HISTORY OF MANKIND
CULTURAL AND SCIENTIFIC DEVELOPMENT
VOLUME VI
THE TWENTIETH CENTURY

PUBLISHED FOR THE
INTERNATIONAL COMMISSION FOR A HISTORY OF THE
SCIENTIFIC AND CULTURAL DEVELOPMENT
OF MANKIND

BY

HARPER & ROW, PUBLISHERS

NEW YORK AND EVANSTON

HISTORY OF MANKIND

CULTURAL AND SCIENTIFIC DEVELOPMENT

VOLUME VI

By CAROLINE F. WARE

K. M. PANIKKAR and J. M. ROMEIN

THE TWENTIETH CENTURY

HARPER & ROW, PUBLISHERS

NEW YORK AND EVANSTON

*Prepared under the auspices and
with financial assistance of the
United Nations Educational, Scientific and
Cultural Organization*

Consultants for
Volume VI

Professor E. N. Anderson
(University of California,
Los Angeles)

Professor K. V. Ostrovitianov
(Academy of Sciences of the Union
of Soviet Socialist Republics)

LIBRARY OF CONGRESS CATALOG CARD NUMBER: 66-20748

INTERNATIONAL COMMISSION
FOR A HISTORY OF THE SCIENTIFIC AND
CULTURAL DEVELOPMENT OF MANKIND

Netherlands
Professor Dr R. Hooykaas
Dr Maria Rooseboom

New Zealand
Dr J. C. Beaglehole

Pakistan
Dr A. Halim
Dr I. H. Qureshi
Dr S. Suhrawardy

Philippines
Professor Gabriel Bernardo

Senegal
H.E. M. L. S. Senghor

South Africa
Professor A. N. Pelzer

Spain
Professor Claudio Sanchez Albornoz
Professor Antonio Garcia Bellido
M. Ciriaco Pérez Bustamante
M. F. Cantera
Professor Emilio Garcia Gomez
Duke of Maura
Professor R. Menendez Pidal

Sweden
Professor Axel Boëthius

Switzerland
Dr Werner Kaegi
Professor Jean Piaget

Syria
H.E. Khalil Mardam Bey

Thailand
Prince Dhani Nivat

Turkey
H.E. Mehmed Fouad Köprülü

Union of Soviet Socialist Republics
Professor A. V. Artikhovski
Professor B. Kedrov
Professor Guber
Professor N. A. Figourovsky
Professor D. V. Sarabianov
Professor V. P. Zoubov
Professor N. A. Sidorova

United Kingdom
Dr Joseph Needham
Earl Russell

United States of America
Professor Eugene Anderson
Professor Salo W. Baron
Professor Norman Brown
Professor J. K. Fairbank
Professor Harold Fisher
Professor G. Stanton Ford
Professor R. H. Gabriel
Professor Oscar Halecki
Dr C. W. de Kiewiet
Professor A. L. Kroeber
Professor Martin R. P. McGuire
Professor H. W. Schneider
Professor Richard Shryock
Professor John Wilson

Uruguay
Professor Carlos M. Rama

HISTORY OF MANKIND
CULTURAL AND SCIENTIFIC DEVELOPMENT

AUTHOR-EDITORS' PREFACE

THIS volume which deals with the twentieth century must, by the nature of the subject, be more tentative and more varied in the range of its materials than those which treat earlier periods. For it has been written in the midst of the events and trends to which it refers and it deals with the many facets of contemporary life for which only the perspective of time can provide a fully integrated view. The material for many parts of the volume has had to be freshly synthesized, since no comprehensive studies were available on which we could rely. Much, in fact, had to be drawn from the direct experience and thought of living people rather than from written sources.

In spite of these limitations, we hope that we have provided a sound and useful approximation to a world view of the main developments of this period in the fields covered by the History. We hope that our labour and the imperfection of our results will stimulate others to use our work as a basis for more adequate and penetrating accounts of these momentous and dynamic years.

Moreover, since every age sees the past through its own eyes, this volume should help to make apparent the viewpoint from which the entire six-volume work has, inevitably, been written. In fact, it is only in the twentieth century that such a History could have been undertaken at all, for only then have people of different culture areas come to know the range of other cultures. Only in the twentieth century have we had access to the knowledge which enables us to see mankind as one.

The preparation of this volume has involved global collaboration. The three author-editors, drawn from the three continents of America, Asia and Europe, have operated under the mandate of the International Commission for a History of the Scientific and Cultural Development of Mankind to produce a joint, not a composite, piece of work. Although the materials for the different sections have been drafted by different members of the group, and in some cases by other collaborators as noted in the acknowledgments which follow, and although the principal author-editor has assumed responsibility for the form and unity of presentation throughout, every part of the volume has been worked over jointly and represents in all respects our combined thought and judgment. In addition to communicating constantly by mail, exchanging written comments on each other's work, and conferring from time to time, we have held three work sessions: first to go over together detailed outlines of each chapter, then to review in detail a draft of about two-thirds of the manuscript and finally to agree on the text as revised in the light of the comments received. That such complete collaboration has been possible and effective is, in itself, an historical fact of the twentieth century.

Since the work deals with the immediate past, we must call attention to the exact years and months during which our work was carried on and during which the comments received on the draft manuscript were formulated. The swift march of events has brought new material which we have wished to include during the course of our labours and have had to ignore once those labours were terminated. Furthermore, changing climates of opinion and changing policies have affected the viewpoints of the National Commissions for Unesco which have taken advantage of the invitation to criticize our work, and have been reflected in the suggestions which they have made as to possible revisions of our text.

We assumed responsibility for preparing the volume in 1954. The bulk of the material was gathered during 1955 and 1956 and most of the text was prepared in 1957-58. The volume was circulated in draft in the spring of 1959 to Unesco National Commissions and scholars associated with the International Commission, with a deadline of November 1, 1959, for the receipt of comments. Final revision of the manuscript was carried out between November 1, 1959, and April 1, 1960, at which time we met in Paris for a final review of the changes which had been made and to reach agreement on all doubtful points which remained.

All comments received by us before the deadline of November 1, 1959, and also those received during the succeeding months if they reached us before the work of revision on the chapter to which they applied had been completed, were given most careful, detailed consideration. Those received by us before April 1, 1960, but after the work of revision on the particular chapter had been done, were studied to see whether any factual error had been noted or any point raised of such importance as to require that we re-do our work. Those received by us during our final work session, April 1-15, 1960, were read but could be considered only where they threw light on the problems which we were still in the process of considering. We terminated our work on April 15, 1960. Comments received after that date unfortunately could not be considered, except in a few special cases.

When we undertook our task, it was our intention to cover the period to 1955, and to close our treatment of each subject by noting the tendencies apparent in the early 1950s. However, some of the changes which have taken place in the second half of the 1950s have been so substantial, and have thrown so much light on the earlier developments which we treat, that we have not thought it wise to ignore them. One might mention, for example, the exploration of space, the emergence of African nationalism as a major force, the breakthrough in the field of health represented by the polio vaccine, the abrogation of the constitutions of many of the new states, the changes in the USSR in the years after Stalin's death, the creation of communes in China. Yet we cannot rewrite our text daily to account for every event between the time of writing and the actual moment of publication. We cannot, for example, accept the suggestion of one National Commission that we add a whole chapter on satellites and space exploration. This must find its place eventually in a succeeding volume.

We have, therefore, brought our account, in the main, to 1955, but have noted major developments in the years 1955–59 when these add significantly to, or throw new light on, the earlier material. We have made no revisions to take account of any events subsequent to April 15, 1960.*

The basis on which we arrived at the content of the volume, its organization and the manner of presentation have been set forth by the principal author-editor in the *Journal of World History*, Vol. V, no. 1, 1959, 'The History of the Scientific and Cultural Development of Mankind: Some Problems of Interpretation'. We need only indicate here the scope, the selection of material drawn from different parts of the world, the way in which we have used terms which carry different meanings in different areas, and the basis on which we have provided bibliographical references for further study.

In approaching the scientific and cultural development of mankind, we have used the concept of 'culture' in the broad, anthropological sense, not in the limited sense which equates culture with certain areas of knowledge and expression. We have written of scientific developments for the intelligent public, not for the specialist, and have, therefore, sought to present these developments in their cultural context and in terms of their effects rather than in technical terms.

A global history which deals with the many-faceted life of mankind in the modern period cannot cover, even superficially, the relevant events in all parts of the world.

We have included concrete material from different countries only as illustrations of the trends which we discuss, and in order to give reality to the generalizations with which we have tried to bring out major tendencies. For every illustration chosen, ten or a hundred others, equally apt and from different parts of the world, might have been cited. We have tried to select these illustrations so as to suggest both the unity and the range of experience in the period under review. No country will find its scientific and cultural

---

* During the five years which have passed while the editorial notes were being prepared, major changes affecting the life of mankind have further altered the twentieth-century world. Cosmonauts and astronauts have soared through outer space, orbiting the globe. On earth, computers and automatic processes daily take over additional functions and the scientific revolution of the first half of the century is fast becoming the technological revolution of the second half. The world groupings and leadership that characterized the decade after the second world war have shifted as changes and divisions within groups have created more complex patterns of interrelationships.

The European Community has become a reality, the Chinese People's Republic has joined the atomic powers, and the new nations of Africa, stepping one after another onto the world stage, have modified the composition and balance of the United Nations. The rising tide of expectations has brought growing tensions as the accelerating rate of development in the industrially advanced countries threatens to leave the developing countries further behind and the Negro protest in the United States has become a revolutionary movement.

These recent events have not found their way into the text or into the bibliography which remains limited to books published through 1960. In some instances, however, they have entered the editorial notes, and material relating to years after 1960 has been included in some Author-Editors' responses. C. F. WARE, March 1965 history presented in these pages. This is expecially true with respect to those aspects which are most deeply embedded in the language and cultural traditions of each unique area of the world, such as education, literature and the arts.

In writing contemporary history, the historian has to make use of terms that are interpreted differently and carry a different emotional weight in different countries and situations—terms such as 'West', 'East', 'underdeveloped', 'totalitarian', 'democratic', 'capitalist', 'communist', 'socialist', and even neutral words like 'bureaucracy'. Since it is impossible to avoid such words or to put a note every time misunderstanding might arise from their use, we must rely on the collaboration of the reader to understand them in the context in which they appear, and to do the same with such imprecise designations of geographical areas as Near East, Middle East, Tropical Africa, Oceania. As far as possible, we have tried to be consistent in the way in which we have used each term and have chosen a neutral rather than a pejorative or emotionally-charged sense. We have, thus, used 'bureaucracy' to refer to the personnel of the large-scale organizations so characteristic of the twentieth century, whether in the state, in industry, in labour unions or in international agencies; we have not used it in the derogatory sense which implies waste and red tape, nor in the limited technical sense of 'rule by officialdom'.

We have, however, used the term 'socialism' in two senses. We have used it in the orthodox Marxian sense for the socialist economies of the USSR, the People's Democracies and the Chinese People's Republic, and we have also used it in the more general sense in which it is used outside of these areas to describe the extension of state responsibility for basic aspects of economic life. We have used the term 'communist' in a political sense to refer to the Communist party and the states under Communist party control; we have used it to refer to the economy or the society only in the technical Marxian sense of the stage which is expected to follow that of socialism.

We have used the term 'welfare state' to indicate a general concept of the role of the state and tendency to act in terms of that role, without implying that the actual situation in any state during the period corresponded to this ideal.

Although this is a history of mankind written for a world audience, the bibliography has been limited—except in very rare instances—to books written or translated in English. It is intended that the French edition will have a principally French bibliography. We have limited ourselves in this way, reluctantly, because any other basis of selection for a volume which touches all the major fields of knowledge and expression and all areas of the globe in the twentieth century is impracticable. If we do not limit ourselves to the language in which the book itself is published, there is no stopping point. We should not be justified in confining ourselves to the major European languages; the official languages of UNESCO or the United Nations would exclude German; and what of works in Arabic, Hindi, Japanese—not to mention Dutch, Swedish, Italian, Polish, Hungarian? Between a bibliography in the language of the volume and one that includes all modern languages there is no place to draw the line. To compile a bibliography of the latter type would be a large and separate task in itself which we must leave to others. We have, moreover, limited the references in the text to material which is directly quoted or cited, since in so comprehensive a work, full documentation would require an elaborate supporting footnote for nearly every statement.

In the preparation of the volume, we have had help from many sources, in many lands and from many fields of knowledge, to which full reference is made in the Note on Editorial Treatment.

CAROLINE F. WARE, *Author-Editor*
J. M. ROMEIN, *Co-Author-Editor*
K. M. PANIKKAR, *Co-Author-Editor*

April 1960.

SUPPLEMENT TO AUTHOR-EDITORS' PREFACE

IT is with profound sadness that I must add a personal supplement to the jointly-signed Preface written on the completion of the text of this volume five years ago. Neither of the co-author-editors has lived to see the work in press, and neither has been able to share responsibility for the author-editors' responses to the editorial notes. I take this opportunity to pay tribute to the extraordinary breadth, intellectual integrity, generosity and dedication of these two brilliant and remarkable scholars and to acknowledge the great privilege that has been mine to enjoy their unstinting collaboration.

In the course of the preparation of the notes by editorial consultants and their review by the Bureau of the International Commission to assure the maintenance of a scholarly tone and elimination of material deemed to be polemic, we received several suggestions for further minor revisions of the text to meet criticisms of commentators. So long as my colleagues were alive, these suggestions were all carefully considered and modifications to which we agreed were made. After Professor Romein's death in July 1962, no further suggestions for alteration could be accepted as the text had to remain intact.

By the time that the final editorial notes were received in June 1964, Sardar Panikkar had also died and I had to assume full responsibility for the author-editors' responses. In this I was guided by our joint decision as to the kinds of responses we would make. We agreed that we would not enter into debate with the editorial commentators with respect to either the accuracy of their observations or the merit of their positions. We agreed to limit ourselves to clarification and supplementation of our text at those points where the editorial comments made it appear that the text needed amplification or documentation or had been misconstrued or might be subject to misinterpretation. The author-editors' notes which appear in the volume have been prepared in conformity with these criteria.

We knew from the start that the pioneer effort of Unesco to bring an international view to the writing of world history would be subject to criticism from proponents of distinct philosophical viewpoints and that such criticism would bear with particular force on the volume dealing with the contemporary period. This has, indeed, been the case.

Criticism of our general approach has come from representatives of three fundamental and conflicting philosophical positions:

1. Traditional western European liberalism which sees the twentieth century as a period of great cultural crisis in which the values of individual freedom and responsibility are at stake.
2. Marxism-Leninism which sees the twentieth century in terms of laws of dialectical historical materialism.
3. The Catholic historical view which stresses the primacy of unchanging spiritual values.

Professor Wilhelm Roepke (Switzerland) voices the traditional liberal point of view:

'What strikes me in the first place is that obviously no effort has been made to interpret the history of the period in question in terms of one of the most profound "cultural crises" which our—or any—civilization has ever seen. When reading these chapters one gets the impression that the authors—in spite of their impressive erudition—have never heard of authors such as Huizinga, Toynbee, Alfred Weber, de Corte, René Grousset, G. Ferrero, A. Rustow, Guardini or myself. In the eyes of all those who take these authors seriously, and who themselves have to be taken seriously, the whole work thus misses its real point. . . .

'What seems to me no less strange, though it is in close connection with this first criticism, is the complete absence of any hint on the political consequence of this cultural crisis. It is significant that the word "totalitarianism" . . . never occurs in this ambitious work, and that its possible connection both with the cultural crisis and the change of our society into a "mass society" has not been mentioned, let alone been analysed.'

From this angle, the volume has been criticized not only for failing to focus on manifestations of totalitarianism as the source of the crisis of these times, but for blurring issues and taking away all the sharp edges from the difference between market economies and collectivist economies, for not showing the dangers and limitations of the welfare state, and for the choice of writers and literary and artistic tendencies to which to give attention in the chapters on literature and the arts.

The Marxist-Leninist view is expressed in the criticisms received from the USSR, Czechoslovakia, Hungary, Poland and Bulgaria. Other possible versions of that view which might have come from the Chinese People's Republic or from Yugoslavia were not received since the former country was not a member of Unesco at the time that the manuscript was circulated for comment (1959) and the Yugoslav National Commission for Unesco was among the several commissions which sent no comments on the draft.

The Marxist-Leninist criticism, as summarized by Dr Vladimir Knigl of the Czechoslovak Academy of Sciences, is that:

'the fact that the authors do not see the economic and political development in the world in the twentieth century from a class point of view leads them to a positivist and unscientific interpretation of the events of this century.'

Dr Ludvik Svoboda of the same institution adds that:

'the basic shortcoming lies in the fact that all the phenomena are enumerated so to speak on one plane, one problem next to the other. The treatise does not show sufficient understanding and does not appreciate sufficiently the appearance of a new social system which will change in the very near future the whole world even more than it did up till now.'

And the Hungarian National Commission for Unesco states that the author-editors' 'objectivist approach':

'seems to provide the only medium of concealing or minimizing the significance of the unquestionable achievements attained by the socialist countries in the cultural and scientific fields. . . .

'Owing to their objectivist approach . . . the authors, instead of analysing facts, merely describe the phenomena they review; they do not explain them, do not reveal the social and economic factors that produced them.'

From this standpoint of historical materialism, the volume is not only criticized for failure to give sufficient place to the achievements of the socialist countries but is charged with minimizing the weaknesses of capitalist economies, obscuring the class basis of society, failing to recognize the potential of the dialectic method for scientific research, and preferring a non-political view of the arts.

The Catholic writer, Professor Oscar Halecki (USA) observes:

'To somebody who does not share the enthusiasm for "the triumph of industrialism" and who is less interested in technological, i.e. material, progress, than in the search for a new humanism based upon spiritual values and individual freedom, that whole important volume seems to deal rather with the economic and social than with the scientific and cultural development of mankind.

'. . . the basic change resulting from the scientific orientation of life and the transformation of the industrial societies is . . . over-emphasized as the main feature of modern culture. . . .

'The question is raised whether any religion can furnish a basis for the great decisions which are required in view of "man's new power". But the main question is whether we need at all any "new morality" and not simply the respect and application of the old unchangeable principles of morality founded on natural law and the belief in God.'

Viewed from this angle, the treatment of many subjects in the volume is found to be open to criticism—the biological sciences, the family, education, population, the spiritual qualities of religion as against the institutional manifestations, the place of religion in the tradition of western Europe, the impact and significance of Christian missions.

The great majority of the notes provided by the editorial consultants consist of the application of these conflicting points of view to the subjects treated in the chapters to which these notes are attached.

Inevitably, in a world sharply divided along ideological lines, we have been charged with bias. Some non-communist scholars have criticized the text for what they consider a 'leftist' viewpoint and a tendency to select and present material in such a way as to show the communist countries in a favourable light. Communist scholars, on the other hand, as their extensive editorial notes indicate, do not think that we have done justice to the communist system and its development during these years.

As author-editors of an historical work undertaken under international auspices with the purpose of bringing an international viewpoint to the writing of history, we have faced a difficult task. We have endeavoured to present all subjects, however controversial, in such a way as to place them in their total context and to enhance understanding from all sides.

The question has been raised as to whether such an approach is feasible, i.e. whether Unesco's objective of bringing to the history of mankind a perspective which the world can share is attainable. Professor Raymond Aron (France) writes:

'In the last analysis, the issue involves a difference as to what history should be, especially the history of an unfinished century. The authors have wished above all for it to be descriptive, neutral, objective, acceptable to everybody. Personally, I believe that it can only be problematic, interpretative, sociological, philosophical, unacceptable to some people.

'Perhaps, within the outlook of Unesco, the authors had to conceive of their task as they have done. But in this case it is Unesco's own conception, applied to the twentieth century, that must be called into question.'

The readers may judge whether this volume fulfils, in whole or in part, the high purpose which inspired Unesco to sponsor a history of the scientific and cultural development of mankind.

CAROLINE F. WARE

March 1965.

K. M. Panikkar was born in Kerala in 1895. After studying at the Christian College in Madras he went to England and attended Oxford University (Christ Church), where he obtained a Master of Arts degree, and the Middle Temple, London, where he was received Barrister at Law.

On his return to India in 1919, he lectured at the Aligarh Muslim University and later at the University of Calcutta. In 1925 he abandoned an academic career to become Editor of the *Hindustan Times*. In 1933 he was appointed Secretary of the Chamber of Princes; later he served as the Foreign Minister of the State of Patiala, and Education and Foreign Minister of the State of Bikaner. He was also Secretary to the Delegation of Indian States at the Round Table Conference in London in 1930.

After Indian independence he was elected to the Constitutional Assembly in 1946, and was a member of the Indian Delegation to the United Nations in 1947.

In 1948 he served as Indian Ambassador to Peking during the change of régime. In 1952 he was Ambassador to Cairo, and in 1956 Ambassador to France. Between these last two appointments, he was a member of the States Reorganisation Committee which established a new basis for the relationship between the Indian States and the Government of India and which redrew the internal boundaries along linguistic lines.

On his return to India after his Ambassadorship in France, K. M. Panikkar sat in the Upper Chamber of Parliament. He ended his career as he had started forty years earlier: as a scholar and a leader of education. He became Vice-Chancellor of Kashmir University, then Vice-Chancellor of Mysore University, a post he occupied until his death.

Well versed in Sanskrit literature, he also had a profound understanding of Asian and European history and literature. He translated many European classics into his native language, Malayalam.

His works, available in many languages, include:

Survey of Indian History (London, 1947), *Hindu Society at the Cross-Roads* (Bombay, 1955), *In the Two Chinas* (London, 1955), *The State and the Citizen* (Bombay, 1956), *Asia and Western Dominance* (1959), *The Afro-Asian States and their Problems* (1959), *The Foundations of New India* (London, 1963), etc., and a series of lectures at the Sorbonne, 'The Confrontation of Two Cultures'.

K. M. Panikkar began his collaboration in the preparation of Volume VI, *The Twentieth Century*, of the *History of Mankind: Cultural and Scientific Development* in 1954. In 1956 he was elected to full membership of the International Commission for a History of the Scientific and Cultural Development of Mankind.

JAN MARIUS ROMEIN, 1893–1962

J. M. Romein, born in Rotterdam, the Netherlands, was educated at the Erasmianum Gymnasium in his native city, and at the University of Leyden. A thesis on Dostoevsky's criticism in the West led to a doctorate of letters. Until 1929 he was a free lance historian, a journalist, and a political analyst concerned with public affairs, especially those of South-east Asia. In this capacity he was one of the first writers to advocate the abolition of every form of colonialism. In 1929 he was appointed to the professorship of the theory of history at the University of Amsterdam, a chair which he held until his death with the exception of the years 1942–44 when he was debarred by the German occupation authorities, and in 1951–52 when he was visiting professor of modern history at the University of Jogjakarta in Indonesia.

His wide interests and the range of his knowledge enabled him to comprehend the complexity of a world in evolution, and his book, *De Eeuw van Azië* (Amsterdam, 1956), was translated into many languages: in English it appeared under the title *The Asian Century* (London: George Allen & Unwin, Ltd., 1962). Among J. M. Romein's works the following are representative of his outstanding contribution to the understanding of man and of history: *Dostojewski in de Westerse Kritiek* (Haarlem, 1924), *De Biografie* (Amsterdam, 1946; German translation, Berne, 1948), *Aera van Europa* (Amsterdam, 1954). In collaboration with A. Romein-Verschoor he published two important works on the history of the Netherlands: *De lage Landen bij de Zee* (Utrecht, 1934), and *Erflaters van onze Beschaving* (Amsterdam, 1938–40; abridged German edition, Berne, 1946). In addition, between 1937 and 1963 there appeared in Amsterdam five volumes of historical essays by Professor Romein. Several were translated into English, German, and Czech.

For a detailed bibliography of Professor Romein's works, see *Prof. Dr Jan Romein, Bibliografie* (Groningen, 1963).

J. M. Romein's association with the International Commission for a History of the Scientific and Cultural Development of Mankind began in 1954 when he was appointed co-author-editor of Volume VI, *The Twentieth Century*, of the *History of Mankind: Cultural and Scientific Development*.

NOTE ON THE PREPARATION AND EDITING OF VOLUME VI

This volume is part of the *History of Mankind: Cultural and Scientific Development*, prepared under the auspices of UNESCO by the International Commission for a History of the Scientific and Cultural Development of Mankind. *The Twentieth Century* will conclude the series of six books which cover the major aspects of the scientific and cultural development of mankind from Prehistory to the present century.

The spirit in which this work was conceived, the motivations which led the General Conference of the United Nations Educational, Scientific, and Cultural Organization to sponsor this project, have been described by the Director-General of UNESCO in the 'Foreword' to Volume I of the *History of Mankind*.* The method that was followed to reach the objectives of the International Commission is analysed by its President in the 'Preface' to the same volume.†

Volume VI, *The Twentieth Century*, was prepared by Dr Caroline F.Ware (United States of America), Professor J. M. Romein (The Netherlands), and H.E. Sardar K. M. Panikkar (India). After elaborating a detailed plan on the basis of the directives of the International Commission, the author-editors, aided by their various associates and advisers, prepared a first version of the volume which was submitted to the National Commissions for UNESCO in all the member states of the Organization and to selected specialists nominated by the International Commission. The observations and suggestions received by the International Commission were carefully examined by the author-editors who revised and corrected the original text to incorporate many of the materials that had been made available to them.

In accordance with the procedure established by the International Commission for all volumes of the *History of Mankind*, the revised text was entrusted to consultants. They were asked to study the final text together with the original comments that had been received, and to prepare editorial notes that would explain some of the differences in historical interpretation which remained after the author-editors had made use of the critical comments in their revision. These editorial notes, which appear at the end of the chapters, reflect many of the divergencies that characterize historical scholarship with respect to fundamental issues in the twentieth century.‡

The two consultants for Volume VI, Professor Eugene N. Anderson (United States of America) and Professor K. V. Ostrovitianov (Union of Socialist Soviet Republics) prepared editorial notes. The author-editors were given the privilege to

---

* See Appendix A to the present volume.

† See Appendix B to the present volume.

‡ The Bureau of the International Commission, after studying carefully the question, came to the conclusion that the diversity in the political, philosophical and ideological spheres which characterizes the twentieth century was so apparent, and the opinions of scholars for whom historical developments obey certain specific principles were so various as to warrant fuller presentation in an additional volume. The present volume, like the other five volumes of the *History of Mankind*, was conceived according to the plan approved by the International Commission: each question was approached in function of the main objectives of the project as a whole, a study of the major social, cultural and scientific developments of mankind in the widest context. The additional volume will contain the contributions of writers from the Soviet Union and other socialist countries, Latin America, Africa, and other regions, and of qualified representatives of various cultural streams who will give well-considered interpretations of twentieth-century history. The presentation of all the parts of Volume VI will be the same, and they will be annotated according to the usual procedures.

supplement or clarify their text in the light of these notes; this additional material is printed in italics.

All the editorial material appearing at the end of the chapters was reviewed carefully by the President and the members of the Bureau of the International Commission. In some instances the Bureau exercised its authority to delete or modify notes which, in its opinion, did not bear on fundamental divergences of views or which were based on secondary opinions or on imperfect evidence.

It will be observed that there are more notes prepared by Professor Ostrovitianov than by Professor Anderson. This is due to the fact that the basic plans for the volumes of the *History of Mankind* had already been approved by the International Commission when Soviet scholars became associated with the project: the *History of Mankind* was under way when the USSR joined Unesco. Consequently, no Soviet scholar had the opportunity to collaborate in the elaboration of the plans of the *History of Mankind* as a whole or of Volume VI, *The Twentieth Century*. The Bureau, taking these circumstances into account, authorized Professor Ostrovitianov to include more notes than normally would have been the case.

In the course of preparing the text, Dr Ware travelled around the world in 1955–56 in order to consult with some five hundred scholars and leaders of thought and action. A multitude of specialists reviewed one or another section of the manuscript and offered valuable comments and suggestions. More than fifty scholars from some twenty countries prepared articles for the *Journal of World History* or special memoranda. All these were helpful, although all could not be published because of lack of space in the *Journal*. Drafts of some chapters were prepared by specialists.

The author-editors and the International Commission wish to acknowledge with warm appreciation all these contributions from the smallest to the most substantial. At the same time, the author-editors assume full responsibility for all parts of the text.

Drafts for chapters were prepared by the following persons:

CHAPTER

VI. *The New Scientific Thought and its Impact*
Dr J. Bronowski, Research Director, National Coal Board, England, prepared the draft and approved revisions.

VII. *Mathematics and Logic*
Dr Marshall H. Stone, Andrew Macleish Distinguished Service Professor, University of Chicago, USA, prepared the draft and approved revisions.

VIII. *The Elaboration of the Physical Sciences*
Dr George W. Wetherill, Carnegie Institution of Washington, Department of Terrestrial Magnetism, USA, prepared the draft and incorporated suggested revisions, using in part material prepared by Dr Edward U. Condon, Professor of Physics, Washington University, St Louis, USA.

XIII. *Development of the Biological Sciences*
Dr Jane Oppenheimer, Professor of Biology, Bryn Mawr College, Bryn Mawr, USA, prepared the draft and incorporated suggested revisions.

XXVII. *Use of Leisure*
Dr Dorothy Jackson (USA), former lecturer in History, University of Western Australia, Perth, Australia, prepared the draft and approved revisions. She also contributed material for Chapter XI (*Communication*) and Chapter XXVI (*Education*).

XXXI. *Tendencies in Literature and the Arts in the Western Culture Areas*
Dr Helen D. Lockwood, Professor Emeritus of English, Vassar College,

Poughkeepsie, N.Y., USA, prepared a large proportion of the draft, reworked all the revisions and collaborated closely throughout.

The following persons reviewed and advised on the plan of the volume and the following parts of the manuscript:

Dr Gardiner C. Means (USA), former Director, Industrial Section, National Resources Planning Board, reviewed the plan for the volume and each chapter as it was drafted, in addition to giving special attention to chapters with economic content—IX, XVI, XXI.

Dr Annie Romein-Verschoor (Netherlands), author and lecturer, reviewed the plan and much of the text as it was drafted, especially Chapters XVII, XXII and XXXI.

Dr Helen D. Lockwood (USA), reviewed the plan and several chapters, in addition to doing special work on Chapters I–V, XI, XVIII, XXVII and XXXI.

Dr George W. Corner (USA) former Director, Carnegie Institution Department of Embryology, reviewed the plan for the chapters on the natural sciences, and reviewed each chapter (VI, VIII, XIII, XV, XVI) as it was prepared.

Dr Ralph Turner (USA), Vice-President, International Commission for a History of the Scientific and Cultural Development of Mankind, was constantly available for advice during the formative stages.

Articles for the *Journal of World History* and memoranda, prepared at the request of the author-editors of Volume VI, or at the request of other author-editors, provided material which was useful in connection with the following chapters, and frequently for chapters other than those listed specifically:

CHAPTER

I. *The Shift in World Power*

Guy Wint (UK), Oxford University, 'South-East Asia in the Twentieth Century', *JWH*, V, 2; John K. Fairbank (USA), Harvard University, 'China's Response to the West: Problems and Suggestions', *JWH*, III, 2.

II. *The Impact of Nationalism and Trend Toward International Co-operation*

E. Z. Karal (Turkey), University of Ankara, 'La transformation de la Turquie d'un empire oriental en un état moderne et national', *JWH*, IV, 2.

IV. *The Triumph of Industrialism*

Yoshio Ando (Japan), University of Tokyo, 'The Evolutionary Process of the Japanese Economy in the Twentieth Century', *JWH*, V, 1.

VIII. *The Elaboration of the Physical Sciences*

G. Tikhomirov (USSR), 'Geographical Investigations' (memorandum); V. Yesahov (USSR), 'Exploration of the Arctic and Antarctic' (memorandum); V. Khain (USSR), 'Geological Surveying' (memorandum).

X. *Transport*

V. Petrov (USSR), 'The Development of Transport' (memorandum).

XI. *Communications*

L. Kalashnikov (USSR), 'Progress of Communications' (memorandum).

XII. *Means of Destruction*

Herbert Rosinski (USA), 'The Twentieth Century Revolution in Warfare', *JWH*, IV, 3.

XIII. *Development of the Biological Sciences*

Jean Rostand (France), 'La biologie au XXe siècle', *JWH*, II, 1.

XIV. *Food and Agriculture*
C. H. Edelman (Netherlands), Agricultural University, Wageningen, 'The Utilization and Conservation of the World's Soil Resources in the 20th Century', *JWH*, VI, 3; Gerhard M. Gerhardsen (Norway), Norwegian School of Economics and Business Administration, Bergen, 'Fishery Developments in the 20th Century', *JWH*, IV, 4; Franz Heske (Germany), Universities of Hamburg and Istanbul, 'The History of Foresty in the World: A Short Survey', *JWH*, V, 3.

XV. *Health and Population*
J. J. Spengler (USA), Duke University, 'Population Changes, 1900–1950: Socio-economic Implications', *JWH*, V, 4; Y. Ashurkov and A. Shevelyov (USSR), 'Care of Public Health' (memorandum).

XVI. *The Scientific Approach to Human Behaviour and Human Relations*
Clyde Kluckholm (USA), Harvard University, 'Developments in the Field of Anthropology in the 20th Century', *JWH*, III, 3.

XX. *Major Changes in Concepts and Ideas*
H. Margenau and J. E. Smith (USA), Yale University, 'Philosophy of Physical Science in the Twentieth Century', *JWH*, IV, 3; M. I. Sidorov (USSR), 'Le développement de la philosophie marxiste dans les travaux de G. V. Plekhanov', *JWH*, Special Number: Contributions to Russian History (1958); A. M. Deborin (USSR), 'Lenin as Philosopher', *JWH*, Special Number, 1958.

XXI. *Economic Institutions*
N. V. Sovani (India), Gokhale Institute of Politics and Economics, Poona, 'British Impact on India after 1850–1857', *JWH*, II, 1.

XXII. *Social Institutions*
Kenneth Little (UK), Edinburgh University, 'African Culture and the Western Intrusion', *JWH*, III, 4; K. K. Datta (India), University of Patna, 'Changes in the Structure of Indian Society in the 20th Century', *JWH*, VI, 2; Saleh A El-Ali (Iraq), College of Liberal Arts, Baghdad, 'Westernization of Iraq' (memorandum); Louis Bernot (France), 'Attitudes des Français devant les techniques modernes', *JWH*, V, 4; L. Pershits (USSR), 'The Settlement of Nomads in the USSR' (memorandum).

XXV. *Religion*
Fazlur Rahman (Pakistan), Durham University, UK, 'Internal Religious Developments in the Present Century Islam', *JWH*, II, 4; Kenneth Cragg (USA), Editor of *The Muslim World*, 'External Pressures and Religious Developments in Islam in the 20th Century', *JWH*, III, 2; Zenryū Tsukamoto (Japan), 'Japanese and Chinese Buddhism in the 20th Century', *JWH*, VI, 3; Louis Finkelstein and Associates (USA), Jewish Theological Seminary, 'Religion in Israel' (memorandum).

XXVII. *Use of Leisure*
N. Karklina (USSR), 'The History of Public and Research Libraries' (memorandum).

XXVIII. *The Self-Image and Aspirations of Nations*
A. B. Pant (India), Indian Resident Commissioner, Sikkim, 'Notes on Certain Problems of Africa', *JWH*, V, 3; Pius Okigbo (Nigeria), Northwestern University, USA, 'Factors in West African Economic History', *JWH*, IV, 1; K. A. Busia (Ghana), University College, Accra, 'West Africa in the Twentieth Century', *JWH*, IV, 1; Diedrich Westermann (Germany), 'The Cultural

History of Negro Africa', *JWH*, III, 4; I. H. Qureshi (Pakistan), Columbia University, USA, 'The Development of Pakistan', *JWH*, IV, 4; H. Kishimoto (Japan), Tokyo University, 'The Self-Image and Aspiration of the Japanese People in the Twentieth Century', *JWH*, VII, 1.

XXIX. *Drives for Cultural Integrity and Recognition*
Nabih A. Faris (Lebanon), American Univerity, Beirut, 'The Arab Countries of West Asia in the 20th Century', *JWH*, V, 1; Nicola A. Ziadeh (Lebanon), American University, Beirut, 'Cultural Trends in North Africa', *JWH*, VII, 1; J. B. Kripalani (India), 'Gandhian Thought and its Effect on Indian Life', *JWH*, V, 2; Gonzalo Aguirre Beltrán (Mexico), Instituto Nacional Indigenista, 'Indigenismo y Mestizaje: Una Polaridad Bio-Cultural', *JWH*, VI, 1.

XXX. *Drives for Individual Freedom and Human Dignity*
Charles Gamba (Australia), Univeristy of Malaya, 'Trade Unionism in Malaya' (memorandum).

XXXI. *Tendencies in Literature and the Arts in the Western Culture Areas*
Jerome Mellquist (USA), 'Twentieth Century Relationships in Painting, Sculpture and Architecture' (memorandum); Mariano Picón-Salas (Venezuela) 'El "Aire" Cultural en América Latina', *JWH*, I, 3; F. L. Baumer (USA), 'Twentieth-Century Version of the Apocalypse', *JWH*, I, 3; A. Kantor and V. Polevoy (USSR), 'Fine Arts and Architecture' (memorandum).

XXXII. *Developments in Eastern Literature and Arts*
S. T. Alisjahbana (Indonesia), 'Le développement de la langue et de la littérature indonésiennes', *JWH*, II, 3; Prabhakar Machwe (India), 'Indian Language and Literature in the 20th Century' (memorandum); I. M. Husaini (Lebanon), America University, Beirut, 'Modern Arabic Literature', *JWH*, III, 3; Mouhammad Khalafallah (Egypt), University of Alexandria, 'L'évolution de la langue et de la littérature arabes au XXe siècle', *JWH*, VI, 1.

In the preparation of the original draft, the individual chapters were reviewed as follows:

Dr A. A. Zvorikine (USSR), Vice-President of the International Commission for a History of the Scientific and Cultural Development of Mankind, offered a detailed alternative plan for the content of the volume.

CHAPTER

VI. *The New Scientific Thought and Its Impact*
Dr George W. Corner.
Dr Merle Tuve, Director, Carnegie Institution Department of Terrestrial Magnetism, Washington, D.C.
Dr Warren Weaver, Director, Division of Natural Sciences, Rockefeller Foundation, N.Y., USA.
Dr George Gaylord Simpson, Chairman, Department of Geology and Palaeontology, The American Museum of Natural History, New York, USA.
Dr Leonard Carmichael, Secretary, Smithsonian Institution, Washington, D.C., USA.
Dr Kenneth Mees, former Director, Research Laboratories, Eastman Kodak Company, Rochester, N.Y., USA.
Dr Percy W. Bridgman, Department of Physics, Harvard University, USA.
Dr Esmond R. Long, former Director, Henry Phipps Institute for the Study and Prevention of Tuberculosis, Philadelphia, Pa., USA.

Dr Robert Oppenheimer, Director, Institute for Advanced Study, Princeton, New Jersey, USA.

Dr René J. Dubos, The Rockefeller Institute for Medical Research, New York, USA.

Dr Bentley Glass, Department of Biology, Johns Hopkins University, Baltimore, Md., USA.

Sir Julian S. Huxley, FRS (UK), Vice-President, International Commission for a History of the Scientific and Cultural Development of Mankind.

Dr Jane Oppenheimer.

IX. *Industrial Production*

Dr Ir. R. J. Forbes (Netherlands), International Council of Scientific Unions, Observer on the International Commission for a History of the Scientific and Cultural Development of Mankind.

Dr Bruce Netschert, Resources for the Future, Washington, D.C., USA (sections on materials and energy).

Prof. P. Sargent Florence (UK), University of Birmingham, England.

Dr Louis Hunter, Army Industrial College, Washington, D.C., USA (sections on materials, energy, plant and equipment).

Mrs Elizabeth Johnstone, Special Assistant to Director-General, International Labour Organization, Geneva (section on labour supply and utilization).

XI. *Communications*

Dr E. I. Green, Bell Laboratories, American Telephone and Telegraph Company, N. Y., USA (technical aspects).

Mr Winthrop Means, Bell Laboratories (technical aspects).

Mr. Henry Ware, American Telephone and Telegraph Company, USA (technical aspects).

Mr Frank O'Brien, former Director, Associated Press Bureau, Istanbul, Rome, and elsewhere (section relating to news).

XII. *Means of Destruction*

Dr Herbert Rosinski, New York, USA

XIII. *Development of the Biological Sciences*

Dr George W. Corner.

Sir Julian Huxley, FRS

Dr George Gaylord Simpson.

Dr Bentley Glass.

Dr René Dubos.

Dr Esmond R. Long.

Dr Robert H. MacArthur, Department of Biology, University of Pennsylvania, USA (section in ecology).

XIV. *Food and Agriculture*

Mr J. C. Ellickson, US Department of Agriculture, Washington, D.C., and other members of the Department (section on agriculture).

Dr A. LeRoy Voris, Secretary, Food and Nutrition Board, National Research Council, National Academy of Sciences, Washington, D.C., USA (nutrition).

Dr E. N. Todhunter, Dean, College of Home Economics, University of Alabama, USA (section on nutrition).

Dr G. M. Gerhardsen (section on fishery).

Dr G. L. Kesteven, Chief, Fisheries Biology Branch, Food and Agriculture Organization, Rome (section on fishery).

Dr R. K. Winters, US Forest Service, Washington, D.C. (section on forestry).

Mr W. E. Hiley, CBE, Dartington Hall, Devon, UK (section on forestry).

xv. *Health and Population*
Dr George W. Corner.
Dr Richard H. Shryock, Corresponding Member of the International Commission for a History of the Scientific and Cultural Development of Mankind, Director, Institute of the History of Medicine, Johns Hopkins University, Baltimore, Md., USA.
Dr Esmond R. Long.
Dr John Blake, The Smithsonian Institution, Washington, D.C., USA.
Dr Guillermo Arbona, Health Commissioner, Puerto Rico (section relating to Puerto Rico).
Dr Frank Lorimer, President, International Union for the Study of Population (section on population).

XVI. *The Scientific Approach to Human Behaviour and Human Relations*
Dr Dorothy Lee, Anthropologist, Harvard University, Cambridge, Mass., USA.
Dr Brewster Smith, Editor, *Journal of Abnormal and Social Psychology*, New York University, N.Y., USA.
Dr Alfred Sherrard, Economist, Washington, D.C., USA.
Prof. A. N. J. den Hollander, Sociologist, University of Amsterdam.

XVII. *The Home*
Dr Dorothy Lee.
Dr Flemmie Kittrell, Department of Home Economics, Howard University, Washington, D.C., USA (section relating to home economics).

XVIII. *The Environment*
Dr Catherine Bauer, Department of Urbanism and Planning, University of California, USA.

XIX. *Treatment and Prevention of Social Breakdown and Provision of Social Services*
Dr A. R. Burns, Department of Economics, Columbia University, N.Y., USA.

XXI. *Economic Institutions*
Dr Alfred Sherrard.
Prof. J. W. Bezemer, University of Amsterdam (part relating to economy of USSR).

XXII. *Social Institutions*
Dr Kathleen Hill, University of Natal, Durban, South Africa (section relating to youth organization).

XXIV. *Military Institutions*
Dr H. Rosinski.

XXV. *Religion*
Dr Douglas Horton, Dean, Harvard Divinity School, Harvard University (general section and section on Christianity).
The Rev. Robert Paul Mohan, The Catholic University of America (general section and section on Christianity).
Rabbi Louis Finkelstein, Dean, Jewish Theological Seminary, New York, N.Y., USA (section relating to Judaism).
Prof. Fazlur Rahman (section on Islam).
The Ven. Prasiddh Kittisiddo, Bangkok, Thailand (section on Puddhism).

XXVIII. *The Self-Image and Aspirations of Nations*
Rabbi Louis Finkelstein (section on Israel).
Dr I. Qureshi (section on Pakistan).
Prof. Fazlur Rahman (section on Pakistan).

Dr Kathleen Hill (section on South Africa).

Miss de Ru, University of Amsterdam (section on South Africa).

Mrs Maida Springer, International Affairs Department, American Federation of Labor-Congress of Industrial Organizations, USA (section on Africa).

Dr Rayford W. Logan, Department of History, Howard University, Washington, D.C., USA (section on South Africa).

XXIX. *Drives for Cultural Integrity and Recognition*

Dr Clarence Senior, Columbia University and Office of Puerto Rico, New York (section on Mexico).

H.E. Prof. Paulo E. de Barrêdo Carneiro, President, International Commission for a History of the Scientific and Cultural Development of Mankind (section on Brazil).

Dr S. Zavala, Vice-President, International Commission for a History of the Scientific and Cultural Development of Mankind (section on Mexico).

XXX. *Drives for Individual Freedom and Human Dignity*

Dr David Saposs, former Research Director, National Labor Relations Board, USA, and former labour economist, US Mutual Cooperation Administration, Paris (section on labour).

Mrs Elizabeth Johnstone (section on labour).

Dr Carl Taylor, former Director, Division of Farm Population and Rural Life, US Department of Agriculture and Ford Foundation Consultant on Community Development, India (section on farmers and peasants).

Dr Annie Romein (section on women).

Dr Dorothy Lee (section on women).

Sra. Esther N. de Calvo, Interamerican Commission of Women, Pan American Union, Washington, D.C., USA (section on Latin American women).

Miss Pauli Murray, Lawyer, New York City, USA (section on Negroes).

Mrs Corinne Robinson, former assistant racial adviser, US Housing and Home Finance Agency, Washington, D.C. (section on Negroes).

Mr Charles Mason, Washington, D.C., USA (section on Negroes).

XXXI. *Tendencies in Literature and the Arts in Western Culture Areas*

Division of Cultural Affairs, Pan American Union, Washington, D.C., USA (section relating to Latin American literature and arts).

The International Commission wishes to thank the National Research Council—National Academy of Sciences of the United States for designating its Vice-Chairman, Dr George W. Corner, as science adviser to the author-editors, and to thank Dr Corner, not only for his helpful suggestions, but for inviting a panel of twenty American scientists to serve as consultants within the fields of their specialities.

The National Commissions for Unesco in the following countries made it possible for the principal author-editor to meet with leading scholars during her visit: Japan, Indonesia, Thailand, Burma, India, Pakistan (the Government of Pakistan extended hospitality and arranged for scholars to come to Karachi from distant parts of the country); Iraq, Lebanon, Egypt, Turkey.

The International Commission also wishes to thank Howard University, Washington, D.C., for granting leave of absence to Professor Ware for two years and two half years, the University of Amsterdam for reducing the academic duties of Professor Romein for a period of two years, and the Government of India for the opportunity to include H.E. Sardar Panikkar in the group of author-editors.

Finally, in the preparation of the volume, the author-editors have had ingenious and dependable research assistance from Dr Dorothy Jackson, Mrs Margaret Carroll, Miss Mary Gresham, Prof. I. Schöffer, Prof. F. de Jong Edzu, and Dr W. G. Heeres.

In elaborating the editorial notes, the consultants utilized materials from the following scholars whose comments and suggestions were also helpful to the author-editors in revising the first draft of the volume:

Members of the International Commission
Sir Julian Huxley, FRS (United Kingdom).
Professor Mario Praz (Italy).
Professor Silvio Zavala (Mexico).
Professor C. K. Zurayk (Syria).
Professor A. A. Zvorikine (Union of Socialist Soviet Republics).

Corresponding Members of the International Commission
The late Professor F. S. Bodenheimer (Israel).
H.H. Prince Dhaninivat (Thailand).
Professor John K. Fairbank (United States of America).
Professor Oscar Halecki (United States of America).
Professor B. Mazar (Israel).
Professor Richard Shryock (United States of America).

Scholars Consulted by the International Commission
Dr Louise B. Ames and Dr Frances Ilg, Gesell Institute of Child Development, New Haven, Connecticut (USA).
Professor Lionel Elvin, Institute of Education, University of London.
Professor Dr A. N. J. den Hollander, University of Amsterdam.
Professor Kenneth L. Little, University of Edinburgh.
Professor J. Presser, University of Amsterdam.
Professor Wilhelm Röpke, Graduate Institute of International Studies, University of Geneva.
Sir George Thomson, FRS, Corpus Christi College, Cambridge University.
Professor C. H. Waddington, FRS., University of Edinburgh.
Professor W. F. Wertheim, University of Amsterdam.

Scholars Consulted by the National Commissions for UNESCO

Austria:	Professor Dr Heinrich Benedikt, University of Vienna.
Bulgaria:	Professor Ignat Emanuilov, Academy of Sciences, Sofia.
	Professor Khristo Khristov, Academy of Sciences, Sofia.
	Dr D. Kosev, Institute of History, Member of the Academy of Sciences.
Ceylon:	Dr S. J. Tambiah, Colombo.
Chile:	Dr Ricardo Krebs, Santiago-de-Chile.
Czechoslovakia:	Professor Radim Foustka, Charles University, Prague.
	Dr Vavro Hajdu, Institute of Law, Academy of Sciences, Prague.
	Dr Ivan Málek, Institute of Biology, Academy of Sciences, Prague.
	Professor Minn Latt, Institute of Oriental Studies, Academy of Sciences, Prague.
	Professor Ludvík Svoboda, Institute of Philosophy, Prague, Corresponding Member of the Academy of Sciences.
	Dr Dušan Zbavitel, Institute of Oriental Studies, Prague.
Hungary:	Professor Tomás Földessy, Institute of Philosophy, Lóránd Eötvös University, Budapest.
	Dr János Jemnic, Associate Member, Hungarian Academy of Sciences, Institute of History, Budapest.

	Dr Vilmos Peschka, Associate Member, Hungarian Academy of Sciences, Institute of Political Sciences and Law, Budapest.
	Dr Gyula Raszszo, The History of War Museum and Archives, Budapest.
	Professor Imre Törö, School of Medicine, University of Budapest.
	Dr László Zsigmond, Deputy Director, Institute of History, Academy of Sciences, Budapest.
India:	Dr Prabhakar Machwe, Sahitya Akademi, India.
Israel:	Professor S. N. Eisenstadt, Hebrew University.
Italy:	Professor Mario Bendiscioli, University of Pavia.
	Professor Silvio Golzio, University of Turin.
	Professor Vincenzo Cappelletti, *The Italian Encyclopaedia.*
Japan:	Professor Masaaki Kosaka, Kyoto University.
	Professor Seiichi Iwao, Tokyo University.
	Professor Suketoshi Yajima, Tokyo College of Sciences.
Korea:	Professor Cho Eui Sul, Yonsei University, Seoul.
	Mrs Chung Bom Mo, University College of Education, Seoul.
	Professor Lee Sang Bek, College of Liberal Arts and Sciences, Seoul.
	Professor Suhr Myung-wun, University College of Education, Seoul.
	Professor Samuel Shahoon Shin, College of Liberal Arts and Sciences, Seoul.
	Professor Minn Young Gyu, Librarian and Professor of History, Yonsei University, Seoul.
	Professor Koh Sung Jae, University College of Commerce, Seoul.
Norway:	Dr Edvard Bull, The Norwegian Folk Museum, Oslo.
Poland:	Professor Eugeniusz Olszewski.
	Professor Boloslaw Skarzynski.
	Professor Bogdan Suchodolski.
	Professor Armin Teske.
Spain:	Professor Pedro Lain Entralgo, University of Madrid.
Turkey:	Professor E. Z. Karal, University of Ankara.
Union of Soviet Socialist Republics:	Dr E. I. Adirovich, Institute of Physics and Technology, Academy of Sciences of the Uzbek Soviet Socialist Republic.
	Academician V. A. Ambartsumyan, Astrophysical Observatory of the Academy of Sciences of the Armenian Soviet Socialist Republic.
	A. S. Arsenyev, Candidate of Philosophy, Institute of the History of Natural Sciences and Technology, USSR Academy of Sciences.
	Academician A. A. Arzumanyan, Institute of World Economics and International Affairs, USSR Academy of Sciences.
	Dr J. P. Averkieva, Institute of Ethnology, USSR Academy of Sciences.

Dr K. A. Beginyan, Institute of State and Law, USSR Academy of Sciences.

Dr L. J. Blacher, Institute of the History of Natural Sciences and Technology, USSR Academy of Sciences.

A. E. Bovin, Candidate of Law, Editorial Board of *The Communist*, Moscow.

F. M. Bourlatsky, Candidate at Law, Editorial Board of *Pravda*, Moscow.

Dr I. S. Braginsky, Corresponding Member of the Academy of Sciences of the Tajik Soviet Socialist Republic, Editorial Board, *Peoples of Asia and Africa*, Moscow.

Professor E. D. Chermensky, Moscow State University.

Dr V. M. Dalin, Institute of History, USSR Academy of Sciences.

Professor A. M. Dyakov, Institute of the Peoples of Asia, USSR Academy of Sciences.

Professor H. T. Eidus, Institute of the Peoples of Asia, USSR Academy of Sciences.

I. K. Ekholm, Candidate of Pedagogy, Academy of Pedagogical Sciences of the Russian Soviet Federative Socialist Republic.

Dr A. A. Elistratova, Institute of World Literature, USSR Academy of Sciences.

Professor L. M. Gatovsky, Corresponding Member of the USSR Academy of Sciences, Institute of Economics, USSR Academy of Sciences.

Dr G. N. Golikov, Institute of Marxism-Leninism, Moscow.

Dr L. R. Gordon-Polonskaya, Institute of the Peoples of Asia, USSR Academy of Sciences.

B. B. Granovsky, Candidate of Arts; *Soviet Encyclopaedia*, Moscow.

Assistant Professor A. N. Grzhegorshevsky, Candidate of Economics, Academy of Social Sciences, Moscow.

Professor A. M. Gurevich, Institute of World Economics and International Affairs, USSR Academy of Sciences.

Professor P. A. Henkel, Institute of Plant Physiology, USSR Academy of Sciences.

Professor M. S. Ivanov, Institute of Ethnography, USSR Academy of Sciences.

Professor V. N. Kolbanovsky, Institute of the Peoples of Asia, USSR Academy of Sciences.

Academician N. I. Konrad, Institute of the Peoples of Asia, USSR Academy of Sciences.

Yu. P. Lisitsyn, Candidate of Medicine, Second Medical Institute, Moscow.

V. B. Lutsky, Candidate of History, Institute of the Peoples of Asia, USSR Academy of Sciences.

Dr A. A. Manukyan, Institute of World Economics and International Affairs, USSR Academy of Sciences.

Professor A. F. Miller, Institute of History, USSR Academy of Sciences.

E. D. Modrzhinskaya, Candidate of Philosophy, Institute of Philosophy, USSR Academy of Sciences.

U. P. Ouryas, Candidate of Law, Institute of State and Law, USSR Academy of Sciences.

Z. M. Pashetkina, Candidate of Economics, Institute of World Economics and International Affairs, USSR Academy of Sciences.

V. M. Polevoy, Candidate of Arts, *Soviet Encyclopaedia*, Moscow.

Professor L. S. Pollak, Institute of Oil Chemical Synthesis, USSR Academy of Sciences.

Dr R. M. Samarin, Institute of World Literature, USSR Academy of Sciences.

Dr V. S. Semenov, Institute of Philosophy, USSR Academy of Sciences.

Dr B. Y. Smulevich, USSR Central Statistical Department, Research Institute, Moscow.

Dr R. Y. Steinman, *Soviet Encyclopaedia*, Moscow.

Dr R. I. Stolper, Institute of Economics, USSR Academy of Sciences.

Academician S. G. Strumilin, Economics Department, USSR Academy of Sciences.

General N. A. Talensky, Institute of History, USSR Academy of Sciences.

V. P. Tikhomirov, Candidate of Economics, Institute of International Relations, Moscow.

Dr S. L. Tikhvinsky, Institute of the World Socialist System, USSR Academy of Sciences.

T. K. Trifonova, Candidate of Philosophy, Institute of World Literature, USSR Academy of Sciences.

V. Tumanov, Candidate of Law, Institute of State and Law, USSR Academy of Sciences.

Academician E. S. Varga, Institute of World Economics and International Affairs, USSR Academy of Sciences.

Dr N. N. Yakovlev, Institute of History, USSR Academy of Sciences.

I. P. Yastrebova, Candidate of Economics, Institute of Africa, USSR Academy of Sciences.

L. I. Yurevich, Candidate of History, *Science*, Moscow.

L. A. Zak, Candidate of History, *Soviet Encyclopaedia*, Moscow.

Professor L. I. Zubok, Institute of History, USSR Academy of Sciences.

United Kingdom:

Mr B. Abel-Smith, London School of Economics.

Mr V. L. Allen, University of Leeds.

Dr A. N. Frankland, Royal Institute of International Affairs, London.

Mr S. J. Gould, London School of Economics.

Mr D. G. MacRae, London School of Economics.

Professor David Mitrany.

Dr Ivy Pinchbeck, London School of Economics.

Mrs B. R. Scharf, London School of Economics.

Professor M. J. Wise, London School of Economics.

United States of America: Professor W. Norman Brown, University of Pennsylvania, Philadelphia.

Professor Herbert B. Callen, University of Pennsylvania, Philadelphia.

Professor Lynn M. Case, University of Pennsylvania, Philadelphia.

Professor Thomas C. Cochran, University of Pennsylvania, Philadelphia.

Mrs Hope T. Eldridge, University of Pennsylvania, Philadelphia.

Professor Holden Furber and Elizabeth Furber, University of Pennsylvania, Philadelphia.

Colonel William R. Kintner, University of Pennsylvania, Philadelphia.

Professor Hans Kohn, College of the City of New York.

Professor R. Strausz-Hupé, University of Pennsylvania, Philadelphia.

Professor Martin Wolfe, University of Pennsylvania, Philadelphia.

Professor Marvin E. Wolfgang, University of Pennsylvania, Philadelphia.

Professor Conway Zirkle, University of Pennsylvania, Philadelphia.

The authors and consultants also utilized critical materials made available by the National Commissions for Unesco of Pakistan, Rumania and Viet Nam.

Cultural Institutions

International Catholic Co-ordinating Centre for Unesco: François Russo, sj, Ecclesiastical Consultant.

International Federation of Catholic Universities: Dr Paul Dezza.

Jewish Theological Seminary of America, New York.

Pontifical Committee on History: Msgr Michele Maccarone.

Pontifical Gregorian University, Rome:

Erveo Carrier, sj, Institute of Social Sciences.

Gicrgio Cruchon, sj, Faculty of Philosophy.

Edoardo Dhanis, sj, Faculty of Theology.

Emilio Gathier, sj, Faculty of Missionary Work.

Giorgio Jarlot, sj, Institute of Social Sciences.

Vittorio Marcozzi, sj, Faculty of Philosophy.

Giuseppe Masson, sj, Faculty of Missionary Work.

Emilio Pin, sj, Institute of Social Sciences.

Coengeno Quinn, sj, Institute of Social Sciences.

Ricardo Garcia Villoslade, sj, Faculty of Ecclesiastical History.

Mrs E. R. Schari, London School of Economics.

Professor M. J. Wing, London School of Economics

United States
of America: Professor W. Norman Brown, University of Pennsylvania, Philadelphia.

Professor Herbert B. Callen, University of Pennsylvania, Philadelphia.

Professor Lynn H. Case, University of Pennsylvania, Philadelphia.

Professor Thomas C. Cochran, University of Pennsylvania, Philadelphia.

Miss Hope T. Eldridge, University of Pennsylvania, Philadelphia.

Professor Holden Furber and Elizabeth Furber, University of Pennsylvania, Philadelphia.

Colonel William R. Kintner, University of Pennsylvania, Philadelphia.

Professor Hans Kohn, College of the City of New York.

Professor R. Strausz-Hupé, University of Pennsylvania, Philadelphia.

Professor Martin Wolfe, University of Pennsylvania, Philadelphia.

Professor Marvin E. Wolfgang, University of Pennsylvania, Philadelphia.

Professor Conway Zirkle, University of Pennsylvania, Philadelphia.

The authors and consultants also utilized current materials made available by the National Commissions for Unesco of Pakistan, Romania and Viet-Nam.

Cultural Institutions:

International Catholic Co-ordinating Centre for Unesco: Francois Russo, S.J., Ecclesiastical Consultant.

International Federation of Catholic Universities: Dr Paul Dezza.

Jewish Theological Seminary of America: Yerushe die.

Pontifical Committee on History: Mgr Michele Maccarose, Pontifical Gregorian University, Rome.

Enzo Carrieri, S.J. Institute of Social Science.

Giorgio Cucchini, S.J. Faculty of Philosophy.

Edoardo Fabiani, S.J. Faculty of Theology.

Emilio Gathier, S.J. Faculty of Missionary Work.

Onorio Janko, S.J. Institute of Social Science.

Vittorio Marcozzi, S.J. Faculty of Philosophy.

Giuseppe Massoa, S.J. Faculty of Missionary Work.

Egilio Fin, S.J. Institute of Social Sciences.

Gregorio Quiroa, S.J. Institute of Social Sciences.

Ricardo Garcia Villoslada, S.J. Faculty of Ecclesiastical History.

ACKNOWLEDGEMENTS

UNESCO, the International Commission, the authors and the publishers wish to thank all those who have kindly given permission for the reproduction of the plates in this book. Acknowledgements are made under each illustration and abbreviated as follows:

Associated Press, New York   AP
Brazilian Embassy, Paris   BRAZILIAN EMBASSY
Centre de Recherches sur les Macro-molécules, Strasbourg   STRASBOURG
Cinémathèque française, Paris   CF
Crawley Development Corporation, UK   CDC
Cunard Line   CUNARD
J. Delville, Delviljem, Rueil-Malmaison, France   DELVILJEM
Embassy of the German Federal Republic, Paris   GERMAN EMBASSY
Ente Provinciale per il Turismo di Roma   TR
Federal Power Board, Salisbury, Southern Rhodesia   FPR
Gemeente Musea van Amsterdam   AMSTERDAM
General Motors, Detroit   GM
Walter Gropius, Cambridge, Mass.   GROPIUS
Harvard University, Mass.   HARVARD
Holland-America Line   HOLLAND-AMERICA
International Business Machines   IBM
International Theatre Institute, Paris   ITI
Japan Art Academy   JAA
Kafil Uddin Ahmed, Dacca   KAFIL UDDIN AHMED
Kunstgewerbemuseum der Stadt Zürich   KGM
N. S. Lamba, Chandigarh   LAMBA
Le Corbusier, Paris   LE CORBUSIER
LIFE Magazine © 1953 Time, Inc.   TIME-LIFE
Magnum, Paris   MAGNUM
Gjon Mili, New York   GJON MILI
Ministère de la Construction, Paris   MCP
Moody Institute of Science, Los Angeles, Calif.   MOODY INSTITUTE
Mount Wilson and Palomar Observatories, Pasadena, Calif.   MWP
Mulk Raj Anand Collection, Bombay   MULK RAJ ANAND
Musée Cernuschi, Paris   CERNUSCHI
Museum of Modern Art, New York   MODERN ART
National Gallery of Modern Art, New Delhi   MODERN ART, DELHI
National Housing Center, Washington, D.C.   NHC
National Museum for the History of Science, Leiden   LEIDEN
Georgia O'Keeffe, for the estate of Alfred Stieglitz   GEORGIA O'KEEFFE
Philips-Industrie, Paris   PHILIPS-IND.
Phillips Collection, Washington, D.C.   PHILLIPS
Pro Helvetia Foundation   PRO HELVETIA
Rabindra-Bharati Society   RBS
Régie Autonome des Transports Parisiens   RATP
Régie Renault, Paris   RENAULT
Scientific Laboratory, Los Alamos   LOS ALAMOS
Shell Berre, France   SHELL BERRE
F. Skinner, Esq., London   SKINNER
Société Nationale des Chemins de Fer Français   SNCF
Société des téléphones Ericsson, Paris   ERICSSON

State of California Department of Public Works, Division of Highways, Sacramento   CALIFORNIA STATE
Swiss National Tourist Office, Zürich   SWISS TOURISM
Swiss Postal Museum, Berne   PTT MUSEUM
Transworld Airlines   TWA
United Nations, New York   UNATIONS
United States of America Delegation to UNESCO, Paris   USA DELEGATION
United States Information Services   USIS
University of California   CALIFORNIA U
University College, Ibadan, Nigeria   IBADAN U
USSR Academy of Sciences   USSR ACADEMY
USSR Delegation to UNESCO, Paris   USSR DELEGATION

CONTENTS

INTRODUCTION: THE TWENTIETH CENTURY AS A PERIOD IN WORLD HISTORY

PART ONE: THE DEVELOPMENT AND APPLICATION OF SCIENTIFIC KNOWLEDGE

Section I—New Scientific Thought

Section II—The Elaboration and Application of the Physical Sciences

Section III—Development and Application of the Biological Sciences

Section IV—Application of Knowledge to Human Behaviour and Development of the Social Sciences

PART TWO: THE TRANSFORMATION OF
SOCIETIES

PART THREE: THE SELF-IMAGE AND ASPIRATIONS OF THE PEOPLES OF THE WORLD

PART FOUR: EXPRESSION

CONCLUSION

ILLUSTRATIONS

ILLUSTRATIONS

PARTS TWO TO FOUR

**(All the plates listed hereunder are to be found between
pages 1190 and 1191)**

MAPS

PART ONE

PART TWO

The maps of Volume VI were prepared by Hallwag A.G., Berne.

FIGURES

Line drawings executed especially for this work by Stella Robinson in collaboration with R. G. Hadlow.

CHARTS

All charts were designed for this work by Stella Robinson in collaboration with R. G. Hadlow

INTRODUCTION:
THE TWENTIETH CENTURY
AS A PERIOD
IN WORLD HISTORY

CHAPTER I

THE SHIFT IN WORLD POWER[1]

IN 1899 the British poet Rudyard Kipling wrote his famous lines: 'Take up the White Man's burden—ye dare not stoop to less.' In 1957 the African state of Ghana took its seat at the United Nations along with eighty other nations of the world. The history of the first half of the twentieth century is the story of the revolutionary shift in power reflected in these two events. For Kipling wrote not alone for the British empire, on which 'the sun never set', but for the French empire with its *mission civilisatrice*, and the Dutch and Belgian, the Portuguese and the German—in short for the white man of Europe who had carried his power and his civilization to the ends of the earth. And Ghana was not unique, for more than a dozen independent countries, formed by those whom Kipling had seen as the white man's 'burden', had already taken their places as sovereign equals in the family of nations.

The world which Kipling knew came to an end in the first world war. The sure hegemony of Europe in the world and the structure at home on which European leadership was based were damaged beyond repair by internecine strife, the shift in the centre of industrial society overseas, especially to the United States, the success of the October revolution in Russia and the mounting nationalism in subject areas spurred on by Europe's own enunciation of the principle of self-determination of peoples. To those who could read the signs, it was apparent that the old order could never be restored. But the illusion of the old Europe in the old world lived on for at least a decade after the war. Only when the great depression of the 1930s added helpless misery at home to political ineffectiveness abroad did those who had dominated both their own societies and their dependent peoples recognize that the world had basically changed. And even then the sense of superiority did not wholly die, but took refuge in the subconscious of many Europeans, where it hampered their ability to see what was really going on in the world at large.

The second world war ushered in the new age whose foundations had already been laid. At the close of the war two great powers, both the offspring of European civilization, dwarfed all others—the United States, which represented the fullest application of industrialism, capitalism and democracy, was prepared to give leadership to what it called the free world; the USSR, which had built a powerful industrial society by the application of communist principles and organizational techniques, aimed to become the most industrially developed country in the world and by its success to influence the direction of economic and political development of other countries.

In what had once been European colonies or spheres of influence in Asia, the Middle East and north Africa, nations which had become newly independent or had been restored to full sovereignty struggled to overcome their handicaps of poverty and lack of economic development and to begin to catch up with the industrially developed countries. To this underdeveloped segment of the world the major contenders for world leadership offered economic aid and appealed for identification of interest, or at least friendly neutrality. The largest Asian country, China, chose the communist way, with the establishment of the Chinese People's Republic in 1949; so also did northern Vietnam and northern Korea. The rest remained outside of the communist orbit during the decade which followed the war, their constitutions drawn mainly on democratic lines, their economies a mixture of capitalism and socialism, and their policy generally one of non-entanglement in the major contest for power which divided the world.

The awakening of tropical Africa was not long delayed. In the new world that followed the second world war, no colonial power could take its position for granted and expect to escape for long the demands of its people: when Ghana achieved her independence, other African areas were already setting their timetables for their steps to statehood.

The old Europe in the new age found itself in a new role. On the one hand, the centre of gravity of European civilization had to a considerable extent shifted overseas, not alone to the United States, but to vigorous members of the British commonwealth, such as Canada and Australia, and to Latin America, where cultures of Portuguese and Spanish origins flourished as dynamically in Brazil and the Spanish-speaking American republics as in the Iberian peninsula. On the other hand European countries, forced back upon themselves, began to find a centre of gravity at home. By 1957 a nucleus of west European countries had agreed to develop a common European market and to exploit the new resources of atomic energy for their common use.

The world at mid-century had become in a very real sense a world society. Revolutionary developments in transport and communication had brought all peoples close to each other. The common language of science and technology carried the same meaning wherever it was applied. The common danger to life on earth from the radioactive effects of nuclear explosions was shared by all.

Though the world was sharply divided politically between the communist and non-communist groups,[2, 3] and divided economically between industrially developed and underdeveloped segments, the common problems of mankind had become the common concern of all. The United Nations provided, at the very least, a forum for world opinion. The World Health Organization united the forces of the world for the eradication of disease. The United Nations Food and Agriculture Organization concerned itself with the world's food and the welfare of the world's farmers and fishermen. The United Nations Children's Fund served children and mothers throughout the world. The United Nations Educational, Scientific and Cultural Organization supported efforts throughout the world to combat illiteracy and ignorance and sought to strengthen scientific and cultural interchange. The employers, workers and governments of the world sat down together in the International Labour Organization to formulate labour standards. The Universal Declaration of Human Rights embodied an expression of the world's aspiration. Mankind at mid-century had awakened to a sense of world community in which all were inescapably involved.

I. HEGEMONY OF EUROPE

At the beginning of the twentieth century Europe still overshadowed the world. Two events may be taken as symbolizing this position: the occupation of Peking (1900) by the combined forces of European nations following the anti-foreign Boxer rebellion, and the Delhi durbar (1903) held to celebrate the coronation of King Edward VII of Great Britain. The first was a demonstration of the helplessness of the most ancient and populous state in Asia, a nominally independent nation, before the colonial powers of Europe; the second was a declaration of faith in the permanence of British power in Asia. China and India, containing between them more than a third of the population of the world, lay prostrate before the might of Europe, together with the domains of the French in Indo-China, the Dutch in the Indonesian archipelago and the subjects of the Russian tsar in central and north Asia.

The European powers, in the course of twenty years (1879–99), had divided among themselves virtually the whole of the African continent. The immense area of the Belgian Congo became the private property of King Leopold of the Belgians; central, west and east Africa were partitioned between Great Britain, France, Germany and Portugal; France extended her authority from Algeria to build up a Sahara empire and to exercise a protectorate over Tunisia; Italy occupied Somaliland and Spain claimed areas in the northwest. Only the historic empire of Ethiopia and the small American-sponsored republic of Liberia stood outside the sphere of European colonialism. The European powers had agreed on the general plan of partition at the Berlin conference of 1885, and had demonstrated by their suppression of such resistance as they encountered that wars against colonial peoples brought victory to colonial powers with little cost in men or arms.

There was at that time no apprehension, not even a faint idea, that a time might soon come when the European nations would have to withdraw from Asia, much less that they might one day be forced to grant independence to nations in Africa. Lord Morley, one of the most liberal statesmen of the time, declared as Secretary of State for India in 1908 that he could not foresee a time when India would be free and self-governing, and the Indian National Congress itself had claimed only 'self-government on the colonial pattern'. Kaiser Wilhelm II had voiced the assumptions of the powers who enjoyed semi-sovereign rights in spheres of influence covering the most fertile and valuable parts of China, when he boasted (1897) 'the German Michael has set his shield, decorated with the imperial eagle, firmly upon the ground. Whoever asks him for protection will always receive it.'*

European hegemony appeared to rest not alone on armed might but on the advantage of European society by all the criteria which measured progress in an industrial age. In Europe were to be found the factories and mines, the

CHART I.   Colonial Empires before World War I (1910–13).
Source: League of Nations. *Annuaire International de Statistique*, v.

railways and steamships, the machines and the harnessed energy that made up the sinews of an industrial society. The *per capita* consumption of the principal source of energy, coal, was one hundred times as great in Britain as it was in China. Viewed in human terms, the vast majority of the people of western

* William L. Langer, *The Diplomacy of Imperialism 1890–1902* (New York, Knopf, 1935), Vol. II, p. 459.

Europe were literate, while less than 10 per cent of their colonial dependants could read; they enjoyed an average life expectancy nearly twice that which prevailed in most of Asia and Africa. The disparity in productive potential and level of living appeared to mark the superiority of European civilization and to provide a basis for continuing dominance. Moreover Europeans, confident of the superiority of their Christian religion, displayed a missionary zeal that followers of other faiths lacked or could not express.

Only the Japanese empire remained outside the sphere of European authority, for the other free Asian countries owed their precarious independence to their status as buffer zones—Siam between Great Britain and France, Afghanistan and Persia between Great Britain and Russia. Once her traditional isolation had been broken in 1853, Japan had sought to acquire European techniques and to use them to defend herself from the fate which had overtaken the rest of Asia. Since 1868 she had pursued a vigorous policy of industrial and military development along western lines, and had combined the aggressive and dynamic spirit of the West with her strong central organization imbued with feudal traditions. Her victory over China in 1895 had placed her in a position to imitate the West in aspiring to become a colonial power in her own right.

The first significant breach in European supremacy came at the very time when Europe appeared to be at the height of its world power. In 1902 Britain concluded a treaty of alliance with Japan. This was a major event, looked at from any point of view. It was the first alliance on terms of equality between a great European power and an Asian state. It was directed frankly against another European state, Russia. Under its terms Great Britain was prepared to entrust to Japan the support of her vital interests in the area of the China Sea. The Russo-Japanese war was rendered possible only by this alliance.

The Japanese victory over Russia in 1905 may well be considered as the event which unleashed Asian nationalism. There had been earlier stirrings, as when Asian nations had received with enthusiasm the news that the Italian army had sustained a major defeat at the hands of the Ethiopians at Adowa (1896). But Italy was a little-known power in the East and though the Ethiopian victory showed for the first time that European nations were not invincible, it did not have the same revolutionary effect as the Japanese victory over the Russian colossus. Moreover the Japanese were victorious not only on land but at sea. Since the time when Khair ud-din Barbarossa commanded the Turkish fleet in the sixteenth century no Asian country had gained a naval victory against a European nation; in fact it was their sea power that had enabled the European nations to exercise authority in Asia. Admiral Togo's victory therefore appeared to most Asian observers as a turning-point in history, as indeed it was. In a short time the news of the famous victory even reached remote villages in Africa by primitive means of communication.[4]

The awakening of Asia may be said to start from that date. In India, especially, its effect was far-reaching. The nationalist movement, which previously had asked only moderate reforms acceptable to some of the more enlightened British civil servants, became a revolutionary force. An extremist party, demanding complete independence and resorting to terrorism, violence and economic boycott as its methods, took the initiative away from the more moderate elements. In China the nationalist parties began, under the leadership of Sun Yat-sen, to plan a revolution.

Elsewhere the feeling was abroad that the time had come to prepare for independence. The nucleus of an independence movement was formed in Vietnam in 1909; a Burmese priest returning from a visit to Japan in 1914 called for a nationalist movement of renovation and liberation of Burma; in Indonesia a small group of western-trained intellectuals tried to revivify the old self-consciousness of the people without asking for help from the Dutch government. All this however might then have led to nothing more than partial reforms had not the war of 1914–18 broken the structure of European power.

That power had already begun to be counterbalanced by the rise of the United States as a world power. In 1900 the opposition of the United States, which insisted on an 'open-door' policy to maintain free access to the Chinese market, had helped to prevent the actual partition of China. In 1905 it was the president of the United States who mediated in the Russo-Japanese war; he proposed terms of settlement which limited the claims of the victor by denying the Japanese indemnity and returning Manchuria to China, and he brought the belligerents together to sign the Treaty of Portsmouth in a harbour of the United States. American investors were beginning to compete with British in Latin America and the nation had shown its readiness to invoke with increased confidence its historic Monroe Doctrine to prevent the intervention of any non-American power on the continents of North and South America.

The American people however were reluctant to enter the world struggle for power outside the continent which they had considered it their manifest destiny to occupy. When the Philippine Islands and Puerto Rico had fallen into their hands in 1898 as the consequence of pursuing their historic western hemisphere policy and aiding Spain's last dependency in the New World in its fight for independence, some leaders had welcomed the new role of the United States as a colonial power and others had accepted it as inevitable.[5] But many Americans, engaged in the task of settling a continent and cut off from Europe and Asia by broad oceans patrolled by the British fleet, retained their traditional desire to avoid entangling alliances. They, or their ancestors, had come to the new continent to escape the conditions of the old—its economic limitations, political or religious restraints, compulsory military service or direct persecution. To them America meant opportunity, not power. They were preoccupied with the quest for a life of freedom and well-being which seemed within reach, at least for their children, and they wanted no involvement in the affairs of Europe which they had resolutely left behind.

The industrial development of the United States was indeed already showing signs of surpassing that of Europe in efficiency, productivity and extent. On the eve of the first world war, the United States was consuming 20 per cent more coal *per capita* than the most industrialized European country, Britain, and was producing 50 per cent of the world's machinery. It was the productive capacity of the United States that was to decide the issue when the European war had become a stalemate in 1917.

II. THE FIRST WORLD WAR—THE GREAT DIVIDE

The dominant position of Europe *vis-à-vis* the rest of the world belied the inner strains within Europe itself, where nations faced each other as from armed camps, and two systems of alliances perpetuated the old concept of balance of power. The enormous and ever-mounting sums of money and the manpower which European powers spent to maintain vast armies and navies were not designed to maintain their superiority over their subject peoples; colonial wars were cheap, and the subject peoples themselves furnished much of the manpower. The armed forces were aimed at European neighbours. Britain was determined to keep her fleet at the combined strength of the next two naval powers; France lengthened the term of conscription in the effort to bring the strength of her forces to those of her more populous neighbour, Germany, while the latter, in turn, increased the number of men under arms.

Once the spark was struck by the murder of the Austrian Archduke Ferdinand at Sarajevo on June 28, 1914, the continent was aflame. For a month efforts were made to localize the conflict, but when Austria finally declared war on Serbia one country after another was dragged swiftly into the fray. Within a week Russia had come to the aid of her ally, Serbia, Austria's ally Germany had declared war on Russia and her ally France, the frontiers of neutral Belgium and Luxembourg had been crossed by German troops and Great Britain, their guarantor, had entered the war. Italy refused to recognize a treaty obligation to the central powers, but subsequently came in on the other side when it appeared that she might use the opportunity to fulfil her irredentist ambitions in the Adriatic.

The conflict, moreover, did not remain European, for almost immediately after her own declaration of war on Germany Britain called on her ally, Japan, and in less than a month from the opening of hostilities in Europe the theatre of war was extended to the Pacific. Before the war was over, zones of combat included also the eastern Mediterranean, the Persian Gulf, the east and south coasts of Africa and the broad Atlantic.

The plans of all the military staffs were based on a short war. But new weapons had made the defence too strong for sudden victory, and within a few weeks the war had settled into a long stalemate which was not broken for nearly four years. As the war dragged on it became more and more a contest of peoples and of economic resources and less one of armies and navies. The submarine warfare by which the Germans sought to overcome the immense

superiority of the British navy destroyed merchant shipping carrying food and
industrial supplies; the blockade of German ports starved the German
economy of essential materials. Meantime the casualties from repeated efforts
to break the stalemate reached staggering dimensions. By the close of the war
more than two-thirds of the 39,000,000 men mobilized by France, Russia,
Germany and Austria had been killed, wounded or captured, and over a third
of the 14,000,000 British and Italian forces.

The European powers emerged from the war with their societies strained
and weakened in every way: in men and wealth, in the balance of their economies and the stability of their political structures and above all in their relation
to new powers rising or beginning to rise in other parts of the world.

As Europe's position declined the United States stood forth as a major
world power. She finally abandoned her historic policy of non-intervention in
Europe's struggles and threw her economic and military weight into the war
in 1917, making a decisive contribution to the victory of the western allies. By
the end of the war she had become a creditor instead of a debtor nation, and
the world financial centre of gravity had started to shift from London to New
York. Even more significantly, the United States defined the terms of the
conflict, 'to make the world safe for democracy'; in President Wilson's
Fourteen Points, she enunciated the bases for a peace settlement. The
principle of the self-determination of peoples provided the rationale for the
break-up of the Austro-Hungarian and Ottoman empires and encouraged the
aspirations for independence among the peoples of Asia, the Near East and
Africa.

Initiative in Asia also passed to the United States. When Japan faced China
with her Twenty-One Demands at the opening of the war, it was the United
States that opposed her. As a power concerned with open trade rather than
colonial domination, the United States viewed the anti-colonial Asian point of
view with considerable sympathy. In the era following the war the emergence
of the United States as a major factor in the Far East impeded the complete
resuscitation of European imperialism, for the colonial powers found that in
the absence of American support it was no longer possible to follow 'gunboat
diplomacy' as of old. American influence, furthermore, prevented a revival of
the Anglo-Japanese alliance and effectively hindered Japan from organizing
the resources of China in support of her own imperialist policies.

In the same year, 1917, that the United States entered the war Russia
experienced the successive revolutions which ushered in the Soviet state. A
decade earlier an abortive revolution had broken out following the defeat of
Russia at the hands of the Japanese in 1905. In the intervening period stern
repression and minor reforms had failed to quell the peasants' unrest or to
check the radical tendencies of the active element among workers and
peasants. In February 1917, with the war dragging on and Russian losses
heavy, a revolution led by the liberal democratic and social revolutionary
parties overthrew the tsar and sought to establish a liberal democratic régime.

Within a few months the revolutionary Bolshevik party of workers and peasants, led by Lenin, swept away the moderate government and seized power in the name of the proletariat. As the first successful revolution in the world to be projected in economic as well as political terms it had an immense impact internationally, for it provided a world-wide stimulus and encouragement to revolutionary movements of workers and peasants and gave an impetus and a socio-economic orientation to liberation movements among colonial and subject peoples.

In the civil war which followed the October revolution, the allied powers intervened to oppose the revolutionary party. The victory of the Bolsheviks in the civil war in spite of this intervention served notice that a new power had been born whose presence would have two profound effects. Not only would it have an unsettling influence on the traditional class structure of the capitalist societies of Europe; the USSR would in time overshadow the western European powers themselves when it stood out as one of the two giants of the modern world after the second world war.

But it was in its impact on the peoples of Asia and Africa that the first world war was perhaps most significant as a turning-point in world history. Once war broke out in Europe the unity of European interests *vis-à-vis* Asia was destroyed as the European nations began to bid for Asian support. Indian soldiers fought in France, and the entire propaganda machinery of the British government in India was utilized to prove to the Indians that Germans were inhuman 'Huns' and 'Boches'. Japan not only joined the war in Asia but was invited to send her navy to the Mediterranean. China and Siam were induced to declare war on Germany; China sent labour battalions to France and other theatres of war, and her allies actively encouraged her to abolish the rights of extra-territoriality and other privileges within China which Germany enjoyed.

The effect of Asians and Africans fighting in Europe in support of European nations against other European nations was unprecedented. The French statesman Alexandre Varenne, on his appointment as governor-general of Indo-China, noted that this participation had proved that peoples have other aspirations than physical well-being, it had awakened in distant lands of the ancient world a feeling of independence, and 'this Orient which the European travellers have discovered and crossed the seas to gaze upon has now crossed the same seas to view us and delve into the secrets of Europe'.*

More important than the actual discovery of Europe by Asians and Africans was the change in the moral position of the European powers. To ask India and Indo-China to subscribe to war loans in order to defend democracy and prevent the imposition of German *Kultur* over the world was to expose the moral weakness of the metropolitan powers to their own subjects. The Indian nationalist leader, B. G. Tilak, made this point clear when he

* Quoted in *L'Asie française* (Paris, March 1926), p. 110.

demanded openly that prior agreement on self-government for India was necessary before India could support the war as a national programme.

The preoccupation of European nations with war, moreover, gave the Asian nations their first major opportunity for industrial development. Japan alone was able to utilize the opportunity to the fullest extent, but industrial progress in India and China during the war period was considerable. The Indian iron and steel industry, for example, was able to establish itself firmly on a modern basis as a result of Britain's steel requirements in the East, and in the period immediately following the war, Indian capitalism began to assert itself and to compete with British capital in India. In China, though the country as a whole was disorganized, a new local capitalism found opportunities in the European concessions.

The rise of the United States and the Russian revolution both contributed to the dynamism of the war period in Asia. When President Wilson enunciated the principle of self-determination of peoples, it seemed like a new revelation. However much Europeans might have looked upon it merely as a useful weapon with which to detach the suppressed peoples of the Austrian, German and Turkish empires, it was acclaimed in Asia, where the European allies least desired it to be accepted, as a doctrine of liberation. When self-determination of peoples was accepted as a war aim the moral position of the nationalist movements in Asia became unassailable; for how could India, which had fought on the side of the Allies on three continents, be denied the right which was being offered to Czechs, Poles, Croats and Arabs within empires engaged on the other side?[6]

The Russian revolution gave strong reinforcement to Asian nationalism, and was a major factor in defining its content in the areas where a strong nationalist movement was not already defined in liberal democratic terms. The declaration of the rights of the peoples of Russia proclaimed the equality and sovereignty of the dependent peoples in the former tsarist empire, emphasizing the principles of national self-determination and ethnic separateness of minorities. This doctrine was highly explosive at the time, whatever its later application, and it had an immense effect in shaping opinion in Asia. Moreover, the Soviets from the beginning declared their support for the national struggles of colonial peoples, and they abdicated the rights of extraterritoriality which, with other European powers, they enjoyed in Asian countries. For the first time there was one European nation which was prepared openly to champion the cause of colonial peoples.

The impact of Soviet policy differed among Asian countries. In China Sun Yat-sen, after failing to secure European support for his parliamentary régime, openly declared: 'We no longer look toward the West. Our faces are turned toward Russia', and he patterned his party, the Kuomintang, on the Russian Communist party. The Indian National Congress on the other hand, with its liberal traditions of nearly forty years, was less impressed by the communist methods. The effect of the Russian revolution on India was mainly to modify the content of nationalism, giving it an economic programme and an emphasis on social reconstruction. In areas where both the national economies and nationalist movements were less developed, as in Indo-China and Indonesia, the appeal of communism as such was greater.

Thus major elements that mark the new epoch in world history and separate it from the previous era had been brought together in the period 1914–18: the emergence of Asia as a factor in world politics, the growing prominence of the United States, the revolutionary character of Russia and the economic and political decay of the European powers. Few people either in Europe or elsewhere, however, realized how completely the situation had changed. It took the devastating economic depression of the 1930s to make it fully clear that the old European order had been permanently shattered. It required the ghastly trauma of the second world war to bring into precarious being the new world shape which, at the close of the first war, might already have been discerned.

III. BETWEEN THE WARS: THE SHADOW OF ECONOMIC DEPRESSION

1. *Decay in Europe* 7

The end of the first world war left central Europe in a state of political disintegration after its superhuman effort to fight the combined power of the rest of the world. The once mighty German empire lay prostrate, its industries severely depleted, its currency in the grip of an unprecedented inflation through which the middle classes were virtually dispossessed. Germany was deprived of her Silesian coalfields and a reduced East Prussia was cut off from the main Reich by a corridor of Polish territory leading to the internationalized port of Danzig. The historic empire of the Hapsburgs was dismembered and the demands of its subject nationalities for independence were recognized. Czechoslovakia was set up, Yugoslavia was formed by the union of Serbia with Montenegro and parts of the Austro-Hungarian empire, while Austria and Hungary became separate, independent states.[8] The imperial capital, Vienna, great cultural centre of eastern Europe, was reduced to the level of a provincial city. Poland was reconstituted from its fragments which had been incorporated at the end of the eighteenth century into Russia, Austria and Prussia. The states of Estonia, Latvia and Lithuania, which had long been part of the tsarist empire, were restored their independence.

The effect of all this was to create in the vital central region of Europe a number of small states, each jealous of its independence, and none with boundaries encompassing adequate economic resources or with a sufficiently strong political and industrial background to enable it to contribute to the stability of Europe.

France, with the prestige of victory, presented a brave front. But though the defeat of Germany left her as the first power on the Continent, the internal strength necessary to uphold her pretensions as heir to the power of

Louis XIV and Napoleon was not there. Her policy was dominated by the fear of a German revival and the recognition that once Germany found her feet again the dangers under the shadow of which France had lived from the time of the Bismarckian settlement would return in an aggravated form. Her former ally, Russia, which had been the counterpoise to German power, appeared to her to have become a potential enemy of western Europe;[9] the British and American guarantee on which France had hoped to build up her security did not materialize, for the United States Senate refused to ratify the Treaty of Versailles; the dream of the Rhine frontier for France was not realized.

French policy was therefore based on an organization of the smaller states of Europe—Poland, the successor states of the Hapsburg empire and the Balkan countries—under her leadership. The Little Entente was France's insurance, but clearly it could give no great support. Neither Yugoslavia, composed of conflicting nationalities, nor Rumania, which had a feudal political structure, could be a source of strength at a time of crisis. Czechoslovakia under the leadership of Thomas Masaryk and Eduard Beneš seemed a dependable ally. Poland appeared to have good military possibilities and French policy, consequently, was to try to develop a strong Poland.

Nor did the internal history of the Third Republic bear witness to a revival of strength. With the war sacrifice of 10 per cent of her active population killed and 11 per cent mutilated, and with an already low birth-rate further reduced, with most of her immense foreign investments wiped out by the Russian revolution and the finances of her client states precarious, her physical and financial position deteriorated perceptibly. These and other factors had their effects on the political fabric. Once peace was restored the political unity of wartime gave way to the characteristic political instability of the French parliamentary system. The popularity of extremist organizations, such as the royalist Action Française and the semi-fascist Croix de Feu, was evidence of a growing uneasiness, as was the growth of the Communist party; a series of political scandals revealed widespread corruption in French politics. A succession of ministries, notorious for their short term in office, proved incapable of dealing radically with the malaise of the nation.

When German revival became a reality and Adolf Hitler set out to tear to pieces the Treaty of Versailles, France found herself in no position to offer effective resistance. Hitler breached the French system of alliances by concluding a treaty with Poland in 1934; he denounced the clauses of the Versailles treaty requiring German disarmament and restored compulsory military service; he refused to continue to pay reparations; he reoccupied the demilitarized Rhineland and denounced the Locarno Pact of 1925 which had guaranteed the border between France and Germany. When civil war broke out in Spain in 1936 France lent no support to the legal republican government with which her own government was in sympathy, in spite of the aid rendered by Germany and Italy to the other side. In 1938, when Hitler annexed the Sudetenland from Czechoslovakia, she stood by while her most valuable ally in central Europe went down. In the early months of the second world war, when the invading German armies outflanked the fortified Maginot line on which France had relied, she showed neither the ability nor the will to resist, and the collapse of France in 1940 was the end of the road down which this once great power had faltered in the inter-war years.[10]

The one European power which retained a semblance of its former character and position after the first world war was Great Britain. The British parliamentary system, deeply rooted in a centuries-old tradition, maintained its vitality. But the British empire only remained intact through its conversion into the British Commonwealth of Nations, and this very act revealed the extent to which power had shifted from the metropolitan centre to the dominions overseas. The self-governing dominions, Canada, Australia, South Africa and New Zealand, had sent their finest troops to the battlefields. They, together with India, claimed a share in the direction of the war, and the imperial war cabinet which included the prime ministers of the self-governing dominions and representatives of India marked a departure from the structure of the pre-war empire in which foreign policy, defence and the right to declare war were the exclusive privilege or recognized function of the mother country. At the peace settlement the dominions and India were accorded separate representation as major participants in the war.

In the years after the war the self-governing dominions claimed the right to act independently in foreign policy. At the Imperial Conference in 1926 a new relation between Britain and her self-governing dominions was formulated as that of 'autonomous communities within the British empire, equal in status, in no way subordinate one to another in their domestic or external affairs though united by a common allegiance to the Crown, and freely associated as members of the British Commonwealth of Nations'. The Statute of Westminster in 1931 confirmed this status and thus allowed the dominions to assume the rights of independent sovereignty with their own foreign policy and diplomatic representatives, though Britain at this time did not relinquish her hold on the Indian empire. While her people still thought in terms of her historic power, her position had already come to depend more on leadership than on dominance. The Irish rebellion during the war had forced the granting of dominion status to the Irish Free State on Britain's doorstep, and it could easily be foreseen that other self-governing or independent units would be formed from segments of the world-wide British empire.

One of the most significant symptoms of the decay of European power was the denial of democracy and the political values of western Europe by a large number of European nations. Beginning with Italy, where fascists under Benito Mussolini marched on Rome and assumed power in 1922, one European state after another, outside the ranks of the western and northern European countries, became anti-democratic and dictatorial in its government. Admiral Nicholas Horthy in Hungary (1920), Primo de Rivera in Spain

(1923), Marshal Joseph Pilsudski in Poland (1926), Augustinas Voldemaras in Lithuania (1928), Antonio Salazar in Portugal (1932) and finally Adolf Hitler's Nazi régime in Germany (1933) showed how great was the denial of the principles of democracy which had been the pride of Europe. In all these countries social unrest permitted dictatorships to rule. Once they were in power, irredentist claims made the dictators' ambitions a threat to stability and peace. The Italian d'Annunzio's romantic action against Fiume in 1919 was perhaps the incident that set the pace but it was only one among many claims, such as those of Poland to Teschen, of Lithuania to Memel, of Italy to Nice and Corsica, of Germany to the Sudetenland.

It was, however, the economic rather than the political weakness of Europe which finally revealed the changed position of the old European societies in the world and precipitated the chain of events which were to bring a radically new structure into being. The weaknesses and maladjustments of the European economies in the post-war years were in part concealed by loans from the United States which helped to carry Europe through the process of reconstruction. A struggle to maintain the value of the French franc produced a political crisis in 1926. In the same year deep-seated labour unrest in Britain expressed itself in a general strike with a larger number of participants than any other strike in history. But it remained for the great depression of the 1930s finally to sweep away the illusion that the world could be restored to its pre-war shape, with Europe the seat of paramount power and the European bourgeoisie the ruling class over colonies abroad and workers at home.

The collapse of the European economies from the precarious readjustment they had achieved in the years after the war was precipitated by the crash of the New York stock market in October 1929, which ended a speculative boom in the United States. The fact that this event could drag down the European economies in its wake was in itself evidence of their dependent state. Two years later, when a measure of confidence had been restored and some recovery achieved, the failure of the principal banking institutions in Austria and Germany sent the European and American economies plummeting further into the economic abyss, their currencies undermined, their industries shut down, their national production reduced by as much as a quarter to a half from its 1929 level, and millions of workers unemployed, their families hungry, their outlook without hope.

Whatever the factors involved in the collapse and in the failure of efforts to bring recovery—and these were still in debate a generation later—the effects of the prolonged depression were far-reaching. They revealed that after more than a century of industrial development the capitalist countries of Europe and America still had too little understanding of their own economies to keep their people continuously employed. The spread and prolongation of the depression throughout the world showed how extremely vulnerable the industrial economies had become to dislocating influences, wherever these might arise. The fact that Britain since the close of the war had had continuous unemployment and that her basic coal industry had been chronically depressed seemed to imply that the European economies might be suffering from fundamental and perhaps incurable ills.

The great depression thus shook the confidence of the European countries in their own societies, it exposed their inner weaknesses to the rest of the world, and it so preoccupied their statesmen with domestic affairs as to sap the vigour of their national policies abroad. It created a fertile soil for the rise of dictators ready to take unorthodox means to meet the crisis, and produced an atmosphere of international impotence which permitted them to pursue their ambitions unchecked.

Against this background of frustration and despair, Adolf Hitler rose to power in Germany in 1933 and embarked on the course that was to plunge the world into war six years later. Hitler's strength lay in the fact that he dared to imagine a wholly new order and to set out to remake the world in this image. The tragedy for Europe was that his vision was a denial of every value which European society and European culture had developed through the centuries. For reason he substituted 'thinking with the blood', and the 'big lie'; for democracy and ultimate confidence in the judgment of the common man, the 'leadership principle' and blind followership by the masses; for respect for individual worth and human life, unmitigated terror, even to mass use of the gas chamber in his campaign to exterminate millions of citizens who happened to be Jews; for the give-and-take of political controversy and the initiative of voluntary organization, the *Gleichschaltung* of all parties, organizations and groups under common direction and into a common mould; for freedom of thought and speech, repression; for freedom of conscience, subservience of the Church to the state; for the authority of law, the secret police—Gestapo— and the perversion of legal principles and practice to serve the leader's ends; for the concept of equality and the brotherhood of man, a hierarchy of roles, in which women were permanently confined to children and home, workers must give up their independent organizations, and the other peoples of Europe and the world must recognize their inherent inferiority and be prepared to bow to their natural masters, the German *Herrenvolk*; for the ideal of a civil order, the military ideal as the norm of society.

With this vision of a new order, he tackled the internal problem of the German economy and the external problem of Germany's status. By a vigorous programme of militarization he set the unemployed to work and converted a labour surplus into a labour shortage. His policy of autarchy to make Germany independent of world trade called for the development of new industries and substitute products to take the place of those from abroad. While the rest of Europe stood by, preoccupied with its struggles to pull out of the depression, he effected a union with Austria, eliminated its conservative clerically-inclined government, and made it an adjunct to his Nazi state. He entered into an alliance with the fascist government of Italy, and he tested out his new weapons by giving aid to the Spanish dictator, Francisco Franco, who successfully overthrew the elected government by civil war. In 1939 he marched on Poland to inaugurate what he announced as a new era for Europe under the hegemony of the Third Reich, which should endure for a thousand years.

2. *Japan's bid for colonial power*

While Europe's Asian colonies were beginning to slip from their rulers' grasp, Japan projected a new Asian colonial empire under her rule. Her island homeland was small and her population large and growing. Her industries depended heavily on foreign trade for raw materials, fuel and other industrial supplies. A substantial part of her food supply was imported from abroad and she had to seek foreign markets. She looked to colonial development to meet her needs. The mainland of China offered many of the resources and markets which Japan required, if these could be brought under control and developed. The principal lack in this area was oil, and this seemed within reach on the islands of the Indonesian archipelago. The plan of Japan's imperialists was therefore to create a land empire to the north-west and an island empire to the south-east, and to organize the whole into an autarchic economy.

The first effective extensions of Japanese authority had been the fruits of her wars with China and Russia; from the former she had secured a food area, Formosa, and from the latter a region of potential industrial development, Korea. During the first world war she had forced her Twenty-One Demands on China to establish a paramount position in important areas of northern China and an attempted protectorate over the Chinese government.

In the decade following the war political leadership in Japan passed into the hands of a democratically inclined faction which acceded to pressures for withdrawal from China and for limitation of naval armaments. But when the world depression destroyed Japan's foreign markets and reduced her people to misery, the militarists, who had regained control, launched a series of moves designed to build Japan into a great Asian power. In 1931 Japan invaded Manchuria, set up the puppet state of Manchukuo and launched a vigorous programme of industrial development to supplement the resources of her crowded islands. In the following years she penetrated farther into China in a succession of aggressive moves and added other Pacific islands to those which she had inherited from Germany at the end of the war. Finally, in 1937 she launched a full-scale war against China which ultimately merged into the second world war.

3. *Growing importance of the United States of America*

The changed position of the United States in world politics was dramatized by her part in the peace negotiations at Versailles. Although Britain and France were represented at the peace conference by experienced statesmen who sometimes outmanœuvred the American president, it was President

Woodrow Wilson who was the principal arbiter of the destinies of the defeated nations. And it was not because she met opposition that the United States failed to follow through and to continue to exercise the political leadership that was hers; her own people were unwilling to assume that role. The American people were loath to have a position of leadership forced upon them in a world whose disorder only confirmed their traditional feeling that they wanted to be free of old-world conflicts. They had risen to the crisis of war but, this duty done, they were eager to return to their preoccupation with the permanent revolution in economic and social life which they were living out —to resume the domestic reforms which President Wilson on the eve of the war had named the 'new freedom', to exploit the new technology that offered a vision of release from back-breaking toil for farmers, workers and their wives and that was introducing the motor car, the radio and leisure into the life of the ordinary man, to return to what President Wilson's successor described as 'normalcy'. In this atmosphere the Senate of the United States turned back to the historic policy of non-entanglement and refused to ratify the treaties and to join the League of Nations of which the president of the United States had been the major architect.

It was only in the political sphere, however, that the United States withdrew from its position of pre-eminence. In the reconstruction of war-torn Europe and the settlement of reparations problems her leadership continued to be effective. No amount of political isolationism, moreover, could conceal the fact that New York had become a major financial centre. The principal European nations were indebted to the United States and the dollar largely replaced the pound sterling as international currency outside the British Commonwealth area. Financial pre-eminence was matched by an unprecedented increase in industrial potential. The United States became the leading industrial producer in the world to an extent that even Britain had never been before.

The revolutionary character of this transformation was not fully perceived, for American industry produced primarily for its own practically inexhaustible internal and hemispheric market while European nations retained a pre-eminent position in the markets of Asia and Africa. But the widening gap between Europe and America in productive efficiency and *per capita* income marked the real shift in the basis of power. The United States had grasped the potentialities of modern industry. When Europeans shuddered, as they often did publicly, at signs of the Americanization of Europe they were frequently reacting, at least in part, to the modernization of their own industrial society which they associated with the United States only because she had accepted the implications of industrialism more completely.

Though the new leadership of the United States was obscured in Europe by her act of self-restraint in the political sphere, in east Asia it was fully apparent. By her firm attitude toward the Japanese claim to control China during the war she had assumed a leadership and initiative which she did not surrender thereafter. After the treaty of Versailles the United States stood forth clearly as the dominant foreign power in the Far East. She became distrustful of Japanese policy as Japan expanded to the island groups near the equator, occupied the Shantung peninsula of China and augmented her naval armaments. The Washington Naval Conference convened by President Harding in 1921 was a clear declaration of American leadership in the East. At the conference the United States secured the dissolution of the Anglo-Japanese alliance, the return of Shantung to China, and an agreement on naval limitation which held down the Japanese navy to three-fifths of either the British or the American and established naval parity between the United States and Britain, though the latter had always tried to keep her fleet at least as big as the sum of her two nearest rivals.

From the Washington conference on, America's authority in the Far East grew steadily, but it was only after 1931 when the Japanese forced the issue in Manchuria that the full nature of American leadership in east Asia became clear. The Japanese occupation of Manchuria led to the Stimson declaration that, in substance, the United States did not intend to recognize any infringement on the sovereignty or territorial integrity of China. Although ineffective at the time this amounted to a declaration against Japanese expansion. Thereafter the United States maintained a steady pressure against Japan by giving aid and assistance to China in her struggle, by working up an impressive solidarity at the League of Nations and in the world against the recognition of Manchukuo and by isolating Japan diplomatically until she finally sought allies in Germany and Italy. It was the Japanese reaction in the attack on Pearl Harbor in December 1941 which provided the occasion for the entry into the second world war of the United States with its vast industrial resources.[11]

4. *The emergence of the Soviet Union as a new power*

From the time of the October revolution the Soviet Union was a force to be reckoned with. Even at its lowest point, when torn by civil war and armed intervention and racked by famine and epidemic, its revolutionary appeal to the oppressed classes of Europe and peoples of Asia was a threat to the established order. The mere fact that the area from the east of Poland to the Pacific, from the Arctic to the borders of China, India, Persia and the Black Sea—the largest single and continuous land area in the world—came under a revolutionary régime was in itself of supreme importance.

From the time of its birth the European powers and the United States opposed the communist state, whose leaders professed a dynamic theory which they claimed to be the absolute political truth of the future, valid throughout the world. But in 1917 the powers were still locked in a life and death struggle, and when they were free to intervene more actively after the end of the war their people were tired of war and weary of superhuman efforts to achieve victory. Their armed intervention met resistance and every-where ended in disaster, though at one time effective Soviet authority was confined to a comparatively small area in the region of Moscow.

When the dust of intervention cleared two things stood out plainly. In spite of eruptions in parts of Germany and a short-lived communist régime in Hungary, which were put down quickly and violently, there was no immediate likelihood that the proletariat of the world would follow in the Russian footsteps. The prospects of an immediate world revolution had become dim.

At the same time it became equally clear that whether the rest of the world liked it or not the Soviet power had come to stay. The Treaty of Rapallo concluded in 1922 between Germany and the Soviets was an unmistakable reminder that, though weakened by civil war, foreign intervention and internal economic crisis, Russia was a factor which could not be ignored in the world. However much the European nations might be repelled by the liquidation of capitalists, landowners and well-to-do peasants (*kulaks*) on economic or political grounds, attracted by the efforts to build a classless society on a socialist basis, worried by the possible contagion of ideas to their own people, or fearful of the revival of Russia's historic territorial aspirations with a new dynamic force, they could not fail to take her presence into account.

The political recovery of the Soviet area reduced to lesser proportions the smaller units in eastern Europe out of which Marshal Pilsudski of Poland hoped to build an Intermediate European Federation. As a result of the leadership which the Russian communists enjoyed as the first in world history to establish the dictatorship of the proletariat, the Communist party of the USSR acted as a guide to the communist parties throughout the world which were united in the Comintern, or Third International.

The economic revival of the USSR after an initial period of unexampled misery had equally far-reaching results. In the face of an economic boycott by the west European nations and the United States the communist leaders had been forced to adopt a policy of heavy temporary sacrifices in order to convert Russia into an industrialized nation. In 1928 they stepped up the pace of industrialization with the inauguration of the first five-year plan. By the eve of the second world war Russia's production of steel had become as great as that of Germany; though her economy had still great gaps, it was already apparent that a powerful industrial state had risen from the ashes of tsarist Russia. After the great depression the prestige of the Soviet Union markedly increased, for its economy was untouched by the crisis and its industrial development went on while in other countries men and machines stood idle.

With the emergence of Hitler and the revival of German military power the relation of the Soviet Union with the European states underwent a change. Throughout the 1920s the Soviet position was one of isolation. Although failure of the intervention in 1922 removed for the time being the immediate threat of direct military aggression, and although the faction of the Communist party which advocated the pursuit of revolutionary socialism in one country triumphed over the supporters of world revolution, the Soviet Union viewed the capitalist countries as essentially hostile neighbours.

From 1929 on, especially after 1931, the Soviet Union began to negotiate non-aggression agreements with her immediate neighbours, Poland, Lithuania and other states on her western borders. In 1932 she entered into a non-aggression pact with France and in the following year signed an agreement defining aggression with the countries to the south, Afghanistan, Persia, Turkey. The Soviet leaders were aware of the great implications of the revival of reaction in Germany, of Germany's desire for expansion to the east, of Rosenberg's theories about the right of Germany to living space in the Ukraine and elsewhere, and of the doctrine of the German geopolitical school whose unconcealed objective was to control the heartland—the vital plains of European Russia. They were also aware that there were powerful groups in western Europe and the United States as well as in Germany who saw in the revival of German power a counterweight to Russia and even hoped that Germany might be the means of ridding the world of the communist threat.

The Soviet riposte to the possibility of Germany being used as the spearhead of western reaction was open advocacy of collective security. In 1934 she was invited to join the League of Nations, and the world began to witness the unfamiliar spectacle of the Soviets as the champions of peaceful settlement of disputes and the literal observance of treaties. In every matter that came before the League—Japanese action in Manchuria, Italian aggression in Ethiopia and German action in different regions of Europe—the Soviet representative became the most vigorous pleader for collective action. The preview of another world war provided by the Spanish civil conflict was everywhere recognized as of supreme importance. Russia saw it as the prelude to a systematic campaign by the fascist powers directed against her, and sent her volunteers and military strategists to aid and lead the Spanish republican forces.

Until the failure of collective security evidenced by the Munich pact in September 1938, the USSR expressed its readiness to join with western European nations against Germany. After the Munich pact, however, the Soviet Union doubted the determination of Britain and France to resist Germany and in the following year entered into a non-aggression pact with Hitler. But when the collapse of France released the German forces for other operations the Russo-German pact became a scrap of paper as Hitler's armies swept eastward over the Russian land. The strength with which the Soviet armies and people stood against the German might and reconstructed their country after untold devastation bore witness to the success with which a largely agrarian, feudal society had been remade into one of the two greatest modern industrial states.

5. *Rising nationalism against colonial powers*

In the heat of the first world war the powers made promises and held out hopes to subject peoples—their own and those of their enemies—which they were reluctant to make good when they no longer urgently needed these people's support. But the impetus to nationalism in Asia and in the Middle East was too great to be checked. Nationalist movements were ready to take advantage of signs of weakness among the colonial powers and of their pre-occupation with problems of economic depression. The Soviet Union afforded a constant example of the possibility of consciously remaking society and it offered direct assistance to the 'toilers of Asia'.

During the war, the Arab peoples within the Ottoman empire were encouraged by the western allies to fight against their Turkish rulers, and they expected that independence would be their reward. Defeat of the Turks brought dismemberment to the Ottoman empire. But instead of achieving independence the Arabs found themselves in varying degrees under the protection or authority of Britain and France. British plans called for direct rule in the valley of the Euphrates, control of the Arabian peninsula and much of the Fertile Crescent through Arab leaders whom she supported as her allies, a protectorate in Egypt, a mandate over Palestine and a working agreement with the sultan of Turkey. The area was crucial, for it had been found to be immensely rich in oil, and oil was becoming the lifeblood of industrial countries as they entered the motor age. The British fleet was being converted from coal to oil and thus could no longer be supplied by home resources.

British hopes of easy dominance in the Middle East were, however, short lived. Turkish nationalists under the leadership of Mustapha Kemal fought for the complete independence of the modern national state which they organized in the Turkish heartland of Anatolia, and achieved their goal by 1923. The rival claims of France in the Fertile Crescent resulted in the driving out of Britain's Arab nominees and the establishment of a French mandate over Syria and Lebanon. The monarchy set up in Iraq pressed for independence. In the Arabian peninsula, King Hussein of Mecca who had originally been supported by the British was driven out of his kingdom by a rival dynastic leader, Abdul Aziz ibn Saud. The Egyptian nationalist movement won its first victory against Britain and gained partial independence for Egypt, a lesson which was not lost on other nationalist movements in the area. Britain's own commitment to the idea of a Jewish homeland undermined her relations with her Arab allies.

French authority in the Middle East encountered even more intense resistance than did the British. Though France sent a series of top military leaders as high commissioners for Syria, she faced open rebellion, and the area under her mandate was in effect held under military occupation. When the French authorities in 1925 went to the extreme of shelling the city of Damascus it was apparent that French persistence was being met by intense and determined Arab nationalist feeling.

Iran and Afghanistan, too, shared the prevailing nationalism in the Middle East. Since 1907 Persia had been divided by Anglo-Russian agreement into two spheres of influence and during the war, in spite of her neutrality, British forces had occupied parts of Persian territory as a step in fighting the Turks and later the Bolsheviks. The Russians in the first flush of the revolution renounced their claims under the Anglo-Russian agreement, and the movement for the recovery of Persian sovereignty was therefore directed mainly against the British. In 1921 Reza Khan seized control and in 1925 deposed the shah, assumed the crown and pushed forward a scheme of modernization. The dominant British influence in the south, exercised largely through the Anglo-Persian Oil Company, was the target of his attack; in 1932 the oil concessions were cancelled, to be replaced by an agreement more advantageous to the Persians. Afghanistan under King Amanullah in 1919 threw off the limitations which Britain had imposed on Afghan sovereignty and was soon afterwards recognized as an independent state.

Thus everywhere in the Middle East nationalism was rising and the European powers, though seeking to assert their influence and to gain new ground, were beginning to be forced to retreat.

The greatest of the colonial areas, India and Burma, emerged from the war with a form of partial self-government which marked a definite breach in the citadel of imperial authority. Under a system known as dyarchy power over education, health, local government and similar matters at the provincial level was transferred to elected representatives, while finance and the maintenance of law, order and defence were reserved to the central colonial government. In the central government half the members of the cabinet were nominated from among Indians and a majority of the legislature was subject to election on a restricted franchise.

The nationalist movement which had grown greatly during the war was not, however, content with this limited arrangement and pressed for immediate self-government. Under Mahatma Gandhi's leadership, the Indian National Congress adopted a dynamic, revolutionary programme based on non-co-operation with the British, a boycott of British goods and organization of the people to prepare them for independence. In this he had the support of a considerable section of the Muslims under the banner of the Khilafat movement.

From 1920 on, the drive for independence never slackened, and it was clear that India was unlikely to remain long under British rule. Britain sought to limit or delay independence by building up the princely states of India in direct relationship with the British Crown and by acceding to the separatist claims of the Indian Muslims. The first of these efforts to prevent the unity of the Indian people was unsuccessful. At the Round Table Conference summoned in London in 1930 in an attempt to reach a negotiated settlement, the princes, whose territories covered over two-fifths of the land area, offered to federate with the rest of India. As far as the Muslims were concerned, they ultimately demanded partition; but they were no more willing than the rest of the people of the sub-continent to remain under British rule. In the negotiations for independence they worked successfully for the establishment of a separate state, Pakistan, out of the provinces in which they constituted a majority.

China offers perhaps the best evidence of the breakdown of European supremacy following the first world war. Refusal of the Chinese delegates to sign the Versailles Treaty, and student demonstrations in Peking in 1919 against the decision of the Allies to permit Japan to occupy Shantung, were portents. At the Washington Conference in 1921 China's claims for equality were conceded in principle even at a time when that country had no effective government. Her representative's demand for tariff autonomy was not opposed by any power and the states concerned agreed under certain conditions to abandon foreign postal privileges not later than January 1923.

During the period between the students' movement in 1919 and the establishment of the national government in 1927 by Sun Yat-sen's successor, Chiang Kai-shek, the most remarkable feature of the Far Eastern situation was the changed behaviour of the western nations in the face of Chinese anti-foreign agitation. When for example the Shanghai police fired on a student demonstration on May 30, 1925, agitation spread to other cities from this great international centre where the Europeans still ruled; in Canton British troops resorted to firing. The Chinese retaliated by an effective blockade of Hong Kong and a boycott of British goods which they maintained for over a year. In the pattern of the relationships which had existed before the war such a blockade would have been answered by gunboats and further concessions would have been exacted as compensation. In 1925 however, though China could not have offered military resistance, Britain did not feel that she could use force and she even took part in a conference in Peking to devise measures to restore China's tariff autonomy at the very time when these hostile demonstrations were going on.

In south-east Asia Indonesia had remained comparatively unaffected by the war, for the Netherlands had not been a participant; but there too nationalism began to be a force in the following period. The Dutch government faced its first serious opposition in the nationalist rebellion of 1926. French authority in Indo-China was also challenged as communism began to spread. But in both these areas movements for independence did not gather effective momentum until the general collapse of colonial authority in the second world war.

IV. THE SECOND WORLD WAR AND AFTER:
NATIONS AND PEOPLES IN A NEW WORLD

The second world war brought into full being the new world pattern which had been building up from the beginning of the century. The pattern had taken shape in the first world war, and its outlines had come to be recognized as economic depression effectively closed the road back, ambitious dictators challenged the old order, the USA and USSR revealed their mounting strength, and the ferment of self-determination marked for early defeat the theory as well as the practice of colonialism.

It was the efforts of dictators to remake and dominate the world—Hitler in Europe and the Japanese militarists in Asia—that precipitated the world conflict. Hitler, pursuing the bold dream of European unity under the Nazi swastika, was prepared to use any measures, at home or abroad, to achieve his goal. Encouraged by the success of his piecemeal measures—in the Rhineland, in Austria, in Czechoslovakia—he believed that he would meet little opposition, and was confident that the new, swift weapons of offence—tanks and planes—would bring quick victory to his arms. With fascist Italy as his ally and communist Russia neutralized for the time being by the Russo-German pact, he took the great gamble of plunging Europe into war.

In the Pacific Japan was prepared to venture with equal boldness. Her daring and successful surprise attack against the United States fleet at Pearl Harbor and US installations in the Philippines on December 7/8, 1941, instantly brought the United States into the war, made the Japanese war in China part of the world war and converted the European war into a global conflict. In a few swift weeks Japan overran the French, British and Dutch possessions in south-east Asia, the Indonesian archipelago and the islands of the Pacific. Announcing her objective as the creation of a Greater East Asia Co-Prosperity Sphere, she organized the oil and other resources of these areas for her defence. In the process she released the colonial peoples from their European rulers and, though she substituted her own authority, destroyed the institutions through which former colonial suzerainty had been exercised and demonstrated to the subject peoples the impotence of those who had been their masters.

The second world war differed from the first in that it was a war of movement; the weapons of offence, especially the tremendous striking power of aircraft, had outstripped those of defence to make warfare once again a matter of attack and counter-attack. Even more than in the earlier conflict it was industrial potential that ultimately won through, as the unprecedented output of American industry poured on to every battlefield, as British production continued in spite of air attacks and as Russian factories beyond the Urals replaced those lost in her western industrial belt.

Far more than before, too, it was the civilian population which bore the brunt; among the many millions of Europeans young and old who perished in the war, scarcely more than a third were military personnel. The high civilian toll reflected not only the character of total war but the ideological basis of the struggle, for, as the resistance and partisan movements throughout Europe bore witness, the war became to a considerable extent a civil war; in addition, the civilian casualties in Europe included the Jews who were marked for extermination.

Most important of all, science changed the scale and manner of warfare; the culminating scientific achievement of the atom bomb, dropped on Hiroshima to wipe out in a single blast some 100,000 inhabitants, made it clear that science had carried the art of destruction to a new level, as radically different from what mankind had known before as had been the change wrought by the introduction of gunpowder in an earlier century. Henceforth the shape of world power was inseparable from the implications of the atomic—and soon the even more terrible hydrogen—bomb, which cast its fearful, radioactive shadow over the entire earth.

The world emerged from the second world war with two great powers towering above the rest, the USA and the USSR. With her homeland undamaged and her industrial productivity enormously increased, the United States was the major source of wealth for reconstruction, as she had been for the supplying of war material. Her world industrial leadership may be seen in the fact that five years after the war, when the European economies had largely recovered, she was producing 43 per cent of the world's iron ore and 45 per cent of its crude steel, 60 per cent of its locomotives and 74 per cent of its motor vehicles, 64 per cent of its radio receivers, 50 per cent of its rayon and 86 per cent of its other synthetic fibres.

In a move to rebuild the shattered economies of Europe and to restore the productive potential of her allies, the United States made available large amounts of money, surplus war material and technical aid, carrying over into peacetime the same concept of partnership in effort which had been the basis of the wartime programme known as lend-lease. In addition, as the sole occupying power in Japan and one of the four occupying powers in Germany, she poured money and effort into the rehabilitation of her former enemies, and stimulated a spectacular revival of their economies. When the United Nations and its specialized agencies were created the United States became the largest contributor, supplying from a third to a half of the budgets of these bodies. Under what was first known as the Point Four Program by virtue of the manner in which the proposal had been presented by President Harry Truman in 1948, she offered substantial technical aid to economically underdeveloped countries in their efforts to modernize their societies and made it possible for numbers of leaders, specialists, and students to visit or study in the United States.

Yet in spite of these unprecedented world commitments the American people retained some of their historic reluctance to become involved in world affairs and to assume the responsibilities of power which circumstances had thrust upon them. They met the demands of war and reconstruction, as they had those of the first world war, in terms of a crisis. They could not again withdraw, as they had when they refused to join the League of Nations, nor did they wish to do so. But they were still mainly preoccupied with opportunities at home, and after more than a decade in a paramount position the American people had yet to develop a clear and positive attitude toward the exercise of world power. Meantime the impact of American industry and private foreign investment was felt in many parts of the world.

Within months of the close of the war it became clear that the western allies and Russia, which had fought side by side after Hitler invaded the Soviet Union, were working at cross-purposes when it came to organizing the peace. The zones into which Germany had been divided for purposes of administration by the occupying powers became a division into two separate entities, as Russia supported the establishment of a communist-led state in its zone to the east, while the areas occupied by the United States, Britain and France in the west formed a federal republic, with West Berlin left as an island within East Germany. In one after another of the countries immediately bordering on the Soviet Union in east Europe, which had been liberated from the Nazis with the aid of the Red army, a coalition government led by its communist element made its way to power and by 1948 all had set up régimes of 'people's democracies', with such support from the Soviet régime or from the Red army as the situation in each case required.

In these circumstances a new contest developed between the Atlantic community, consisting of western Europe and America, and the communist bloc, composed of Russia and the east European states. The contest became global when the Communist party in China gained power in 1949 and the Chinese People's Republic joined the communist camp.

The policy of containing communism led the members of the Atlantic community to support the non-communist governments of countries on the periphery of the communist orbit, notably Greece and Turkey; to transport supplies to West Berlin by airlift when access by land was cut off; to form an Atlantic alliance with international forces under unified command; and to create looser alliances in the Pacific and the Middle East.

The policy brought open conflict in Korea and Indo-China. In 1950 the majority of the non-communist countries, following the initiative of the United States, joined in military resistance to prevent the incorporation of South Korea into communist North Korea which had been allocated to Russian administration at the close of the war and had been organized as a communist-led state in a manner similar to East Germany. The Security Council of the United Nations, acting in the absence of the USSR which boycotted the session, declared North Korea an aggressor; for the first time in history troops of many nations fought under the flag of an international organization, the flag of the United Nations. The conflict was held to a stalemate by the entrance of the Chinese People's Republic on the side of North Korea after the battle had reached the frontier of China itself. This act of support for a country which had been declared an aggressor was the main stated reason for excluding the Chinese People's Republic from membership in the United Nations during the following years. In Indo-China resistance to the spread of communism became intertwined with the long, unsuccessful struggle of France to retain her hold on the area and led to the division of the territory in 1954 into a northern region under communist control and the states of Vietnam, Laos and Cambodia under non-communist leadership.

In both Europe and Asia, it was the resources of the United States which furnished a large part of the military strength deployed around the periphery of the communist-dominated area, in the form of American forces stationed in Europe, north Africa, the Middle East, the Arctic, the Pacific and various points in the western hemisphere, and in the form of military aid to other countries. In the 1950s there were hundreds of American military installations, large and small, outside the continental United States which had been established by agreement with host countries for common defence or on Pacific islands formerly held by Japan which had become United Nations trust territories under United States administration.

In contrast to the United States, whose homeland had remained undamaged, the USSR suffered war devastation even greater than that of defeated Germany, for the fighting which had raged over her western area had destroyed her cities, levelled an estimated third of all her urban homes, ruined factories and laid waste the land. She owed her survival and ability to make a rapid recovery in part to the foresight of her leaders who, expecting war in the west, had established much of her heavy industry east of the Urals, and to the transfer of activity to that region from the west during the war.

Yet in spite of wartime destruction she not only regained her strength and renewed her advance in production but, within less than five years, she ceased to be the only communist state in a non-communist world and became the centre of a communist group extending from the Pacific to Berlin and from Siberia to Indo-China. With the accession to communism of the countries of east Europe and the Chinese People's Republic, what had been but a single instance of a communist state became, within a short period, a competitive world system controlling a third of the world's population and equipped with the latest technology in science, industry and armament.

In the middle years of the twentieth century there were thus two worlds, one calling itself the 'free world', the other the communist world. But each believed only in one world—its own. To the free world, that of the communists loomed as a threat to its power, its institutions and its values. To the communist world, its doctrine and its system alone had universal validity.

The policy of each was to stand firm against the expansion of the other and to seek means of extending its system. The Kremlin tolerated no deviation from the general party line and repressed without hesitation signs of defection among its east European associates, notably the 1956 revolt in Hungary, put down as a counter-revolutionary movement with the aid of Soviet troops.[12] Yugoslavia, however, maintained a national communist régime isolated from the Soviet-led communist group. Outside the communist area the Communist party of the Soviet Union worked to strengthen its ties with the communist parties in other countries and supported national liberation movements. The free world, in turn, looked for chinks in what the British wartime leader, Sir Winston Churchill, dubbed the 'iron curtain', through which to reach and appeal to the people under communist control, and they tightened their own security systems in various ways against communists at home, making the Communist party illegal, raising bars to immigration and travel, excluding known or suspected communists from certain positions, especially those of responsibility and trust, and otherwise restricting democratic freedoms. Both groups set up military–political blocs and enhanced their military potential.

With the world thus divided, and with the new and terrible weapons making it plain that another full-scale war could mean hardly less than suicide for humanity, the cold war—as the relations between the two worlds in the 1950s came to be called—took the form of the building up on either side of deterrent forces of nuclear arms, borne first by ever-swifter, jet-propelled planes travelling faster than the speed of sound, then by guided missiles traversing outer space.

The contest took the form, too, of advances in science, technology and production. The USSR declared her intention to challenge the leadership of the United States in industrial production, and sought to accelerate her rate of industrial expansion with each five-year plan. Her notable scientific progress was grounded in the distinguished Russian scientific achievements of pre-Soviet days, it was stimulated from the beginning of the Soviet régime by a policy of staking national progress on scientific advance, and it was supported by a vigorous programme of mass education in which scientific subjects played a central role. When the USSR succeeded in placing the first earth satellite in outer space in October 1957, the world knew that the leading nation of the communist world was in the front rank in the vital field of scientific advance on which modern society had come more and more to depend.

While the two major powers and their associated worlds pursued their competitive courses, the new nations liberated from colonial rule struggled to establish stable political institutions and to find effective means to develop their economies and raise the level of living of their people. They wanted no part in the cold war and resisted the efforts of both protagonists to make them take sides. On the one hand their governments and other institutions were generally patterned on those of Europe or the United States and it was in terms of European principles of freedom and democracy that they had fought for their liberation. On the other hand they saw in the Soviet Union a country which had used economic planning and the central direction of national effort to achieve rapid industrialization—the goal which they ardently sought—and they saw the largest of the economically underdeveloped areas, China, choosing the same route.

It was clear, however, that the issue in the world contest between rival systems would inevitably depend to a major degree on the fate of these neutral uncommitted nations of the Indian sub-continent, south-east Asia, the Middle East and Africa. Both dominant groups therefore sought to draw them to their side, by strategic appeals and by offers of economic and technical aid. And within each new country rival elements attempted to push their governments in one direction or another. At times such conflicts impeded the difficult, central task faced by all these countries—that of converting ancient, technically primitive, often densely populated agrarian societies into modern, prosperous economies in which their people could aspire to standards of living more nearly approaching those of the technically developed countries of the world.

The mounting importance of this part of the world was reflected in the emergence of an Afro-Asian bloc. In 1955 twenty-three Asian and six African nations, from Japan to Liberia, assembled at Bandung, Indonesia, in an historic conference of Afro-Asian nations. At the Bandung conference the assembled nations declared, in essence: 'Here we are, The time has passed when the world can act as though we did not exist'.

Even at the close of the second world war it was not immediately apparent how deeply tropical Africa had already been stirred by the nationalism that was abroad in Asia and the Middle East, and by the evident decline of the imperial powers. To be sure, the policy of reserving to white settlers the best land in the highlands of Kenya had been challenged before the war by a British-educated African leader, Jomo Kenyatta, and Britain's announced policy in West Africa during the war was to prepare for ultimate independence. But few people were prepared for the swiftness with which a vague hope was converted into practical, determined steps toward independence in one African area after another.

In 1956 the Anglo-Egyptian Sudan voted for independence rather than either union with Egypt or a continuing tie with Britain. The Gold Coast chose the name of an ancient African kingdom, Ghana, when it celebrated its independence from Britain in 1957. By then other British African areas such as Nigeria and Uganda were on the way to independence. Where the population included European settlers, as in Kenya, the Central African Federation and Tanganyika, the question was not whether these areas would become independent but what would be the relations among the European, Indian and African elements when independence was secured.

France hoped to retain her Sahara empire by her traditional method of assimilating as Frenchmen the educated African *élite* and incorporating overseas territories into the French body politic; but already in 1946 she had admitted the principle of self-government, by 1957 she had granted her West and Central African territories a measure of autonomy, and in 1958 Guinea became the first of these territories to withdraw from the French community and set itself up as an independent African state. The long struggle over Algeria threatened the stability of France itself, as the French minority in Algeria fought to keep the country a part of France while the Muslim majority waged a war of liberation. Belgium hoped to find some formula for a partnership which would keep the immensely rich Congo tied into the Belgian economy and the Belgian state, but she could not resist mounting restiveness and yielded to the demand for independence. Portugal, making no concessions to the idea of African separatism, virtually sealed the borders of her African territories in the effort to exclude contamination from outside. The full effects

of the awakening of Africa had only begun to be seen at mid-century, but that
this awakening was a major new political reality of world importance none
could overlook or deny.

Another major area whose potential importance had only begun to be
recognized internationally was Latin America. Although the republics of
South and Central America had enjoyed independence since the early
nineteenth century, most had continued to be predominantly agrarian with
semi-feudal economies; in some, large sections of the indigenous Indian population had remained outside the main stream of national economic and political
life. They thus shared many of the problems encountered by other economically underdeveloped countries in their efforts to overcome illiteracy and
poverty and to achieve balanced economic development. At the middle of the
century Latin America, with the most rapidly growing population of any
region, with a wealth of resources to be developed and lands to be settled and
with an aroused determination to achieve greater economic independence and
progress, appeared likely to become an increasingly important factor in world
affairs.

Meanwhile the countries of Europe in the decade after the second world war
faced the need to find a new basis for effective survival, stability, security and
prestige. Though western Europe had lost much of its ability to exploit vast
resources overseas, it still constituted an area of some 300,000,000 people with
the highest level of education and technical skill of any comparable body in
the world, with many of the resources on which to base a strong economy and
with a potential market capable of sustaining highly productive industry as
did the home market in the United States.

A first step toward European economic integration was the creation of the
European Coal and Steel Community shortly after the war. Since the crucial
problem of Europe as a self-based economy was fuel, the possibility of
developing atomic energy as a source of power offered an attractive alternative
to continued dependence on oil from the politically uncertain Middle East. In
1957 six European nations—France, West Germany, Italy, Belgium, Netherlands, Luxembourg—formed a common organization, Euratom, to exploit
this new resource. At the same time they took steps to open their markets to
each other's products and agreed to develop a common European market in
the heart of western Europe with which other European countries might later
become allied.

These steps marked the beginnings of a new kind of Europe, no longer the
Europe of competing colonial powers but a technically advanced, interrelated
entity within the modern world. The growth and vigour of the European
economies in the 1950s was evidence of their continuing vitality and new
potentiality.

Though the world at mid-century was sharply divided, this very division
created conditions which required organization of the world community. The
creation of the United Nations as the second world war was coming to a close

Cartography Hallwag Berne

R U S S I A

C H I N A

TIBET

NEPAL BHUTAN

DIA   BURMA

Andaman Is.
(Brit.)

Nicobar Is.
(Brit.)

Ceylon

SIAM   INDOCHINA

BRITISH
MALAYA

SUMATRA

JAVA

Ocean

Cocos Is.
(Brit.)

KOREA

J A P A N

Ryukyu Is.
(Jap.)

Bonin Is.
(Jap.)

MACAO
(Port.)   Formosa (Jap.)

HONGKONG (Brit.)

PHILIPPINES
(USA)

N. BORNEO

SARAWAK

BORNEO

Celebes

Molucca

Pelew Is.
(Germ.)

Marianas
(Germ.)

Guam (USA)

Carolines (Germ.)

NEW GUINEA

TIMOR
(Port.)

AUSTRALIA
(Dom.)

Tasmania

Midway Is.
(USA)

Wake I. (USA)

Marshall Is.
(Germ.)

Biamarck Is.
(Germ.)

Gilbert Is.
(Brit.)

Ellice Is.
(Brit.)

Solomon Is.
(Brit. + Germ.)

New Hebrides

New Caledonia
(Fr.)

Fiji Is. (Brit.)

Loyalty Is. (Fr.)

NEW
ZEALAND
(Dom.)

COLONIAL EMPIRES 1900

[To face page 32

Cartography Hallwag Berne

T U N I O N

MONGOLIA

C H I N A

Kurile Is.

J A P A N

KOREA

Midway Is. (USA)

NEPAL—BHUTAN
Sikkim
PAK.
INDIA
BURMA
MACAO (Port.)
HONGKONG (Brit.)
Taiwan
Ryukyu Is.
Bonin Is. (Jap.)
Wake I. (USA)

THAILAND
VIET-NAM
CAMB.
PHILIPPINES
Marianas (USA-Tr.)
Guam (USA)

Andaman Is. (Brit.)

N. BORNEO
BRUNEI
SARAWAK
BORNEO
Pelew Is.
Carolines (USA-Tr.)
Marshall Is. (USA-Tr.)

Nicobar Is. (Brit.)
Ceylon
MALAYA
Trucial States
SINGAPORE
SUMATRA
I N D O N E S I A
JAVA
Molucca
Celebes
NETH.
GUINEA
(In dispute between Netherlands and Indonesia)
NEW GUINEA (Austr.-Tr.)
Bismarck Is.
Nauru (Austr., N. Zeal. Brit.-Tr.)
Gilbert Is. (Brit.)

Indian Ocean

TIMOR (Port.)
Ellice Is. (Brit.)

Cocos Is. (Brit.)
Solomon Is. (Brit)
Fiji Is. (Brit.)

New Hebrides (Brit. + Fr.)
New Caledonia (Fr.)
Loyalty Is. (Fr.)

A U S T R A L I A

NEW ZEALAND

Tasmania

INDEPENDENCE SCHEDULED

Sierra Leone
Tanganyika
Uganda
Ruanda-Urundi
British West Indies

COLONIAL AREAS 1960

[To face page 33

expressed the urgent sense, far more intense than it had been when the League of Nations was set up after the first world war, that international organization was indispensable to human survival.

In the presence of competing world systems the United Nations and its specialized agencies afforded a means through which the members of both groups could communicate with each other and could work together on matters of common concern which transcended their differences, although the absence of the world's most populous nation, the Chinese People's Republic, impaired the universality of these agencies. Moreover, the United Nations was the principal channel through which the new nations made their world presence felt. Although the former great powers continued through the 1950s to dominate the United Nations Security Council, the Assembly where each nation had an equal voice came more and more to take on the tone of the new nations as, one after another, they joined its ranks.

And it required only a glance at the faces of the Assembly delegates to make it clear that this was no longer a white man's world. For the shift in world power that had taken place in half a century was not only from the old, imperial European core to the new leaders of the communist and non-communist worlds. Less pronounced but no less real was the trend from the dominance of the white to the equality of non-white peoples. In a world where populations that classified themselves as white numbered no more than perhaps a quarter of the whole, and where the equality of nations and peoples was coming to be accepted in principle, the darker peoples could not fail to play a growing role. Though racial prejudice was far from dead and determined groups fought to maintain white supremacy within their own societies —in South Africa, in Kenya, in southern parts of the United States—a white skin had ceased to be the badge of privilege or superiority which it had been in the world which Rudyard Kipling had described.

International co-operation, moreover, was playing a part in the efforts of newly developing nations to gain some of the scientific and technical knowledge which had remade the industrialized segments of the world. In the new structure of power, these peoples had the conscience and self-interest of mankind on their side in their efforts to rise. This provided a new dynamic for world relationships and an imperative which gave international organization a practical as well as a political role.[13, 14]

NOTES TO CHAPTER I

1. Professor E. N. Anderson suggests the following discussions of historical writing for perspective on the method and approach of this volume:
   Raymond Aron, *The Dawn of Universal History* (London, 1961).
   Geoffrey Barraclough, *History in a Changing World* (Norman, University of Oklahoma Press, 1956).

Isaiah Berlin, *Historical Inevitability* (New York, Oxford University Press, 1954).
Herbert Butterfield, *Christianity and History* (London, 1943).
Herbert Butterfield, *History and Human Relations* (London, 1951).
R. G. Collingwood, *The Idea of History* (New York, Oxford University Press, 1946).
H. P. R. Finberg (ed.), *Approaches to History* (London, 1962).
Romano Guardini, *The End of the Modern World* (New York, 1956).
H. Stuart Hughes, *Consciousness and Society* (New York, 1958).
Jacques Maritain, *On the Philosophy of History* (New York, 1957).
Hans Meyerhoff (ed.), *The Philosophy of History in Our Time. An Anthology* (New York, 1959).
L. B. Namier, *Avenues of History* (London, 1952).
Karl Popper, *The Poverty of Historicism* (Boston, 1958).
Social Science Research Council, *Theory and Practice in Historical Study*. Bulletin 54 (New York, 1946).
Social Science Research Council, *The Social Sciences in Historical Study*. Bulletin 64 (New York, 1954).
Fritz Stern (ed.), *The Varieties of History* (New York, Meridian, 1956).
Caroline F. Ware (ed.), *The Cultural Approach to History* (New York, Columbia University Press, 1940).

2. Professor C. K. Zurayk comments: 'There is a constant mention of the "Communist and non-Communist worlds". It seems to me rather unfortunate that we have to describe the Western World negatively and to place it after the communist world. I realize the great difficulty of choosing an appropriate positive term, such as Free, or Democratic, etc. Although "Western" is open to many objections, it is still, I believe, better than a negative term.' Professor Wilhelm Röpke writes: 'When the authors say that the world was sharply divided politically between the Communist and the non-Communist groups, and divided economically between industrially developed and "underdeveloped" segments, the picture they give cannot be more wrong. It obscures the fact that the division between the communist and the non-communist world is not only political, but ethico-cultural and economic and in all these aspects the most profound that could be imagined. It can in no way be compared with the dividing lines within the free world itself.'

3. *The Author–Editors call attention to the fact that the term 'Western' is used throughout the text to refer to occidental culture and is not used in a political sense.*

4. Professor M. S. Ivanov, Professor A. F. Miller, and other personalities who examined this question, stress that it was above all the Russian revolution of 1905–7 that exercised an effective influence upon the development of the national-liberation movement of the peoples of the East in 1905–12 (the so-called 'awakening of Asia'). Thus V. Chirol, an English writer who was at that time *Times* correspondent in India, described the impact of the 1905 events on India in the following way: 'But there were Indians to whom it meant even more than a mere humbling of a great European power by an Asiatic race. It meant also a mighty blow to the autocratic system in Russia and to that system the Indian extremists never tired of likening a system of Indian Government concentrated in the hands of an all-powerful bureaucracy. British officialdom in India was denounced as the counterpart of the *chinovniks* who ruled and ruined Russia in the name of the Tsar, and to be fought if necessary with the same weapons which the Russian revolutionists were learning effectively to employ' (V. Chirol, *India*, London, 1926, p. 114.).

The Indian democrats who supported Tilak—a leading figure in the Indian liberation movement—published clandestinely a number of pamphlets in which they brought to the attention of the public the libertarian ideas of the Russian revolution of 1905–7 and the methods of struggle employed by the Russian revolutionaries. (See *Sedition Committee Report*, Government of India, Home Dept., Calcutta, 1918, pp. 42–4.)

E. G. Browne, an English author, cites in his work a letter from Teheran written by an eye-witness of the events that inaugurated the revolution in Persia: 'The Russian revolution has had a most astounding effect here. Events in Russia have been watched with great attention, and a new spirit would seem to have come over the people' (E. G. Browne, *The Persian Revolution of 1905–9*, Cambridge, 1910, p. 120).

One of the founders of the first Young Turk committee, 'Unity and Progress', Dr. Abdullah Djevded, wrote as follows in an appeal entitled *To My Turkish Compatriots*, despatched from Geneva early in 1907: 'To the entire oppressed population, Moslem and non-Moslem—unite! Poor and rich, weak and strong, women and men, young and old—unite! Look at Russia, look at Persia. . . .' The Young Turk newspaper *Türk*, published in Cairo, appealed to its readers 'to take as your example the magnificent ideas of the Russian revolution' (No. 118, June 1, 1906).

The liberation ideas of the Russian revolution had a great impact on the programme of Covenant Society (T'ung-meng Hui), the Chinese revolutionary organization founded in 1905 by Sun Yat-sen. Its theoretical organ, the journal *Minpao*, established in Tokyo in October 1905, printed in each issue long articles about the Russian revolution, the situation in Russia, and the history of the Russian revolutionary movement. In a number of these articles reference was made to the significance of the revolutionary events in Russia for China (See 'Democracy and the Perspectives of Revolution in China', No. 4, 1905; 'Salvation from Inexorable Ruin', Nos. 18, 19, 20, 1905; 'The Revolutionary Ideology', No. 25, 1905, and others).

5. Professor L. I. Zubok stresses that the Spanish-American War of 1898, which led to the Philippines, Cuba, Puerto Rico and Guam coming under American control (*Foreign Relations of the United States for 1898*, p. 940) inaugurated an era of imperialist wars, i.e. wars for the re-division of a partitioned world. The war showed that the most powerful capitalists in the United States were no longer content with the internal market alone, and set themselves the task of capturing markets in the world at large. From this time onwards expansionist theories came to exercise an ever greater influence upon the orientation of US foreign policy. The late Charles Beard, the American historian, refers to Admiral Mahan, President Theodore Roosevelt and Senators Henry Cabot Lodge and Albert Beveridge as the four 'wildest agitators' for an expansionist policy by the United States in the 1890's (C. Beard, *Giddy Minds and Foreign Quarrels: an Estimate of American Foreign Policy*, New York, 1939, p. 16).

It was at this time that the United States set out to capture the enormous Chinese market. But since China was already partitioned into 'spheres of influence' by the other powers, the United States enunciated the doctrine of 'open doors and equal opportunities', which enabled its goods to penetrate into these 'spheres of influence' and the Chinese territories leased to other powers. The annual account of the Bureau of Foreign Trade of the State Department for the fiscal year 1896–7 already contains the statement that the provision of equal opportunities in China 'will undoubtedly bring tremendous profits to United States industrialists, in view of the demand for provisions and goods of various kinds which they will be able to satisfy' (A. W. Griswold, *The Far Eastern Policy of the United States*, New York, 1938, pp. 56–7).

The principle of the 'open door' was put forward in identical notes despatched on September 6, 1899, by US Secretary of State, John Hay, to London, Berlin and St. Petersburg (see McMurray, *Treaties and Agreements with and concerning China*, New York, 1921, Vol. I, pp. 221–35).

Professor Zubok's point of view is endorsed by Academician D. Kosev who considers that the authors' attempt to portray the war between the United States and Spain in 1898 as a just war is a failure. This war bore an imperialistic character for both parties. As a result of the war the United States became a colonialist power, through its seizure of the Philippines.

Professor László Zsigmond believes that the facts do not bear out the view that the United States had no colonial ambitions, and that the Philippines and Puerto Rico became subject to the United States only as a result of the chain of circumstances. He notes further that the authors do not take account of the difference between the interests of American finance capital and those of the American people.

6. Doctor of Historical Sciences N. N. Yakovlev notes that the principle of the self-determination of peoples was advanced for the first time in the 'Declaration of the Rights of the Peoples of Russia', published on November 15, 1917, and also in the address 'To All Toiling Moslems in Russia and the East', signed by Lenin (December 3, 1917). So far as the declaration of W. Wilson is concerned, which was published on January 8, 1918, this was largely a propagandist document. The author himself found

it necessary to limit his promised 'basic principles' by sanctioning an accompanying official commentary. On the eve of the Paris Peace Conference, T. Roosevelt, giving expression to the majority view in Congress, emphasized that neither Wilson's fourteen points, with their four conditions and five appendices, nor any other of his statements any longer reflected the intentions of the United States. (See *Documents of American History*, ed. by H. Commager, New York, 1945, p. 331.) Of Wilson's twenty-three conditions (including addenda), only four were incorporated into the peace treaties with a measure of accuracy. Senator H. C. Lodge, dealing with the fact that the 'Fourteen Points' programme had been buried at Paris, wrote that the first point, about the elimination of secret negotiation, was infringed at Versailles; the principle of freedom of the seas (point two) was also discarded—this principle could not be carried through on account of British resistance. Point Three, in Lodge's opinion, was never seriously considered by anyone. Point Four 'related to a reduction of armaments. Nothing was done about that in the Treaty of Versailles, except the disarmament of Germany. . . . The League has since then done nothing about it. . . . 'The fifth point related to the adjustment of colonial claims, which seem to have been settled by the victorious Allied Powers taking all the colonial possessions of Germany everywhere. 'Point six related to the evacuation of Russian territory, and that of course was not dealt with at all accord- to the methods set forth by Mr Wilson, but was more or less temporarily and violently disposed of in the process of events which could not have been foreseen at that time. . . . (H. C. Lodge, *The Senate and the League of Nations*, New York and London, 1925, pp. 92–4).

7. Professor E. N. Anderson notes that the subject of decay in Europe has been discussed at length in both popular and scholarly writings, not merely during the interwar years, to which the author-editors apply the term, but during the entire century. Communist and fascist writers of all kinds agreed that the traditional western civilization, referring primarily to that of Europe, had decayed, and many West Europeans shared the same view, although for other reasons. Oswald Spengler's *Decline of the West* appeared soon after World War I, André Siegfried's book documenting the decay of England, *England's Crisis*, was published in 1931, Alexander Werth wrote of the *Twilight of France 1933–1940* (1942), and Pertinax published *The Gravediggers of France* in 1943. Non-Westerners like Gandhi and Nehru and leaders of the Muslim world saw in the European passion for war evidence of spiritual decay; an American historian has recently written that 'Europe ended its century of progress in an orgy of violence from which it never recovered' (Gordon A. Craig, *Europe since 1815*, London, 1961, p. 488). Writers noted that the area whose fate they were discussing shrank in size under the impact of communism and fascism, considering the strength of the forces hostile to the traditional civilization as evidence of decay. Some authors found evidence of decay in certain aspects of European life, especially in the political, economic and social areas, but they were impressed with the vigour of activity in scholarly fields like physics and mathematics, medicine and psychiatry, and in literary, artistic and musical creativeness.

The victory over fascism and the revival of political and economic life in Western Europe have led to a reassessment of the interwar views. Several commentators upon the present manuscript have taken exception to the use of the term 'decay of Europe' to refer to the interwar period. Professor Zurayk prefers the phrase 'decline in power' or 'decline in influence'. Professor Halecki thinks that the 'consequences of . . . the "Decay of Europe"' are 'overemphasized' and regards the expression as 'being inevitably offensive to Europeans, especially in contrast with the much more sympathetic approach to all other peoples'.

The development of a 'European Spirit' since World War II has been much discussed as a reality, and some writers define Western Europe as a Third Force, which maintains itself as an independent political and cultural unity between the communist bloc and the non-European world. See *L'Espirit européen* (Neuchâtel, 1947) as an example: it is a complete record of the proceedings of the first 'Recontres Internationales de Genève', held in the summer of 1946.

8 Professor Lázló Zsigmond makes the point that the cause of the collapse of Austria-Hungary and the formation of national states was the national-liberation movement

of the peoples who inhabited the area. Mention should also be made, in his opinion, of the formation of the Hungarian Soviet Republic in 1919.

9. Professor László Zsigmond expresses the opinion that it was not Soviet Russia that was the enemy of Western Europe, but the reverse: the imperialist Western Powers, which between 1919 and 1922 organized the intervention against the Soviets, were hostile to Soviet Russia.

10. Professor Lázló Zsigmond believes that in 1940 the French people were capable of resistance but lacked determination. The 'collapse' was the result of treachery on the part of certains groups within France.

11. Professor L. I. Zubok maintains that the political manœuvres directed by the United States against the extreme and overt forms taken by Japan's expansionist course in the late 1930s were half-hearted. Thus, for example, US Secretary of State Cordell Hull, at the same time as he called for the Japanese aggressors to be restrained, told the Japanese ambassador in a conversation on June 13, 1937, that the United States was taking up a 'friendly, impartial position' towards Japan in connection with the conflict in China (see *Papers Relating to the Foreign Relations of the United States: Japan 1931–41*, Washington, Vol. I, p. 321). On September 28th Hull wrote to the American observer at the League of Nations that the United States was not prepared to take part in collective sanctions against Japan (*Peace and War: Foreign Policy, 1931–41*, Washington, 1943, pp. 381–2). Throughout the period of Japanese aggression, almost up to the attack on the United States, a number of extremely influential American companies and trusts continued to supply Japan with very important types of strategic raw materials that she lacked, as well as with military *materiel*. In 1937 American commercial exchanges with Japan amounted to $288 million—considerably more than in the preceding year. In 1938 the total amount of American military supplies exported to Japan rose by 34·3 per cent, including metals by more than 300 per cent, machinery by 200 per cent, and aeroplanes almost by 500 per cent (T. Bisson, *American Policy in the Far East, 1931–40*, New York, 1940, p. 85). Even after the denunciation of the Japanese–American commercial treaty of 1911 (on July 27, 1939), Japan continued to receive strategic military supplies from the United States: in 1939 sales exceeded the 1938 level by 34 per cent.

12. The class character and causes of the events in Hungary in 1956 are explained in the resolution of December 1956 passed by the Central Committee of the Hungarian Socialist Labour Party and in the resolutions of VIIth Congress of this party (December 1959). In these resolutions it is stated that the counter-revolution was brought about by four simultaneously operating factors: the errors of the former sectarian leaders of the Hungarian Workers' Party, the (treacherous) activity of the revisionist group of Imre Nagy, the internal bourgeois counter-revolutionary forces, and the subversive activity of world imperialism. Since the 'counter-revolutionary uprising unleashed in Hungary on October 23, 1956, threatened not only the Socialist achievements of the Hungarian people, its national independence, but also the entire socialist order, peace in Europe and in the world as a whole', the new-formed Hungarian 'Revolutionary Workers' and Peasants' Government turned for aid to the armed forces of its ally, the Soviet Union, in order to prevent an armed intervention by the Western imperialists and to avert a lengthy civil war. The fraternal support given by the Soviet Union was a remarkable demonstration of allied loyalty and proletarian internationalism, which prevented further bloody crimes by the white terror, helped the forces of Socialism to smash the armed forces of counter-revolution, and averted the danger of war.' (*A Magyar Szocialista Munkáspárt VII. Kongress-zusának jegy-zökönyve*, Budapest, 1960, pp. 563–4).

13. The text has been severely criticized by scholars in the West European liberal and Catholic traditions for avoiding the use of the term 'totalitarian' and not treating totalitarianism as such as one of the central developments of the period. Professor Wilhelm Röpke

(Switzerland), Professor Hans Kohn (United States) and Professor Giorgio Janiot (Pontifical Gregorian University) believe that failure to focus upon totalitarianism as such affects the entire perspective from which events of this period are interpreted.

14. *The Author-Editors have not wished to minimize the significance of the tendencies to create monolithic societies and to reject the concept of the pluralistic, open society which has dominated the development of Western Europe and the spread of West European culture and influence around the world since the sixteenth century. They have avoided the term 'totalitarian' because it seems likely to impede rather than to facilitate the effort to see and analyse the similarities and differences in the institutions, social and political objectives and practical realities of the different regimes which have been established or maintained during these years. They have tried to use more precise, less comprehensive and less emotionally charged terms in order to examine the reality of all types of regimes, seeking the inner consistency of each and noting how their institutions reflect common or differing responses to conditions of industrial society and currents of thought of the period.*

CHAPTER II

THE IMPACT OF NATIONALISM AND TREND TOWARD INTERNATIONAL CO-OPERATION

AMONG the Fourteen Points which President Woodrow Wilson proposed as a basis for settlement of the first world war were two which embodied major dynamic trends of the twentieth century—the principle of self-determination of peoples and the proposal to form an international organization which should afford mutual guarantees of political independence and territorial integrity to great and small nations alike. To Wilson, with his ideal of a world order composed of free and democratic peoples, these were complementary proposals, each in line with the imperatives of the age. Both were welcomed by the peoples of the world as offering hope for the fulfilment of their deepest aspirations. Yet in a measure they reflected conflicting trends, nationalism versus internationalism. The resolution of the conflict between these two trends was the central and incomplete process of the years which followed.[1]

Wilson conceived of nationalism as a liberating force—and so it proved to be, not only in the east European areas which he had primarily in view but even more importantly in the colonial empires to which Lenin in the same period addressed his call for the liberation of subject peoples. But the idea of self-determination also gave a new lease on life to the driving, aggressive, competitive nationalism which had come to a tragic head in the first world war.

Wilson hoped that the international organization, the League of Nations, would hold aggressive nationalism in check and protect the aspiring nationalism of liberated peoples from the designs of their stronger neighbours. But the forms of nationalism which developed in the following years were more virulent than those previously known. The international organization was powerless to avert the ensuing conflict. A second holocaust was the awful price paid by the world.

When the world once more emerged from the hell of modern war, liberating nationalism and desperately needed internationalism again became the foundations of the world's peace and reconstruction. Liberating nationalism this time found expression in the new nations of ex-colonial peoples who emerged as a new world force. Internationalism was embodied in the United Nations and its many specialized agencies.

The new internationalism differed from the old both in the comprehensiveness of the international organization and in the nature of the divisive forces with which it had to cope. For the issue in the decade following the second world war was not only whether internationalism could stand up to aggressive nationalism but whether it could bridge the gulf in a world which was ideologically divided. Its task was to enable the 'free world' and the communist countries to live together and the liberated peoples to develop as free nations in peace.

I. THE IMPACT OF NATIONALISM [2,3]

Nationalism, which provided so much of the dynamic force for the shift in world power in the first half of the twentieth century, was in essence a state of mind in which the supreme loyalty of the individual was accorded to the nation-state and his identity as a person was bound up with membership in his nation. National loyalty replaced or overshadowed other forms of loyalty —personal loyalty to feudal lord or other leader, loyalty to family, village, craft or religious group. As an alternative to these personal loyalties nationalism offered identification with a broader and more generic concept, the people. The national state was an instrument by which the combined power of a multitude of men could be focused on a common goal, on the basis of the common obligation of all to a common entity.

Since modern nationalism implied the identification of state with people, its corollary was that people should form nation-states of their own. This was in contrast, not only to the concepts of more limited loyalty to feudal lord, town, monarch or religion, but to such traditional concepts of universality as Christendom or Islam, and to such supra-national political structures as the Ottoman, Austro-Hungarian and Russian empires.

Modern nationalism not only identified the individual with the nation-state in his political loyalty but identified civilization with national differences. By substituting the vernacular language, the folk traditions and the historic experience of each national unit for a language of international culture and a concern for universal truth, it added the concept of national civilization to that of national political identity.

The kinds of nationalism which were at work in the twentieth century differed in their temper and implications. In one of its forms, most vigorously manifested in the heritage of the American revolution, the spirit of nationalism was associated with the rationalism, liberalism and humanism of the eighteenth-century Enlightenment. In the theory of that time the act of nation-forming was a voluntary act—the social compact which John Locke and Jean-Jacques Rousseau had formulated on the basis of the traditional concepts of natural right. Peoples had become nations because they had chosen to band together to establish civil authority. The nature of this process implied the continued active participation of the people, who were the state. The national state was a rational expression of recognized human need, a defence against personal aggression and a stepping-stone to the liberation of mankind.

The terms in which President Wilson asked for the self-determination of peoples were those of liberal nationalism, for this was his tradition and that of his nation, most of whose people had become Americans by choice in successive waves of immigration.

Throughout much of the nineteenth century in Europe nationalism was associated with the rising or dominant middle classes. In the national state of that time 'the people' were the propertied classes who, alone, enjoyed the suffrage in most countries. The interests of the state—identified with the goals of nationalism—were primarily the interests of the commercial and industrial groups. It was they who most thought of themselves as the nation. The aristocracies of Europe had many family ties abroad, and a more international outlook. The non-propertied elements in the population—small or landless peasants, industrial workers—who did not participate politically did not identify themselves psychologically with the nation-state in the same degree as did the *bourgeoisie*.

In the late nineteenth and early twentieth centuries identification with the nation-state spread through more strata of European society as these became literate and were incorporated more completely into national life. By the outbreak of the first world war the process was so far advanced that alternative loyalties could not stand against loyalty to the national state. Leaders of European labour thought that the common interests of the working classes were greater than national interests and they counted on these ties to prevent a resort to war. But the Second International, which united the socialist parties of Europe and represented the solidarity of labour, broke down in 1914 in the face of the national feeling of the working classes who followed their leaders in supporting their governments. Any lingering reservations were overcome by the impact of total war.[4]

European nationalism in the nineteenth and early twentieth centuries tended to be expansionist and competitive. Expressing dominant commercial and industrial interests, it pressed for markets, raw materials and opportunities for foreign investment. How aggressive the nationalist drive might be depended in each case upon the position of the particular country. Britain, which had been the first to develop modern industry and whose empire contained twice the geographical area and seven times the population of the next largest imperial power, France, could advocate free trade and enjoy a comfortable sense of national identity and superiority without the necessity for intense, nationalistic passion. By contrast, Germany, whose unification, industrial development and entrance into the competition for empire came late, felt the need to struggle to make a 'place in the sun' for itself as a great power.

Aggressive nationalism drew much of its spirit and rationale from the concepts of nationalism formulated by the nineteenth-century German romantics in a non-rational, non-liberal spirit. In this theory, nationalism was deemed to rest on the *Volksgeist* expressing man's instincts, not his reason, to reflect the circumstances of birth and blood and to derive from historic experience, not conscious choice. This concept of nationalism emphasized

EUROPE AND MIDDLE EAST
BEFORE WORLD WAR I

ICELAND
(Danish)

NORWAY

SWEDEN

DENMARK

GREAT BRITAIN

IRELAND

THE NETHERLANDS

BELGIUM

LUX.

GERMAN EMPIRE

SWITZERLAND

FRANCE

SPAIN

PORTUGAL

R U S S I A

AUSTRIA-HUNGARY

RUMANIA

SERBIA

MONT.

ALBANIA

BULGARIA

GREECE

ITALY

OTTOMAN EMPIRE

PERSIA

ARABIA

EGYPT
(British Protectorate)

TRIPOLITANIA
(Italian)

Morocco Algeria
(French)

Tunis
(French)

Cartography Hallwag Berne

loyalty to an entity which transcended those who made up the nation, and it was compatible with authoritarian rule. It tended to view the uniqueness of each nation as permanent and divisive rather than as an aspect of common brotherhood.

Competitive nationalism built up world tension, and though the broadened base of nationalism led to social reform at home, it tended to enhance the emotional component of nationalism abroad and to strengthen its romantic, irrational, non-liberal aspects. The final expression of competitive nationalism was the first great war of peoples.

This was the kind of nationalism that Wilson hoped to hold in check by international organization, as did all who rallied to him eagerly at the close of the war, convinced that the response to the tragedy of some 13,000,000 dead and 7,000,000 permanently disabled must be, 'Never again'.

While nationalism permeated the societies of western Europe and the Americas, the concept was growing stronger in eastern Europe and Asia, to produce ferment among the peoples of the Austro-Hungarian, Russian and Ottoman empires, to break out in anti-foreign attacks in China and to reach colonial India with the establishment of the Indian National Congress in 1885. In these areas, as in Europe, it was at that stage mainly the rising middle classes of civil servants, professionals, clerical workers and merchants which became the bearers of nationalism. Even in such an area as Indonesia where the middle class was small, the first nationalist movement in 1908, *Budi Utomo* (Fair Strive), was composed of western-trained intellectuals, and it was followed some years later by a half-religious, half-nationalist movement of merchants, *Sarekat Islam*, which was joined by other groups such as school teachers and clerks.

In the areas to which nationalism spread, as in the lands of its origin, devotion to the nation-state came in time to embrace broader segments of the population. As nationalist movements in colonial areas became mass movements they inevitably also became movements for the reconstruction of society as well as for its liberation from foreign yoke.

Asian nationalism thus followed a course of development similar to that in Europe but at a very much more rapid pace. The process of national identification, first with ruler, then with *bourgeoisie* and finally with the totality of the people, that had taken place in Europe gradually through some four hundred years was virtually completed in Asian countries in as many decades. In Africa the pace was faster still.

European nationalism had developed along with the growth of political and economic institutions. It had taken shape in nations which functioned as going concerns and whose economic and political basis was strong and broadening. It had expanded to embrace broader classes in the population as these became more active participants and beneficiaries.

Asian nationalism, however, developed among the intellectuals and then among the masses of the people long before an adequate institutional basis for national life had been established. In so doing it released an immense

EUROPE AND MIDDLE EAST
AFTER WORLD WAR I

Cartography Hallwag Berne

emotional force which could provide a great stimulus to national efforts and at the same time could overshadow the practical realities of national progress.

The first impact of the stimulus to nationalism from the enunciation and acceptance of the principle of self-determination of peoples was to loosen the hold of multi-national empires, to encourage national movements among minorities within national states, such as the Flemish in Belgium or the Catalans in Spain who wanted the use of their own language, to strengthen movements for independence, as in Ireland, and to give great encouragement to nationalist movements among colonial peoples.

These were generally liberating effects but they contained within themselves disturbing tendencies. How small a group was a people or a nation? In an economically interdependent world an invitation to every minority with historic consciousness to seek statehood was an encouragement to the fragmentation of society. The romantic concept of national history as a basis for nationalism, moreover, led immediately to conflicting claims, especially in eastern Europe where each country appealed to the period in history when the element with which it was identified nationally had ruled over the largest area. The idea that people of the same ethnic background belonged together, furthermore, brought claims for reunion with fellow-nationals living outside the national area. The wholesale exchange of Greek and Turkish populations in Asia Minor and Macedonia in 1922 removed millions of people from what had been their homelands for many generations, to bring them under the jurisdiction of their 'own' national states. These were but the first of many groups of displaced persons who were to become one of the twentieth century's most characteristic and tragic monuments to nationalism. For those minorities who had no nation to which to go, the liquidation of the Armenian population of Turkey foreshadowed the fate that was later to befall the Jews in Europe.

Within a few years of the hopeful enunciation of the principle of self-determination aggressive nationalism reasserted itself with renewed vigour. Japanese nationalists launched their expansionist venture in Asia, while in Europe a type of aggressive nationalism arose which went far beyond any hitherto known. First in fascist Italy and then in an even more extreme form in Nazi Germany, the implications of romantic nationalism were pushed to their furthest limits. The individual's supreme loyalty to the nation-state became his complete subjection to it; his identification with the aims of the nation became the surrender of every independent basis for organization; the nationhood of birth and blood became Aryanism, extermination of the Jews and the concept of the 'great-German Reich' composed of all German peoples wherever they might be; and finally the claimed natural superiority of the German folk was taken as a warrant for the expansion of the German state. This was the new, aggressive nationalism of the 1920s and 1930s which took the world to a second world war.

After the second world war, nationalism remained a major world force. It brought the liberation of the peoples of Asia and Africa. Its most aggressive forms appeared, for the moment at least, to have been checked. In the decade after the war it seemed to be compatible with the new internationalism. But by the middle of the twentieth century nationalism had shown itself to be a dangerous as well as a creative force in the life of mankind. And the interrelations among political units, both within and between states, had become infinitely complex in a world which was increasingly interdependent and at the same time increasingly bent on self-determination.

II. THE GROWTH OF INTERNATIONAL CO-OPERATION

The very forces making toward nationalism pressed at the same time beyond nationalism to international co-operation. Industry had required wider territory than the local village or feudal domain, and the national state had been in part an answer to its need for markets, for regulations extending over a large area to permit transactions under cover of law, uniform monetary systems, guarantee of contracts and legal recourse in case of their violation, as well as for transport facilities, financial institutions, labour recruitment and all the elements of modern industrial society. But as industry expanded and technology made possible fast transport and communication, national boundaries became too narrow, national regulations and facilities were insufficient, and many types of international bodies were set up. The International Telegraphic Union dated from 1865 and the Postal Union from 1874; international conventions for patents and copyrights were adopted in the 1880s; the International Court of Arbitration was established at The Hague in 1899. Starting with the International Geodetic Association in 1864, virtually all fields of science were internationally organized, as were many of the arts. International co-operation in the field of labour had been inaugurated with the First International in 1864, followed by the Second International in 1889.

The groundwork thus already existed for a major effort at international organization when the nations, staggering to their feet after the long, disastrous strain of the first world war, found the need for such organization to be imperative.

1. The League of Nations

Yet the League of Nations was radically new in conception and structure. For it proposed to commit states in advance to certain courses of action, and to provide judicial machinery which nations might, if willing to do so, use for the adjudication of disputes.

The Covenant of the League of Nations, drafted as an integral part of the treaty of Versailles, provided in its preamble that:

The High Contracting Parties, in order to promote international co-operation and to achieve international peace and security by the acceptance of obligations not to resort to war, by the prescription of open, just and honourable relations between nations, by the firm establishment of the understandings of international law as the actual rule of conduct among Governments, and by the maintenance of justice and a scrupulous respect for all treaty obligations in the dealings of organized peoples with one another, agree to this Covenant of the League of Nations.

Three points stood out clearly: the obligation not to resort to war; the creation of a new international law as the actual rule of conduct among governments; and scrupulous respect for all treaty obligations. These were not to be merely pious expressions; the Covenant provided machinery by which they should be enforced. Any member who might resort to war in disregard of its covenants was 'deemed to have committed an act of war against all other members', and these undertook to subject the covenant-breaking state immediately to economic sanctions by cutting off all trade and economic relations with it. Collective security supported by sanctions was a revolutionary principle.

A complementary provision, meant to develop the new spirit of international law under which the states were to settle their disputes, created a Permanent Court of International Justice, which should be 'competent to hear and determine any dispute of an international character' referred to it by the parties and to give an advisory opinion on any question or dispute referred to it by the Council or Assembly of the League of Nations.

In an effort to prevent disagreements from developing into disputes which might threaten the peace the Covenant gave every member 'the friendly right' to bring to the attention of the League's Assembly or Council any circumstance which might disturb 'the good understanding between nations on which peace depends', thus affording the League an opportunity to intervene and mediate.

The League was intended as a world organization and not merely a continuation of the concert of Europe. It was to include in its membership every independent state. The Latin American states and five Asian countries—Japan, China, Siam, Persia and India—were original members of the organization; India, though not independent, was admitted to membership on the ground of her exceptional contribution to the war. In the League's Assembly member states were represented on a basis of sovereign equality. Its Council, however, reflected the structure of world power, for the allied great powers, Britain, France, the United States, Italy and Japan, were to be permanent members, while four others were to be elected periodically from among the rest.

But the League, in fact, never became a world organization. The principle of universality suffered a staggering blow from which it never recovered when the United States decided not to join the organization. Also, Germany and the Soviet Union, though admitted later with permanent seats on the Council, were not associated with the League in its formative stages. Japan, Germany and Italy subsequently withdrew when they wished to act in defiance of the League's decisions.

The Assembly, which included all the smaller countries, met only annually at the League's headquarters in Geneva as a sort of international gathering. The League's authority was exercised by the Council whose permanent members tended to make the League their instrument. Furthermore the guarantee of the territorial integrity of nations included the overseas possessions of European states, thereby aligning the League on the side of the imperial powers against nationalist movements.

The authority of the League was soon tested. Challenged by the new and virulent form of nationalism, it was quickly shown to be ineffective. In 1923, a few months after Benito Mussolini had marched on Rome to establish the first of the fascist states, Italy became involved in a controversy with Greece. Instead of negotiating the dispute she sent a twenty-four hour ultimatum to the Greek government, which in turn appealed to the League of Nations; but before the League could even meet, Italy had bombarded and occupied the island of Corfu. The League merely handed over the matter to the Council of Ambassadors. Mussolini had proved to the world the impotence of the world organization.

From that time on, no major issue was decided by the League. The Locarno pact of 1925 and other attempts by the powers to find direct remedies for their fears were in fact confessions of the League's ineffectiveness. When Japan invaded Manchuria in 1931 the League found that even with the active support of the United States it was in no position to enforce any decision against the invader. The only result of its declarations and actions, including non-recognition of the puppet state of Manchukuo, was Japan's withdrawal from membership in the League. This incident removed all doubt as to the League's fatal weakness.

The League did invoke economic sanctions when Emperor Haile Selassie of Ethiopia in 1935 appealed to it for support in the face of Mussolini's attack on his country. But the response of the member states was so half-hearted that the damage to the League's prestige was far greater than to the Italian economy, although Italy was lacking essential raw materials and highly vulnerable to a systematic cutting off of supplies. The apparent indifference of the European statesmen to the fate of the last historic free state of Africa seemed to the weak nations and the colonial peoples of the world to confirm their suspicions that the League was no more than a cloak for the continuation of the old power politics of the 'haves' at the expense of the 'have-nots'. The League stood helplessly by while Hitler, one of whose early acts was to withdraw Germany from the League, scrapped one provision of the Treaty of Versailles after another, and it made no serious attempt to use its authority when Italy and Germany intervened directly in the Spanish civil war in 1936. Its only firm gesture, the expulsion of the USSR on the charge that the

Soviet–Finnish conflict of 1939–40 constituted aggression, came after the second world war had already broken out.[5]

Thus the first effort to create an international world organization which would ensure collective security failed to check the aggressive nationalism of the fascist powers and to avert a second world war.

Yet although it failed in its major task, the League of Nations, through the technical bodies it established, the studies which it conducted, conferences it organized and conventions which it formulated in many fields, contributed substantially to the building up of a world community and helped to develop the habit of approaching matters of common concern in international terms. Its most notable and enduring achievements were in the field of labour, where the International Labour Office through patient and unspectacular work brought workers, employers and governments together to develop world standards and principles concerning hours of work, industrial health and safety, employment of children and young people, maternity protection, protection of wages and related matters. The International Labour Office became so well established in its work and so generally accepted that it survived the shock of the second world war to emerge as one of the specialized agencies of the United Nations.

In making provision for the administration of Germany's former colonies and of part of the former Ottoman empire, the League developed three classes of mandates, adapted to the presumed political maturity of each area, under which administration was to be primarily for the benefit of the people of the area, not the mandatory power. The latter was responsible to the international body for the conduct of its rule. Although the system as it worked out was a long way from achieving its announced goals, it helped to undermine the principle of colonial authority and laid a basis for the trusteeship system of the United Nations.

In many social fields as well, such as health, nutrition, international traffic in women and in drugs, highway safety, population study, the League developed practical machinery for international co-operation and laid the basis for the United Nations and its specialized agencies. Its International Institute of Intellectual Co-operation presaged the formation of UNESCO.

Thus the practice of international co-operation was built up in numberless ways, at the same time that the destructive forces of aggressive nationalism were precipitating world conflict.

2. *The United Nations*

Although the outbreak of the second world war put an end to the League of Nations, it was clear that a new international structure must emerge once hostilities should cease, and during the war steps toward this objective were taken. The declaration of principles contained in the Atlantic Charter, formulated in 1941 by the British prime minister, Winston Churchill, and the president of the United States, Franklin D. Roosevelt, was adhered to by fifty-seven countries before the end of the war. Declarations of their intention to create a world organization were made by representatives of Great Britain, the United States, the Soviet Union and China at Moscow in 1943 and by Churchill, Roosevelt and Stalin at Teheran in the same year. Draft proposals for a general international organization were formulated in 1944 at Dumbarton Oaks in the United States as a result of conversations between the United States, the Soviet Union and Great Britain to which China was later a party. Finally, as the war was drawing to a close in April 1945, forty-six nations sent delegates to a meeting in San Francisco, USA, to formalize the creation of the United Nations Organization and agree upon its charter.[6]

The purpose of the United Nations as stated in the preamble to its charter was broader than that of the League of Nations, for it reaffirmed 'faith in fundamental human rights, in the dignity and worth of the human person' and it called specifically for employing international machinery 'for the promotion of the economic and social advancement of all peoples' as well as 'to unite our strength to maintain international peace and security'. Like the Council of the League, the United Nations Security Council was composed of five great powers as permanent members—Great Britain, USA, USSR, France and China —and rotating members elected for two-year terms from among other states.

The United Nations succeeded, where the League had failed, in becoming genuinely a world organization. As the former colonial peoples gained their independence they took their places one by one in the international body. Year after year the membership grew. Fifty nations signed the charter on June 26, 1945, to bring the organization into existence; by 1957 there were eighty-two with more to come as successive African states should achieve their independence. For areas still in colonial status, it exercised supervision of former mandates and other trust territories and its Trusteeship Council called upon all metropolitan governments to supply periodic reports on the administration of their dependencies. However much the great powers might seek to use the United Nations, it could not be regarded on the whole as the bulwark of their interests. The main gap in the organization's structure during the 1950s was the absence of the Chinese People's Republic with nearly a third of the world's population.

The chief channel for the influence of the smaller countries came to be the United Nations Assembly which grew in importance through the years. The influence of the League's Assembly had been slight; though it had held some dramatic sessions, as when Emperor Haile Selassie appeared before it to plead Ethiopia's cause, the League had acted almost entirely through its Council. The drafters of the United Nations charter expected a comparable development. But in the early period of its existence some members of the Assembly, notably the delegate of Australia, made an effort to bring more and more subjects before the Assembly for debate and to establish its independent right to take up and act by majority vote upon matters of its choice. At the same time the Security Council was persistently split by the division between communist and non-communist countries and prevented from action by the veto which each permanent member enjoyed and which was used no less than seventy-seven times by the USSR in the course of the first ten years as its way of maintaining its point of view in a body where four of the five permanent seats were held by non-communist powers.7

In these circumstances the United Nations Assembly became a forum for the expression of world opinion—opinion which came more and more to reflect the views and aspirations of those who had played little or no part in the League of Nations.

In the first decade of its existence the United Nations functioned in the shadow of tension between the communist and non-communist blocs. It acted in 1950 to declare North Korea an aggressor and to mobilize member nations in South Korea's defence, but the action was taken by the Security Council at a moment when the USSR chose to boycott the session and was not present to exercise its veto.8 When Israel marched against Egypt in 1956 and Britain and France sent an expedition against Suez, world opinion, mobilized through the United Nations Assembly, halted the Suez expedition and caused the withdrawal of the victorious Israeli and Franco-British forces; the United Nations assumed responsibility for policing the Egypt–Israel truce line with an international police force and, by agreement with Egypt, for clearing and reopening the blocked canal. Simultaneously, however, United Nations protests failed to halt the use of Soviet troops to suppress a revolt in Hungary and the secretary-general of the United Nations was denied entrance into Hungary either as a mediator or as an observer.9

After fifteen years the most striking thing about the United Nations was that it had withstood the world forces constantly threatening to tear it apart. Although nations had walked out of its meetings, none had left the organization. Whatever its failures, its efforts persisted in the deep conviction that some kind of international organization must be kept alive.

Meantime, through its many specialized agencies, its Economic and Social Council, its Commissions on Human Rights and on the Status of Women, its Technical Assistance Board and its other instrumentalities, it developed a great body of co-operative international activity in economic and social fields. The World Bank for Reconstruction and Development provided an international means for bringing foreign capital into underdeveloped areas without the imperialist implication which such investment had often carried in the past. International technical assistance missions in agriculture and health, welfare and industry, education, administration and countless other fields responded to requests for aid from governments around the world. UNESCO acted as a stimulus to intellectual co-operation. Through all these practical programmes the United Nations pursued its declared purpose 'to promote social progress and better standards of life in larger freedom'.

3. *Tendencies in international law*

Along with the creation of international organizations went the development of international law. The League of Nations mandate system involved a direct assumption of international responsibility. So also did the recognition of state-lessness as a status under international guarantee, in response to the problem created by large numbers of refugees from revolutionary régimes; travel papers based on this special status became a factor of considerable importance. The conventions drafted by the International Labour Organization came to constitute an internationally recognized code of labour standards, while those relating to the control of white slave traffic and narcotics imposed direct obligations upon the signatories. And though its efforts were unsuccessful, the League of Nations did attempt to enforce sanctions against two major powers, Italy and Japan, for what it considered breaches of international law. The collective action of the majority of members of the League in protest against the Italian invasion of Ethiopia deserves to be remembered as the first effort to enforce an international decision against a major power.

The most noteworthy step was the creation of the Permanent Court of International Justice by the League of Nations. Although only those countries which agreed to do so were bound to accept the jurisdiction of the court when a case was brought against them, and though the basic issues involving the peace of the world did not come before the tribunal for adjudication, the court decided thirty-two international cases during its eighteen years of existence, and in no case was its judgment defied. Its work was carried on after the second world war by the International Court of Justice created by the United Nations.

The establishment of the United Nations and its specialized agencies was accompanied by a further growth in international law—the gradual evolution of a system of enforcement manifested in the creation of token international forces such as the neutral commission in Kashmir and the international police force in the Gaza strip and the Sinai peninsula; in the decision to halt war as in the case of the two 'police actions' of the Dutch in Indonesia or to engage in war on behalf of the United Nations when the sovereignty of a country was invaded as in Korea or the Anglo-French attack on Suez; and in the growing tendency of the United Nations to override the plea of internal sovereignty where human rights were involved, notably in resolutions condemning racial policies in South Africa and discussions of French military activity in Algeria. On a regional basis, the Organization of American States provided mutual guarantees of non-intervention among the states of the western hemisphere and the League of Arab States undertook a somewhat similar function in the Middle East. Efforts to unite western Europe envisaged the pos-sibility of a European parliament, growing out of steps toward economic co-operation.

In short, the developments during this period bore witness to the growth of a collective consciousness and a desire on the part of the world community to enforce, even against powerful nations, certain moral and ethical principles, thus giving them the force of international law.[10]

NOTES TO CHAPTER II

1. Academician D. Kosev argues that it was the October Revolution in Russia, and not Wilson's Fourteen Points, that exercised the principal influence upon the spread of the revolutionary movement in Europe and the national-liberation movement in the East.

The same point is made by Professor László Zsigmond, who finds it impossible to agree with the authors' statement that national self-determination and national independence are incontrovertibly connected with the Fourteen Points of President Wilson.

Professor L. I. Zubok and Doctor of Historical Sciences V. M. Dalin note that the Great October Socialist Revolution opened a new era in history—the era of the collapse of imperialism and the establishment of a new socialist society—and exercised a decisive influence upon the destinies of peoples the world over. It brought about a mighty upsurge in the revolutionary and national-liberation movement in all countries and marked a new stage in the struggle of the working masses for socialism. From the time of the October Revolution onwards the development of world history has proceeded under its steady influence. The period immediately following the socialist revolution in Russia (1918–23) is known as *the period of revolutionary upsurge* in the capitalist countries and *the upsurge of the national-liberation movement* in the colonial and dependent countries.

J. Nehru, Prime Minister of India, and President Sukarno of Indonesia, assess the significance of the October Revolution in the following words:

' . . . I had no doubt that the Soviet revolution had advanced human society by a great leap and had lit a bright flame which could not be smothered, and that it had laid the foundations for the "new civilization" towards which the world would advance.' (J. Nehru, *The Discovery of India*, New York, 1946, p. 17).

'During the October Revolution the Russian people showed the peoples of Asia who were fighting colonial oppression that the working class could overthrow the mighty power of a cruel feudal regime, in this case the tsarist autocracy, and build the new society of which they dreamed. This great historic event, which took place beyond the limits of the Asian continent, had a striking effect upon the peoples of Asia who were struggling for national independence, and enhanced their confidence that in the long run they too would win victories in their struggle for justice, if they fought in an organized manner and with all the determination they could command. After the success of the October Revolution in Russia, the struggle of the Asian peoples for national independence, against the oppression of the invaders, burst forth with fresh intensity.' (Sukarno, 'The Influence of the October Revolution on the Awakening of the Peoples of Asia', *Pravda*, October 11, 1956.)

See also the following:

Velikaya Oktyabrskaya revolyutsiya i mirovoye osvoboditelnoye dvizhenie ('The Great October Revolution and the world-wide Liberation movement') Moscow, 1958).

Mezhdunarodnoye znacheniye Velikoy Oktyabrskoy sotsialisticheskoy revolyutsii ('The international significance of the Great October Socialist Revolution') (Moscow, 1958).

Vsemirno-istoricheskoye znachenie Velikoy Oktyabrskoy sotsialisticheskoy revolyutsii ('The world-historical significance of the Great October Socialist Revolution') (Moscow, 1957).

Velikiy Oktyabr i narody Vostoka ('The Great October Revolution and the Peoples of the East') (Moscow, 1957).

Die Auswirkungen der Grossen Sozialistischen Oktober Revolution auf Deutschland, Bd 1–4, (Berlin, 1959).

Tim Buck, *1917–1957. Forty Years of Great Change* (Toronto, 1957)
Contributii la studiul influentei Marii revolutii socialiste din Octobrie in Romunia (Bucuresti, 1957).
Culinović, F., *Odjeci Oktobra u jugoslavenskim krajevima* (Zagreb, 1957).
Winston U. Solberg. *The Impact of Soviet Russia on American Life and Thought* (Cambridge, Mass, Harvard University, 1952).
Velka Rijnova Socialistcka revoluce v dejinach a kulture Ceskoslovenska (Praha, 1958).
Wplyw Rewolucji Październikowej na ruch spółdzielczy (Warszawa, 1958).
K. M. Panikkar, *Asia and Western Dominance* (London, 1954).
J. Romein, *De Eeuw van Azie* (Leiden-Brill, 1956).
J. Ingenieros, *Los tiempos nuevos* (Buenos Aires, 1957).
O. Brandao, *Russia Proletaria* (Rio de Janeiro, 1923).
A. Pereira, *Russia avanza* (São Paulo, 1924).
E. Recabarren, *Lo que vi en Russia* (Santiago de Chile, 1923).
K. Liebknecht, *Reden und Aufsätze* (Hamburg, 1921).
K. Mammach, *Der Einfluss der russischen Februarrevolution und der Grossen Sozialistischen Oktoberrevolution auf die deutsche Arbeiterklasse* (Berlin, 1955); and others.

2. Candidate of Philosophical Sciences E. D. Modrzhinskaya cannot agree with the way in which the authors treat the concepts of 'nation' and 'nationalism'.

(1) Following a school of thought that is widespread in the West, the authors understand by the word 'nation' first and foremost a state organization. Undoubtedly the creation of a state is an important element in the development of a nation; nevertheless it cannot be considered an indispensable sign of nationhood, since there have been, and still are, nations which have not had or do not have their own national state. To maintain that every nation must have its state would imply that many colonial and semi-colonial peoples that have not yet won statehood, but are still fighting for it, are not nations. Historical materialism teaches that the nation is an historically constituted, stable community of people, formed on the basis of a common language, territory, economic life, and psychological make-up manifested in a common culture.

All these hall-marks of nationhood are interconnected, and the presence of all of them is necessary before a particular community of individuals can call itself a nation. Nations first came into being during the epoch of developing capitalism, although certain elements of nationhood (language, common culture, etc.) were already formed during the pre-capitalist era.

(2) Nationalism is treated by the authors as though it were identical with some sort of 'national feeling in general'; the nationalism of ruling groups is equated with the patriotism of the popular masses, which they also call nationalism; and the nationalism found in colonial and dependent countries is confused with the aggressive nationalism of the colonialists. Soviet scholars take the view that nationalism is the expression of the policy of the bourgeoisie in the form of ideas and concepts, and that it reflects the attitude of the bourgeoisie to its own nation and to other nations; in other words, nationalism is a constituent element of bourgeois ideology. During the period when capitalism was in the ascendant, i.e. when bourgeois nations were first coming into being, nationalism was linked with a fierce and bitter struggle against feudalism and feudal exploitation. The broad mass of the people rose in revolt against feudal society; they were interested in the liquidation of serfdom and oppression by the privileged classes of feudal society; and in so far as the bourgeoisie fought against the feudal order, and genuinely acted on behalf of the nation as a whole, to that extent bourgeois nationalism had a progressive, general-democratic character. But victory in the struggle against feudalism paved the way for a new, capitalistic form of exploitation. A radical difference appeared between the class interests of the bourgeoisie, and the bourgeois ideology that reflected them, and the interests and ideology of the working masses. As capitalism developed, so this contradiction between the exploiters and the exploited became ever more intense. It is natural that in the era of the highest and last stage in the development of capitalism, imperialism—when there is a very deep gulf between the interests of the monopolists and the broad masses of the people —aggressive imperialist nationalism should have revealed particularly clearly its essentially anti-popular and reactionary nature. However, in this historical epoch, but in different concrete circumstances—

in countries where a struggle is being carried on against imperialist oppression—bourgeois nationalism has a progressive character in so far and inasmuch as it has a general democratic character and is directed against imperialist oppression.

This point of view is endorsed by Dr. Vavro Hajdu, who points out that the authors frequently identify the nation with its ruling class, and present the actions and interests of the ruling class as the actions and interests of the nation as a whole. Hajdu also considers that the authors' approach 'to the problem of nationalism is fundamentally incorrect, particularly in so far as the philosophical aspect is concerned. The efforts towards integration in Europe are presented as a new form of internationalism.'

3. *The Author-Editors have used the term 'nation state' to designate a state based on the presumed loyalty of all citizens and their presumed common interest and identity vis-à-vis other political units. They have used the term 'nationalism' to designate: (1) the aspirations for separate identity and political autonomy of a group of people identified by a common language, religion, culture, descent or tradition, and (2) the aspirations of a nation state to further what it regards as its interests as a body politic.*

4. Professor László Zsigmond, Dr Vavro Hajdu and Professor L. I. Zubok emphasize that a decisive part in bringing about the collapse of the Second International was played by its leaders, J. Guesde, H. Hyndman, E. Vandervelde and K. Kautsky, who adopted a position contrary to the resolutions passed on war and militarism with their participation at the Stuttgart congress (1907) and Basle congress (1912) of the International. At the beginning of World War I they repudiated internationalist slogans and supported their governments. See, for example, the declaration by the Social-Democratic fraction in the German Reichstag on August 4, 1914, to the effect that it supported the government in the war and was voting for the war credits requested (*Vorwärts*, August 5, 1914).

5. Doctor of Historical Sciences N. Yakovlev notes: The resolution on the exclusion of USSR from the League of Nations was taken on December 14, 1939, by the Council of the League. A pretext for this step was found in the armed conflict between the USSR and Finland. Of the 15 members of the Council only 7 voted in favour of the resolution: Great Britain, France, Belgium, Bolivia, Egypt, the Union of South Africa, and the Dominican Republic, i.e., less than one half of all the members and, besides, among the States voting there were two—Egypt and the Union of South Africa—which at that time were directly dependent upon Great Britain. Therefore, the resolution of the League of Nations could not have normal validity.

6. Doctor of Historical Sciences N. N. Yakovlev stresses that the first of the Powers belonging to the anti-Hitler coalition to declare officially that it was necessary to set up a new international organization was the Soviet Union. The declaration on friendship and mutual assistance signed between the USSR and Poland on December 4, 1941, stated: 'After the victorious conclusion of the war and due punishment of the Hitlerite criminals it will be the task of the Allied states to secure a lasting and just peace. This can be attained only by a new organization of international relations, based on the uniting of the democratic countries in a durable alliance.'

7. Doctor of Historical Sciences N. Yakovlev notes:
(1) When drafting the UN Charter, the American and British governments attached enormous importance to the principle of unanimity of the Great Powers in this Organization—the principle later known as 'the veto'. At that time unanimity of the Great Powers in the United Nations was regarded in Washington and London as a *conditio sine qua non* of the existence of the United Nations Organization. On this question there was not the least disagreement between the USSR, the USA, and Great Britain. C. Hull, the US Secretary of State during the war years, emphasizes in his *Memoirs:* ' . . . There was no question in our minds, . . . that the vote of the permanent members of the Council should be unanimous on questions involving security. This was the so-called veto power. We were no less resolute than the Russians in adhering to this principle. . . . ' (C. Hull, *Memoirs*, New York, 1948, Vol. II, p. 1683.) E. Stettinius, who succeeded C. Hull as Secretary of State, pointed out that both the military and the civilian American leaders were anxious that the principle of unanimity of the Great Powers should be accepted. E. Stettinius wrote: 'The fact . . . that a major argument

against American participation in the League of Nations had been that membership
would commit us in vital matters was of real significance in determining American
support of the veto power by the permanent members (of the Security Council)'. (E.
Stettinius, *Roosevelt and the Russians: the Yalta Conference*, New York, 1949, p. 19.)

(2) The representatives of the Western World also used the 'veto'. For example, in
1956 Great Britain and France made use of the power of veto when in the Security
Council there was raised the question about the cessation of Anglo-Franco-Israeli
hostilities against Egypt.

8. Professor L. I. Zubok and Dr Vavro Hajdu stress that the declaration that the Democratic People's Republic of Korea was guilty of aggression contradicts the facts. The
facts show that aggressive actions were begun by the government of South Korea,
relying upon the support of the USA. See the book I. F. Stone, *The Hidden History of
the Korean War* (New York, 1952); also 'Documents and Materials Exposing the
Inspirators of the Civil War in Korea': *Documents from the Archives of the Rhee Syngman
Government* (Pyongyang, Ministry of Foreign Affairs of the Democratic People's Republic
of Korea, 1950).

9. See Note 12 to Chapter I.

10. Professor László Zsigmond notes that, when enumerating various international organizations, the authors make no mention whatsoever of the Third International and
other international labour organizations, such as the World Federation of Trade Unions.

CHAPTER III

THE NEW ROLE OF THE STATE
AND ITS COMPETING FORMS

I. DEVELOPMENT OF THE INCLUSIVE STATE

IN the twentieth century the political state became more inclusive and demanding than it had ever been before. This was true in respect to those who participated in it, those whom it reached and served, and the scope of its functions and activities. The electorate on which governments rested was everywhere extended.

At the beginning of the century the governments of even the most advanced democracies rested on a limited franchise, for although direct property qualifications for voting had been gradually removed, indirect ones such as educational qualifications remained in some places, and women did not enjoy the right to vote. Outside western Europe, the Americas and Oceania political participation was far more restricted. Russia and the Ottoman empire were under autocracies; Japan, under a divine emperor, had a parliament based on limited suffrage; the empire of China was still ruled by the Manchus; few colonial peoples knew the meaning of the ballot, for even such legislative bodies as functioned in British-occupied India were elected on a restricted and indirect franchise.

By mid-century the position had changed radically. In the countries of Europe and the Americas the conception of 'the people' had, as a result of many kinds of movements and struggles, been enlarged to include virtually all adults—men and women, workers and property holders, peasants and landlords. This was true regardless of the form of the state; however authoritarian a government might be its electoral base was conceived to be the entire adult population. The newly established countries of Asia generally provided for universal suffrage in their constitutions. There still remained large areas of the world where the political structure did not rest even in theory on the majority of the people, notably in the Union of South Africa where the African and Coloured peoples were excluded from political participation, in parts of tropical Africa still under colonial rule and in some theocratic states of the Islamic Middle East. But the vast majority of the world's populations enjoyed more political rights than at any time in the world's history.

Not only were political rights extended, but the state took note of all elements in the population. In 1900 only a few countries had an accurate census of their populations; still fewer kept records of their people's illnesses and causes of death, their occupations and employment, their education and housing, their marital status and incomes. At mid-century most governments compiled such data from year to year or decade to decade, as a guide for national policies and as a basis for observing the results of policy in terms of the total population. Even where indigenous populations within the borders of the state still lived a tribal or otherwise isolated life apart from the general society—in South and Central America, the United States, the USSR, China, India, New Zealand, Australia—governments declared the welfare of these enclaves to be a state responsibility and took steps to make them more fully a part of the body politic.

Even more distinctive of the twentieth century was the increased scope of the state's activity. The liberal democratic state of the nineteenth century interfered as little as possible in the affairs of the people and left the individual free to go his own way so long as he did not endanger the state or engage in activities contrary to law and accepted ethics. The state was not expected to assume direct responsibility for promoting the welfare of its citizens beyond the relief of paupers, measures to check epidemics, and such education as might be required to enable people to perform their duties as citizens. As late as the first decade of the twentieth century some outstanding students of political theory in Britain regarded the introduction of social insurance in that country as the beginning of the end of democracy.

The modern state, however, ceased to be merely a bystander while its citizens pursued their several interests. It provided public utilities, medical services and social insurance; it recognized housing as a national concern; it used taxation as an equitable method of providing for national welfare and fiscal and monetary policy to promote full employment. The mounting requirements of industrial society and the concept of the state as including all the people thus changed the state's functions, its responsibilities and its direct activities.

These trends were present in all twentieth-century states regardless of their form, their history and the stage of their economic development. Although countries which had gone furthest along the road of public responsibility for the people's welfare, such as the Scandinavian countries or the USSR, were poles apart from those at the other extreme which had hardly made a beginning, such as Saudi Arabia or Yemen, the general direction of development was the same. Even where there was active resistance to widening the basis of participation, as in the Union of South Africa, the scope and functions of the state were enlarged and the state undertook in some measure to serve the total population.

The issue in the twentieth century was thus not whether or not the state should enlarge its scope and reach all the people. The two issues which produced revolution, war and terror and which at mid-century still divided the world into competing camps were: what should be the state's form and, in extending its activities to reach all the people, was it primarily as their servant or as their master.

II. EXTENSION OF LIBERAL DEMOCRACY BEFORE THE FIRST WORLD WAR

At the opening of the century, liberal democracy was widely accepted in principle throughout the western world as the norm toward which societies were tending. In practice popular sovereignty was far from a reality, for not only restricted suffrage but lack of economic security and education made it ineffective. Autocracies remained in many parts of the world but, in the optimistic view of the liberal thinkers of the West, these were assumed to be the relics of an unenlightened past, as in China, Turkey or Russia, or they were regarded as deviations from the norm, as in Latin American countries where dictators from time to time seized the government of states with democratic constitutions.

To say that liberal democracy was the accepted norm of the West is not to deny that the existing autocracies were prepared to resist with utmost rigour efforts to bring this principle to their realms; the ruthlessness with which the Russian tsar put down the revolutionists in 1905 bore ample testimony. Nor is it to ignore the anomaly of autocratic colonial rule imposed on subject peoples by states which were among the leading exponents and practitioners of liberal democracy at home—Great Britain, France, the Netherlands.

But in spite of these factual situations few in the West were prepared seriously to challenge liberal democracy in principle. In a guide for newspaper readers and debaters published in 1903 by John Bertram Askew, neither democracy nor dictatorship appeared on a list of some 250 controversial topics. The only related questions listed were whether or not members of parliament should be paid, whether parliaments should be shorter, and questions involving freedom of speech and opinion, religious equality and how much honour should be paid to the intellectual professions. A few voices were raised to accuse democracy of cultivating mediocrity, of creating a servile state and of being incapable of decisive action, but these were individual dissenters and not yet part of a critical chorus.

1. Broadening base of liberal democratic states

As a dynamic principle, both within states where it was the prevailing form and in its spread to other areas where it was not traditional, liberal democracy had two facets, liberty and equality. Liberal democracy of the nineteenth century stressed liberty—the freedom to think and speak, to assemble and worship, to engage in free enterprise for economic gain. The state was conceived as an instrument which should create the conditions for the pursuit and enjoyment of freedom. In theory this was freedom for all, within the limits of the infringement of the freedom of others, and in this sense it was egalitarian. But in practice the inequalities of society, in access to wealth, to education, to the means of expression, often limited or even negated freedom.

In the late nineteenth and especially in the early twentieth century, a growing recognition that the reality of democracy was bound up with a closer approach to the ideal of equality was reflected in a mounting tendency to broaden democracy's base. In its most general and obvious form this trend involved extending the franchise, first to males who lacked property and then to women. Equally important was the trade union movement and the accompanying extension of labour influence into the political field. The trade unions played a major part in reducing the disparity of status between workers and other segments of the population.

The organization of labour was not achieved without a bitter struggle during which its opponents appealed to the principle of individual freedom against the efforts of workers to achieve equality of bargaining strength through collective action. But gradually what had been regarded as a conspiracy in restraint of trade came to be tolerated in principle as a legitimate form of voluntary association, then protected in its right to function and its members assured by law of their right to join without intimidation by employers. By the middle of the twentieth century the trade union had become a recognized, integral part of a modern liberal democratic state.

The trade union movement was only the most important of the many tendencies to broaden the base of democracy in traditionally democratic countries and to reduce inequality during these years. Movements to increase the participation of women in national life, through enlarged opportunities for education and employment as well as suffrage, reduced the disparity of status between men and women. Efforts were also made to extend equality of rights and opportunities to such disadvantaged elements in the population as Negroes or Jews or religious or national minorities. These movements gained momentum over the years, but in the early decades of the century they were already in the process of converting states which had been mainly the expression of the propertied males of the dominant ethnic element into more nearly comprehensive and egalitarian democratic societies.

The extension of government activity to include social insurance, labour legislation and health and welfare services was a reflection of this change. For these measures served the interest of the broadened electorate as the interests of the middle-class electorate had been served by the former system of *laissez-faire*. Although it was not until the second quarter of the century that the concept of the welfare state as an expression of liberal democratic principles emerged clearly, the trend was present and the first elements of policy already initiated before the first world war. The war itself accelerated the trend, for the improved conditions achieved or promised during the conflict were at least partially retained or secured thereafter; the American war slogan 'to make the world safe for democracy' made the doctrine of equality more popular in Europe; the post-war collapse of some European currencies and the decline of others destroyed or reduced much inherited wealth.[1, 2, 3, 4]

The economic crisis of 1929–33 gave an added impetus to the consolidation of the role of the state and the extension of its functions as governments intervened more and more deeply in economic life in the effort to revive their depressed economies and to reinstate their unemployed people. Finally, during the second world war, all the belligerent countries assumed direct controls over many aspects of national life and generally retained some features of these controls when the war was over.

In the countries which had been formed by European settlement overseas, where feudal institutions and rigid class structures had never existed—the United States and Canada, New Zealand and Australia—liberal democracy was taken more completely for granted than in older societies, and the broadening of its base came earlier and more thoroughly than where older institutions hung on. Manhood suffrage had prevailed throughout most of the United States from the early nineteenth century and universal public education was well established in most sections before the middle of the century; Negroes, however, were still effectively excluded from the polls in some states during the twentieth century in spite of national law, and women only secured the vote on a national scale in 1920. New Zealand and Australia were in the vanguard in many types of social legislation.

2. *Spread of liberal democracy to new areas*

In the first decade of the twentieth century liberal democracy became the ideal of the rising *bourgeoisies* in eastern Europe, the Middle East and parts of Asia and the inspiration for movements of reform. Universal manhood suffrage was introduced into parts of Austria–Hungary in the first decade of the century, but the Hapsburg empire was a long way from the pattern of the parliamentary democracies of western Europe. Within the autocracies of Russia, Turkey, Persia and China, and in imperial Japan, revolutionary or reform movements attempted to achieve the beginnings of democracy.

In Russia the *bourgeoisie* in 1905 demanded from the tsar constitutional reforms and guarantees of civil rights, and they were joined by a general strike of Moscow workers and by revolts of peasants seeking to eliminate the hold of landlords. The 1908 revolution of Young Turks was carried out under the banner of 'liberty, equality, fraternity and justice' by a combination of young Turkish emigrants in Paris and a Committee for Unity and Progress composed of discontented officers and freemasons in Turkish towns.[5]

Inspired by the Russian and Turkish efforts, young Persian intellectuals with western education led a movement in the same year which, with some British backing, was successful in forcing a quasi-liberal constitution on the shah; the parliamentary body set up in response to this movement survived through the vicissitudes of the following fifty years.[6]

Japan had adopted parliamentary forms along with other western institutions after the Meiji restoration in 1868, but the franchise was extremely restricted and the retention of many of the strongly feudal features of Japanese

society had kept parliamentary processes from becoming more than superficial phenomena. Within Japan, however, repeated reform movements
sought to modify the feudal structure and to give the forms of political
democracy some reality. Even the dowager empress of China found it necessary to concede constitutional reforms in 1905, but these came too slowly to
check the revolutionary movement led by Sun Yat-sen which converted
China into a republic in 1911 with institutions which attempted to embody the
kind of liberal democracy which Sun had learned in the West.

None of these movements resulted in the establishment of effective liberal
democratic states, but they reflected the extent to which the principles had
spread and had become the ideal in terms of which discontent with autocratic rule or status in world affairs expressed itself.

These same ideals also penetrated colonial areas. This was most notable in
India which had the longest and most thorough exposure to British parliamentary thought and institutions, and possessed a considerable middle class,
but it occurred to some degree wherever western-trained elements began to
seek leadership in colonial areas. Such ideals could not find expression in the
years before the first world war, but the fact that they had been assimilated
and engrained in the aspirations of the colonial leaders became evident a
generation later when the peoples gained their independence and made these
ideals the basis of the constitutional systems of their states.

III. CHALLENGES TO LIBERAL DEMOCRACY
IN THE INTER-WAR YEARS

During the inter-war years liberal democracy of the western type was
challenged in theory and in practice both from the right and from the left,
both from fascism and from the revolutionary communist movement, and it
was subjected to sharp attacks from critics within its own ranks who raised
doubts about its premises, criticized its practices and expressed fear of its
impact. The few voices in western Europe which had been heard to question
democracy or deny its goals in the early years of the century became a chorus
by the 1930s. They were even joined by some few voices from Britain, and
some from the United States where democracy was taken for granted, who
feared the masses as a downward-levelling force or assailed democracy as the
worship of incompetence. The economic depression of the 1930s offered an
added cause for losing confidence in a political system which appeared unable
to cope with economic decline.

The many dictatorships which gained power in eastern Europe, the
Balkans, the Iberian peninsula and parts of Latin America during these years
were evidence that, under the conditions of the period, liberal democracy had
insufficient vitality in the areas where it lacked strong roots to organize new
states successfully or to sustain the reforms which it achieved in others. They
did not, however, offer a new ideological challenge. They were essentially
feudal or military dictatorships, sometimes reinforced by clerical support as

in Spain, Portugal and Austria, and they represented the old pattern of resistance to the democratization of feudal societies.

1. The challenge of fascism

More serious was the challenge of fascism which struck at the basic assumptions and values of democracy, not merely at its institutional forms. Liberal democracy rested on an acceptance of the essential worth and dignity of the individual, whose welfare was the *raison d'être* of the state; by definition, the state was his servant, not his master. It assumed that men were rational and could act responsibly so that the state might be entrusted to their judgment. The institutions characteristic of democracy were implicit in these assumptions and values—legal guarantees of certain individual rights against arbitrary action by other individuals or by the state itself, including the right to hold and express opinions and to form voluntary groups such as political parties for such purpose; acceptance by the minority of majority rule and respect by the majority for minority rights.

Fascism denied these basic assumptions about man—his rationality, his potentiality for responsible action and his basic value as an individual. It denied that the essential purpose of the state was to secure the freedom and welfare of the individual and asserted the value of the state as an end in itself. Far from trusting the judgment and capacity of the people, fascism exalted the leadership principle and made irrational loyalty a substitute for rational choice. On these premises, the fascist states scorned and suppressed democratic institutions—parliamentary forms, party organization as a means of expressing diversity of opinion, and all the personal freedoms which the liberal states guaranteed.

The challenge from the fascist, national socialist and other dictatorships in the inter-war years placed liberal democracy on the defensive. Obvious weaknesses in the parliamentary systems of some countries, such as the instability of the parliamentary régime in France, lent colour to the attacks on parliamentary principles as such. These weaknesses were not characteristic of the countries where democratic processes were rooted in a long experience of voluntary civic activity and responsible local government. They appeared in areas where parliamentary institutions had been superimposed on an administrative structure, as in France, or on feudal localism as in Italy, or on clerical dominance as in Spain and Austria, or on paternalistic authoritarianism as in Germany.

The requirements of modern warfare had forced a great extension of state power during the war and had offered an example to those who would make a principle of the paramount authority of the state and the subordination to it of the individual citizen. The growth of economic power in the hands of great corporations made the nineteenth-century image of free enterprise and competitive individualism obviously false, and the democratic states found themselves forced to regulate many aspects of economic life. The imperatives of modern industrial society seemed to call for principles of integration rather than of individualism and competition, and its highly technical and complex character required a more sophisticated form of administration and a more technically competent bureaucracy than had been implied by the ideal of the *laissez-faire* state. In addition, modern techniques of communication placed immense power in the hands of those who controlled the mass media and the means of mass propaganda—power which the state might use or might have to control.

Although the dictatorships differed as between those which were merely dictatorial in practice, such as those of Marshal Pilsudski in Poland, King Alexander in Yugoslavia and traditional dictators in parts of Latin America, and those which made a principle of the fascist alternative to democracy, they had certain features in common. All discarded or repressed parliamentary institutions and the party system on which they rested and substituted a single party; all limited freedom of speech and discussion and brought most or all organizations and institutions into a common pattern; all were anti-individualist and in one way or another substituted corporate entities for the individualism of old-style democracy, although only fascist Italy, clerico-fascist Austria and Portugal specifically sought to create something like a corporate state.

Pro-fascist elements who challenged democracy from the right were able to take advantage of the liberal democracies' fear of the opposite challenge from the left. In one state after another dictators rose to power claiming to be defenders of the nation against the menace of revolutionary socialism or communism.

2. *The challenge of communism*[7]

The basis for the attack on liberal democracy from the left differed fundamentally from that of the right, though the challenge was no less sharp and the methods employed, both to destroy democracy and to govern in its place, had certain features in common.

In challenging liberal democracy, the communists accepted many of the fundamental assumptions that fascism denied. They, too, viewed man as a rational being whose judgment in the long run could theoretically be trusted, and they regarded the state as the product of rational action, not as a mystical entity. The charge against liberal democracy was that it was not in reality democratic. The *bourgeois* capitalist state, in this view, was incompatible with the welfare of the people to which it gave lip service, for the liberty which it cherished was only the liberty of those who owned the means of production to exploit those who did not. In the Marxian view, state power was always exercised solely by that part of society which owned the instruments and means of production.

Liberal democracy in theory took no account of class as a phenomenon. In practice it functioned in European societies which were strongly stratified along class lines and in North America and Oceania where class structures, though far less rigid and historically engrained than in Europe, were nevertheless real. In societies which were still feudal and authoritarian the class division was even sharper. The socialist challenge stressed class as the major social reality and accused liberal democracy of being in fact only a cloak for the dominance of the *bourgeoisie*.

Communism differed from liberal democracy in its view of the individual's relation to society. Unity of social and individual interests was a central concept according to which the individual, as a cell in the organism that is society, derives his rights from the society and realizes his purpose and his individual development in service to it.

The party system also differed fundamentally from that of the liberal democracies. Whereas in the liberal democratic states political parties were the means of organizing and expressing the differences of opinion and interest presumed to exist, the Communist party considered itself the vanguard and instrument of the working people in a state where differences were being eliminated with the elimination of class. It was a select, trained and disciplined body which carried responsibility for the interests of the proletariat. The Communist party was thus the central organization, the leading and guiding force within the state.

In the operation of the communist state all organs of state power constituted a single system conforming to the principle of democratic centralism as formulated by Lenin, i.e. the principle of elective organs and the subordination of lower organs to higher ones. The system was conceived as permitting the power over state matters to be concentrated in the hands of a central authority while encouraging maximum initiative of the population.

The various organs of state and party, and of such other bodies as trade unions and women's and youth organizations, were elected by universal suffrage, generally from lists which the voters could accept or reject rather than by choice among competing candidates. Active discussion of matters referred by higher organs enabled the lower units to understand and help to carry out central decisions and provided the central organs of the party and state with reflections of popular opinion which they could take into account in arriving at decisions. In the USSR a million or more people came to serve as deputies in organs of state power and millions of citizens were members of regular committees of the Soviets. In 1957 an estimated 40,000,000 took part in discussions of the draft law for the reorganization of industrial and building management.

In Marxist-Leninist theory the dictatorship of the proletariat was conceived as a temporary device for transferring power from the dominant *bourgeois* class to the proletariat and eliminating the *bourgeoisie*. The ultimate objective was the creation of a classless society which should, finally, no longer require a strong, dictating state. According to this view the state would eventually 'wither away', for as all citizens would be drawn into the management of economic and cultural affairs, functions performed by state organs would be gradually taken over by social organizations and in the ultimate communist society there would no longer be any need for organs for the government of people, only for the government of things, i.e. the economy. The history of the first forty years of communist rule in the Soviet Union was marked by Stalin's dictatorial power, but after his death in 1953 the Soviet Communist party condemned the policy of mass repression. From 1957 on, a number of central state functions were decentralized, but the state continued to be the main instrument of social change and the party kept its leading role.

The concept that the state is a temporary phenomenon, that the party is a leading and guiding group rather than an all-inclusive body to which all must belong, and that there should be active social participation, distinguished the communist concept of the state sharply from the fascist concept of the state as a mystic entity embodying the leadership principle. Yet though these systems were based on opposing political and socio-economic principles both were, in theory and in practice, fundamentally at variance with the principles and practices of liberal democracy.[8]

IV. LIBERAL DEMOCRACY AND DICTATORSHIP AT MID-CENTURY

Though challenged from both right and left, and the object of many doubts and questions expressed from within, liberal democracy at the middle of the twentieth century retained a strong position in the world and democratic principles maintained their appeal. Liberal democracy held its ground and prospered in its old strongholds—in the British Isles and the United States, in Canada and the Scandinavian countries, in the Low Countries and Switzerland, in Australia and New Zealand. It stood firm in principle even where it was breached in practice, notably in Latin America where although dictatorships continued to rise, democratic principles continually reasserted themselves in one country after another when they had been temporarily lost.

Liberal democratic principles provided the basis for the constitutions of most of the new states created after the second world war by formerly colonial or subject peoples. But the application of such principles under the historic conditions of liberation was far from simple. Institutional forms inherited from colonial powers had evolved under the conditions of the home country and were not necessarily suited to the needs of former colonial states. In fact some principles and institutions were directly at variance with the cultural traditions of the areas.

Except in the communal village structures of some areas, democracy as a functioning process was almost unknown outside India and Pakistan where some local machinery based on elective principles had been in operation. More fundamentally, the principle of democratic obedience to majority decision was an alien concept. Furthermore, the difficulties of adapting democratic systems inherited from colonial powers were complicated by the particular forms of such institutions. In Indonesia the multi-party system with an elaborate method of proportional representation inherited from the Dutch produced no less than fourteen contenders for the vote of the inexperienced Indonesian citizen in the country's first national election in 1956. The British two-party system had the virtue of simplicity, but it depended on the willingness of the defeated minority to function as a loyal opposition instead of defying the authority of the state.

The new states, moreover, came into existence at a time when governments of all types carried far greater responsibilities than those which older democratic governments had faced in their early stages. Their efforts to achieve rapid economic and social development intensified these responsibilities, and gave rise to doubts as to whether the methods of liberal democracy were adequate to the tasks. Indonesia's president, Sukarno, for example, sought a formula for what he called 'guided democracy' in the effort to provide some of the positive direction he observed in communist countries without resort to dictatorship. A decade after their creation the newly independent states, with the possible exception of India, were far from having made a working reality of the democratic principles which their constitutions professed. In fact many of the original democratic constitutions were superseded or set aside in favour of some form of central authority designed to facilitate positive, immediate action and to permit the development of new political forms adapted to the needs and traditions of each area.

Everywhere there was a tendency for democratic states to take on the characteristics of a welfare state and to incorporate a measure of what was originally projected as part of the socialist ideal and came to be loosely called socialism. In the new and the revised constitutions adopted in the decade following the second world war by more than thirty countries outside the communist areas, responsibility of the state for many aspects of health, education and welfare were specifically set forth as obligations of the state. Socialism, which had originally been offered as a challenge to and basic criticism of liberal democracy, was in a large measure incorporated into the practice of the democratic states. Acceptance of the principle varied markedly from country to country, and difference in practice did not necessarily coincide with difference in professed policy. Socialism might be loudly denounced while much of the actuality was being adopted, or loudly proclaimed but haltingly applied. In spite of the fact that India's announced policy was to develop a 'socialist pattern of society' while the United States preached 'free enterprise' and opposed 'socialism', a far larger proportion of the national income was spent through government channels in the United States and a much wider range of services was publicly provided than was the case in India during these years.

In the years after the second world war what might be termed old style dictatorships continued, for example, in the Iberian peninsula and in certain of the Latin American republics, where some dictators fell, some rose and others retained long established control. These pragmatic dictators based their rise on military force and maintained their position essentially by that means. They offered no ideological justification for seeking power, beyond the maintenance of the *status quo*. They were generally thrown from power by military means. In the course of these years the tendency was for their number to decline, but some very tough ones survived and there was no assurance that others would not gain power.

The principal fascist dictators, who had appealed not merely to force but to an alternative political ideal, went down to defeat and destruction in the second world war. Democratic forms were installed by the victorious powers in West Germany and Japan, and continued after the withdrawal of occupying forces. Italy restored the parliamentary system which Mussolini had destroyed. But in Argentina Juan Perón established a fascist government in 1943 and tried to organize fascist movements in other parts of the South American continent until he was ousted in 1955. The Nationalist party which came to power in the Union of South Africa in 1948 adopted some of the Nazi principles and techniques. A decade after the death of Hitler and Mussolini there was still no guarantee that their doctrines might not be reborn and their methods applied again.

Communism, meantime, scored signal successes and showed great vitality. The effective industrialization of the Soviet Union gave it great appeal in underdeveloped areas seeking to remake their societies at a rapid rate. In the post-war years it gained control of eastern Europe, spread to China and organized a third of the population of the world. Politically, its success in the Soviet Union was achieved not by emphasizing the features common to or closely related to liberal democracy but by those most at variance. Soviet dictatorship under the leadership of Joseph Stalin did not hesitate to restrain by vigorous action any attempt to oppose party leadership. By purges against politicians, engineers or generals he eliminated all deviation from the party line. Stalin's successors acted in a much more lenient and flexible but no less effective way. Similar methods were also adopted by the Chinese communist state.

Yugoslavia alone among the communist states deviated from the Soviet pattern of democratic centralism, choosing to isolate itself from the international communist movement, and experimenting with more decentralization, though still retaining strict party control.

Modern states, whatever their form, extended their functions to meet the needs of industrial society and to involve, in some way, the total population. As they expanded their functions all types developed extensive bureaucracies, which in turn became major elements in their societies. All governments, moreover, had at their disposal the new means of mass communication, with the vast powers to reach and influence people which these afforded. In the course of the twentieth century the modern state, whatever its political form, thus became an increasingly dominant factor in the life of mankind.

NOTES TO CHAPTER III

1. Some scholars in the liberal tradition of the West criticize the text for failing to discuss the extension of state activity as a threat to freedom. Professor Wilhelm Röpke writes: 'It is hardly scientific to write on social services without mentioning that the welfare state is a very serious problem, economically, politically and morally and far from being a "progress" under all circumstances.'

Those who look with greatest distrust on the welfare state fear that it will destroy freedom and lead to totalitarianism. They distrust the effects of the expansion of the functions of the state, and they correlate the loss of economic individualism with the loss of political, social and intellectual freedom. They refuse to believe that the state, as envisaged by the proponents of the welfare state, can act as a 'positive economic force' (J. M. Clark) or as a means of 'ensuring the general welfare of all its members' (Kenneth Boulding). Instead, they prophesy that if the trend toward the welfare state continues, western civilization is doomed to follow 'the road to serfdom' (F. A. von Hayek).

At the other extreme are scholars, of whom J. K. Galbraith in *The Affluent Society* (Boston, 1958) is one, who attack the failure to canalize a larger share of national wealth through government, and who contrast the low level of spending and inadequate standards for public services with the high level of mass spending and the abundance of goods in the private sector of modern capitalistic economies.

A majority of scholars and of policy makers probably take an intermediate position in the matter, accepting the principle of using the state as an instrument to achieve common welfare objectives but remaining concerned about the question of how to acquire the benefits of expansion of governmental activity while avoiding disadvantages. They believe that the welfare state has become essential, that it has developed necessary services and institutions, and that it is approved and desired by the masses, not merely in advanced industrial countries but in countries struggling to build a modern economy and society. They consider it essential to preserve individual responsibility and initiative and are therefore alert to safeguard individual rights and to keep governmental activity within the bounds of the clearly essential. Even in the Scandinavian countries, where the concept of the welfare state is thoroughly accepted, there is a lively issue of public policy as to how far state-directed activity should go—beyond the minima already established—in making available to all citizens benefits commensurate with the nation's wealth.

Among other works on the subject, Professor E. N. Anderson suggests the following:
Kenneth E. Boulding, *Principles of Economic Policy* (New York, 1958).
Colin Clark, *Welfare and Taxation* (Oxford, 1954).
John Maurice Clark, *Economic Institutions and Human Welfare* (New York, 1957).
Sheldom Glueck (ed.), *The Welfare State and National Welfare. A Symposium on Some of the Threatening Tendencies of Our Time* (Cambridge, Mass., 1952).
Frederick A. von Hayek, *The Road to Serfdom* (Chicago, 1956).
Frederick A. von Hayek, *The Constitution of Liberty* (Chicago, 1960).
Bertrand de Jouvenal, *The Ethics of Redistribution* (Cambridge, 1951).
I. M. D. Little, *Critique of Welfare Economics* (New York, 1957).
Alan T. Peacock (ed.), *Income Redistribution and Public Policy* (London, 1954).
Wallace P. Peterson, *The Welfare State in France* (Lincoln, 1960).
Wilhelm Röpke, *A Humane Economy: the Social Framework of the Free Market* (2nd ed., Chicago, 1961).
Richard Titmuss, *Essays on the Welfare State* (London, 1959).

2. Candidate of Juridical Sciences V. Tumanov notes:
(1) Advocates of the theory of the 'welfare state' hold that in the western states economic policy is directed towards raising the standard of living of the population as a whole and liquidating abuses by the monopolies through their subjection to controls. However, the facts show another thing: in 1950–51, for example, the US government handed over to the monopolies for exploitation 278 industrial enterprises built up during World War II at the taxpayers' expense. The thesis that the State 're-distributes' the national income in favour of broad segments of the population, in the first instance through the medium of fiscal policy, does not correspond to the facts either. Between 1949 and 1960 the

amount of income tax paid in the USA increased by more than double, from 17·9 to 38·6 milliard dollars, and the social insurance tax by three and a half times, from 2,477 to 8,644 million dollars. (See *Economic Almanac*, 1960, p. 426.)

Many sociologists hold that the first task of the welfare state is to liquidate unemployment (see, for example, R. M. Titmuss, *Essays on the Welfare State*, London, 1959). However, the western states of to-day are incapable of dealing with this problem. According to official statistics in 1961, there were about 8 million unemployed each month in the USA, Canada, Great Britain, France, Western Germany, Italy, and Japan—most of them in the United States (see *Monthly Bulletin of Statistics*, U.N., February 1962). With regard to the social services rendered by the 'welfare state' (unemployment assistance, social insurance, etc.), it is worth quoting the words of the British sociologist Crossland, one of the defenders of the 'welfare state' theory, who was compelled to admit that, 'at the present time the working class pays more in taxes than it receives in the form of social expenditure' (C. R. Crossland, *The Future of Socialism*, London, 1957, p. 44).

(2) It is undeniable that in a number of 'liberal democratic' states during the twentieth century there has been a certain extension of the voting rights enjoyed by the citizens of these countries. However, formal universal suffrage is in practice restricted by various kinds of qualifications and restrictions. (See Note 10 to Chapter XXIII.)

3. *On the question of the welfare state, the Author-Editors write:*
   '*As we have noted in the Preface, we have used the term "welfare state" to indicate a general concept of the role of the state as a positive instrument to promote the welfare of its citizens. The development of this concept, and the wide range of actions growing out of it, is an important phenomenon of the twentieth century. We have chosen to discuss it using the term which is widely current, without implying the realization of any specific actuality in respect to state benefits or services. We recognize that the term "welfare state" could be given a very precise meaning, such as that offered by V. A. Tumanov* ("Le Welfare State. Est-il un mythe ou une réalité ?", Journal of World History, *VII, 1 (1962), p. 224), i.e. a state in which all citizens are entitled to receive the benefits* (Mr Tumanov says the "necessities") *made possible by the level of public wealth. If we had accepted such a limited definition, we should have had to seek some less familiar term with which to discuss the great extension of public services and the acceptance by the state of responsibilities not regarded as within its function in previous centuries.*'

4. *In regard to unemployment in capitalist countries, the Author-Editors draw attention to the following table which shows the wide difference among capitalist countries in the extent of unemployment during the period 1954–60. It includes the countries for which the United Nations could compile reasonably comparable data, although the footnotes to the table indicate that even these data differ considerably in source and therefore in meaning. No comparable figures are available for any of the communist countries except Yugoslavia, since these countries state that full employment is provided under their systems.*

UNEMPLOYMENT, 1954–1960

(Percentage Unemployed)

	Austria	Belgium[1]	Canada	Denmark	Germany[2] Fed. Rep.	Ireland[3]	Italy[4]	Japan
1954	7·9	10·9	4·6	8·0	7·0	8·1	10·0	1·5
1955	5·7	8·4	4·4	9·7	5·1	6·8	9·8	1·6
1956	5·4	7·0	3·4	11·1	4·0	7·7	9·9	1·5
1957	4·9	5·5	4·6	10·2	3·4	9·2	9·0	1·2
1958	5·3	8·5	7·1	9·6	3·5	8·6	9·0	1·3
1959	4·8	9·5	6·0	6·1	2·4	8·0	8·7	1·3
1960	3·7	7·5	7·0	4·3	1·2	6·7	7·9	1·0

	Nether-lands[5]	Norway	Puerto Rico	Sweden[6]	UK	USA[7]	Yugo-slavia
1954	1·9	1·3	15·4	2·6	1·5	5·6	3·3
1955	1·3	1·2	14·3	2·5	1·2	4·4	2·7
1956	0·9	1·4	13·0	1·7	1·3	4·2	3·9
1957	1·2	1·4	13·0	1·9	1·6	4·3	4·3
1958	2·3	2·3	13·9	2·5	2·2	6·8	5·9
1959	1·8	2·2	13·8	2·0	2·3	5·5	6·7
1960	1·2	1·7	11·5	1·4	1·7	5·6	6·1

This series (from the International Labour Office) generally represents the total number of persons wholly unemployed and temporarily laid-off and is derived from unemployment insurance statistics, employment office statistics, or from sample surveys of the labour force. In using this series, consideration should be given to the source of the data. In general, the figures relating to percentage unemployed are calculated by expressing the number of unemployed in a given period as a percentage of the total number of employed and unemployed persons in the group considered during the same period.

(1) Including persons partially unemployed.
(2) Unemployment among insured members of trade union funds.
(3) Excluding agriculture, fishing and private domestic service.
(4) Percentages relate to economically active population (1951 population census).
(5) Excluding persons employed on public relief work.
(6) Prior to 1956, trade union statistics, excluding commercial workers; beginning 1956, unemployment among members of unemployment insurance funds.
(7) Prior to 1956, excluding Alaska and Hawaii.

Source: United Nations, Monthly Bulletin of Statistics, February, 1962.

5. Doctor of Historical Sciences E. D. Chermensky stresses that the Russian revolution of 1905–7 was the first people's revolution of the imperialist epoch. It faced the task of overthrowing autocracy and destroying the relics of serfdom which permeated every sphere of economic and social life. . . . The economic basis for all these feudal relics was the ownership of land by the nobility. For this reason the agrarian question, i.e. the struggle by the peasants to liquidate the landed estates, was the principal feature of the bourgeois-democratic revolution in Russia. The Russian revolution was bourgeois-democratic according to its objective content, but it differed radically from the bourgeois revolutions of the seventeenth, eighteenth, and nineteenth centuries, which took place at a time when capitalism was in the ascendant and the bourgeoisie was still a revolutionary class. The revolution of 1905–7 took place in the epoch of imperialism, the development of which is characterized by the decay of the capitalist system and the intensification of social and political contradictions of every kind. By the beginning of the twentieth century the Russian working class had not only emerged as an independent social group, a class separate from the common mass of toilers, but had already acquired a considerable experience of class struggle, had created its own Marxist party and was acting as the most advanced and well organized political force in the country. . . . The Russian bourgeoisie, alarmed at the scope of the labour movement and bound by a multitude of ties to the reactionary landlords and to tsarism, was afraid of the democratic revolution. This resulted in the emergence, in the historical conditions of Russia, of a paradoxical situation, which V. I. Lenin described as follows: 'The victory of the bourgeois revolution in this country is impossible as the victory of the bourgeoisie. . . . The prevalence of a peasant population, with the heavy bondage imposed on it by large-scale land ownership of a semi-serf nature, the strength and consciousness of the proletariat, already organized in a socialist party—all these events lent a specific character to our bourgeois revolution.' (V. I. Lenin, Collected Works, 4th Russ. Ed., Vol. XV, p. 41.)

The specific character of the Russian bourgeois-democratic revolution consisted in the fact that its entire development, its scope and forms were determined by the struggle of the proletariat. Mass strikes—that characteristic proletarian form of struggle—played a major part in arousing the peasantry to the revolutionary struggle and in preparing the people's armed uprising against autocracy. That is why the leading role in the revolution of 1905–7 was assumed by the working class, with the peasantry, which was vitally interested in the destruction of the survivals of serfdom, becoming its ally.

6. In the opinion of M. S. Ivanov, Doctor of Historical Sciences, the Persian revolution of 1905–11 took place under the direct influence of the Russian revolution of 1905–7, and not of the Young Turk revolution, which began in 1908. See note 4 to chapter I.

7. Candidate of Juridical Sciences V. A. Tumanov states that the first socialist state in history was established in Russia as a consequence of the Great October Socialist Revolution of 1917. As a result of the popular democratic revolutions that occurred during and after World War II a number of other new socialist states came into being in Europe and Asia. The 600 million strong Chinese people embarked upon the path of socialist development. Much earlier, and in different historical circumstances, the Mongolian People's Republic came into being. The rise of new socialist states in Europe and Asia resulted in socialism ceasing to be confined to a single country and becoming a world system. The socialist state is the political expression of the new socialist system of economy, based on public ownership of the instruments and means of production. In a socialist society the means of production are the property, not of the privileged classes, but of the entire people, and for this reason the state power also belongs to the people.

The development of the socialist state passes through two principal stages. The first of these coincides with the period of transition from capitalism to socialism. During this period there still remain relics of the classes which have been overthrown by the revolution. These remnants of the bourgeoisie and the landlords offer stubborn resistance to the gigantic efforts in the sphere of economic organization, cultural and educational work, and the diffusion of democracy to the broadest masses of the population, made by the proletarian power. Because of this, the task of crushing the resistance of the exploiting classes is one of the main functions of the socialist state.

All progressive revolutions have had to overcome resistance by the classes that they have thrust from power. The socialist revolution brings about the profoundest social transformations of all. For this reason it has to overcome particularly stubborn resistance, which is intensified by support from external forces (e.g. the intervention of foreign powers against the young Soviet state, the support given from abroad to the Kuomintang regime in China, etc.), which in alliance with the peasantry and the other sections of the toiling population, effects the political leadership, wages a struggle against the remnants of hostile elements and dismisses them from power. The socialist state of this period constitutes the dictatorship of the proletariat.

Once socialism has scored decisive victories in all spheres of public life, there begins the process of the transformation of the dictatorship of the proletariat into the state of the entire people—an organ that expresses the interests and will of the people as a whole. In the USSR this process began in the mid-1930s, when socialism had won decisive victories in the towns and in the countryside.

It was reflected in the 1936 Constitution, which consolidated the victory of socialism in the USSR by the further development of democratic forms. However, the threat of armed attack, and then the war, and also the errors committed during the period of the Stalin cult, acted as a substantial brake upon the process of rapid development. Nevertheless these factors could not prevent the development of socialist society and its political superstructure in accordance with the laws that govern such development. Once the final and complete victory of socialism (the first phase of communism) had been accomplished, and society went over to the building of communism on an extensive scale, the dictatorship of the proletariat had fulfilled its historic mission and had ceased to be necessary in the USSR so far as the tasks of internal development were concerned. The Soviet Union became a state of the entire people. This was reflected in the new programme of the Communist Party of the Soviet Union (1961).

Other socialist countries, which are at the stage of building a highly-developed socialist society (for example, the Czechoslovak Socialist Republic, the Bulgarian People's Republic, the Rumanian and Mongolian People's Republics) have already entered upon the process of the transformation of the dictatorship of the working class into the state of the entire people. The forms of the socialist state are such as to make a living reality of that most important democratic principle, the maximum involvement of broad masses of the people in the administration of society and in government. This is accomplished, in the first place, by means of a fully democratic electoral system; in the second place, by drawing into the work of all state organs broad active elements of the population; and in the third place, by the consistent development of social control over the activity of all organs of government and officials.

In the countries of people's democracy the forms of political organization have differed in a number of ways from those in the land of the Soviets (e.g. existence of people's or patriotic fronts, a multi-party system, etc.)—the result of the particular historic conditions governing the establishment of socialist states in these countries. However, the basic features of the Soviet and People's Democratic forms of government are the same: in both cases the form of government is republican, ensuring a plenitude of power to popular representative organs; in both cases the organizational and legal principle governing the entire state structure is democratic centralism; in both cases the apparatus of the new state power developed as a result of the destruction of the old military-bureaucratic apparatus (although this process of destruction took a different course where historical circumstances were different), and in its composition and principles of activity contributes to the maximum realization of popular sovereignty. The territorial organization of the socialist states accords with the principle whereby the state apparatus is brought as close as possible to the population and production; in multi-national states the principle of socialist federalism has created all possible opportunities and prerequisites for the elimination of national oppression of any kind, and for the voluntary association of free and equal nations and peoples within the framework of a single state.

The fact that the socialist state is a state of the entire people finds reflection in the further democratization of the forms whereby the authority of the state is implemented. During the period of transition from socialism to the higher phase of communism the main trend of development, so far as the socialist state is concerned, is the far-reaching extension and perfectioning of socialist democracy, the active part taken by all citizens in administering the state and guiding economic and cultural construction, the improvement of the work of the state apparatus, and the strengthening of popular control over its activity. During this period an increasingly important role is played by the system of representative organs—the Soviets (increasing number of deputies, broadening of their powers, etc.). Broad segments of the population come to be associated with the work of the Soviets and the executive apparatus. Simultaneously a number of important functions are handed over from the state organs to public organizations. There takes place a growth of direct democracy, implying in particular the practice of placing the most important government measures and legislative proposals before the whole people for discussion. There is a further democratization of the structure and forms of activity of the state apparatus (the principle of periodical removal of officials from their posts, extension of the electoral principle, etc.). The citizens of the socialist state come to enjoy stronger material and juridical guarantees of their broad democratic rights and freedoms.

In the socialist state there exist numerous public organizations, powerful trade unions with extensive rights, organizations of women, young people and so on. Among these public organizations a central position is occupied by the Communist Party, which is the leading and directing force in the state. The basic principle underlying the activity of the Party is its link with the masses. The Party is the vanguard of the working people.

It is not essential that in a socialist state there should only be one party. Where class differentiations still remain, it is possible that several parties should exist (as in the German Democratic Republic, or the Chinese People's Republic).

One of the most important principles of the socialist system is the unity of public and private interests. This gives wide scope for the development of the individual, for the vigorous growth of science and art, and for creative personal initiative. The fundamental principle of socialism is 'from each according to his ability, to each according to his work'. Socialism is only the first phase of communism. When the principle of 'from each according to his ability, to each according to his needs' has been realized, there will be unlimited opportunities for the comprehensive development of the individual.

Scientific socialism does not regard the state as something permanent and unchanging. As socialist society effects the transition to communism the socialist state system gradually develops into communist public self-government. As democracy expands, and all citizens are drawn into the administration of economic and cultural affairs, many functions that were previously performed by state organs gradually fall to the competence of public organizations.

Public functions analogous to those currently exercised by the state in the administration of economic and cultural matters will be preserved under communism, but will change their character and become perfected as society develops. Their nature and the means of realizing them will be different by comparison with the situation under socialism. The organs concerned with planning and accounting, with management of the economy and the development of culture, which at the present time are state organs, will lose their political character and will become organs of public self-government. Communist society will be a highly-organized community of working people. They will live in accordance with generally-accepted rules of communist conduct, the observance of which will have come to be felt by all men as necessary and customary.

8. The treatment of communism in this chapter has been criticized by several scholars on the ground that the Author-Editors have treated official communist ideology as if it were reality, have overrated the communist maintenance of many forms of democracy and have understimated what these scholars regard as the danger of the dictatorship of the proletariat and Lenin's formula for party leadership. Some of those expressing this view are Mrs B. R. Scharf (United Kingdom), Professor Hans Kohn (United States), and in more general terms Professor Coengeno Quinn (Pontifical Gregorian University) and Professor Robert Strausz-Hupé (United States).

CHAPTER IV

THE TRIUMPH OF INDUSTRIALISM

IN the twentieth century industrialism became the dominant, moulding force in the countries of its origin; it spread into new areas and it offered a goal to which much of the world came to aspire.

By the opening of the century it had fundamentally modified the life of western Europe and the United States and was penetrating elsewhere. In the first half of the twentieth century it revealed its capacity to raise the levels of living of entire societies, to transform one aspect of life after another and remake patterns of occupations and social relations, to shrink the globe by its mastery over distance, to provide a basis for more terrible warfare than the world had ever imagined and to modify the nature and functions of the state.

I. PROCESS OF INDUSTRIALIZATION

Twentieth-century industrialism was both an extension of the factory system and commercial economy of the nineteenth century and a new growth whose dimensions, speed of development, scientific basis and phenomenal productivity made it a powerful, dynamic force. The essence of modern industry was its dependence on and interrelation with science and its mass-production character. It not only rested on a scientific base but its whole method was characterized by the same qualities of rationality, experimentation, systematic organization and acceptance of change which were the essentials of the scientific approach; and it supported scientific research as an essential part of its own development. By harnessing energy and converting it to productive labour it created the equivalent of 500 to 1,000 extra hands for each worker employed, and thus replaced an immense amount of grinding human toil and made the modern industrial worker enormously productive.

The inner dynamics of modern industry pressed constantly for expansion, drawing more and more workers into its orbit, seeking ever wider markets for its products, stimulating constant efforts to improve methods, reduce costs of production and apply available scientific knowledge and providing an impetus to continuing scientific research.

The growth of industry was responsible for great migrations of people: millions of European peasants who streamed across the Atlantic in the late nineteenth and early twentieth centuries to supply the insatiable demand of American industries for workers, and were still coming in large numbers to Canada and parts of South America in the mid-twentieth century; more millions who left their farms for mines and factories in their own or neigh-

bouring countries of Europe or within North America. Countless others
became part of the expanding industrial population of the USSR or went out
to Australia, or moved to Japanese cities, or migrated from China to Manchuria in one of the largest mass migrations in history.

As industrialism developed in the countries where it became dominant, it

CHART II.   World Industrial Production, 1913–59 (index: 1937=100).

Source: W. S. and E. S. Woytinsky, *World Population and Production*, 1953, p. 1002,
and *U.N. Statistical Yearbook*, 1960.

ushered in a system of mass consumption which was as revolutionary in its impact as the factory system had been in the preceding century. For it meant a new pattern of life for masses of people and a reduction of the gulf which

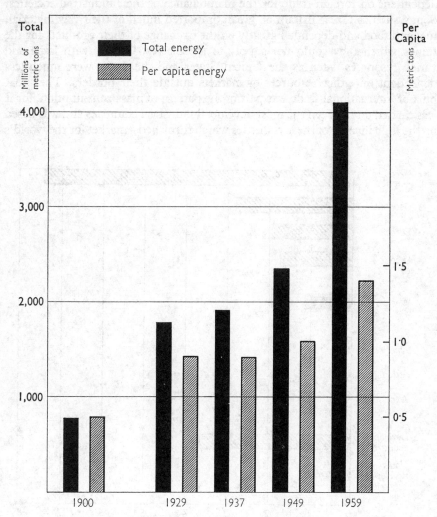

CHART III. World Production of Energy, 1900–59 (excluding work animals, wood, peat, bagasse, manure, etc., fuel).

Source: *U.N. Statistical Yearbook*, 1960, Table 120.

separated those who were able to enjoy the fruits of civilization and those who toiled to produce them. Mass production, which could not find its market in a limited class of the rich, forced the spread of material benefits to a wide segment of the population.

The main output of the most industrially developed countries was for their home market and most of the products which their people consumed were produced within the area. Countries differed in the degree to which they were dependent on foreign trade for the maintenance of their industrial societies. Some, such as Great Britain or Japan, imported much of their raw material, fuel and food and depended greatly on the exchange of their products for the things which they could not supply to themselves. Others, with large and varied resources, such as the United States and the USSR, were much less dependent on either resources or markets outside their borders. The great bulk of international trade was part of the pattern of mass consumption, for it was carried on between the most developed industrial countries and was based on the high income of these countries which furnished a market for the world's

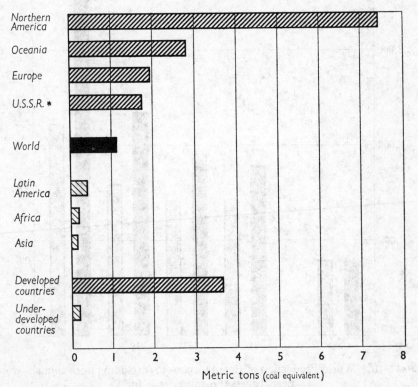

*U.S.S.R. figure includes 36 small countries with aggregate population of 20 million

Northern America = Canada and U.S.A.

Developed countries = North America, Oceania, Europe, U.S.S.R.

Excludes work animals, wood, peat, bagasse, manure etc., fuel *

CHART IV. *Per Capita* Consumption of Energy, 1950, by regions.

Source: U N, *World Energy Supplies*, Statistical Papers, Series J, No. 1.

varied industrial products that the people of the non-industrial countries could not afford to buy.

Modern industry provided the incomes to sustain a mass market, for the rising productivity of its workers enabled it to pay higher and higher wages.

CHART V. Increase in Output per Man-hour, USA, 1899–1957 (index: 1929=100).

Source: U S Department of Commerce: *Historical Statistics of the U.S.A.*, p. 599.

In the most highly mechanized of the industrial countries, the United States, the average output per hour of labour in manufacturing more than doubled in these fifty years. The real income of workers rose correspondingly, so that the worker in 1948 was able to buy with twenty-eight hours of work what a typical worker of 1914 had had to work sixty-five hours to purchase. The mechanization of agriculture increased the productivity of the agricultural worker to a similar degree, raising the farmer's income and lowering food costs to the urban worker. The modern worker also enjoyed new leisure, for the average work week in industry was shortened by a third between 1900 and 1950.

The result of industrialization was thus to spread higher levels of income and leisure through the society. An estimated 60 per cent of US families in 1950 enjoyed real incomes, adjusted for changes in the prices of the things that they bought, as high as those which only 30 per cent had enjoyed in 1935. At the other end of the scale less than 8 per cent of the families in 1950 were receiving incomes as low as those received by 20 per cent in 1935. Comparable data are not available for earlier years, but according to other estimates the incomes of 30 per cent of income-receivers in 1951 were the equivalent of those received by the upper 7 per cent in 1918.

Although twentieth-century industrialism offered the basis for high levels of living for whole societies, this was an actuality only in those areas most thoroughly and modernly industrialized. At mid-century it was still only a potentiality in the areas whose industrial development was either less complete or less based upon the use of modern techniques, and an aspiration where industrialization had barely scratched the surface and was being eagerly sought as a road to national welfare.

Industrial production remained concentrated during the first half of the twentieth century in the countries where it had its origin and early development. At the middle of the century approximately 80 per cent of industrial production was still centred in the countries which had accounted for 98 per cent in the late nineteenth century—Great Britain, western and central Europe, Russia and the United States. In spite of the tendency of industrialization to spread, the only new areas where industrial development was sufficient to make a substantial contribution to the world's industrial production were Japan, Czechoslovakia, Canada, Australia, Poland, India and Argentina. In the last three of these countries and in most of the rest of the world, agriculture continued to employ well over half of the labour force—60 per cent or more in most countries of Latin America and east Europe, at least 75 per cent in most of the countries of Asia and north Africa, and, together with hunting and gathering, over 90 per cent in the rest of the African continent, exclusive of the European population of South Africa.

The general result of industrial development during these years was to widen the gap in real income between the industrial and the non-industrialized countries, and particularly between the latter and the countries of most advanced industrial technology and organization which had not been set back by wartime destruction: the United States, Canada, Australia, Sweden and Switzerland. In the non-industrial countries production rose little during the century while population in most areas increased, holding *per capita* incomes as low as or lower than in the past. In the United States, Britain and the Commonwealth countries, meantime, *per capita* income more than doubled, and it nearly trebled in Sweden. At mid-century *per capita* income in most of the Latin American, Asian and African countries was less than 10 per cent that of the United States and less than 20 per cent that of Great Britain. In many parts of these areas the disparity was far greater.

Acceleration in the rate of development in the industrial areas threatened to widen the gap still further and intensify the impatience and frustration of

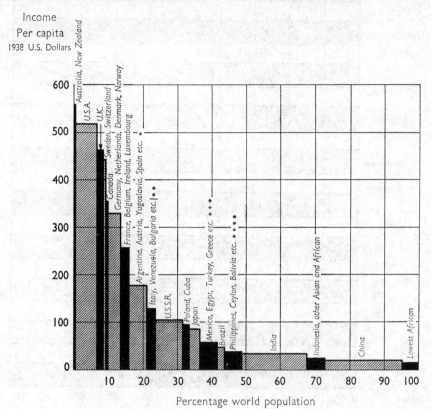

* Includes Hungary, Czechoslavakia, Finland, South Africa
* * Includes some other South American
* * * Includes some other North and Central African, and South American
* * * * Includes some other Central and South American, Asian and North African.

CHART VI. Distribution of World Income, 1938. *Per capita* (height of bars) and total (area of bars).

Source: Woytinsky, *World Population and Production*, pp. 389–96.

the 'have-nots'. Technological advance in the decade after the second world war stepped up the rate of production spectacularly in many lines. Measures in the capitalist countries to check the recurrence of depression offered the prospect that rates of growth during this decade would be maintained or exceeded. In the communist countries ever-higher production goals and the

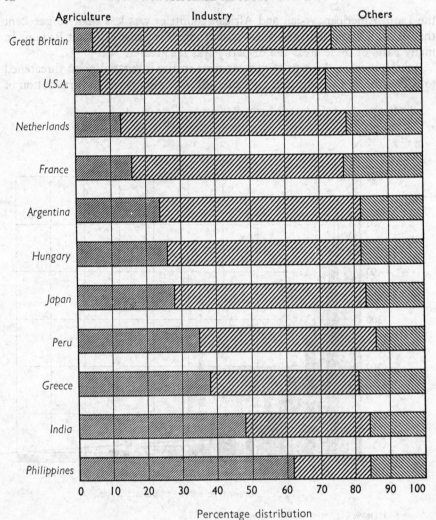

Source: Woytinsky, *World Population and Production*, pp. 430, 433.

determination of the USSR to outstrip its capitalist rivals promised a maximum acceleration of industrial output and potential. As the industrial
countries became more wealthy their resources for capital investment in
further expansion became greater.

Most fundamentally of all, science itself constantly widened the gap.
Industrial development became increasingly dependent on highly developed
scientific and technical skills which the non-industrial countries could only

hope to build up slowly. The new science required such a high degree of knowledge and scientific sophistication that few outside the advanced scientific milieux were able even to understand the research of others, let alone carry it forward. Although the non-industrial countries had available to them the techniques which the industrial countries had evolved by slow degrees, and though they were prepared to make heroic efforts to catch up with their richer neighbours, the momentum of modern industrialism and the revolutionary pace of science kept carrying the developed countries further ahead.

The path of industrial development was not a smooth one during these years. On the one hand it was abnormally stimulated by war; on the other, industrial growth was periodically set back by depressions, war destruction and revolution. Industrial output fell off in Europe and America because of economic depression in 1907 and 1921, and the collapse of the 1930s was so severe that it shook the capitalist industrial countries to their foundations, shut down factories, sent unemployed workers into the streets, slowed down technological progress, caused the destruction of agricultural products for lack of markets and undermined the faith of many people in the ability of industry to fulfil its promise. At the lowest point of the 1930 depression production in the countries whose economies were most depressed—the United States and Germany—dropped by nearly a half from 1929 levels and it fell a third or more in several other industrial countries; in some countries as much as a quarter of the entire labour force was unemployed. The magnitude of the wasted manpower of these depression years in the United States alone was estimated as sufficient to replace the nation's entire physical capital, to rebuild its railways three times over or to supply a new, modern house for every family in the country.

Although the socialist economy of the USSR was free from economic crises and depressions, it suffered severely, as did the European economies, from war devastation. The first world war set back the industries of western, central and eastern Europe, and that of the USSR suffered additionally from the civil war and intervention of 1918–20. The destruction and disruption from the second world war was even greater. The war laid waste one-third of the urban housing of the USSR and uprooted one-third of its people; it reduced the *per capita* real income of the German people to hardly more than a third of the pre-war level or half of that which they had enjoyed at the opening of the century. Wars and military preparations diverted much industrial production from uses that would enhance economic well-being. The actual increase in industrial output in the industrially developed countries was thus kept well below the potentials which science, industrial technology and industrial organization made possible.

By mid-century industrial activity, which had been under few restraints and virtually no guidance at the beginning of the century, was everywhere subject to a considerable degree of control. The leaders of the Bolshevik revolution of 1917 were convinced that the capitalist organization under which industry had initially developed could only make the rich richer and the poor poorer and would inevitably lead to recurrent economic collapse, and that a socialist economy was necessary in order to secure the benefits of industrialism without its disadvantages. In the USSR and most other communist countries industry was under central government direction.

In non-communist countries governments found themselves increasingly called upon to intervene to regulate one aspect of economic life after another. They adopted a variety of measures to protect workers, consumers, small business and investors, and to guide development by controls over the volume of money, the flow of capital and international exchange; they used their tax and spending policies to try to maintain economic stability. Countries that were newly aspiring to achieve the benefits of industrialization used planning, regulation and government spending to stimulate industrial activity.

The uses to which the potentialities of industrialism were put could differ markedly under different economic and social systems. Where production was guided by the demands of consumers and the efforts of producers to make a profit in meeting those demands, industrial capacity was devoted to a wide range of consumer goods, including those required by government for civil and military purposes, and to rival efforts by producers to stimulate consumer wants in directions which they found profitable. In such circumstances, the level of incomes and their distribution determined the extent to which production met the wants of the many or of the relatively wealthy few and was directed toward necessities or less essential products. Where there was central control and administration of production, as in the socialist economies, a comparable industrial potential could be directed, in line with the purposes and judgment of those in control, to the rapid expansion of the industrial and military base and to such consumer goods as were deemed necessary and appropriate.

Production could be directed toward the creation of an autarchic economy, as in Nazi Germany, or devoted to militaristic purposes as in Japan from 1926 to the outbreak of the second world war. In time of war all belligerent countries took steps to focus their industrial potential on war requirements. Newly developing countries were under great pressure to plan their economies in order to devote their limited capital resources and technical skills to the most urgent purposes.

Industrialism thus offered the basis for the development of various types of societies well supplied with material goods. Its essential processes made certain common demands on all, and thus in a measure shaped a common new culture, but it did not wholly determine the form of the increasingly affluent societies which it made possible.

II. THE SPREAD OF INDUSTRIALISM

The spread of industry from its early home in Great Britain, western Europe and the United States to the regions of eastern and southern Europe, the overseas areas of the British commonwealth, and into the non-industrial regions of Asia, Africa and Latin America followed distinct patterns. In parts of Europe outside the original nucleus and in areas of European settlement abroad the expansion of industry reflected the gradual spread of enterprise either through investment from other countries or through the establishment of mines or factories with local capital. In much of Asia, Africa and Latin America the introduction of industry represented either the effort of foreign capital to exploit the natural resources of a colonial or economically undeveloped area, or the struggle of a newly aroused state to enhance its national status and raise the living standards of its people.

1. Extension of enterprise

In eastern Europe substantial industrial developments based on the coalfields and textile industries of Poland and the iron and ceramics industries of Bohemia brought important parts of the region into the industrial fold before the first world war. Thereafter industrialization followed a chequered course. Growth was halted temporarily by the destruction of the first world war and the economic reorientation involved in the establishment of new national states. It had barely been resumed when the world economic depression brought another sharp set-back, and then the disorganization and destruction of the second world war followed. In the years after the war there was another reorientation as the further industrial development of eastern Europe took place under communist leadership and in close relation with the economy of the USSR.

Industrial development in the British commonwealth countries, especially Australia, and also in India, received a great stimulus when the first world war cut off normal European supplies. Canadian industry developed as a natural extension from the United States and experienced the same types of industrial growth. In these areas of transplanted European culture industrialism took root and flourished in the same manner and even more freely than in the older areas. These countries provided their own markets for diversified, balanced interdependent production, and participated as industrial producers and consumers in the general flow of world trade.

2. Foreign investment

No such general industrialization took place in the areas which were penetrated by foreign capital in search of profitable investments in raw materials to supply the insatiable demands of European and American industry: copper and gold in Africa, tin in Bolivia and Malaya, rubber in Malaya and Indonesia, iron in Labrador, petroleum in Venezuela, Borneo, Sumatra, and the Persian Gulf, coconut oil on the islands of the Pacific, uranium in the Belgian Congo and many other products elsewhere. Where industry reached new areas by means of foreign enterprises which developed mines or oilfields, rubber plantations or jute mills, it had little effect in industrializing these countries,

RELATIVE IMPORTANCE OF AGRICULTURE, ca 1950

Cartography Hallweg Berne

Percent economically active males
in agriculture and related activities

under 25 percent

25 – 50 percent

50 – 75 percent

over 75 percent

although it did provide sources of income, introduce some new knowledge and skills and develop some supporting institutions. Operating under the protection of colonial rule, or with the aid of unequal treaties such as those with China and Turkey giving extra-territorial jurisdiction or spheres of influence to Europeans, or under agreements negotiated with local governments as in Latin America or the oil-rich Arab states, these enterprises constituted enclaves within the non-industrial areas where they functioned. Equipment, technicians and managers were brought in from outside; products flowed out. Profits from the enterprise, gained from sale of the product abroad, went mainly to the foreign investors or were spent abroad to pay for equipment and to buy the things which entered into the standard of living of the foreign personnel and the small group of local people who were associated with management.

The wages of labour were not sufficient to provide a substantial market and thus to stimulate other local production. Sometimes imported products found their way into the company store of a foreign concern and thence to the local worker's home. But the kind of spiral which was set in motion in industrial countries, when local production for a local market generated income which provided a further market and stimulated production of other products, was almost wholly absent under the conditions of foreign enterprise in underdeveloped areas.

Local interests sometimes sought to encourage foreign investment of this sort, but often they resented bitterly the return of profits to the country of the capital investors; the privileges exercised by representatives of foreign firms were offensive to the dignity and self-respect of the people of the locality. Some local governments secured royalty agreements and imposed taxes which retained large profits from these foreign enterprises, as in the case of oil profits in Venezuela and the Persian Gulf. But such revenues often went to enrich the ruler or a limited group in power, and even when they were used for public purposes they were more likely to be spent on roads, hospitals or schools than invested in local productive enterprise, and they did not substantially alter the non-industrial character of these countries.

3. *Conscious efforts to industrialize*

Quite different in process and results were the conscious efforts of nonindustrial countries to remake their economies and to achieve the advantages of industrialism for their own people. Japan was the first to make this effort, starting in the late years of the nineteenth century and gathering momentum from the early twentieth. Russia after the October revolution undertook to build a great industrial empire on the narrow but scientifically and technically grounded base of pre-Soviet Russian industry. Mexico and Argentina led the Latin American countries in the extent to which they expanded the industrial sector of their basically agrarian societies, and remained in the forefront as other Latin American countries undertook national programmes of economic development in the years after the second world war. At mid-century the Asian countries, released from colonial control or Western economic domination, were straining to achieve the most rapid industrial development within their power, either seeking this objective within the framework of democratic political institutions and a partially capitalist economy, as did India, or adopting the communist course, as did China.

(a) *Japan*. Each of the conscious efforts at self-industrialization reflected the direct aspirations of a nation and its concept of national progress. For Japan the determination to remain free from the encroaching colonialism of the western powers led her in the late nineteenth century to seek industrialization as a basis for military strength. The pattern of industrialization reflected the unique situation of a compact, nationally integrated society, capable of responding to a national leadership which undertook to change its orientation.

Japanese industrialism was built on the foundations of pre-industrial society and did not destroy them. The feudal structure of that society with many small centres of prestige and power provided a source of widespread entrepreneurial initiative; a substantial class of merchants and artisans producing for the imperial court and the feudal households offered a supply of skilled workers; an agricultural economy unable to support an expanded population furnished a reservoir of unskilled labour; a number of urban centres around the court and feudal administrative units could readily become a series of industrial centres when linked by sea or rail and provided with electric power.

Since the objective of Japan's industrialization was to make possible a strong military position, the government gave its major support to the development of heavy industry through state operated, financed or sponsored enterprises. But the country lacked materials for such industries, and it was necessary to seek these from outside through trade, territorial expansion or investment abroad. Accordingly Japan developed export products which did not depend on the scarce materials and capital needed for the major sector and could be produced with a minimum of machinery by the labour of girls drawn from rural areas and by the use of the capital resources and initiative of the poorer gentry and merchant classes. In the early years of the twentieth century Japan moved into the world markets as a large supplier of cheap textiles, toys and wooden and glass objects. To reduce dependence on the uncertainties of this market she then sought direct control of resources outside her immediate borders, developing Korea and invading Manchuria in order to tap the coal and iron of that rich region.

As basic heavy industry developed and light export industries grew to help sustain it, a third sector of Japanese industry emerged to meet the demands of the home market. Wages earned in industry, though low, constituted a source of buying power which supported a variety of additional industries; workers in these industries, in turn, became part of the market for a growing, diversified range of production. In spite of its military orientation Japanese industrial development was thus a balanced and largely self-sustaining growth.

By the end of the first quarter of the twentieth century Japan had become one of the major industrial nations although, with her dense population, her *per capita* income never equalled that of any European country except the poorest among them—Rumania, Bulgaria, Greece or Portugal—or amounted at any time to as much as a fifth of that of the United States. But on the eve of the second world war her aggregate production amounted to two-fifths that of Great Britain and four-fifths that of France, and was exceeded by no other countries except the United States, Germany and Russia. Less than half of her labour force, which had become educated and technically trained, remained in agriculture.

(b) *The USSR.* The industrialization of the USSR, within the framework of a communist society, followed a vastly different course, under the differing conditions provided by the large area, rich natural resources and heterogeneous population of the Soviet Union and by its revolutionary social system. In contrast to Japan which retained much of its pre-industrial structure, the communist revolution eliminated the feudal centres of wealth and potential leadership. In addition, the USSR undertook to industrialize agriculture at the same time that it developed industry, while Japan left its agricultural system essentially unchanged. As soon as the Russian industrial programme gained momentum after 1928, moreover, it operated in the presence of a labour shortage rather than a reservoir of surplus rural workers as was the case in Japan. Socialization of the basic means of production and centralized utilization of economic revenue through the state budget made it possible, for the first time in history, to effect deliberate industrialization according to a uniform economic plan.

Soviet industrialization was very largely self-contained, drawing from accumulations of the socialist economy. Except for some initial acquisition of machinery and the hiring of foreign technicians in the early stages, the Soviet Union had little dependence on imports or need to seek an export market in order to finance them. It was, therefore, able to concentrate almost wholly on the development of heavy industry in order to lay a basis for industrial expansion and the mechanization of agriculture and to provide the military strength made necessary by a far from friendly environment. By means of widespread technical education at every level, in factory, school, labour institute and university, it developed the technical personnel essential for industrial growth.

In concentrating initially on heavy industry the USSR departed from the pattern which had characterized industrial development in most other countries, where textile and other light industries led the way. Its system of planning enabled it to start with production of capital goods before there was a developed market for the industries they would supply. It also made it possible to prevent consumer industries from developing in response to domestic demand as they did in the older industrial countries and in Japan, and to limit this type of production to what were considered the minimum needs of the people during the period of concentration on heavy industry. The expansion of consumer industries, planned to follow when heavy industries should be sufficiently well established, was delayed by the military demands and the physical destruction of the second world war and by the military build-up which continued in the face of world tensions in the post-war decade. Although levels of consumption remained low for some time and *per capita* income in the USSR in the early 1950s was still less than a third of that in Canada or Switzerland, the light goods and food industries were expanding rapidly and consumption was rising. The high rate of industrial growth in the 1950s revealed a dynamic economy prepared to bid for world industrial leadership.[1]

(*c*) *Economically underdeveloped countries.* The underdeveloped countries of Asia, Africa and Latin America which consciously strove for economic development after the second world war had their eyes primarily on the gulf in living standards between their people and those of the industrially developed countries, and on the problem of how to make the best use of their own resources for their own people. The vision of plenty, or at least of the reduction and ultimate elimination of want, led them to initiate programmes to stimulate economic activity, establish machinery for planning, undertake technical education, explore sources of capital and seek to develop managerial skills.

In launching these efforts they recognized that they were embarked on fundamental changes in their societies, for the experience of the industrially developed countries had shown that industrialization did not take place partially while the rest of life remained unchanged. It could not fail to break down the status structure of Asian societies or to bring detribalization to desert peoples and African tribes.

Industrialization involved a reorientation of the essentially colonial economies of these countries as well as their expansion. This process was far from simple, for existing structures of trade and finance tended to perpetuate dependence on countries of advanced economic organization.

Still more, industrialization involved a change in outlook, for it produced and required general technical-mindedness and a network of institutions to keep an industrially organized and mechanically equipped society in operation. The widespread use of automobiles and radios was almost as dependent on petrol service stations every few miles and radio mechanics in every neighbourhood as on automobile and radio factories, while mechanized agriculture required either that every farmer become a mechanic or that tractor stations be set up throughout the rural areas. Many sad examples of agricultural or other machinery introduced into non-industrial areas and wastefully abandoned for lack of mechanics or spare parts served as warning that piecemeal industrialization would not be effective.

The countries which aspired to rapid industrialization in the middle of the twentieth century had many advantages as well as many problems. They had access to the latest techniques, so that some of the most modern factories in the world were to be found in countries beginning their industrial development, yet they lacked the technical personnel required to make use of the latest devices. They were unhampered by the presence of existing investments in older machines or methods and could adopt new techniques without opposition from vested interests. In this they had some of the same advantages that latecomers to industrialization in the nineteenth century, such as Germany and the United States, had enjoyed over the pioneer industrial country, Britain. New energy sources and new materials that were being developed, including atomic and solar energy, light metals and plastics, promised to free the newly industrializing countries in time from dependence on traditional energy sources—coal, oil, water-power—and on some of the conventional materials such as iron which many of them lacked. At the same time these developments created a new dependence on scientific and technical knowledge.

The international atmosphere, moreover, was favourable to the success of their efforts, for the technically advanced countries were prepared in some degree to share their know-how and to help them to move ahead. The flow of technical knowledge was far from free, for private companies protected their trade secrets and patents, and governments tried to guard knowledge deemed vital to national defence. But there was a growing recognition that economic as well as political colonialism of the old type was doomed, and that countries which had benefited from industrialization would serve their own self-interest if they helped to reduce the gap between the levels of living of the 'have' and the 'have-not' peoples. International agencies provided channels for technical assistance and some financial aid toward this end.

Yet although the desire for industrialization was general, the absence of trained technicians, experienced managers, and institutions, habits and attitudes associated with modern enterprise presented serious obstacles. The great problem was how to mobilize the means, the understanding and the will to effect the transformation necessary to bring substantial benefits to non-industrial areas.

The situation was far more difficult than that which had accompanied the industrial development of Europe and North America. The first 150 years of industrialization had coincided with the opening up of new, sparsely occupied lands in the Americas, Siberia, Australia. In Europe and North America industrial development kept ahead of population growth, while open lands provided an additional outlet for European peasant populations. The combination of new lands, colonial wealth and a moderate rate of population growth had enabled Britain and western Europe to achieve the momentum of industrialization. Even so, the transformation of the peasant societies of eastern Europe had still not been achieved.

The non-industrial countries of the mid-century did not have these advantages. There were, indeed, vast empty lands, arid or formerly inaccessible, which new technology was making available for settlement. But to conquer these new frontiers required great resources and scientific skills. The new countries could not draw on the wealth of distant colonies, nor did they experience moderate rates of population increase. On the contrary, modern medicine was reaching every part of the globe, to wipe out age-old diseases which had kept population growth in check. In nearly every non-industrial area death rates were dropping sharply and population was growing at an accelerating rate. The measures taken to promote economic expansion in the decade after the second world war, though extensive, were small in relation to the task, and in some instances they could hardly do more than prevent economic conditions from becoming worse. During the 1950s none of these countries reached the point where its industrial development was self-generating and self-sustaining.

The central questions which industrialization posed for these countries were perhaps as much cultural as technical: Did they have the drives which industrial development required and could the integrity of their societies be maintained and the benefits of industrialism also be enjoyed? Since the cultures of all the countries at an advanced stage of industrialization gave value and dignity to work, could industrialization be achieved by those where work had been traditionally regarded as an indignity or a curse to be avoided or unloaded on to the backs of others if possible? Since the culture of the capitalist countries sanctioned the quest for private gain, was capitalistic development possible where personal gain was an unworthy objective for those groups in the population which had the wealth, education and prestige that would make them potential sources of industrial leadership? Could some commitment to the welfare of society provide the necessary moving spirit and some non-authoritarian form of planning provide the method in countries which did not wish to adopt authoritarian political forms or to support their industrial programmes and economic policies by the kinds of force which were employed by communist states to direct economic development?

The most basic problem for these countries lay in the need to develop a scientific orientation and to master not merely techniques which could be imported or readily learned but the immensely complex and austere disciplines of scientific knowledge and thought which alone could sustain modern industrial society.[2, 3, 4]

NOTES TO CHAPTER IV

1. Doctor of Historical Sciences G. N. Golikov asserts that the authors give a distorted picture of the policy of socialist industrialization as carried out in the USSR. The necessity for high tempos of industrial development in our socialist state was dictated by the country's technical and economic backwardness, the heritage of tsarist Russia, and the threat of intervention by aggressive imperialist states. In December 1925 the fourteenth congress of the VKP(b) (All-Union Communist Party (Bolsheviks)), guided by the

teaching of V. I. Lenin on the maximum development of heavy machine industry and the electrification of the country, put before the Soviet people the task of carrying out the socialist industrialization of the USSR, creating the material and technical foundation of socialism, and turning the country from one economically dependent on the capitalist states into a socialist power. The concrete tasks that had to be solved in the course of industrialization were as follows: the re-equipment of old plants and factories on the basis of new technology; the creation of branches of industry that had not existed in pre-revolutionary Russia; the construction of factories for building machines, machine tools, motor vehicles, chemicals and metallurgical works; the organization in Soviet Russia of the production of motors and equipment for electric power-stations; an increase in the output of metals and coal; the establishment of a new defence industry to strengthen the Soviet Union's defensive might; the construction of tractor plants and enterprises producing modern agricultural machinery, thereby creating the material and technical foundation for agriculture and making possible the transition from millions of small individual peasant farms to a system of large-scale collective farming. In contrast to the capitalist countries, which as a rule began their industrialization with the development of light industry, the Soviet Union launched on industrialization with the development of heavy industry.

The solution of all these very complex economic tasks necessitated the overcoming of difficulties, and above all a search for the tremendous capital investments which industrialization required. In the hands of the socialist state were the key positions in the economy: factories, plants, land, transport, banks, foreign trade and so on, and this opened up opportunities for the socialist accumulation of resources for industrialization. The party and government stimulated the political activity and zeal for labour of all the working people, mobilizing them in their struggle to bring down production costs, raise the productivity of labour, and lower costs of production.

As a result of the fulfilment of the First Five-Year Plan at the beginning of 1933 the Soviet Union was converted from an agrarian country into a socialist Power with an industrial base and a collective-farm economy. The share of industry in the economy rose to 70·7 per cent in 1932.

The foundation of a socialist economy had been built. Unemployment had been eliminated and the conditions created for an uninterrupted improvement in the material position of the working people in town and countryside, and for a rise in their cultural level.

2. The text has been criticized for accepting the anti-colonialism formula too uncritically. Professor Giorgio Janiot finds the text one-sided in its analysis of capitalist colonialism and calls attention to the investments made by the colonial powers which have left real wealth in the form of income and installations and 'serve to put the decolonized countries on the path of economic and industrial development'. Professor Lynn M. Case thinks that the authors should not have stopped with a statement of the difficulties encountered by some of the new states, but should have suggested that independence might have been premature.

Professor E. N. Anderson observes that it is true that some of the newly independent states are too small and lacking in resources to provide a viable base for economic development. The immediate tendency of the new African states to form one or another sort of union testifies to their recognition of this fact, as do similar steps toward the establishment of common market or other integrating relationships among groups of older economically under-developed countries such as the Central American republics. At the same time, independence has provided the indispensable basis for measures designed to reorient local economies with the prime object of raising the income and levels of living of the population rather than of providing raw materials for foreign industry or tropical products for foreign consumption.

3. Doctor of Historical Sciences L. I. Zubok underlines that the principal difficulties facing the under-developed countries are the consequence of several centuries of colonial rule and the exploitation of these countries by imperialism.

Several Western European sociologists are attempting to prove that the colonial regime was really a blessing for the enslaved countries and propound the thesis of the civilizing mission of colonialism. For example, Cardinal Mercier defines colonialism as a collective act of mercy accomplished by more developed nations on behalf of unfortunate races and as being the inevitable consequence of cultural superiority (*'Cahiers Internationaux de Sociologie*, vol. XVII, July–December 1954, p. 8).

The facts would have it differently. In resources and ancient culture alone, the rich African continent lost nearly 150 million people as a result of the hunting of the Negro and other acts of the colonialists (cf. Jacques Arnault, *Procès du Colonialisme*, Paris, 1958, p. 87). In three hundred years, its population fell from one-fifth of the population of the world to one-fourteenth; 90 per cent of the inhabitants could neither read nor write; the numbers engaged in the industrial production of the capitalist world accounted for only slightly more than 1 per cent.

In the post-war years, the question of aid to under-developed countries has not disappeared from the agenda of international conferences. Thus the industrially developed countries possessing modern techniques and qualified personnel can make a significant contribution towards easing the tasks faced by the peoples of the under-developed countries. But the whole problem is that of the conditions under which this aid will be furnished.

The basic task confronting the under-developed countries is that of the swifter development of the forces of production, and to increase production sharply in order to meet the urgent needs of the population. The basic approach towards solving this problem is to increase productive labour and the mechanization of production. However, many Western economists starting from obvious premises, apparently consider that since the under-developed countries have a large surplus of free labour and are very short of capital, they should concentrate on creating undertakings with little mechanization and use manual labour to a much greater extent (cf. the article of the American theoretician H. W. Singer in *Social Research*, Spring 1953, pp. 25–6; B. Higgins in *Land Economics*, vol. XXXI, No. 3, August 1955 and others).

In speaking out against the industrialization of the under-developed countries, the Western powers are endeavouring to promote the backwardness of those countries so that they can exploit them. They consider the best form of assistance to be different government loans and grants and the export of private capital so that in the end it leads to the outflow of enormous sums from the country in the form of percentages, dividends and so on. The overwhelming part of Western aid takes the form of arms deliveries and the sale of agricultural surpluses. Industrial equipment is virtually never provided and insignificant amounts are allocated for technical experts. Quite often the aid is tied to some political condition or other.

As a result, imperialistic exploitation of the under-developed countries still goes on to-day. For instance, according to the British oil information office, out of the 496·2 million tons of oil produced in 1960 in industrially under-developed regions, nearly 433·2 million tons, or more than 87 per cent, was obtained by firms controlled by American, English or Dutch capital.

Thus, one of the primary tasks in the economic advancement of the under-developed countries still remains the removal of the consequences of colonialism and the struggle with neo-colonialism in all its forms.

See:

Kolonializm včera i segodnja [Colonialism yesterday and to-day] (Moscow, 1964).

E. D. Modrzhinskaya, 'Zaščitniki sovremennogo kolonializma' [The advocates of present-day colonialism] and V. Kolontai, 'Protivniki ěkonomičeskoj nezavisimosti slaboraz-vityh stran' [Opponents of economic independence for under-developed countries] in the collection *Istoričeskij materialism i social'naja filosofija sovremennoj burzuazii* [Historical materialism and the social philosophy of the present-day bourgeoisie] (Moscow, 1960).

Kolonializm i mežimperialističeskie protivorečija v Afrike [Colonialism and international imperialistic contradictions in Africa] (Moscow, 1962).

Y. Y. Etenger, *The expansion of the Federal German Republic in the Arab countries and Africa*.

4. *The Author-Editors make the following additional comment to the question of the economic development of former colonial countries:*

The problems faced by one-time colonial countries in their efforts to develop viable economies and to begin to close the gap between themselves and the economically developed countries are increasingly preoccupying the world community, and are revealing themselves as more complex than any of the simple formulae about "colonialism". The United Nations have declared the decade of the 1960's as the "Development Decade" in the effort to focus world intelligence, good will, and practical co-operation toward this end. The crux of the matter lies, in part, in the problem of generating or securing sufficient investments to mount a modern economic development process. This has been one of the major concerns of the successive Indian Five-Year Plans.

The inescapable need to draw on expertise and investment funds from abroad in order to develop local resources and begin to meet the aspirations of the people presents a double problem: (1) the organization of such assistance on the part of the countries in a position to render it, and (2) its use by the developing countries in a manner which avoids the reintroduction of forms of dependency which independence has sought to break. The establishment of the United Nations Special Fund for Development, the creation of a variety of aid and loan systems by the countries of Western Europe, the USA and the USSR, and measures to attract and promote private investment on the part of both capital-receiving and capital-supplying countries have been among the efforts to meet the situation. The developing countries have endeavoured to avoid a monopoly of influence by seeking funds and technical assistance from a number of countries and, wherever possible, by utilizing the aid of international agencies.

It has become increasingly apparent that in the interdependent modern world where industry, technology, politics, and many forms of communication afford a multiplicity of means for influencing peoples, the concept of 'colonialism', 'anti-colonialism' or 'neo-colonialism' is too simple to describe these interrelations or the problems which once-colonial countries share with other economically under-developed states which are seeking modernization.

See:

Rupert Emerson, From Empire to Nation: the Rise to Self-Assertion of Asian and African Peoples (*Cambridge, Mass., 1960*).

John Petrov Plamenatz, On Alien Rule and Self-Government (*London, 1960*).

Robert Strausz-Hupé (ed.), The Idea of Colonialism (*New York, 1958*).

CHAPTER V

THE CHANGING SOCIETY

THE developments of these years brought social and cultural changes no less drastic than the shift in power and the changes in the political and economic systems of the world. These social changes reflected three major factors: the development and impact of science and technology, the interaction between cultures characterized by advanced technology and the cultures of other parts of the world: and the processes of revolution aimed at the conscious remaking of societies. In the industrial countries industrialism remade the patterns of life. In the non-industrial areas changes in outlook and social organization were even more radical than those in the industrial countries, which by the opening of the twentieth century had already gone far toward adopting a scientific orientation.

The interaction between technically advanced cultures and other societies modified the traditional social patterns and stimulated a renaissance of the cultural values and vitality of many areas. The process became a universal one throughout the world, though it operated in differing manners and degrees under conditions of colonial impact and liberation from colonial rule, or where contact was through trade and investment, or where isolated peoples were becoming integrated into modern states of which they formed a part, as were some Indian populations in Central and South America and some of the Asian peoples within the Soviet Union.

Revolutionary movements which undertook to build new societies brought other forms of fundamental social changes. The October revolution in Russia followed by the socialist reconstruction of Russian society stands out as the major conscious revolutionary transformation of the first half of the twentieth century, but this was not the only revolutionary phenomenon. The Mexican revolution which began in 1910 went far toward destroying the social pattern based on large-scale landholding, as did the revolutionary peasant movements in eastern Europe after the first world war and revolutions in Bolivia and Cuba in the 1950s. Under the leadership of Ataturk, the Turkish revolution of the 1920s remade the legal structure, the position of women and the place of religion in the state. The people's democracies of eastern Europe, and especially the People's Republic of China, profiting by the experience of the USSR, undertook to build socialist societies leading toward communism, in line with the situations in their respective countries. Every country which successfully freed itself from colonial rule projected more or less directly a new social pattern which it sought consciously to realize.

These trends radically altered the relation between classes and groups of people, both within and among societies. They had the effect of uprooting many millions of people and brought a staggering rate of population growth far above anything which the world had ever known. The disruptions of two world wars loosened many social bonds. Cultural impact combined with the spirit of nationalism to bring new outlooks. The growth of large organizations, both political and economic, created a new framework for the individual and placed new demands upon him.

The children born into the second half of the twentieth century, in all parts of the world, entered a milieu radically unlike that which their immediate forebears had known before the opening of the century.

I. IMPACT OF INDUSTRIALISM ON THE SOCIETIES OF INDUSTRIAL COUNTRIES

In the industrial countries the new industrialism penetrated rapidly through all segments of life. At the opening of the century, even in the most industrially advanced areas, many aspects of life were largely untouched. Only the beginnings of industrial transformation were then present. Railways carried great loads of men and goods four or five times as fast as a lightly loaded horse could travel, steamships doubled the speed and multiplied the tonnage of fast sailing vessels, and the telegraph, followed by the telephone, brought the first swift communication; but highway travel was still at a horse's pace, man was earthbound, and wireless communication was not in use; the machine gun and heavily armoured battleship presaged mechanized warfare, but barely hinted at its future extent; agriculture had begun to use mechanical equipment and the first of the mechanical household appliances, the sewing machine, had entered the home; the organ grinder was able to entertain city children with mechanically produced music.

But at the opening of the century transport and communication, warfare, agriculture, the home and the arts had only begun to be modified. During the first fifty years of the century—in fact during the first quarter—these and many other aspects of life were partly or fully industrialized by the application of machine technology or by their incorporation into the industrial structure.

The most dramatic change came in transport and communication. Man's relation to distance had already been so revolutionized by railways, steam navigation and telegraph that a second revolution in transport and communication hardly seemed possible. Yet the changes brought by motor transport, and especially aviation and radio communication, were no less drastic than those from steam and telegraphy. In the course of the twentieth century motor vehicles brought to every doorstep served by a street or road transport as rapid as that provided by all but the fastest trains. Air travel multiplied maximum ground speeds as much as the railway and motor car multiplied the speed of the horse, and the aeroplane was bound by no rail or road or blocked by mountain, desert, sea or arctic ice. When aircraft began to exceed the speed of sound after the second world war, there appeared to be virtually no limit to the rate of travel that might be obtained and each new record, such as the non-stop circumnavigation of the globe at the equator in forty-five hours in 1957, was merely a temporary record, for single jet-planes had already reached speeds which would cut that record in half. Earth satellites circled the globe through outer space in one and a half hours.

In short, whenever it was essential to bring people to a given spot—for rescue on land or sea, for quick medical attention, for diplomatic conference, for wartime destruction—the barrier of distance was virtually eliminated. Instantaneous communication by telephone and radio, telephoto and television completed the conquest of distance and the reduction of the size of the world. The chance for men to live in isolation or seclusion grew rapidly less; few places on the globe could not be reached by plane and none was beyond the potential reach of a radio voice.

Mechanization of warfare and the application of industrial methods to the production of implements of war not only brought the unprecedented horrors of mass warfare in the prolonged stalemate of the first world war and the aerial bombardments of the second and led to the nuclear arms race of the post-war decade; it changed the place of war in society, for it converted the whole community into a military target and all but eliminated the old distinction between soldier and noncombatant.

The mechanization of agriculture, which had begun with the commercial production of the iron plough in the second quarter of the nineteenth century, had reached considerable proportions with the introduction of the reaper and harvester on North American wheat fields later in the century. But it entered a new phase with the development of the tractor on the eve of the first world war and the application of electric power on the farm. The use of tractors, which largely replaced horse-power on the commercial farms of North America and much of western Europe and Russia, substituted the petroleum industry and motor manufacture for the land and the farm labour that had supported horses and raised their feed; together with a wide variety of mechanical attachments, it enabled a single farmer on a fully mechanized North American farm to perform some tasks which required the labour of four men on a partially mechanized European farm and as many as forty men in the traditionally operated agriculture of Asia. The use of farm machinery, moreover, forced the farmer to become a mechanic. More fundamentally, new agricultural technology, which included the use of a host of commercially produced fertilizers, chemical insecticides and improved seeds, and the introduction of a variety of experimentally tested methods of cultivation, transformed the farmer from a conservative follower of custom and tradition into a scientifically minded experimenter and innovator.

Industrialism reached into the home, taking to the factory such traditional home tasks as the making of clothing, laundering and the preparation and preservation of many kinds of food, and bringing into the home mechanical appliances for cooking by electricity or gas, sewing, cleaning, laundering and refrigeration. It played a part in changing the position of women as it drew them out of the home to follow their traditional tasks into the factory, and as it freed them from endless home drudgery and enabled them to engage in other occupations, and to take a fuller part in other aspects of family and community life.

Industrialization had its impact, too, on the use of leisure. Mass entertainment for those to whom industry gave new leisure was itself mass-produced by the new motion picture, radio and television industries. Aiming at mass audiences, these new media enlarged the horizons of the many, though they often offended the taste of the few, and they became an integral part of the life of modern societies, involving a vast network of productive units and employing a large body of people with very specialized skills.

The mass production of newsprint and technical developments in printing, telecommunication and radio, together with the spread of mass literacy which industrialism demanded, revolutionized the press. From a relatively simple instrument which provided political and business information and editorial opinion for a limited group of merchants, politicians and other men of affairs, the daily press became an increasingly complex mass-vehicle for the transmission of a wide range of news and information to satisfy the curiosity and provide entertainment for the general public. Mass audiences and new techniques for printing, photography and sound recording had the dual effect on the arts of stimulating the tendency to cater to mass taste and of making works of the finest quality available to the many.

In these and many other ways the life of the industrially developed countries became permeated by the features of industrialism—mechanization, mass production and the scientific attitude. Much remained unmechanized and unorganized—in the home, in the practice of the liberal professions, in various services and in the arts—but daily life was touched at almost every point by industry's structure or its products, and the scientific attitudes of rationality and acceptance of change penetrated even into those aspects which were not modified by mechanization or productive organization.

Industrialization radically changed the occupational structure of the industrial countries. Skilled craftsmen who had constituted the aristocracy of labour lost their position as their trades became obsolete; unskilled workers found themselves replaced by machines. In their places a new group of trained engineers and managers, technicians, salesmen, statisticians, office workers, advertisers, operatives and mechanics arose to plan, design, manage and carry on the processes of modern industry and distribute its products. New occupations developed in wholly new industries such as radio or aviation, motion pictures or plastics. With mounting requirements for scientific research and diversified education, with more wealth and greater leisure, professions and service occupations expanded and the numbers

of scientists, teachers, doctors, nurses, entertainers, restaurant keepers and
providers of holiday and travel facilities multiplied.

The old class structure fell before the changes in occupations and sources
of income. Where a landed aristocracy had dominated, men of industry
shouldered them aside, leaving hollow titles with waning prestige. The old,
small middle class of professionals, tradesmen and skilled craftsmen was
overshadowed by a vast new army of industrial technicians, administrators
and every sort of white-collar worker.

Modern industrialism, in fact, tended to push the bulk of the population
toward the middle class. Although it did not eliminate the distance between
richest and poorest and wide disparities remained, it steadily reduced the
proportion which fell in these extremes and tremendously expanded the
great middle group. Rising incomes reduced distinctions in consumption
patterns, clothing and manner of living; rising levels of general education
blurred the line between the educated and uneducated; mechanization and
automation reduced the need for unskilled labour; large organizations
produced a host of bureaucrats; taxation to support the social services which
industrialism made necessary skimmed off some of the extra resources of the

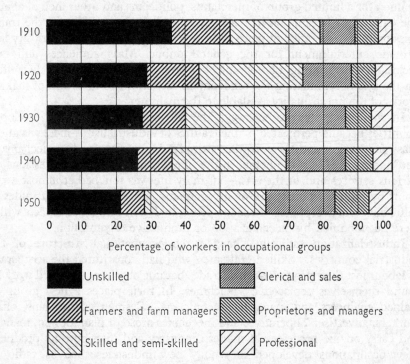

CHART VIII. Shift in Occupations, USA, 1910–50, percentage of workers in
occupational groups.

Source: J. F. Dewhurst and Associates, *America's Needs and Resources*, 1955, pp. 730, 731.

rich, and pushed them closer to the general level; these same services raised
still further the real incomes of the lower groups.[1, 2]

The trend may be clearly noted in the change in income distribution in
Britain and in the United States. In Britain the highest income receivers at
the opening of the century were receiving an estimated 1,500–2,000 times the
amount received by the average industrial worker; in 1950 they received
only 12–15 times the worker's income. Social expenditures, which involved
for the most part a redistribution of real income, amounted to 18 per cent
of national income in 1951 as compared with 5.5 per cent in 1913.

CHART IX.   Distribution of Family Income in the USA, 1929, 1956 (percentage of
families).
Source: Committee for Economic Development, *Economic Growth in the United States*, 1958.

In the United States the average income of the two lowest fifths of the
population, before taxes, increased between 1935 and 1950 by 78 and 81 per
cent respectively, while that of the top fifth increased by only 34 per cent and
of the highest 5 per cent only 17 per cent. The income pyramid in the United
States in 1955, even without adjustment for taxes, showed a concentration of
incomes in the middle groups in marked contrast to the many very poor and
few very rich typical of most non-industrial areas. The trend toward this
type of income pyramid in all advanced industrial countries was so marked
that it was sometimes referred to as a bloodless revolution.

With industrialization came the progressive urbanization of society. At the
opening of the twentieth century there were only eleven cities of over 1,000,000
population; in 1950 there were 49 such cities or 63 if surrounding metropolitan areas as well as central city are included. The largest city at mid-century,

Tokyo, had more than twice the population of London in 1900, then the largest of the great cities. The number of urban centres with more than 100,000 people was approximately 280 in the earlier year and some 850 in the latter. Nearly 80 per cent of the population of England and Wales was already living in urban districts before the first world war. From a half to nearly two-thirds of the population in western European countries, the United States and Australia were urban dwellers at mid-century.

But figures of urban population tell only part of the story, for urbanization was not confined to the cities. Penetrated by arterial roads, served by electricity, equipped with farm machinery, reached by radio and motion pictures, rural areas lost their isolation and much of their distinctive character. In a broad sense the entire life of the industrial countries became urbanized.

The full meaning of this change for human life and society was a matter of great concern to teachers and scholars, statesmen and philosophers, parents and artists who tried to adapt themselves and to guide or lead others. Some, impressed with the age-long dependence of human beings on a small group of family or neighbours for their sense of belonging and source of values, thought that the rootless, heterogeneous impersonality of the city left the urban individual lonely, incomplete and without the means of developing his full personality. Others were concerned lest the multitude of forces beyond his control and the impact of information, ideas, values and opinions which did not grow out of his direct experience, should rob man of the independent judgment which he could exercise within the limited sphere of his former life and make him a follower and mirror rather than a master of his own thoughts.

Others, however, saw the city as providing a new, rich ground for human development, offering a wide range of fare to nourish the mind and senses and of contacts and experiences to enrich the personality. They thought that the new associations in trade unions, professional bodies, scientific circles, or with others of common interests, the new loyalties of broader scope, and the new opportunities to travel and observe offered the masses of men a chance to develop potentialities for which earlier societies had given no scope. Whether those who viewed the urban milieu with alarm or with hope had the truer insight, there was no doubt that urban industrialism was remaking the lives of a large and growing segment of mankind, as old relationships and old certainties gave way to new experience.

It was the impact of industrialization which pressed the state to assume new functions and expand its role—to protect its citizens against the insecurity of income which industry brought and the hazards of life for which the traditional extended family no longer offered a cushion; to cope with the practical problems of transport, utilities, health and safety which came with city living; to exercise a measure of control over powerful industries; to develop the facilities for education which industrial society required. As governments in industrial countries expanded their services to meet these demands, they employed large and growing numbers of citizens and gathered through taxation a large part of the national wealth. Even in a country which retained a vigorous economy of private enterprise and consciously sought to minimize government activity, such as the United States, the number of civilian government employees, federal, state and local, mounted from 6·3 per cent of the total civilian labour force in 1930 to 10·5 per cent twenty-five years later, while the portion of the national income absorbed by taxation, including that used for military expenditures, rose from less than 10 to over 20 per cent. Canada more than tripled its civil service employees from 1925 to 1950. In countries more frankly devoted to the welfare state, the role of government expanded still further, and in those with state-directed economies the vast army of state employees came to include a large proportion of the citizenry, and most of the national income flowed through the hands of the state and its agencies.

In all fields industrialization brought large-scale organization that often overshadowed the individual. Gigantic corporations were matched by huge trade unions built up to bargain with them. Both organizations involved large bureaucracies. The individual participant in modern industry, whether he was a worker or a part of management, faced the central problem of how to maintain his sense of self in the midst of bigness—of the corporation, the trade union and the community in which he lived.

Modern industry also set its stamp on the intellectual, religious and artistic development of the time. It gave direction to much scientific investigation, both through support for research in its own establishments and as the industrialization of warfare led to heavy military expenditures in scientific fields. In addition, science depended on modern industry for the elaborate equipment and instrumentation indispensable to much advanced experimental research. In the social sciences, too, industrialism provided a powerful stimulus, for the problems to which modern sociology, psychology and human geography addressed themselves arose in large measure from the unsettling effect of the urban milieu, the breakdown of old values and the uncertainty in human relations which industrial society brought.

The challenge offered to philosophy and religion by the dominance of practical, rational and dynamically changing industrial forces was met by both adaptation and rejection. Dialectical materialism, pragmatism and logical positivism, in spite of their contradictory approaches to basic philosophical problems, were all expressions of the rational and practically oriented spirit of industrial society; secular defection from religion and modernism in religious dogma were their counterparts in the field of religion. But response to the impact of industrialism also found expression in the philosophy of existentialism with its psychological rejection of industrial society and often despair in the face of its problems; it also took the form of reaffirmation of religious orthodoxy or mystical religious faith.

In the arts new processes such as photography, new materials and new industrial techniques put their mark on the visual arts and architecture, while mass audiences and mass production methods affected the nature and quality of literature, drama, screen and music. The artist in industrial society had to come to terms with its mass character or retreat into social isolation.

Industrialism thus transformed the societies which it came to dominate, reaching into every phase of life. By destroying old habits, old ties, old responsibilities and old certainties it created a mobile, changing, uncertain way of life. By opening wider horizons, creating new and broader relationships, breaking down barriers of distance and social class it set the stage for a new phase of human living. By lightening man's burden of toil and poverty it released immense human energy.

For the first time in human history a society of abundance became a reality, not merely the myth of a golden age or utopia. The first country to experience this new phenomenon, the United States, was clearly only the vanguard in mankind's movement toward this condition. The United States owed the priority of its abundance to a number of circumstances. It represented the projection of European civilization under the advantageous circumstances of a continent rich in resources. It had inherited and developed those European political, economic and social institutions which favoured full and rapid economic and social development, with a minimum of rigidity. These factors had combined to produce a high level of technology and organization geared to a large domestic mass market. In the twentieth century the United States was free from the destruction of war, yet was stimulated by wartime demands to achieve rapid advances in productivity. Similar conditions produced similar results in Canada, Australia and New Zealand.

In the 1950s it was already apparent that it was only a matter of a short time before many other countries of advanced technology would also become affluent societies. Britain and the countries of northern and western Europe were well on their way. Rapidly rising production and relatively slow rates of population growth brought *per capita* income in these countries by the end of the 1950s close to that of the United States a decade earlier and their levels of mass consumption were becoming similar. The main roads of Britain and the Continent were becoming as crowded with pleasure vehicles as those of North America. Japan exceeded all other countries in the late 1950s in the completeness of home electrification while a very high rate of economic expansion was raising levels of consumption in other lines. The USSR proclaimed its intention of outproducing the United States and it defined the communist society which it was approaching as a 'society of abundance'. The shape of abundance might vary substantially under the differing circumstances of different societies. But whatever the variations, the phenomenon as it actually appeared during these years was of immense historic importance in itself and of concern to mankind throughout the world.

II. CHANGE IN THE POSITION AND STRUCTURE OF NON-INDUSTRIAL SOCIETIES

It was the vision of this abundance, of the potentialities of industrialism for releasing human energies and opening up new possibilities for human development, that led the non-industrial countries to seek its benefits for their own societies, however long the road and however many the problems which would be encountered before the potential benefits could reach a large proportion of their populations. Whether in the radical, high-speed pro-gramme for China's great 'leap forward', or in the dedication of India to the task of modernization within the framework of traditional and liberal values, or in the aspiration of African peoples to bring themselves abreast of the new times, the elimination of man's poverty and the pursuit of abundance was the goal.

Many of these peoples had already experienced the impact of industrialism on their societies long before they began actively to seek its benefits. Wherever tea or rubber, indigo, tin, petroleum, jute, copra and countless other raw materials were produced, local societies had felt the effects of fluctuations in world markets, shifts in world demand and in the competitive position of different regions, changes in technology, and the impact of wars and de-pression. In addition the commercial products which reached their markets had often undermined local crafts and modified the balance of their economies even when the items involved, such as paraffin, thread or utensils, made up only a small part of local consumption. Twentieth-century industrialism accelerated the rate of social change and reached areas which had been largely untouched by the expansion of trade and investment in the preceding century.

The new means of transport and communication meant a breakdown of isolation, new possibilities for development, and a new importance for regions which had been inaccessible. From the time of the great European explora-tions the whole world had been linked by its seas, and the major centres of development had been in coastal areas. The coming of the railway had opened up the interiors of some continental regions and had linked them with the coasts; the opening up of the North American continent was associated with the introduction of the railways during the second half of the nineteenth century; the trans-Siberian railway was a factor in the penetration of Siberia; railways connected the interior of the Indian sub-continent with the port cities. But it was the highway, the motor car and the aeroplane of the twen-tieth century that were bringing the interior regions into new accessibility and new prominence—the vast interior of Asia where such ancient historic centres as Tashkent, lost during the era of the sea routes, flourished anew, or the region of Sinkiang which offered a new frontier rich in resources to populous China, or the interior of the South American continent, or the heart of Africa whose riches were only beginning to be unlocked in the middle of the twentieth century.

For some peoples, following their traditional ways, the new transport took away their functions and destroyed the basis of whole societies. Nomadic peoples of the west Asian and African deserts, whose camel trains had provided the transport and whose desert fighters had furnished the military forces of the areas, found themselves displaced by motor lorries and armoured tanks. With these new developments the last remnants of nomadism, once the way of life of many of the world's peoples, were disappearing from the face of the earth.

For the peasant village, which still at mid-century was the home of the majority of the world's inhabitants, the integrity of self-contained village life was fast breaking down. In varying degrees and with greater or less rapidity the mutual dependence of village members and their independence from the outside world was undermined from many directions—by the entrance of commercial goods to replace the products of village crafts, by the substitution of cash crops for subsistence agriculture, by the drift of workers from village to town, and by the coming of roads, education, radio communication and motion pictures to bring new people and ideas that had no place in the structure of village life. The individual, whose role had been defined and whose horizon had been bounded by the pattern of village relationships, gained alternative bases from outside the village society for his image of himself, his actions and his relations with his fellows. By mid-century the peasant village in nearly all parts of the world was no longer a complete and integrated society in itself, but a society in transition whose integration into the broader society that was emerging had not yet been achieved. Where governments were making conscious efforts to guide the transition they sought both to strengthen the village as a unit under the new conditions and to develop urban centres which would sustain the surrounding villages.

With the breakdown of isolation and of village integrity went the loosening of social relationships which had been part of the traditional structure of essentially static societies. The joint family was weakened everywhere, not only where it was under direct attack as in communist China but where, as in modern India, new legal structures favoured its dissolution as a legal entity, or wherever individualizing forms of economic opportunity drew its members into new relationships. The breakdown was most drastic in the detribalization of Africans who were drawn into mines or industries and whose entire structure of tribal relationships, values and controls found no place in the Europeanized urban society of which they formed the labour base.

Traditional bases of social stratification, by caste or other distinction which defined status, were modified. New classes of technicians or others whose position rested on their functional role in a changing society challenged the superiority of those who derived their position from a social system and tradition which was being replaced. With new political power, classes emerged which had never before enjoyed social or political status. Adult franchise identified the entire community with the state, and its exercise awakened groups which had been submerged for ages and gave them both a vested interest and a manner of sharing power at all levels. This tendency was most conspicuous in India, in the rise of former 'untouchables' and members of lower castes through the operation of democratic processes which were used to further social and economic change.

By the middle of the century radical social and economic changes were thus under way and many old values had been undermined, while new values appropriate to the altered character of these societies were yet to take shape.

III. POPULATION CHANGE[3]

1. *Uprooted people*

In no previous period had such great numbers and so large a proportion of the people of the earth been uprooted from their ancestral homes and forced to find new homes and establish new relationships in an alien environment. The twentieth century might, indeed, be known as 'the century of the uprooted'. In the early decades the great stream of European immigrants who had first trickled and then poured from Europe to the New World since the seventeenth century rose to a flood. When the United States put up the bars and limited immigration after the first world war, the volume was sharply reduced, but some flow continued to North and South America and to Oceania whenever economic conditions offered favourable opportunities and war did not prevent movement. Many millions of Chinese migrated to Manchuria in search of economic opportunity. The movement of Russian population into Siberia, which was already considerable during the tsarist régime, was immensely stimulated by the development of great new industrial centres in this region of the USSR. Other movements of population in response to economic opportunity included the steady flow of Chinese to south-east Asia, of Indians to Malaya, Burma, East Africa and the Caribbean and of Africans from tribal areas into the mining regions of the Union of South Africa and the copper belts of the Rhodesias and the Congo.

The flow from farms or villages to the expanding metropolitan and industrial centres went on both within and between countries. Some workers migrated only seasonally or temporarily, such as the Polish and Italian workers who formed a large part of France's seasonal labour supply before the second world war, and the nearly half a million Algerians who worked in metropolitan France in the 1950s, intending to return home with their earnings. Especially in newly industrializing areas, workers tended to retain their village roots and to return, or at least to plan to return, after a period of earning in factory or mine. The labour force of African mines and mills at mid-century was still very largely composed of temporary workers whose place was taken after a period of months by others who also expected to remain for a temporary period. But for most migrants the transfer was complete and permanent, and the new and growing urban populations of industrial and non-industrial countries alike were composed of people who had cut themselves off from their roots.

The most uprooting movement of people during these years, however, was not the drift of workers into areas of expanding economic opportunity but the tearing of people from their homes as a result of political and religious strife. The uprooting and resettlement of some 14,000,000 Muslims and Hindus at the time of the partition of India and Pakistan was the greatest single movement of people in a short time that the world had ever seen. But these were only the largest groups. The shift of Greek and Turkish populations in 1922 was followed by the exchanges of populations forced by Hitler in eastern Europe during the second world war. Refugees and expellees from revolution, civil war and oppression fled Russia after the October revolution, Germany and Italy during the Nazi and fascist régimes, Spain in the 1930s and eastern Europe after the second world war. To these movements must be added the flight to Palestine of Jews who survived the Nazi efforts at extermination, the displacement of nearly a million Arabs in the creation of the state of Israel, the repatriation of several hundred thousands of Turks from Bulgaria in the 1950s, and the flow of nearly a million refugees from North to South Vietnam when the French were forced to withdraw and the country was partitioned in 1954. All these and lesser movements elsewhere made the displaced person a twentieth-century type. The problems which he presented and the attitudes which he brought from his experiences became important elements in the outlook of the period.

2. *Mounting numbers*

The most dramatic feature of the world's population was the speed-up in its rate of growth. In the first half of the century, in spite of wars of unprecedented destructiveness and one of the most fatal epidemics of modern times, the influenza epidemic of 1918, the annual rate of increase in the number of people was nearly half again as great as during the last half of the nineteenth century and nearly twice that of a hundred years before. Yet by the decade of the 1950s the growth since 1900 appeared slow, for the rate had jumped to almost double the average for those fifty years.

In earlier periods of the world's history upward spurts in population had come with expansion in the means to sustain life. In the twentieth century they reflected the new means to postpone death. As modern medicine developed the capacity to control or prevent one disease after another, it raised the survival rate and extended the life span of those whom it reached. Until the second world war its major impact was on the industrially developed countries whose death rates declined steadily, creating a wide disparity between the life expectancy of their citizens and those in underdeveloped areas. But in the years after the war modern medicine penetrated to most areas where death rates had remained high, dramatically wiping out ancient scourges such as malaria, sharply reducing infant mortality and radically altering the balance between births and deaths. Death rates plummeted while birth rates stayed high, and countries such as Mexico faced the prospect that their populations might double in a mere twenty years.

The reduction in death rates in the industrially developed countries brought only a moderate acceleration of population growth, for the process was gradual and it was accompanied by a decline in births as the rational attitudes characteristic of industrial society were extended to family planning. Possessing ample and expanding economic resources and social institutions, these countries faced no serious problems in feeding, educating, employing and housing their growing numbers; in fact several of the European countries during the inter-war period were more concerned with their low birth rates and slow population growth than with the reverse. For them the principal result of the lowered death rates was to change the age composition of the population and convert the aged few into a large body of senior citizens. This was a change of considerable social and cultural importance but it was not disruptive and, even when higher birth rates brought new increases after the war, the impact was absorbed for the time being at least, though not always without difficulty, especially in housing and the expansion of educational facilities.

But in most non-industrial and partially industrialized areas rapid population growth presented grave problems. The most immediate difficulties arose where there was already pressure on the land, as in the Nile valley, Java, parts of China, India and Pakistan, the Andes, and where traditional methods of agriculture and small subsistence farms could not sustain additional numbers. In such areas increasing rural poverty set in motion a migration to the cities which exceeded in volume the available urban jobs, produced a large body of unemployed or semi-employed people and created a massive demand for housing, education and other facilities. Even where empty lands awaited settlers and ample resources could sustain a much larger population in the future, as in Brazil and some other parts of South America, the situation was not simple; for the number of new children to be educated, families to be housed and workers to be employed placed a heavy strain on existing resources and called for a rate of economic expansion and degree of institutional adaptability most difficult to achieve. Ever-increasing numbers threatened to undermine the determined efforts to reduce illiteracy and poverty and the steps designed to create the economic momentum which alone could convert the additional people from a burden to an asset. The situation was a precarious one, for unsuccessful attempts to satisfy the demands for services which modern peoples everywhere had come to regard as their due could not only impede economic development but imperil political stability as well.

For the world as a whole the prospect of greater and greater numbers on what seemed like a shrinking globe, and the differential rates in different parts of the world, made the population problem a live issue for the first time in world history.

IV. NEW CULTURAL ORIENTATIONS

With these changes in social structures and relationships went changes in attitudes and cultural orientations. Western man had to learn to see himself, not as standing at the pinnacle of human development, but as one among many peoples, each with its own cultural integrity and dignity, and its own right and ability to demand respect. Eastern societies derived new attitudes from their contact with the West, and these attitudes in turn became part of the dynamics of their own development.

The most radical concept which penetrated eastern societies was the doctrine of change. In Asian countries generally, the accepted view of society was of a stable condition based on immutable principles and unchanging institutions. Change meant decline, a fall from moral standards, and was therefore to be resisted at all costs. This was so marked a feature of Asian life that reformers had always taken the greatest possible care to insist that they were not demanding anything new but were calling for a restoration of something lost.

But from the early twentieth century the young men who returned from their higher studies in western universities to provide intellectual leadership in the emerging national movements in Asia made the principle of change an article of faith. The scientific approach to such daily problems as public health and sanitation brought home to the ordinary man the idea that change can be a normal feature of human life. More than merely accepting change, moreover, Asian societies began to conceive of the possibility of progress. For example, while the Hindu sacred text, the *Gita*, had taught a doctrine of continuing social adjustment, and the Buddha had preached the doctrine that all things change, it was only when these ancient teachings were re-examined in the context of the western idea of progress that they were seen as containing the idea that change is the basis of life.

When change came to be accepted as desirable and progress became an ideal, time acquired a new importance. In generally stable societies the time factor was not a major consideration; the joint family was a continuous institution and as a result the urge for achievement or for quick results was not great. The breakdown of the joint family combined with other influences to change the idea of time, for the family head of the single family unit had a direct responsibility for the welfare of the immediate group. A more competitive approach to life, a sense of urgency and a desire to achieve provided new motivations to individuals.

One dimension of time was a new historical sense which developed as European scholars delved into Asian history and Asian students turned to the discovery of their own past. The first effect of the world consciousness that was already being awakened before the end of the nineteenth century was to show Asians to themselves in an inferior world role. But as the work of European scholars brought to light evidence of the peoples who had built empires, established colonies and spread their cultures through trade and travel, Asian peoples were able to develop a self-image which could undergird their nationalism with the reality of their own pasts.[4]

The political nationalism which successfully challenged western hegemony thus became at the same time a revival of national cultures. The reassertion of cultural traditions took the form of revitalizing traditional religions, renewing interest in traditional arts such as the dance and in local languages and literatures, and rescrutinizing the traditional values of the society. At times it was a conservative revival, often led by the most orthodox religious element, which sought to re-establish traditional forms of authority and modes of life in the face of influences which were bringing change. More often it expressed efforts to relate the modernization of society to the vital and positive elements which had come from the past.

At the other end of the scale, attitudes toward the individual and toward human life also underwent fundamental change. The notion of human equality was alien to the traditions of eastern societies; yet by the time that these countries achieved political independence they were ready to write into their constitutions the principles of democratic equality, majority rule and, generally, universal suffrage, including suffrage for women. Though these principles had rarely been fully assimilated, their mere enunciation marked the change in outlook which had taken place by the middle of the twentieth century.

In the attitude toward life itself, the old fatalism and the dependence on religious practices, charms, special offerings or prayers to cure illness and ward off misfortune were yielding nearly everywhere before the demonstrated efficacy of modern medicine. The almost universal demand for doctors and hospitals reflected the new view.

Thus the scientific approach to life, the basis for the transformation of the industrial societies in these years, was entering into the outlook of the non-industrial societies as well, to point the direction of their development in the years ahead.

NOTES TO CHAPTER V

1. Professor László Zsigmond points out that it is impossible to agree with the authors' assertion that in 'modern industrialism' the differences between the various classes of the population are tending to disappear, and that with the disappearance of a clearly-marked contrast between wealth and poverty a majority of the population comes to consist of members of the so-called middle classes. This is a mistaken assumption that has no basis in actual fact. Dr János Jemnitz agrees with Professor Zsigmond and remarks that the term 'middle class' as used in this work is too vague and imprecise. It can cover the technical intelligentsia, managers and technicians—social groups which cannot all be considered as belonging to one and the same class. . . . We note that such professional groups as engineers, lawyers and bankers are lumped together (as the uppermost section of the middle class). This classification is superficial. The rise in the living standards and cultural niveau of the working class leads the authors to suppose that class divisions are tending to lessen, since in their view the working class is rising to the level of the middle class. This problem undoubtedly merits closer analysis than is given in the present work. Attention should be paid to such factors as the role of property as a link between members of a particular group, sources of income, and class relationships. If the latter are taken into account, it becomes impossible to speak of 'the disappearance of classes'. Doctor of Philosophical Sciences V. S. Semenov points out that the theory that the growth of the 'middle class' represents a 'new path' of transition from capitalism to a classless society is fundamentally anti-scientific. It is based on the concept of 'social stratification', and proceeds from the premise that social groups are to be distinguished by secondary and derivative characteristics: ideas, outlook, psychological attitudes, education, spiritual culture, biological characteristics, way of life and behaviour, nature of employment, level of income, and role in the organization of the labour process. This approach disregards the decisive and basic attribute of social classes: men's relationship to the means of production. The very term 'middle class' is exceedingly imprecise. In 1949 Harry Truman, President of the USA, declared that the American 'middle class' comprised individuals and families with earnings of 10,000 to 25,000 dollars a year. Included in the 'middle class' were officers, members of the free professions, some wealthy farmers (i.e. capitalists), 'administrative personnel and self-employed persons' (small property-owners, artisans, owners of shops and the like), office and commercial employees, and a large segment of the skilled workers. At the present time many American sociologists and government bodies include in the 'middle class' from 60 per cent to 80 per cent, or more, of the US population, thereby embracing the greater part of the working class and a sizeable element of the capitalist class.

The Danish sociologist J. Havemann considers all skilled workers members of the 'middle class'. The British labour theoretician G. D. H. Cole assigns to the 'middle class' members of the most varied social groups, from entrepreneurs (except the largest) to shop-assistants and typists.

The German sociologist Helmut Schelsky (Federal Republic of Germany) assigns to the 'middle class' everyone who accounts himself a member of this class, irrespective of his actual social position (see H. Schelsky, *Die Wandlungen der deutschen Familie in der Gegenwart*, Hamburg, 1954).

It is impossible to concur in the view that the 'middle class' is tending to swallow up gradually all other classes of the population. Thus, for example, the urban and rural petty bourgeoisie, employees and intelligentsia, taken together, formed the following percentage of the working population of the USA in the years stated:

1870	1910	1950	1954
47·2%	43·2%	43·5%	44·1%

(Third World Congress of Sociology, *Transactions*, Vol. III, p. 70; J. A. Kahl, *The American Class Structure*, New York, 1957, pp. 13, 67). The thesis that with the growth of the 'middle class' income differences disappear also does not accord with the facts.

It is characteristic that in his address to the Third World Congress of Sociology the American scholar Kurt B. Mayer stated that 'the image of America as a society where "everybody is middle class" has persisted long after it ceased to be in accordance with economic and social reality' (Third World Congress of Sociology, *Transactions*, Vol. III, p. 71).

2. *The Author-Editors explain the sense in which they have used the term 'middle class' as follows:*

In using the term to refer to the relative expansion in the portion of the population which has substantial access to the fruits of production, enjoys corresponding aspirations and patterns of living, and engages in occupations which require education and carry responsibility and some prestige, they have chosen to use the term in its common, imprecise sense to apply to essentially imprecise phenomena.

'Class' may be defined in a number of ways. The term always implies position on a scale from lower to higher, but it may be limited to economic position, applied primarily to social position, or used in a more general way to designate status within a society; it may be based on stratification in relation to occupation, income, consumption, education, social recognition or prestige, power. The relevance of one or another factor to what is happening to class structure depends on the definition. If 'class' is defined in terms of relationship to the means of production, i.e. limited to economic relationships and, within these relationships, to the factor of power, it is irrelevant to consider such factors as actual levels of real income, disparity or lack of disparity in income, similarity or dissimilarity in levels of living, or occupational patterns. If 'class' is defined in terms of social strata and standards of living, however, such factors are of central importance.

The Author-Editors have chosen to use the term in a broad socio-economic sense which includes all of the factors mentioned above. In so doing, they are taking no position as to how the term should be used in other works.

Evidence of the tendency for the middle class, in the sense used in the text, to expand may be seen in the following trends in occupations, income distribution, and relation between the earnings of industrial and professional workers in the United States:

OCCUPATIONAL DISTRIBUTION OF EMPLOYED PERSONS IN THE UNITED STATES—1900-60

Per cent

	1900	1910	1920	1930	1940	1950	1960
Professional, technical and kindred workers	4·1	4·7	5·4	6·8	7·5	8·6	11·2
Farmers and farm operators	20·0	16·5	15·2	12·3	10·4	7·5	4·2
Managers, officials and proprietors, except farm	5·9	6·6	6·6	7·4	7·3	8·8	10·6
Clerical and kindred workers	3·1	5·4	8·0	8·8	9·7	12·2	14·7
Sales workers	4·5	4·7	4·9	6·4	6·6	7·0	6·6
Craftsmen, foremen and kindred workers	10·7	11·5	13·0	12·9	12·0	14·2	12·9
Operatives and kindred workers	12·7	14·5	15·7	15·8	18·4	20·3	18·0
Private household workers	5·5	5·1	3·3	4·1	4·6	2·5	3·3
Service workers except private house-workers	3·5	4·6	4·5	5·8	7·1	7·8	9·1
Farm labourers and foremen	17·6	14·4	11·8	8·8	6·9	4·4	3·9
Labourers, except farm and mine	12·4	12·0	11·6	10·9	9·5	6·7	5·5
	100·0	100·0	100·0	100·0	100·0	100·0	100·0

Source: *U S Department of Commerce*, Historical Statistics of the United States, *and* Statistical Abstract of the United States, 1964.

REAL FAMILY INCOME OF FAMILIES AND UNATTACHED INDIVIDUALS IN THE UNITED STATES
(in 1954 dollars)

	Income after Income Taxes (percent. distribution)					Income before Income Taxes (percent. distribution)				
	Under 2,000	2,000– 4,000	4,000– 6,000	6,000– 10,000	Over 10,000	Under 2,000	2,000– 4,000	4,000– 6,000	6,000– 10,000	Over 10,000
1929[1]	35·8	38·9	13·5	7·6	4·2	35·8	38·9	13·5	7·6	4·2
1935–6[1]	42·2	33·8	14·2	6·6	3·2	42·2	33·8	14·2	6·6	3·2
1941						30·8	31·3	21·5	12·1	4·3
1947						19·3	32·3	24·9	16·6	6·9
1950	20·7	32·8	26·4	14·9	5·2	19·8	30·5	25·7	17·4	6·6
1955	16·9	28·0	28·5	19·1	7·5	15·9	25·4	26·2	23·1	9·4
1960	15·7	24·9	25·7	23·1	10·6	14·8	22·4	23·5	25·8	13·5
1962	14·8	23·6	25·0	24·7	11·9	13·9[2]	21·2	22·6	27·0	15·3

	Average Income after Taxes	Average Income before Taxes
1929	$3,791	$3,791
1935–6	3,343	3,343
1941		4,161
1947		4,877
1950	4,526	4,943
1955	5,070	5,618
1960	5,570	6,193
1962	5,815	6,490

Percent. Increase in Real Income after Taxes
1935–36 to 1962

Families in:	%
Lowest Fifth	112
Second Fifth	127
Third Fifth	85
Fourth Fifth	100
Highest Fifth	48

Source: U S Department of Commerce, Survey of Current Business, April 1964.

(1) In 1929 and 1935–6, personal income taxes were low and no figures for after-tax income are available. The before-tax figures have been included in the after-tax columns as substantially representing the after-tax distribution. The first year for which after-tax figures are available is 1950.

(2) It should be noted that over half of the families and unattached individuals with incomes (in 1954 dollars) of less than $2,000 in 1962 were unattached individuals such as young persons entering the labour market, older persons leaving the labour market and working only part time, etc.

AVERAGE ANNUAL EARNINGS OF MANUFACTURING PRODUCTION WORKERS, PUBLIC PRIMARY AND SECONDARY SCHOOL TEACHERS, COLLEGE (UNIVERSITY) TEACHERS, AND ENGINEERS IN THE UNITED STATES. 1929–1954

| | Manufacturing Production Workers[1] | School Teachers | College Teachers | Engineers[2] | Ratio of Earnings of Manufacturing Production Workers to Earnings of: | | |
					School Teachers	College Teachers	Engineers
	$	$	$	$	%	%	%
1929	1288		3056	3468		42·1	37·1
1930	1196	1420	3065		84·2	39·0	
1931	1073		3134			34·2	
1932	878	1417	3111	2820	61·9	28·3	31·1
1933	866						
1934	966	1227		2520	78·7		38·3
1935	1035		2666			38·9	
1936	1121	1283	2732		87·4	41·0	
1937	1239		2843			43·6	
1938	1148	1374	2861		83·5	40·4	
1939	1229			3324			37·0
1940	1298	1441	2906		90·3	44·7	
1941	1533						
1942	1907	1507	2914		126·5	65·4	
1943	2240		3039	4008		73·7	55·9
1944	2376	1728	3331		137·5	71·3	
1945	2298		3277			70·1	
1946	2253	1995	3465	4884	113·0	65·0	46·1
1947	2557		3736			68·4	
1948	2762	2639	4123		104·7	67·0	
1949	2802		4234			66·1	
1950	3033	3010	4354		100·7	69·6	
1951	3294						
1952	3492	3450	5106		101·2	61·3	
1953	3664			6216			58·9
1954	3665	3825			95·8		

Source: US Department of Commerce, Historical Statistics of the United States, *and US Department of Labour*, Employment and Earnings Statistics for the United States, 1909–62.
(*1*) *Based on average weekly earnings.*
(*2*) *Based on median monthly salary rates.*

3. Professor E. N. Anderson notes that:
    'The treatment of population in this chapter and in Chapter XV is open to the criticism that it minimizes the impact of catastrophic events in the period—the enormous losses through war, revolution, famine and forced migration—and, further, that it fails to discuss the role of migration, not merely in Europe but in Asia as well, as an instrument of population adjustment and its relation to economic conditions and social and political tensions. It is to be noted that, in spite of tremendous loss of life in World Wars I and II, the deficit in Europe and Russia in manpower was soon overcome by natural increase, and there was no absolute decline, apart from the gap in the number of births during the war years, in the population of these areas.'
    For further discussion consult:
Dudley Kirk, *Europe's Population in the Interwar Years* (League of Nations, 1946).
Eugene M. Kulischer, *Europe on the Move: War and Population Changes, 1917–1947* (New York, 1948).

Bruno Lasker, *Asia on the Move* (New York: Institute of Pacific Relations, 1945).

Ministry of Information and Broadcasting, India, *Millions on the Move: The Aftermath of Partition* (Delhi, 1949).

Joseph Schechtman, *Postwar Population Transfers in Europe 1945–55* (Oxford, 1962).

Joseph Schechtman, *On Wings of Eagles* (New York, 1961).

Joseph Schechtman, *Population Transfers in Asia* (New York, 1949).

H. J. Wiens, *China's March toward the Tropics* (Hamden, Conn., 1954).

4. Candidate of Juridical Sciences E. A. Bovin notes that it is not ideas that make history, but history that makes ideas. The awakening and consolidation of a sense of nationality has its roots primarily in actual social-economic processes (the formation of capitalist relations and the emergence of a national bourgeoisie).

PART ONE

THE DEVELOPMENT AND APPLICATION OF SCIENTIFIC KNOWLEDGE

SECTION ONE

NEW SCIENTIFIC THOUGHT

CHAPTER VI

THE NEW SCIENTIFIC THOUGHT
AND ITS IMPACT*

THE most creative cultural development of the twentieth century was the emergence of a new scientific outlook and its impact on the thought and life of mankind.

Beginning at the opening of the century, scientists conceived a new view of nature and her laws which made as sharp a break with the thought which preceded it as the scientific inquiries of the sixteenth and seventeenth centuries had made with the thought of the Middle Ages.

The new scientific thought may appropriately be termed the second scientific revolution. The first great scientific revolution had evolved the scientific method of inquiry. Looked at from the perspective of the twentieth century the unfolding of scientific thought between 1500 and 1700 appears critical in the creation of modern civilization. According to one contemporary historian, Professor Herbert Butterfield, it 'outshines everything since the rise of Christianity and reduces the Renaissance and Reformation to the rank of mere episodes'.†

The first scientific revolution was an intellectual revolution; it taught men to think differently. Only later was this thought put to a new kind of practical use, in the industrial developments which gave modern civilization its outward character. By the end of the nineteenth century the scientific method had not only brought profound changes in outlook; science was remaking the world, root and branch.

The second scientific revolution, too, began as an intellectual revolution. About the year 1900 the view of nature which the first scientific revolution had established began to exhaust its successes and to meet its first failures. Delicate new phenomena were found here and there which the established view of nature and her laws could not unravel. As a result scientists began slowly and with many hesitations to form a new conception of the processes of nature and a new assessment of scientific activity itself. The shift in outlook was subtle but it went very deep.

Like its predecessor the second scientific revolution spread slowly from the minds of the specialists who conceived it. In the course of fifty years its practical consequences reached far; many of the spectacular applications of science in the years following the second world war grew out of the new

---

* This chapter was prepared by Dr. J. Bronowski.

† Herbert Butterfield, *The Origins of Modern Science* (G. Bell & Sons Ltd, London, 1950), p. viii.

concepts and the new approach. In time it began to transform the outlook of the layman as well as the scientist and to enter the minds and affect the lives of people in all parts of the world.

I. THE STATE OF KNOWLEDGE IN THE 1890s

The character of the revolution in scientific thought can only be understood against a background of the knowledge and thought at the end of the nineteenth century.

1. *Physical sciences*

In most respects the physical sciences seemed in the 1890s to have reached almost the frontiers of knowledge. There existed a coherent theory of the structure of matter which explained the known phenomena. According to this theory all matter consists of atoms, which form a regular arrangement when matter is in the solid state, but become progressively more loosely held together when matter passes into the liquid and then into the gaseous state. About eighty essentially different kinds of atoms were already known. These were known chemically to fall into cyclic groups, with marked similarities of physical and chemical activity in any one group. But nothing was known or conjectured which could explain either the differences between atoms of one kind and those of another, or the similarities among the different kinds of atoms which belong to one cyclic group.

Since the atoms were conceived, as the Greeks had named them, indivisible, there was indeed no sense in which either their differences or their likenesses could be discussed. For to explain a material difference one must presumably point to some underlying difference either in make-up or in arrangement. An indivisible atom would have neither make-up nor arrangement. On this view each kind of atom is a fundamental entity, complete and self-contained; its properties could be described but they could not be traced back to any deeper underlying principles.[1]

The different kinds of atoms were known to combine in many different chemical structures. Descriptive laws had been found which pictured how the atoms in such structures fit together. It had been guessed that the atoms of sodium and chlorine, when they combine chemically to make table salt, hold each other in place by occupying the corners of a cubical lattice. It had been deduced that in some hydrocarbons the carbon atoms form long, open chains, and in others they are linked, six at a time, in closed rings.

These pictures of chemical structures had proved themselves to be powerful guides to discovery, particularly in the study of carbon-containing substances which run through all the processes of life. They had already made it possible to synthesize many new substances. Nothing was known however of the forces which are presumably at work when atoms are held together in such stable structures.

Scientists recognized of course that the physical world does not consist simply of matter but also of forces between the pieces of matter and of radiations which pass from one piece of matter to another. Of the known forces the most important historically remained the force of gravitation which Isaac Newton (1642–1727) had first conceived to spread from every piece of matter throughout all space. Newton had thereby with one stroke brought order and understanding into the motions of all the heavenly bodies, and his achievement seemed as supreme in 1890 as on the day that the *Principia* had been published, in 1687. Earlier in the nineteenth century, when the distant planet Uranus seemed not to be keeping time, the astronomers John Couch Adams (1819–92) in Britain and Urbain Jean Joseph Leverrier (1811–77) in France had calculated what lesser planet must be disturbing it. Working with no knowledge of one another and with nothing but pencil, paper and Newton's laws, each calculated where such a planet must be. And sure enough, when the great telescope at Berlin had been turned to the spot calculated by Leverrier, there had been Neptune clear to the eye, and spectacular in its vindication of Newton's laws.

Also known were the forces of electricity and of magnetism, and it was now established that each could induce the other. Moreover, James Clerk Maxwell (1831–79) in the 1860s had given theoretical reasons for believing that such a radiation as light might be an electromagnetic disturbance propagated through space. If this was so then electromagnetic disturbances might well create other forms of radiation which had not been detected hitherto, and the young Heinrich Rudolf Hertz (1857–94) had just produced new radiations of this kind; they later turned out to be the radio waves. New radiations were also detected in 1895 by Wilhelm Konrad von Röntgen (1845–1923) which came to be called X-rays. It was becoming clear that visible light covers only about an octave in the range of electromagnetic radiations, and that the range extends for many octaves on either side, up from the ultra-violet to the short X-rays, and down from the infra-red to the long radio waves.

The question remained as to what carries these electromagnetic radiations from one point to another. Sound was known to be a physical disturbance of the air; it is propagated in the air and it is the air which carries its waves from point to point, and indeed forms them. If the air is pumped out of a hollow glass ball no sound can cross it. Yet light still crosses it. What carries the light waves? And what carries the other electromagnetic radiations, of which light is only one waveband to which the human eye happens to be sensitive?

To this question the nineteenth century answered: the aether. This was the universal medium which scientists posited to carry the different radiations through space. Thus the aether was thought to carry light from the stars to us, and the warmth of the sun on which our lives depend. It had in fact to carry from place to place all that energy which is not directly transmitted by the movement of matter. To do this, however, it turned out that the aether as a transmitter of energy had to have extraordinary and in many ways contradictory properties quite unlike those of any known material. For this reason the aether was the outstanding puzzle to scientists at the end of the nineteenth century.[2, 3]

2. *Mathematics*

There had been striking extensions in the field of mathematics, the discipline upon which the physical sciences always leaned heavily and to which they owed much of their success. Although in Britain mathematics had been particularly concerned with problems relating to mechanics and physics, on the continent of Europe pure mathematics had reached new levels. The non-Euclidean geometries had been discovered. Rigorous methods had been found to discuss infinitesimal and infinite quantities. It had been shown that the distinction which the Greeks had known, between numbers which can be written as fractions and those which cannot, can be further refined; it is possible to give precise definitions of numbers, for example the ratio between the circumference of a circle and its diameter, which cannot be expressed by any algebraic equation at all. A whole field of work was opened in the study of new functions and the application to them of mathematical processes which hitherto had been confined to linear spaces. New methods had been found for attacking some of the beautiful problems in the theory of numbers.

To both the pure and the applied mathematician in the latter part of the nineteenth century, however, mathematics remained at bottom an affair of measurements and therefore of numbers. Their cast of mind might be epitomized by a remark attributed to the German mathematician L. Kronecker (1823–91): 'God made the whole numbers: everything else is the work of man.' The basic numbers, the whole numbers, were something that had to be taken for granted; they were, in a sense, God-given.[4]

3. *Biology*

The great upheaval in the nineteenth century had been in biology, as a result of the publication in 1859 of *The Origin of Species* by Charles Darwin (1809–82). Darwin's achievement was twofold. He marshalled a vast body of evidence supporting the theory that evolution had occurred, and he discovered a scientifically acceptable mechanism for its occurrence.

The argument for evolution was reinforced by the discovery at about the same time of the unit common to all living forms, the cell. One living creature differs from another in the number of cells set aside for different uses and in the complexity of their organization. But, as Theodor Schwann (1810–82) established in 1839, all are built from cells, and basically therefore all can be pictured as different assemblies from the same units.

Darwin's development of the principle of natural selection was as important for biology as were Newton's *Principia* for mechanics and astronomy, though in a different way. It made the variety and development of life scientifically comprehensible. All organisms are variable, and some of the variation is heritable. Artificial selection by man can accumulate desirable heritable variations to produce new breeds. In nature there is overproduction of off-spring, and therefore a struggle for existence.[5, 6] Individuals with favourable heritable variations will tend to survive in greater numbers. A species can therefore change gradually in the course of generations. Darwin called this principle of the differential survival and reproduction of favourable heritable variations natural selection.

The weakness of Darwin's theory of evolution by natural selection lay in the absence of a science of genetics—the mechanism by which variations arise and heritable characteristics, including new variations, are transmitted.[7]

The nineteenth century had discovered that all existing life arises from pre-existing life—i.e. that life is self-reproducing matter; that most known forms of life consist of cells containing an organized nucleus; that most growth entails the division of cells, including the accurate division of the nuclear system; that reproduction in single-celled organisms is by division of cells, in multicellular organisms by detached single cells or groups of cells.

In sexual reproduction the nuclei of two detached single cells unite. But it was still widely believed that this involved some sort of blending or fusion of whatever was transmitted. If so, the offspring of a cross would become pro-gressively less differentiated and heritable variations would tend to disappear. This dilemma was not recognized as having been resolved until after 1900. Meantime, however, granted the undoubted fact that variations do occur and that some are heritable, natural selection remained a valid principle. Much of later nineteenth-century biology was devoted to reinterpreting biological facts in its light.

Classification, comparative anatomy, embryology and other old divisions of biology became transformed by the hypothesis of evolution. But the impact of Darwin's work was far more extensive than within the limits of the old biology itself. Perhaps no single discovery since Copernicus produced an impact of such force as did Darwin's on all those fields of science and philo-sophy which touched on the position of man in the universe. Recognition of the fact that man is subject to the same biological laws as other organisms and can no longer consider himself biologically apart from them led not only to the breakdown of old religious beliefs but also to the development of new philosophical doctrines and to many new psychological insights.

4. *Social sciences*

The social sciences in their empirical form had hardly come into being by the 1890s. The French philosopher Auguste Comte (1798–1857) had insisted that the positive method of thought which characterized the natural sciences was the highest stage of human reason and must be applied to human behaviour through the scientific study of sociology. But although his positivist principles gained wide popularity they produced few attempts to determine the workings of society from examination of the social data which were begin-ning to be accumulated. The careful collection and objective scrutiny of evidence in the social field had been carried furthest by the school of scientific historians which had been developed in the German universities and had spread thence through Europe and America. Anthropologists had only begun to analyse systematically the observations of the customs of primitive peoples recorded by travellers, missionaries and colonial administrators and had not developed their own techniques for observing these fast-disappearing social forms.[8] The first attempt to survey social life in a modern city, Charles Booth's *Life and Labour in London,* was undertaken in 1890.[9]

A considerable body of social theory had however been formulated in the effort to describe and predict social phenomena. Economic theory purporting to explain economic behaviour under conditions of competitive capitalism had been elaborated during the nineteenth century on the foundation laid by Adam Smith's *Wealth of Nations* (1776) and the eighteenth-century assumption that human motivation is rational. Economists on the European continent and in America built up a picture of the operation of an economy governed by the law of supply and demand, where the essence of economic relationships is an exchange in which each seeks to maximize his advantage and minimize his cost, and in which supply and demand are equated by a flexible price; they developed a system of mathematical equations in which to express the totality of these economic relationships. In this view of society, which provided the rationale for a *laissez-faire* policy on the part of government, self-seeking by each individual would furnish the motive power for the economy, bring continuous economic progress and convert the advantage of each into the good of all.

An alternative body of theory, developed by Karl Marx (1818–83), arrived at a different estimate of the results of self-seeking in a capitalist economy. Focusing his attention on the process of production and the relation of employer and employed in the factory system, he saw capitalism leading, not to continuous economic progress, but to progressive disparity between the capitalist exploiter and proletarian worker and to successively severe economic crises. Following on the one hand the German philosopher Georg Wilhelm Friedrich Hegel (1770–1831), who viewed historical development as a dialectical process of struggling opposites which he saw as the self-deploying of the World Spirit, and taking on the other hand the view that not spiritual but material factors are dominant to human motivation, Marx formulated dialectical materialism as a concept of historic development and predicted that class struggle will lead to eventual revolution and the ultimate creation of a classless society.[10]

Other social theorists applied the theory of evolution to the analysis of society. In the hands of Herbert Spencer (1820–1903) the concept of the survival of the fittest reinforced the conclusions of the *laissez-faire* economists and justified the position of those individuals or peoples who rose to wealth and power in the competitive struggle. Anthropologists assumed that societies passed through stages of evolution from lower to higher states and that primitive societies were survivals from states through which more advanced societies had already passed.

The alternative formulations of the nature of society had in common an assumption of progress, whether through the process of competition, dialectical materialism or evolution from lower to higher stages of civilization.

With respect to the psychology and behaviour of individuals much of the evidence on which theories were based had been drawn from the introspection of philosophers. The concept of the human organism as a mechanism which responded to stimuli, borrowed from the mechanistic conceptions of the physical sciences, led Wilhelm Wundt (1832–1920) at Leipzig and his pupils in Europe and America to undertake psychological studies of stimuli and response in an experimental approach to the understanding of human behaviour. On the further assumption that physical differences were associated with qualities of character, intelligence and higher or lower development, some sociologists attempted to establish the existence of criminal types and physical anthropologists looked for evidence of racial characteristics. The French sociologist Émile Durkheim (1858–1917) made a beginning in the 1890s toward the study of group psychology by examining the process by which the interactions of individual consciousnesses produce syntheses in the form of religious beliefs or value judgments that carry authority because of their collective character.

II. THE OUTLOOK BEFORE 1900

Underlying scientific knowledge and thought in all areas ran several strong common assumptions. Almost all thought conformed to four basic preconceptions, or unspoken ways of looking at nature, which at once reflected and directed the thought of the age.

First was the principle that nature proceeds by a strict chain of events from cause to effect, the configuration of causes at any instant fully determining the events in the next instant, and so on for ever. This principle of determinism, of cause and effect, left no uncertainty in nature.

Apparent uncertainty was presumed to be the reflection of ignorance; if there were full knowledge, it would always be possible to predict the future precisely. This had been said explicitly by the French mathematician Pierre Simon Laplace (1749–1827) in a famous passage. If we were given, said Laplace, the whereabouts and the speeds at this instant of every atom in the universe, then we should be able to forecast their whereabouts and speeds at every instant afterwards. We could therefore predict without the smallest uncertainty the fate of the entire universe, its molecules and its men, its nebulae and its nations, from now into eternity. Indeed we could do more than this, because we could go backward in time as well as forward and reconstruct the past also to eternity.[11]

With the principle of determinism was coupled a second principle which

Incidental antiproton

Antineutron invisible to chamber

π^+

π^-

π^+

π^+

FIG. 1. The particle of interest is an antineutron. The antiproton enters from the top and proceeds for a short distance. Its path is seen to stop abruptly. At this point the antiproton collides with an ordinary proton producing a neutron and an antineutron both of which are invisible to the bubble chamber as they have no charge. However, the antineutron makes itself known by annihilating with another nucleon in the lower centre of the picture. The annihilation produces 5π mesons with an energy greater than 1,500 million electron volts. (See Plate 1a opposite.)

[*California U.*

(b) *Atomic explosion, Los Alamos, July 16, 1945, 15 seconds after detonation*

[*Los Alamos*

⊢——⊣ 100 METERS

[MWP　　(a)

2　ASTRONOMY I

(a) *200-inch Hale telescope pointing to the zenith; seen from the East*

(b) *60-foot radio telescope, Agassiz Station, Harvard University*

(b)

[HARVARD

(a)   [MWP

3   ASTRONOMY II

(a) *Galaxy NGC 5194–5 photographed by the 200-inch Hale telescope*

(b) *The hidden side of the moon photographed by Lunik III, 1959*

(b)

[USSR *Academy*

Leiden

4   MICROSCOPY I

(a) *Optical microscope, Zeiss-Winkel*, 1954

(b) *Electron microscope, Philips EM* 200, c. 1960

(a)

(b)

[Philips-Ind.

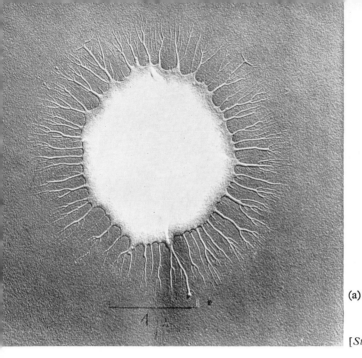

(a)

[*Strasbourg*

5   MICROSCOPY II

(a) *Particle of DNA made up of a large number of molecules which when submitted to the action of water vapour flow out into branches comprising a very small number of DNA chains; enlarged about 33,000 times. (Photo by Dr R. Vendrely and Mme S. Steiner)*

(b) *Bacteriophages (streptomyces griseus phage); enlarged about 60,000 times*

(b

[*Delviljem*

Report from IBM Yorktown Research Center, New York

OPTIMUM CONTROL OF DYNAMIC SYSTEMS

A dynamic system is one whose present output depends not only on the present value of the input but also on its past history. To maintain the output as close as possible to a set of desired values, the input is generated from a knowledge of this history as expressed by the state of the system, which must be constantly monitored, and the input-output relationships.

Since the contribution of random disturbances and the effect of the monitoring process itself cannot be precisely determined, statistical procedures must often be relied upon. The difficulties owing simply to the large number of interrelationships involved are magnified in practical cases by the need to perform calculations in real time and to take into account the cost of the control effort. A group of scientists and engineers at the IBM Yorktown Research Center are trying to make this problem manageable through work in stability theory and the development of analytical techniques that take full advantage of the capabilities of digital computers.

The group has employed the Second Method of Lyapunov (a 19th Century Russian mathematician) to distill the necessary and sufficient conditions for the control of certain classes of nonlinear systems. The virtue of this method is that it allows properties of a solution to be studied from the structure of the differential equation, independent of particular solutions. The aim is to set up a scalar function over the state space so that the energy along each solution decreases. This assures that the system—linear or nonlinear—is globally stable.

Members of the group have demonstrated the unifying effect of working directly in the time domain. They have also attempted to simplify the computation through dynamic programming—a technique for solving multistage problems one stage at a time, successively embedding each solution into the next more general solution. The next step is to bring together the various results in a theory of self-optimizing control systems.

IBM. RESEARCH

Investigate the many career opportunities available in exciting new fields at IBM.
International Business Machines Corporation, Dept. 000, 590 Madison Avenue, New York 22, New York

[IBM

expressed the exact spirit of science: the quantitative principle. According to this principle science consists of measuring things and setting up precise relations between the measurements. Lord Rayleigh (1842–1919) expressed this in another famous passage by saying that our ideas become clear only as they become quantitative, so that only that which is measurable is susceptible to scientific, and indeed to exact, discussion and can truly be described as knowledge. On this view nature should ultimately be described by numbers— co-ordinates in space, times of events and coefficients which describe physical properties; and knowledge of nature advances by working out the relations between these numbers.[12]

The third underlying principle, which concerned the transitions of nature from one state to another, was the principle of continuity. It expressed the sense, deeply engrained in the outlook of the age, that the movements of nature are gradual. They may seem sudden and startling—a flash of lightning, an explosion, the eruption of a volcano. But the suddenness, said the scientific thought of the time, is only apparent.

To the nineteenth-century mind the processes of nature move imperceptibly from instant to instant. Between any two instants there is another, shorter instant; between any two positions there is an intermediate position. If any sequence seems abrupt or inexplicable it is only necessary to divide it into smaller sections. And the division could be carried on for ever; the processes of nature are infinitely fine and continuous.[13]

With these the nineteenth century pictured in nature and in science a fourth principle: the principle of impersonality. The scientist saw himself not as a person but as an instrument—passionless, unprejudiced and somehow more than human. Nature appeared as a great impersonal machine, going on its imperturbable way, which the human observer could only peek at. And the process of watching this wonderful engine was conceived as a passive one. The scientist did not invent, he saw. He did not use his imagination, but his obser-vation. He did not create order among the natural phenomena; he humbly found it. Even viewing himself as an instrument, he did not recognize any interaction between that particular instrument and the phenomena under observation.[14]

In this way the nineteenth-century scientist cut himself off from the imaginative and the creative arts. Determinism, measurement, continuity and impersonality were parts of one vision: the vision of science as remote from the uncertainties and stresses of everyday life.

III. THE REVOLUTIONARY DISCOVERIES

Around the turn of the century the facts of scientific discovery compelled scientists to give up this vision of science and the outlook on nature which it embodied. A number of discoveries were made and a number of irregularities were confirmed which could no longer be squared with the principles which underlay the accepted scientific theories. As scientists faced the implications of the new discoveries they developed a fundamentally new view of nature and of scientific activity.

1. *Physical sciences*

In the physical sciences, which had seemed so near to completion, there turned out to be range upon range of new facts and concepts beyond the edge which had appeared to place a limit to further progress. The view of nature since 1900 which physics revealed was richer and wider than the nineteenth century dreamt, and did more than the speculations of philosophers to change the outlook of the century.

(a) *The structure of the atom.* The fundamental unit of matter, the supposedly indivisible atom, was found to have structure and parts.

The discovery came from experiments in the passage of electric current through gases at low pressure which gives rise, roughly, to the phenomenon seen in neon lighting. In this phenomenon electricity streams from the cathode down the tube.

The unsolved problem of the time was whether the rays of electricity streaming down the tube are mere waves of electricity or are particles. In 1897 Joseph John Thomson (1856–1940) proved conclusively what others had already almost proved, that the cathode rays are particles, and he showed that they must be more than a thousand times lighter than the lightest atom. Moreover he showed that their behaviour was the same whatever gas he had in the tube and whatever metal he used for cathode.

Thomson had discovered the electron within the supposedly indivisible atom. Later, Thomson's pupils, led by Ernest Rutherford (1871–1937), found the structural relation of the parts to one another. They proved that the electrons spin in a cloud of orbits round the heavy kernel or nucleus of the atom. In particular, Niels Bohr (1885–   ) showed that the leap of an electron from one orbit into another always releases the same quantity of energy; and he thereby brought the new quantum physics into the understanding of atomic structure.

The nucleus still seemed indivisible, but Henri Becquerel (1852–1908) in 1896 had already shown that some atoms could change their chemical nature, spontaneously and without known cause. He and others after him, including Madame Marie Curie (1867–1934), discovered radioactivity, essentially the breaking up of a nucleus.

Later physicists who focused their attention on the nucleus finally established the possibility of fission in the atom. Until 1932 it was constantly supposed that if the nucleus had parts, the parts would be electric charges. In that year however James Chadwick (1891–   ) showed that the evidence pointed conclusively to the existence of some part of the nucleus which is electrically neutral; and there emerged the modern picture of the nucleus as made up of two kinds of fundamental particles, positive protons and neutral neutrons, held together by an unexplained binding energy.

The discovery of the neutron provided a particle which could bombard the nucleus without being driven back by electrical repulsion. It thus became conceivable that the nucleus could be entered, made unstable and so caused to release its enormous binding energy. Such an action, if it released further neutrons, could be self-propagating. And so it turned out. In 1938 the German physicists Otto Hahn (1879–   ) and Fritz Strassmann (1902–   ) proved that such fission can take place in atomic variants or isotopes of uranium. The structure of the once indivisible atom could not only be described; it could be destroyed.

(b) *Relativity*. Space and time, which in the Newtonian system had been assumed to be absolute, were found to be relative. This revolutionary discovery was made in the effort to resolve discrepancies between observation and theory, particularly questions raised by the peculiar characteristics of light which became evident through efforts to determine the character of the aether, and by observations which showed a relation between mass and energy.

The new set of unit particles that entered into physics with the discovery of the electron gave some ground for thinking that all matter might be a configuration of electric charges. J. J. Thomson, who had long worked at the mathematics of this theory, had already shown in 1881 that a moving electric charge would appear to have mass. Now the fast-moving electrons were found to change their mass with their speed, and a relation between mass and energy began to seem probable.

But energy should surely be carried by a medium. The puzzle remained, how to detect this all-pervading medium, the aether. An experiment had been devised by Albert Abraham Michelson (1853–1931) and Edward Williams Morley (1838–1923) in 1887 which should have made it reveal its presence. Michelson and Morley argued that if the aether were a medium which carried waves of light as the air carries sound or the sea water waves, it should be possible to detect the passage of the earth through the aether and thereby throw light on the character of the aether itself. For example, if a ship is moving on a calm sea, the ripples it sends out seem, from the ship, to travel along the line of the ship's movement at a different speed from that at which they travel at right angles to the line of movement. These differences can be used to calculate the speed of the ship through the sea; and Michelson and Morley expected to calculate the speed of the earth through the aether by a refinement of this method.

Alas, light obstinately insisted on travelling at the same speed, in whatever direction it was sent into the aether and regardless of the motion of the source of light. That is, light covered a given distance across the earth's surface in the same time, regardless of how fast or in what direction the earthly object which was sending out the light was moving. The speed of light was found to be absolute; it did not behave as did other speeds such as sound or water waves, which are affected by how the sender is moving through the medium—air or water—which carries them.

This sensational misbehaviour was a scandal to classical science for several years. Eminent physicists such as George Francis Fitzgerald (1851–1901) and eminent mathematicians such as Henri Poincaré (1854–1912) proposed various corrections including ones which would have the effect of cancelling out the speed of the earth through the aether. But though Poincaré went far toward a reformulation it was left to a young man of 26, Albert Einstein (1879–1955), to publish in 1905 a paper which put the matter into natural perspective.

Einstein looked for no minute error of formulation in the laws of physics, and for no ingenious device to correct them. Instead he followed a philosophical procedure first proposed by the Austrian physicist Ernst Mach (1838–1916). He set himself to look at the unwritten assumptions on which the laws themselves were built and asked whether it might not be there that the flaw in the physics of the nineteenth century was hidden.

The unwritten assumption which he challenged was that space and time are given to us absolutely. That this was no more than an assumption had been clear to Isaac Newton when he himself had made his great discoveries as a young man of 23, but the lesser scientists who followed him had rarely spared it a thought. They accepted space and time as boxes provided by nature ready-made, within which the events we observe take place.

But, asked Einstein, are space and time given to us ready-made? How does the physical observer carry out the process of measuring them? For example, how do two observers at a distance apart compare their times? They can do so, he noted, only by sending a signal from one to the other, and the signal itself takes time to travel through the space between them. The signal, in fact, is a ray of light or a similar electromagnetic wave or disturbance, and its speed cannot be taken out of the measurement. It follows that there is no abstract and impersonal way in which we can define 'now' for all observers everywhere at once. Every observer has only his own 'here and now'. In our experience of the physical world, space and time cannot be wholly separated from one another; each is part of a single reality. And the passage of light signals from one point of space to another is the essential link between the time at the two points.

With this analysis, which constitutes the Special Theory of Relativity, Einstein solved the paradox of the experiment by Michelson and Morley once and for all.[15] His view remained fundamental to physics from the time of the publication of his paper.

Moreover, once space and time were related, as Einstein related them, by light-signals, mass and energy were also related. Einstein showed in the same paper that his theory of relativity implied a fundamental equivalence between mass and energy. The relation between them could be expressed by an equation which involves the velocity of light as a fundamental constant; each particle of matter represents an energy which can be measured by the product of its mass with the square of the velocity of light, $E = mc^2$. Mass and energy were thus seen to be two different ways of experiencing a single reality.

(c) *The quantum.* Energy, which the nineteenth century had assumed to be continuous and infinitely divisible, was discovered to consist of discrete units which could not be subdivided.

In the nineteenth century matter had been thought to consist of separate atoms but energy was thought to be passed from one piece of matter to another continuously. That is, it was assumed that we can transfer as small an amount of energy as we please from one piece of matter to another. Unlike matter energy was assumed to be capable of being divided and divided again into smaller and smaller quantities, without limit, for ever.

There were however some phenomena in the radiation of energy from a hot body which obstinately did not fit into this scheme. Mathematicians were puzzled but no one had thought of challenging the fundamental assumption. Then in 1899 the theoretical physicist Max Planck (1858–1947) did so— diffidently, but with startling consequences. He showed that the distribution of energy which goes into the different wavelengths when a hot body is radiating could be explained, and perfectly explained, but only on a different assumption.

We must, said Planck, assume that the energy is sent out piecemeal, in individual flashes, as it were unit by unit; that it does not ripple away from the radiating body continuously but goes out like a stream of bullets. The bullets, the pieces, are indeed very small but—and this is the crux of the explanation —their size for any one wavelength is fixed; they cannot be further subdivided. On any one wavelength, energy can be transferred only in units of one fixed quantity. Planck called this minimum quantity a quantum.

Max Planck was aware that his explanation broke radically with classical physics. Yet he remained loath to press forward to the full implications of what he had done. That was left to younger physicists, among whom one of the boldest was again Albert Einstein. These younger men did not hesitate to say what Planck's discovery implied.

It implied that energy has a structure, a certain graininess or coarseness, rather as matter has. Just as matter can be broken down into its fundamental particles but no further, so energy can be broken down into quanta but no further. The quanta play somewhat the same part in the movement of energy that the fundamental particles—protons, neutrons and electrons—play in the arrangement of matter.

If this is so, Einstein reasoned, then radiation of one wavelength—say, the yellow light of sodium—must be made up of quanta which are all equal. When sodium atoms glow these equal quanta are fired off individually, as if they were in a sense particles of light. This view of light as a stream of separate particles or photons was singled out as one of Einstein's major contributions to physics when he was awarded the Nobel prize in 1921.

But a basic puzzle still remained: if light can be pictured as made up of separate particles, how does it come also to behave as if it moved in a wave? An answer to this question was given by Max Born (1882–   ) in the 1920s. The waves of light are waves of probability—waves which describe only where we are more and where we are less likely to find an individual photon at any instant. And if we fix our attention on an individual photon, its position at any instant can be described only by a probability; it is not determined but probable.[16]

2. *Mathematics*

These changes in the outlook of physics went hand in hand with new interests in mathematics. In one way the connection was obvious: the new physics needed new kinds of mathematics. But in another way the connection was more subtle. It was as if mathematicians and physicists, often without knowing of one another's thoughts, came to be interested at the same time in the study of such subjects as discontinuity and probability. Pure mathematicians who were quite divorced from physics often seemed to have worked out a technique even before physicists needed it. By contrast, where mathematics was closely tied to physics, as in Britain, mathematicians often did not develop in advance the techniques necessary to express the revolutionary new ideas in physics.

(a) *The statistical approach.* Although the study of probability and of mathematical statistics had started in the Renaissance when problems of insurance and of gambling were first posed, it was only about the year 1900 that the central and critical concepts in statistical reasoning began to be laid bare. These rested jointly on the mathematics of reasoning about probabilities developed in the eighteenth century and on the theory of the distribution of errors of observation worked out by Carl Friedrich Gauss (1777–1855) at the beginning of the nineteenth century.

The essence of statistical reasoning, as developed by Andrei Andreevich Markov (1856–1922) and A. Liapunov (1857–1918) and others in Russia and by Karl Pearson (1857–1936) and, later, Ronald Aylmer Fisher (1890–   ) in Britain, was that it did not deal with clear-cut and self-evident issues, black versus white. It dealt with phenomena which may be described, and often may be explained, in a number of different ways, where therefore it is necessary to make a judgment and choose the description or explanation which seems to fit the evidence best. What mathematical statistics could do was not to take the place of such judgments, but to provide tools to help in restricting the area of judgment and in guiding the judgments by furnishing a quantitative basis, consistent from one occasion to another.

Statistical reasoning was unnecessary to describe and explain clear-cut phenomena such as the force of gravitation. It does not require statistical reasoning to demonstrate that a piece of matter will fall to the ground if it is dropped, nor to establish convincingly that the force of gravitation which is postulated to explain this effect will also explain the movements of the moon and of the planets. The phenomena and the explanations are clear-cut, they can be formulated in precise equations, and as soon as this had been done by Isaac Newton the agreement between observation and explanation was seen to be self-evident.

In a less clear-cut issue, for example the effectiveness of a drug, the situation is very different. Every experiment designed to determine the drug's effectiveness is overlaid by unavoidable and substantial variations: patients are in many stages of a disease; their response is inevitably affected by many factors in their general health and physical condition.

Statistical techniques offer a way to extract positive results in a variable field such as this. In essence they ask how often the result which has been found might have been obtained by mere chance. By calculating this they make it possible to distinguish between observed results which might have occurred by chance and those which show a degree of consistency which would be unlikely to arise from chance and which may therefore be presumed to be related to the influence whose effect is being studied.

The statistical approach is essentially simple in conception. At bottom it divides observed phenomena into two parts, those which are random, attributable to chance, and those which are systematic, representing an effect. That is, the statistical approach recognizes that an effect can be isolated only to a certain degree of accuracy and that in order to determine whether an effect is real it is necessary to compare its area of uncertainty with the accuracy to which it can be measured. The effect must be judged relative to the error to which the estimate is liable. If the effect stands out plainly above the error, the result may be considered significant. But if the effect turns out not to be large when compared with the inherent errors of measurement, then it has not been established as significant. It may in fact exist but its area of uncertainty is too large to permit such a conclusion. The only hope then is to assemble more observations until they reduce the area of uncertainty to a point where the conclusion, though still not free from uncertainty, becomes useful.

(b) *New concepts of structure*. Mathematicians about the year 1900 came to take a new interest in problems of relation and of structure. The statistical approach embodied a less rigid and in some ways a more subtle and elaborate sense of the relation between events than was expressed in the nineteenth-century conviction that everything could be said by a few precise numbers. Mathematicians showed a growing interest in logical connections and in the general relations which could be pictured geometrically.

An important school of modern geometry was created in Italy, largely by the inspiration of Corrado Segre (1863–1924). Beginning from the neglected work of such German pioneers as Hermann Grassmann (1809–77), it explored the properties of non-Euclidean spaces and, later, the algebraic functions which can be constructed in them.[17, 18]

Other geometers took the liberation from the restrictions of Euclidean space even further. Led by Henri Poincaré, among others, they began to investigate the most general movements by which one geometrical figure can be distorted to the shape of another—by which the closed surface of a cube can be stretched to fit the surface of a sphere, but cannot in any way be stretched to fit the surface of a ring. This subsequently became the subject of topology and proved one of the richest fields in modern mathematics.

At the same time the local and smaller-scale properties of non-Euclidean constructs were studied, under the inspiration of the work of Georg Friedrich Bernhard Riemann (1826–66).[19, 20] From this work there developed a wider form of the differential calculus which later turned out to be essential for the mathematics of relativity.

In this and other extensions of traditional mathematics there was evolved a new basic concept: the concept of the operation. It caused mathematics to be regarded not as a set of numbers held together by equations but as a set of structures turned into one another by operations. Attention shifted, for example, from the differential coefficient as a measure to the operation of differentiation as a process. The mathematician came to see himself actively, as a man who carries out new operations.

(c) *Logic and mathematics.* The basic assumption of mathematics, that the whole numbers are God-given and things in themselves, was subjected to the same kind of scrutiny as was the physicist's assumption that space and time are absolutes. Mathematicians at the turn of the century began to recognize that the whole numbers describe relations between things. As space and time describe physical relations, numbers describe logical relations; the number 2, for example, describes some logical relation common to all the pairs of things that can be imagined. They saw that numbers would have to be worked out and defined, from the ground up, as relations. Giuseppe Peano (1858–1932) and others set out about 1900 to formulate such logical definitions for numbers, and more generally for the operations of arithmetic. Alfred North Whitehead (1861–1947) and Bertrand Russell (1872–   ) went further and tried from these beginnings to establish all mathematics as a formal expression of logical relations.

In the course of this work Whitehead and Russell uncovered some unexpected assumptions in the very foundations of mathematics. At the same time they showed that the symbolic expression of thought, either in language or in other symbols, requires much subtler analysis than had been given it hitherto. Much of the philosophical analysis of the twentieth century, and particularly the philosophical movement begun by Russell's pupil Ludwig Wittgenstein (1889–1951), was set in motion by these discoveries in the semantics of all symbolic forms of expression.

Among the difficulties which Whitehead and Russell did not resolve, however, was the searching question posed by the mathematician David Hilbert (1862–1943): is it really self-evident, is it even true, that when a system of axioms such as that of Euclid has been set up, every true proposition can be proved from the axioms and every false proposition can be disproved? Is it not possible that there are propositions which can neither be proved nor disproved in a finite number of steps?

In 1931 Kurt Gödel (1906–   ) showed that it is indeed possible. Any logical body of mathematical thought which has an axiomatic basis rich enough, in a technical sense, to permit the formulation of significant statements and questions also turns out to be rich enough to permit the asking of questions which are unanswerable within the system. These questions are unanswerable, not for the practical reason that they are too difficult; they are theoretically unanswerable.

This finding opened a chasm in the very foundation of mathematics—the assumption that all the propositions in a system of mathematics either follow from or contradict its axioms. It dealt the notion of truth and falsehood a severe shock, for truth can no longer be based on mere formal consistency ii there are propositions which, within a given system, are neither true nor false in any effective sense. It undermined the method of developing science from a set of axioms but offered no alternative method. The full effects of this discovery would only appear as they spread outward from arithmetic and mathematics to the empirical sciences.

3. *Biology*

Advances in the biological sciences about the turn of the century seemed less radical than those in physics. Their consequences however were as far-reaching, and in the long run precipitated a change in outlook which was equally profound.

(*a*) *Genetics.* The problem which had been raised by evolution was the discovery of a mechanism of inheritance which could preserve variations between individuals, especially those which conferred a biological advantage on those members of a species in whom they had happened to occur. The great opening attack on this problem had in fact already been made by an Austrian monk, Gregor Mendel (1822–84), who before the end of the nineteenth century had carried out a thoughtful series of experiments in the breeding of plants, chiefly peas. The significance of these experiments was not appreciated even by those who knew of them. Certainly they were at variance with the deepest preconceptions of his contemporaries.

About the year 1900 Mendel's papers attracted the attention simultaneously of a number of biologists who were interested in heredity. Several of these biologists perceived that Mendel's work gave a radically new view of inheritance and laid the groundwork for the new study which would make it possible to understand how evolution had been able to fix advantageous strains and to form new species.

The mechanism of inheritance which Mendel conceived was very simple—and there is evidence that he had conceived it on theoretical grounds even before he put it to the test of experiment. In Mendel's view such a trait as, for example, the colour of the peas which he studied in his monastery garden is fixed by a pair of factors, later called genes, one inherited from each parent. If both genes in the pair are the same, of the type which causes the pea to be green or that which causes it to be yellow, then the pea will indeed be green or yellow. But if one gene is of one type and one of another, then the colour of the pea is determined by whichever type is dominant, in this case the gene for green colour, and not by the type which is recessive, in this case the gene for yellow colour.

The biological difference between a green pea which has both genes of the same kind and a green pea which has a dominant green and a recessive yellow gene, Mendel pointed out, lies in the ability of the second pea to hand on the recessive gene to the next generation. Since only one of the pair of genes is contained in the reproductive cell, the pea will hand on the gene for green to half its descendants and yellow to the other half. If the pea is crossed with a green pea which also happens to possess genes of both kinds, a quarter of the descendants will, by chance, receive yellow genes from both parents and these peas will be yellow although both parents are green.

Here, then, is a mechanism which does not average the variations of individuals. Once a genetic difference has been established in an individual, this mechanism will preserve it. The difference might spring only from a recessive gene, and this might remain submerged in the population for many generations. But it would continue to be handed on from generation to generation, and now and again it would reappear in the mating of individuals both of whom happened to carry the same recessive gene.

One question had still to be answered in order to elucidate the working of evolution: are all genes already present in a population or can new genes appear in it? And can genes alter or be altered? A preliminary answer to this question was made about 1900 by Hugo de Vries (1848–1935), who demonstrated that certain plant deviants or sports bred true. His studies indicated that the hereditary constitution does change from time to time, and he named the spontaneous change mutation, although subsequent investigations found that the phenomena which he had observed did not constitute true genetic mutations. Later, other workers demonstrated and analysed other types of mutation which provided specific gene change. Thus not only are the determinants of heredity that are already present constantly being shuffled, but also new forms of determinants are continually appearing. The ever-varying combinations of old and new determinants generally affect the reproductive success of their bearers. They are, then, the material on which natural selection operates, with directive evolution and adaptation as a result.[21]

(b) *The nature of living matter.* The origin and character of life has always interested some biologists. Study of chemical characteristics and reactions in the organism focused the pursuit of this question on the chemical and other features which affect the growth and behaviour of cells, and launched the new twentieth-century science of biochemistry.

The discovery of the mechanism of inheritance in the genes was consolidated by the study of the structure and division of plant and animal cells. It was shown that cells contain microscopic structures which are string-like and which, because they can be stained, were called chromosomes. These chromosomes lie in pairs in the cell, and divide when the cell divides. The position of the genes was located by breeding experiments and statistical methods; in addition, microscopic study showed dark spots in some chromosomes presumed to coincide with the presence of genes, though they were never regarded as genes made visible.

The chromosomes and the genes on them appeared to be complex chemicals. It was found that they can be altered by strong chemical or physical action—by irradiation with X-rays, for example, or treatment with mustard-gas. If chromosomes in the reproductive cells have been altered in this way, then the offspring will show differences which can be inherited from one generation to another.[22] Thus microscopic chemical structures in the sperms and ova were seen profoundly to affect the living creature which grows from them, not merely for one generation but for many. In addition, from other points of view, much study was given to those points of a fertile ovum from which the specific organs of the full-grown animal take their beginnings, and to the chemical stimuli which can direct and change their growth.

New speculation on the possible transition from dead matter to living being was stimulated in the 1920s by the study of viruses.[23] Some plant diseases, for example of the tobacco plant, were found to be induced not by bacteria but by simpler structures. These structures can be isolated from the plant and in that state can be crystallized as chemicals. The crystals are in themselves quite inactive when isolated; yet when they are brought into contact with a healthy tobacco plant the plant becomes diseased. When an infective agent of this kind, called a virus, was first identified it seemed to some to stand on the threshold between dead and living matter, with a foot in each.

But the viruses turned out to be more complicated than was first thought. It became fairly clear that they are not independent agents, and that they are multiplied as a result of the altered metabolism of the host plant. In the presence of its host, the tobacco plant, the dead chemical becomes active; it deflects the host's metabolism in such a way that more virus is produced, and a disease results which spreads over the leaves of the plant.

Nevertheless there was evidence that the activity of the viruses does reside in their chemical structure. Moreover the chemical structure of the viruses was found to bear a likeness to that postulated for the genes which influence the development of living cells. Many biochemists hoped to find in the chemistry of the viruses a bridge across which dead matter steps to life.

If a living thing is defined as one that is capable of reproducing itself in the same form, the problem is to find a mechanism which shall give a chemical arrangement of atoms this property of copying itself.

Toward the middle of the twentieth century a possible mechanism was identified by which a chemical could copy itself and ensure that the copy would match the original. It was shown that some of the important constituents of living cells are chemicals, nucleoproteins, whose atoms are arranged in a special form. F. H. C. Crick (1916–   ) and J. D. Watson (1928–   ) showed that a fundamental unit in these, deoxyribose nucleic acid (DNA) has a molecule which consists of two spirals each made up of a string of atoms. These two strings of atoms match one another and are joined by crosslinks in such a way that the two spirals wind in and out of one another.

Many chemists believed that this is a form peculiarly adapted to copying itself. If one spiral should break away from the other, new atoms could join on to each spiral only at the places where they were found on the other spiral. In this way each spiral could induce the formation of another spiral of the same kind, linked to it at the right places. This chemical structure was recognized as holding a possible key to the problem of life.

It was of additional interest because it was seen to play a role in the heredity of widely diverse organisms. A number of other chemical substances proved also to be indispensable in the vital processes of very different organisms; vitamins for instance were shown to be as important in the metabolism of bacteria as in that of man. The chemical bonds of one particular molecule, adenosine triphosphate (ATP), were discovered to be responsible for the transfer and utilization of energy in all life processes. A particular class of compounds known as enzymes, primarily protein in constitution, were shown to be the prime regulators in many biological processes.

Thus features of organisms became apparent which substantiated at a biological level the hypothesis that all organisms are related to one another. But the biochemists of the first half of the twentieth century did not confine themselves to the mere confirmation of the evolution hypothesis. They went far towards explaining many varied and important vital phenomena in molecular terms, and thus made great strides in bringing to biology the same standards of accuracy and objectivity which had characterized the more exact physical sciences for a long time. In doing this they gave further ground for the growing conviction that all living processes, those of the mind as well as those of the body, can be traced back to material causes.[24, 25]

4. Social sciences

In the long run the visible and explicit changes in the conditions of life brought by the physical sciences might not prove to be the most important. For the twentieth century began to explore the minds and social behaviour of people. The practical effects of these pioneer studies did not leap to the eye. Yet they might lead to an understanding of man which in time would change the foundations of civilization.

(a) *Learning and conditioning*. The manner in which learning takes place had long been the subject of speculation and of educational theory. In the eighteenth century the philosopher David Hartley (1705-57) had singled out association as an important process in human thought.

About the year 1900 the Russian scientist Ivan Pavlov (1849-1936) began a long study of association in animals. He developed a technique for associating one stimulus with another and measuring the response when either of the stimuli was present. For example he associated the stimulus of ringing a bell with the stimulus provided by presenting the experimental animal with food. The response to the food could be measured by the amount of saliva produced. After a number of repetitions the animal came to associate the ringing of the bell with food and to produce saliva when the bell was rung, even if no food was presented. The action by which an animal salivates at the sight of food is automatic, a natural reflex. Pavlov called the action by which it comes to salivate at the sound of the customary bell a conditioned reflex.

He made a detailed study of conditioned reflexes: how they are formed, how they can then be inhibited and even destroyed, how they can once again be revived. On this study he based an interpretation of all animal and human habits, which he conceived as an elaborately linked array of conditioned reflexes. His work was of great importance in showing empirically that association enters deeply into behaviour.

Later studies covering areas which Pavlov did not explore found that the process of learning, in animals and in man, is more varied and more subtle than he supposed. Studies of animal behaviour by Konrad Lorenz (1903–), N. Tinbergen (1907–) and others brought out the role of instincts in the learning process and the variety and richness of symbolic stimuli to which animals respond, and offered new insights from observation of animals in their native environments where they were not limited by controlled laboratory conditions. The importance of exploratory behaviour of children and animals as a first condition of learning was also established. Whereas Pavlov's work tended to foster a purely behaviourist approach to individual psychology, other approaches made it clear that human responses are not developed in isolation one from the other, but in terms of a structure of relationships or *Gestalt*, built up in the mind.

(b) *Motivation*. No less far-reaching in implications for human behaviour were Sigmund Freud's (1856-1939) explorations into the drives and desires that lie below the surface of man's consciousness. As this Austrian physician studied his neurotic patients and sought ways to relieve their mental anguish, he traced many of their neuroses to suppressed desires which generally outraged the taboos of society and which grew out of experiences in early childhood. He assumed that normal people also possess these same desires but are able to repress them successfully or to canalize them into socially acceptable forms of behaviour.

On the basis of these observations Freud developed a theory as to the innate drives with which each individual is born, especially the impulse to love and to be loved, and of the manner in which these drives work themselves out during his growth and development. He formulated the concept of the unconscious as the repository of the desires which the individual suppresses as he acquires his sense of himself and his ability to conform to the norms of his society. Neurotic persons, he concluded, are those who have been unable to handle the process of repression successfully and whose unconscious is loaded with unmanageable desires which rise threateningly to the surface, or, often in disguised form, produce unacceptable behaviour. He developed the method of psychoanalysis as a tool of research and a means of treatment, to explore the nature of the suppressed experiences and desires and, in treatment, to bring them to the patient's consciousness in order that he might be helped to deal with them.

Freud's pioneer speculations had a profound effect on thinking men and women. His observations and theory destroyed both the eighteenth-century picture of man as a rational being with rationally motivated behaviour, and the mechanistic concept of the human organism as simply a series of responses to external stimuli. Other psychologists who followed gave prominence to other human drives in addition to those which Freud stressed. His analysis made only a start toward unravelling the complex processes in the life of the mind, conscious and unconscious, and in the formation of human personality. But Freud made men aware, inescapably, how much irrational forces and hidden motives lie behind human behaviour.[26]

(c) *Culture and race.* The new insights into man's individual motivation and behaviour were paralleled by new perspectives on his social forms which undermined the assumption that western civilization was a culminating stage in social evolution.

Interest in folklore and in the customs and arts of primitive peoples during the nineteenth century had resulted in numerous publications, such as the collections of folk tales by the brothers Jakob Ludwig Karl Grimm (1785–1863) and Wilhelm Karl Grimm (1786–1859), and in the establishment of ethnological museums. The classical scholar James G. Frazer (1854–1941), attempting to trace to its beginnings the classical story of the Golden Bough, had explored the legends of many nations and the rituals of many religions and had found evidences of similar practices such as symbolic magic and fertility rites among peoples widely distant in time and place. The publication of his accumulated materials in *The Golden Bough* (1890) had prompted the question: were these likenesses produced spontaneously, by a common mental process which all men share, or did they point to a single or a few centres of origin of human culture from which such practices had spread over the world?

Answers to these and related questions were sought in detailed studies of the surviving cultures of primitive peoples. Franz Boas (1858–1942) and his students studying the cultures of North American Indians and Bronislaw Malinowski (1884–1942), A. R. Radcliffe-Brown (1881–1955) and their associates studying island cultures in the Pacific and tribal cultures in Africa found great differences among peoples and yet likenesses also, in that all cultures, in one way or another, reflected common human needs. They found little evidence of the successive stages from lower to higher societies which the social evolutionists had projected, for social forms appeared in a great variety of combinations. Moreover some similarities, such as those which Frazer had noted, proved to have quite different meanings when seen in the context of a total culture. These studies made it apparent that all the social institutions, value systems and patterns of behaviour in any society are interrelated and that the culture must be seen as a whole if one would understand its parts and the people who are shaped by it and who pass it on to their children.

Franz Boas also cut the ground from under the assumptions of racial superiority by his study of the *Mind of Primitive Man* (1901) in which he found that the mental processes and capacities of the primitive Indians whom he studied were comparable to those of civilized men, differing only in the cultural experience and norms to which the processes were applied. His observations were reinforced by the persistent failure of efforts to link mental capacity with physical characteristics.

The anthropologists' findings on culture and race were not fully accepted until political events changed the balance of world power and forced those who had assumed that they belonged to a superior culture and race to reassess themselves and their cultures. They did however provide a basis for such a reassessment and the beginnings of a new understanding of man in society.[27, 28]

IV. THE CONCEPTS BEHIND THE DISCOVERIES[29, 30]

Even more profound than the body of new facts uncovered in the sciences from the opening of the twentieth century was the movement in the underlying assumptions of science. This subterranean movement in outlook—in the way scientists thought about nature and laymen in time came to think—was the real scientific revolution of the twentieth century. It grew out of the process of coming to terms with the new facts and it provided the new approach which carried scientific progress forward at an accelerated rate.

1. *Structure*

A noteworthy feature of twentieth-century science was that much of it lacked the rigid numerical character which was thought essential to science in the nineteenth century. Preoccupation with number and measurement was overshadowed by a growing interest in structure.

In the social sciences concepts which offered powerful ways of organizing knowledge to make it more orderly and penetrating, such as those created by Freud and Pavlov, came to be recognized as in every sense scientific, though they were seldom amenable to measurement or even to comparison. In the biological and the physical sciences, also, science was seen less and less as an accumulation of numerical measurements and more and more as a complex of logical and empirical relations. It was the relations, the connections between phenomena, the structure of the network of connections, which interested the scientist.

The bacteriologist would not give a numerical answer to the question of how a sulpha drug prevents the multiplication of bacteria. His explanation would be in terms of the geometrical structure of the drug: the atoms in the drug are arranged on the same pattern as the atoms in one of the foods which the bacteria need; thus the bacteria accept the drug, as it were by mistake, deceived by the shape in which its atoms are arranged.

So the cosmologist became less interested in the age of the universe than in the logic by which an age could be ascribed to it; and he was less interested in the size of the universe than in whether its size implies that it is open or closed. The nuclear physicist was fascinated by the strange relations between the numbers of different particles in a stable nucleus, not because the numbers were interesting in themselves but because they might provide a clue to the structural arrangements of particles which make a nucleus stable.

The quantitative principle was not thrown overboard, for science cannot exist without precise data. But it ceased to dominate the minds of scientists as it had in the nineteenth century. The twentieth-century scientist saw the accumulation of measurements no longer as an end but as a means. He needed exact numbers not for their own sake but as a step towards framing what he was really looking for, the laws which express the structural relations in nature. The quantitative principle became subservient to something more profound—the concept of structure.

2. Discontinuity

The nineteenth century assumed continuity in nature; yet discontinuity had already been established in the atomic division of matter. Physicists, however, did not then appreciate its significance.

Discontinuity as a principle was brought into the open when energy also was shown to have an atom-like structure and to travel on any one wavelength in quanta of a definite size. Once it had been demonstrated that energy cannot be divided indefinitely and cannot be transferred continuously, the nineteenth-century principle of continuity disappeared from physics. The underlying structure of the world was accepted as discontinuous. And with the recognition that both matter and energy exist and act only in discontinuous units of definite sizes, the possibility of an exact description of the universe was seen to be an illusion.

The need to turn to statistical methods had long been accepted in fields such as biology where the environment in which an experiment is conducted clearly contributes a background of unavoidable variations—differences between one experimental animal and another or in temperature and other conditions from one day to the next. Conclusions have to be drawn from such experiments which represent not finality but the preponderant weight of evidence. There always remains a possibility that the conclusions will be modified, and any numerical results in them are necessarily surrounded by some area of uncertainty. In the traditional view the reason for the appeal to probabilities in these areas was only the lack of complete knowledge; if perfect knowledge of the small fluctuations in background could be secured, even a biological experiment might in theory be perfectly precise and conclusive.

But the new discoveries in physics made it clear that it was really senseless to talk, even in principle, of having complete and exact knowledge. For knowledge is limited by the extent to which it can be supposed that things remain fixed, even in principle. And when for example scientists attempted to fix precisely the quantity of light reflected, say, from the page of a book, they found that the pointer on the light meter trembled; the quantity of light cannot be held steady any more than can the atoms which make up the pointer.

The fact that the pointer would tremble was already known in the nineteenth century. It had been discovered by the botanist Robert Brown (1775–1858) when he observed under the microscope the trembling of vegetable spores on the surface of a liquid. But the full implication of the Brownian movement was not grasped until the twentieth century.

The implication which came to be recognized is that in a universe in which matter and energy are atomic there is a limit to the accuracy of every description. Every description, however short the time which it covers, is an average taken over that time; because matter and energy make discontinuous jumps we cannot, even in principle, reduce the interval of time of any description of them to nothing. The pointer will tremble on any instrument that can be devised, however delicate, however carefully controlled and however shielded from all outside fluctuations. For in a universe in which matter and energy are both atomic, they themselves provide a background of sudden and discontinuous fluctuations which cannot be excluded.

In a continuous universe one could regard the statistical variability of results simply as errors of measurement which would disappear if one took more and more accurate readings at shorter and shorter intervals of time. But in a universe in which matter and energy are both discontinuous the difference between one measurement and another is no longer only an error of the observer. Nature herself is supplying a statistical distribution of events from one moment to the next, in discontinuous jumps.

3. *Uncertainty and chance*

The principle of uncertainty which the twentieth-century scientist came to accept, however, went far beyond the impossibility of making the measuring instrument precise. It went to the nature of matter and energy which the scientist sought to observe. Uncertainty in describing the course of the electron was implied in the very character of the electron itself.

From 1900 the ideas of quantum physics could not be made to match with the classical mechanics of particles. Fantastic properties had to be given to an electron whenever it sent out or took up a quantum of energy. The difficulties grew until in the 1920s it began to be seen that it was simply impossible to make a theory to describe these minute happenings and still hope to keep it rigidly laid out in the classical pattern of causes and effects.

The difficulty was apparent, for example, in the behaviour of electrons when an atom radiates one of its characteristic colours, such as a yellow line of sodium. It gets the energy for this when one of its electrons makes the leap from one of its characteristic orbits to another. This leap takes no time and does not pass through the space between; the electron disappears from one orbit and instantly appears in another. It did not seem to make much sense to call something with this behaviour a particle or even to ask whether what appears in the two orbits is the same electron. Neither did it make sense to give the electron one place at one time in its orbit; its possible positions are spread round the orbit like a wave. The electron, in short, was seen to behave as an electron and nothing else, with its own unusual but definite laws; and words like particle and wave were mere metaphors, each of which describes an aspect, and no more, of the whole algebra of its behaviour.

When for example light from a sodium lamp was beamed through two holes in a screen, the light was found to ripple from the two holes in waves which overlap to form a pattern of dark and bright bands. These waves are made up of single photons of light sent out by the leaps of single electrons. But through which hole any one photon goes, to take its place in the pattern of dark and bright, no one can tell. The single photon, the piece of energy, is set off on its journey and it appears at the end in one of several possible places. This is all that can be said of it; it is useless to ask more.

Useless, that is, so long as one insists on following single photons one by one. For one finds that the units of energy, as of matter, obstinately contradict the dogma of classical mechanics which declares that the processes of nature must be infinitely predictable. What one finds to be predictable is the statistics of collection—that half the light goes through each hole, and makes a pattern of dark and bright bands.

The conviction that there is no way of describing the present and the future of these tiny particles and events so that they appear completely determined was put into a formal principle in 1927 by Werner Heisenberg (1901–   ) and given the name of the 'principle of uncertainty'.

Heisenberg showed that every description of nature contains some essential and irremovable uncertainty. For example he found that the more accurately he attempted to measure the position of an electron the less certain he could be of its speed. The more accurately he tried to estimate its speed the more uncertain he was of its precise position. The future of the particle can never be predicted with complete certainty because it is impossible to be completely certain of its present. The future of these small-scale events can only be predicted with some range of alternatives, some uncertainty. And once any uncertainty in prediction is recognized, in however small and distant a corner of the world, then the future is essentially uncertain—although it may remain overwhelmingly probable.

The principle of uncertainty refers to very small particles and events. But these small events are not by any means unimportant. They are just the sorts of events which go on in the nerves and the brain, in the giant arrangements of atoms in the chromosomes, or in the behaviour of matter under extremes of heat or cold.

The discovery of the principle of uncertainty had a profound effect. At first it brought a severe shock to scientists accustomed to think, in nineteenth-century terms, that a law of nature is a rigid conjunction in which a known cause is described and a definite effect predicted from it. For it meant that nature could not be described as a rigid mechanism of causes and effects. What had seemed to be a clear relation of cause and effect was only a statistical accumulation, in which the uncertainties of the minute individual events averaged themselves out. Yet the successes of science in the nineteenth century had been won by fitting nature with a causal mechanism.

Scientists were accustomed to think that if a law of nature has been rightly determined a given procedure will always be followed by the same result. They were not accustomed to the idea that it will sometimes be followed by one result and sometimes by another or that one result is more probable than another. They did not expect to find the word 'probable' in a law of nature. To the nineteenth century the word 'probable' was a confession of ignorance —ignorance which could, in principle, be removed. But the twentieth-century scientists could not hope to remove the word 'probable' from the laws which govern very small events. They knew that the tiny events which take place within atoms cannot be described by laws which contain any stronger word than 'probable'; that in this sense chance is inherent in nature.

By the second quarter of the twentieth century the principle of uncertainty was no longer a strange or unsettling idea. To the later generation of physicists it seemed altogether natural and sensible. It did not seem to them to have taken the order out of science. Rather it had the effect of taking out the meta-physics and focusing upon the purpose of science: to describe the world in an orderly scheme or language which will make it possible to look ahead. It left no place for such general beliefs as Laplace's assertion that if we knew the present completely we could completely determine the future. According to the principle of uncertainty there simply is no sense in asserting what would happen if we knew the present completely; we do not, and plainly we never can. The principle allows no assertions at all about whether we could or could not predict the future of an electron, supposing that we knew this or that about its present. It merely points out that we cannot completely know its present.

To the scientists who grew up in the twentieth century the principle of uncertainty stated in special terms their fundamental view of science—that science is a way of describing reality; it is therefore limited by the limits of observation and it asserts nothing which may not in principle be tested by observation; anything else is scholastics, not science. The nineteenth century was dominated by Laplace's belief that everything can be described by its causes. To the scientist of the twentieth century this was no less scholastic than the mediaeval belief that everything is contained in the First Cause.

4. *Operation*

The twentieth century also evolved a radically new view of the relation between the scientist and what he observes. Man came to be seen not as a detached observer but as an irremovable part of his observations.

The nineteenth century was inspired by a belief in the impersonality of science and of all knowledge. It assumed that all its concepts, such as space and time, exist absolutely and outside of the observer. It assumed a sharp division between the observer and the natural world which he observes. Nature was regarded as a chain or network of events which unroll themselves in imperturbable sequence, and of which the observer is a witness but not a link.

When Albert Einstein examined the hidden assumptions in the physics of his boyhood he saw that this view of the relation between nature and those who observe it is simply unrealistic. He did not ask whether such a view was tenable in some abstract sense but whether it was practical. Does science in fact record impersonal events? Can it separate the fact from the finding, and distil the event from the observation of it?

Once Einstein had asked these questions the answer was plain; and the answer was 'No'. He saw that physics as the scientist actually practises it does not consist of events; it consists of observations. And between the event and those who observe it there must pass a signal, a ray of light perhaps, a wave or an impulse, which simply cannot be taken out of the observation. Event, signal, and observation: this is the relationship which Einstein recognized as the fundamental unit in physics. Relativity is the understanding of the world not as events but as relationships.

This was the fundamental change which relativity induced in all scientific thought. It brought the observer into the observation and, through it, into the formulation of the law. This of course did not mean that the law of nature was at the mercy of the individual observer. On the contrary, relativity and its extensions usually stipulate that a given law of nature must be so stated that it is equally applicable to all observers.

Thus science in the twentieth century was no longer a great heap of facts, each complete, self-contained and impersonal. It was a way of giving order which included the process by which facts were obtained. Facts were not given to the scientist by nature; he had to get them himself. Science thus became an activity, a sequence of operations that had to be carried out by people.

What the scientist found could not be divorced from his operations. The length of a stick cannot be divorced from the operation of measuring it, or the time on two clocks from the operation of comparing them.

In the same way it is possible to regard the principle of uncertainty as stating a limitation imposed by the presence of an observer. That is, one can consider that the behaviour of an electron is disturbed by the act of observing it and this is the reason why it cannot be described precisely. If for example an observer wanted to see the electron, he would have to shine a light on it, and this light would give some of its energy to the electron and so would change its course. Thus the act of observation would itself change the conditions which he was trying to describe; and in so small a unit as an electron the change would be important.

Twentieth-century science was able to gain new insights into reality only because it recognized the status of the observer, of the scientist in his work. It learned to understand the structure of the world more deeply because the scientist no longer tried to isolate the facts of nature from the operations by which he sought to find them.[31, 32]

V. THE UNIFYING OUTLOOK

Thus the underlying assumptions on which the nineteenth century formed its picture were replaced. In place of the quantitative principle, the scientist of the twentieth century thought of himself as pursuing a concept of structure. In place of the principle of continuity, the scientist recognized that the underlying structure of the small-scale world is discontinuous. In place of the principle of determinism or cause and effect, he recognized that the smallest units of matter and energy follow laws which can only be described by probabilities and whose predictions are therefore always surrounded by an area of uncertainty. In place of the impersonality of science came an understanding that the operations of the scientist enter inextricably into his findings. These were revolutionary changes in the outlook of science, and they make it appropriate to speak of a second scientific revolution.

The total effect of the new outlook was to overthrow the stark and mechanical image of the scientist serving an inhuman truth, remote from the everyday world, which the nineteenth century set up. Its place was taken by a richer image in which the scientist saw himself as carrying out an essentially human and personal activity, from which he must create an order, an understanding of the world by the projection of his own mind.

This was the most subtle change which took place in the view of science and of all knowledge. The twentieth century broke with the view that knowledge is passive, that it accumulates the facts that nature provides like a card index, and that the scientist need do nothing more than keep the index accurate and tidy. Instead it saw knowledge as a constant activity.

It ceased to ask that a law of nature be formulated as if there were no observers; it asked only that it be formulated in such a way that it looks the same to all similarly placed observers. When it asked that a law should be universal, it did not ask for a formulation which would hold in the absence of human observers. It asked, rather, for a formulation which should be valid for them all, however different their circumstances. This was the new meaning of universality.

At the same time it gave to the seeker after knowledge a creative role which science in the past had denied. A fully deterministic universe, as Laplace pictured it, carried the implication that everything that men do is already determined. On this nineteenth-century view man invents nothing and adds nothing to the world. Everything is wholly conditioned by past events.

This interpretation of nature as a machine ticking inexorably on a wholly determined course was no longer implied by the facts of twentieth-century physics. For the facts of physics left no room for any theory which does not include an unpredictable chance element in every forecast. The facts of modern physics say, for example, that one half of the atoms in a piece of plutonium will undergo radioactive disintegration in 25,000 years, but they do not say which half. Nor do they say of any specified atom in a piece of plutonium whether it will or will not disintegrate in the next 25,000 years, or in any other period of time.

To the scientists of the mid-twentieth century there appeared no possibility that there could be hidden somewhere a theory which would allow them to make exact forecasts of this kind about the small-scale events in the atom. In fact the mathematician, John von Neumann (1903–57), showed that any deterministic law which exactly predicted the occurrence of such phenomena would contradict some of the known and established facts of physics.[33, 34]

The concept of chance, as it entered into modern physics, did not mark any relaxation of scientific rigour. It was as clear and well defined as was the principle of strict cause and effect in the past. The area of uncertainty with which it was necessary to surround predictions was as well formulated and as intellectually lucid as was once the point of certainty. These were the tools of the new science, more supple and less familiar than those of the past, and highly practical, but no less scientific for that.

VI. THE SCIENTIFIC IMAGINATION IN ACTION

As science and all knowledge came to be regarded as personal activities, the scientist was placed in a new relation to his theories. Isaac Newton did not think of himself as inventing the law of gravitation, and Charles Darwin did not think of himself as creating the theory of evolution. They thought of themselves as uncovering what had always been there. Each pictured the law which he discovered as wholly objective, something which existed in itself, as positively as a stone or a clockwork.

The modern scientist saw this as too simple and too impersonal a view of knowledge. He presumed that the laws of nature did have an existence in themselves but that their character was more delicate, more elaborate and immensely more varied than anything that men were able to trace. Therefore the order that the scientist could find in nature was surely only one of many orders which might be found. And the particular order found by the scientist was thus in part created and imposed by his own imagination.

Let us consider a concrete case. Isaac Newton thought that each piece of matter was attracted to every other piece by a force of gravitation. The forecasts which he based on this law were almost entirely successful until the end of the nineteenth century. But they were not entirely successful. They failed, for example, to predict a small but obstinate discrepancy in the orbit of the planet Mercury.

In 1916 Albert Einstein published the General Theory of Relativity. This included all the predictions Newton had made and in addition it correctly accounted for the irregularities in the orbit of Mercury. It also forecast a remarkable phenomenon, the bending of the path of light towards massive objects. This was confirmed by observations on the total eclipse of the sun in 1919.

The General Theory of Relativity in its turn opened up a new series of problems. Einstein came to formulate it in such a way that it implied a closed universe. But it was then shown, mathematically, that the size of a closed universe cannot be stable; it must either expand or contract. And indeed, in 1924, Edwin P. Hubble (1889–1953) observed that the light from distant galaxies is increased in its wavelength in a way which is naturally explained by assuming that all the galaxies are moving away from one another. A whole new field of cosmology was thus opened up.

Einstein's General Theory of Relativity was not simply an enlargement of Newton's laws which adjusted them to cover a wider range of phenomena. It was a wholly new way of looking at the phenomena. It threw overboard the idea of a force of gravitation, and indeed the whole concept of force. In its place it regarded the interaction of massive bodies—and of light—purely as a geometrical effect, caused by geometrical irregularities in a four-dimensional space–time.

There was thus no intellectual link at all between the mechanism which Newton conceived to be driving the planets and the new mechanism which Einstein conceived.[35] Yet the predictions which both gave, for example for the orbit of the earth, were nearly always indistinguishable.

The laws of nature, as the twentieth century saw them, might thus be conceived in forms which philosophically are widely different and which may yet give almost the same predictions. The choice which a theoretical scientist may make among possible forms of law is therefore by no means inevitable. The particular order which he finds in nature is in some ways a projection of his mind.

In this century many new connections were found between the different phenomena of nature. Albert Einstein, who was always striving for new unifying ideas, showed how to connect time with space, mass with energy, and gravitation with the structure of space. To the end of his life he was still working on a unified field theory, which was intended to find a link also between gravitation and electricity.

J. J. Thomson, Ernest Rutherford and Niels Bohr elaborated a model of the atom which drew together a mass of diverse phenomena, all the way from electricity to chemistry. In 1932 James Chadwick showed that other atomic phenomena would fall into the same order if there was postulated the existence of a heavy fundamental particle without electric charge, the neutron. Once again a new concept unified and gave meaning to the varied and scattered phenomena of nature.

Such profound concepts came to be recognized as products of the scientific mind. In the thought of the twentieth century the scientist might seem more restricted in his freedom than the poet or painter and to be more bound by the facts to which his creativity must conform. But these restrictions do not affect the essence and character of the imaginative process. Relativity, the theory of atomic structure, the concept of the unconscious, the Mendelian laws of inheritance, were seen as works of the imagination. They were triumphs of the human mind, for they found or created order where there was the appearance of disorder, they singled out among the workings of nature certain striking trends, and they imposed an intellectual unity on the lifeless mass of phenomena.[36, 37]

When the twentieth-century scientist was seen to enter so personally into his work and, by implication, its practical consequences, his relationship to society also altered. The change in relation of the scientist to his contemporaries and in his own sense of responsibility grew naturally out of the new sense of science as a personal activity.

VII. SCIENTIST, TECHNICIAN AND LAYMAN

The twentieth century thrust the achievements of its scientists into daily life at a breath-taking rate. The legend of the remote scientist, living in a world of his own thoughts and blundering into discoveries whose practical importance he did not understand, survived only in the comic strips. No scientist of the mid-twentieth century, however abstract his work, could be sure that it would not sooner or later have a technical application. Few would be so rash as to boast, as had the mathematician Godfrey Harold Hardy (1877–1947) in his book *A Mathematician's Apology* (1940), that their work could not conceivably do anyone the least practical harm or the least good. Many physicists had in fact learned their approach to mathematics from the pioneer work of Hardy himself.

Yet the new and remote worlds within the atom, the cell or the universe which the modern scientist explored demanded such specialized knowledge and techniques in order to be perceived that they set the scientist apart from his fellows. He possessed the key to mysteries as inaccessible to the layman and as crucial to his well-being as those which any priesthood had monopolized in other societies. The public had to depend on him and to give him its trust and support; he, in turn, faced the age-old problem of how to communicate the meaning of his knowledge to those who must act in the light of it and whose actions, in turn, affected his work. For the scientist no longer saw himself merely as a man who supplied others with the facts and left them to make what they could of them. Understanding that what he found, however factual, had practical implications, he came to recognize a responsibility for bringing these implications home to others.

In turn, the practical world influenced the direction of scientific advance. This was not a wholly new development, for the direction in which science has looked, its background interests and its long term problems, have always been influenced by the preoccupations and the needs of the societies in which scientists have worked. Each society and age has created a climate of interest in its special problems. The fundamental scientist, immersed in this climate of interest, has tried his gifts on such of these problems as have challenged his curiosity; and his choice of specific problems may have been more or less directly determined by the existence of facilities for research enabling him to pursue the lines of investigation which he finds challenging.

1. *Support for scientific research*

To an ever-increasing extent during the twentieth century facilities for scientific research were provided by government agencies, industries, professional bodies and private foundations with practical objectives. Universities shifted much of their emphasis from humanistic to scientific studies, and special types of research in universities were often stimulated by subventions from agencies which hoped for usable results.

The most spectacular scientific break-through, the release of energy by atomic fission, and later by fusion, was achieved in direct pursuit of a military objective during and after the second world war. In the decade after the war enormous sums were invested in scientific research by virtually every major country as part of its expenditure for national defence, sums which often overshadowed research expenditures by public or private bodies along other lines.

Such orienting of much scientific research toward defence, although tending to distort its direction, was less narrowing than might at first appear, for total war involved not merely weapons but every other aspect of operation and survival—transport, communication, control of disease, synthetic production of materials, food and agriculture, genetics—in short the whole range of life to which science had been and might be applied. The exploration of outer space, conceived for purely scientific purposes as part of the research programme of the International Geophysical Year, 1957–58, came to be linked with military efforts to design missiles which could travel through space and re-enter the earth's atmosphere.

As governments expanded their functions they supported research along many other lines, notably public health, agriculture, power, transport, communications and construction, social processes and social problems. Industries spent huge sums for technical research, either within a single enterprise as in the Bell Laboratories of the American Telephone and Telegraph Company, famous throughout the world for work in the field of communications, or in research establishments maintained by groups of enterprises producing steel, petroleum or other fuels, chemicals, plastics, artificial fibres, radios, aircraft or motor vehicles.

Applied research was not confined to practical matters, for it came to be recognized that next steps in application often depended on fundamental scientific discovery, whether of radiation affecting the possibility of travel in outer space or of biochemical factors able to unlock secrets of cancer. Research in the Bell Laboratories, for example, ranged from speech formation to the abstract theory of information. Military research extended into such remote mathematics as the theory of strategic games. Coal research in Britain gave special attention to the fossil flora found in coal. Most strikingly, the work done by Hans Bethe (1906–   ) and others in the 1930s in elucidating the source of the sun's energy pointed the way to the development of a first bomb in which hydrogen was fused to helium. But theoretical work in Russia, Britain and in the United States at once pressed further than this, and devised a fusion reaction on a new principle. Comparable examples of the close link between fundamental research and practical needs could be found in many fields, including communication engineering and plant breeding.

Several factors tended to make the support of scientific research by government and industry a noteworthy feature of the twentieth century and to increase this tendency with the passing years. As science pervaded more and more aspects of life, societies looked to their scientists to contribute to national survival and well-being; science itself became an instrument of national defence and a means by which national industry could compete in world markets, public health could be achieved, air and road accidents reduced, long-distance communication perfected, agricultural production promoted. In addition the tremendous cost of equipment required for experimental work, especially in the field of nuclear physics and in the exploration of outer space, made generous support essential; even the wealthiest of the American universities found themselves hard pressed to equip laboratories where their nuclear physicists could engage in pioneer research, and several of them joined together after the second world war to support such a laboratory in common. Furthermore, many problems could not be studied effectively by a single scientist but required the collaboration of a group of specialists, and the organization and funds to bring them together and support their work.

The use of scientific theory and technology by governments and industries brought profound ethical problems to scientists and dangers to the development of science itself. The teamwork necessary for large-scale research not infrequently brought pressures for conformity and discouraged originality and brilliance. Though the interaction of many minds could be stimulating it could also lead toward a consensus of mediocrity which excluded disturbing questions.

Discoveries made by scientists working in industrial laboratories generally became the property of the company, which then could determine their use, and the scientist's contract of employment often restricted his further work along the same line either within or outside of the enterprise. When scientists worked for the government, problems of national security often demanded secrecy. Walls were thus raised around the individual scientist, and loyalty to country brought him into conflict with the most basic of scientific loyalties, the pursuit of truth and the free flow of knowledge.

By no means all scientific discovery in the twentieth century, however, depended on costly experiments or the co-operative work of many specialists. Patience and imagination often proved more important than complex equipment in yielding new scientific insights, especially in the biological and social sciences. Important characteristics of the scattering of light, known as the Raman effect, were discovered by the Indian physicist Chandrasekhara Venkata Raman (1888–   ) with a minimum of equipment and much careful mathematical work, in 1928.

Even in nuclear physics very significant discoveries continued to be made by theoretical physicists, often working where costly equipment could not be provided. In the 1930s the Japanese physicist Hideki Yukawa (1907–) predicted the existence of mesons on theoretical grounds, before these particles had ever been looked for and before giant machines were built to produce them.

Similarly, two Chinese theoretical physicists, T. D. Lee (1926–) and C. N. Yang (1922–), working in the United States, devised an experiment to test the assumption that atomic phenomena should be symmetrical. Unexpectedly, in 1956, the experiment disproved this basic assumption in physics and opened an exciting new field of study.

Whether the scientist worked alone or in a group, experimentally or theoretically, in academic seclusion or employed by government or industry, his own creative imagination and scientific curiosity remained the driving force leading to new discoveries. And in spite of security regulations, trade secrets and governmental or industrial direction of some research, much freedom for the exchange of information remained, while the nature of science itself constantly called for such exchanges. Regardless of national or other boundaries, scientists continued to share their observations and thus build up a cumulative body of knowledge as they had been doing since the beginning of modern scientific inquiry.

2. *Communication between scientist and layman*

The close link between scientist, technician and layman placed a burden on the scientist to make the implications of his findings clear and understood by others. In the twentieth century this became an ever more necessary and more difficult task. It was more necessary because the impact of science on the life of mankind forced non-scientists constantly to make judgments involving its use, and they needed understanding in order to make such judgments soundly. It was more difficult because of the lack of a language in which scientists could communicate to laymen.

The imperative need for the scientist to bring home to others the meaning of his discoveries was intensified at mid-century by the threat to the very existence of mankind from nuclear explosion and the release of radioactivity. These fruits of scientific effort not only placed on scientists the heavy responsibility of making their implications understood; they faced the scientist with a basic ethical conflict. In choosing what search to pursue and what instruments to make, scientists were forced to think in terms of their ethical duties as well as their duty to uncover laws of nature. The judgment and understanding required of the scientist went beyond his competence as a specialist in his field.

Yet as the sciences grew more specialized and their researches more detailed it became difficult for the individual scientist to present his thought in the total context of science. With his special vocabulary of words and symbols he was often scarcely able to communicate even with other scientists outside his field who also had special vocabularies and symbols of their own. To make the nature and meaning of his discoveries understood by the public was even more difficult.

The difficulty was enhanced by the fact that up to the middle of the twentieth century the new scientific discoveries had not yet yielded a compact organizing principle which could be seen to run through all sciences and would bring order to the scattered disciplines, in the way that the elucidation of the principle of cause and effect had brought order into the scattered knowledge of the seventeenth century.

The absence of such a general principle was a handicap to the scientist, above all, in his relations with the public. For the relations depended on the existence of a language which the scientist felt to be sufficiently accurate and which nevertheless the public could understand. Newton's *Principia* had created such a language of communication between scientist and public for its time, and Darwin's *The Origin of Species* had done so for its period. The principles which underlay these books could be grasped by the public which thus gained an insight into scientific method and a vocabulary of scientific fact.

The language which would make the new science immediate to the public had not yet been created by the middle of the twentieth century; it was an open question whether it could be created until a unifying principle should have been distilled from the revolutionary thoughts in the science of this century, as the unifying view had slowly taken shape after the first scientific revolution. Meantime, the public remained bewildered by the new science because it lacked a language and the habits of thought which a language formalizes. Thus bewildered, it could not readily exercise its responsibility for the use of the new scientific findings and it sometimes blamed the scientist for making discoveries which could be put to destructive use.

3. *The scientific outlook in daily life*

Yet a scientific outlook did come to penetrate into the daily life of the time and some of the new scientific concepts, at times diluted or distorted, became part of current thought. In areas where the scientific point of view was accepted—and these were constantly growing, both geographically as more people came in contact with modern techniques and in wider areas of daily life—people came to respect facts and to approach them rationally and empirically. This was particularly noteworthy not only in practical matters relating to industry or travel but in the field of health where new knowledge supplanted traditional practices at a strikingly rapid rate.

Perhaps the most significant evidence of the extent to which science had entered the outlook of the twentieth century was the acceptance of change as a continuous and fundamental phenomenon, and adaptation to its accelerating pace. Not only was this true of the western countries where the expectation of change had become a well-established attitude. In the historically more static societies of the East, where change had been looked upon as defection from eternally established norms, it became the order of the day.

Equally fundamental was the concept of new potentialities which science brought and the public accepted. All over the world people who for centuries had taken poverty and disease for granted saw in the methods and the fruits of science a new possibility of human fulfilment. In the first half of the twentieth century this vision altered the outlook of mankind.

Specific concepts from the new science were incorporated into attitudes and thought. Chief among these was the idea of relativity. Though often enough misunderstood, the idea of relativity as a revolutionary concept in physics impressed on moralists, artists and the man in the street the notion that, from other points of view, reality may appear different, and yet be as valid as that which they themselves perceive.

The concept of uncertainty also entered the popular mind and many people learned to think statistically in terms of chance and probability rather than in terms of the certainty of direct cause and effect. Concepts derived from psychological studies of learning and conditioning and Freudian analysis of personality formation entered into the lore associated with the rearing of children. The scientist's sense that the observer is inevitably a part of that which he observes was reflected in the inner perspective of the modern writer. And the fact that physics became concerned with atomic structure also influenced painters and sculptors to portray what they saw as discontinuous structure rather than as surface appearance.

In the swiftly changing world of the twentieth century science was thus an ever-growing force, constantly yielding new facts and new capabilities which brought changes in structures, activities and relationships, often before it had developed the means to deal with the results of such changes.

The chapters which follow will examine this process in the elaboration of scientific thought and the application of scientific knowledge as the dynamic interplay between knowledge and action remade one aspect after another of the life of mankind.

NOTES TO CHAPTER VI

1. Already at this time many scientists, Dr L. Pollak points out, including men as well known as Helmholtz, Lodge and Stoney, thought that the atom was not simply an indivisible structural element. But as yet there was no direct experimental proof that this was the case.

2. Dr L. Pollak reminds that the development of statistical concepts in the molecular-kinetic theory of gases (Maxwell, Boltzmann), of statistical mechanics (Gibbs), and the statistical interpretation of the second law of thermodynamics (Boltzmann) introduced entirely new elements into physics, which were to play a decisive role in the development of this branch of science during the twentieth century.

3. *The Author-Editors call the attention of the reader to the treatment of probability theory and statistics in Chapter VII, pages 172–3.*

4. Candidate of Philosophical Science A. S. Arsenyev says that L. Kronecker's view of the 'God-given' nature of whole numbers can scarcely be considered characteristic of the mathematicians of the last quarter of the nineteenth century.

5. In the opinion of Academician Ivan Malek the principle of natural selection is explained incorrectly, in a Malthusian fashion. As Karl Marx and Friedrich Engels pointed out, writes Academician I. Malek, Darwin was mistaken in making use of Malthusian ideas and referring to them, but this does not detract from the essential correctness of Darwin's teaching on natural selection.

   Both writers realized how ironical it was that Darwin should apply to animals and plants the anti-humanist Malthusian idea that mankind was multiplying in geometrical progression, while holding that the means of existence, i.e. those very same animals and plants, were multiplying in arithmetical progression—and in this way demonstrate, without realizing it, the absurdity of this idea. In refutation of Malthus' theory it is sufficient to point out that the population of the world, and Great Britain in particular, has risen several times since the time when Malthus wrote, but that the average consumption per head of food products, far from diminishing, has actually increased to a significant extent.

   The 'struggle for existence', i.e. natural selection, as Darwin understood it, is never the consequence of overpopulation. It is rather the reverse: overpopulation, which facilitates the survival of a particular species in conditions unfavourable to existence and development, is itself the consequence of selection; this means that only those species survive which are capable of compensating, by reproduction, for periodical curtailment of their numbers.

6. *The Author-Editors call attention to the fact that the explanation presented in the text is that given by Darwin.*

7. Academician Ivan Malek emphasizes that at the time when Darwin published his work, and even much later, nothing was known about the inheritance of the minor variations which Darwin considered the prime factor in natural selection; nevertheless subsequent discoveries in the realm of genetics have not required any essential corrections to be made to the theory of natural selection, with one exception: we now know that some of these minor variations, and in particular those included in the concept of instable variability, are not heritable and therefore cannot be subjects of selection. On the other hand, study by geneticists of natural populations of animals and plants has revealed a fairly large number of heritable variations—the so-called micro-mutations.

8. Candidate of Historical Sciences J. P. Averkieva points out that by this time there had already appeared such classical works on the history of primitive society as L. Morgan's *Ancient Society* (1877) and F. Engels' *The Origin of the Family, Private Property and the State* (1884).

9. Candidate of Juridical Sciences A. E. Bovin reminds that a work which appeared much earlier than that mentioned in the text, and which was far more profound in scope, was F. Engels' *The Condition of the Working Class in England* (1845).

10. In the opinion of Soviet scholars, the assessment given in the text of the scientific legacy of Karl Marx is incomplete and essentially erroneous.

Prior to Marx and Engels the realm of social phenomena was considered an unassailable citadel of idealism. All philosophers were convinced that what determined the life of a society were men's ideas and the struggle between them. Of course, one can detect individual elements of a Marxist approach to society in the views of a number of predecessors of Marx: among the French materialists, the advanced British economists, Feuerbach, Hegel, and the utopian socialists. But these were only surmises which did not alter the general situation—the complete domination of idealism over matters concerning human history.

Marx and Engels overcame idealism in this sphere as well, by applying dialectical materialism to social phenomena and creating the theory of historical materialism. The main significance of this theory lies in the fact that it turned the study of society and its laws into a science, which like other sciences was capable of providing precise data, on the basis of which the course of events could be predicted and social development guided in the necessary direction. In evolving the theory of historical materialism an important part was played by an examination of capitalist society. Far more graphically than other social formations, capitalism and the class struggle between the proletariat and the bourgeoisie revealed the contradictions of material interest that underlie the antagonism inherent in any class society. As Marx and Engels wrote in the *Communist Manifesto*, the bourgeois epoch had 'simplified the class antagonisms'; it has substituted for exploitation veiled by religious and political illusions 'naked, shameless, direct, brutal exploitation'. Their profound objective analysis of the capitalist system refuted the idealist conception of history and led to the incontrovertible conclusion that the main motive force in the development of society is not reason, not ideas, but material needs, the production of material values. This investigation into the motive force of capitalist society also threw light on the whole of man's past. The anatomy of the bourgeois system could, in a manner of speaking, provide a key to the anatomy of the entire previous development of society. Marx and Engels showed that in the development of society, as in the world of nature, there existed objective laws independent of the consciousness and will of men. They discovered the general laws governing all social progress. This is the content of historical materialism.

The emergence of historical materialism, as a science elucidating the laws of social development and a method of studying social phenomena, was not the product of mere chance but of the logical development of society and scientific philosophical thinking. Previously the inner link between social processes, between the causes of historical events and the events themselves, had been obscured from view and therefore difficult to discover; but with the development of capitalism this link was becoming more and more simple and obvious.

The course of history was accelerating. From the English Revolution onwards, and particularly after the French Revolution of 1789–94, events followed upon one another with great rapidity; class contradictions were becoming sharper; clashes took place, and the working class appeared upon the stage of history. These were the social premises that made possible the creation of the science of the laws and motive forces governing social development. The tempestuous events of the late eighteenth and early nineteenth centuries showed that human society had not crystallized into a form valid for all time, but was changing and developing. Although the course of history was marked by certain zigzags, by and large the trend of social development was, and is, upwards.

Advanced social thinkers such as Hegel, the British classical political economists, British and French historians of the 1830s and 1840s, and some pre-Marxist philosophical materialists (Helvetius and others) were feeling their way towards a scientific view of society and history. But everything done in this sphere before Marx was purely tentative—an approach to a correct scientific attitude, but not a scientific theory, not an integral well-founded view of the historical process. The creation of historical materialism was the great scientific achievement of Marx and Engels—an exploit that had world-historical significance for the theory and practice of revolution, for the cause of communism. Marx and Engels were only able to create historical materialism and Marxism as such because they were the ideologists of the most progressive class in society—the working class, which was interested in discovering the truth, in the forward march of society, and not in perpetuating old outmoded social relationships.

Historical materialism arose as the result of the application of dialectical materialism to society and the study of social phenomena, and to the history of society. For this reason the laws and categories of historical materialism cannot be understood in isolation from the tenets of dialectical materialism. Thus, for example, when studying the laws governing the movement of class societies, which historical materialism discovered, the law of class struggle and social revolution, it should not be overlooked that these laws constitute one specific form of the universal dialectical laws of the unity and conflict of opposites, the struggle between old and new, positive and negative, and the transformation of quantitative changes into qualitative change.

In conformity with the general materialist world outlook historical materialism proceeds from the assumption that social being is primary and social consciousness secondary, or—to put this in another way—that it is not ideas that determine life, but life, social existence, that determines ideas. But what do we mean by 'social being?' We mean the material life of society, and in the first instance the social production of material values and the relations formed between men in the course of production. In an antagonistic society these relationships are relationships between classes. Before men can occupy themselves with science, art, religion, philosophy or politics, they have to drink, eat, clothe themselves—and for this they have to produce foodstuffs and clothing, build houses, and create means of production. Without the production of material values social life is impossible. The production and reproduction of material values constitutes the vital foundation of a society. If production were to cease all intellectual and spiritual activity would become impossible and society would perish. Therefore the key to the structure and development of society must be sought, not in men's consciousness, not in their political, philosophical, religious, or moral ideas, but in the mode of producing material goods.

The material life of society is basic and determinant, whereas spiritual life is reflection of material life. This by no means implies, as bourgeois critics of Marxism falsely assert, that Marxists underestimate or play down the significance of the spiritual life of society, the role of ideas, consciousness, reason, science, art, or politics in social life or history. On the contrary: by declaring social consciousness, social and political theories to be a reflection of social being, Marxists are thereby simply giving a scientific explanation of the spiritual life of society, the origin and development of ideas. Marxists consider that social ideas play a very important part in the life and development of society. It may be added that the bourgeoisie has had to pay for its vulgar superficial ideas about Marxism, and in particular about historical materialism. Thousands of nonsensical treatises have been written criticizing Marxism and blowing it to smithereens on the grounds that it allegedly ignores or minimizes the role of ideas, ideals, the spiritual element, and so on—and now the bourgeoisie has suddenly discovered that Marxist ideas, the ideas of communism, are spreading more and more widely and possess irresistible force. Bourgeois politicians and ideologues have therefore raised a cry about 'pernicious' communist propaganda and 'subversive' activity by communists. At the present time the bourgeoisie is compelled to admit more and more frequently that it has no great ideas which it could put forward in opposition to the ideas of communism. The classical formulation of the basic principles of historical materialism was given by Marx in the preface to his book *A Contribution to the Critique of Political Economy*: 'In the social production of their life men enter into definite relations that are indispensable and independent of their will, relations of production, which correspond to a definite stage of development of their material productive forces. The sum total of these relations of production constitutes the economic structure of society, the real foundation, on which rises a legal and political superstructure and to which correspond definite forms of social consciousness. The mode of production of material life conditions the social, political and intellectual life process in general. It is not the consciousness of men that determines their being, but, on the contrary, their social being that determines their consciousness.

'At a certain stage of their development the material productive forces of society come in conflict with the existing relations of production, or—what is but a legal expression for the same thing—with the property relations within which they have been at work hitherto. From forms of development of the productive forces these relations turn into their fetters. Then begins an epoch of social revolution. With the change of the economic foundation the entire immense superstructure is more or less rapidly transformed.

'In considering such transformations a distinction should always be made between the material transformation of the economic conditions of production, which can be determined with the precision of natural science, and the legal, political, religious, aesthetic or philosophic—in short, ideological forms in which men become conscious of this conflict and fight it out. Just as our opinion of an individual is not based on what he thinks of himself, so can we not judge of such a period of transformation by its own consciousness; on the contrary, this consciousness must be explained rather from the contradictions of material life, from the existing conflict between the social productive forces and the relations of production. No social order ever perishes before all the productive forces for which there is room in it have developed; and new, higher relations of production never appear before the material conditions of their existence have matured in the womb of the old society itself. Therefore mankind always sets itself only such tasks as it can solve; since, looking at the matter more closely, it will always be found that the task itself arises only when the material conditions for its solution already exist or are at least in the process of formation' (K. Marx, *A Contribution to the Critique of Political Economy*, Karl Marx and Frederick Engels, *Selected Works in Two Volumes*, Moscow Foreign Languages Publishing House, 1958, Vol. I, pp. 362–3). These propositions were formulated one hundred years ago. The whole subsequent course of social development, all the foremost and greatest events of our time, and in the first place the victory of socialism in the USSR, the people's revolution in China and other countries of Europe and Asia, where socialism is being successfully constructed, have confirmed wholly and fully the laws of social development discovered by Marx and Engels.

11. Candidate of Philosophical Sciences A. S. Arsenyev points out that the authors mistakenly equate mechanistic determinism with determinism as such. Furthermore, A. Arsenyev adds, already at that time the materialistic dialectic was in existence, and this provided the means for a much deeper understanding of causality.

12. Candidate of Philosophical Sciences A. S. Arsenyev reminds that the quantitative principle was criticized from the dialectical point of view, by Hegel, already at the beginning of the nineteenth century—and not in the twentieth century, as the authors write. The correct solution of the problem of quality and quantity was given not by the natural sciences, but by philosophy.

13. Candidate of Philosophical Sciences A. S. Arsenyev reminds that the authors regard the principle of continuity as one of the principles of the scientific method of the eighteenth and nineteenth centuries. It is necessary to add that the question of continuity and

discreteness has been solved by the dialectic. What the authors present as the modern point of view (recognition of discreteness alone) is a one-sided abstraction, just as erroneous as its counterpart.

14. Candidate of Philosophical Sciences A. S. Arsenyev points out that the 'principle of personality' adduced by the authors in opposition to the principle of 'impersonality' in fact implies a subjectivist concept of science verging on apriorism.

15. Candidate of Philosophical Sciences A. S. Arsenyev thinks that this is not true. The theory of relativity does not explain the result of the Michelson experiment—i.e. it does not give it any physical interpretation. It presents it without contradiction, provided that certain limiting postulates are imposed on the physical world.

16. Dr L. Pollak considers that this statement is misleading unless the following is added:
   In 1924 L. de Broglie developed the idea that matter could behave either as a wave or a corpuscle, putting forward the hypothesis that each particle of matter (electron, etc.) also has the properties of a wave. In 1926 E. Schrödinger worked out the theory of the wave mechanics of the atom. According to this theory the behaviour of an atomic structure could be examined and explained with the aid of a kind of wave function.
   Max Born showed that this function could be interpreted as giving a certain measure of probability that a particle exists at a particular point in space at a particular moment in time. Many idealist philosophers, without any serious scientific foundation, have linked Schrödinger's probabilist interpretation of wave function with an indeterminist concept of the microcosm.

17. László Mátrai, Corresponding Member, Hungarian Academy of Sciences, writes that it is incorrect to say the non-Euclidean spaces were first studied by followers of Corrado Segre, whose work was based on that of Hermann Grassman. It is generally acknowledged that the first in the field were Bolyai and Lobachevsky.

18. *The Author-Editors call attention to the fact that the text does not make the statement attributed to it in the preceding note.*

19. Candidate of Philosophical Sciences A. S. Arsenyev reminds that fruitful systems of non-Euclidean geometry were also elaborated by N. I. Lobachevsky (1792–1856) and J. Bolyai (1802–60).

20. *The reader is referred to Chapter VII, p. 169, for discussion of non-Euclidian geometry.*

21. Doctor of Biological Sciences P. Henckel asserts that K. A. Timiryazev was one of the first to point out that the nature of heredity is to be ascertained, not by establishing statistical patterns, but by physiological studies. He noted that the rules set down by Mendel are not universal. Timiryazev offered a classification of heredity, distinguishing between simple and complex heredity. Simple heredity is observed during vegetative reproduction, and complex, in crossing. According to Timiryazev, complex heredity is subdivided into: (1) mixed heredity, when one part of the organism displays the traits of one parent, and the other part, of the other parent: (2) merged heredity, when the traits of the parents are merged, giving rise to new traits; (3) mutually excluding heredity, when the traits of one parent alone are displayed. In this latter type, two categories of cases are observed: (*a*) when the offspring shows no variety (Millardism) and (*b*) when the offspring does show variety, usually beginning with the second generation (Mendelism). The work and achievements of Michurin's genetics have confirmed Timiryazev's view of heredity and have yielded important practical results in the field of plant and animal selection.

22. Doctor of Biological Sciences P. Henckel writes that major changes in the nature of organisms are not always attributable to alteration of the number or structure of chromosomes.

23. Doctor of Biological Sciences P. Henckel points out that viruses were discovered by the Russian scientist D. O. Ivanovsky, who specialized in plant physiology. He was the first to demonstrate, on the basis of studying the tobacco mosaic virus, the corpuscular nature of viruses and to describe the crystalline insertions of viruses (Ivanovsky's crystals) in the cells of a diseased plant.

24. Candidate of Biological Sciences L. Ya. Blyakher expresses astonishment and concern that the authors should apparently be inclined to question whether all biological phenomena are at all times susceptible to a materialist explanation.

25. *The Author-Editors note that the text expresses no view on this matter.*

26. Doctor of Historical Sciences Yu. P. Averkieva underlines that Freud's theory is a speculative one: its propositions are based in the main on the intuition and imagination of the investigator, and not on rational methods of experiment worked out in detail. This theory has never enjoyed much success in Eurasian countries, and especially not in the Soviet Union. The authors ought to emphasize that modern neo-Freudianism, like Freudianism in the past, is most widespread in the USA, but that even there it is being subjected to well-founded criticism, not only by sociologists and ethnologists, but also by psychologists. See, for example, Yu. P. Averkieva, 'Etnofreidizm v S.Sh.A.' (Ethnofreudianism in the USA), *Sovetskaya etnografiya* (Soviet Ethnography) (1962), No. 4, pp. 3–15; H. Wells, *Pavlov and Freud* (New York, 1956); R. Piddington, *An Introduction to Social Anthropology* (London, 1957), Vol. 2; O. Klineberg, 'Tensions affecting International Inderstanding', *Social Science Research Council Bulletin* (1950), No. 62.

27. Doctor of Historical Sciences Yu. P. Averkieva writes: In this section the authors state that the investigations of ethnologists and students of folk-lore at the beginning of the twentieth century allegedly 'undermined' faith in the doctrine of social evolution created by Morgan, Taylor and others; furthermore they justify the anti-historical approach to the study of social history employed by the functional school of bourgeois ethnologists, with their relativism and conception of holism. This approach is at present rejected by most Western scholars, who have made a sharp turn towards the theory of evolution. The anti-historical trend and its worthlessness from a scientific point of view are examined in the following works: D. A. Olderogge and I. I. Potekhin, 'Funktsionalnaya shkola v etnografii na sluzhbe britanskogo imperializma' (The Functional School in Ethnology at the Service of British Imperialism) in the volume of essays entitled *Anglo-amerikanskaya etnografiya na sluzhbe imperializma* (Anglo-American Ethnology at the Service of Imperialism) (Moscow, 1951) pp. 41, 66; J. Steward, *Theory of Culture Change: Methodology of Multilinear Evolution* (Urbana Ill., 1955); *Evolution after Darwin* (Chicago, 1960), Vol. II; F. Voget, 'Man and Culture' *American Anthropologist* (1956), Vol. 58, No. 6.

28. *For a fuller discussion of the various trends in anthropology in the twentieth century, see Chapter XVI, infra, and Clyde Kluckhohn, 'Anthropology in the Twentieth Century' in* Journal of World History, *III, 3 (1957), pp. 754–77.*

29. Doctors of Physical and Mathematical Sciences E. Adirovich and R. Steinman give the following estimation of Sections IV, V and VI: In these sections, the authors seek to demonstrate that there is a radical difference between the science of the twentieth century and that of the eighteenth and nineteenth centuries. It is pointed out in the text that the most important scientific achievements of the twentieth century are the quantum theory and the theory of relativity, although the account of the former is confined to an account of the principle of indeterminacy, and the theory of relativity is considered solely from the angle of the role of the observer. The authors say almost nothing at all about the most important achievement of twentieth-century physics: the creation of the physics of elementary particles. Yet this is a major revolutionary step towards the establishment of a single physical picture of the world, a single theory of matter. The discovery that many elementary particles change into one another according to certain laws and form systems combining matter and field has thrown much light on the way in which particles interact upon one another, and has shown the connection between different types of matter and the types of motion and interaction associated with them. The theory of relativity has shown that space and time are inter-connected, and also connected with the distribution and movement of masses—which the authors, incidentally, ignore completely, since they say nothing at all about the general theory of relativity. Quantum mechanics, and in particular quantized field theory, the fundamental ideas of which are also overlooked in Chapter VI, have led to a re-examination of the

questions of the particle and its dynamical motion, the limitations of the concept of the individual in nature, and the correlation of the movements of identical particles forming a single system.

The basic ideas of twentieth-century physics are set out here in accordance with the canonical scheme of positivist ideas (collection of measurable magnitudes instead of study of the objective world; hyperbolization of the relationship between uncertainties, and treatment of this as signifying a limitation of the possibilities of cognition, instead of the inadequacy of macro-characteristics when dealing with micro-particles; the concept of the observer bringing order into the phenomena he studies; the concept of chance as lack of causality, etc.). A reader of this chapter would draw the conclusion that such treatment is generally accepted, and is even the sole possible interpretation that could be given to the findings of modern physics. But one may refer, for example, to the works of Blokhintsev, Fock, de Broglie, Bohm and other scientists, whose views, however different they may be from one another, are at sharp variance with the conception put forward in Chapter VI. The modern scientific ideas contained in this chapter, presented as characteristic of the modern world-outlook and modern scientific method, are in fact nothing more than negative demonstration of the inadequacy of the principles underlying the old metaphysical method. Moreover, the ideas put forward here as characteristic of the modern scientific world-outlook (for example, the ideas of indeterminism, uncertainty, the 'personal' character of science, etc.) in reality testify to the absence of proper scientific method. They lead science into a blind alley, and in the last resort to the revival of theology. At the same time the text of this chapter contains not a word about the materialistic dialectic, which solves the questions of the relationship between chance and necessity, between relative and absolute truth. Many natural scientists abroad are evidencing great interest in the materialist dialectic. It is gradually becoming, and in future undoubtedly will become, the generally accepted method of scientific inquiry. For the moment, however, in science a stubborn ideological struggle is in progress—one which has not been reflected by the authors of Chapter VI.

30. *The Author-Editors call the reader's attention to the language of the text, pages 130 and 146. The account on pages 143–150 is an exposition of the inadequacy of macro-descriptions when applied to micro-particles and to micro-phenomena. It does not deal with individual theories (for example, that of de Broglie and that of Bohm) which attempt, in different ways, to set up new systems of description for the behaviour of micro-particles. For fuller treatment of elementary particles, see Chapter VIII, pp. 194–203. For the General Theory of Relativity, see page 151.*

31. Candidate of Philosophical Sciences A. S. Arsenyev writes that in making this statement the authors are making the law of nature dependent upon the observer, i.e. they are assuming that matter does not exist objectively, independently of the observer. It does not make any difference if one substitutes all observers for a single observer: this merely leads to the Bogdanovist concept of truth as 'socially organized experience' (truth is what everyone agrees to be true).

32. *The Author-Editors call the reader's attention to the exact language of the text, which does not deal with the metaphysical question of the independent existence of matter apart from the observer but with the nature and basis of the observer's knowledge. See also pages 149 to 152.*

33. Doctor of Physical and Mathematical Sciences E. I. Adirovich and Dr R. Steinman think that Neumann's theorem of concealed parameters, which stated that it was impossible to describe a system 'fully' within the framework of quantum mechanics, is incorrectly treated by the authors as proof that the views put forward in Chapter VI are the only possible treatment of the findings of modern physics. In actual fact the essence of the matter lies, not in our supposed inability in principle to obtain complete knowledge, not in 'the inexactness of measurements', but in the objective absence of the possibility of an absolute isolation of an individual (of a particle or a system) from external impacts; this accounts for the non-universality of dynamic regularities.

34. *By way of clarification, the Author-Editors note that von Neumann's theorem is presented only as a confirmation of the inability to make exact forecasts of small-scale events.*

35. László Matzai, Corresponding Member, Hungarian Academy of Sciences, thinks that the authors are clearly exaggerating the differences between the scientific thought of the twentieth and nineteenth centuries. It is not as though there were an unbridgeable gulf between classical and modern physics. Lorentz's transformations make possible an exact transition from one system to the other. It is highly symptomatic that Lorentz's name is not even mentioned as one of the greatest physicists of our age.

In general the authors' interpretation of Einstein's theory of relativity is dangerously close to philosophical relativism and even to subjective idealism.

36. Doctor of Historical Sciences Yu. P. Averkieva points out that Soviet scientists are astonished, to say the least, to find the semi-scientific Freudian concept of the unconscious included among the triumphs of the human mind together with the theory of relativity and the theory of atomic structure. As has already been pointed out in the note 26, *supra*, Freudianism is only popular in the USA, and can therefore lay no claim to a place among the theories and concepts that have had a global impact. See also *Sounemennaya amerikanskaya etnografiya: sbornik statey* (Contemporary American Ethnography: Collection of Articles) (Moscow, 1963); H. J. Wells, *Pavlov and Freud* (New York, 1956).

37. *For the influence of Freud in countries other than the United States, see references* in Note 3 of Chapter XVI *and the following: Benjamin Nelson*, Freud and the Twentieth Century *(New York: Meridian Books, 1958), Leopold Bella, ed.*, Contemporary European Psychiatry *(New York: Evergreen Books, 1961).*

CHAPTER VII

MATHEMATICS AND LOGIC*

URING the twentieth century a profound change took place in the understanding of the nature of mathematics and in particular of its connections with logic and with physical reality. It was beginning to be clear that this change marked one of the most significant intellectual advances in the history of mankind, the full implications of which could not be prophesied.

The brilliant and varied achievements of twentieth-century mathematicians tended in some measure to obscure the revolutionary character of the underlying mathematical currents of the times. And furthermore, the recognition of the true state of mathematical affairs was not altogether easy because it was not apparent just when or where mathematicians made so clean a break with the past as the physicists did around 1900. In the history of modern physics the price which had to be paid for the new knowledge of the atom and the nucleus was the virtual abandonment of the theoretical foundations of physics as they had been painstakingly elaborated up to the end of the nineteenth century. In mathematics nothing so drastic or so spectacular took place. On the contrary there was a continuous and on the whole accelerated development from the sixteenth century to the mid-twentieth century, when mathematical activity attained a volume and an intensity the like of which had never been seen before.

The new conception of mathematics evolved bit by bit in the midst of this increasing activity, growing quite naturally and logically out of the discoveries of earlier mathematicians, particularly those of the nineteenth century. It provided new insights and a radically different philosophical attitude towards the role and the responsibilities of the mathematician without requiring that he abandon the principal achievements of earlier generations or reject the successful working practices and techniques of his predecessors. The emergence of the new ways of thinking about mathematics was too recent to permit an adequate appreciation of how profoundly they might alter the course of mathematical development. Nevertheless they had already produced clearly observable effects in stimulating and strengthening creative work in pure mathematics, and they promised to exert a strong overt influence upon the multiplying uses of mathematics in understanding and controlling the phenomenal world for human ends.

While the changes in mathematics represented some of the most far-reaching and significant changes produced in the course of the century, they were not of a kind to strike a casual observer with the same force as many

* This chapter was prepared by Dr. Marshall E. Stone.

others which accompanied them and which were indeed more or less directly caused by them. If the educated public by and large was reasonably well aware of the revolution which shook the foundations of physics, the same could hardly be said in reference to mathematics. Relatively few had any comparable knowledge or grasp of the fundamental progress which had occurred in the latter field. For the majority of mankind, chiefly concerned with the practical impacts of science and little or not at all with its intellectual roots, the most striking and impressive changes were those which impinged directly, intimately and decisively upon men's daily lives.

The powerful influences let loose by modern science were already beginning to affect society as a whole in such drastic ways that their true import could be grasped only by interpreting them as the agents and determinants of an entirely new and different cultural stage in the evolution of the human species. But beneath this transformation and subtly moulding the evolution of its consequences lay the potent role of mathematics whose influence bade fair to become ever more powerful and pervasive in science and in the other affairs of men. For the perception of new mathematical patterns in nature and of new forms in mathematics itself lies at the root of all science and all its applications.

The emergence of mathematics in the twentieth century upon an entirely new level of thought and action finds a unique and striking parallel in the history of Greek mathematics. The fundamental new discovery made by the Greeks, on which the whole edifice of their mathematics rested, was that the facts of empirical geometry fall into a logical pattern, accessible to description and analysis in terms of logic alone. In the relatively short span of two or three centuries the mathematicians of ancient Greece succeeded not only in grasping the logical structure of geometry but also in developing logic itself as a powerful tool for the discovery of new mathematical propositions. In spite of having left unsettled a certain number of details which actually were not put entirely straight until the end of the nineteenth century, they had done the essential things needed to show that geometry, far from being a strictly empirical science, can be developed from a few empirical axioms solely by means of logical inference. This was beyond all doubt or argument one of the few outstandingly great achievements of the human intellect. The mathematical insights of Thales and Pythagoras had a profoundly stimulating effect far beyond the bounds of mathematics itself and, from the beginning, exercised a powerful directive influence upon the historical development of Greek thought.

The new insights gained during the twentieth century had in essence exactly the same kind of deep fundamental significance for mathematical science as those of the early Greek mathematicians in the sixth century B.C. A comparison with the pioneer period in Greek mathematics strengthened the confidence of mathematicians that the intense and remarkably successful mathematical activity of the day was but a prelude to a still more brilliant era in the development of mathematics.

I. DIVORCE OF MATHEMATICS FROM THE PHYSICAL WORLD AND IDENTIFICATION WITH LOGIC

According to their understanding of the essential nature of mathematics, twentieth-century mathematicians identified mathematics as the study—comparative as well as intrinsic—of general abstract systems, each one an edifice built of specified abstract elements and structured by the presence of arbitrary but unambiguously specified relations among these elements. They recognized further that neither these systems nor the means provided by logic for studying their structural properties have any direct, immediate or necessary connection with the physical world, beyond what may be implied by the statement that thought takes place in the brain. In short, mathematicians reached what is to all appearances the ultimate stage of generalization and abstraction in their modern characterization of mathematics.

To describe the virtually absolute divorce thus permanently established between mathematics and the phenomenal world, Bertrand Russell said that in mathematics we do not know what we are talking about nor whether what we say is true. Because of the purely formal character thereby attributed to mathematics it is appropriate to liken mathematics to a game—or better, to an infinite assortment of games—in which the pieces and moves are intrinsically meaningless and the interest lies in perceiving and utilizing the patterns of play allowed under the rules. It was significant of the profound change which took place in mathematics that more and more mathematicians were approaching their subject in a spirit indistinguishable from that in which a devoted chess-player regards his beloved game. How sharp was the contrast between the twentieth-century attitude and that of earlier generations may be appreciated by recalling the pioneering achievements of such eighteenth- and nineteenth-century mathematicians as Leonhard Euler (1707–83), Pierre Laplace, Augustin Cauchy (1789–1857) and C. F. Gauss in various branches of applied mathematics. In the modern scientific life of the twentieth century pure mathematics was distinguished from applied, and the pursuit of mathematics for its own sake was recognized as a natural, fruitful and culturally desirable form of human activity.

As mathematics thus loosened its ties with the direct study of nature, it formed much closer ones with logic. In fact the line of demarcation between mathematics and logic was almost entirely erased by researches completed during these fifty years. On the one hand the modern characterization of mathematics reduced mathematics to the application of logical procedures to entities—namely, mathematical systems—which can be completely described in the language of logic. Thus all of mathematics was subsumed, in a precise technical sense, under logic. On the other hand the formalizations of logic through the use of appropriate symbolisms led directly to associations (on the meta-mathematical level, at least) with certain mathematical systems—specifically, for instance, with Boolean algebras, polyadic Boolean algebras or other somewhat similar algebras. Thus logic, in its formal or symbolic aspect, assumed more and more the character of a special branch of mathematics.

It is worth while retracing the evolution of this view of mathematics as a totally abstract, strictly logical and fully independent discipline. The starting-point was the dissatisfaction felt even in antiquity with the parallel axiom of Euclid according to which, in the geometry of the plane, a point and a line not incident with one another determine exactly one line incident with the given point and not incident with the given line. Does this statement reflect a self-evident property of points and lines in the physical sense? Does it or does it not follow logically from their other properties as summed up in the remaining axioms of the *Elements*? In seeking to answer these questions Girolamo Saccheri (1667–1733) discussed in the manner of Euclid a series of interesting consequences to an alternative for the parallel axiom, arriving finally at one which asserted a property of the line in his view 'repugnant to the nature of the straight line'. With this he congratulated himself upon having vindicated Euclid's inclusion of the parallel axiom among the postulates for geometry. What he had actually done was to show that the parallel axiom could be replaced by another which he felt to be more 'natural' and 'self-evident', and because he did not push this exercise of his logical faculties quite far enough he missed an opportunity to discover non-Euclidean geometry.

This opportunity was fully appreciated and seized upon in the early nineteenth century by Wolfgang and Johann Bolyai (1775–1856 and 1802–60), Carl Friedrich Gauss and Nikolai I. Lobachevski (1793–1856) who independently discovered hyperbolic non-Euclidean plane geometry, in which the parallel axiom is not satisfied. Gauss hesitated to publish his results, thus leaving the honours of this important discovery to be shared by the Bolyais and Lobachevski. Gauss sought to decide by physical measurements whether the geometry of space is Euclidean or Lobachevskian, using as a criterion the angle sum of a triangle (which is two right angles in the first case but less than two right angles in the second). He concluded that measurements of the accuracy he could attain were incapable of producing a decision.

Thus two internally consistent but mutually incompatible mathematical systems were available for describing physical geometry. It was impossible to imagine that either of them had, at the expense of the other, the advantage of a necessary connection with the physical world. It was likewise impossible to choose between them, then or conceivably for a good many years to come, on the basis of physical observations. The development of projective geometry by Jean Victor Poncelet (1788–1867), Georg F. Riemann's formulation of a general theory of space within the framework of metric differential geometry, and the comparative study of these different geometries by such eminent mathematicians as William K. Clifford (1845–79), Arthur Cayley (1821–95) and Felix Klein (1849–1925) all contributed to the emergence of the modern view described here.

As in geometry, so also in algebra it became evident that mathematics has to deal not with one number system but with infinitely many, displaying many common features but at the same time having their individual peculiarities. Among these the real and complex number systems remained the ones of principal interest for geometry, analysis and mechanics, though the role of other number systems in geometry began to emerge at the end of the nineteenth century as a consequence of the axiomatic studies undertaken at that time, and thereafter they became well established and familiar.

The increasing variety in mathematics and the technical difficulties met in connection with handling new problems, above all in mathematical analysis, led to an intensified interest in logic and its relation to mathematics. The result was the rapid development of new methods and new concepts which marked substantial advances and shed much light on many difficult or subtle problems in these fields. The symbolic treatment of logic by George Boole (1815–64), Ernst Schroeder (1841–1902) and Giuseppe Peano, the creation of set theory and transfinite number theory by Georg Cantor (1845–1918), and the logical analysis of the real number system by Julius Dedekind (1831–1916) and Gottlob Frege (1848–1925) prepared the way for Bertrand Russell and Alfred North Whitehead's monumental treatise *Principia Mathematica* (1911) which established in minute detail the central facts concerning the identification of mathematics with logic.

These, briefly, were some of the main steps toward the perception of mathematics as an entirely abstract discipline inseparable from logic. It is difficult to imagine how this view might be further developed and modified, except through the development and modification of views concerning logic itself. Thus in a certain sense the process of rendering mathematics abstract, which started in prehistoric times when men first began to conceive that numbers could be detached from the objects they were used to enumerate, reached a more or less definitive stage beyond which it is not possible to go without probing still more deeply into the nature of logic.

II. RELATION BETWEEN PURE MATHEMATICS
AND APPLIED FIELDS

The establishment of a new relation between pure mathematics and applied involves an accommodation which would have been forced, quite apart from theoretical considerations, by the increased specialization resulting from the struggles of mathematicians to cope somehow or other with the extremely rapid growth of mathematical and scientific knowledge. Paradoxically, the more uncompromisingly mathematics was conceived as being in principle independent of its applications, the more did productive contacts between mathematics and other scientific fields multiply and flourish. The cultivation of the abstract seemed to lead to success in handling the concrete, no doubt because independence implies a greater degree of flexibility in forming contacts between pure mathematics and the areas where it may be applied. The more that is known about mathematical systems on their own account, the more numerous are the opportunities for making mathematical progress in fields where traditional forms of mathematical analysis have so far proved inadequate or powerless. A long experience has taught that the working contacts between pure mathematics and applied are mutually beneficial, each influencing the other in stimulating and fruitful ways.

This lesson was confirmed in the twentieth century. In theoretical physics, for example, mathematics was called on to play new and unexpected roles in relativity theory, quantum theory and field theory, all of which were developed in this period. Some of the mathematics required in the study of these branches of physics was already available even though previously little studied or applied by physicists. In particular, tensor analysis, spectral theory and group theory were all in relatively advanced stages of development before being put to use in these newer parts of physics. As a result of the interest aroused by their important new applications, both spectral theory and group theory were stimulated to new growth in the period after 1930.

The mathematical structures abstracted from observation and experience as models for certain aspects of the physical world—a Riemannian geometry of the space-time manifold in the case of large-scale phenomena, and an algebra of operators on Hilbert space in the case of the small-scale realm of atomic and nuclear phenomena—were the most complex and elaborate encountered in any branch of applied mathematics up to the middle of the century. The models used in treating the classical parts of physics such as the dynamics of continuous media (solids, liquids and gases) and statistical mechanics are certainly considerably simpler, in spite of the fact that they offer mathematical difficulties with which mathematicians were still unable to cope. In other fields of science the models developed tended to be still simpler; in some areas, such as the behavioural sciences, mathematics was only beginning to play a role and had not yet been drawn upon for anything but extremely modest contributions. In view of the tremendously complex situations with which the behavioural sciences have to deal, however, it seemed probable that the initial appeal to quite simple and elementary mathematical models would open the way eventually to theories fully as complicated and mathematically involved as those accepted in modern physics.

One of the exciting features of intellectual life in the twentieth century was the proliferation of applied mathematics in a great many different directions, some of which were already indicated by the researches of the preceding century and some of which were entirely new. Because of its close relationship to physics, chemistry was strongly influenced by the radical developments in physics, particularly in so far as the molecular domain is concerned; in some respects the boundary lines between physics and chemistry may even be said to have disappeared, once an effective theoretical understanding of the behaviour of molecules had been made possible through the application of the appropriate kinds of mathematics. The newer discoveries in biochemistry were undoubtedly preparing a similar demolition of the frontier barriers between chemistry and physics on the one hand and certain branches of biology, particularly genetics, on the other. The analysis of genetic phenomena on the basis proposed by Mendel was given an elaborate mathematical form during the first part of the twentieth century; the next step lay in the search for the mathematical mechanism which enables giant molecules to act as the carriers of hereditary traits.

The study of human behaviour had inspired a certain number of efforts towards the use of mathematics as a tool of analysis before the end of the nineteenth century, but only in the second quarter of the twentieth century was enough success achieved to inspire a fairly large-scale attempt to put this study on the same basis as the natural sciences. The kinds of model used in these pioneering attempts were often quite different from those employed in the older sciences and in more than one instance even required the creation of new branches of mathematics. The most conspicuous example is von Neumann's theory of games, which provides a penetrating analysis of a wide variety of competitive situations and has direct applications in the theory of economic behaviour. But communication theory, though more closely connected with classical mathematics and originally developed with an eye upon engineering applications, was providing insights fully as valuable into the nature and use of language. It would be impossible to catalogue here all the aspects of human behaviour for which mathematical models were proposed during these years, but by way of illustration one or two more might be mentioned—for instance the learning process and some general features of social organization.

At mid-century many of the applications of mathematics suggested as aids to the analysis of men's behaviour as individuals or as members of social groups were speculative, and were a long way from being brought to the point of sharpness and precision which can reasonably be expected of them before they may be considered fully successful. In many cases the mathematical discussion of proposed models was too difficult and the opportunities for collecting appropriate observations too rare for this gap between theory and practice to be easily narrowed in a satisfactory way. Nevertheless, a plausible speculative analysis in terms which can be subjected to something a little better than trivial logical transformations is often very helpful in trying to grasp a complex situation, long before any detailed inferences can be drawn. For this reason there is justification for thinking that substantial progress in the mathematical treatment of the social sciences was being made from the 1930s on.

A feature common to many of the mathematical models which were introduced in widely different sciences was their incorporation of the basic concepts of probability theory. For this reason they are generally called statistical models and their mathematical study requires the use of techniques developed in the theory of probability and statistics. While most of these statistical models were proposed during the twentieth century, the idea of using them was a discovery of earlier times. Thus the statistical model on which the kinetic theory of matter is based was introduced by James Clerk Maxwell during the previous century. The models used in quantum-theoretical physics are also statistical models, and the assertions couched in terms of them are statistical assertions about the elementary particles. The models actually used for the study of matter in bulk—that is, of gases, liquids and solids treated as continuous media—can, in theory at least, be inferred as limiting or asymptotic forms of the statistical model proposed in the kinetic theory where matter is treated as an aggregate of discrete molecules. Thus the theory of probability lies at the foundations of modern physics. It plays no less important or indispensable a role in genetics, communication theory or game theory and quite generally is an essential component of a major part of analytical thinking about the biological, psychological and social behaviour of man.

The theory of probability and its statistical applications took their origins in the sixteenth century and were quite extensively developed by the end of the eighteenth. The two succeeding centuries saw this development carried very much farther ahead, on both the theoretical and the practical sides. As a branch of mathematics probability theory came to be identified as a part of general measure theory, and many of its central problems received beautiful solutions in this framework, particularly the ergodic theory of George D. Birkhoff (1884–1944) and John von Neumann which removed a puzzling difficulty at the heart of statistical mechanics and opened up interesting new avenues for technical progress in probability theory itself. The basic meaning of statistics for the study of all sorts of natural phenomena became very much better understood and appreciated than it was fifty years before, as the statistical models proved their effectiveness and versatility. Thus probability and statistics, if not at all new, certainly played a much more prominent and characteristic role during the twentieth century than they did in any of its three predecessors. The key to their success was that they made it possible to deal effectively with very large numbers of like objects at a time when the attention of scientists was shifting from individuals or small numbers of individuals to large aggregates of them.

An extremely practical development equally characteristic of the twentieth century was the invention and utilization of high-speed electronic computers. The dream of building powerful machines which could surpass the capabilities of human calculators was by no means a new one. In particular, Charles Babbage (1792–1871) during the nineteenth century had already conceived and worked on such a machine, introducing principles of design which continued to be of use in the computing art. The extraordinary development which took place in the twentieth century was stimulated by the rising demand for speedier and more versatile means for computing the solutions to problems in engineering and applied mathematics.

Modern computing devices were made possible by the conjunction of progress in two apparently unrelated directions, in electronics and in the formalization of mathematics and logic. While the machines developed in the 1950s were subject to various limitations, particularly as concerns their capacity for retaining or remembering data required in the course of an elaborate computation, they were exceedingly powerful and versatile. Their introduction therefore produced a marked alteration in the relations between mathematics and computing procedures. Since a machine of advanced design can handle at high speed almost any programme of successive elementary calculations which can be framed in logical terms, there was far less need than formerly for treating the computational aspects of a mathematical problem as an integral part of its discussion or solution in mathematical terms. These aspects became the direct concern of specialists in the writing of programmes for the machine. Such specialists needed to know both mathematics and the nature of their machines in order to choose the most economical ways for carrying out the computations desired in a wide variety of situations. They were engaged, therefore, in a task which has close contacts with logic as well as with algebra and analysis, and were beginning to build up a theory of computation which would eventually be ranged among the various branches of applied mathematics.

The capacity of the electronic computers was sufficiently great for them to be applied to furnish detailed information about areas which had hitherto been pretty much closed off because the necessary calculations were too massive to undertake and still not massive enough to be handled through asymptotic approximations. For instance, the treatment of management and decision problems leads to a mathematically rather simple model but one which in general contains too many variables for easy computation and too few for the application of asymptotic formulae. The theory of this model, known as linear programming, would therefore be of fairly restricted practical interest if it were not for the high-speed computer.

The modern machines offered new possibilities for the study of certain models for selected aspects of human behaviour. When for instance a description of what takes place in a social situation involving a group of individuals with assumed types of reaction can be formulated, the result can sometimes be converted into a mathematical model for the behaviour of the group and its implications calculated with the aid of a suitable machine. Since models of this kind often involve a number of variables in the range where direct computation had been the only way of getting at their mathematical properties, the machine was becoming an important research tool for the social scientist.

Thus, as these examples show, the improvement of computing devices and of skill in using them could be expected to give strong stimulation to the various branches, old and new, of applied mathematics. There were likewise possibilities for interesting uses of electronic computers in studying questions in pure mathematics, particularly those where empirical evidence is needed before general theories can be formulated or those where it is necessary to treat a limited number of special cases left aside by a general discussion.

III. ADVANCES IN PURE MATHEMATICS

The advances which took place in pure mathematics itself from 1900 on can be explained only in technical terms, but certain salient features of the growth of mathematics in the twentieth century may nevertheless be noted. In trying to describe them there is no better way than to examine the different branches into which mathematics traditionally may be divided: algebra, number theory, geometry, analysis and logic. It is not possible to give an adequate picture of the rich and varied discoveries made since the beginning of the twentieth century in each of these separate branches; but a correct impression of the unprecedented level of activity reached by mathematics can perhaps be conveyed by a brief survey going beyond the mere mention of statistical facts such as the number of mathematicians primarily engaged in research—some 3500 in the late 1950s—or the volume of their publications, an idea of which can be gained by inspecting an abstracting journal such as *Mathematical Reviews*.

1. *Algebra*

Algebra probably had a more spectacular development than any of the other branches of mathematics, because it not only underwent an extensive internal transformation but also penetrated deeply into all the rest, with a notable unifying influence. Inasmuch as algebra deals with very general mathematical systems indeed—an algebra in the widest sense is simply a mathematical system in which the relations are finitary and functional, being expressible therefore in terms of abstract operations upon its abstract elements—it is by no means surprising that algebras should occur in all sorts of places and thus provide unifying bonds among the various branches and parts of mathematics. Internally algebra took the path toward abstraction and latterly gave an increasing amount of attention to systems beyond the traditional ones. Thus in addition to studying groups, rings, fields, vector systems and linear algebras, modern algebra was also concerned with general multiplicative systems (or systems with binary composition), various non-associative rings and algebras, lattices, and so on. A number of general theorems about algebras in the widest sense were established and may be thought of as constituting a kind of 'universal algebra'.

Algebra has always played an important part in geometry and in the twentieth century it extended and deepened its connections there. Indeed there are some portions of geometry—namely, algebraic geometry and combinatorial topology—which it more or less came to dominate. Whenever there is question of transformations or of operations on geometric entities, algebra has a geometric role to play; the classical instances are the introduction of co-ordinates and the reduction of geometry to the study of transformation groups. As mathematicians took a broader and more abstract view of algebra they discovered more of such applications of algebra to geometry. On the other hand the formulation of geometrical problems in algebraic language presented algebra with new types of questions and led to new algebraic techniques and theories. A good example of the influence of geometry upon algebra is found in the case of homological algebra, which resulted from the development of certain techniques in combinatorial topology.

2. *Number theory*

Number theory has always been closely allied to algebra, providing it with many of its central problems. While many of these problems, be they concerned with the integers or with more general algebraic number systems, can be treated algebraically, some have also strong ties with analysis. Numerous problems of additive and multiplicative number theory have indeed been attacked by analytical methods with considerable success. One of the most concerted efforts along this line was made early in the twentieth century when Riemann's programme for studying the distribution of the prime numbers by means of the zeta-function was pushed extremely hard but with only partial success. Later there was a tendency to reduce the use of analysis to a minimum, often with much better success than might have been anticipated. Thus an 'elementary' proof of the prime number theorem, without use of the zeta-function, was carried through only in the 1940s. Some of the problems of number theory have connections with algebraic geometry which are extremely illuminating and which in certain cases have suggested the way to a solution. Such was the case for the multiplicative number theory of algebraic function fields and the study of the associated zeta-functions, where the analogue of Riemann's programme proved to be feasible. The history of number theory during the twentieth century records a whole series of brilliant contributions. Some solved old problems, some made significant advances short of complete success; but, as always in this difficult field, all bore the stamp of virtuosity.

3. *Geometry*

Geometry is a branch of mathematics which it is hard to characterize in a satisfactory way. On the one hand it has close ties with algebra, as has already been noted. On the other it has firm bonds with analysis. At times it almost appeared that geometry might be torn asunder, one part being absorbed by algebra, the other by analysis. Certainly, with the execution of the modern programme of treating algebraic geometry over a very general base field of co-ordinates, this part of geometry seemed to have been firmly appropriated by the algebraists. Differential geometry, however, is inseparable from analysis and the number of its problems requiring powerful analytical methods for their solution seemed to be increasing. Of course, geometry unites operational and continuity considerations, and the split mentioned above results in part from an attempt to examine these separately. Just as the examination of strictly algebraic features resulted in the creation of the modern form of algebraic geometry, so the isolation of the continuity considerations initiated that part of geometry known as topology.

Topology is hardly a very recent arrival on the mathematical scene, as it goes back at least to Leonhard Euler's (1707–83) Königsberg bridge problem, but by far the greater portion of its development took place during the twentieth century. This development was perhaps the most intensive undergone by any branch of mathematics since 1900. Topology itself was pulled in two directions, because some parts of it can be put in algebraic terms and treated by algebraic methods. These parts were drawn closer to algebra, and the remaining parts, where the fundamental continuity properties have to be kept to the fore, were thus somewhat separated from the others. Even in differential geometry, where the use of real or complex co-ordinates makes the continuity properties an essential feature of the whole subject, there are important algebraic aspects. These enter either through the combinatorial topological properties of a differentiable manifold or through the use of tensor algebra to characterize the local linear structures over the manifold.

The development of geometry during the twentieth century was on the whole opportunistic and not very well co-ordinated. Advances pushed far ahead into new territory in certain directions while there was little or no progress in others. The problems which were of interest at the opening of the century were in many cases replaced by others and almost forgotten. There was more concern with foundational questions than with technical problems of the classical kind. At mid-century, with advances in algebra, topology and analysis providing the means for attacking hitherto refractory problems, geometry was beginning to make very substantial advances of a fundamental kind, and it seemed reasonable to expect a very brilliant period for geometry during the following years.

4. *Analysis*

In some ways the emergence of functional analysis may be considered to be the most characteristic technical feature of twentieth-century mathematics. Functional analysis is, for one thing, essentially a creation of this century; and it is, for another, the central meeting-place of algebra and topology. In fact if one looks at the basic structures studied in modern mathematics one sees three fundamental types—the algebraic systems as described above; the topological spaces or mathematical systems in which only continuity relations are given; and the partially ordered systems, not previously mentioned. Partially ordered systems are primitive and simple as there is only one relation of order given in them; and they have direct connections with algebra through lattice theory and with topology through set-theory. When a system has simultaneously algebraic and topological or ordinal properties, coupled together in a reasonable way, it may be called a topological algebra (or more specifically, a topological group, topological field, topological vector space, and so on).

Such mixed systems became the prime objects of study in modern functional analysis. They arise frequently as abstractions from classical analysis, which is directly concerned with functions of a real or a complex variable and the standard analytical operations upon them. The experience from the 1920s onwards showed that it is very fruitful to focus attention on these abstractions, studying various kinds of topological algebras on their own merits and applying information obtained about them to the solution or clarification of more concrete problems of analysis. This point of view involved a shifting of attention from individual problems of function-theory to problems concerning aggregates of functions. Inasmuch as geometry also is concerned with the union of algebra and topology, the language of geometry is useful in describing many of the structures met in topological algebra and, when used in connection with topics of analysis, often presents the latter under a helpful geometrical aspect. The theory of Hilbert spaces, Banach spaces and their generalizations, and the theory of linear operators on such spaces became central in modern functional analysis and provide illustrations of the importance of this kind of abstraction for mathematical progress. The theory of topological groups, which received special attention because of its significance for quantum theory, can be considered as a part of functional analysis, as it is concerned in fact with a generalization of harmonic analysis from the case of the additive group of the real numbers to the general case of a group with continuity properties. One of the signal achievements of twentieth-century mathematics was the solution of the fifth problem of a celebrated series proposed by David Hilbert in 1900, showing that under suitable restrictions upon a topological group it can be co-ordinatized as a group of analytical transformations of an analytical manifold into itself.

A part of analysis which is especially close to the traditional core of the subject and also to its applications, and which was nevertheless strongly influenced by modern functional analysis, is the theory of partial differential equations. One can perhaps gain a better appreciation of the significance and power of the new ideas in analysis by seeing what they can accomplish in a difficult classical domain than by looking at their success with newly formulated problems. At any rate it is a noteworthy fact that by the mid-twentieth century modern functional analysis had been throwing a rather bright light upon the theory of partial differential equations for some thirty years and was probably the most effective single factor in the steady advances made in that theory. Even in the case of linear equations with constant coefficients, where knowledge was still hardly more than rudimentary, progress had been made in recent years only with the aid of the theory of distributions and would have been impossible otherwise. Thus the modern approach in this important area of mathematics more than justified itself by its successes with old problems as well as new.

5. Logic

To give an accurate account of recent technical advances and discoveries in symbolic or mathematical logic would require a patient examination of subtleties best appreciated against a broad mathematical background. Stimulated by Hilbert's bold proposal to establish the adequacy and freedom from contradiction of at least one fairly substantial portion of mathematics as formalized within a suitable symbolic logical system, logicians began to look more closely at the structural features of certain versions of the so-called 'first-order predicate calculus' and corresponding formalizations of set-theory and arithmetic. In the 1930s Kurt Gödel made the astonishing and extremely disconcerting discovery that for a wide variety of formal systems—in particular, for one combining the first-order predicate calculus with a formalized arithmetic—adequacy and freedom from contradiction are incompatible. More precisely, he showed that there are propositions of formal arithmetic which cannot be proved or disproved—in other words, which are undecidable—by means of the formal apparatus of the first-order predicate calculus as applied to the formal axioms given for arithmetic so long as the system is consistent, but that this is not due to any inadequacy of the first-order predicate calculus taken by itself. A related but independent result was Alonzo Church's (1903–   ) discovery that no systematic procedure can be prescribed for deciding which formal statements or sentences in first-order predicate logic are provable. Independently, A. M. Turing (1912–54) presented this result in a more picturesque form by showing that none of a wide class of 'machines' which he described could furnish such a decision.

Thus logic suddenly burgeoned with these and other paradoxes of an extremely subtle nature, difficult to comprehend and impossible to ignore. The mechanism which produces such paradoxes came to be much better understood, and the paradoxes therefore seemed rather less astonishing than they originally did. Their challenge was not one whit less for all that. Most of the paradoxes invite philosophical discussion, but those due to Church and Turing also have a bearing on another aspect of formal logic. This is because the latter raise the question as to whether or not the brain is a mechanism subject to the limitations explicitly established by Turing for his machines. It did not seem likely that any of these problems would be soon resolved by purely technical means, or even by anything short of new and highly original insights. In the meantime logicians and mathematicians were busy with other problems of a more technical nature and less philosophical interest, refining and enlarging concepts of logic as a formal discipline.

IV. EXPOSITION AND TEACHING OF MODERN MATHEMATICS

The rapid growth of mathematics during the twentieth century, and the accompanying extensive alterations in its general nature and its technical content, made it vitally necessary for mathematicians to concern themselves in an active way with the exposition and teaching of modern mathematics. At the level of exposition there was a growing need for presentations of the new subject-matter of mathematics and its organization into systematically arranged and perceptively correlated chapters. The most ambitious attempt to provide such a presentation, with every detail of definition, notation and demonstration carefully worked out, was that made by a number of French mathematicians banded together in the name of Bourbaki. Beginning in the 1930s this group worked steadily, with some changes of membership, to prepare a general statement of modern mathematics in the form of an encyclo-paedic treatise. After twenty years of work they were, naturally enough, still far from their goal and were forced to undertake a revision of the volumes they had already published. A considerable part of what was written in the treatise of Bourbaki dealt with set-theory, general topology, algebra and linear functional analysis—precisely the topics which were being developed to an unusual degree and which therefore presented the greatest problems for an expositor.

The new mathematics also created need for a thorough reform in mathematical instruction at all levels, to the end that elementary mathematics in the schools might be thoroughly modernized, better articulated and better adapted to the requirements of youth in a technological civilization. A very considerable portion of the mathematics taught at the advanced university level in the 1950s was not taught at all thirty or forty years before. As a result it became necessary to compress and condense the mathematics taught in schools and in the earlier university years as preparation for advanced instruction in the modern spirit. In consequence there developed an increasingly disturbing gap between school mathematics and university mathematics in many parts of the world, one symptom of the grave crisis which was overtaking education in the new scientific age. In the debates, the experiments and the organized efforts stimulated by this profound crisis in education, mathematics was at the very centre of the struggle to make the scientific knowledge of the times more accessible to the common man and to increase its cultural and technological role in the interests of mankind as a whole. In view of the nature of mathematics and its potentialities for the future of science, this could not be otherwise as mathematics entered the second half of the twentieth century.

SECTION TWO

THE ELABORATION
AND APPLICATION OF
THE PHYSICAL SCIENCES

CHAPTER VIII

THE ELABORATION OF THE PHYSICAL SCIENCES*[1]

I. INTRODUCTION

THE rapid increase of scientific and technical knowledge brought a concomitant increase in specialization as it became necessary for a single individual to master a great wealth of detailed knowledge in order to keep abreast of even a narrow field of inquiry. It became a cliché to contrast the 'narrow specialist' of the twentieth century with the 'universal genius' of the past. However, concurrent with this trend toward specialization there was a unifying trend. Whereas in former times one man might be able to strive at the frontiers of knowledge in several fields such as physics, chemistry and geology, there was little unity in the subject-matter in these areas of knowledge. Physics and chemistry appeared to be separate and well-defined disciplines. In general, geologists rejected the notion that the rocks they studied were amenable to understanding by the laws of chemistry and physics. Application of physics to astronomy was limited to celestial mechanics in which Newton's laws of motion were used to predict the movement of astronomical objects.

In the twentieth century the isolation of the various physical sciences was disappearing as a consequence of the development of a universal theory of matter. The knowledge of the properties of atoms and molecules gained by the nineteenth-century chemists and the mechanical laws and electromagnetic theory of the physicists were extended and unified by new discoveries, particularly by the discovery of the existence and properties of the elementary particles, especially the electron, proton and neutron, and by the development of quantum mechanics. As a result of this unification the boundaries between physics and chemistry became much more arbitrary, being drawn at least as much by tradition and historical accident as by any inherent difference in the subject-matter.

Physical science in the middle of the twentieth century, whether pursued in the name of physics, chemistry or some other science, largely consisted of extending still further the theory of matter and applying it to all imaginable portions of the physical world. A unified theory of matter was being applied with equal confidence to increase man's understanding of the properties of familiar metals, of the material in the core of the earth and of the most distant regions of the universe. Much of biology was being approached as a

* This chapter was prepared by Dr. George W. Wetherill.

physical science, and there were few astronomers who did not refer to themselves as astrophysicists. The development of the new theory of matter was the central development of twentieth-century physics and chemistry and the new understanding of the structure of matter which it provided transformed the disciplines of geology and astronomy.

In addition to its success in integrating the physical sciences, this new development had incalculable importance to technology. Whole industries developed as a consequence of man's increased understanding of the nature of matter. Basic discoveries were frequently translated into commercial products within a few years, while on the other hand the products of the most highly advanced technology provided the tools without which much of the basic research would be impossible.

II. THE NATURE OF MATTER

1. *The heritage of classical physics and chemistry*

By the end of the nineteenth century a great and satisfying synthesis of macroscopic phenomena had been achieved. To the classical work on mechanics of the seventeenth and eighteenth centuries had been added a new understanding of thermodynamics and electromagnetic phenomena, the latter principally as a consequence of the experimental work of Michael Faraday and the theoretical contributions of James Clerk Maxwell. Maxwell had succeeded in unifying in a few simple equations such diverse phenomena as the attraction of oppositely charged bodies, the rotation of electric motors and the reflection of light. The three fields, mechanics, electromagnetism and thermodynamics, had been integrated by the far-reaching principle of the conservation of energy.

Yet even within this grand system some inconsistencies remained until Einstein's Special Theory of Relativity in 1905 provided a key to the principal unsolved problems. The delicate experiments by Michelson and Morley* had failed to detect any motion of the earth with respect to the hypothetical aether, whereas the classical theory of light led scientists to expect such a motion. Einstein showed that it was possible to write the laws of mechanics and electromagnetic theory in such a way that they would be identical in all systems of co-ordinates moving at constant velocity with respect to one another. In this theory the velocity of light is the same in any of these co-ordinate systems, thus explaining the negative result of the Michelson–Morley experiment.

To accomplish this result Einstein altered slightly the classical equations of mechanics, together with the equations used to convert data measured in one co-ordinate system to its equivalent in a relatively-moving co-ordinate system. These changes in the laws of mechanics were so slight that the discrepancies which they corrected had been undetected in the previous experimental data.

* *Supra*, p. 131

However, many experiments were subsequently designed and performed to test the predictions of the Special Theory of Relativity and the theory was strikingly confirmed. Thus, early in the twentieth century the Special Theory of Relativity completed the grand synthesis of macroscopic physics and formed the capstone to this monument of nineteenth-century thought.

Looking back at nineteenth-century physics from the mid-twentieth century it appeared that much of the completeness of this synthesis arose from the choice of phenomena of interest to the physicist. There were vast classes of physical phenomena which the classical physics could never explain. For example, when an electrical discharge is passed through hydrogen the light emitted by the gas is confined to certain discrete wavelengths, referred to as spectral lines. This set of wavelengths forms the characteristic spectrum of hydrogen which is different from the equally characteristic spectrum of any other element, say, nitrogen. These spectra were an important practical tool in physics, chemistry and astronomy. Classical models of an atom were constructed in an attempt to explain these spectra, but classical physics proved unable to say just why a given element was capable of emitting certain wavelengths and not others.

Another example can be drawn from the theory of elasticity which was greatly developed during the nineteenth century. This theory is founded on the assumption known as Hooke's law, which states that when a body is deformed the deformation is proportional to the force causing the deformation, or as more commonly expressed, the strain is proportional to the stress. The factor of proportionality between the strain and the stress is called the elastic constant and will in general depend on the type of deformation. Thus the elastic constant for deformation by twisting is generally different from that for deformation by stretching.

Early in the nineteenth century there was a serious controversy among various leading physicists and mathematicians who were engaged in developing a theory of elasticity as to how many different constants it was necessary to specify in order to describe the elastic properties of a body. One school held that two were necessary, one to describe the resistance of the body to stretching and the other its resistance to twisting. The other school maintained that only one constant was necessary and if this one were given the other could be calculated. The fundamental difference between the theories proposed was that the one-constant school made certain assumptions about the forces between the atoms and molecules of which the body was composed, whereas the other did not.

While there were always advocates of the one-constant view, it was characteristic of nineteenth-century physics that the main stream of progress in the classical theory of elasticity followed the two-constant view and the great successes made by this theory by the end of the century were accomplished by two-constant theories. The reason for this was that in the nineteenth century any theory which depended on the assumed atomic structure of a body was doomed to failure because an adequate theory of atoms and their interactions simply did not exist. The two-constant theory depended only on more general principles such as the laws of mechanics and thermodynamics which were well established by the middle of the nineteenth century. However, as a result of the new understanding of the structure of matter it became feasible actually to undertake the calculation of the elastic constants from more fundamental principles, and even to understand the circumstances under which Hooke's law will fail to be valid.

As illustrated by these examples, scientists of the last century made repeated efforts to explain phenomena which depended on the microscopic structure of matter. These attempts were seldom successful except in a few cases such as the classical kinetic theory of gases. However, the successes of classical physics in the macroscopic realm were so great that these difficulties were not taken very seriously and the state of the science was generally regarded as being eminently satisfactory.

Nineteenth-century chemistry, too, had constructed a comprehensive system of chemical elements and their interrelationships which was regarded as complete, though it rested on empirical observations whose rationale was unexplained. The early work along lines laid down by Antoine Laurent Lavoisier (1743–94) in the late eighteenth century had identified many chemical elements, studied the simpler reactions between them, and had established that elements, to a very good approximation, combine in weights proportional to small whole numbers. At the beginning of the nineteenth century John Dalton (1766–1844) had conceived that this law of multiple proportions could be explained if a given chemical element was composed of identical, indestructible atoms of matter of a definite weight, and with this theory he had laid the foundations for the subsequent development of chemistry.[2]

The atomic theory had led to the development of precise techniques for the determination of atomic weights and many of the analytic procedures which continued in use had their origin in this work. It also provided an interpretation of the concept of valence. The valence of an element represents the relative proportions in which hydrogen combines with a given element. For example, one atomic weight (one gram) of hydrogen reacts with one atomic weight (35.5 g.) of chlorine to form hydrochloric acid whereas in the analogous reaction with oxygen two atomic weights of hydrogen are required to react with one atomic weight (16 g.) of oxygen. Therefore chlorine is said to have a valence of one while oxygen has a valence of two. In terms of the atomic theory the oxygen atom is thought of as being able to link with two hydrogen atoms whereas the chlorine atom links with only one. This property of valence, like atomic weight, is a fundamental property of an element and therefore, in accordance with the atomic theory, must represent some property of the atoms of that element.

In 1869 Dmitri Ivanovich Mendeleyev (1834–1907) had succeeded in connecting the atomic weight, valences and many other properties of the elements by his famous periodic system which showed how the properties of the elements tend to be repeated when arranged in order of increasing atomic weight. On the basis of this discovery it was possible to predict the existence and properties of a number of missing elements, some of which were quickly discovered.

There had also been a great development of organic chemistry following the successful synthesis of urea from inorganic matter by Friedrich Wöhler (1800–82) at Göttingen in 1828, which had disproved the idea that there was a fundamental difference between organic and inorganic matter. Many new compounds had been synthesized, their reactions understood and the structural form of their molecules established.

In the field of physical chemistry the laws of thermodynamics had been applied to the problem of chemical equilibrium leading to the formulation of the law of mass action; the techniques of electrochemistry had been established and the groundwork was laid for a theory of the rate of chemical reactions.

Great as these achievements were, the underlying foundations of nineteenth-century chemistry were largely empirical. There was no reason known why atoms should unite themselves into molecules in some ways and not in others. Studies of the ionic salts such as sodium chloride suggested that the binding was electrical in nature, but on the other hand there was the vast number of compounds of carbon in which the binding did not seem to be electrical. There was no reason known why the properties of the elements should repeat themselves as shown by Mendeleyev nor why some compounds such as water were liquid under ordinary conditions whereas others such as methane were gaseous. The whole field was badly in need of a generalization to replace the rapidly growing collection of empirical facts. As the result of the combined efforts of physicists and chemists the development of the theory of the nuclear atom and the laws of quantum mechanics during the twentieth century provided this generalization.

2. The development of the new theory of matter

(a) *The nuclear atom model.* It has commonly happened in the development of science that great new discoveries do not follow naturally from questions logically raised as consequences of earlier work. In some cases they seem to stem more from technological advances which permit new types of measurements to be made. The discoveries which led to the breakdown of classical physics and opened the way to the explosive development of atomic physics in the twentieth century can be traced to the invention of a greatly improved vacuum pump by Heinrich Geissler (1814–79) in 1855, and further improved by other workers. While these pumps were very slow and inefficient by modern standards, they were so great an improvement over earlier ones that many scientists were encouraged to make experiments on gases at low pressures. In particular they studied the electrical properties of such gases and discovered many new phenomena such as the bright discharges familiar in neon signs and beams of particles which they named cathode rays. J. J. Thomson, working at the Cavendish Laboratory in Cambridge, England, showed that these cathode rays were the same regardless of the material which produced them, and formed the conclusion that they were atoms of electricity or electrons.

Using similar cathode-ray tubes Konrad von Röntgen in 1895 discovered a new type of radiation which could penetrate opaque material and which he named X-rays. It was suspected at the time that these rays were related to the fluorescence produced in the glass wall of the apparatus by the bombardment of the cathode rays. X-rays had immediate medical application, but perhaps even more important for the development of science was the fact that their discovery stimulated the French scientist Henri Becquerel to conduct a series of experiments on fluorescence, using naturally fluorescent minerals containing the element uranium. These experiments led to the discovery of natural radioactivity in 1896.

Naturally radioactive elements were found to emit three distinct kinds of energetic radiations in processes by which these unstable heavy atoms spontaneously transmute from one chemical element to another; the three types of radiation were called alpha, beta and gamma before their real nature was known. As a consequence the naturally radioactive materials proved to be extremely valuable as sources of high-energy particles which could be used in other studies of the nature of matter. Further study showed that the alpha radiation consists of a stream of relatively heavy, positively charged particles known to be high-speed nuclei of helium atoms. The beta radiation consists of a stream of much lighter, negatively charged particles, of the same nature as the electrons of cathode rays except that they possess much more energy of motion than any cathode rays which could be made with the technical means available at that time. Finally, the gamma radiation was found to be like electromagnetic radiation X-rays, but of even shorter wavelength.

The most decisive experiments in this field were those made by Ernest R. Rutherford in Manchester, England. He studied (1911) the angular scattering of high-speed alpha particles as they went through thin foils of various materials. His work showed, in the cases where the particles were deflected through moderately large angles (10 degrees or more), that the deviation was the consequence of a strong interaction of an alpha particle with a single atom of the scattering foil, not the cumulative effect of weaker interactions with many atoms in the foil. From quantitative study of such angular scatterings, especially at large angles, Rutherford inferred that the positive electricity in the atom was not spread out through the whole atom of diameter about 10^{-8} cm, but would have to be concentrated on a small nucleus which could not have more than ten-thousandth the diameter of the whole atom. Moreover, by comparing the way in which various elements scattered alpha particles he found the relative amounts of positive charge in the nucleus of different elements.

In this way was born the concept of the nuclear atom, i.e. that atoms consist of a small centre of positive charge about 10^{-12} cm. in diameter surrounded by an equal negative charge in the form of electrons at a distance of about 10^{-8} cm. The positive charge on the nucleus was thought of as arising from a number of positive atoms of electricity called protons, analogous to the negative electrons. This concept thereafter formed the basis of all understanding of matter. In the normal state each nucleus is surrounded by enough negatively charged electrons to make the atom as a whole electrically neutral. All the atoms of a given chemical element resemble each other in having the same nuclear charge, and hence the same number of electrons moving around outside the nucleus. This number is called the atomic number, usually denoted by Z.[3] Thus the chemical elements stand in one-to-one correspondence with the integers, from one for hydrogen through 2 for helium, 3 for lithium, 4 for beryllium, 5 for boron, 6 for carbon, 7 for nitrogen, 8 for oxygen, on up to 92 for uranium, the largest value of Z for a naturally-occurring chemical element.

About this same time J. J. Thomson devised an instrument called a mass spectrograph by means of which the relative masses of individual atoms could be determined. With this instrument it was soon learned (1910) that not all atoms of the same chemical element are alike in mass. Thus the atoms of neon ($Z = 10$) are found to be of three kinds, with masses $A = 20$, 21 and 22 on a scale of which ordinary hydrogen has a mass number $A = 1$ and ordinary oxygen has $A = 16$. Such different kinds of atoms of the same chemical element are called isotopes. In terms of Rutherford's nuclear model these experiments showed that nuclei can have a range of masses for a given positive charge Z.

Hardly had Rutherford made his basic discovery of the need for a nuclear model than this idea was taken up and pursued with extraordinary fruitfulness by Niels Bohr. He was then a young Danish theoretical physicist who had recently gone to Manchester to continue his graduate studies. Bohr undertook to develop Rutherford's nuclear atom model by learning more in detail of the behaviour of the outer electrons and how this behaviour was related to the emission or absorption of light by a gas made up of many such atoms. In order to do this he had to make some drastic departures from what then seemed fully-established consequences of the known laws of electromagnetism. According to what was then known, the electrons ought to move around the nucleus in orbits. Being accelerated as they move, they ought to radiate electric waves, like the oscillating charges which generate radio waves. As they radiate they would lose energy and move faster in smaller orbits, and thus the frequency of the emitted light would steadily increase. Thus a gas of many such atoms ought to emit a continuous spectrum of frequencies, in sharp contradiction to the discrete sharp-line spectrum that is actually emitted.

To overcome this difficulty Bohr postulated that the atoms can only exist in sharply-defined discrete energy levels, implying that the electron orbits could have only definite sizes and shapes. He next postulated that an atom emits a unit or quantum of light radiation by making an abrupt transition or jump from a higher to a lower energy level, and absorbs radiation by an analogous transition from a lower to a higher energy level. Finally, he supposed that the frequency of the light emitted or absorbed in such jumps is equal to the difference in energy of the initial and final levels divided by Planck's quantum constant, $h = 6.55 \times 10^{-27}$ erg-sec.

With these simple but daringly radical postulates he was able to give a direct quantitative interpretation of the spectrum of atomic hydrogen. His work was quickly taken up by others, who proceeded to show how its natural extension could explain many detailed features of more complex atomic spectra.

A great fever of excitement was let loose in the world of physics by one success after another of the Rutherford–Bohr atom model. Soon the model was extended to give an account of the rotation and vibration spectra of diatomic molecules which were thereby interpreted to give quantitative data about chemical bonds between the atoms in such molecules. As illustrated by this latter development, during the next two decades physics and chemistry were rapidly joining to form one science with common fundamental laws which were becoming increasingly well understood.

(b) *The development of quantum mechanics.* Although Bohr's use of quantum jumps to interpret emission and absorption of light by atoms or molecules was radical by the standards of nineteenth-century physics, this assumption was a natural next step since the original idea of the light quantum had already been introduced by Max Planck in 1900. Planck was led to the idea by theoretical analysis of the radiation emitted by hot bodies. Because of its radical nature and the difficulty of the reasoning involved, the light quantum idea did not have much influence on physics until Einstein used it in simpler ways in 1905.

Since early in the nineteenth century light had been regarded as a wave motion. By the end of that century these waves were known to be waves of electric and magnetic force, and the mathematical laws governing their propagation were well understood. According to the light quantum idea as used by Bohr and Planck it is supposed that the energy exchange occurring when atoms emit or absorb light is discontinuous, in such a way that in a single elementary process energy is always emitted or absorbed in units which are always the same for light of a definite frequency, being in fact equal to $E = h\gamma$ where E is the quantum of energy, γ is the frequency of light and h, Planck's constant, is a universal constant whose value has to be determined from analysis of the observed phenomena.

In 1905 Einstein also used this idea to explain some puzzling phenomena observed in the photoelectric effect. This effect, which became familiar in electric eyes for opening doors in stores or garages and in the television camera, consists of the observation that when light falls on a metal electrode electrons are emitted from the metal. Thus it seems that the beam of light is able to knock out electrons from the metal. However, it was observed that when the intensity, and thereby the energy, of the beam of light is increased the energy of the emitted electron does not increase but remains the same. The number of electrons emitted increases but it was expected from the wave theory that, since the energy of the incident light beam is greater, the light should be capable of knocking out electrons with greater energy, and there-fore their energy should also increase.

The experimental result, puzzling according to the wave theory, becomes clear from the point of view that light is absorbed in quanta, the energy of one quantum being directly given to one electron. In this way Einstein showed how the photoelectric effect gives evidence of absorption of light in quanta, pointing the way to the incorporation of the same principle in Bohr's theory of emission and absorption of light by atoms.

According to Einstein's Special Theory of Relativity, any particle having energy, as does the light quantum, ought also to be the carrier of a definite amount of momentum. This conclusion gained experimental support in the studies in 1923 by Arthur H. Compton (1892–   ) on X-ray scattering, leading to the discovery of what came to be called the Compton effect. Thereby the reality of the light quantum became even more definitely accepted by physicists.

Although Bohr's ideas had great success and gave an immense stimulus to the study of atomic and molecular spectra, the exact detailed calculation of the energy levels of atoms other than hydrogen raised a number of difficulties. By 1920 many features of the complex spectra of many-electron atoms had been analysed, but there were puzzling details even about the structure of the relatively simple spectrum of sodium and the other alkali metals, and also about the behaviour of spectra when the emitting atoms are in a magnetic field (Zeeman effect). In 1925 it was found possible to patch up the Bohr theory by assuming that the electron is more complicated than being just a charged particle and that it is also endowed with a fixed amount of angular momentum, like a spinning top, and a magnetic moment, like a tiny bar magnet. These properties, called electron spin, became a firmly established central part of all atomic theory.

In the decade following Bohr's first paper on his atom model in 1913 no one did more than Bohr to keep the attention of scientists focused on the fact that its principles were far from complete or satisfactory. That electrons in atoms do not behave like particles obeying Newton's laws of motion was evident, and some partial rules about the nature of the departure from them were known. It was clear that classical mechanics needed to be replaced by a new quantum mechanics which would agree with classical mechanics when applied to large systems and give differing but correct results when applied to atomic systems. To discover the laws of quantum mechanics was the crucial problem of theoretical physics in the early 1920s.

The answer to this problem came from two directions, not at first recognized as providing the same answer. Louis de Broglie (1892–   ) published (1924) a paper in which he suggested that since light seems to have a dual nature, in some ways appearing to be a wave and in other ways a particle, this duality might also apply to electrons and protons, and that these particles might also have wave properties. Erwin Schrödinger (1887–   ) of Zürich took up the idea two years later and put it in a more definite mathematical form, discovering the equations of quantum mechanics in a form called wave mechanics. These equations formed the basis of the methods of treating atomic systems thereafter.

The other approach to the subject was initiated in 1925 by Werner Heisenberg and led to a formulation of quantum mechanics in which physical quantities were represented by a kind of mathematical quantity called a matrix. Matrix algebra was at that time quite unfamiliar to most theoretical physicists, a fact which, when combined with the physical novelty of the new concepts, made for great difficulty in their assimilation.

By 1927 the new methods, wave mechanics as developed by de Broglie and Schrödinger and matrix mechanics as developed by Heisenberg, were recognized to be the same theory in two different mathematical cloaks.

Experimentally the new ideas gained quick support through the discovery in 1927 of electron diffraction. It was shown that electrons when scattered by a crystal behave as if their motion were governed by the associated wave motion postulated first by Louis de Broglie, and they are diffracted much as light waves are diffracted by a diffraction grating.

The new ideas introduced a complete break with the ideas of classical mechanics. In the theory which originated with Newton, motion was fully determined by the initial positions and velocities of the moving parts and the forces acting on them. However, it was now seen that at the atomic level the motions were undetermined and that the wave function of Schrödinger serves to indicate only probabilities or relative likelihoods of the various possible motions.[4, 5] In 1927 Heisenberg completed the recognition of the essential nature of the indeterminate elements of the quantum theory by showing that they had their origin in the impossibility of making certain measurements of infinitely great precision.

These new ideas proved to be extraordinarily fruitful in the following thirty years. To a new generation of physicists and chemists they seemed perfectly natural. But at first the implications of uncertainty were resisted vigorously by many theoretical physicists. Thus Albert Einstein, while recognizing the many successes of the mathematical formalism of quantum mechanics, refused during the remainder of his life to believe that the indeterminacy aspects represent a fundamental and final limitation of knowledge. Instead he believed that these ideas represent only a temporary lacuna in our understanding which he expected would somehow be filled in by future discoveries.

The first main consequence of the discovery of the mathematical laws of quantum mechanics was that it permitted a highly detailed completion of the theory of atomic spectra and opened also the way to a greater understanding of the nature of the chemical bond between atoms in molecules. The simplest type of molecule is the hydrogen molecule, formed by the bonding together of two hydrogen atoms. Each hydrogen atom has a nucleus consisting of a single proton to which is bound a single electron. Until the advent of quantum mechanics there was no known reason why these hydrogen atoms should join to form a hydrogen molecule.

In 1927 Walter Heinrich Heitler (1904–   ) and Fritz London (1900–54) in Zürich showed that an attraction between these two atoms should arise in a way that is peculiar to quantum mechanics and has no counterpart in classical physics. These exchange forces provide not only a quantitative understanding of binding in the hydrogen molecule but give a qualitative picture of the nature of chemical bonds in other more complex molecules and also an understanding of the reasons for chemical valence.[6] The new theory also gave a clear understanding of the fundamental structural distinction between solids that are insulators and solids that conduct electricity.

The new theory clarified the fundamental basis for the periodic system of the elements. The regularities exhibited in the periodic system obviously reflect some more fundamental underlying principle. In 1924 Bohr attempted to explain the periodic system in terms of his atom model but although he was certainly on the right track the ambiguities inherent in his theory made a definitive explanation impossible. During the next few years, the discovery of electron spin, the exclusion principle and the quantum mechanics of Schrödinger and Heisenberg permitted the resolution of these ambiguities.

According to these new ideas the simplest atom is that of hydrogen with one electron bound to the nucleus. This electron will be, in its lowest energy state, characterized by the quantum number $n = 1$. In the next heavier atom, that of helium, there is an additional electron having this same quantum number, but this second electron will be spinning in the direction opposite to that of the first. According to the exclusion principle proposed by Wolfgang Pauli (1900–58) in 1925, no more electrons can be added with $n = 1$, and this shell is said to be closed[7]. The other inert gases—neon, argon, krypton, xenon—share this property of having their last electron shell closed. In the next heaviest atom, lithium, the third electron must be in the next shell, characterized by the quantum number $n = 2$. The alkali metals—lithium, sodium, potassium, rubidium, caesium, and francium—share this property of having one electron in the next higher shell above the closed shell characteristic of the inert gases. It is this similarity in the configuration of the outermost electrons which produces the similarity in the chemical properties of these groups of elements, since the outermost electrons are the most effective in the interactions leading to chemical reactions. The exclusion principle, together with the equations of quantum mechanics, show that this second shell, $n = 2$, can hold eight electrons. When this second shell is closed the total number of electrons is $2 + 8 = 10$. The element with an atomic number of 10 is neon, the second insert gas. The next element is the alkali metal sodium with one electron in the shell $n = 3$. Continuation of this reasoning led to an understanding of the reason why all the other groups of elements such as the alkaline earth's and the rare earths had similar chemical properties.

The links between chemistry and physics which were forged by the Bohr theory were strengthened by the development of quantum mechanics. In the next decade great strides were made in fundamental chemistry as numerous investigators took advantage of the sudden increase in understanding made possible by the new theory. Modern theoretical chemistry as well as solid-state physics largely consists of a continuing exploitation of this theory.

(c) *The early development of nuclear physics.* The developments in physics and chemistry initiated by the Bohr theory and crowned with the successes of quantum mechanics form the subject known as atomic theory which deals with aspects of the atom outside the nucleus but in which the internal structure of the nucleus itself is not considered. At the time of the great success of atomic physics and chemistry in the late 1920s little had been done to extend the pioneer work of Rutherford in the study of the nucleus itself. As early as 1919 Rutherford had succeeded in transforming one type of nucleus into another. He bombarded nitrogen gas with alpha particles and found that high-energy protons were emitted indicating that an alpha particle enters a nitrogen nucleus for which $A = 14$ and $Z = 7$ and knocks out a proton, leaving an isotope of oxygen of mass 17. However, the total yield of such particles was extremely small so that further effective work on nuclear reactions had to await the development of large electrical devices which are able to accelerate large numbers of protons and alpha particles up to energies of several million electron volts.

In the excitement of working out the consequences of the new discoveries in atomic physics during the 1920s the physics of the nucleus was largely neglected. But when atomic theory seemed to be well established around 1930, many physicists returned to the study of the nucleus and to the development of the necessary accelerating devices.

The production of a nuclear reaction with artificially accelerated particles was first achieved in 1932 by John Douglas Cockcroft (1897–   ) and E. T. S. Walton (1903–   ) at the Cavendish Laboratory, Cambridge, England. After that the study of nuclear reactions was carried out on a large scale in many laboratories with the aid of particles accelerated in the cyclotron as first built by E. O. Lawrence (1901–58) in California in 1931 and in the electrostatic belt machines of the type introduced about the same time by R. J. Van de Graaf (1901–   ) in Princeton, USA.

In other ways the year 1932 was an important one in the development of nuclear physics. In that year James Chadwick discovered the existence of a third kind of fundamental particle, having no electric charge and a mass nearly the same as that of the proton. Because of its electrical neutrality he named this particle the neutron. It was quickly pointed out that many difficulties could be accounted for by supposing the atomic nucleus to consist of both protons and neutrons. In the following quarter-century this view of the constitution of the nucleus was so overwhelmingly successful as to leave no doubt of its correctness. Although subsequently other kinds of fundamental particles were discovered it remained true that all ordinary matter consists of only the three kinds of particles: protons, neutrons and electrons. Thus the various chemical elements are characterized by having a nucleus containing Z protons and K neutrons. The mass number A equals $K + Z$. Around this nucleus is a cloud of electric charge containing Z electrons.

Also during this same year a heavy isotope of hydrogen, deuterium, was discovered by H. C. Urey (1893–   ) at Columbia University, USA, and a new kind of particle, the positron, by Carl D. Anderson (1905–   ) in California.

The discovery of deuterium or heavy hydrogen was particularly important for nuclear physics in that its nucleus, called the deuteron, consists of but one neutron and one proton and therefore must have the simplest possible nuclear structure: a simple bond between a proton and a neutron. Deuterons can be accelerated to high energies in cyclotrons and other accelerators and used to produce nuclear reactions when they bombard targets of various elements. Writing d for deuteron, n for neutron, p for proton, α for alpha particle, we can distinguish (d,n), (d,p) and (d,α) reactions in which the deuteron enters the target nucleus and respectively a neutron or a proton or an alpha particle is emitted. Within a few years after 1932 many such nuclear reactions had been studied in considerable detail.

The discovery of the positron was important because it was the first of the elementary particles of transient existence to be discovered, and because it provided a confirmation of some peculiar predictions growing out of Paul A. M. Dirac's (1902–   ) theory (1928) in which the quantum mechanics of a single electron was put in a form consistent with Einstein's Special Theory of Relativity. Dirac's theory led to the conclusion that for each kind of elementary particle (one that is not structurally built of other particles) there should exist a related anti-particle, which would be its opposite in various ways. For the electron the anti-particle is the positron, a particle having the same mass as the electron and the same numerical value of electric charge, but the positive kind instead of the negative.

According to Dirac's theory a positron and an electron can mutually annihilate each other upon colliding, and in their place two quanta of gamma radiation are produced. Since there are so many electrons present in ordinary matter, a positron, somehow made, can have only an extremely transient existence before being annihilated in an encounter with one of the many electrons in its environment. For this reason positrons cannot play any role in the structure of matter under ordinary conditions. The positrons that were discovered by Anderson are generated as a result of bombardment of the earth's upper atmosphere by high-energy cosmic rays and are found to suffer the kind of annihilation processes predicted by the Dirac theory. This discovery served as a great stimulus to more intensive studies of cosmic radiation and high-energy particle physics, which became a branch of physics of immense importance in the 1940s and 1950s.

By the late 1930s progress in the understanding of nuclear matter and in the elementary particles of nature occurred so rapidly and on so many fronts that it is exceedingly difficult to present a complete or even a one-dimensional narration of these important events. One of the major problems of nuclear theory was the understanding of radioactivity. The mechanism by which alpha particles are emitted quickly received a simple explanation in terms of the new quantum theory, but the nature of the process by which beta particles (high-energy electrons) are ejected from beta-active atoms remained a great mystery until 1934, when Enrico Fermi (1901–54) published the theoretical treatment which formed the basis of all subsequent work on the subject. The problem of beta-emission is different from that of alpha-emission in two respects. On the one hand there are sound theoretical reasons for believing that atomic nuclei do not contain any electrons. Hence one part of the emission process must involve the creation of the to-be-emitted electron out of some of the charge and energy (= mass) that is already present in the nucleus. While physicists already had some ideas concerning creation and destruction of particles from the Dirac theory and its confirmation in Anderson's positron discovery, such ideas were new and unfamiliar in the early 1930s.

The other major mystery in this field was the continuous-energy spectrum of the emitted electrons. The experimental evidence indicated that all the beta-active nuclei of a certain kind are alike both before emission and after emission. Therefore a certain definite amount of energy would be available for the emission; so all of the emitted electrons ought (by the principle of conservation of energy) to come out with the same energy. But instead, experimental work showed that actually they come out with a wide statistical distribution of different energies, ranging from a maximum value down to as near zero as can be found in view of the experimental difficulties.

The solution to this puzzle was originally put forward by W. Pauli in 1931 in a suggestion that perhaps two particles are emitted in the beta-decay and the same total energy in each case is divided between them in different ways in different individual occurrences of beta-decay, but that one particle is of such a nature that it escapes direct detection. Thus the evidence for the existence of the new particle became the need to account for the missing energy, just as a business man might infer the existence of a thief he never sees from the observed lack of the proper amount of cash in the till.

To carry off energy and escape detection, the particle would have to be electrically neutral and have a mass less than that of an electron. Enrico

Fermi called this hypothetical new particle the neutrino, the Italian for little neutron.

Accordingly, then, the basic process was this: one of the neutrons in the beta-active nucleus must have a certain probability of converting itself into a proton while simultaneously creating an electron and a neutrino which are then ejected from the nucleus. Using the mathematical formalism of quantum mechanics Fermi made certain plausible postulates about the process which proved fruitful in giving a detailed account of the shape of the continuous spectrum and the factors governing the rate at which beta-decay occurs.

In the years after 1934 this theory had extraordinary development. George Gamow (1904–   ) and Edward Teller (1908–   ) in 1936 introduced more general mathematical forms for the process. For twenty years this theory proved useful for correlating a wide range of details about beta-decay until in 1956 T. D. Lee and C. N. Yang discovered that the whole structure had been erected on a basis involving an incorrect assumption, known as the conservation of parity. This seemed at first to complicate matters by introducing many new theoretical possibilities, but it subsequently appeared that among these new possibilities are some which make it possible to complete the understanding of beta-decay theory in a very satisfying way.

(d) *Nuclear stability, artificial radioactivity and fission.* The naturally occurring radioactive atoms are thus energetically unstable and are found to disintegrate in two ways: by alpha particle emission and by beta and neutrino emission by the process just described. Most of the atoms known in nature are apparently quite stable and do not disintegrate in either of these ways. These questions, therefore, arise: what determines which kind of nuclei are stable, and are there other ways of disintegration that can relieve instability? Much of the work in nuclear physics in the 1930s and 1940s revolved around the study of these questions.

Study of the general problem of nuclear stability was greatly advanced during these years by the development of mass spectrographs of high precision. With these instruments the relative masses of most atomic species were known to a precision of better than one in a million. Even the earlier work was accurate enough to indicate that the mass of an atom is definitely less than the sum of the masses of its separated constituents, usually by amounts less than 1 per cent. This difference is called mass defect.

Mass defect is a direct consequence of the equivalence of mass and energy ($E = mc^2$) as discovered by Einstein in 1905. When an atom is formed by the coming together of its separated constituents energy is released which goes away carrying some of the mass with it, so the resulting atom has less mass than the materials from which it is made. If on the other hand an atom is unstable and spontaneously disintegrates into lighter atoms and particles with the release of energy, then the initial atom must have greater mass than the sum of the masses of the materials into which it disintegrates.

Thus the precise measure of atomic masses gives a direct indication of their energy of formation or disintegration; this is the reason why so much effort continued to go into measuring atomic masses with the maximum precision attainable. The sum of the masses of a neutron and a hydrogen atom is 2·0171311 atomic mass units, which exceeds the mass of the deuterium atom by 0·0023886, which is proportional to the amount of energy released when a neutron is captured by a hydrogen atom to form a deuterium atom. Similarly, the mass of two deuterium atoms is 4·0294850, exceeding that of one ordinary helium atom by 0·025611. This is proportional to the amount of energy which would be released if a way could be found to cause deuterium atoms to join to make helium. Reactions like these do occur in the sun and stars to maintain their radiation, and they occur explosively in hydrogen bombs.

With the accumulation of the knowledge of large numbers of precise masses, the mass differences in various nuclear reactions could be correlated with experimentally measured energy release. In this way, thirty years after Einstein's theoretical discovery of mass-energy equivalence, that principle was quantitatively confirmed with high accuracy on dozens of nuclear reactions.

Trends of the measured masses show that the nuclei become unstable except in the narrow band of related (Z, N) values that characterize the naturally occurring nuclei. It is this fact which explains the occurrence of artificial radioactivity. In an (α, n) type of reaction an alpha particle (consisting of two protons and two neutrons) is caught and a neutron is emitted, so the result from bombardment of a nucleus containing Z protons and N neutrons (Z, N) is $(Z + 2, N + 1)$. If this is outside the band of stable nuclei it may be radioactive, i.e. it may spontaneously disintegrate. In 1934 Irene Curie (1897–1956) and her husband Frédéric Joliot-Curie (1900–   ) in Paris discovered instances in which the product was radioactive but emitted positrons instead of electrons. Thus it became clear that the process of beta-decay could include positron-neutrino emission by change of a proton into a neutron, as well as the originally discovered process of electron + neutrino emission by change of a neutron into a proton. Which occurs in a particular instance depends on whether the nucleus is unstable by having too many protons or too many neutrons. In the years which followed it became possible to make artificial radioactive isotopes of both types for nearly every element. These proved to be enormously valuable in chemistry and in biology.

Apart from their intrinsic importance, studies of artificial radioactivity were to lead in the next few years to the discovery of nuclear fission, the neutron chain reaction and the development of nuclear weapons. This chain of events started in 1934 when Fermi and associates, working in Rome, made a systematic study of the artificial radioactive isotopes produced by neutron capture in various elements. As this process produces a nucleus containing too many neutrons to be stable, the kind of beta-decay which occurs is electron + neutrino emission in which one of the excess neutrons changes into a proton.

Among the elements bombarded with neutrons by Fermi and his group was uranium. Adding a neutron to a nucleus puts it on the neutron-rich side of stability. Therefore if stability is acquired by beta-emission, an electron will be ejected and the atomic number is increased by one. By bombarding uranium with neutrons one might expect to produce atoms beyond uranium, the transuranic elements, which do not exist in nature. Fermi's group found a large variety of radioactive materials produced this way which were at first interpreted as being the new transuranic elements.

But in 1938 two chemists, Otto Hahn and F. Strassmann, showed that most of the observed activity due to the reaction of neutrons with uranium was not due to the expected formation of transuranic elements. Instead it was due to an unexpected new process called fission. In this the uranium nucleus, rendered highly unstable by the capture of a neutron, splits into two roughly equal parts which fly apart from each other with great speed. Further investigation showed that the direct fission products are not the same in each instance of each disintegration; instead, a wide variety of fission products is formed. These are all on the neutron-rich side of stability and so are radioactive with subsequent emission of negative beta particles.

An important feature of the fission process is the fact that, besides the two major fragments, there are on the average between two and three neutrons which get free. It is this fact that makes possible atomic bombs and the controlled release of power from uranium. Usual sources of neutrons are costly and weak. In the fission process one neutron is used to cause the fission and about three are released, so there is a gain of two. Hence if these two can be fully utilized to cause fission the next stage will give four, the next eight and so on. Such a multiplicative process is known as a chain reaction, and raises the possibility of producing very powerful neutron sources as well as the release of huge quantities of energy. (Pl. 1a.)

These basic ideas were all known to physicists of many countries within a few months of the discovery of fission, i.e. by the summer of 1940 when Hitler's armies had overrun the European continent and an invasion of Great Britain appeared imminent. That it might be possible to use a fission chain reaction as an explosive weapon was immediately obvious, and consideration of this possibility was under discussion in several countries.

Although the basic ideas underlying a possibly explosive chain reaction based on uranium fission were known, many of the quantitative parameters of the process were quite inaccurately known at the time. It was not certain that an explosion could actually be made to occur nor what minimum size was called for. What was known was that even to answer such questions would call for a vast amount of experimental research, expensive in materials and in the use of skilled manpower. If the project of making a uranium fission bomb could be carried out at all it would be at the price of an enormous effort, for which success could not with confidence be forecast in advance.

By the summer of 1940 military secrecy was imposed on this field of work in various countries. In Germany the work was put under Werner Heisenberg; little progress, however, was made in the five years that remained of Hitler's régime. In Britain a project was also initiated but, with the intensification of the German aerial attacks on Britain, it became clear that a project of the necessary magnitude could not be carried on in that country. In the autumn of 1941 arrangements were made for the British to contribute their scientific talent to a combined effort with the United States to carry on a large project in the USA. With the entry of the United States into the war at the end of 1941 these plans were given high priority with the result that the first fission bomb was tested in June 1945 at Los Alamos, New Mexico, USA. When the USSR started its development work was not made public; however, the Soviet Union successfully tested such a bomb about three years later. (Pl. 1b.)

However far-reaching these events might be in military technology and international politics, they did not directly add appreciably to knowledge of fundamental science. They had some indirect effects, for now governments wished to spend much more on scientific research than ever before. Also the uranium reactors, built to supply the transuranic element plutonium ($Z = 94$), another fission bomb material, provided unlimited supplies of by-product radioactive materials which found wide applications in research in chemistry, in biology and in many areas of technology. In the early 1950s nuclear reactors, using the controlled uranium fission chain reaction to supply heat to make steam to drive steam turbines, had been developed in the United States to propel submarines and in various countries, principally in Britain and the USSR, to produce electric power.

(e) *Post-war period: cryogenics, solid-state physics, new elementary particles.* Three major areas of experimental research developed greatly in the post-war period. These were cryogenics, the study of the properties of matter at extremely low temperatures: solid-state physics, in which the results of experimental data such as X-ray spectra are combined with quantum mechanics of the electrons to give new insights concerning metals, semi-conductors and insulators; and the discovery and study of high-energy particles, in cosmic rays and through their artificial production in very large electrical particle accelerators. Many of the fundamental discoveries in these fields had been made earlier in the century. In the post-war period these older discoveries were exploited, many new discoveries were made and the total scientific activity in these fields increased enormously.

The study of the thermal properties of matter down to very low temperatures is needed to gain information about their chemical behaviour at ordinary temperatures. This fact long served as a major stimulus to cryogenic research. In addition there are two peculiar properties of special materials which occur only at temperatures where the thermal agitation of ultimate parts is greatly reduced. Certain metals exhibit the phenomenon known as superconductivity when they are colder than a certain temperature. In this state all resistance to the flow of electric current vanishes, so an electric current, once started, flows indefinitely without appreciable diminution. The effect is more than a simple reduction to zero of the electrical resistance, for it is accompanied by unusual magnetic behaviour known after its discover, Walther Meissner (1882–   ), as the Meissner effect. At usual pressures helium becomes liquid at $4°K$ and then abruptly, when cooled below $2 \cdot 18°K$, changes over into a different liquid form which is called a superfluid because it is characterized by extraordinary flow properties. Its behaviour is as if the viscosity of the fluid abruptly became zero, analogous to the vanishing of the electrical resistance of a superconducting metal; but also the fluid shows other peculiar flow properties that require more sophisticated modes of description than merely saying that it has zero viscosity. A great deal of experimental and theoretical work went into the study of the superconducting and superfluid states but, as late as 1958, it could not be said that the basic principles were well understood.

In the field of solid-state physics many new experimental techniques were developed to measure the microstructure of solid matter. For example, the development of the field emission microscope greatly facilitated the study of surface phenomena and made it possible to attack such problems as the migration of tungsten atoms on the surface of a tungsten crystal. The technique of nuclear magnetic resonance, originally developed by nuclear physicists, permitted solid-state physicists to explore the internal magnetic fields occurring in solids and molecules. The well-established method of studying crystal structure by X-ray diffraction was supplemented by neutron diffraction. One advantage of this new method is that, in contrast to X-ray diffraction, it permits the identification of the position of light atoms such as hydrogen in a crystal containing heavy atoms.

The older method of X-ray crystallography provided the means for determining the detailed arrangement of atoms in crystals. Since the arrangement of atoms in a large molecule is not much affected by the circumstance of the molecule's being in a crystal, X-ray diffraction becomes more generally a tool for studying the structure of complicated molecules. Here a basic discovery was developed to the point where structural crystallographic work became a professional speciality in its own right, with distinct areas of specialization within it according to the worker's interests in amorphous materials like glass and organic polymers, metals and alloys, silicate minerals, or proteins and other macromolecular compounds of biochemical interest.

X-ray crystallography was making rapid progress toward the detailed determination of the structure of proteins and of the deoxyribonucleic acids which appear to be the stuff determining modes of life, growth and heredity of most living things.*

To physicists one of the most exciting new frontiers to be opened up was the study of a whole new class of high-energy particles whose presence was first detected in cosmic rays. This field of work originated with a sugges-

* *Infra*, Chapter XIII.

tion by H. Yukawa in 1935 that an understanding of the forces which hold the atomic nucleus together would be facilitated by supposing the existence of a new type of particle, intermediate in mass between electrons and the 1,836 times more massive nucleons. Because they were intermediate in mass they were called mesons. Two years later the Yukawa hypothesis seemed to receive a beautiful confirmation when, independently, such mesons were discovered in cosmic rays. However, it soon appeared that the story was more complicated than was at first supposed because these experimentally discovered mesons were found to interact with nuclei so weakly that they could not possibly be the agents of the nucleon-nucleon interaction for which purpose Yukawa first postulated their existence. This meant that either Yukawa's idea was wrong or another kind of meson remained to be discovered.

The war caused a long hiatus in which physicists could not follow the challenge of this dilemma. A full decade elapsed until the discovery in 1947 of the other kind of strongly interacting mesons which behave more like those which Yukawa had postulated. These were found in high-altitude cosmic-ray studies, whereas the kind found earlier were most abundant at lower altitudes in the earth's atmosphere.

Mesons became the object of intensive study by physicists all over the world. To distinguish them, the ones occurring at high altitudes which interact strongly with nucleons are called π-mesons or pions; and those occurring at low-altitudes which interact weakly with nucleons are called μ-mesons or muons. Pions were found to be of three types, the electrically neutral, and those having either a positive or a negative electric charge of the same amount as that of an electron. The positive pions and negative pions seem to have the same mass, 273 times that of the electron, but the neutral pion has a smaller mass, 264 times the electron mass. The muons are always charged, positively or negatively, the amount of charge being the same as that of the electron. No evidence for a neutral muon had been found. Both positive and negative muons have a mass $206 \cdot 8$ times that of the electron, definitely less than the mass of either neutral or charged pions.

The pions and muons are all unstable, disintegrating spontaneously into other particles in small fractions of a second. For this reason they cannot be the primary cosmic radiation. Rather it was thought that the primary cosmic radiation consists mainly of high-energy protons with a lesser component of high-energy nuclei of several other kinds of light atoms. How these nuclei get their energy and whence they come was one of the great unsolved problems of astronomy. Encountering the outer layers of the earth's atmosphere they collide with nuclei of these atoms and generate pions by processes which in 1948 were reproduced in the laboratory with the large synchrocyclotron at Berkeley, California.

The charged pions spontaneously decay in flight within one hundred millionths of a second, giving rise to muons of the same charge and presumably neutrinos and anti-neutrinos. The neutral pions have a life that is a million times shorter, decaying into gamma rays, or into gamma rays and electron-positron pairs. The charged muons in turn decay into electrons or positrons accompanied by neutrino and anti-neutrino pairs. This they do at a rate that is one hundred times slower than that of the decay of the charged pion, so that the muons have a mean life of 2·2 microseconds.

Just when physicists were getting the relations and properties of these mesons worked out, the picture was further complicated by the discovery of several more kinds of unstable particles in cosmic radiation. These are charged and uncharged K-particles, or kayons, of about 966 electron masses, the uncharged lambda (Λ^0) particle of about 2,181 electron masses, hence more massive than the normal protons and neutrons, and the charged ($\pm$) and neutral sigma particles (Σ) of masses around 2,330 times that of electron, and probably others. Those whose mass exceeds that of normal protons and neutrons are called hyperons, so there are Λ and Σ^+, Σ^- and Σ^0 and other kinds of hyperons. The mesons include the kayons and the various pions and muons. Finally, in 1955 the negative proton was discovered in Berkeley, California, by Emilio Segre (1905–) and associates.

This unexpected wealth of unstable particles opened up a vast range of new problems for experimental and theoretical research. At first the experimental study was held back by the extremely small numbers of such particles that occur in the natural cosmic radiation. In 1930 nuclear physics had been limited in a similar way. The sources of natural radioactive particles used by Rutherford were too weak to allow much further advance. The development of the cyclotron and other accelerators allowed the use of intense beams of protons, deuterons and alpha particles, and from the results of experiments using such beams the properties of these particles were discovered. Very large accelerators were therefore being built to produce beams of these new unstable particles, and by means of similar experiments to permit the working out of their properties.

The understanding of matter developed during the first half of the twentieth century was sufficiently complete to serve as a fundamental basis for all chemistry, all of atomic physics and most of nuclear physics. But it did not yet provide an ultimate theory of matter. The study of why particles of certain masses are stable and others are not, the characteristics of these particles and their interactions was the main frontier in the quest for such an ultimate theory.

III. THE NATURE OF THE EARTH

The new theory of matter brought new insight into the nature of the earth and unity into the study of its surface, its atmosphere and its deep interior. It began to transform geology from a mainly descriptive science to an experimental and theoretical one, although at mid-century much knowledge of the earth remained at the descriptive level.

1. *The surface of the earth*

By the opening of the twentieth century the description and classification of rocks was well advanced. Although geology was a late-comer among the physical sciences and the revision of ancient and medieval notions of the earth did not begin until the end of the eighteenth century, extensive work in palaeontology and petrography during the nineteenth century had established these largely descriptive fields.

In palaeontology the French biologist Georges Cuvier (1769–1832) led the way in showing how scraps of bones in gypsum deposits could be combined with an understanding of anatomy to reconstruct the form of an animal never before seen by man. As a result of the labours of nineteenth-century palaeontologists extinct organisms were classed into species, genera and orders which gave a new dimension to descriptive biology. In combination with Darwin's great synthesis of biological data in his *Origin of Species*, this detailed and tedious work had an incalculable impact on man's concept of his place in nature.

In petrography, the description and classification of rocks, perhaps the most significant single development during the nineteenth century, arose from a technical invention. The polarizing microscope, invented by the Scottish physicist William Nicol (1768–1851) in 1828, had made it possible for the petrographer to examine thin sections of dense rock in the same detailed way that a biologist examines the cells of a plant or animal. As the nineteenth century ended, petrography led to the new science of petrology in which emphasis shifted from the description of rocks to the problems of their genesis and distribution. This shift in emphasis was made possible both by the great wealth of petrographical data which had been accumulated and by the growing understanding and synthesis of physics and chemistry.

During the twentieth century geologists came to realize that the crystallization of rocks such as basalt and granite follows the same laws of physical chemistry as the crystallization of chemical compounds in the laboratory. By application of reasoning based on understanding of these laws of physical chemistry petrologists were able to show that some of the facile explanations of geological phenomena previously advanced could not be correct.

For example, one of the major problems of geology is to explain the diversity of rock types. In a small region of a few kilometres extent one often finds different igneous rocks which nevertheless probably had a common origin. This phenomenon had usually been explained as resulting from 'liquid immiscibility'. It is a well-known fact of experience that certain liquids do not mix with one another, for example oil and water. It had been supposed that, upon cooling, an initially homogeneous mass of molten rock, called a magma, split into two or more immiscible liquid fractions which then crystallized to give the different types of rocks which are observed. N. L. Bowen (1887–1956) showed the result of such a process would be entirely different from what is observed in nature. According to his reasoning the rocks which result would contain many minute droplets of material of different chemical composition rather than distinct homogeneous rocks as observed in the field. Furthermore, careful laboratory experiments indicated that melts of the composition of the observed rocks could actually be mixed in all proportions. Thus the explanation failed on two counts.

Bowen then suggested an alternative explanation which did fit with the facts of physical chemistry. After various minerals have successively crystallized from the magma to form one type of rock, physical forces such as gravity separate these crystals from the residual magma. As a result of the subtraction of the chemical compounds in these early crystals, the chemical composition of the magma has been changed. The subsequent crystallization of the residual magma therefore produces a different type of rock. Repetition of this process of fractional crystallization can result in the type of variation observed in nature. Similar combinations of physical reasoning and careful laboratory work enabled petrologists to learn much about the actual processes by which rocks are formed in nature, although many fundamental questions remained unanswered.

Bowen's theory of differentiation due to crystallization did not, however, provide a complete solution to the problem of the diversity of volcanic rocks, in particular to their division into the two main groups of basalts and granites. In the second quarter of the twentieth century new ideas began to gain ground. According to these, granites were not formed as a result of intrusion from below of a magma or the late crystallization products of a basalt magma but as the result of the change—granitification—of various older sedimentary, metamorphic and volcanic rocks due to the displacement of their minerals by feldspars and quartz upon the deposition of alkalis (K, Na) and silica and upon the removal of the superfluous alkali earth (Ca, Mg) and iron. The magma origin or metasomatic origin of granites, and the mechanism of granitification assumed in the latter case, remained highly controversial questions.

2. *The age of the earth*

One of the major problems in geology is the question of the age of the earth. At the opening of the nineteenth century most men in the Christian world, including scientists, had accepted the view that the earth was only about 6,000 years old. As a consequence of this belief it had been necessary for geologists to squeeze all the events which combined to produce the present geological record into this short length of time.

The work of the great pioneer geologists James Hutton (1726–97) and Charles Lyell (1797–1875) helped to free the science from this encumbering opinion. They presented striking evidence that the geological record was the product of ordinary familiar causes, such as erosion, operating over great expanses of time. The need for a longer time-scale was accentuated by the requirements of the evolutionists later in the nineteenth century and it appeared that the earth must be hundreds of millions of years old rather than merely a few thousands.

No sooner had this scientific opinion prevailed over the theological one than it was challenged from another source, the calculations of the British physicist Lord Kelvin (1824–1907), who concluded that the earth and sun could be but a few tens of millions of years old. Consideration of the known sources of solar energy led Kelvin to believe that the sun could not have been radiating heat for more than about a hundred million years; furthermore, if the earth were originally molten its surface regions would have cooled sufficiently in about twenty-five million years to conflict with the observed rise in temperature encountered in deep mines. These conclusions seemed formidable at the time, and they gave rise to serious controversies.

The discussion was soon ended, however, in a most unexpected way by the first contribution of nuclear physics to geology, the discovery of radioactivity in 1896. This discovery showed that the radioactive elements uranium and thorium formed an almost inexhaustible source of heat which had not been included in the calculations of Kelvin, and which would suffice to produce heat in the earth for many thousands of millions of years. By the 1930s it was realized that the heat of the sun is caused by a different type of nuclear effect, the fusion of hydrogen nuclei into the nuclei of helium, accompanied by the production of heat.

During the twentieth century radioactive decay contributed to knowledge of the age of the earth in another way. It was soon realized that the radioactive transformation of uranium and thorium into lead furnishes the basis for an absolute method of geological age determination. Minerals such as uraninite contain uranium and thorium but initially very little lead. As time goes by the uranium and thorium in the mineral decay into lead at a known rate. By measuring the total amount of lead produced in this way, together with the amount of uranium and thorium, one can calculate the time which has elapsed since the original formation of the mineral. The first ages calculated by this method were published in 1907 and showed that many of the rocks on the earth were hundreds of millions of years old. Although the nature of the radioactive transformation was little understood, these early age-determinations were approximately correct and the subsequent development of nuclear physics and of powerful new analytical techniques made it possible to date a great many geological occurrences in this way.

After the second world war the older methods based on the disintegration of uranium and thorium into lead were supplemented by new methods which utilized in a similar way the disintegration of potassium into argon and rubidium into strontium. As a result of these measurements ages as great as 3,400 million years were found in the Kola peninsula of the Soviet Union, and rocks at least 2,500 million years old were found in many places throughout the world. The earth itself must be older than this, but just how much older was hard to say. Indirect arguments based on comparison of the ratios of the isotopes of lead on the earth with the corresponding ratios in iron meteorites indicated a probable age for the earth of about 4,500 million years.

Nuclear physics made a number of other contributions to geology. Measurement of ages by the amount of radioactive carbon present in geological materials and in organic residues contributed to the study of more recent geological history, which includes such events as the great ice ages. This was in addition to the great importance of carbon-dating for archaeological studies. Still another example of the application of nuclear physics to geology was the work initiated by H. C. Urey and his colleagues in which variations in the ratios of stable isotopes of the light elements hydrogen, carbon and oxygen were utilized in geological investigations. Continuation of this work yielded information concerning such problems as the temperatures of the prehistoric oceans, the origin of natural waters and the fractional crystallization of a magma.

3. The interior of the earth

In the nineteenth century geological thinking had been concerned almost exclusively with the surface features of the earth. Relatively little was known about its interior. From astronomical measurements it was possible to calculate the total mass of the earth as well as the fact that this mass was concentrated toward the centre of the earth. Measurement of the temperature in mines apparently indicated that the interior of the earth was much hotter than the surface. Extrapolation of these thermal gradients led to the conclusion that the deep interior of the earth is so hot that it is liquid, if not gaseous. But from observations of earth tides, Lord Kelvin arrived at the opposite conclusion, that the earth as a whole is very rigid.

Great advances in the understanding of the earth's interior were made during the twentieth century. These advances were largely due to the growth of seismology, the study of earthquakes. An earthquake is caused by the sudden fracture of rocks within the earth—usually near the surface of the earth. As a consequence of this fracturing, waves are radiated which are sufficiently strong to penetrate the entire earth. These seismic waves are mechanical vibrations like sound waves, but are mostly too low in frequency to be audible to the human ear. Other seismic waves are formed which travel along the surface of the earth. By combining the classical theory of elastic wave propagation with observations of these seismic waves, seismologists succeeded in deducing much information concerning the structure of the earth's interior. In fact these seismic waves were almost the only practical way to probe the deep interior of the earth.

Early in the century studies of seismic waves showed that the earth is divided into two principal regions—the core, largely liquid with a radius of about 3,500 kilometres, surmounted by a solid shell called the mantle about 2,900 kilometres thick. In 1909 A. Mohorovičić (1857–1936) in Zagreb discovered that above the mantle is a thin skin of lower density which has been named the crust. The boundary between the crust and the mantle was named the Mohorovičić discontinuity in honour of its discoverer. Underneath most of the continental regions it lies at a depth of about 35 kilometres below the surface of the earth, while under the oceans it occurs at a much shallower depth.

As a result of much detailed work seismologists were able to give a fairly exact account of the way in which the velocity of sound waves varies with depth, and from these results it proved possible to infer the variation of density with depth as well as other properties of the earth's interior. After the second world war seismic studies were aided by the use of man-made explosions to replace earthquakes as a source of seismic waves. This method had the advantage that the time and place of the initial shock were accurately known and did not have to be calculated from the observations as is the case with earthquakes. Using chemical explosions, seismic studies of the earth's crust were made on several continents as well as at sea, and nuclear explosions produced seismic waves sufficiently strong to penetrate the deep interior of the earth. Data from these nuclear explosions gave further information bearing on the existence and properties of a solid inner core within the liquid core of the earth.

At the same time much thought was given to the nature of the Mohorovičić discontinuity which forms the base of the crust. For many years it had been assumed to represent a chemical discontinuity; the crystal rocks were thought to contain a high concentration of the lighter elements, while upon entering the mantle the composition was thought to change abruptly to rocks richer in iron compounds and having a greater density. However, support increased for the view that there is no major chemical change at the Mohorovičić discontinuity but that the observed increase in density at this depth arises from the presence of high-pressure modifications of familiar minerals. Laboratory work in which a number of these high-pressure modifications appeared at pressures and temperatures appropriate to the depth of the Mohorovičić discontinuity strengthened this surmise and was one of the considerations which led to plans to drill a deep hole through the discontinuity into the mantle to put the hypothesis to a direct test.

4. The atmosphere of the earth

During the twentieth century substantial information was accumulated about the earth's atmosphere as well as about its interior.

In the nineteenth century it was known that as one goes higher in the atmosphere, to heights of a few kilometres in balloons or on mountains, the air becomes less dense and the temperature drops. It was generally thought that if one went to greater elevations the density and temperature would steadily decrease, the density approaching zero and the temperature approaching $-273\,°C$, the absolute zero of temperature.

About the turn of the century Léon P. Teisserenc de Bort (1855–1913) in Paris sent balloons to altitudes of about 14 kilometres and discovered the surprising fact that above about 11 kilometres the temperature no longer dropped but assumed a constant value of −60°C. Thus it was discovered that the earth's atmosphere consists of at least two layers; the lower he named the troposphere, and the upper region the stratosphere. The boundary between these two layers is known as the tropopause, where the famous belt of high wind called the jet stream is found. Most ordinary weather phenomena such as clouds and storms take place in the troposphere, although it appeared possible that the stratosphere might be important in practical meteorology.

In the period prior to the second world war the greatest altitude accessible to direct observation by unmanned balloons was about 30 kilometres. However, the inability of scientists to probe the upper atmosphere directly did not prevent them from investigating its properties. Increased understanding of the nature and properties of matter combined with new observational techniques made it possible to infer much about the upper atmosphere from measurements made at the ground.

One important indirect method for probing the stratosphere was developed as a consequence of the observation that guns fired in London at Queen Victoria's funeral were heard unusually far to the north, and that during the first world war artillery fire from the Western front was frequently heard in England. It was shown that the sound waves which were radiated toward the sky were being refracted back to earth because of a temperature gradient in the atmosphere above the constant-temperature region discovered by Teisserenc de Bort.

By careful study of this phenomenon it was shown that the temperature actually increases in the region from 30 to 60 kilometres and that at the height of 60 kilometres the air temperature is about 90° C, considerably hotter than the temperature at sea-level. Studies of the velocity and luminosity of meteors, principally by Fred L. Whipple (1906–   ), led to the same conclusion for the region from 30 to 60 kilometres and showed further that the temperature then decreases well below 0° C at an altitude of 80 kilometres and then begins slowly to rise again at greater altitudes. Thus the temperature variation in the atmosphere proved to be quite complex in contrast to the simple uniform decrease accepted at the beginning of the century. The observations on meteors also provided data on the density of the atmosphere up to an altitude of about 100 kilometres.

Concern with problems of electrical conductivity led to the identification of a third layer, known as the ionosphere. At the surface of the earth most of the very short wavelength, ultra-violet radiation from the sun has been absorbed by the atmosphere. However, in the stratosphere and above, high-energy protons are able to break chemical bonds and thus induce a number of photochemical effects. One of the most important of these effects is the conversion of small amounts of oxygen into ozone in the region from 20 to 50 kilometres, as demonstrated in 1934 by measurement of the absorption bands of ozone in the solar spectrum. It is this ozone which is responsible for absorbing most of the biologically harmful ultra-violet radiation. At even greater altitudes the ultra-violet radiation is effective in removing electrons from normally neutral atoms to form positive ions. The presence of these free charged particles, electrons and ions, causes the atmosphere to become a good electrical conductor above an altitude of 70 kilometres.

Late in the nineteenth century it had been suggested that there was a conducting layer somewhere in the atmosphere, in order to explain the day-to-day variations in the earth's magnetic field. Little attention was paid to this suggestion and it was almost forgotten at the time Guglielmo Marconi (1874–1937) made his pioneer investigations in radio transmission in 1901. Since physicists had shown that radio waves travel in straight lines like light it had been expected that the curvature of the earth would prevent long-distance transmission of radio signals. Nevertheless Marconi succeeded in sending signals across the Atlantic.

The idea of a conducting layer which would reflect the radio waves back to earth was then revived by Arthur E. Kennelly (1861–1939) in the USA and Oliver Heaviside (1850–1925) in Britain. That radio waves from a distant station do indeed come down from the sky was demonstrated in Britain by Edward Appleton (1892–   ) and M. A. F. Barnett (1901–   ) in 1924. In 1925 Gregory Breit (1899–   ) and Merle A. Tuve (1901–   ) in the USA demonstrated beyond doubt the existence of the conducting layer by a technique which was the forerunner of radar. Radio signals were transmitted vertically into the sky and echoes were received from the conducting layer. By measuring the time required for the radio signal to go up and back, the height of the conducting layer was determined.

This conducting region forms the third major division of the atmosphere, the ionosphere. It was found that the ionosphere contains several layers of different conductivity which are designated in order of increasing height as the D, E, F and F_1 layers, the last beginning at an altitude of about 250 km. The part of the atmosphere beyond the ionosphere is called the exosphere. Here the density of the atmosphere is so low that individual atoms and molecules seldom collide with one another and thus are able to revolve in satellite-like orbits around the earth.

The development of the V-2 rocket by Germany in the second world war provided a means for direct probing of the upper stratosphere and ionosphere. After the end of the war many V-2 rockets, and later rockets of more advanced designs, were fired into the upper atmosphere. The accuracy of the earlier data was greatly improved but on the whole these direct observations were in agreement with the conclusions already obtained by indirect methods. After 1957 the use of artificial satellites provided a way of making a sustained series of observations in the ionosphere and exosphere. It was expected that the continued development of this approach would result in many highly instrumented and possibly manned observing stations in the upper atmosphere and would thus greatly facilitate the collection of information regarding this outermost region of the earth.

IV. THE NATURE OF THE UNIVERSE

At the opening of the twentieth century the motions of the planets and satellites of the solar system were understood in precise detail. To a high degree of accuracy they were fully predictable on the basis of calculations based on Newton's laws of motion and Newton's inverse square law of gravitation. Only in the case of the planet nearest the sun, Mercury, was there a discrepancy: the direction of perihelion was observed to advance by a measurably larger amount than could be accounted for by perturbations by the other planets. This last discrepancy was removed by substituting (1916) a slightly modified law of gravitation from Einstein's General Theory of Relativity which explained the advance of Mercury's perihelion without spoiling the vast number of other details in which Einstein's and Newton's laws each agree equally well with observations. Although refinements of detail continued to be made, astronomers thereafter regarded celestial mechanics as essentially a fully worked out branch of their science.

The attention of astronomers therefore turned more and more to stellar astronomy, including the study of the sun and of the gaseous and dust clouds of interstellar space. They examined the distribution in space of stars and of clouds of dust and gas, and the structure, constitution and evolutionary development of these astronomical phenomena.

1. *New techniques of observation*

Prior to 1932 all data studied were based on observation of the visible, near-ultra-violet and near-infra-red light emitted by the stars that is able to penetrate the earth's atmosphere. Early in the century effort was concentrated on building larger telescopes for dealing with this light; the largest projects were construction of the 100-in. reflector on Mt Wilson and later the 200-in. Hale reflector on Palomar Mountain, both in southern California. At the same time there was a steady increase in the large telescope facilities in the southern hemisphere, especially at the Mt Stromlo observatory of the Australian National University near Canberra. Improvement of southern hemisphere facilities was of especial importance, for it became known that this part of the sky contains more objects of fundamental interest than does the northern. (Pl. 2a.)

An entirely new method of stellar observation was made possible by the discovery that certain radio waves come from interstellar space. Radio astronomy makes use of the transparency of the earth's atmosphere to electromagnetic waves in the range of wavelengths from 1 cm. to about 10 metres.

The source of such radio waves was discovered in 1932 by Karl Jansky (1905–50) in New Jersey and knowledge of them extended by Grote Reber (1911–   ) in Illinois in the following years. After the second world war this field of study was cultivated vigorously in many countries, particularly by the Australian radio physicists. Very great expansions of astronomical knowledge were expected as a result of the construction of many large radio telescopes, which are large paraboloidal metal reflectors at the foci of which are placed receiving antennae for picking up the received radio waves and leading their energy to amplifying and recording devices. (Pl. 2b.)

The scope of astronomical observation was still further extended when it became technically possible to make observations with instruments carried above the opaque blanket of the earth's atmosphere. At mid-century many observations in the far-ultra-violet were being made with instruments carried aloft by rockets or high-altitude balloons, or by combinations of both in which a rocket was carried by balloon most of the way to the top of the earth's atmosphere and then fired vertically upward. Such techniques opened the possibility of knowing much more about detailed mechanisms by which changing solar conditions affect the earth.

Toward the end of 1957 a great impetus to studies of this kind was given by the successful launching by the Russians of the first artificial earth satellite. They demonstrated the feasibility of putting into an orbit several hundred miles above the earth's surface an object of several thousand pounds weight that can be equipped with astronomical observing equipment and means for automatically transmitting the data of observation by radio to stations on the earth. Because such satellites can remain above the earth's atmosphere continuously for many months or even years, they can accumulate data much more effectively than occasional rocket shots of a few moments' duration. (Fig. 2.)

2. *The distribution of stars in space*

At the beginning of the twentieth century the distance of stars was determined by measuring trigonometric parallax—the shift in their apparent direction from the observer due to the orbital motion of the earth around the sun. But the stars are mostly so far away that only very few of them give a measurable parallactic displacement, even though displacements as small as 0·01 sec. of arc were measurable by mid twentieth-century techniques.

A star at a distance such that the radius of the earth's orbit subtends an angle of 1 sec. at the star is said to be at a distance of 1 parsec. which is equal to 206,265 times the earth–sun distance. A light-year is the distance light goes in one year, which is 5·88 million million miles. A parsec is 3·26 light-years or about 19 million million miles. Only about 5,000 stars are near enough for direct measurement of their distance by the parallax method.

A great advance was made early in the century with the discovery by

Fig. 2. Diagram of the Russian satellite Lunik III, the automatic interplanetary station which photographed the far side of the moon. 1: illuminator for photographic apparatus; 2: motor for guiding system; 3: solar pickup; 4: sections of solar battery; 5: shutters of temperature control system; 6: heat screens; 7: aerials; 8: apparatus for scientific investigations. (See plate 3b.)

Henrietta Leavitt (1868–1921) and Harlow Shapley (1885–   ) of a new way of determining stellar distances. There is a type of variable star called a Cepheid variable, of which thousands are known, whose brightness dwindles slowly and then rises abruptly. The time for one cycle of such brightness variation is called a period. Working on stars which are near enough for their distance to be measured by the parallax method, Miss Leavitt discovered a relation between this period of variation and the absolute mean brightness, i.e. its brightness as seen at a standard distance. The brighter the star the longer the period. Shapley recognized that, since the observed period of such a Cepheid variable tells its absolute mean brightness, astronomers could use this together with its observed apparent mean brightness to infer its distance away from us. The method was widely used during the first half of the century, and with the large telescopes gave distances for this kind of star out to far greater limits than is possible with the parallax method.

The twentieth century saw a great advance also in understanding the relationship of the sun and solar system to the rest of the stars in space. The most obvious organization of the stars in space is the plainly visible Milky Way, a band in the sky near which there is an unusually great density of visible stars. In this aggregation of stars, known as 'our' galaxy to distinguish it from the several hundred million other similar aggregations which make up the known universe, the great circle which passes through the densest parts is called the galactic equator. The fact that the number of visible stars thins out rapidly in directions away from the galactic equator indicates that the galaxy is a vast disc-shaped region occupied by stars.

Prior to the twentieth century the fact that the density of stars at various places around the galactic equator is roughly the same was thought to indicate that the sun's location is near the centre of our galaxy. But researches of Shapley in the 1920s on distribution of globular clusters of stars showed this not to be so, and led to estimates that our solar system lies about 9,000 parsecs from the centre of the galaxy and that the diameter of the galaxy is 30,000 parsecs and its thickness about one-tenth as much. These dimensions are roughly ten times greater than the estimates that were prevalent in the nineteenth century.

Possibilities of probing the structure of our galaxy to its centre were opened up by the development of radio astronomy. Towards the centre of the galaxy and near its plane there is a vast amount of dust and interstellar gas that tends to obscure the light coming from these directions and make the Milky Way look not much brighter toward the galactic centre (in Sagittarius) than in the opposite direction. Radio waves, however, are less obscured by dust than is visible light. Observations revealed that the stars of our galaxy seem to be more numerous along several spiral arms out from the centre, indicating that the general structure of our galaxy resembles that of the spiral galaxies external to ours that can be seen as telescopic objects.[8]

Motions of a few nearby stars relative to us can be calculated from direct observation of slow change of their apparent direction. But a much more important method, since it is not limited to the nearby stars, was derived from the Doppler effect. This technique was first developed in the late nineteenth century and made the basis of a vast amount of observational work during the next seventy-five years. According to this the lines in the spectrum of a light source that is moving towards the observer are shifted in wavelength toward the violet and, if moving away, toward the red. The amount of the wavelength shift is measured and serves as a direct indication of the speed of motion, or radial velocity, towards or away from the observer.[9]

From this technique came the discovery of spectroscopic binaries. These are pairs of stars which revolve around each other so close together that they cannot be resolved as two in the largest telescopes but whose motions are clearly revealed by the regular variation of the wavelength shifts in their spectrum, as their orbital motion causes first one and then the other of them to move towards us while the other moves away. In the second quarter of the twentieth century statistical study of the radial velocities of stars in our galaxy in different directions from us furnished a basis for an overall picture of the motions in the galaxy. The picture that emerged was of a good deal of random chaotic motion of the stars in the galaxy, superimposed on an orderly motion of rotation around the centre. As with the planets in the solar system, the period of revolution is longer at greater distances from the centre. At the sun's distance from the centre the period of revolution is about 200 million years. From this it appears that the total mass of the galaxy is of the order of one hundred thousand million times that of the sun. Perhaps half of this is in stars and the other half is spread out in interstellar dust and gas.

Outside our galaxy a vast number of other galaxies were known whose sizes are roughly comparable with that of ours, and whose distances apart are large compared with their own dimensions. Nearest to ours are the Magellanic clouds, two irregularly shaped aggregations about 25,000 parsecs away, and each about one-tenth the diameter of our galaxy. The two nearest and best-studied spiral galaxies are Messier 31 in Andromeda and Messier 33 in Triangulum each about 500,000 parsecs from us—about twenty times as far from us as the diameter of our own galaxy. (Pl. 3a.)

During the first half of the century, astronomers devoted a great deal of attention to the study of these galaxies external to ours, particularly at Harvard, at Mt Wilson and at the Lick Observatory in California. Edwin P. Hubble of the Mt Wilson Observatory estimated that about 100,000,000 of them existed within the range of instruments then available. In directions away from the plane of our Milky Way they show a remarkable statistical uniformity of numbers. The marked apparent absence of them in directions near the Milky Way was therefore taken as evidence that the uniformity of their numbers in all directions is masked by the obscuring effect of clouds of dust and gas in our own galaxy.

Thus the picture as developed during the first half of the twentieth century was that man lived on a little planet going around one of the millions of stars in our galaxy which is but one among millions of similar galaxies in the known universe.

The discovery concerning external galaxies that excited the most attention and speculation was that made at Mt Wilson by Hubble. By studying the spectra of the light from these galaxies he found the lines to be shifted toward the red. Interpreted as Doppler shifts, this gives evidence that the galaxies are moving away from us. He found, moreover, that the fainter ones which it is natural to suppose are the most distant ones have greater red shifts; in fact the data are most simply interpreted by supposing a proportionality of the speed of motion of a galaxy away from us to its actual distance from us.[10]

This showed the universe to be expanding. Hubble's rule of proportionality of speed to distance seemed to apply out to the limit of the faintest objects that could be reached with the great telescopes in California.

3. *The structure and development of individual stars*

Along with this enlarged view of the extent of the universe came a rapid development of knowledge concerning individual stars, such as the sun. While earlier observers merely estimated apparent brightness of total light and made rough qualitative remarks about colour, the subject was completely transformed in the late nineteenth century with the introduction of the spectroscope, making possible detailed analysis of the light emitted by a star. In the twentieth century, study of stellar spectra progressed with the scientists' increasing ability to interpret spectra as revealing specific details about chemical composition and physical conditions in the source emitting the light.

From these studies the great fact emerged that the stars are made of the same chemical substances as occur on earth. The lines of varying width and intensity in the solar spectra are characteristic of the kinds of atoms and molecules in the star's outer atmosphere and of the physical conditions of temperature and gas pressure existing in the stellar atmosphere. They serve to show which chemical elements are present in the stars because of agreement of the wavelengths registered with those produced in terrestrial sources of known composition.

The relative intensity of the different lines in the spectra, including the question of presence or absence, varies greatly from star to star. On the basis of study of many tens of thousands of stellar spectra, a system of classification into spectral types was devised, largely the work of Annie J. Cannon (1863–1941) of Harvard University which came into universal use. The vast amount of attention given by astronomers to stellar spectroscopy was indicated by the details on the spectra of 225,000 stars contained in the Henry Draper Catalogue of Stellar Spectra, published (1885–1924) by the Harvard College Observatory.

A great step forward in understanding the relation between the intensity of the spectral lines and the physical condition in a star's atmosphere was made by Megh Nad Saha (1893–1956) of Calcutta. He applied general thermodynamic theory to the problem. From this work emerged the surprising fact that the great observed differences in stellar spectra are mostly due to differences in temperature and density, with the chemical composition of the stellar atmospheres being nearly the same. Such studies showed that the stellar atmospheres are more than 98 per cent hydrogen and helium. Oxygen and magnesium make up another 1 per cent, leaving less than 1 per cent for all other elements.

With the rapid accumulation of large amounts of quite precise information about stellar atmospheres and with the great development of physical theories of atomic structure that occurred in the first half of the twentieth century, it began to be intellectually profitable to inquire into the internal constitution of stars, the nature of the source of the energy which they continually radiate, their genesis and the paths and time-scales of their evolution. The second quarter of the century was particularly fruitful in the development of theories dealing with these questions.

In the nineteenth century the only energy source known was that involved in the release of gravitational energy by steady contraction of the star. But calculation showed that such a source could not maintain the sun's radiation for more than about a hundred million years whereas there is ample geological evidence that the climatic conditions on the earth have been roughly the same for a hundred times longer than that. Discovery of radioactivity and the subsequent development of nuclear physics very early gave rise to the idea that the necessary energy source must involve nuclear changes related to atomic transmutations. But ideas of this kind had to remain vague and unspecific until 1936 when enough progress in nuclear physics had occurred to enable Hans A. Bethe in the USA and C. F. von Weizsäcker (1912–   ) in Germany to produce detailed and specific nuclear mechanisms by which energy could be released under conditions that actually prevail in stellar interiors.

At mid-century astronomers were far from having an adequate understanding of the genesis and development of stars. These were generally supposed to get started by gravitational contraction of interstellar gas and dust; at this stage the energy liberated by gravitational contraction heats the material up to a temperature of some ten million degrees, at which nuclear reactions can occur to provide the supply of energy needed for the full life-cycle of the star's development. But the specific details of such processes were not yet fully worked out.

V. THE APPLICATION OF BASIC SCIENCE TO TECHNOLOGY

The discoveries which brought advances in basic understanding of the nature of matter, of the earth and of the universe were made for the most part by men motivated solely by a desire for increased knowledge of the physical world. The extent to which these basic discoveries were exploited technologically and made the basis for industrial and other developments varied greatly from field to field. All of the major advances in the field of communication can be traced to the fundamental scientific discoveries of Faraday, Maxwell and Hertz as developed by engineers and inventors such as Alexander Graham Bell, (1847–1922), Thomas A. Edison (1874–1931) and Marconi. An outgrowth of the communication industry, the electronics industry, also had strong ties to the basic research of the late nineteenth and early twentieth centuries.

In contrast to this, the field of transport developed largely without the aid of workers in the fundamental sciences. At first this was even true of aeronautics, where it might have been expected that the classical science of aerodynamics would have played a fundamental role. However, unlike classical electromagnetic theory, the classical aerodynamics was principally concerned with the solution of mathematical problems of little practical interest, and the early understanding of the principles of flight was left to engineers to discover empirically. Through the work of Ludwig Prandtl (1875–1953), Theodore von Karman (1881–   ) and others, the physical basis of the principles of practical aerodynamics were gradually understood. After the second world war there was a major emphasis on applying fundamental physics to problems of aeronautics in university research centres, government laboratories and industrial research facilities.

While the development of the theory of the nuclear atom and quantum mechanics seemed at first to be far removed from practical application, the insight which these discoveries gave to the nature of matter was of great technological importance, notably to chemistry and to solid-state physics. A great amount of fundamental research in the latter field was undertaken in industrial research laboratories with such practical consequences as the development of the new amplifying device, the transistor. The techniques developed by geologists and geophysicists to study the earth had very rapid commercial application, principally by the petroleum industry. Routine procedures of oil prospecting made use of seismological, geomagnetic and gravity surveys. The high-pressure techniques of the physicist and petrologist were adopted for the commercial synthesis of industrial diamonds.

The discoveries made by nuclear physicists during the 1930s had enormous practical consequences. The work on artificial radioactivity in 1934 led directly to the discovery of nuclear fission in 1938 which in turn led almost immediately to the development of nuclear weapons, and during the postwar period to the further development of reactors for the production of power and unlimited supplies of artificial radioactive isotopes which could be put to countless industrial and medical uses.

The fundamental scientific work leading to the later type of nuclear weapon, the thermonuclear or hydrogen bomb, was recognized as having potentially more practical importance than all the previous applications of basic science to industrial purposes. The rise of modern industry had been at the expense of an ever-dwindling supply of fossil fuels. The use of uranium fission could extend the available energy sources a few centuries, but eventually the sources of uranium, like those of coal and petroleum, would become exhausted. However, the development of thermonuclear power using the water of the oceans as a fuel would provide an inexhaustible source of power for the service of man. At mid-century, scientists in Britain, the USSR and the USA were working intensively on this problem, recognizing that if the necessary thermonuclear reactors could be designed and built, one of the gravest threats to the long-term survival of an advanced industrial civilization would be overcome.

The conscious exploitation of basic science by industry was in its early stages. Before the second world war it was rare for industrial firms to employ physicists and applied mathematicians; their technical personnel had been trained almost exclusively in engineering. In the post-war years industries were adding to their technical staffs men who were familiar with the fundamentals of the modern theory of matter, in addition to those trained in the more well-established engineering techniques. While research in industrial laboratories continued to be oriented toward the production of usable products, the approach was at a more fundamental level than in the past, and the relationship between basic science and technology was becoming ever closer. [11,12] (Pl. 6.)

NOTES TO CHAPTER VIII

1. Doctor of Physical and Mathematical Sciences E. I. Adirovich writes that Chapter VIII suffers from the following grave shortcomings: (1) the entire physics of the twentieth century is reduced to microphysics, but at the same time there is neither a proper exposition of the fundamentals of the theory of relativity, nor a proper analysis of its role in cosmogony, field theory, or the physics of elementary particles; (2) only a brief and superficial exposition is given of such important branches of physics as the theory of solids, the physics of low temperatures, semi-conductor electronics, and others; (3) no information is given about the achievements of Soviet physics.

2. Doctor of Physical and Mathematical Sciences E. I. Adirovich writes that in addition to Lavoisier and Dalton mention should be made of Lomonosov and Proust.

3. Doctor of Physical and Mathematical Sciences E. I. Adirovich points out that it would be wrong not to mention at this point H. Moseley. Moseley was one of the scientists who fell victim to the first World War.

4. Professor Khristo Khristov, Member of the Bulgarian Academy of Sciences, writes: The fundamental idea of quantum theory is given in a very simplified form. The remarks in the text could apply to any classical static theory. It should be noted that quantum mechanics rejects the classical view that the co-ordinates and impulse of each particle of matter have at each moment objectively fully determined values (which we can either know or not), and as a result there is a new definition of the very concept of the nature of a particle, which is now determined by its wave function. This definition of the nature of matter is just as determinist as that given by the classical theory, because a wave equation is of the first sequence in regard to derivative time.

5. *The Author-Editors stress that within the classical concept of determinacy, the statements in the text concerning the quantum theory could not apply to any classical static theory.*

6. Doctor of Physical and Mathematical Sciences E. I. Adirovich writes that the reduction of the chemical bond to 'exchange forces' will not explain anything to the reader. The essence of the chemical bond in quantum mechanics can be fully explained by means of the Pauli principle and an examination of the nature of a united atom and disunited atoms.

7. Doctor of Physical and Mathematical Sciences E. I. Adirovich thinks that the question of the content in quantum mechanics of Mendeleyev's periodic law—so important both in science and in everyday life—is set forth too summarily and in language too specialized for the general reader.

8. Doctor of Physical and Mathematical Sciences E. I. Adirovich says that it should be pointed out that Soviet scholars were the first to photograph the centre of the galaxy.

9. Doctor of Physical and Mathematical Sciences E. I. Adirovich writes that A. M. Belopolsky was the first to prove the applicability of the Doppler effect to light. Mention should also be made of the work of Academician G. A. Shayn, who developed a method for determining the velocity of the axial rotation of stars, from the form of their spectral lines, which was of great importance for cosmogony.

10. Academician V. A. Ambartsumyan underlines that only one conclusion is possible: that the metagalaxy is expanding. Idealist philosophers see in this proof that the universe began to expand from a single point, i.e. as confirmation of religious views that there was a single act of creation.

    In actual fact there is nothing supernatural about the process of expansion of the galactic systems. In the universe scientists see various systems of heavenly bodies which are distinguished from one another by the nature of the movements within them. Some of them are extremely stable, others are not. An example of a very stable system is the one revolving around the sun. The earth has already made milliards of revolutions around its sun, and in all probability it, as well as the other planets, will remain a member of the solar system for a long time to come. A similarly high degree of stability is found in the double stars, i.e. systems consisting of two suns. However, the so-called aggregations of stars, containing hundreds or thousands of stars, are far less stable. Calculations have shown that each star can only make a few revolutions around the centre of gravity of the aggregation. In the larger stellar systems this instability is still more marked. The Soviet scientist B. Vorontsov-Velyaminov has published a magnificent atlas of dual and multiple galaxies, from which the instability of such large stellar systems is clearly visible.

    Expecially interesting are the data relating to individual aggregations of galaxies in the metagalaxy. It has been shown that many of them are disintegrating. This is apparent from the fact that the velocities of individual galaxies in such aggregations are very great in relation to one another. In the view of many astronomers this means that when the aggregation appeared the galaxies received such high velocities that the forces of Newtonian attraction were from the very beginning too weak to hold them back. In just the same way the metagalaxy, too, is expanding because its individual members received very high velocities at the moment of its formation. Thus science proves that there is nothing supernatural in the fact that the metagalaxy is expanding. Moreover, Einstein's general theory of gravity gives us a theoretical foundation for the proposition that very large systems are unstable on account of the very character of Einstein's law of gravity.

11. In spite of the fact that the Author-Editors have presented a series of chapters on the application of the physical, biological, and social sciences, following discussions of the major scientific developments in each of these fields, they have been criticized for not showing adequately the interaction between science and other aspects of the culture. Professor Herbert B. Callen writes with respect to the physical sciences: 'I would have expected the account to stress the interrelationship between science and culture. Many accounts have been given of recent scientific developments, and many of cultural evolution, but seldom has the strong interaction between these two been explored.' Professor S. N. Eisenhardt remarks with respect to the chapters on the application of the social sciences (Chapters XVII to XIX): 'Not enough emphasis has been given to the utilization of social science in various applied fields . . . and to the ways in which

social science services become institutionalized as professional service roles in different fields, such as industry, agriculture, settlement, counselling, etc.'

Professor E. N. Anderson comments that these criticisms serve to underline the immense difficulty of tracing the multitudinous and vastly complex interrelations between science and other elements in modern society.

12. *The Author-Editors limited themselves to general treatments of the application of the physical, biological, and social sciences after attempting to find a more precise way to identify significant specific relationships. For example, the authors consulted several industrial specialists in an effort to determine what had been the most important scientific 'breakthroughs' in the technology of their industries. The specialists countered with the question, 'Which "break-through"? The basic scientific discovery, the recognition of what the discovery could mean, the actual invention, the experimental stage of innovation, or the later, perhaps minor, modification which made the use of the invention economically feasible?' By the time that the authors had traced the process for a single feature of the technology of one industry, it was apparent that only very general relationships could be treated in a volume of history such as this.*

CHAPTER IX

INDUSTRIAL PRODUCTION

I. INTRODUCTION: THE SPREAD OF TECHNOLOGY

THE technological development of the twentieth century followed a common course throughout the world, despite difference in levels of development and in social institutions. In a broad sense, technology like science constituted a common pool of knowledge, available to all who commanded the understanding, skill and resources to make use of it. Engineers throughout the world shared common procedures for applying basic scientific knowledge to problems of production and within their respective fields of specialization could talk a common language; trade secrets were only a very minor deterrent. Workers in steel, textile, automobile or chemical factories could quickly find themselves at home in plants of the same industry wherever they might go.

The common aspects of twentieth-century technology were derived from its essentially scientific base, although the extent to which advancing science was put directly into practice varied markedly from one field to another. Until the advent of the scientific age science and technology had followed largely independent paths, the one academic, in the hands of scholars, the other empirical, in the hands of craftsmen. Science had been an area of speculation and study through which man might enhance his understanding of his world; the craftsman had generally drawn his principles as well as his techniques from tradition and experience, not from a body of knowledge most of which lay far outside his ken. But from the beginning of modern industry the gap between science and technology had been gradually narrowed, and in the twentieth century it was bridged by a large and rapidly growing corps of engineers, applied scientists and technicians, as inventions based on scientific discovery overshadowed those arrived at by trial and error.

The great mass of technology that was derived from the physical sciences rested on Newtonian principles and on the basic discoveries in physics, chemistry, astronomy or geology that had already been made before the end of the nineteenth century. By the middle of the century, however, the new scientific discoveries were becoming the bases for major technological advances, especially in the fields of electronics and the use of atomic energy.

It would be impossible to detail the innumerable technical developments of importance during the years under review. The host of discoveries, inventions and new arrangements that affected industry, transport, communication, warfare and all aspects of daily life were cumulative and interrelated. Often the steps in their development were obscure and comprehensible only to those who understood related processes. Even the effort to identify key developments leads to the dilemma of what to single out from the continuum of invention and innovation—an initial concept, a first discovery, a later discovery making the first one technically usable, a third making it economically feasible or a fourth converting a process of limited applicability into one of widespread usefulness. Inventions and techniques which at the time of their development appeared of minor significance later proved to be among the key events. At any given time only those whose impact had already been felt could be identified with assurance.

The chapters which follow therefore confine themselves to the common features and major trends that run through the technological developments of these years and the changes in way of life which the new technology made possible or imposed. An examination of these trends, and of their most advanced forms, yields a view of the direction in which mankind was moving, but not a realistic picture of the uneven actuality at any time. If the direction of trend is taken for a description of actuality, the account may seem exaggerated, unreal or idealized. Yet it is not irrelevant to contemplate these same trends in global terms, for the extension of the most advanced technology to areas still using primitive methods was already in process. In the rapidly moving world of the twentieth century it was not at all fantastic to consider the face of India if its *per capita* supply of motor vehicles should even begin to approach that of the United States, or the drain on world resources if China should utilize paper at a *per capita* rate approaching that of Canada, or the effect of using the uranium mines in the Congo to provide a vast source of energy to its African neighbours.

In considering the main trends, however, and recognizing many of them as irreversible and bearers of permanent changes in the life of mankind, it is important not to overlook lesser, sometimes partly counterbalancing tendencies. In the main, for example, twentieth-century developments were toward mass production. But the very cumbersomeness and complexity of mass-production processes left the door open for small, specialized operations which had the flexibility that mass production sacrificed for the economy of repetitive operations. In the mid-twentieth century, countries or segments of industries with a tradition of quality and specialization, as in France and Switzerland, were exploiting high-level technology in the latter manner.

The mounting drive for the development and introduction of new techniques was world-wide, gathering momentum in industrial centres and catching up the less developed areas in its sweep. But the drive was stronger in some areas than in others and, although the general tendency was for the pace of technical advance to accelerate, pressures were more intense and conditions more favourable in some periods than in others.

In general the most advanced techniques of industrial production, transport, communication and warfare were to be found in the countries of advanced scientific and industrial development. In the nineteenth century these had been the countries of Europe, especially Great Britain and Germany, and they continued to be centres of innovation. By the opening of the twentieth century the United States was taking the lead technologically and it remained in the vanguard in many fields throughout the first half of the century. By mid-century the USSR was coming to the fore, especially in some lines such as the long-distance transmission of high-voltage electric current and the propulsion and guidance of objects in space.[1, 2]

The most advanced technology was not however always to be found in the most fully developed areas. Although the process of technological advance was cumulative, each new development providing the momentum for others, existing techniques could act as a block as well as a stimulus, for they represented a large investment of capital and a vested interest for both owners and workers. Just as the factory system had developed more vigorously in England in the eighteenth century than in France where handicraft industries were more highly developed, and as German industry had overcome its late start by introducing the most recent designs while Britain was burdened by old equipment, so in the twentieth century some of the most up-to-date methods were to be found in newly industrialized sectors of advanced industrial countries or in plants based on the most advanced foreign models in countries in early stages of industrial development. The absence of antiquated equipment and the freedom from vested interests thus at least partly balanced the advantage of prior development.

Yet although underdeveloped areas could and did install modern plants, they remained mere borrowers, dependent upon technical developments elsewhere until they had the scientific, engineering, managerial, vocational and capital resources to carry forward the process of invention and innovation. It was the presence of a technological complex rather than of specific examples of advanced technology which distinguished the industrially developed from the newly developing areas.

Many factors acted as a stimulus to technological advance. Pressures to substitute mechanical for human labour were great wherever there was a relative shortage of manpower or high wages, a chronic situation in the United States and one of the reasons for its high level of mechanization. Such pressures were intensified by national drives which identified national progress or survival with technical advance.[3] Wartime needs brought many practical applications of existing knowledge which might otherwise have taken decades to work out. German technical development was stimulated by the Nazi effort to achieve autarchy and again in the intensive drive to re-establish the German economy after the defeat and destruction of the second world war. The revolutionary society of the USSR staked its survival and its future on intensive technological progress and spared no effort to introduce the highest degree of mechanization attainable throughout industry, agriculture and all parts of the country. Even in the Chinese People's Republic where manpower was abundant, the national drive to remake Chinese society and re-establish China's position as a world power included efforts to use and improve the most advanced productive methods, as well as to use modest devices to supplant primitive practices, such as the wheelbarrow to replace the carrying pole.

Incentives for technical development, which were generally strong in time of prosperity when demand for the products of industry was high, investment funds were available and the opportunities for the profitable exploitation of new techniques appeared ample, were weak in time of depression when opportunities seemed poor and manpower was unemployed. They were weak where vested interests in older processes were strong, where funds for investment were scarce, where management was conservative and where the institutional structure of the society obstructed or was unfavourable to technical change. They were weak where there was an abundant supply of cheap labour.

The technology of the production process itself, however, often dictated the choice between machine and worker even when labour was plentiful. Oil companies built the same types of installations in Latin America, the Middle East or south-east Asia where labour was cheap as they did on the east coast of the United States where it was among the highest priced in the world. As machine technology developed, the alternative of using cheap labour tended to become less attractive economically and the presence of available workers did not slow down the mechanization process. This was one of the dilemmas which faced the newly industrializing countries as they turned to industry to provide a basis for raising the levels of living of their people, yet could not employ the very ones most in need of work.

A further difficulty faced both the newly industrializing and the smaller industrialized countries. The processes of research, invention and application tended to become so costly that only the biggest nations with the most abundant resources in capital and highly specialized technicians could afford to finance and manage them. This difficulty was most conspicuous in respect to the development and use of atomic power.

Yet although advancing technology, paced by advancing science, carried much of its own momentum, institutional factors arising from non-technical sources affected the application of science and technology to industry, transport, communication and warfare. For the most part institutional factors tended increasingly to favour technological progress.

Industrial production in the twentieth century depended upon organization and upon techniques which made large-scale complex organization possible. Without rapid and reliable transport and communication, without effective record keeping, without the organizational structure and operating processes to make use of the technical potential, and without the political and social systems which would permit and sustain the myriad transactions involved, the effort to put technological advances into practice could only have broken down in chaos and confusion. The social inventions of the twentieth century were no less essential for the application of scientific knowledge to material production than were the more strictly physical aspects. Management was as important a technical development as electronics.

Legal institutions, taxation and public policies provided a framework within which the momentum of technical change worked itself out. Access to materials depended upon ownership rights and royalty systems as well as on the advancing technology for prospecting and extraction; tax systems could hold back exploitation or encourage wasteful methods. Throughout the period most institutional arrangements favoured the exploiter of material resources and few serious obstacles stood in the way of the use of materials as fast as technology permitted. A growing movement for conservation of resources placed some restraint on wasteful practices; more effective were the technical developments themselves that permitted better and more complete use. Where subsoil resources were sought by foreign enterprises, as was the case for a large proportion of the oil reserves and for minerals in Central and South America, Asia and Africa, the terms of their exploitation became an issue of national sovereignty and international relations. But the widespread insistence on national rights over local resources merely effected a division of profits more favourable to the government of the country where resources were located; it had little effect on the actual use of materials or the manner of their technical exploitation.

Public policy entered into the availability and cost of energy to an increasing degree as an ever-growing proportion of industrial power was supplied in the form of electricity. Not only was the available supply of electric power directly affected by the public undertaking of great hydro-electric projects, valley developments and, latterly, the beginning use of atomic energy; the transmission of electric power and its cost was everywhere subject to public control, by ownership or regulation, and to policies which determined where and how it would be supplied. The tendency was to regard the provision of cheap power as a public investment in national and local development and to favour projects and policies tending to expand the supply and lower the cost.

Patent systems designed to encourage the invention of new processes were well established in Europe and America before the development of modern industry. How far this device to secure to the inventor the proceeds from his invention actually stimulated technological advance is not clear, for it could also act as a deterrent to innovation. In some industries at least, patent guarantees attracted the investment of capital in new processes to which existing enterprises were blind or which they feared might undercut their established position. In the development of radio, for example, independent capitalists in Britain and the United States backed companies formed to exploit Marconi's wireless patents and, later, the patents on receiving devices and tubes, while the well-established telephone, telegraph and electrical manufacturing companies showed no interest in this new field. Elsewhere patent systems were accused of facilitating monopoly and examples of the buying up of patent rights in order to suppress rival inventions were not unknown.

In any case the importance of patents as a stimulus to invention and innovation declined as industrial and governmental research laboratories rather than the lone inventor became the principal sources of technical innovation. Even where patents existed there was some tendency to forgo their use; automobile manufacturers in the United States, for example, adopted a system of cross-licensing of all patents among members of the automotive manufacturers' association, and the entire American industry developed on this basis; the most radical innovation in electronics after the vacuum tube, the transistor, was made freely available by its inventors and passed rapidly into use. The USSR and other communist countries discarded patents on the principle that inventions which might increase productivity must be the property of all the people, although they offered various rewards to encourage invention.

The factor most subject to institutional rather than purely technological influences was the utilization of labour, which came to be hedged about in all industrialized or industrializing countries by minimum standards and requirements based on human rather than purely technological considerations. Throughout the industrial world, and increasingly in industrializing countries as well, limitations with respect to such matters as child labour, hours of labour, working conditions, wages and social security took similar forms, along lines expressed in the conventions formulated by the International Labour Organization. At the same time technological advance itself made it possible to think in terms of limitations on hours of work and minimum levels of income and security for all.4

In a broad sense the total milieu in the industrial countries favoured technological development. In western Europe the old structure of custom, feudal privilege and craft regulation had largely broken down by the beginning of the century. In the United States, Canada, Australia and New Zealand it had never existed. In the USSR it was destroyed by revolution.

Environments strongly favourable to technical development existed in many countries. The spirit of individual and group enterprise and of innovation received strong cultural sanction in the United States; German science and technology paced the world in many lines; Britain retained its scientific and technical leadership in others. Japan's national programme of industrialization took the form of copying and adapting new industrial techniques as fast as they were developed elsewhere. The USSR oriented its highly centralized and directed society toward production goals and threw the full weight of its support to technical education and research. In non-industrial countries where the milieu favoured the perpetuation of traditional methods rather than innovation and change, leaders recognized that programmes designed to provide a new technical base for rising living standards could only succeed as part of a broad cultural reorientation.5

On a yet more fundamental level the scientific spirit itself was the most essential ingredient in the twentieth-century technological development. The whole structure of modern technical advance rested on a rational spirit of free inquiry. To the extent that this spirit dominated, the conditions existed for the rapid growth of scientifically based technology and the transformation of society at its hands; only where this spirit penetrated could any but a limited, imitative development be anticipated. Man's growing command over nature in the twentieth century thus involved a three-way relationship between science, technology and the social milieu, each producing, supporting and depending on the other.

As applied to industrial production, modern technology involved the discovery and creation of new materials and new uses for old, the harnessing and use of energy in new forms and from new sources, the designing of new machines and new organization for industrial plants, the development of an increasingly capable labour force and its more productive use, and the evolution of management techniques.

During the first fifty years of the century one single industrial country, the United States, used more of the earth's minerals than had been withdrawn from the earth's crust for man's use in all preceding history. The *per capita* amount of energy harnessed for man's use tripled for the world at large and more than quadrupled for the country with the highest energy consumption in 1950. Mechanical power, substituted for human effort, first replaced physical labour for lifting, hauling, pushing, twisting and pressing; then it replaced manual skills as craft processes were analysed into their component steps and machines were devised to perform each process; by mid-century electronic computing and control devices able to observe, select, calculate and command more accurately and swiftly than the human eye and mind were beginning to be used to perform many of the steps in the managerial process. Mechanization thus altered successively the nature of work and the requirements which men must meet in order to become productive members of society.

The stream of products that emerged from mines, mills and factories entered the standard of living and transformed the way of life of the world's industrial countries. The productivity of twentieth-century industry not only made possible much release from toil but it enabled those who, throughout the ages, had sustained civilization by their labour but had shared few of its fruits to become partakers as well as producers.[6]

Every industry as it grew in size and complexity depended on the presence of countless subsidiary industries providing its materials, gauges, parts or machines. It depended on a trained labour supply, able to operate machines and keep them in repair; often it required mechanics ready to repair its products after they reached the consumers. It depended on a sufficient body of purchasers able and willing to buy its output, and upon the means of communication with this market and transport to it, as well as communication with and transport from its sources of supply. It depended too on financial resources, on legal protection and regulation of its dealings, on the physical facilities such as water, power, streets and houses required for its operations and for the living of its employees, on the social resources which its workers required. It depended in short on a whole industrial complex of which industry itself, though it was the core, was only one interrelated part.

The economic institutions which provided a framework for industrial activities were elaborated in the capitalist countries as industrial development required, and were carried to the distant parts of the world to which industry penetrated. An alternate set of institutions, facilitating the same essential industrial processes, were developed within the communist orbit. Economic motivations—work, production, a high standard of living—were sanctioned by the cultures of the countries where the industrial complex flourished during these years.*

II. MATERIALS

Basic to industrial development in the twentieth century was the growing ability to use more and more kinds of materials to serve man's needs and wants. In one sense twentieth-century technology was the greatest user of resources that the world had known; in another sense it was the greatest creator, for it transformed one after another of the elements in the land, sea and air into forms which man could use.

In the middle of the twentieth century a United Nations Conference on the Conservation and Utilization of Resources held at Lake Success, New York, in 1949 opened with a review of the world's critical shortages in minerals, fuel and energy, forest resources and food. Simultaneously the president of the United States appointed a Materials Policy Commission to answer a question which would have seemed absurd to that resource-rich country fifty years before: has the United States the material means to sustain its civilization?

Both groups were aroused by the possibility that economically usable supplies of many materials on which industrialization had hitherto rested might become exhausted. Estimates of known or suspected supplies of copper, tin, zinc and lead, for example, indicated that, at the rate of world consumption at mid-century, those which could be exploited by current methods at current costs would be used up well before the end of the twentieth century. Moreover, since the rate of consumption in the industrial countries was many times that of the rest of the world and population was expanding steadily, the rate of consumption could be expected to increase as industrialization spread. If the non-industrialized part of the world should reach the European rate of consumption, estimated resources of these particular metals would be exhausted in ten to twenty years. Yet the United States was already using the principal minerals at three to five times the European *per capita* rate and petroleum seventeen times as fast.

At the same time twentieth-century technology expanded the world's

* See Chapter XXI, Economic Institutions.

industrial resource base in a number of ways: by making possible the discovery, extraction, transport and use of unknown, inaccessible or low-grade materials which could not be used before; by so refining, combining and treating minerals as to make a given supply do much more work more effectively; by creating new materials from common substances through chemical processes and by improving ways of preserving materials and re-using them.

Early industrial development had depended chiefly on the nearby, readily exploitable and richest veins of coal, iron and other minerals. The iron and coal of Lorraine and the Ruhr, the British 'black country', and the fields in the eastern United States accounted in 1900 for as much as four-fifths of the world's output of coal and three-fifths of its iron ore. Less bulky minerals which could stand higher transport costs had been sought out in many parts of the world and drawn to industrial centres from their richest sources— manganese from Russia and Brazil, tungsten from China, nitrate from Chile, tin from Malaya, nickel from Canada, mercury from Spain, zinc from the United States, silver from Mexico, gold from South Africa. With the methods of 1900 and the ratio of demand to resources, only the best and most accessible seams of coal were mined and the best grades of ore exploited, while the smelting process discarded as waste many materials that later methods were able to recover and use. Most mineral deposits were discovered by prospectors who penetrated to an area on foot or horse and used simple tools to test outcroppings that looked promising. The great bulk of the earth's minerals remained unexplored.

From the time of the first world war newly developed geophysical methods of prospecting made it possible to detect subsurface minerals in areas which could not have been explored by old methods without great difficulty and cost. Large sections of the United States, Canada, Sweden, South Africa and Russia and several parts of Latin America were surveyed, and areas likely to repay exploratory drilling were identified by the use of devices which registered and recorded variations in the magnetic susceptibility and specific gravity of rock formations and differences in the electric conductivity and elasticity of the earth's crust. These methods so reduced the cost that they revolutionized the scope of mineral exploration and brought to light vast new oil and ore reserves in the years before the second world war. Developments in electronics and aviation during that war effected a second revolution in prospecting methods. Geophysical exploration from the air could be carried on in a fiftieth to a two-hundredth of the time required for ground surveys and could be done at a tenth to a twentieth of the cost even with expensive equipment.

In spite of all these improvements in prospecting methods great areas of the earth's surface in South America, Africa, northern Canada, Asia, Australia and Antarctica still remained unexplored at mid-century and no reliable estimates could be made of the world's total mineral reserves. The means for such exploration were at hand, however, and the undertakings of the International Geophysical Year (1957–58) sought to expand the world's knowledge of its hitherto undetected reserves.

Technical developments in transport, mining and the recovery of metal from ore made the exploitation of distant and difficult sources not only physically possible but economically feasible. By the middle of the century ore was being mined far into the Arctic, high in the Andes mountains and deep in the jungles of South America and Africa, and oil was being pumped from under the desert, the jungle and the sea. Nickel was being mined on the Arctic shores, iron and titanium in sub-Arctic Labrador, and Canadian uranium was being carried 500 miles by inland waterways open only between June and September; jungles, disease and distance had been overcome to open the great Northern Rhodesia copper belt, the lead, zinc and copper mines in remote sections of south-west Africa, the uranium and copper deposits of the Belgian Congo, the ironfields of interior Venezuela and Brazil and the ore resources of Siberia and north China. Oil was pumped through pipelines from the Persian Gulf to the Mediterranean, from Texas, USA, to the eastern seaboard and central United States, and across Venezuela.

Mechanization of mine operations changed mining methods and extended the scope of profitable mining. Electricity in underground mines made it possible to replace the miner's pick, to use motors instead of donkeys to drag the loaded cars, to replace the dangerous miner's lamps by electric lighting, and to use powerful blowers forcing refrigerated air to ventilate much deeper diggings. Miners' productivity increased sharply even where the richer seams had already been worked and the poorer or less accessible were being exploited. In coal-mining in the United States, for example, output per worker more than doubled in the first half of the twentieth century although the working week was cut almost in half. By 1957, 85 per cent of the cutting and loading was done mechanically and 59 per cent of the cleaning, whereas in 1900 only a quarter of the cutting and none of the loading or cleaning had been mechanized. Towards the middle of the century continuous, automatic machine cutting, loading and transporting of coal and ore from the face to the pit mouth was beginning to eliminate blasting to dislodge the material being mined.

Heavy equipment for moving earth—the giant bulldozer and steam shovel —introduced strip mining where ore or coal was not too far below the surface, removing the earth cover and scooping out the material with a minimum of time and labour. Strip mining in the United States, which began shortly after 1920, accounted for nearly a quarter of that country's coal-mining at mid-century; in the USSR it increased from 4 per cent in 1940 to 19 per cent in 1957. The use of flame for boring into rock too hard to drill opened up very large reserves of taconite which could not be worked for its iron content by traditional methods. Drilling for oil, meanwhile, was reaching greater and greater depths as new metal alloys increased the cutting power of the drills.

Developments in metallurgy played a major part in expanding usable resources, for they made it possible to recover metal from lower grades of ore, to extract a larger proportion of the metal content, to separate out and refine to much greater purity the several minerals contained in each ore body, and to combine or treat metals so as to derive materials with new properties. The froth-flotation process proved much more efficient than older methods in separating out and concentrating a large range of ores; by placing pulverized ore in a succession of chemical solutions each type of mineral could be floated out in the froth of its appropriate chemical. Electrolytic refining gave greatly increased purity and made it possible to recover many rare metals, such as cobalt and platinum from the refining of copper and nickel, by passing an electric current through appropriate chemical solutions in order to deposit one or another of the component elements.

With these new processes, slag piles surrounding old smelters became virtual mines in themselves from which formerly wasted products were extracted, and little remained to be cast on to the slag heaps of new smelters except the ubiquitous silicon, whose possibilities were only beginning to be exploited at mid-century. Introduction of dust precipitators and collectors into the smoke-stacks of smelters, together with devices for capturing and converting smelter gases, not only recovered large quantities of materials that were formerly wasted but protected the people and vegetation of the surrounding area from harmful dust and fumes.

Although ore once withdrawn from the earth cannot be replaced, its initial use in industry did not necessarily mean its destruction as a future resource, for the re-use of the material in discarded products offered a source upon which industry could draw. As industrial output accumulated over the years dumps, especially those for old cars, junk yards, and demolished buildings contained a large metal supply. With the improved methods of recovery in use at mid-century it was estimated that 60–65 per cent of iron, copper and lead, 40 per cent of aluminium, and 20–25 per cent of tin, nickel and zinc could be recovered and re-used after their initial fabrication. Scrap already provided nearly half of the iron, over a third of the lead, copper and aluminium and a quarter of the zinc going into the furnaces in Great Britain and the United States. While a substantial proportion of this was waste produced in the process of manufacture itself, such as the remains of steel sheets after forms had been stamped out, and thus did not provide a supplement to newly mined ore, much was old scrap from discarded objects of manufacture. As the stock of metals in use grew constantly, so did the quantity returning as old scrap, and the proportion of the total supply coming from this source tended to increase over the years.

New methods of extraction made available to industry metals which had formerly appeared only in the laboratory. These furnished the basis for an array of special steel alloys and for the substitution of light metals for the materials—iron, simple steel and wood—on which modern industrial develop-ment had originally been based. Special steel alloys, hardened or strengthened or given special properties by admixtures of molybdenum, nickel, chrome, vanadium, cobalt, titanium and other minerals, met a wide variety of specialized needs. Tungsten carbide, developed for general use in the 1920s, lengthened the life of machine tools by twenty-five to a hundred times and greatly increased the speed at which they could be operated or the precision of the finish which could be obtained.

Such special alloys and new metals were essential, for modern industry required materials which would stand up and perform under conditions to which no previous materials had been subjected. Metals used in steam turbines had to withstand pressure of 5,500 lb per square inch and temperatures of 1,150° F, as compared with 170 lb of pressure and 280° F of heat in 1900; aircraft engines had to operate at terrific heat and great speed for many hours, and must not fail. Piping, which was once judged adequate if it allowed no more than a drop or so of leakage per minute, had to be absolutely without leakage when used to carry radioactive materials in atomic installations. The refining of zinc to a purity of 99·9 per cent during the first world war was hailed as an advance, but a transistor required silicon with no more than one part of impurity to a hundred million parts of pure metal.

Where lightness was a consideration aluminium, which had begun to be produced commercially at the opening of the century, became the most extensively used and cheapest metal next to steel. By mid-century it was not only being used as the basis for the aircraft industry and in other places where steel, because of its weight, would not serve, but was being widely substituted for steel and other materials in many types of construction and fabrication and was replacing copper in wire for electrical transmission. From the time of the second world war magnesium began to share the position occupied by aluminium as rapid improvements in its processing lowered its cost and made it economical to take advantage of its extreme lightness and considerable strength.

Both aluminium and magnesium required large amounts of electric current in their production; the rapid growth in their supply and drop in price depended on the expansion of power generation. Raw materials for both were widely distributed, aluminium in small concentrations in most earths and magnesium in sea-water. Up to mid-century aluminium was being manufactured only from rich bauxite deposits containing 50–60 per cent aluminium oxide, located chiefly in southern France and Italy, British and Dutch Guiana, the United States, Hungary, the USSR, Jamaica and Ghana. Magnesium however had begun to be extracted from sea-water in 1937 by a procedure which had been regarded as fantastic when it was proposed in the early part of the twentieth century, and at mid-century a large part of the world supply was coming from that source.

On the heels of magnesium another widely distributed substance, titanium, came to be recognized as a new metal with great possibilities, when a satisfactory process for making it in a pure and usable form was developed toward the middle of the century. New techniques for smelting iron from titano-magnetic rock not previously regarded as a source for either iron or titanium produced a slag containing an ample workable supply of titanium and helped to reduce its cost. As a metal both lighter and stronger than most steels and extremely resistant to heat and corrosion, titanium was used in alloys for such purposes as jet engines even while its cost was still high. An even more costly metal, zirconium, was being used in nuclear installations, primarily because of its resistance to corrosion and acid. The most abundant mineral in the earth's crust, silicon, was also beginning to enter into industry in silicone plastics and, experimentally, in other forms.

As techniques were improved for separating out the components of a given piece of rock and more was known about the values and uses of a wider and wider range of minerals, the exhaustion of traditional resources seemed less of a threat to continued industrial growth. Since ordinary granite rocks contain most minerals in some proportion, it was technically possible to take practically any rock which might be at hand, pulverize or dissolve it, and sort out the component elements for use in whatever combination local industry might require. Sea-water, already yielding magnesium, could be utilized for others of the many minerals which it contained. Air had already proved to be a source for nitrogen used in fertilizers and might be tapped for other elements. To the extent that these possibilities might be economically realizable, a virtually unlimited material basis would be available for industry in practically any part of the world which possessed the necessary technical knowledge, equipment and power.

One of the most spectacular and revolutionary contributions of technology to the supply of industrial materials was the creation of new substances, known generally as plastics, either in imitation of natural products or to provide something which had no counterpart in nature but which possessed properties desired for a particular use. Using chiefly hydrocarbons which could be derived from many sources—coal, petroleum, coal tar, cellulose from wood pulp or sugar-cane waste—the chemical industry learned how to put together enormously complex chains of atoms by a process known as polymerization to produce tough fibres, sheets or moulded forms. Since the variety and complexity of the chains which could be created was almost unlimited, it became possible to introduce many different properties, both by the chemical elements included and by the process of treatment. Additional possibilities were being introduced by the use of silicones instead of hydrocarbons as a base.

The prototypes of plastics had been developed before the turn of the century in the form of celluloid and bakelite. The first of the synthetic fibres, artificial silk or rayon, was in use in the 1890s and its manufacture by various methods became well established in the first two decades of the twentieth century. In the 1930s a number of new plastic materials began to be produced commercially, especially in Germany where they served as *ersatz* or substitute products for natural fibres and other materials in short supply.

The full potentialities of plastics, however, only began to be envisaged during and after the second world war with improvements in their quality. Such critical war materials as nylon for parachutes and synthetic rubber to keep motor transport in operation when natural resources of rubber were cut off emphasized the importance of synthetic products. Plastics manufacturers turned from efforts to devise substitutes as good as some natural product to the development of materials with characteristics which natural products lacked, and they supplied an enormous range of fibres, sheets, shapes, paints, and substances which could be mixed with other material such as wood or glass to give them new properties.

The development of plastics was paralleled in the production of glass, a material also based on a resource, sand, which was unlimited and readily accessible. Although glass-making was a very old art, glass became a cheap material in general use only after a machine process for bottle blowing was introduced at the beginning of the twentieth century. In the course of these years glass became a highly versatile material as ways were developed to preserve its imperviousness to corrosion and its transparence while over-coming its brittleness and fragility. Types of glass were developed of such hardness as to be bullet-proof, of such heat resistance as to be used in labora-tory equipment subjected to intense heat, of sufficient strength for building blocks and wall panels, and of a flexibility which could be drawn into fine fibres and woven into fabrics. Its transparent qualities could be so controlled as to let through or exclude either ultra-violet or infra-red rays, or to be transparent from one side and opaque from the other. In combination with plastics, fibre glass was moulded into boats, car bodies, wall panels and translucent roofs that were strong, light and of low cost.

Concrete had begun to supplement brick, stone and wood as a structural material in the second half of the nineteenth century; during the twentieth century it became one of the most widely used materials for the construction of industrial plants and for most large urban buildings, bridges and main roads. Although it had the advantage of being made from plentiful material found in many localities and of being easy to handle, the large amount of cement and reinforcing steel required for strength made this a heavy building material, eminently suited for foundations but bulky when used for super-structures and roofs. New concretes, made by mixing in such things as saw-dust, volcanic ash and certain lightweight minerals or by adding chemicals, were lighter and more versatile. Panels for roofs and partitions could be pre-fabricated, preinsulated and transported with relative ease. Prestressing of concrete, to give strength to beams at the place where strain was greatest, substantially reduced the amount of cement used and achieved the same strength with only a fraction of the usual reinforcing material. Other materials such as gypsum, sugar-cane waste or asbestos were pressed and chemically bound into sheets for use in building construction, and insulating materials were made from glass fibre or other non-conductors of heat in order to reduce the thickness of wall required for warmth or to conserve heat. (Pl. 11a.)

Although the industrial development of the twentieth century rested primarily on the use of metals, plastics, cement and glass, wood continued to serve many of its old purposes and, in combination with plastics or subjected to chemical treatment, was put to new uses. New techniques gave wood new properties and extended available resources by utilizing lower grades and much of what had been discarded as waste. At mid-century high consumption of wood was associated with a high degree of industrialization, as was evidenced in the fact that the *per capita* consumption of timber, lumber and plywood in North America was five times that of Central and South America, while in Europe, with very much more limited forest resources, it was some 16 per cent greater.

One of the largest consumers of wood was the paper industry. New processes were designed for making cheaply the enormous volume of newsprint consumed in the countries where literacy was general and for many types of strong, sturdy or absorbent papers. They converted paper from a scarce item to be cherished and re-used to a cheap, plentiful material produced with the idea that much of it would be destroyed. Cartons and corrugated boxes took the place of wood, metal and cloth containers; disposable tissues, towels, napkins and paper cups offered cleanliness and convenience and reduced the transmission of germs, especially in public drinking and eating places and washrooms. These many uses raised the *per capita* consumption of wood pulp in the principal paper-consuming countries, the United States and Canada, to five times that of European countries other than the Scandinavian, and twenty-five to a hundred times that of most of the rest of the world.

While new techniques enabled the paper industry to use quick-growing types of trees, the enormous expansion in demand for paper constituted a mounting drain on forest resources, and together with industrial demand continued to press on the world's wood supply. With a long history of forest conservation, timber in most European forests was felled during much of the twentieth century at a rate which balanced growth, but wartime demands and requirements for post-war reconstruction upset the balance and led to cutting in excess of the rate of growth. In North America, where virgin forests had seemed inexhaustible, interest in forest conservation began to be aroused only in the first decade of the twentieth century, scientific forestry practices were slow to take hold, and at mid-century cutting was exceeding annual growth by as much as 50 per cent.★

The use of all these materials was not only dependent on technological developments but also on the conditions under which they were made available to those who might exploit them.

Control over mineral resources and their exploitation at the opening of the century was vested generally in the owners of surface land; it was on this

★ See Chapter XIV, section on Forestry.

basis that the coal and iron resources which sustained nineteenth-century industrialization had been mined. Since the size of landholdings, the interests of owners and the terms on which they were willing to lease the right to mine below their soil did not necessarily coincide with the most rational and technically sound methods of extraction, mining was often uneconomic and wasteful, as for instance where a multitude of small units brought out only the best from each spot, leaving the rest of the seams difficult or impossible to work. Royalties to landowners were often a heavy charge against mining operations. Where minerals lay below the public domain, as in much of the United States, Canada, Australia, and in some parts of South Africa, or in areas claimed by various colonial governments, the system known as free mining prevailed. Under this system a prospector could exploit the minerals which he discovered if he met the established requirements for registering his claim, developing it within a specified period and making the prescribed payments to the government.

In the case of petroleum the fact that a single underground pool could be tapped at many points and drained through any one of the wells which reached it led to highly competitive and wasteful drilling. When oil was struck in an area where there were many surface-owners, the original driller quickly sunk as many wells as he could in order to pump oil out fast, while his neighbours rushed to drill on their land in order to pump out their share before it was gone. Forests of derricks in the oilfields of Rumania, Mexico and the United States bore witness to the results of the surface-owner's right to drill and the driller's right to pump all that he could draw. This system proved so wasteful of oil, and so uneconomical in its tendency to glut the market irrationally, that governments intervened to establish controls over the rate at which oil could be withdrawn.[7]

Since many of the mineral and petroleum resources developed in the twentieth century lay in industrially undeveloped areas and were sought by foreign concerns, the terms on which they could be exploited were determined by the relations between the governments of these countries and the foreign oil, steel and mining companies. The companies received concessions from the governments to search and exploit and undertook costly and highly uncertain exploration in the hope of finding rich resources which would yield a high profit in return.[8]

Because of the vital importance of oil and minerals to the development of modern industry and to national security, these resources came increasingly to be regarded as national assets rather than private possessions and governments extended their control over the manner of their exploitation. Mexico and others of the Latin America countries laid claim to all subsoil resources not yet being worked and then extended their claim to those already under concession, sometimes nationalizing the entire industry as in the case of Bolivian tin. These governments and those in the Middle East granted concessions for oil and other minerals on terms which assured that a proportion of the returns should be paid to them. When terms already granted appeared unsatisfactory they insisted upon and secured larger proportions of the returns, and asserted their right to nationalize the operation on the principle that the resources lying below the earth were the birthright of the political unit beneath whose soil they lay. Mining operations were wholly nationalized in Russia immediately upon the establishment of the Soviet state, and by the communist régimes in the eastern European countries after the second world war. Great Britain nationalized mineral rights before the second world war and took over the entire coal industry after the war. The major part of Holland's coal mines, developed to meet the shortage of the first world war, were state-owned.

Countries dependent on sources outside their borders for supplies of minerals vital to their industry adopted the practice of stockpiling supplies against a possible emergency. In time of war and during years of tension, governments exercised rigid controls over the flow of metals in international trade in the effort to withhold such materials from opponents as well as to assure their own supply.

Although the range of resources which were being used by the middle of the twentieth century far exceeded the few, simple and obvious materials which had provided the basis for nineteenth-century industrialization, scientists and engineers agreed that they had only scratched the surface of potentialities. Only about one-third of the known elements were extensively used in industry, another third were in very slight use and the remainder were still entirely outside the scope of industrial application.

At mid-century divergent answers were being given to the question of whether man by his command over nature was so exhausting the resources of the earth as to lay an unsound basis for future generations, or whether the process of technological development itself was so enlarging the range of possibilities that the balance was on the side of ever more abundant resources rather than of their depletion. Some chemists claimed more limitless possibilities than others saw for the materials creatable through the chemical industry. Some mineralogists were disturbed by the exhaustion of old minerals while others envisaged the utilization of new. Some thought that economy in the use of materials was tending to balance new demands, pointing to the single pound of material per horsepower in high-speed aircraft engines as compared with the one thousand pounds of material per horsepower in the early internal-combustion motor, or the negligible amount of materials and power required for heating and cooling by means of such new devices as the reversible heat pump.

Three points only were clear: that at mid-century the limits of technological possibilities in developing resources on the basis of already known scientific principles were nowhere in sight; that the future pattern of resource use would undoubtedly involve as fundamental a shift as that of the preceding fifty years, which had seen the replacement of wood and coal by petroleum for fuel, of wood and brick by concrete and steel for construction, of iron by alloy steel, aluminium and magnesium in much machinery, and of wool, cotton and leather by synthetic fibres and plastic materials; and that the essential resource upon which mankind would depend for its industrial future was not any specific physical material but technology itself.

III. ENERGY

Power lay at the heart of industrial society, for it was the use of energy to operate machines and implements that increased productivity and altered the character of the production process itself. The use of energy was the chief measure of a society's degree of industrialization and mechanization. Following the oft-quoted dictum of Lenin, 'Communism is Soviet rule plus electrification of the whole country', the USSR expanded its production of electricity more than a hundredfold during its first forty years, it put into operation in 1959 the largest hydroelectric project in the world and it was feeding its growing volume of power into an immense grid designed to extend from Leningrad to eastern Siberia. Japan's thorough electrification after the first world war sustained her nation-wide industrial development. For the people of central Africa the great Kariba dam on the Zambesi was the surest evidence of Africa's emergence into the modern world. The Chinese People's Republic, in its determination to provide a base for massive industrialization, projected a dam for the Yangtze river designed to produce more than ten times the power generated by the Grand Coulee dam in the USA, which had been the largest hydroelectric installation in the world in 1955.

In the first half of the twentieth century the world's supply of energy from mineral fuel and water power increased threefold. The energy actually put to work increased very much more because the efficiency with which supplies could be used doubled for the world as a whole during this period.

Almost all of the increase however was in the highly industrialized countries. On a *per capita* basis in 1950 the only country outside North America, Europe and Oceania that was using one-tenth as much energy as the highest energy-user, the United States, was Israel. With the exception of Japan no Asian country used as much as 5 per cent. India, the Asian country with the second largest industrial output, used less than 2 per cent as much energy *per capita* as did the United States, while Indonesia, Pakistan, Burma and Thailand used less than 1 per cent. The Latin American and Caribbean countries ranged from Argentina with slightly less than 10 per cent the *per capita* energy consumption of the United States to Haiti with ·003 per cent. The disparity between the energy consumption of the industrial and non-industrial areas had been growing as the consumption of the former increased. It would clearly require heroic efforts by the industrializing countries to close the energy gap.

The sources of power upon which industrial development depended changed markedly during these years, and at mid-century further major changes appeared to be in sight.

At the opening of the century the world was drawing about 40 per cent of its non-human energy from work animals, wood fuel and wind and 60 per cent from mineral fuels, almost wholly coal. At mid-century more than 80 per cent

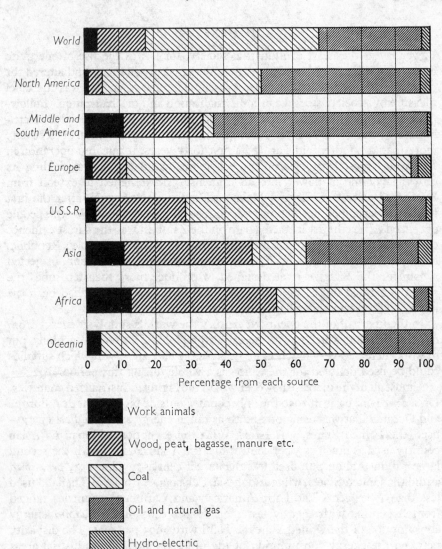

CHART X.   Supply of Energy by Continent, 1948. (Percentage from each source.)

Source: Woytinsky, *World Population and Resources*, p. 931.

7 ELECTRIFICATION I

High tension lines

8
INDUSTRIALIZATION I
Early automobile
assembly line, c. 1910

INDUSTRIALIZATION II
*Automated assembly
line,* 1955

[Renault

(a)   [FPI

The Kariba Dam, Zambesi River, 1960

(a) *General view*
(b) *Detail of the construction*

(b)   [FPI

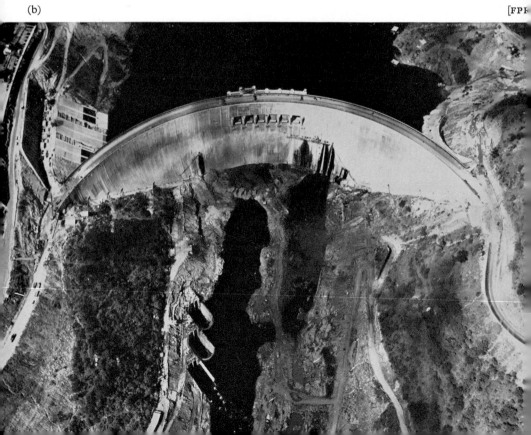

came from mineral fuels and water power, and of this coal supplied only three-fifths while more than a quarter came from petroleum and the rest from natural gas and hydroelectric power.

In the industrial countries the shift was much more complete. The United States in 1900 was already drawing nearly 98 per cent of its work energy from mineral fuels, almost wholly coal. In 1950 coal supplied a quarter of the work

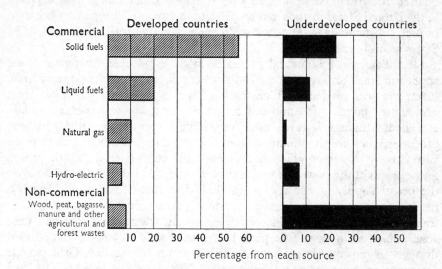

CHART XI. Consumption of Energy in Developed and Underdeveloped Countries, 1959. (Percentage from each source.)

Source: UN, *World Energy Supplies*, Statistical Papers, Series J, No. 1.

energy used, as against 58 per cent from petroleum, 15 per cent from natural gas and less than 2 per cent from hydroelectric power. Western Europe (OEEC countries, 1953) at that time was drawing over 80 per cent of its energy from coal, about 15 per cent from petroleum, 3 per cent from hydroelectric sources and a negligible proportion from natural gas.

Whatever its source, energy came to be delivered for use in two principal forms, electricity for more or less stationary operations and the internal-combustion engine—petrol or diesel—for mobile power. Steam continued important but tended more and more to be converted into electricity rather than to be used directly. Diesel engines were also extensively used for electric power generation, specially in small installations. In cold climates considerable energy of course continued to be used directly in the form of heat.

In the early stages of industrial development industry had been closely tied to its power base. Power transmitted directly by means of shafts and belts from water-driven wheels or stationary steam engines had limited factory location to the immediate vicinity of these sources. Machines within a factory had to be arranged in such a way that they could be connected mechanically with the power source and much of the factory space was filled with moving belts.

Although the electric motor was known before the end of the nineteenth century it only began to be used in industry in the first quarter of the twentieth century and to determine the character of industrial processes in the second quarter. Electric motors provided 5 per cent of manufacturing motive power in the United States in 1900 and 80 per cent in 1950. In Europe they began to be used substantially in the 1920s and remained less general than in the United States at mid-century.

Electrification of industrial processes made it possible for power to be applied in small or large volume and at places distant from the power source. Electricity was carried by high-tension lines as much as 300 miles from generating points; at mid-century the distance was being greatly extended. Although factories using very large amounts of electricity in their processes, such as aluminium refining plants, found it advantageous to be sited close to power supplies, most plants could be situated with little regard to the origin of the power on which they depended. In some areas, moreover, the power supply of one region was linked to that of the next through a common grid permitting the substitution of current from one source for that from another as demand fluctuated; especially where grids spanned time zones, they could distribute peak loads. In Britain a well-developed grid throughout the country gave great flexibility in power supply. Grids on the European continent were to some extent linked internationally. The grid under construction during the 1950s in the USSR, designed to link all parts of the Soviet Union, carried power at higher voltages than were used elsewhere and thus permitted long-distance transmission without serious loss. (Pl. 7.)

Electricity, moreover, revolutionized the factory itself. It was no longer necessary to arrange machinery to permit the transmission of power by shafts and belts, with consequent crowding and danger to workers from moving parts. Power could be delivered to any spot within the plant, equipment could be arranged for convenience in handling the material that was being processed, individual machines, and even parts of machines, could be operated independently of one another, and many small operations which had had to be done by hand because mechanically delivered power was too clumsy could be performed with electrically driven hand tools plugged into a current outlet at the work bench. A major result of eliminating the shafts and belts used in the transmission of mechanical power was to allow clear space for equipment conveying materials to and through the work site.

Some industrial processes, especially construction, involved operations which could not be carried on by fixed machines and for these, as well as for all types of transport, the internal-combustion engine provided power in the necessary form.

The essential principles of the reciprocating engine operating by fuel ignited under compression were known, and their application was worked out during the late nineteenth century. The four-stroke engine in which highly volatile gas and air are mixed in a carburettor, compressed and ignited by a spark had been in commercial production since 1877, and in 1897 Rudolf Diesel had made practical the two-stroke engine in which a charge of lower-grade fuel is self-ignited at the high temperature produced by the high compression of the air into which it is injected.

Both these types of engines were gradually improved and adapted to the multitude of purposes to which they were applied, as experience, new materials and new methods of refining fuels permitted. Diesel engines were developed mainly for heavy duty, such as railway locomotives, very large lorries and stationary equipment, while petrol engines of equal power but perhaps only 5 per cent of the weight were designed for aircraft, and petrol engines of every size drove motor cars and all manner of mobile equipment in factories and on farms.

An alternative type of internal-combustion engine, the gas turbine, had also been designed and placed in successful operation at the opening of the century, but its practical use depended upon the development of metals which could resist extreme heat. In reciprocating engines materials had to resist the peak heat only during the moment of explosion, but in the turbine the process was continuous and speeds extremely high. When the jet propulsion principle began to be applied to aircraft during the second world war, i.e. when the exhaust gas was used as the driving force instead of being treated as waste, the high-speed turbo engine proved the most suitable type. Once the metallurgical problems were solved, turbo-jet engines became standard for military aircraft and for a rapidly increasing proportion of civilian planes. In the development of missiles and space vehicles, the ram-jet principle and new fuel gave even greater power. While these new instruments were developed primarily for airborne and space travel, they extended the range of possibilities for the application of energy to productive tasks.*

The rapidly rising level of fuel consumption in the industrial countries, and the enormous prospective needs in the rest of the world, brought to the fore the problem of whether the world's energy resources were sufficient to continue to sustain industrial activity and growth.

With the rate of petroleum consumption rising rapidly, fears were repeatedly expressed that petroleum might be in short supply by the end of the century. In 1942 the world consumption of petroleum products exceeded for the first time the new supplies discovered during the year. At the rate of increase in consumption at mid-century, the proved supplies would have lasted little more than fifty years. But unproved supplies in the Middle East were thought to be many times the proved amounts, great fields in the Sahara were being opened up, and exploration for new resources was being carried on in many parts of the world. Improved methods of extraction,

* See Chapter X, Transport.

including the flooding of fields to force out oil left in the ground after pumping—sometimes amounting to as much as the total which had been pumped out of the field—increased the yield from known sources. Other technical developments opened the possibility of extracting oil from shale.

Some scientists, however, predicted that a substantial proportion of petrol supplies would be derived from coal rather than petroleum before the end of the century. World reserves of coal remained large, with little immediate prospect of exhaustion, though some of the older sources on both sides of the north Atlantic were becoming less and less productive.

On the basis of data and analyses presented to the 1955 Geneva conference on the peaceful uses of atomic energy, it appeared that world reserves of conventional fuels were sufficient to meet increasing needs for a hundred years. But the location of reserves did not match areas of consumption, and it appeared that few regions of the world would be able to meet their energy requirements by the end of the century from these sources without a considerable increase in price.

Although only a small proportion of the energy consumed in the world at mid-century came from hydroelectric power, this source had gained in importance and immense resources remained untapped. Estimates as to the amount of water power available were necessarily uncertain in view of constantly changing technology which made it possible to harness more remote and difficult flows. It appeared however that an amount equivalent to half the total energy which the world was consuming at mid-century might be derivable in the future from the great resources in the Himalayas, Africa, the Andes, the Amazon and the Orinoco, the Columbia River basin of the United States and Canada, and the great rivers of Siberia and China. In addition the power potential in the ebb and flow of the tides had not been exploited to any substantial extent. Nearly half of the world's estimated untapped water power lay in Africa, approximately one-eighth each in Asia, South and Central America and the USSR, and the remainder in North America, Europe and Oceania.

Only about 13 per cent of the world's usable water power had been harnessed, including more than 60 per cent of that available in Europe, half of the North American supply, 3–6 per cent of the usable potential in South and Central America, Oceania and the USSR, a negligible amount in Africa, and some 13 per cent in Asia, almost wholly in Japan and Korea. Among the countries of the world only Japan, France, Sweden, Germany, Switzerland, Austria and Italy had tapped their water power resources anywhere nearly to the full, measuring these resources in terms of the minimum flow during the dry seasons of the year without considering the additional supplies that might be stored from rainy periods.

Great hydroelectric projects were at the heart of the USSR's industrial development programme. Dams and generating stations on the Volga and Dnieper rivers were included in the early five-year plans and these were promptly reconstructed after the destruction suffered during the second world war. In the period after the war the Soviet Union was doubling its hydro-electric capacity every five years, with gigantic projects on the Siberian rivers, at least one of which was designed to generate more than twice the volume of electricity put out by any existing plant elsewhere in the world.

Other countries seeking industrialization gave hydroelectric projects a central place in their national plans. India looked to her great rivers as a major source of much-needed power; her Damodar Valley project was designed to form the basis of a great steel complex. The Chinese People's Republic, short of equipment but determined to lay a basis for economic development, set some 20,000,000 of its people to work on river projects during its first decade of existence. The high Aswan dam on the Nile, the Volta River project in West Africa and the Kariba dam on the Zambesi in the Central African Federation marked the beginnings of major developments on the African continent. (Pl. 10a, 10b.)

It was characteristic of hydroelectric projects that they could be undertaken as multi-purpose enterprises, for flood control, inland transport and irrigation as well as power generation. The concept of river valley development, first made famous by the Tennessee Valley Authority (TVA) in the United States in the 1930s, became the basis for multi-purpose projects in many countries, with one or another aspect dominant—flood control and inland navigation in China, irrigation in India and Egypt, power generation in the USSR—but with most or all features included in the total plan.

At the middle of the century two major new sources of power were beginning to be exploited, atomic energy and solar energy. Atomic power, first developed for purposes of destruction, was being harnessed practically for industrial use; the USSR, Britain, and the United States all placed atomic generating stations in operation for the commercial production of electricity in 1956 and 1957. The 1955 Geneva conference on the peaceful uses of atomic energy revealed a great range of experimental undertakings which indicated the likelihood of early and eventually widespread use of atomic power for industrial purposes, especially in those areas where other sources of energy were scarce or costly. Nuclear fuels, it found, were abundant—many times more abundant than the world's coal reserves—and could be obtained at a reasonable price. Several types of machines were successfully extracting energy from nuclear fuels at costs already not much higher than that of energy obtained from coal or petroleum. Since costs could be expected to drop below those of energy from coal or oil, atomic power generation appeared to offer a practical resource to countries where there was sufficient technical personnel to operate the complex mechanisms. European countries joined in 1953 to form a permanent European Organization for Nuclear Research (CERN) which set up an international laboratory in Switzerland. In 1957 they established an organization, Euratom, to develop atomic energy for practical use. The USSR set up a Joint Institute for Nuclear Research in Dubna to co-ordinate the activities of scientists from socialist countries. In 1957 the International Atomic Energy Organization, with headquarters at Vienna, came into existence as a specialized agency of the United Nations.

Investigations were also under way to find means of utilizing thermonuclear fusion as well as atomic fission for power generation following the development of this process in connection with the hydrogen bomb. Since the materials for the latter process were far more plentiful and cheap than the uranium on which atomic fission depended, these experiments opened the possibility of an even more universal and ultimately economical source of power. The problems of radioactive contamination or danger had not yet been solved, nor was there yet a supply of atomic scientists and technicians who could design and operate installations in some of the regions where such power might be of particular importance. There was little doubt however that atomic energy would become a major source of industrial power in the future.

Extensive work was also in process at mid-century to draw power from the enormous volume of solar energy reaching the earth, especially in the tropical areas and in arid zones of constant sunshine. Solar energy was already being used successfully on a partial or experimental basis, to distil fresh water from the sea, for irrigation pumps and other small engines, for stoves and high-temperature furnaces and for charging electric batteries. The principal problem in the utilization of the sun's rays, the very small amounts in which solar energy reaches any given point, was being overcome by constant improvements in design. A practical solar battery for boosting small amounts of electric current had been installed on rural telephone lines in the United States, and had attained the relatively high efficiency level of 11 per cent; a large solar plant to generate electricity and pump water was under construction near Abidjan, in West Africa. Marked progress was being made in Israel. At the first world symposium on solar energy held at Tucson, Arizona, USA, in 1955 some 900 scientists and industrialists from thirty-four countries and all continents met to discuss scientific and practical aspects and to view examples of more than fifty different solar devices.

While the possibilities of atomic energy were of greater importance to countries with limited sunlight and high rainfall such as Great Britain and northern Europe, and although the fact that the sun could generate power only during daylight hours presented storage problems in all regions, solar energy seemed to offer to tropical and arid areas a hopeful possibility for a plentiful and ultimately cheap source of power.

IV. INDUSTRIAL PLANT AND EQUIPMENT

1. *Productive equipment*

It is obviously impossible to discuss in any detail the variety of equipment to produce every imaginable type of product, but it is possible to note in broad terms some of the characteristics of design and operation which marked the major trends of twentieth-century development.

The features which most distinguished the productive equipment of twentieth-century industry from that of the nineteenth century were the widespread use of electrical and chemical rather than primarily mechanical processes and the increasing extent to which operations were automatically controlled. Nineteenth-century machinery was almost wholly mechanical in design and operation, and much of the productive equipment of twentieth-century industry also represented a refinement and elaboration of mechanical principles. But electrical and chemical processes gained in importance, over and above the use of electrical energy to drive equipment, and became vital to many key industries.

Electric processes revolutionized many aspects of metal producing and metal working industries, both in the extraction of metals from ores and in the production of alloys. Electric furnaces provided the higher and better-controlled temperatures needed for making special steels and other high-grade metal alloys. Electric welding was used in much metal working in place of riveting, reducing costs and improving quality; it permitted the virtual flowing together of joined surfaces without weakening or distortion and, together with various forms of electric soldering and brazing, it became the principal method for joining metal parts. Induction heating of materials was used to give different parts of the same object quite different properties of strength or hardness. Electro-erosion methods of cutting and processing metals supplemented mechanical cutting.

Electrolytic processes for the extraction of metals became the basis for aluminium and other light metal industries. Electromagnetic attachments on the pick-ups of cranes were used for moving masses of iron and steel. Electric charges in gases produced such instruments as neon lights. Electric cooling systems provided air conditioning, refrigeration and freezing treatment. Electric power greatly facilitated the design of automatic devices and powered X-rays to detect imperfections.

The most striking use of electricity to perform vast new functions was in the field of electronics. From 1906 onwards the vacuum tube, with its capacity to capture and amplify infinitesimally small amounts of current, and after 1948 the transistor also, not only revolutionized communications,* but became the basis for a multitude of devices to control industrial operations.

Another large proportion of twentieth-century production depended upon chemical processes, sometimes in conjunction with the use of electric current as in electrolytic methods for refining metals, sometimes in combination with mechanical processes as in powder metallurgy where metal sheets were formed under great pressure from metal powders, and sometimes as an entire chemical process in plants producing synthetic fibres, plastics, photographic film and other man-made materials from chemical elements. In other

* See Chapter XI, Communications.

types of production, such as oil refining, chemical processes were used to affect materials rather than to create them. Not only in essentially chemical industries themselves, such as drugs, fertilizers and synthetics, but in many other lines chemical treatment figured at some step in the production process.

Although major innovations were most generally based on electrical and chemical processes, mechanical devices retained their importance and were greatly refined. In metal producing and using industries, machines were developed to permit continuous operation of both rolling and casting, to cast by a variety of improved methods which minimized the necessity for subsequent machining, to handle metals in a non-molten state as in cold rolling of steel and other plastic deformation of materials. Mechanical handling of other types of material was elaborated with great precision and complexity.

Many of the most important mechanical innovations depended upon the arrangement of equipment rather than on any specific operation. Workers or machines, each repeating simple actions, were so arranged that the product could pass from one to the next without loss of motion or the need to carry partially worked products elsewhere or to store them until they could be put through the next step.

The assembly line, introduced by Henry Ford in the automobile industry in 1909 and extended to many types of production, established the principle of the moving belt which brings the product to one worker after another, each of whom performs a limited function during the short time that the object is before him. Once the simple, repetitive components of a production process have been so organized as to be part of a continuous flow, with each bit of material or part arriving at the right place at the right moment, machines can frequently replace workers. In many industries long, complex systems of production came to be carried through by machines from start to finish. Engineers were increasingly called on to design whole systems, not single machines, and each new device had to be engineered in terms of its place in a series of operations, not merely for the specific function which it must perform. (Pl. 8.)

Elaborate assemblies timed for a continuous flow and dependent on having every component at the right place at the right time became more and more complex. Since lack of any one part would hold up the entire costly operation, large producers tended to manufacture their own parts rather than to depend upon suppliers who might fail to meet their deliveries because of a breakdown, strike, fire, transport difficulty or excess number of orders. But in the manufacture of complicated products such proliferation of processes often became cumbersome and introduced uneconomic variety into the operations of a single enterprise. The opposite tendency was for a plant to concentrate on a single component and to perfect techniques for its economic production. This interplay between the tendency to integrate more and more processes in order to achieve a continuous flow and the tendency to specialize in order to achieve maximum economy went on constantly in the competitive economies, and the same problem presented itself in the planned economies in the choice between alternative forms of organization and design.

All kinds of processes became increasingly automatic through the application of the cybernetic principle of self-regulation or feed-back, i.e. the use of devices which enable the machine to respond automatically to conditions created by its own operation and thus to adjust itself in order to maintain the desired condition. The principle itself was not new; it had entered the early stages of industry with the first governors on steam engines that controlled the delivery of steam to regulate the speed. But early types of automatic controls were based on simple mechanical principles. The availability of electricity greatly enlarged the scope of such controls. Electric switches which would respond instantly to the receipt of an electric impulse permitted the installation of many new types of control devices such as thermostats which registered temperature and transmitted an electric signal to cut off or turn on a fuel pump or blower in order to maintain constant heat. (Pl. 9.)

The development of electronic devices so stepped up the use of self-regulatory controls as to make these a central feature, not merely an incidental part, of production technology. These extremely sensitive instruments were designed to control immensely complex operations with a precision which far exceeded that which could be supplied by the human hand or by mechanical or cruder electrical means. Their introduction at an ever-accelerating pace was so dramatic that in the decade after the second world war they seemed to be bringing a new stage in technological development which earned the name automation.

In some industries, such as some oil refining and chemical works, whole processes were beginning to be controlled by electronic memory devices, or computers, which recorded information and instructions and transmitted them to a chain of machines in such a way as to keep the machines supplied, adjust all steps from raw material to finished product, automatically remove the finished product and wastes, inspect the product for imperfections and measure its quality, keep the machinery oiled and in running order, stop the process if anything went wrong and keep a record of what had been done. The cost of installing elaborate automatic processes made them particularly suitable for large mass-production operations that could be expected to produce sufficient volume over a period of time to repay the initial cost.

With the coming of atomic energy a further resource for efficient and economical automatic control of even greater precision and penetration was furnished by the radioactive isotope. From the initial experimental introduction of radioactive particles as tracers, their use grew by leaps and bounds. They were soon being relied upon for such purposes as detecting faults in metals or machines, registering the amount of wear on important parts, controlling the gauge of rolled steel, paper or plastic sheeting or checking the quality of oil travelling through a pipeline.

The production of equipment of all types depended upon the machine-tool industries, on the machines that made the machines and the technical personnel with the knowledge and experience to design and construct new equipment for new purposes. These industries were both the foundation and the mainspring of industrial development. Although the basic tools for machine production—lathe, drill press, metal plane, and machines for milling, boring, shaping and grinding—had been developed in the nineteenth century, their improvement through the use of high-speed steels, the introduction of new electrical and chemical techniques for working metals and the application of automatic devices transformed machine-making technology. In the machine-tool industries all the most refined techniques that were developed in any line were brought to focus to permit a degree of precision undreamed of at the beginning of the century.

The development of machinery was a cumulative process which depended on continuous improvement in design based on experience in use, the introduction of new materials and precision instruments as they were developed, the availability of parts or elements from other industries, and a corps of highly skilled and imaginative designers and mechanics with sufficient resources to carry out their ideas. The more complex and single-purpose the machine, the more costly the retooling for a change in design of the product to be made. In order to avoid both inflexibility and the need to discard old equipment, there was a tendency to design basic multi-purpose mechanisms to which different special-purpose parts could be attached. With the progress of standardization many machines became assemblies of standard parts which could be replaced as needed for repair or to vary the machine's operation.

In some fields, as for example military equipment during periods of war or intense international rivalry, changes in design came so rapidly that retooling was needed almost before the machinery to produce the original model was in operation.[9, 10] In the competitive economies changes in models in order to stimulate demand for the product, as in the automobile industry, led to periodic retooling as part of the pattern of industry; but on the other hand a strong company seeking to protect its investment sometimes bought up and suppressed a new design in order to avoid the necessity of discarding existing productive equipment.

Production of machinery was heavily concentrated in the most highly industrialized countries. Prior to the second world war 85 per cent of the world's machinery was being produced in the United States, Great Britain and Germany, with the remainder distributed among several west European countries, the USSR and Japan. In volume, the United States passed Britain and Germany and for a period after the war was producing more machinery than the rest of the world combined, though this relationship was changing with the restoration of the European economies and the expansion of output in the Soviet Union. British mining machinery, German electrical equipment, Swedish ball bearings and Swiss high-precision devices occupied special places on the world market. Japan offered a number of economical types of machines, generally less sturdy in construction but lower in cost than those produced in Europe and America. The Soviet Union developed extensive machine-making capacity to supply its expanding industries, often designing and constructing very large units for its typically large-scale establishments and making wide use of automatic controls. In the decade after the second world war it supplied equipment for the industrial expansion of the people's republics, and was beginning to offer industrial equipment to other parts of the world.

The concentration of machine production in highly developed industrial countries reflected the fact that more than any other branch of industry machine tools depended upon the highest skills and the most varied resources of the entire scientific–industrial complex.

2. *Size of plant*

Wider markets, greater mechanization and the techniques of mass production brought a trend toward large-scale industrial establishments. The very large plants, and even more the large firm with several separate factories, came to be the dominant unit in many fields. In the United States and Great Britain an increasing proportion of workers were employed in large plants in spite of the fact that these were usually more highly mechanized and required fewer workers for a given volume of output than did smaller units. In the planned development of the USSR, with its large domestic market and central direction, large-scale units were established wherever possible, especially in basic industries.

Industries differed from one another however in the characteristic size of their establishments, and these differences persisted. The garment industries for example retained small shops since their technology did not require large-scale operations and small shops gave flexibility. Heavy industries such as steel or automobile manufacture tended toward large plants for economy in mass production. It was not clear how far the general trend toward the large plant reflected technological developments and how far it resulted from the shift toward the kinds of industries in which large-scale operation was particularly advantageous.

Even in many industries dominated by the large plant, moreover, the small establishment did not disappear. While large plants produced standard, bulk products, smaller units turned out specialized items, parts for large-scale manufacturers, and things for which demand was less steady and the risks often greater. In some countries small plants were encouraged by public policy on the ground that they preserved competition, or that they were less vulnerable to physical attack than large units, or that they were essential to balanced industrial development. India at the start of its industrial expansion made special efforts to encourage small establishments, particularly in smaller communities, in the effort to keep workers from concentrating in the cities. In Japan, where there was a sharp dichotomy between large-scale enterprise operated by a small group of large concerns and the small and medium-sized family firms, small plants tended to serve as the shock-absorbers of industry, receiving orders from the large, continuously operating plants when times were good and being left without work in slack periods. In countries too small to provide a mass market for some types of product, only those industries which produced for foreign trade could operate large-scale units.

Although there was much discussion as to the optimum size of industrial plant there was little agreement even for particular industries and particular countries. One trend however appeared clear. Large enterprises had the capacity to grow larger and larger as technical processes, management methods and efficient communication made it possible to operate very large factories effectively and many separate plants under common direction.

3. *Plant location*

Industrial plants tended to be localized in certain areas, partly in relation to raw materials, partly in relation to the market for their products and chiefly in relation to the presence of other plants and other industries. The shift in their source of energy from direct water power to steam and then to electricity gave them flexibility and much freedom to choose a site which appeared favourable.

In different countries similar industries tended to follow similar patterns of location. Those which worked a bulky raw material or a perishable commodity whose transport was costly or difficult, such as cement plants or fish or vegetable canneries, clung near their source of supply. Those such as bakeries or machine shops or printing establishments, which supplied the market with a perishable or bulky product or carried on an operation which included services, were located near their customers. Some which required extremely large amounts of power, such as aluminium processing plants, sought a cheap power source. A few, making dangerous products such as explosives, required isolation and space. But a large proportion of all industrial establishments, limited by none of these factors, simply gravitated to an industrial zone.

The nature of most industries made it advantageous for them to be close to others. They were mutually dependent for the products which entered into manufacture; they wanted to be near a supply of workers with varied skills and to be able to attract skilled and imaginative management; they depended on many supporting services such as printing, financing, advertising, repair; they needed access to transport, power and information. Once a locality had acquired these features it acted as a powerful magnet to draw more plants to it, with a pull so strong that even the danger of bombing in wartime could not overcome it.

Yet some contrary factors tending to disperse industry grew in importance during this period. The possibilities for using electricity as a basis for dispersion were well demonstrated in Japan, where a combination of electrification and extension of railways after the first world war spread industry through the country into many towns and cities of differing sizes. The development of rapid transit systems permitted workers to commute long distances to work and the flexibility of motor transport for both products and workers also made dispersion possible when other factors were favourable. Air transport enabled managers and executives to supervise plants at a distance one from another. High land costs in central urban areas and ordinances excluding plants which emitted unpleasant odours or noxious substances contributed to the dispersing of industry outside major centres. Some industries or individual plants moved to new locations which offered cheap labour.

Nevertheless the tendency toward local industrial concentration remained strong even where positive public efforts were made to counteract the tendency in order to reduce problems of urban congestion. Great Britain after the second world war established new medium-sized towns with facilities to attract industries. Communities at a distance from industrial districts in the United States offered low taxes, reduced rents and cheap power to try to induce industry to locate there. For a time new industries in the USSR were excluded from the larger cities. India's community development programme included the development of small industrial centres linked to surrounding villages. But the disadvantages of isolation in small industrial communities proved a powerful obstacle to dispersion, and industry tended wherever possible to spread its plants within industrial regions rather than to scatter them more widely through non-industrial areas.

4. The factory as a place of work

The factory of the nineteenth and early twentieth century was more often than not ugly, dark, poorly heated or cooled, noisy, grimy and often a dangerous place where workers were exposed to dust, heat, damp or physical injury. Some of these conditions were inherent in the processes themselves— the heat of molten metal, the clang of a forge hammer or the slap of an automatic loom, the constant motion of whirring shafts and moving belts; some merely reflected indifference to the conditions under which human beings were expected to work.

Many of the technical changes in industrial processes brought changes within the factory which made possible the light and airy modern plants which came to set the standards. The substitution of electric motors for moving belts laid the basis for clean well-arranged factories. Air-conditioning and electric lighting provided temperature and humidity control and sufficient light in all places. The atmosphere of the plant was adjusted to provide optimum conditions for manufacturing the product and this usually meant a constant level of heat and humidity and the elimination of dust. Where automatic controls were used, gauges and controls could be placed in a separate room where conditions could be adapted to the comfort and efficiency of the workers. The number of factory tasks that had to be performed under hazardous or unpleasant conditions was greatly reduced by the new technological processes.

Modern factories, moreover, were designed to stimulate the efficiency and productivity of workers by the impact of their surroundings. Colours which lent a cheerful atmosphere replaced the traditional drab walls. Machines were painted in such a way as to facilitate the identification of different parts. The result was not only to raise worker morale but to encourage cleanliness and increase safety and efficiency. Some factories found that productivity was increased when music was played continuously.

Factory design attracted the talents of some of the most imaginative architects in many countries, who could take full advantage of new materials and functional design without being restrained by traditions which limited their freedom in the construction of homes and public buildings. They not only created efficient interior work spaces and well-proportioned building units but set the industrial plants amid lawns and made industrial districts into features of a city plan instead of the eyesores which the older industrial areas had been.

Model factories were by no means representative of the conditions under which the majority of industrial workers laboured, especially in older industrial countries, older centres within such areas, and older industries, for many obsolete buildings remained in use or were occupied by small or struggling concerns when their original owners moved to more up-to-date quarters. But new factories as they were built took on these characteristics. It was a far cry from the conditions of English workers described by Friedrich Engels in 1843 in *Die Lage der arbeitenden Klasse in England*, or from the crowded loft from which New York garment workers leapt to their death in the Triangle fire of 1910, to the industrial parks which commanded the approaches to many cities in the 1940s and 1950s. In the words of the International Labour Office: 'It is hard to imagine a sharper contrast than that between the typical drab, dark, smoke-ridden nineteenth-century factory and the model factory of the twentieth century, light and airy, with attractive interior colour schemes, in well-laid-out grounds with lawns, trees and flower beds. The model factory is not yet typical, but it sets standards that more and more factories are approaching.'*

V.   LABOUR SUPPLY AND UTILIZATION

Changing technology greatly altered the kinds of labour required by industry and the manner in which workers were used. In the countries of advanced industrial development mechanized mines and factories and the vast network of mass production and distribution called for workers with many new capacities. These needs were met by the development of an educated, trained and responsible labour force and its use under conditions which enhanced its

* International Labour Office, *Higher Productivity in Manufacturing Industries* (Geneva 1954). Studies and Reports, New Series, no. 38, pp. 159–160.

productivity. At the same time the goods which industry produced entered into the worker's standard of living and provided much of the motivation for his effort. Industrial labour thus both contributed to production and became its beneficiary.

In the non-industrial areas the situation was different. There the expansion of industrial-type employment, whether in mines, in developing industries or in plantations which functioned as factories in the field, generally failed to keep pace with the drift of workers away from subsistence agriculture, and industries were therefore under few pressures to make efficient use of labour which was plentiful and cheap. Foreign companies often depended upon workers from abroad for the higher levels of skill. Only gradually did industrial labour in the developing countries begin to take on some of the characteristics of the labour force in the older industrial areas, though the trends were in the same direction; in none of these countries did workers begin to provide a mass market for industry's products.

1. *Unskilled labour*

In the early stages industry had required large numbers of unskilled workers to perform repetitive tasks and tend simple machines. The need for such workers continued to some extent, for as soon as machines were devised to replace workers on simple operations, the more complex processes that formerly required skill were broken down into a series of steps which unskilled or semi-skilled workers could perform. The tendency, however, was toward the use of semi-skilled operators rather than the types of unskilled workers who supplied mainly physical or mechanically repetitive labour.

Industry recruited these workers wherever it could find a cheap supply of hands, tapping groups whose other means of livelihood were inadequate. Most of the unskilled workers were drawn from agriculture, both within the industrial countries and from abroad. British industry had already absorbed almost the entire supply of rural workers by the opening of the twentieth century; less than 10 per cent of the British labour force remained in agriculture at that time and only 5 per cent by 1950. Other industrial countries sucked great numbers of their rural workers into industry, until by mid-century less than a fifth of the labour force in such countries as the United States, Canada, Australia, the Low Countries, Germany and Sweden remained on the land. In addition, American and Canadian industry drew heavily on peasant immigrants from eastern and southern Europe as did, to a lesser extent, some of the industries of western Europe and of other overseas areas. Japan's industries drew on a pool of available rural labour throughout their development. South Africa brought native Africans as labourers into its mines and factories.

Workers could be drawn from agriculture into industry during this period without cutting down on the needed supply of food because of three main factors: the highly productive virgin land which had been opened up in North and South America, Oceania and southern Russia was producing ample supplies of wheat and meat to feed the industrial populations of Europe and America; in areas of subsistence agriculture under-employed or under-productive workers, scraping a living from poor or subdivided land, left agriculture as fast as other employment became available; and in regions of advanced agriculture the great increase in productivity resulting from technological improvements released much labour from the farms.

Women were also a major source of factory labour, especially in light industries such as textiles and garment-making. Throughout the period under review women continued to constitute from a quarter to a third of the industrial labour force of most industrial countries and more than 50 per cent in Japan prior to the second world war.

The essential quality required of unskilled workers was the ability to respond to the discipline which the productive process and the machine imposed. They must perform reliably and accurately the task on which the work of the next in line depended, with the endurance to sustain a uniform rate and quality of output throughout the work period. New workers had to adjust to industrial discipline in order to become effective members of the industrial labour force. Especially for those who entered industry from agriculture, this involved a new manner of work and way of life, and the transition was usually accompanied by much instability in employment, absenteeism and the need for training. Workers accustomed to following the seasons and their own rhythm of work found themselves bound to the pace of the machine, required to perform a prescribed task at a prescribed time, dependent on the work of others and having others dependent on them.

Adjustment to the discipline of industrial production was thus an experience common to large numbers of twentieth-century men and women in most parts of the world. In an effort to expedite the process, employers who had little regard for their workers as human beings placed them under various forms of pressure, such as holding gang bosses responsible for seeing that their gangs performed their tasks, or imposing financial penalties on workers for failure to meet norms or for irregularity in attendance or performance. Those employers who were more aware of social factors tried to create some of the social conditions which would contribute to stability, as did groups of employers in several Latin American countries who made use of social workers with this objective. The USSR developed a number of systems for inducting new workers, publicizing workers' performance and placing responsibility for sustaining rates of output on fellow workers. By mid-century some progressive industries in some countries were making positive efforts to avoid placing workers in tasks for which they were not suited, and were attempting to plan work tasks, schedules and methods of supervision that were more consistent with human needs; some tried to enable workers to understand the significance of their contribution to the total work process and to derive satisfaction from group participation.

Because the principal qualities which factory operatives required were flexibility and stamina, industry tended to employ younger workers by preference. The bulk of factory employees were young adults. The young children who had made up a large part of the factory labour of the early nineteenth century were no longer used. Laws requiring school attendance and prohibiting child labour had already sharply limited the employment of children under 14 by the opening of the twentieth century, and by mid-century children had almost disappeared from the industrial labour force. Those between 15 and 20 were employed extensively, but the proportion of boys of this age who entered employment dropped substantially as opportunities for secondary education increased and more of the available jobs required education. The proportion of boys aged 15–19 at work in Great Britain dropped from 92 to 83 per cent between 1901 and 1951, and the proportion aged 14–19 in the United States fell from 64 to 40 per cent in the same period.

2. Skilled workers

Industry continued to need workers with a variety of skills acquired through substantial periods of training or apprenticeship, but traditional and specialized skills were constantly made obsolete by new techniques. To survive in the face of changing technology, skilled workers must be above all adaptable; they had to have a basic understanding of machine processes in order to handle various types of machines and the ability to be quickly trained and retrained for specific jobs. Often the technological change required not merely retraining but a quite different category of workers. The demand fell for craftsmen shaping the product by hand tools, but increased for toolmakers, for mechanics to set up and repair machines, and for draughtsmen to prepare blueprints. With complicated and delicate machinery to be safeguarded and employed as fully as possible, supervisors and foremen became particularly important.

Many who possessed old skills were reduced to unskilled or semi-skilled tasks, forced to learn entirely new trades or faced with unemployment. Older workers, proud of their crafts and accustomed to command good wages on the basis of them, repeatedly tried to resist the introduction of new procedures which could displace their type of work. The relatively slow rate of technological development in the construction industry, for example, reflected in part the success of building-trades workers in many places in defending their traditional methods. New techniques were more readily introduced where defenders of old skills were few or their organized efforts to resist change were weak.

Skilled operatives were produced within the factory by upgrading of semi-skilled workers, and they also entered industry from outside as young workers with vocational training or with good general education which enabled them to learn specific tasks quickly. The speed with which workers were upgraded varied with the state of the labour market. When labour was in great demand, as in times of rapid industrial expansion and during war, every effort was made to bring workers up to higher levels of skill and to devise the most efficient means of doing so. In periods of unemployment, when many workers were employed at tasks below their level of skill, the upgrading and training process slowed down. In the expansion of American industry each successive group of immigrants or of migrants from rural areas moved up the job ladder as they acquired factory experience and command of English, while new groups of immigrants or migrants filled the least skilled and poorest paid jobs.

Individual companies and sometimes whole industries set up in-service training schemes. Such schemes tended to expand as industries came to need a larger proportion of trained workers. Some of the larger industrial corporations developed full-fledged programmes of technical and general education at all the levels of knowledge and skill which their operations required, and enrolled large proportions of their workers in courses designed to fit them for new jobs within the enterprise. During the first world war, and to a much greater extent in the second world war, governments took an active part in helping industry to provide such training through the development of training techniques, preparation of manuals and guides, and consultant services to plants engaged in war production. The USSR at all times made special provision to expedite the process of upgrading by offering courses of study for factory workers and placing great social pressure on workers to take advantage of them so that there would be a continuous supply of trained workers rising from the ranks.

For young people headed for industrial employment the educational systems of the industrial countries provided schools which offered vocational training to supplement or replace the apprenticeship methods by which skilled trades had traditionally been learned. Such training was both included within programmes of general education and offered in special technical schools or institutes.* Some of the older trades continued to be learned by apprenticeship methods, often controlled by craft unions, and apprenticeship schemes were developed in some countries for certain of the newer occupations. Thus skills related to mechanical operations and industrial production might be acquired either in school or on the job, and employment in such occupations was open to those who qualified by both of these means.

Industry often failed to employ certain types of workers, however, for a variety of reasons. Some potential workers were excluded from the opportunities to secure training. Vocational schools or classes offering some types of mechanical training were often open only to boys, even in countries where co-education was the general rule. Although women came to be freely admitted to institutions of higher education and could enter the professions in most countries, they often remained barred from skilled trades. A study of women's employment in Latin America in the 1950s revealed the almost complete exclusion of women from vocational training, except in the needle

* See Chapter XXVI, Education.

trades, and thus from most industrial employment above the unskilled level. Where prejudice against the employment of certain categories of workers existed, as it did against Negroes in many places and types of work, schools were reluctant to offer training to those who would not be able to secure jobs, and opportunities to enter apprenticeships were frequently closed.

When there was a shortage of workers, however, industry used and trained types of workers whom it had regarded as inadequate or undesirable. Under the impact of war women were employed in large numbers in tasks for which they had not been used before. Many of those recruited for such tasks during the first world war were dropped during the post-war economic slump, but after the second world war high levels of general employment led to the retention of women in many jobs which they had entered for the first time during the war. Industry also found that it could use older people and those suffering from various handicaps such as blindness, crippling or loss of limbs. During the second world war many older workers were called back into industrial jobs and proved to be adaptable and capable of retraining. Handicapped persons were successfully placed in tasks for which they had been presumed to be unfit, and after the war laws in some countries required employers to include a certain proportion of war-injured among their workers. The particular faculties needed to perform specific jobs were closely analysed and many such workers were put to work where their capacities could be used and their deficiencies disregarded.

3. *Technicians*

As industry applied more scientific knowledge and more elaborate technology it depended more and more on technicians, engineers and scientifically trained workers rather than on either unskilled workers or skilled machine operatives. The work force of factories or mines using automatic machines and controls or elaborate chemical processes was largely engaged in maintaining and repairing equipment, testing and inspecting materials as they passed through the production process, designing and constructing machines or developing new products. The more automatic controls replaced workers on the production line, the more need there was for people to design and construct the automatic devices and the machines which they controlled.

For these highly technical tasks industry required men and women with a wide range of scientific and technical training, from little more than the vocational skills acquired by the trained operative up to the highest level of scientific competence and imagination. The need for this type of worker expanded enormously as the rate of mechanization accelerated after the second world war.

To meet this large demand industrial countries stepped up their programme of higher technical education, expanding the technical faculties of their universities, offering other training at the university or post-university level, founding higher technical institutes and establishing scholarships and grants for technical, engineering and scientific training.

For countries in all stages of industrial development the expansion of higher technical education became a major concern in the years after the second world war. The USSR made its vast programme of technical education, symbolized by the towering structure of the Moscow University with more than 1,000 laboratories, the heart of its effort to achieve the highest level of industrial production in the world. Britain moved to fill the gap between its small, outstanding group of advanced scientists and its vocationally trained labour force by greatly expanding its training facilities for technicians of all sorts. American industry and government joined in offering grants to attract a larger proportion of university students into engineering and scientific fields. Newly industrializing countries such as India and China devoted substantial amounts of their comparatively limited resources to the development of a corps of technicians and scientists capable of leading their industrial effort.

The ever-changing process of industrial development brought first one type of labour into short supply and then another. At mid-century the shortage in both the industrially advanced and the newly industrializing countries was in engineers, chemists and other highly trained personnel. The introduction of such radically new techniques as the production of power in atomic reactors, for example, was directly dependent upon the rate at which the necessary atomic technicians and engineers became available.

4. Clerical and administrative personnel

A fourth group of workers became increasingly necessary as industry became more highly organized and complex and more geared to a mass market. These were the clerical and administrative staffs who were cogs in the organizational machinery through which industry was carried on and who manned the services on which it depended. From file clerks to managers they made up an industrial bureaucracy of office workers, salesmen, accountants, advertising men, bank clerks and supervisors that absorbed a growing proportion of the labour force of industry. Although automatic record systems and computing devices took over many routine white-collar tasks, the organizational as against the physical aspects of industry continued to require a large and growing number of workers.

For this part of industry's labour requirements the essential qualifications were general education combined with specific skills such as stenography or accounting and with qualities of personality and understanding of human relationships which their responsibilities involved. To meet these needs the curriculum of general secondary schools in many places was expanded to include a variety of commercial courses, and separate commercial schools specialized in this type of training. Schools of commerce and business admini-stration at both secondary and university levels offered technical training in such subjects as accounting and administration, together with a programme of general education featuring the social sciences.

5. Recruitment of labour force

In order to recruit labour and bring the available worker together with the available job, industrial countries developed employment services and programmes for vocational selection and guidance. They also set up safeguards against abuse of workers in the recruiting process. In the industrializing countries safeguards were less adequate and only a beginning was being made toward establishing employment services.

In the early stages of industrial development and continuing to a very considerable degree in most countries, the labour force for expanding industry drifted into the localities where it was needed in an informal manner as news of new opportunities travelled to family members, friends or neighbours. The great bulk of rural–urban migrants in each country, and the millions of European peasants who sought new opportunities overseas, changed their locality and found their places in industry in response to general rumours of opportunities and personal information from those who had gone before.

Employers in their turn depended upon word of mouth, from old to new employee, to recruit a large proportion of their workers. Sometimes a personal contact by employer or foreman supplemented the contact of old to potential worker, as when young Japanese girls were brought from rural communities to work for relatives or family connections in cities, or an Italian *padrone* contracted to supply a work gang of his compatriots for an American or Argentine employer.

As industry came to require a variety of special experiences or training, the informal hit or miss method of recruiting labour and finding jobs no longer sufficed. Private individuals, trade unions, professional associations and governments established employment services to enable employers to find suitable workers and workers to find suitable jobs. That this was no simple problem was evidenced by the fact that the International Classification of Occupations prepared by the International Labour Office in 1949 listed more than 50,000 separate categories of employment.

The impetus for the establishment of employment services came from quite opposite directions: from the need to meet the problem of unemployment and from the effort to cope with labour shortages in time of war. The oldest systems, those of Germany and Great Britain, owed their establishment to concern over unemployment. Several German municipalities established employment exchanges following the industrial depression of 1893–94; the British system, set up by Act of Parliament in 1909, was the outgrowth of a royal commission's study of unemployment. The labour shortage during the first world war, however, was what made the recruiting and effective placement of workers a matter of national concern and led to the establishment of public employment services in many countries.

At the close of the war the International Labour Organization at its first meeting in 1919 demonstrated how widely the need for employment services was accepted when it adopted a convention calling for the establishment by each ratifying state of a system of free public employment agencies under the control of a central authority with advisory committees representing workers and employers. During the inter-war years thirty countries adhered to this convention and by mid-century thirty-three countries had ratified it, while a number of countries not adhering to the convention, such as Canada, Australia and the United States, also had established public employment services.

As employment services developed and functioned they continued to reflect their twofold origin. In countries which had schemes for unemployment insurance or assistance they were apt to be linked with this system, and the receipt of unemployment benefits was usually made dependent upon registration at an employment exchange and the acceptance of suitable work offered there; in a number of countries these services in themselves were the chief device for trying to deal with unemployment. At the same time the ever-shifting character of the labour market led some employment offices to serve as centres of vocational guidance, especially to young people and to older workers displaced when their skills became obsolete; in the latter role they undertook systematic studies of occupational requirements and trends and used performance and aptitude tests to determine the probable fitness of workers for particular occupations. In newly industrializing countries the principal need was for vocational guidance and training, to meet the critical shortage of skilled and technical workers and managerial personnel without whom there could be no employment for the mass of unskilled workers who drifted to cities much faster than jobs became available. The system introduced in the 1950s in Colombia, of interest to other Latin American countries, taxed all substantial employers to maintain a national labour training and recruiting service which made estimates of national requirements for trained workers and arranged with industries to offer needed types of training and to recruit candidates from among their employees.

Since employment services acted as intermediaries between workers and employers they were in a position to give priority to the interest of one or the other group—to try to find for employers the workers whom they most wanted or to find for workers the jobs which they most desired. The ILO convention called for advisory participation by representatives of both workers and employers in relation to the administration of the service. Workers however sometimes alleged that the prejudices of employers were allowed to dictate the choice of workers recommended by the service, while employers complained that the service forced upon them workers who did not suit their needs. The more the process of labour recruiting was placed upon an objective basis of analysis of the job to be done and the matching of qualifications to tasks, the more technical became the role of the employment services and the less likely to be biased toward the interests of either employers or workers.

Where the state dominated economic activity, and generally in time of war, recruitment of workers on a voluntary basis was supplemented by conscription or the freezing of workers in their jobs. In Nazi Germany certain categories of workers in tasks essential to the rearmament programme were tied to their jobs. Young people in the USSR, who received training for the specialities that were in short supply, were routed to jobs where they were needed, and during most of the period under review workers in general were not allowed to quit their jobs without permission; in the period of intensive industrialization, numbers of criminals, especially offenders against the state, were shipped for corrective labour to mines or other distant places where conditions were especially hard and it was difficult to attract workers on a voluntary basis. In South Africa taxes which could only be paid by earning cash wages were used virtually to force Africans to work in the mines, and the system applied in Portuguese Africa was even more direct. Various limitations on labour mobility were imposed in some other countries in circumstances of labour stringency.

During the first world war few restraints were placed on the free movement of workers from one job to another, except in Germany and for some French soldiers sent to work in munitions industries, but in the second world war all the belligerent countries restricted the right of workers in critical types of employment to change their jobs and gave priority in hiring to industries associated with the war effort. The Nazis used several millions of forced slave labourers from occupied countries to man their war industries.

The general result of institutionalizing the recruitment of labour was to introduce into the process a rational system of study, job classification, objective determination of fitness and vocational development; but the system was very far from complete even where employment services had the longest history or the most ambitious programmes.

6. Conditions of employment

In all industrial and most non-industrial countries standards were established by law for the conditions under which labour might be used. The developing body of social and labour legislation in the different countries was both influenced by and reflected in the standards adopted by the ILO from 1919 onwards. These standards gradually became the norms for employment and conditions of work in countries all over the world.

Such regulations generally excluded young children from labour in industry and limited the employment of older children in dangerous trades; they regulated work of women in hazardous employment or at night; they provided codes for industrial safety, maternity protection and protection of workers' health; they limited hours of work and prescribed rest periods; they established minimum wages and in some cases principles of wage policy such as equal pay for equal work. In some countries where discrimination against certain classes of people was practised because of race, religion or other such factors, these discriminations in employments were forbidden by law. To carry out these regulations governments set up systems of labour inspection and administration.

(a) *Job tenure*. Within this framework, which evolved through the years, the industrial worker was employed for wages and normally worked and was paid only when the employer had a job which he wanted him to do. This manner of employment rested on the assumption that labour was to be bought on essentially the same basis as materials and would similarly enter into the direct cost of production. Employment of workers only for the time in which they were actually engaged in work gave flexibility to industry, permitting it to expand or contract, to vary from season to season, to shift from one kind of product to another, to change locality and to substitute machines for workers with a minimum of friction. For workers it meant basic uncertainty and insecurity of tenure.

In this situation employers and workers often sought different ends. Employers wanted to have a supply of labour available and they wanted labour to be mobile, ready to go where jobs were offered and to leave places where industry no longer needed them rather than to remain as a permanent burden; but they also wanted labour to be steady and reliable, not too ready to quit and seek another job. Workers for their part wanted a measure of security, freedom from the fear of being laid off and the necessity of moving away from their community in search of work; but they also wanted freedom to quit and to work or not work as they desired. When labour was scarce employers were especially anxious to hold on to their workers; when jobs were scarce workers were especially anxious to hold on to their jobs.

The trend during the twentieth century in the industrially advanced countries was toward greater stability of employment and job security for workers, assurance of a job for longer periods at a time, protection of job tenure and more careful and systematic use of workers by employers. Cyclical fluctuations in economic activity in the capitalist economies and technological displacement continued to threaten workers with loss of their jobs. But much of the day-to-day uncertainty which had first characterized industrial employment was modified or removed.

Increased job stability was one of the objectives of labour organizations. They insisted that the principle of seniority in dismissals and re-engagement be written into the collective contracts. They also sought guarantees of continuous employment, or at least of pay, for a longer period than the hour, day or week by which workers were customarily engaged. In the first quarter of the century such efforts brought little job security. As late as 1937 an American labour union in a mass-production industry numbered among its victories in a successful strike that the company agreed to lay off no worker with less than twenty-four hours' notice.

By mid-century, however, the situation had changed so radically that some of the leading American industries such as automobile manufacture and steel, under pressure of trade union demands for a guaranteed annual wage, agreed to assure workers the opportunity to work up to a specified number of weeks during the year or to pay the equivalent of their wages if no work was offered.

Industries on their own initiative adopted the practice of keeping their labour force continuously at work. The more elaborate and expensive their equipment, the greater the waste of allowing it to stand idle; the more they required trained and specialized workers, the less could they afford the cost of re-engaging and retraining them.

Governments also intervened to stabilize the worker's income and some-times to place pressure on employers to regularize employment. Beginning with Great Britain in 1911, most of the industrially developed countries adopted some form of unemployment compensation by the state for workers who were dismissed from their jobs and were unable to find new employment within a short time. The original British scheme, and the first state unemployment compensation scheme in the United States, attempted to encourage employers to avoid fluctuations in their demand for workers by requiring a lower contribution to the unemployment fund from employers with stable records, or granting them a rebate. Later schemes in these countries and schemes else-where, however, taxed regular and irregular employers alike, since their purpose was to maintain workers' income and the causes of unemployment were largely beyond the employers' control.

(b) *Hours of work*. The length of day for which workers were employed was fixed by custom, the employer's choice, agreement between workers and employer or by law. Few workers were employed to work for less than the standard working day. Factory operations started and stopped at regular times and required a full complement of workers throughout the period, and industry was reluctant to employ workers on any other basis. Although many types of workers were available for part-time work—women with homes to care for, young people pursuing education, older or infirm workers with limited strength—they were only used by industry during wartime or other period of labour shortage, as a method of recruiting future technicians or in response to social pressure.

Standard hours of work in industry fell steadily during these years. Some labour unions from their earliest formation had worked to reduce hours below the period from sun-up to sun-down, which had been normal in the first part of the nineteenth century. By the opening of the twentieth century the ten-hour day and six-day week had been widely established, although industries which required continuous operation, such as steel, continued to work twelve-hour shifts, day and night. Organized workers all over the world were calling for reduction of hours to eight.

In the early years of the twentieth century, studies in the United States of the effect on production of workers' fatigue brought out the fact that up to a certain point workers actually produced more per day in some occupations if their hours of work were less and they were allowed rest periods. The results of these studies helped to reinforce the claims of workers who demanded the eight-hour day as a means of receiving, in the form of leisure, a share of the new wealth created by modern industry. Such claims had been put forward by the First Socialist International in 1866 and by American and British trade unions in the same decade. The Second International had made it a major issue after 1888.

The eight-hour day was instituted for employees of the United States government in 1868 and in Australia and New Zealand it became general in industry before the first world war. The USSR made it standard immediately following the October revolution. When the International Labour Organization was established in 1919 the first convention which its joint body of

CHART XII.   Trend in hours of work, 1850–1955. Europe and USA.
Estimated Average Weekly Hours.

Source: Woytinsky, *World Population and Production*, p. 367; ILO *Statistical Supplement*, March 1962.

employer, worker and government representatives adopted and recommended to member states called for the eight-hour day and forty-eight hour week. In spite of widespread acceptance of the eight-hour day as a norm, however, a strike to abolish the twelve-hour day in the American steel industry failed in that same year, and not until several years later was the eight-hour day finally introduced in that industry.

Increased productivity, by permitting higher hourly wages, made shorter hours possible without reducing the workers' total earnings. As productivity continued to increase markedly in the succeeding decades, workers in industrially advanced countries agitated for a further reduction to forty hours a week, usually in a five-day week, and the ILO recognized this norm in principle at its session in 1935. At mid-century, however, the eight-hour day and forty-eight hour week were still the prevailing norm in the majority of countries, although the world-wide movement for the forty-hour, five-day week was very strong. Collective agreements in a number of countries, notably Australia, Canada, USA and Great Britain, and in some other European countries, frequently specified the norm as forty-four or forty hours, with anything over that limit paid as overtime; in some countries, among them France, New Zealand and the United States, overtime was defined by law as over forty hours per week.

Once hours of work had been reduced to a point where the worker's health was not impaired and his productivity would not be increased by further reduction, the issue of still shorter hours became a question of the relative value of more leisure as compared with the additional goods which more work could produce. The International Labour Office attributed the strong continuing pressure for shorter hours to:

(1) the continuous rise of production and productivity, bringing with it higher material standards of living and making it easier to afford, at least in the more highly developed countries, any loss of potential output which shorter hours of work might entail, (2) the accelerated rate of technological progress which gained momentum as a result of war and post-war developments, and (3) a widespread desire for increased leisure; leisure needed for its own sake—to live in conditions of human dignity; and leisure required to compensate the stress and strain of modern industry and modern life.*

The world-wide trend toward shorter hours of work resulted in the establishment of the eight-hour day as a norm in the non-industrial as well as the industrial countries. As industry developed in these areas it was forced to adopt this general work pattern, in contrast to the pattern of long hours which had prevailed in the early days of industrial development in Europe and the USA. This provided an added pressure to use methods which would raise labour productivity even where the supply of unskilled workers was very great.

The same considerations which brought, and made possible, shorter hours also led to the introduction of paid holidays. At the opening of the century holidays with pay were the privilege of managers and some few salaried employees; they were virtually unheard of for industrial workers. By mid-century fifty-four countries had enacted legislation requiring the granting of paid holidays to workers of many types, and such annual holidays, as well as individual paid bank or festival holidays, were included in most collective

* International Labour Office, *Reduction of Hours of Work*: report to the governing body, 131st session, Geneva, 6–10 March, 1956, p. 2.

contracts. The practice of providing paid holidays for industrial workers, first introduced on a large scale in the USSR at the time of the October revolution, spread most rapidly after the second world war and there was a tendency to lengthen the period from one week to two or more.

(c) *Wages*. The wages which industrial workers received were determined by a combination of factors, chiefly the supply of available workers, the productivity of labour, the relative bargaining strength of workers and employers and the limits stipulated by law. These factors produced a wage structure which constituted the customary level and relationship among wages for different occupations and skills at any particular time and place. In European countries the wage structure ordinarily included a marked differential between the wage paid to men and to women.

The wages of unskilled workers were most likely to reflect the available supply and the provisions of law rather than productivity or bargaining position. Where there was a large flow of new workers from rural areas or when jobs were scarce and skilled workers dropped into the unskilled group because of depression or technological unemployment, there was little to prevent such wages from falling. On the other hand it was the wages of unskilled workers that most sharply reflected tight labour markets, for when jobs were plentiful these workers could leave lowest-paid employment for better positions.

The adjustment of the wages of unskilled workers to supply and demand was limited, however, by laws which set a minimum level below which no industrial worker could be paid. Such laws began to be enacted in the industrial countries before the first world war following the pioneer measures in Australia which inspired the British Trade Board Act of 1909. They became increasingly general in the inter-war years and were common throughout the world by the years after the second world war, though many workers remained unprotected by them. Minimum wage laws were based on the assumption that industry should not be allowed to use workers without paying them at least what was presumed to be needed for their own and their family's survival, although the level established was often closer to the rate which reflected supply and demand than to one based on worker's needs.

The wages of skilled workers were most frequently set by collective bargaining, for it was among such workers that trade unions took root earliest and most firmly, especially in Great Britain and countries with similar labour movements. In some countries and industries the effective organization of skilled workers on the basis of their trades enabled them to bargain collectively for substantial wage increases and to establish a wide differential between the earnings of such workers and of unskilled and semi-skilled operatives.

In the course of the half century the general level of wages in all the industrial countries rose markedly, reflecting the great increase in productivity during these years. In spite of sharp fluctuations downward in time of depression and upward in time of labour shortage, the trend of real wages, adjusted for change in the prices of things bought by workers, was upward over the years. Precise comparisons between years and among countries are difficult because of changes or differences in the items bought by workers, the length of the work week, taxes withheld from wages, the socially provided goods and services available to workers which did not have to be charged against their wages, and the groups of workers included in the computation. But there can be no doubt that the trend was present and was shared in varying degrees and forms by all industrial countries.

The greatest proportionate increase came at the bottom of the wage scale, as the combination of minimum wage laws, the elimination of many unskilled tasks by machines, the spread of union organization to unskilled as well as skilled workers, and the period of high labour demand during and after the second world war combined to raise the wage floor. As a result the gap in wages was narrowed as between skilled and unskilled jobs, traditionally low-paid and higher-paid industries, and men and women. The wage difference between skilled and unskilled workers in machine making, printing, electric power and construction in the principal industrial countries exclusive of the USSR in 1954 amounted on the average to approximately 20 per cent. In 1938, when employment had been slack, skilled wages in these industries had averaged 25–40 per cent above the unskilled. Some industries, such as textiles, clothing or tobacco manufacturing, were and remained low-wage industries as compared with such industries as petroleum, metal products or automobile manufacture, partly because their labour force included a larger proportion of unskilled workers or women. But though average wages in the high-wage industries continued to be one-third to two-thirds higher than those in the low-wage group, more than double in the case of Japan, the difference at mid-century was less than it had been before the second world war. Women's wages too were coming closer to those of men, partly because women were entering a wider range of better paid jobs and partly because the movement for equal pay for equal work was gaining momentum. In most countries at mid-century, however, the average earnings of women in industry were still only about two-thirds of those of men and different rates for similar jobs still remained common in some fields.

Wages were paid to industrial workers on the basis of the time worked or the work done; they were paid in cash and in the form of a variety of benefits such as paid holidays and retirement and sickness allowances. Piece-rates designed to stimulate the efforts of workers to greater production were common in certain industries, such as clothing manufacture, where the individual could affect the amount of production by his own effort and where his contribution to production was clearly measurable. In highly mechanized processes, where the rate of production was determined by the machine and the exact contribution of one worker could not be distinguished clearly from that of another, piece-rates were less applicable and payment on a time basis prevailed.

In the period under review conflicting factors influenced the trends in methods of wage payment. The effort to achieve high productivity led to the adoption of incentive systems of pay. The USSR abandoned the policy of relatively equal time-rates which had been adopted in the early period of Soviet administration in favour of incentive systems which greatly favoured the highly productive worker. Some use was made of group incentive payments in that country but these were progressively replaced by individual payment based on the worker's output.

In European countries there was an increasing tendency to use incentive pay as industries strove to raise productivity during and after the second world war. In 1951 the ILO found that the various forms of payment by results in use in European countries were quite generally yielding both higher productivity and higher wages than comparable operations where workers were paid on a time basis. The proportion of industrial work performed at piece-rates or under incentive plans had increased in several countries since before the war, and amounted to more than half in Norway and Sweden, over a third in West Germany and Great Britain and 70 per cent in Hungary. Such systems, however, were recognized as tending to place workers under strain which could impair their health and efficiency.

In the United States incentive systems were strongly opposed by organized labour. Systems known as 'speed-up and stretch-out' had been introduced in the early part of the twentieth century in textile and other industries which, the workers maintained, placed them under excessive pressure by using the production of the faster workers as a norm and then re-defining the norm upward as the rest of the workers became geared to the new speed. Although the stretch-out practices had generally been abandoned by mid-century, trade union leaders in the United States remained almost unanimously opposed to incentive systems of pay. The workers who were under such systems, about a quarter of all wage and salary employees, were chiefly in the production of apparel, footwear, textiles, cigars and some special metal products, and in retail sales and repair, rather than in the major, highly mechanized industries. In the latter, wages were tied to productivity in general rather than to the production of the individual worker, as collective contracts came to provide for an automatic wage increase based upon the assumed annual increase in productivity of the industry as a whole.

In addition to cash wages workers received a variety of benefits which augmented their real income from work, although the extent to which these constituted a net addition depended on whether they were based in part on contributions by workers or were paid for wholly by employers or the state. The tendency was for these fringe benefits to multiply and to constitute an increasing proportion of the labour payment. Paid holidays, sick leave, pensions on retirement, accident compensation, medical services in the plant, often family allowances to supplement basic pay, recreational and educational facilities and day care for the children of women workers all supplemented the worker's cash income. Among the members of the European Coal and Steel Community—Holland, Belgium, Luxembourg, France, West Germany and Italy—in 1953 these payments augmented the steel-worker's average hourly earnings by amounts ranging from 30 per cent in Belgium and Luxembourg to 52 per cent in Italy. Benefits and allowances were less in some other industries, but for French employers as a whole social benefit payments amounted to nearly 40 per cent of their total labour costs.

The effectiveness of all types of wage rewards as a means of drawing workers into the labour market, holding them there and stimulating their effective performance depended upon the cultural setting within which industry was carried on and the value placed by potential workers on money as against other things. In countries with a traditional non-money economy or limited wants, higher wages sometimes reduced rather than increased the willingness of the worker to work, for the worker could satisfy a limited desire for money in a shorter period and enjoy leisure or some other pursuit in the rest of his time. Mining companies in remote rural areas of Latin America, for example, found wage incentives ineffective in securing steady work until they stocked their company stores with products which appealed sufficiently to workers and their wives to provide an incentive to acquire more money. The imposition of taxes that could only be paid by cash earnings performed the same function in various parts of Africa. Where the things that workers wanted were in short supply so that money appeared of little use, as in some Asian countries, the provision of workers' housing was regarded as more effective than additional wages in making industrial employment attractive. Even in such countries as the United States, Australia and New Zealand, where a high material standard of living acted as a powerful incentive and the workers' desire for goods seemed unlimited, the desire for leisure offered a serious alternative to some, while others worked at more than one job to earn enough to satisfy their wants.

(d) *Working conditions*. The physical and psychological conditions under which work was carried on changed dramatically as technical changes in industrial processes made for both safer and pleasanter work-places. But factory employment continued to expose many workers to serious hazards. In spite of great improvements in factory design, replacement of moving shafts and belts by electric outlets and substitution of mechanical for human operations at many points of danger, industrial accident and disease continued to take a heavy toll.

Under the common law employers had been liable for injuries to their workers on the job only when they were sued and could be proved to be at fault. By the time of the first world war most industrial countries had taken steps to make employers legally responsible and to require them to pay compensation for work injuries. At mid-century the social security systems of more than forty countries included compensation for injury or death due to work accidents. Germany, with the oldest and most complete system, required its employers to insure themselves against workers' claims in order to make sure that they could meet these obligations. Most United States employers were also required to be covered by insurance, as were the British coal operators.

Employers were thus placed under pressure to cut down accidents, since the cost for insuring themselves against accident claims was commonly based upon their safety record. Insurance companies developed a corps of specialists in accident prevention who provided consultation services to plant managers and conducted studies of accident patterns. Plant designers laid out new factories with the safety of workers as a central consideration. These measures brought spectacular reductions in industrial accidents in some industries and a general decline over the years in the rates of death and injury per number of workers employed. The actual volume, however, remained large. Though the overall death rate from industrial accidents in the United States was cut in half between 1913 and 1953, no less than 15,000 people were killed in the latter year and nearly 2,000,000 injured more or less seriously. In the 1950s approximately 3 per cent of the US labour force was involved in work accidents annually; the British rate had been reduced to 2 per cent while in Australia 9 per cent of all industrial employees suffered injuries. Industrial safety was coming to be recognized as a major problem in newly industrializing countries.

Many technical developments, moreover, increased the hazards to which workers were exposed, especially from injurious chemicals, dust and fumes, and added the hazard of industrial disease to that of work accidents. Special clothing to protect workers, devices permitting workers to operate controls from a distance shielded from contact with injurious substances, limited periods of exposure, wet-drilling and other measures to suppress dust and fumes, and careful instruction of workers in safety practices were used to guard workers from the consequences of industry's increasing use of substances harmful to man. The International Labour Organization sought to establish limits of safe exposure and to provide a guide for the framing of regulations and the adoption of measures to safeguard workers' health.

Still more serious, at mid-century, was the danger of radiation from the use of atomic energy, not alone in the nuclear reactors themselves, but in exposure to radioactive dust in the mining of uranium and to radiation in the plants for uranium refining, and in the handling, transport and use of by-products such as the radioactive isotopes which by the 1950s were already in widespread use in industry. The World Health Organization in 1956 offered a detailed programme for the prevention of radiation exposure, and the ILO brought together a group of experts in 1957 who drew up a comprehensive code of safety rules and practices for the protection of workers, wherever radioactive material was used. Various countries, notably France, were instituting training programmes for public health, engineering and administrative personnel. The problems in this area, however, still remained unsolved and extremely grave.

While these changes in the conditions of employment during the first half of the twentieth century substantially modified the life of the industrial workers, the nature of the industrial process itself remained basically unchanged. However generous the remuneration, whatever amenities might be provided to make the factory a safer and pleasanter place of work, and regardless of the economic system, industrial employment made the worker an instrument of production. It placed him under constant strain to keep up with the assembly line at the pace set and the time prescribed, whether he actually operated a machine or performed one of the other myriad tasks on which the vast, driving industrial mechanism depended. Efforts to humanize the industrial process could mitigate its impact on the worker but could not alter its fundamental character.

VI. MANAGEMENT

Industrial management supplied the momentum, organization and direction for twentieth-century industrial development. As industry became more complex, with larger units and a greater range and intricacy of interrelationships, the management process became more and more complicated and those responsible for it made up a growing proportion of the industrial labour force. The number of salaried employees in industry expanded in relation to the number of wage earners and a high and growing proportion of managerial, administrative, clerical and related workers in the labour force distinguished the more industrialized countries from those where industry was less developed.

The vital task of management was to bring together information, make decisions on the basis of such information, secure the execution of these decisions, evaluate results and build and maintain a working organization. Whatever the position of industrial management—whether operating for private gain or as the agent of a corporation, a co-operative body or the state —its drive, capacity for organization and decision, imagination, attitude toward innovation, ability to use the knowledge of many specialists and the resources of society, and its skill in relating its activity to that of others largely determined the effectiveness of the industrial process.

In the early stages of industrial development in the nineteenth century merchants who knew the markets and some men of technical ingenuity who also possessed organizational skill and speculative daring had provided industrial leadership, relying on rule-of-thumb procedures and shrewd guesswork. Twentieth-century industry required more systematic direction. Management practices were subjected to scientific analysis and study and, especially after 1920, management was developed into a professional field, with a body of principles and methods taught in schools of business administration, set forth in manuals and discussed in professional meetings and technical groups.

New and constantly developing techniques enlarged the scope and increased the precision of each area of management responsibility—choice of product, design and operation of the physical process of production, securing and using the necessary materials, machines, power and labour, selling or otherwise disposing of the product, financing the operations and building and maintaining a functioning organization.

1. *Choice of product*

For the obvious first step of determining what to produce, management needed to know the nature of the potential product, what it could do, and where and how it was in actual or potential demand. It had to decide what grades, qualities or types to produce and in what volume; and it had to determine continuously whether the product was still wanted, was profitable to make, could be improved, could be made more cheaply, and was preferable to alternative products which lay within the enterprise's capacity to produce. In the free economies which depended on the market, the technique of the market survey, which was elaborated and widely used in the second quarter of the twentieth century, provided a picture of potential demand which supplemented the flow of orders upon which producers had formerly depended for evidence of the demand for their goods. With the aid of rapid communication, record-keeping and computing devices, managers of large concerns kept before them a continuous picture of where their products were being sold, to whom and at what rate, and could note and respond to changes as they occurred. In planned economies, where the choice of what to produce and how much was determined by a central plan after consultation with the managements of particular units, the same type of information was helpful in proposing and determining future assignments and quotas.

It was not enough, however, for the industrial manager to decide what product should be made; he had to ensure that each unit produced would conform to specifications and be uniform in quality. In contrast to handicraft products which bore the imprint of the maker, it was the essence of mass production that identical products should be turned out in volume. When a customer ordered from a sample, he counted on receiving a supply that exactly matched, not an assortment of more or less close approximations. Standard specifications were necessary in order that the mass-production process could be set up and carried on, purchaser and seller could know that a transaction was clearly understood by the other, and materials, parts, screws or other products of one industry could be reliably used in the design of products by another and would fit when put together with products from other sources. The more complex and interdependent industry became and the more refined its products, the more necessary it became to establish standards, definitions and testing techniques in order to maintain quality control.

Prior to the first world war standardization was largely confined to the large companies which sought to take advantage of mass-production methods and it was chiefly applied within the plant rather than on an industry-wide basis, although a few standards, such as the gauge for railway tracks, had been established and adopted as clearly essential. In general, producers offered a great variety of things which differed in no essentials, but varied sufficiently to make their combination impossible, such as electric light bulbs which fitted only certain sockets, or screws of the same thickness with many different threads so that nuts which fitted one bolt could not be used on another. Some cartels and trade associations started before the first world war to encourage concentration on standard items or agreed on standard descriptions of products made to certain specifications. The British Engineering Standards Association, founded in 1901, brought the first national approach to the development of standards and remained the only such organization and effort up to the first world war.

The impact of that war brought standardization into industry through the enormous demand for articles which met military specifications. By the close of the war the advantages to industry from the adoption of standards, both in reducing costs and increasing flexibility, led to the organization of national standardizing bodies in most industrial countries. Standards boards or committees were formed in Germany in 1917, the United States in 1918, Japan in 1921 and Russia in 1925. The first of a series of pan-American conferences on standardization was held in 1924 to facilitate international commerce within the Western hemisphere, and the International Standards Association was formed in 1926. First for basic materials and then for a wider and wider range of goods, standard dimensions were agreed upon, within countries and in some cases internationally, to permit interchangeability of parts, standard nomenclature was adopted to assure identification, standards of performance were defined in terms of such factors as resistance to abrasion, heat resistance or strength under pressure, standards of safety were formulated and standard tests were devised.

An important aspect of the movement for standardization was a reduction in the number and variety of products where such variety appeared to serve no useful purpose. A series of conferences between members of different industries and users of their products in the United States in the 1920s resulted in the elimination from mass production of some three-fourths of the varieties of common building materials and household furnishings; varieties of paving brick, for example, were reduced from 66 to 11, of woven wire fence from 552 to 69 and of the sizes of bed springs and mattresses from 78 to 4. In the years after the second world war a similar effort at standardization and simplification, especially for standard types of mechanical equipment, was intensified in the USSR and eastern Europe as part of the programme to raise productivity and bring a closer integration among these economies.

Standard specifications, nomenclature and tests provided industrial management with a device of major importance to the operation of industry, for they made possible a great increase in the rationalization of production and conduct of trade. By mid-century a high degree of standardization had been developed within each of the industrially developed countries, but international differences persisted, including differences in measuring systems, and these impeded the flow of international trade, complicated management's task where an enterprise produced for both domestic and foreign markets, and presented serious difficulties to newly industrializing countries dependent upon imported equipment and faced with the problem of whose standards to follow in developing their own industrial designs. Differences in the voltage and rate of oscillation of the electric current supplied in different countries presented an increasingly troublesome problem as more and more industrial farm and household equipment was operated by electricity.

International military organization offered an incidental stimulus to international standardization among the western European countries. In the effort to secure effective communication and international interchangeability of equipment, the North Atlantic Treaty Organization set up a special department to promote standardization of procedures, military weapons and communications systems. This attempt at international standardization immediately encountered the differing national standards which governed many of the civilian items needed for military purposes.

2. Production control

Industrial management had to plan and operate the processes of production on the basis of knowledge of possible techniques, and choice of alternative methods and arrangements. Rational organization of industrial production was as vital to the high productivity of twentieth-century industry as machinery, power or other applications of technology.

All factory systems involved a flow of material through a series of steps timed to follow one after another. The task of production management was to refine this process with such accuracy of timing and precision in the successive steps as to avoid waste motion, delays, bottlenecks, idle workers or machines, materials or goods piled up at any point, breakdowns, waste of materials or excessive numbers of imperfect products.

Techniques for effecting these objectives were developed gradually and continuously in each specific industry, but major improvements affecting industrial processes in general were stimulated by such diverse developments as Frederick W. Taylor's methods of scientific management which were introduced in a number of factories in the United States after 1910, by Henry Ford's establishment of the assembly line, by Walter Rathenau's leadership in the rationalization of German industry in the first world war and by the Stakhanovite movement in the USSR.

Taylor introduced the practice of making careful detailed studies of the motions of workers and machines in order to determine whether changes such as the rearrangement of machines, adjustment in height of the workers' stools, or substitution of a horizontal motion for one requiring lifting or stooping, would reduce the time required and lessen the workers' fatigue. He demonstrated to management and workers that each task consisted of a series of distinguishable, time-consuming movements which could be scientifically analysed and rationally planned and that such rationalization would speed up output, increase labour productivity, cut costs and permit the payment of higher wages. Henry Ford's assembly line added the feature of the continuous flow. Walter Rathenau brought standardization and simplification of procedures from top to bottom in the management process. Stakhanovism enlisted the active and alert attention and creative imagination of worker, foreman and manager in the continual process of seeking more rational and efficient arrangements and design.

The key to successful production was the continuous flow, whether in a skyscraper being built in a crowded city street where materials had to be used as fast as they arrived, an automobile plant where hundreds of different materials and parts entered the plant at one end and were driven away as finished cars and lorries from the other, a shipyard where prefabricated parts were assembled on a waiting keel, or a meat-packing establishment where animals entered the plant and emerged as meat, hides, glue, fertilizer, shortening, bristles and a dozen other products. The production manager's basic guide was the flow chart which provided the plan and the basis for detecting bottlenecks.

The great precision in production flow was made possible by quick methods of communication, both within the plant and with suppliers of materials or receivers of finished goods, by transport systems which could be relied upon to deliver on schedule, by accurate and systematic recording devices which made it possible to know what was happening at any moment and to study past records for evidences of imperfections in the flow, and by calculating mechanisms which made it possible to examine the interaction of a multitude of factors. As electronic computers began to be used they immensely increased the range and intricacy of the interrelations which could be analysed, and they revealed possible economies which slower and more partial methods had been unable to suggest. In some plants the introduction of closed-circuit television which enabled the production manager to keep the production process continually in view provided an additional means of detecting flaws in the system.

3. *Personnel administration*

Good labour relations and increasing labour productivity were essential to effective operations and a test of good management. The majority of employers in most industrial countries were slow to adopt a rational and co-operative approach toward their labour force in the early years of the twentieth century. They clung to the idea that low wages were the way to keep down labour costs and that labour organization and collective bargaining threatened their control and ability to maintain this policy.

Management interest in ways to increase labour productivity began to grow when the scientific management movement showed the possibilities for raising productivity through careful job analysis; Henry Ford's deliberate policy of high wages, short hours and systematized work brought high profits with low prices; the establishment of labour-management committees in British, German and American factories during the first world war proved fruitful in meeting the increased production required by war.

Labour unions were initially suspicious of this interest on the part of management, for they feared that it would take the form of pressure on workers to increased exertion without increased pay or would lead to technological displacement. But where unions succeeded in securing acceptance from management and where good working relations replaced mutual antagonisms, they sometimes undertook time and motion studies of their own in order to be in a position to negotiate with employers over the workers' share in the fruits of increased productivity. Some unions, in fact, took the initiative in recommending improvements in work organization, in order to enable their employers to stay in business in the face of competition or declining markets, or to expedite a changeover from civilian to military production, as did the clothing workers' union in the United States in the depression of the 1930s, and the automobile workers' union at the beginning of the second world war.

Studies of worker efficiency in the 1920s and 1930s, especially those by Elton Mayo at an electrical manufacturing plant in Hawthorne, USA, brought out the importance of psychological factors and added a new dimension to personnel management. Since these studies were conducted by industrial engineers who were engaged in the training of business managers, they entered quickly into the thinking of leading industrialists and led to the establishment of personnel departments in large concerns, the training of men to conduct these departments in the light of the latest psychological knowledge, the training and retraining of supervisors, the establishment of systematic personnel practices with respect to such things as rest periods, sick leave, job tenure and promotions and, in some large companies, to educational programmes, recreational opportunities and a variety of social services. Additional studies sought evidence as to the most effective ways of conveying instructions to workers and receiving suggestions from them, and of maintaining worker morale, interest in the job and loyalty to the concern.

In some countries and industries labour management committees functioned in respect to various aspects of the enterprise's operation, and elsewhere less formal methods of consultation and joint agreement on matters within the plant were maintained. Management and labour joined in carrying out terms agreed to in collective contracts and in making the machinery for settling grievances or disputes work smoothly. Although personnel management differed greatly among enterprises and from one country to another, ranging from paternalism to indifference, from co-operative relations with organized labour to bitter antagonism, and from the persistence of sharp class lines and cultural differences to the blurring of such distinctions, management policies and methods in industrially developed countries were increasingly designed to achieve high labour productivity by recognizing workers' needs and stimulating their response as human beings.

By the close of the second world war rising productivity was accepted by management and labour alike in the industrially advanced countries as necessary to their own and their nation's welfare. This recognition of common interest did not by any means eliminate the conflict and often antagonism between management and labour over their respective shares in the fruits of industry. But it did become a basis for collective bargaining negotiations and for the fixing of wage structures and other conditions where, as in the Scandinavian countries, these were arrived at by nationally established procedures.

In the United States, following the lead of the United Automobile Workers' contract of 1946, wage contracts began to call for an annual wage increment designed to pass on to the workers automatically a portion of the expected increase in productivity. In the decade following the war productivity teams composed of workers and employers from one or another industry visited other countries, chiefly coming from European countries to the United States, with a view to sharing the experience gained in raising output. Of the fifty-eight British productivity teams which visited the United States, three-fourths cited the workers' appreciation of the need for higher productivity as one of the reasons for the high level of productivity in America and half mentioned the progressive attitude of management.

The joint interests of labour and management in increased productivity were put to a severe test by the accelerated rate at which new automatic processes were introduced, for the large displacement which could result from a single, complex computing device brought great uncertainty as to the full impact of these changes on workers and how benefits from the resultant effects on productivity would be shared.

In the Soviet Union, and countries following its economic and technical lead, a principal means of organizing the productive process and stepping up productivity was to set production goals which would be met and if possible exceeded. Workers were encouraged to devise means to exceed their quotas or to suggest improvements, and were rewarded and honoured for so doing. The role of trade unions was to assist in the meeting of production goals by helping to train workers for their tasks, and by maintaining work morale and discipline. A variety of devices such as group competition between sections of a plant or between plants, public display of production records of individuals and groups, and the stimulus to productive effort offered by five-year plans and other national or local objectives all served to enhance the productivity of the labour force.

Yugoslavia counted on the workers' interest in success to maintain and increase productivity. The direction of enterprises was in the hands of workers' councils with authority to choose whether to use the earnings, after taxes, for reinvestment, social expenditures or direct bonuses to workers.

Both in capitalist and communist economies the second quarter of the twentieth century thus saw a growing tendency to treat workers as partners in industry rather than merely as tools, to humanize work and to transform the worker from an item of cost into an active participant in the productive process. The process was far from complete and in most places there remained undercurrents of labour strife, but the tendency was nonetheless real.

This trend was formalized in various types of management–labour co-operation throughout the industrially active parts of the world. By 1950 twenty-nine countries, including nearly all European countries, both western and eastern, whatever the form of their economy, had well-established systems of management–worker co-operation in single enterprises, in industries or on a national basis, while less comprehensive forms of such co-operation existed in another half-dozen countries. Some of these systems owed their initiation to wartime patriotism and the danger of wartime sabotage; some were established contractually and others by legislation; they often reflected social as well as economic objectives and used social means to achieve economic goals. The object of all such systems, according to the ILO, was to unite the different elements engaged in production in the common task of raising social standards by a continuous increase in productivity.

4. *Merchandising*

Mass-production industry was as dependent on mass methods of distribution as on the production line itself; the industrial manager had to choose his merchandising methods and keep a constant check on their results.

The flow of goods to the consumer through the channels of distribution had to be as streamlined as the flow of materials through the assembly line in the plant. Devices for systematic recording, swift communication and automatic computing played the same role in mass merchandising as in control of mass production. Methods of selling which had served to distribute a relatively small number of items to a relatively small segment of the population were wholly inadequate to the task of routing masses of products to masses of people.

Mass merchandising, like mass production, involved breaking down the total process so that it could be performed in a series of simple steps by relatively unskilled persons, and then substituting where possible an automatic operation for unskilled labour. Towards this end, products were sold in packages which carried their own description and sales appeal and did not depend on the salesman's detailed knowledge of the merchandise or ability to convince the buyer; brand names were used as a means of identification and appeal. Mail-order companies reached millions of buyers with catalogues which earned the name of 'wish books'. 'Five and Ten Cent' or 'Uniprix' stores offered many common, small, low-priced items, or other products put up in small amounts to sell for a standard low price. Self-service stores stocked with clearly marked items required only someone to place products on the shelves and someone to add up the customer's purchases and take his money. Automatic vending machines dispensed such things as cigarettes, candy, bottled beverages, milk, handkerchiefs or stockings, in public places such as railway and bus stations or factories. Some business concerns built up a selling organization to reach the public directly or by means of agents; others sold only through intermediaries.

Mass consumption required that the potential consumer should know about and desire the product; advertising provided the link between mass production and the mass market. The more plentiful and varied the supply of industrial products became—the more affluent the advanced industrial societies—the greater the use of advertising to stimulate and guide consumption, and advertising became as high-powered and systematized as the other processes which were part of industrial management. While the primary function of advertising was to inform the buyer, and governments made efforts to hold advertisers to that function or at least to check false and misleading claims, the aim of high-powered advertising became increasingly to influence and not merely to inform. Using every modern medium of communication to attract attention and interest, advertisers sought to arouse the desires of the people for the products of industry.

In planned economies there was not the same need to press products on to the market, but choices among possible methods of distribution still had to be made. During the period under review, when production in the planned economies was heavily concentrated on producers' goods, the principal problems related to methods of allocating the limited supply of consumer goods. As these economies became more affluent, new problems of distribution began to appear.

5. Financial management

The problems of financial management grew in complexity along with the physical aspects of production and distribution. Both in capitalist economies where management was under the necessity of showing an eventual profit or going out of business, and in planned economies where financial as well as physical balances had to be maintained, management needed to translate physical operations into financial costs and returns.

The tools of financial management were largely the same as those of physical management and their use went hand in hand. Detailed analysis of the physical processes of production and distribution provided the essential basis for detecting detailed costs that might be modified, and instruments for recording, analysing and computing intricate physical relationships were equally useful for financial accounting.

The need for elaborate systems of cost accounting gave rise both to a distinct profession of accountants, trained in their discipline and licensed to practice, and to the design and construction of ever more elaborate business machines.

Accounting had already been recognized as a specialized skill in western Europe and the United States by the latter part of the nineteenth century. In the first quarter of the twentieth century professional associations of accountants in these countries established criteria for training and competence to qualify for the title 'certified public accountant'. Industrial managers depended on the technical knowledge of these specialists to analyse the financial aspects of their operations, to design and set up systems for keeping necessary records and supplying a continuous financial picture, and to review and audit their accounts periodically.

Mechanization of the financial processes began in the last quarter of the nineteenth century with such early devices as the typewriter, cash register and comptometer. As these and other machines for duplicating, calculating and tabulating were introduced, the clerks who had laboriously copied information and entered it by hand in the ledgers of nineteenth-century firms were replaced, first by a battery of typists who made simultaneous copies of each record, subsequently by punch card operators who punched coded information on cards which sorting machines analysed and tabulated automatically, and then by electronic systems which noted, stored, computed and reported information as desired. The use of business machines was accelerated phenomenally in the decade after the second world war, as may be seen in the experience of the world's leading manufacturer of business machines which quadrupled its sales from 1945 to 1955 and increased the number of engineers in its employ more than twelvefold.

6. *Organization*

Industrial management had to build and maintain going organizations which grew in size and complexity as the scope of industry widened. The scale of production resulting from modern technology required the creation of a joint stock company, government enterprise or corporation, co-operative body or other large structure.

The effective operation of an industrial bureaucracy presented many of the same problems of form and administration as were encountered in government agencies and other large bodies. It involved problems of authority, responsibility and motivation, and the need to assure that efforts by members of the organization to attain their own goals would contribute toward the objectives of the organization as a whole.

In view of the growing importance of large-scale organization in modern life, much systematic study and experiment was carried on in an effort to understand more clearly how to build an effective organization and maintain its vitality. Studies of organizational structure analysed such problems as the proper relation between the function to be performed and the authority and responsibility of the person assigned to perform it. They distinguished between the staff functions of providing information and advice and the line functions of making decisions and issuing directives. They considered the number and kinds of people who can be effectively supervised directly by a single individual, and evaluated the need for subordinate divisions, the effective balance between centralization and decentralization and alternative bases for forming departments or other units. Studies of the processes which take place within an organization dealt with such matters as how decisions are actually reached and what conditions favour a sound decision-making process. They observed group interaction taking place within committees, conferences or staff groups and tried to determine the size, composition and method of conducting a group which was likely to stimulate its members and further its purposes. They sought means of effective communication, in order that directions and suggestions might be given in such a manner as to be heard accurately and fully understood.

As the findings of these studies were assimilated by industrial management through formal study in schools of business or public administration, conferences, or inquiries on the job, the task of industrial management came to be seen more and more clearly as one of human relations. It was one of the ironies of the twentieth century that the more technology extended the power of man over nature and spread mechanization, the more crucial became the factor of human relations to those engaged in the conduct of industry.

VII. THE PRODUCTS OF INDUSTRY IN MODERN LIFE

The new products of industry, many of them unknown or not in use at the opening of the twentieth century, transformed the daily life of the people of industrial countries and of those in the urban centres of non-industrial parts of the world. Merely to enumerate the broad categories of products and the areas of life which they touched would be beyond the scope of this chapter. Motor vehicles not only provided unheard of mobility but placed ordinary individuals, at the wheel of a car, in command of tremendous power and in constant jeopardy on the road. Communication devices—telephone, radio, television—placed the home in contact with distant places and brought into the home all manner of information, experience and ideas. The gramophone made the best as well as the most popular music available anywhere. The cinema not only offered a principal form of mass entertainment but set new styles, undermined old habits and opened new horizons. The high-speed camera captured events and people around the world. Improved lighting and heating brought increased comfort into daily life, while refrigeration helped to make foods available the year round.

The housewife's tasks were expedited and lightened. She was enabled to prepare nutritious meals and keep the home clean and comfortable with the aid of a multitude of household appliances, such as refrigerators, vacuum cleaners, washing machines, gas and electric stoves, automatically operated heating and air-conditioning devices. New materials based on glass, cement, plastics, treated wood or composition boards entered into house construction; plumbing systems contributed to sanitation. Clothing materials made from artificial fibres could be washed and quickly dried without pressing. From the chemical industries came a variety of paints, lacquers and other surface protectors against weather or corrosion, together with dyes, drugs and detergents. A multitude of canned, frozen and dehydrated foods offered a varied diet and reduced the time for food preparation.

The small motor, both electric and petrol powered, served many purposes in the home and on the farm as well as in industry, operating a variety of tools and appliances, pumping water or fuel, running boats, fans, gramophone turntables, lawn mowers. Tractors and other power on the farm lightened the farmer's tasks. An endless array of objects and devices, small and large, for utility, amusement or adornment, were used in all walks of life.

Some people regarded the mass of industrial products as a burden and overlay upon the life of mankind, with life becoming standardized and man a slave to his gadgets. Some looked nostalgically towards the past while others insisted that more human values were associated with a simpler way of life and questioned whether material advance brought additional human happiness or merely added pressure, diversion and confusion. Proposals were even made that the process of invention be arbitrarily halted for a period in order that social institutions and man's ability to live with his new powers over nature might have a chance to catch up.

But the large numbers of people who inhabited the great urban areas of the world could not live without the resources which industry had brought them, and even those who withdrew to a simple life away from the pressures of industrial society depended on many of its fruits for their survival. The products, organization and processes of modern industry had become inextricably interwoven with the life of a large segment of mankind.

Yet one vital question remained: in an affluent society would man be able, and would he be inclined, to look on his material well-being as a means to a richer human life and not merely as an end in itself?

NOTES TO CHAPTER IX

1. Academician A. A. Arzumanyan writes: The economic competition over the last decade between the Soviet Union and the United States, between the socialist and capitalist world systems, has led to a radical shift in the balance of forces. Socialism has entered upon a period in which its power is steadily expanding, while the general crisis of capitalism is becoming increasingly severe. Capitalism is being edged out by socialism, and is losing one position after another to its rival.

The new stage in the general crisis of capitalism is characterized by a narrowing of the gap between the Soviet Union and the United States.

The Soviet economy is developing far more rapidly than that of the United States. Over the seven years 1954–60 industrial output in the USSR rose by an average of 11·1 per cent per annum, while that of the USA rose by 2·5 per cent. The socialist world system as a whole is also growing much faster than the capitalist world. Over the last ten years industrial production in the socialist system as a whole rose by an average of 13·6 per cent per annum, whereas the corresponding figure for the capitalist countries was 5 per cent. At the present time the industrial output of the socialist countries accounts for approximately 36 per cent of world output, as compared with 27 per cent in 1955.

Socialism is surpassing capitalism not only in rates of growth, but also in the absolute increase of industrial output. Between 1953 and 1960 the average annual absolute increase of total industrial production was approximately twice as great in the USSR as in the USA. In 1950 Soviet industrial production was about 30 per cent that of the United States, whereas now the figure is more than 60 per cent.

Academician E. S. Varga draws the same conclusion: In its pace of economic growth the Soviet Union has left the capitalist world far behind, and despite the heavy blows dealt to its economy by the civil war, the intervention, and the second World War, is now firmly established as Europe's largest, and the world's second largest, producer of industrial goods (E. S. Varga, '40 let rosta sotsializma i upadka kapitalizma' ('40 Years of the Growth of Socialism and Decline of Capitalism'), in *Novoye Vremya* (New Times) 1957, No. 4, p. 5). The United Nations data support the point of view of the Soviet scholars, and provide evidence of the low rate of growth of most of the principal capitalist countries.

See also Note 1 to Chapter XXI.

2. *On this question the Author-Editors would like to add the following material:*

The tables below, prepared by the United Nations in an attempt to show comparative rates of economic growth during the decade of the 1950s, are the most nearly comprehensive series available for any period. They have been rearranged in declining order of reported rates of growth. The United Nations reports the communist countries separately because their basis for calculating growth differs substantially from those used by other countries. The former exclude economic activities not contributing directly to material production, such as public administration and defence, personal and professional services and similar activities. There are no comparable figures for the non-communist countries making the same exclusions, and therefore there is no way of telling how the comparative figures here reported would differ if converted to the same base.

For the non-communist countries, average per capita income in 1958 is also indicated. It will be noted that the countries of relatively high per capita income show growth rates during this period of about 4 per cent or less, with the exception of the German Federal Republic and Iceland. Middle and low per capita income countries vary widely in their rates of growth. No corresponding per capita income figures are available for the communist countries.

AVERAGE ANNUAL RATES OF GROWTH OF REAL GROSS DOMESTIC PRODUCT, 1952–60,[1] AND PER CAPITA GROSS DOMESTIC PRODUCT IN 1958[2]

Country	Period	Percentage rate of growth Total	Per capita	Per capita product in US dollars, 1958
		%	%	$
Israel	1952–60	9·6	5·8	579
Japan	1954–60	9·5	8·4	285
Trinidad and Tobago	1952–60	9·2	6·0	529
Algeria	1952–57	8·8	6·4	220

Country	Period	Percentage rate of growth		Per capita product in US dollars, 1958
		Total	Per capita	
		%	%	$
Jamaica	1954–59	8·0	6·3	357
Taiwan	1952–60	7·5	3·7	114
Germany, Fed. Rep.	1952–60	7·2	6·0	920
Venezuela	1952–60	7·2	3·1	715
Puerto Rico	1952–60	6·5	5·7	581
Greece	1952–60	6·2	5·2	307
Brazil	1952–60	6·0	2·8	252
Rhodesia and Nyasaland	1955–60	6·0	3·4	161
Italy	1952–60	5·9	5·4	493
Austria	1952–60	5·8	5·6	656
Philippines	1952–60	5·7	2·4	192
Iceland	1952–59	5·6	3·4	946
Guatemala	1952–60	5·4	2·4	164
Thailand	1952–60	5·2	1·7	77
Portugal	1953–60	4·9	4·2	212
Netherlands	1952–60	4·8	3·4	767
Korea, Rep.	1954–60	4·8	2·5	104
Finland	1952–60	4·7	3·6	751
Ecuador	1952–60	4·7	1·4	180
Turkey	1952–60	4·7	1·8	201
Burma	1954–60	4·6	3·4	51
Nicaragua	1952–59	4·6	1·2	220
Colombia	1952–59	4·5	2·2	301
Cambodia	1952–58	4·3	1·6	86
Congo (Leopoldv.)	1952–58	4·2	2·0	87
France	1952–60	4·2	3·4	1089
Indonesia	1952–58	4·2	2·2	69
Switzerland	1955–58	4·1	2·8	1338
Sweden	1952–60	3·9	3·2	1309
Malaya, Fed.	1956–60	3·9	0·7	218
Denmark	1952–60	3·8	3·1	975
Nigeria	1952–56	3·7	–	81
Norway	1952–60	3·4	2·4	1012
Honduras	1952–59	3·4	0·4	192
Canada	1952–60	3·3	0·6	1767
Luxembourg	1953–58	3·3	2·6	1332
Chile	1952–59	3·2	0·9	352
Cyprus	1952–60	3·0	1·2	410
India	1952–59	3·0	1·3	67
Peru	1952–57	3·0	0·7	150
Ceylon	1952–59	2·9	0·4	122
United Kingdom	1952–60	2·7	2·2	1084
USA	1952–60	2·6	0·9	2324
Pakistan	1954–60	2·6	0·5	54
Belgium	1952–59	2·6	2·0	1093
Argentina	1952–60	1·9	0·2	476
Syria	1954–60	1·7	−2·2	144
Ireland	1952–60	1·4	2·0	472
Paraguay	1952–60	1·4	−1·0	126
Morocco	1952–60	0·9	−1·9	159

AVERAGE ANNUAL RATES OF GROWTH OF REAL NET MATERIAL PRODUCT

		Percentage rate of growth	
Country	Period	Total	Per capita
		%	%
China (Mainland)	1953–58	12·6	9·5
USSR	1952–60	9·9	8·0
Yugoslavia	1953–60	9·3	8·1
Bulgaria	1954–60	8·4	7·3
Rumania	1952–60	8·3	6·9
Poland	1952–60	8·0	6·1
Czechoslovakia	1952–60	7·0	6·0
Hungary	1952–60	5·5	4·8

The figures shown in these tables are computed as average annual geometric rates of growth expressed in percentage form for the periods indicated. They are based on the estimates of real gross domestic product or of real net material product which appear for the individual countries elsewhere in the same Yearbook. Conceptual differences and other details concerning the basic data are indicated in the country tables. It should be noted that the methods used to obtain estimates of gross domestic product at constant prices and the years to which these prices relate vary widely between countries. The concept of material product used by the countries with centrally planned economies relates to the total value of goods and productive services, including turnover taxes, produced by the economy in the course of the year. The industries covered are generally agriculture, mining, manufacturing, construction, transportation and communication, trade and catering. Economic activities not contributing directly to material production, such as public administration and defence, personal and professional services and similar activities, are not included.

In order to minimize the influence of single terminal years on the computed growth rates, the estimates of real product were averaged and centred for the first three and last three years of each period for which data were available, for example, the figures shown for the period 1952–60 represented rates of growth based on estimates of average real product in the periods 1951–53 and 1959–61.

(2) With respect to the statistics of per capita product in US dollars, the estimates in this table should be considered as indicators of the per capita production of goods and services of the countries represented and not as measures of the standard of living of their inhabitants. No particular significance should be attached to small differences between the estimates of two countries because of the margin of error inherent in the method of estimation.

Source: United Nations, Yearbook of National Accounts Statistics, *1962, Table 2a, 2b and 3*

3. Professor L. M. Gatovsky writes: In all countries engaged in the construction of socialism the process of industrialization has a number of features in common: the socialist nature of industrialization; a planned economy; high rates of growth; resources obtainable by utilizing the advantages of socialism; the development of socialist emulation, and others besides. At the same time there are also certain differences in the process of industrialization connected with the economic, political and natural geographical conditions in each particular country, its level of industrial development, science and technology, the structure of industry, productive capacity, existence of cadres of skilled workers, the role of foreign trade, etc. In the People's Democracies the concrete forms of industrialization and the rates of growth differ in many ways from the forms and growth rates that characterized socialist industrialization in the USSR—which at that time was the only socialist country in existence, and was compelled to create in the shortest possible time a first-class industry able to supply the economy with all the manufactured goods it required. . . .

All the People's Democracies benefit by economic and scientific-technological aid from the USSR and the entire socialist camp, and obtain a great economic advantage from the international socialist division of labour. The People's Democracies need not therefore develop their industries at such an intensive pace as was adopted in the

USSR, and do not have to set themselves the task of manufacturing products of all kinds (only China faces the problem of building an entire system of new branches of industry). Each country has the opportunity to develop those branches of industry for which economic and natural conditions are most favourable. To a greater extent than was possible in the USSR during the period of industrialization they can take into account the economic efficacy of investments in human and material resources. (L. M. Gatovsky, 'Ob obshchikh zakonomernostyakh i osobennostyakh stroitelstva sotsializma v razlichnykh stranakh' ('On the general laws of development and the specific character of socialist construction in different countries'), in: *Mirovaya sotsialisticheskaya sistema khozyaystva* (The Socialist World Economic System), Moscow: Gosplanizdat, 1958, pp. 67–8.)

4. Doctor of Economic Sciences A. A. Manukyan writes: The length of the working day, wage rates, etc., are determined by the struggle of the working class and the existing social system, rather than by the level of labour productivity. As the American Senator Paul Douglas remarked: 'I grew up in New England and I know the cotton mills and woollen mills of New England prior to the coming of unionism paid extremely low wages and worked extremely long hours.' (Trade Agreements Act Extension, Hearings before the Committee on Finance, US Senate, 85th Congress, 2nd Session, June–July 1958, pt. 2, Washington, p. 1071). It may be added that in the Soviet Socialist Republic the 8-hour working day was introduced in 1917, whereas in 1919, in the USA, a country with a higher level of labour productivity, a strike for the 8-hour working day was cruelly suppressed.

5. Doctor of Economic Sciences A. A. Manukyan writes: Prior to the twentieth century, and to a certain extent even prior to the end of the first quarter of the twentieth century, industrial development was in essence the achievement of Europe alone—first and foremost of Western Europe and the Eastern part of North America and also Japan. Outside these territories there were only small islands of industry, mainly the manufacture of textiles or mining, situated at great distances from one another, almost lost to view amidst the endless spaces of countries completely untouched, or barely touched, by industrial development.

The history of industrial production thus affected directly only a tiny minority of mankind. It was only from the 1920s onwards that the greater part of the human race began to be involved in industrial development.

The reason for this development of industry—within the limits of a few favoured countries—lay in the fact that under capitalism whole continents of colonial, dependent and semi-dependent countries were methodically converted into sources of raw materials and markets in which the metropolitan countries, pursuing their own interests, could dispose of their products. Through the very nature of its social and economic organization capitalism does not facilitate the general unlimited development of industry, in all countries and continents. The obstacles that stand in the way of the development of mankind's productive forces were overcome for the first time in Russia in 1917, as a result of the victorious Great October Socialist Revolution. The socialist system opened up new opportunities for the development of the productive forces of society, such as were unknown to capitalism and which it was incapable of realizing, and showed in practice that rapid industrial development was possible outside the framework of capitalism, without its aid or guidance.

The opening up of this new socialist path of industrial development, and the proof given of this vitality in a country hitherto as backward as Russia, was a turning-point in the history of mankind, so far as industrial development was concerned; it also vastly expanded the opportunities available for economic, scientific, technological and cultural development. After the second world war and the formation of the world socialist system the overwhelming majority of mankind obtained for the first time in history a real opportunity to develop industry, science and culture and to free itself of centuries of poverty and insecurity.

6. On the Soviet view of the distribution of shares, see note 5 to Chapter XXI.

7. Doctor of Economic Sciences A. A. Manukyan writes: The authors mention the high costs and other difficulties involved in the exploitation of mineral resources, resulting from the existence of a large number of surface owners.

In this context, mention should be made of the depletion allowances obtained by, for example, the US oil companies, the gross amount of which exceeds actual investments by 10, 20 and more times. These were a means of subsidizing individual surface owners and oil companies in the USA at the expense of the state. In the years 1925-53 this expenditure amounted to 23,397 million dollars (Department of Agriculture, Appropriations for 1959: Hearing before the Sub-Committee of the Committee on Appropriations, House of Representatives, 85th Congress, 2nd Session, 1958, Pt. I, Washington, 1958, pp. 158 ff.). In the socialist countries mineral resources belong to the whole people and are worked in the interests of society.

8. Doctor of Economic Sciences A. A. Manukyan observes: The international oil companies obtain their high rates of profit, not because prospecting in, say, the Middle East is expensive and fraught with risk, but for precisely the opposite reason. The cost of locating an oilfield and obtaining oil from it is dozens, even hundreds of times cheaper in the Middle East than in the United States. According to latest data, in 1947-60 this cost amounted to: 106 cents in the USA, 58 cents in Canada, 23 cents in Venezuela, 10 cents in the Far East, 1 cent in the Middle East. The profits drawn by the big oil concerns are 100, 200 or 300 per cent of their outlays.

9. A. N. Grzhegorzhevsky, Candidate of Economic Sciences, observes that the clearest demonstration of the distorted development of technology under capitalism, especially at the present stage of its general crisis, is its subordination to purposes of destruction. In capitalist countries technology is today developing most rapidly in those branches (atomic energy, cosmic research) concerned with the production of means of destruction. It is those branches that increasingly dominate the trends of technical 'progress' and receive priority in the introduction of new equipment and new production processes. It is no exaggeration to say that the fate of a particular industry, from the point of view of its technical development, is determined in the main by the fact whether or not it obtains military contracts which can ensure mass production in large series. It goes without saying that the development of technology in the branches of the war industry can find partial application in other fields of capitalist production as well. But it is the characteristic feature of such development that the most important technological advances are achieved, as the facts prove, in war industry.

Yet technology is a most important element of productive—and not destructive—forces. This development of the technology of capitalist production does not testify to normal technological progress. See: A. N. Grzhegorzhevsky, 'Contradictions in the Development of Technology at the Present Stage of the General Crisis of Capitalism', in the book: *Usileniye zagnivaniya Kapitalizma v usloviyakh novogo etapa obshchego krizisa* ('Increased Decay of Capitalism in the Conditions of the New Stage of Its General Crisis') (Moscow, 1961), pp. 103-4.

10. *See Chapters XI and XXIV for discussion of total war and the impact of military considerations on industry, technology and even science in all major countries. The spectacular scientific and technical achievements of the USSR as well as the USA in space exploration and long-range guided missiles testify to this impact.*

CHAPTER X

TRANSPORT

T HE most spectacular application of scientific knowledge in the twentieth century was in the field of transport. The motor car transformed much of the pattern of living on the earth's surface. The aeroplane lifted man from the earth that had always bound him and carried him swiftly and freely over seas and deserts, jungles, mountain heights and polar ice, indifferent to the barriers which had hemmed him in or blocked his course.

Steam and machines had already brought a revolutionary change in transport in the nineteenth century. Thanks to the railway and the steamship, man had been freed for the first time from the limitations placed upon his mobility by his own powers of locomotion, those of draught animals and the propulsion of the wind. The 500,000 miles of railway lines which extended rapid, cheap, safe and dependable transport to most inhabited regions of the globe had opened up resources and markets and had provided a basis for modern industry. This first revolution in transport had brought new relationships and a great sense of change and expansion. Few dreamed, however, of the revolution in transport which lay ahead.

The second was even more spectacular than the first, for it freed man from the limitations of the earth's surface itself, and it was even more pervasive for it placed in the hands of millions of ordinary individuals the means which gave them almost complete mobility and it broke down the isolation of all except the most remote areas.

In the industrialized countries the influence of the motor car can hardly be exaggerated. What in the early years of the century was an experimental vehicle, of interest to technical experts, racing enthusiasts and a few rich men, became a necessity in the life of millions of families, the cornerstone upon which their manner of living was built. It became a symbol of prestige and status and the basis of a major industry. It led to the enormous extension of roads and provided the basis for a network of services of supply and repair. It introduced a new and serious threat to life in the danger from high-speed vehicles. It loosened the relationships which were based on proximity and thus modified social patterns and altered horizons.

In the less industrialized areas the motor car had not, by mid-century, yet come to play the role of a personal vehicle in the lives of a large proportion of the population or changed whole patterns of life and human relationships. It was important in economic development, in providing public transport, for civil administration and military transport, and as a pleasure vehicle for a small wealthy element. But with the process of economic development the use of the motor car expanded steadily, presaging a time when it would begin to give mobility to the general population as it had in the most industrialized areas of the western world.

The aeroplane, on the other hand, had perhaps an even more revolutionary impact on underdeveloped than on industrialized regions, although the main volume of air travel and transport was in the latter areas. In the industrialized countries the aeroplane was mainly an accelerator; it speeded up an already fast system of rail and motor transport, making intercontinental and trans-continental travel a matter of hours instead of days or weeks. It speeded up the processes of business, administration and holiday travel but it did not create a radically new situation in civilian life. Its most far-reaching impact in the industrialized areas was in time of war, when it exposed civilian popula-tions to aerial bombardment and transformed whole cities into military objectives.

In the underdeveloped regions of the world, however, the aeroplane was an innovator which brought an end to isolation and opened up regions to which access was most difficult. In one sweep, the people of the high valleys of the Himalayas, of the Amazon jungles, the African bush or the deserts of Central Asia were placed in contact with the world community. However tenuous the link, it was present and real. The Arctic and Antarctic wastes which had offered a grim challenge to explorers could be flown over routinely or made the basis for scientific expeditions supplied by air.

In the middle of the century a third revolution in transport was just beginning as the first vehicles travelled into outer space, opening a new era in which the speeds and distances of air travel were dwarfed to insignificance, and men could think in terms of exploring not merely the earth and its atmosphere but other parts of the solar system.

I. MOTOR TRANSPORT

Efforts to develop self-propelled vehicles which would travel on the road had begun shortly after the invention of the steam engine, but the lumbering devices contrived by various designers in the late eighteenth and early nineteenth centuries long appeared to be merely dangerous nuisances. It was not until 1896 that the British Parliament repealed its law of 1835 requiring a man with a red flag to go in front of any mechanically propelled road vehicle and limiting the latter's speed to four miles per hour.

In the last quarter of the nineteenth century, and especially in the 1890s, much work was carried on in France, Germany, Britain, Austria and the United States to develop practical designs of both vehicle and motor. The horse-drawn carriage provided the starting-point for vehicle design; motor power was furnished by steam, electric batteries and various types of internal-combustion engines. When pneumatic tyres became available in 1889 they provided an indispensable basis for increased speed.

Out of experiments in many places and with many elements of design, the essential features of the automobile emerged around the turn of the century. A few steam models tried for several years to establish steam as a practical alternative to internal combustion, and electrically driven vehicles retained some popularity as long as it was necessary to crank petrol-driven motors by hand. But as petrol cars became more dependable the advantage of not having to wait until steam was generated gave them clear superiority over the steamers, and the self-starter took away the principal advantage from electric propulsion.

Once the petrol-driven, internal-combustion motor car had established itself as the dominant mechanical road vehicle its use expanded with great rapidity, and the industries, services, regulations and know-how related to the operation of such vehicles became part of the economic structure, the legal system and the education of the industrialized segments of the world. By 1955 motor vehicles in the United States were more numerous than homes; there was one motor vehicle for every 2·6 persons in the population. Comparable figures for other countries showed one vehicle per 4·4 persons in New Zealand, one per 9 persons in Denmark, the best supplied of the European countries, one per 70 persons in the USSR, per 92 in Brazil, per 98 in Japan and per 4,975 in China. Five years later cars on British roads had increased to one per 6 inhabitants, and comparable increases were bringing crowded roads to the European continent. Although a dozen or more countries had vigorous automobile industries, the major quantitative development in automobile production came in the United States, where at mid-century more than two-thirds of the world's passenger cars and half of its lorries and buses were being manufactured.

During the second decade of the twentieth century the whole character of the vehicle, as well as its method of manufacture, was changed by the introduction of mass production. Henry Ford in Detroit, USA, conceived the idea of a car designed for the masses, and started in 1909 to produce his Model T by an assembly-line method which made this low-priced car possible. Manufacturers in other countries, such as Citroën in France (1919), soon began to produce for the mass market, and other American manufacturers sought to compete with Ford for the large number of potential American car users. Gradually a pattern developed by which each major producer placed on the market a car which furnished mass sales and other cars for higher income levels. In the United States the low-priced models of the three principal manufacturers provided more than half of total annual passenger car sales in the 1950s.

As distinctive automobile models were developed the motor car became, like its predecessor the horse-drawn carriage, an object of conspicuous consumption. Automobile manufacturers began to emphasize features other than the mechanical excellence of the car in order to encourage the tendency to use the motor car not only as a means of transport but as a means of display.

In the United States the low-priced cars copied the style features of the higher-priced models until the cars on the road became almost equally elaborate and virtually indistinguishable.

Various improvements in design offered the traveller not only increased comfort but, more importantly, increased safety. The metal turret top of the closed car and other features of the metal body made it possible for the car to withstand a very severe impact without collapsing and crushing the occupants. Safety glass, made by laminating sheets of glass with plastic in such a way that the glass would crack but would not break, removed the extreme danger from cutting in case of accident. Hydraulic brakes offered greater security than those which operated mechanically and improved tyres reduced the likelihood that the car would be thrown out of control by a tyre burst. The automobile remained a dangerous vehicle and automobile accidents consti-tuted a major source of death and injury, but these safety features were among the factors which made it possible to place so powerful an instrument in the hands of the public and turn it loose on the public highways without inviting complete disaster. (Pl. 14a, 14b.)

Vehicles designed for military transport included features which were subsequently adapted for civilian use. The jeep, developed in the second world war as a small powerful passenger vehicle capable of traversing very rough terrain, proved immensely useful to farmers, woodsmen, prospectors and in any areas where roads were inadequate and the ordinary automobile, built for the well-surfaced highway, could not travel.

Motor lorries were manufactured in many sizes and types for a wide variety of cargo transport. At first lorries were used chiefly to carry relatively small loads short distances while railways hauled the long-distance heavy or bulky loads. In time, however, large transport vehicles began to compete with the railways as carriers of many types of freight. Huge trailers, detachable from the motor vehicle which drew them, could be loaded at a factory or warehouse and then picked up for hauling to a near or distant destination.

The production of motor vehicles and the building of roads, both of which steadily improved in quality and increased in scope, made motor transport a major factor in economic life by the middle of the twentieth century. Road transport vehicles were carrying a growing proportion of the world's freight, including the vast bulk of all short-haul loads. Motor transport had also be-come the chief means of passenger travel. Even excluding private vehicles, buses rather than trains were providing the means of inter-urban travel for the majority of passengers in more and more areas.

The enormous volume of motor travel required a great range of facilities. First and foremost were the highways. The roads surfaced with sand or gravel which had served for the traffic of horse-drawn vehicles were soon found to be entirely inadequate for motor transport. The car or lorry whipped up a cloud of dust, loosened and wore the surface and broke down the road-bed with its weight. The unsuitability of existing roads for motor travel was dramatized in 1903 when so many of the drivers in the Grand Prix automobile race from Paris to Madrid were blinded by dust and crashed that the race was called off in mid-course to save the lives of the surviving drivers.

The basic construction for road-building developed by Macadam in Britain at the end of the eighteenth century continued to be used, but asphalt or other binding material provided a solid surface. For major highways carrying heavy high-speed traffic, slabs of reinforced concrete were laid over well-drained road-beds whose depth and material were adjusted to local conditions of soil, moisture or frost. For safety and to permit high-speed travel, motor roads were widened, straightened and, on major routes, divided by a central barrier to prevent head-on collisions.

As long-distance motor travel increased, efforts were made to separate through traffic from local by providing special through motorways. Italy took the lead in the 1920s with the construction of *autostrade*, which could be entered only at specific points and from which pedestrians and slow-moving traffic were excluded. In the 1930s Germany constructed a series of *autobahnen* for military purposes, and the USA began to develop an elaborate network of limited-access high-speed highways, the first of which, the Pennsylvania Turnpike, was opened to traffic in 1940. These fast throughways permitted extremely rapid automobile travel from city to city. In 1957 there were nearly 4,000 miles of such motorways in West and East Germany and formerly German Poland, about 600 miles in the rest of Europe, mainly Italy, and some 2,500 miles in the United States. (Pl. 11b.)

Motor travel depended upon the ready availability of fuel, since each vehicle carried only a limited supply. The oil resources on which the whole system of motor travel and transport rested were localized in a few areas, at first the USA and northern South America, Rumania and southern Russia, then the Persian Gulf, the Indonesian archipelago and the Arabian peninsula. The pipelines, tanker fleets and tank cars which brought petrol great distances to points of use were the lifelines of the motor age. In areas where traffic was heavy, retail petrol-supply points were necessary at frequent intervals along the roads and the petrol service station became a ubiquitous institution.

The motorist was almost equally dependent on being able to find services of repair. When the motor car was a new instrument, driven only by people with special knowledge and interest in it as a mechanism, drivers carried their own tool-kits and some spare parts, and were equipped to make repairs to tyres, motor, or mechanical parts if these should break down on the road. As the motor car itself became much more complex and was driven by millions of men and women who had no specialized mechanical knowledge, motorists ceased to be able to make their own repairs and counted upon finding a mechanic not too far away if anything went wrong. Many service stations combined repair with petrol-supply services and kept on hand the spare parts most usually needed; and associations of motorists provided road patrols or emergency repair crews constantly on call.

Motor travel brought an immense expansion in overnight accommodation and a change in its form to suit the mode of travel. Hotels were urban phenomena. Especially after the railway replaced stage-coach travel and rendered unnecessary the roadside hostelries for man and beast, travellers found overnight accommodation in the towns, frequently near a railway station. But motorists did not want to struggle through congested traffic to the centre of a town where there was no place in which to park their car for the night.

At first private citizens who lived on main roads offered tourist accommodation in their spare rooms; then they built small one-room cabins with space at the side for the car. It was a small step to convert these groups of cabins into a more elaborate motor hotel or motel, and then to design motels equipped with many of the features of urban hotels. By mid-century the highways approaching many cities in the United States and Canada, as well as those in tourist and holiday areas, were lined with such motels and the pattern was spreading to other countries. For motorists who travelled by caravan or carried camping equipment, municipalities, public parks and private landowners offered caravan and camp sites equipped with water and sanitary facilities.

Motor traffic urgently required regulation, and all countries placed legal restrictions on the use of the roads. The most basic regulation, specifying the side of the road on which a vehicle shall drive, was first enacted in Britain by the Highway Act of 1835 which prescribed left-hand driving for carriages and animals, replacing the common law principle that permitted driving anywhere on a public highway. Britain was also one of the first countries to establish a practical speed limit—14 miles an hour in 1896, raised to 20 miles per hour in 1903. In 1930 Parliament abolished all speed limit for private cars and motor cycles, but the high rate of fatalities which followed led to the re-establishment four years later of a limit, 30 miles per hour in built-up areas, though the speed of private vehicles remained unrestricted on the open road. Continental European countries also imposed speed limits in built-up areas. Traffic regulation in the United States remained the responsibility of states and municipalities, which established different speed limits and other regulations for their highways and streets.

Motor vehicle regulations included the licensing of those who were permitted to drive on the highway, and generally required a certain age and demonstrated ability to handle the vehicle before such licence would be granted. Drivers were required to carry their licences at all times, and were subject to fine, arrest or revocation of licence if found driving without a permit or in an unsafe manner.

It was essential, however, that drivers passing from one jurisdiction to another should know what was expected of them. Model vehicle and traffic regulations were formulated and adopted by many jurisdictions, and reciprocity was arranged in respect to licensing and other requirements. The League of Nations developed a motor traffic convention in 1926 providing for international driving licences and uniform danger signals. This convention was put into effect generally in European countries and some others. Interrelated American motor traffic conventions were developed for the Western hemisphere by the Pan American Union in 1930 and 1943. The United Nations carried forward the League of Nations' work and developed uniform international symbols for road signs so that safety would not depend on the driver's knowledge of the language of the country.

Yet in spite of the elaborate systems of traffic regulation, the toll of motor accidents mounted steadily as more and more vehicles, with more and more capacity for speed, crowded the streets and highways. More than 35,000 people perished annually from motor accidents in the United States in the 1950s. In Great Britain during the second world war the number of road deaths was more than two-thirds as great as the fatalities from air raids, in spite of the fact that motor travel was severely limited by petrol rationing.

The menace to life and limb was not the only disadvantage brought by motor traffic, along with its many advantages. Congestion of roads leading into cities and of city streets grew worse with each passing year, often virtually nullifying the advantage of speedy motor travel by reducing traffic to a crawl across bridges or along main thoroughfares. To this was added the problem of parking. Much street space which would otherwise have been available for travel was occupied by parked vehicles, but still the driver often searched vainly for a place to leave his car. Fumes from the exhaust of thousands of vehicles became a menace to health; studies of factors producing smog, of the possible causes of lung cancer, and of the aetiology of other diseases sought to assess the impact of exhaust fumes on the public. Noise, too, contributed to the wear and tear of city living. In an effort to halt the constant grating of motor horns on the nerves of city dwellers, major cities forbade the use of the horn within the city limits, but the traffic roar continued.

The cultural impact of the motor car on virtually all aspects of life was tremendous in the countries where its use became general. The impact was most conspicuous in the United States, but as the number of motor cars in Europe mounted by leaps and bounds in the prosperous years which followed the recovery from the second world war, European life was increasingly affected in the same ways. The automobile was part of the equipment for living of over 70 per cent of the families in the United States by 1955; one family in ten owned two cars or more.

The motor car furnished the link between the place of living and the place of work; it provided the means for social contact, so that individuals were decreasingly dependent for their social life on those who lived in their neighbourhood, or even in their town. Motor travel became a favourite means of recreation and the motor car gave access to other sources of recreation also, such as ball games, racecourses, swimming and boating resorts. The automobile could affect patterns of courtship; it could promote some types of family activity and impair others; it might become a bone of contention between members of the family who might wish it for alternative uses. At best it occupied a very large place in the family budget and, when used as an expression of social status as well as a means of transport, it often strained the budget severely.

Not the least of the automobile's influences was the psychological impact of its use. Behind the wheel of a car every man was a master, in command of tremendous horsepower, able to inflict enormous damage, having to yield to no one so long as he respected the traffic rules—a king indeed. Small wonder that the adolescent could hardly wait until he reached the legal age at which he might enjoy this sense of manhood, and that he was sometimes tempted to abuse it.

The impact of the motor car on the city itself was not less than on its individuals. Older cities had tended toward central congestion as activities crowded into sites which were as accessible as possible to rail or ship terminals, or to other centrally located activities within the city. Only the high cost of centrally located land and the sheer fact of physical congestion limited the number and proportion of the city's business, industry, and population which responded to these centripetal tendencies.

The motor car largely reversed the process. On the one hand it made access to the suburbs easy and interconnections between one suburb and another possible. On the other it reduced the centre of the city to an impossible snarl.

Shops which had sought central sites to serve the greatest number of customers began to establish branches on the outskirts; suburban shopping centres with ample parking space came to serve those who lived in the outer parts of the city, as well as suburban residents. Factories, too, were located in open spaces where land was cheaper, factory buildings could be designed with less congestion, and where employees could have acres of land on which to park their cars. And always the suburbs grew and grew, spreading out in what came to be known as the urban sprawl, the characteristic living pattern of the motor age.

The motor car contributed, too, to a rootless manner of living. Caravan homes—though not numerous in proportion to those who lived in houses—introduced an element of impermanency into communities where they were located and developed a population of wanderers with no local ties. Migration in search of jobs, the constant need and opportunity to make new social contacts, the breakdown of every type of isolation—these were all parts of the restless, on-the-move pattern which the motor car had brought to mid-twentieth-century life.

II.   AIR TRANSPORT

The aeroplane added a new dimension to men's lives. The limitless future of the plane was immediately presaged when the Wright brothers, on December

17, 1903, made their famous flight at Kitty Hawk, North Carolina, USA, to demonstrate the possibility of powered flight by a heavier-than-air vehicle. Once the possibility had been established, the rest was simply a matter of progressive refinement. (Pl. 15a.)

Constantly increased knowledge of aerodynamics provided the basis for improvement in aircraft design. The Wrights' two flimsy wings supported by struts were replaced by a single wing shaped to get the maximum lift from the air flow. In turn, what came to be a conventional design of wing, fuselage and tail gave way in the fast military planes to flying wings of various shapes.

The internal-combustion petrol engine used for power was greatly enlarged, its power and speed enormously increased, and its fuel more and more highly

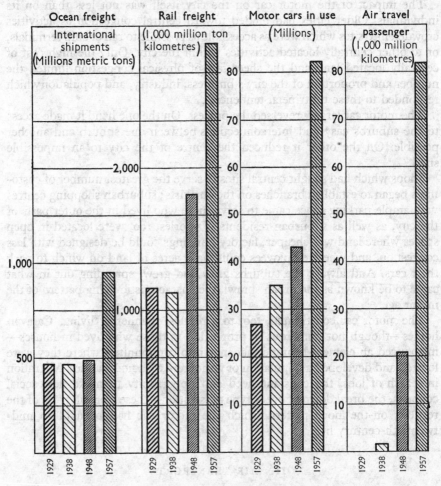

CHART XIII. Transport and Travel—Sea, Rail, Motor, Air, 1929, 1938, 1948, 1957.
Source: U.N. Statistical Yearbook, 1960.

refined. During the second world war, the jet principle of propulsion by explosive thrust instead of by whirling propeller was introduced in fighter planes, and it spread in the decade after the war to most types of military aircraft and then to commercial planes, first in combination with the 'prop' or propeller, and finally in designs first put into use by the British and the Russians, in wholly jet-powered commercial planes. (Pl. 15b.)

A constant succession of new light metals and metal alloys, immensely strong and resistant to very great heat, made it possible to build larger and larger planes and motors operating at higher and higher speeds. Means of pressurizing the passenger cabin were devised when it became practicable to fly at great altitudes. Control devices were perfected to make the plane manageable under every sort of condition—de-icers to prevent the formation of ice on the wings in passing through cold and moist air, an all-important protection against additional weight and unmanageability, wing flaps to give increased lift at slower landing speeds, reversed propellers to brake the plane on landing, automatic course-following controls, and finally radar to give the pilot eyes to see through fog and dark.

All of these developments combined to enable planes to beat their own records for speed and distance continually, and to carry larger loads more safely. For a time it appeared that the speed of sound constituted a barrier to further acceleration, but once the sound barrier was broken in 1947 there seemed no bar to greater and greater speeds. The record in January 1957 stood for the moment at 1,182 miles per hour, nearly twice the speed of sound. At almost every step military aviation paced civilian in technical developments, especially in speed and power, but in time the military advances were adapted for civilian use.

The following table indicates dramatically the rapidity with which speed and distance were increased.

Time required to cross the US from New York to the west coast		Record non-stop flights (miles)
1908	—	77·5
1911	—	460
1923	26 hr.	2,516
1933	10 hr. 5 min.	5,308
1946	7 hr. 28 min.	11,236
1955	3 hr. 45 min.	—

Prior to the first world war the aeroplane was still an experimental instrument. An airman was a daring individual. His principal activity, and often his source of income, was to manœuvre his plane for the benefit of spectators attending a fair or flight exhibition. In the first world war military aircraft were used for reconnaissance, accompanied by fighter escorts to protect their operations; only toward the close of the war were a few bombers put in the air.

Commercial aviation was the product of the inter-war years. Contrary to the expectation of many people that the aeroplane would follow the course of the motor car, there was only a limited development of private flying and the private ownership of small planes. Private plane owners included farmers overseeing large ranches in the western United States or Australia, a few groups of fishermen who used small privately operated planes to spot schools of fish, an increasing number of large corporations which used company planes to transport their executives, a few flying enthusiasts or some rich men who used private planes to reach hunting or fishing camps. For the most part civilian flying remained on a commercial basis, and grew enormously in volume in all parts of the world.

By the middle of the century air transport had become a principal means of long-distance passenger travel. In 1955 it accounted for more than a third of all passenger traffic in the United States, and in 1958 the number of trans-atlantic air travellers exceeded those crossing by surface vessel. Except for mails and some perishable cargo, planes were not yet carrying an important proportion of the world's freight.

Planes were however used for many civilian purposes other than passenger and cargo transport. They patrolled forest areas on the look-out for forest fires, prospected for minerals, conducted aerial surveys, photographed and mapped terrain, sprayed or dusted farmlands with insecticides, flew relief supplies to people marooned by flood or snow and brought medical assistance to out-of-the-way places. In the USSR they were used to carry newspaper matrices so that the same paper could appear simultaneously in national and provincial capitals. In countries such as Iran or Arabia, where populations had been isolated by difficult or impassable terrain, planes permitted rulers to maintain contact with their subjects in far-away corners of their realms and brought them a sense of national belonging. The helicopter, which required no landing field, could take off vertically and could hover close to the ground, was particularly well adapted for rescue work or to deposit forest-fire fighters behind a blazing area and then lift them safely out, as well as for mineral prospecting and for hoisting operations on construction jobs in inaccessible sites.

The importance of the aeroplane in areas of difficult terrain, great distances and sparse population was evidenced by the particularly rapid and extensive development of civil aviation in Latin America, Canada, Australia and the USSR. The oldest of the Latin American airlines, Avianca of Colombia, originally established in 1919, carried more cargo in the 1950s than any other scheduled airline in the world. In a country such as Colombia, which is broken up by mountain ranges into self-contained valleys, the plane provided a basis for national integration and development. Brazil, with its immense undeveloped territory, had some twenty airlines in operation in the 1950s flying more than 100,000 miles of route. All of the principal Latin American countries established one or more airlines and by the 1950s had ceased to depend on the foreign aid, at first German and French and later North American, with which their civil aviation had been started.

Canada started after the first world war to use aircraft for surveying and patrolling its vast forest area and maintaining communication with remote settlements. By the time that a major company, Trans-Canada Airways, was formed in 1937 to fly the main domestic routes and provide international service, Canada had been covered by a network of many small airlines spanning great distances and connecting up its sparsely settled territories. Australia, from 1921 on, depended more and more on aviation to link the cities and settled areas which ringed its vast interior desert and to reach the lonely stations of ranchers and sheep farmers in the interior. For the USSR air service offered access to its central Asian regions and brought Siberia, once a symbol of inaccessibility and distance, within reach of the capital; airlines in the Asian part of the USSR were first organized in 1924 and regular service between Moscow and eastern Siberia was established in 1930.

Many of the world's international air routes were established by the British, French, Dutch and Belgians in the 1920s and 1930s to serve their overseas empires. British Imperial Airways Ltd., chartered in 1924 and subsidized by the British government, was charged with special responsibility for developing routes throughout the Commonwealth. In the decade 1927–37 it extended its routes via Cairo and Baghdad to all parts of India, Burma, Malaya, Australia and Hong Kong, and it surveyed the routes through Africa which it began to fly after the interruption of the war. By 1931 the French were flying to Indo-China and to several parts of the French African empire. The KLM, supported from its start in 1919 largely by the Dutch government, extended its service from Europe first to Indonesia in 1924 and then to the Dutch West Indies in 1934. Belgium's Sabena airline included service to the Belgian Congo. Germany, with no overseas colonies after the first world war, concentrated on service to South America, first by Zeppelin and then also by plane, and helped to develop civil aviation in several Latin American countries.

The United States developed civil aviation more slowly than many other countries, in part because it had few inaccessible areas or overseas dominions. The principal early development in the US was for the flying of the mails. Once American commercial aviation began to boom, after Charles Lindbergh's dramatic solo flight from New York to Paris in 1927, it attracted travellers at such a rate that US airlines in 1955 were flying more passenger miles than all the rest of the world's airlines, exclusive of the USSR and China, combined. The first passenger services across the north Atlantic (1939) and the Pacific (1935) were inaugurated by the Pan American Airways.

The first commercial airlines were struggling private ventures, but soon the recognition of their national importance led to their being subsidized by governments, either directly or by such devices as a generous contract for carrying the mails. By the years after the second world war, nearly every country except the smallest had its airline, not alone for internal travel but for international travel and transport as well. A trend toward international air unions was inaugurated with the formation in 1950 of the Scandinavian Airlines System which brought into a single air-traffic organization the airlines of Sweden, Norway and the oldest of all national airlines, the Danish Air Lines established in 1918.

Concern for public safety in view of the great hazards involved in flying, together with the necessity for adequately constructed and carefully regulated airfields and the international aspects of air travel, led governments to establish regulatory bodies, and to develop rigorous national and international codes of both safety and conduct.

The first step in international air traffic control was a convention adopted in Paris in 1919, providing that private aircraft should be permitted to fly over the territories of participating states, but not extending this privilege to commercial air service. In 1944 representatives of fifty-four nations met in Chicago, USA, to seek agreement on commercial air rights and on international air traffic. Owing to a basic conflict over how far international aviation should be competitive and how far it should be regulated so as to assure a proportion of the traffic to the carriers of different countries, no general agreement was reached and the right of foreign passenger planes to fly into any territory remained subject to agreement between the two countries involved in each case.

The Chicago meeting did however produce a convention on international civil aviation covering technical regulations, standards and procedures, which was signed by virtually all companies providing international air passenger service outside the communist zone. The International Civil Aviation Organization (ICAO) with headquarters in Montreal, Canada, which was set up as a result of the Chicago conference, became a specialized agency of the United Nations. The sanitary aspects of air travel and airport conditions, of extreme importance in view of the danger of the spread of disease by air, was brought under international control by a convention signed at The Hague in 1933. After 1946 the World Health Organization took over responsibilities in this area and issued comprehensive international sanitary regulations for airports to safeguard world health.

By the mid-1950s air travel throughout the world generally conformed to common standards and procedures, and only a few of the detailed amenities associated with the flight were likely to remind the passenger where he was and by what airline he happened to be travelling.

With all these developments commercial flights became safer and people generally overcame the fear which had made them reluctant to use this mode of transport. What was at first a luxury form of travel gradually became an everyday means of reaching a destination. The volume of air passenger miles mounted steadily.

Although the record of air safety was impressive, the increasing size of the planes made disasters when they occurred more costly in lives. The collision of two large airliners over the western American desert in 1956 sent 128 people to their death. Each crash was a spectacular reminder that the air was never wholly safe.

Great precautions were essential around the principal airfields where planes landed and took off minutes apart and where a delay in schedule because of bad weather or mechanical difficulty could mean additional planes circling the field waiting for a signal to descend. The highly skilled traffic directors in the control towers, equipped with radar to watch the approaching planes as well as radios to hear the pilots' reports and give instructions, were hard pressed to keep track of the complex traffic pattern. Military aircraft travelling at supersonic speeds added to the hazards in the sky. By the late 1950s it was becoming apparent that in order to avoid disaster in the air something faster and surer than human communication and observation would have to be employed to control air traffic if the trend toward more and faster planes were to continue, and electronic controls were beginning to be used.

III. PIPELINES

The expansion of motor and air travel, together with other uses of the internal-combustion engine, required the transport of an immense amount of liquid fuel. Increasingly, this was carried by pipelines through which oil and petrol were pumped from wells or refineries to distant markets or ports. As liquid fuels gained in both absolute and relative importance, pipelines became a significant part of the world's transport system.

The first pipeline through which petroleum could be pumped was laid in Pennsylvania, USA, in 1865, six years after oil production began. As the production of oil in the United States expanded, many thousands of miles of pipelines were constructed from centres of production to distant consumption areas. In the 1950s some 80 per cent of the world's oil pipeline capacity was still in the United States, but pipelines were built to carry at least a substantial proportion of the output of the fields opened up in other areas—in Russia where pipeline construction, begun in 1917, was extensive, in the Middle East where oil from the region of the Persian Gulf was pumped to the eastern Mediterranean, in South America and south-east Asia where it was piped to the ports, and in North Africa to carry oil from the Sahara. In the 1950s lines were being built within Europe, from northern and southern European ports, to distribute the oil on which the European economy was coming increasingly to depend.

Pipelines provided the sole means of transport for natural gas which was carried long distances, mainly in the United States and Canada but also in the USSR, France and Italy. They were even beginning to be used for solid products which could be transported in powdered form, such as coal, limestone and some dry building materials.

IV. RAILWAYS

Although the revolution in transport in the twentieth century was brought by the automobile and the aeroplane, railways continued to be the largest carriers of freight and the most indispensable links in the industrial system.

Their military importance for troop transport remained great, because of the large numbers of passengers that could be carried in one load. Their relative importance in the total transport picture, however, declined.

Passengers travelled by motor car or bus for short distances and by plane for long ones. Railways found their passenger travel dropping off; they reduced their passenger service in order not to lose money running half-empty trains, but they thereby discouraged passenger travel further by the absence of trains at convenient times; on the less travelled routes, railways abandoned passenger service altogether.

For freight, also, motor transport competed effectively with rail for short hauls, especially since a motor lorry could be loaded at the point of shipment without having to be reloaded at the freight terminal, and could deliver direct to its destination. Goods shipped in small lots required less handling when sent by lorry than when they had to be packed into a large goods wagon with many other shipments. Savings in handling often meant greater speed from shipping point to destination and less damage to cargo, and thus gave the lorry an advantage over the train in the shipping of perishables and breakables. High-value freight which was light, especially that which was also perishable, could be transported advantageously by air. At the other end of the scale, water transport had always offered serious competition to rail for bulky non-perishable items such as iron ore or coal, which did not need to be transported rapidly.

Although railways remained the backbone of the industrial transport system their position deteriorated steadily and they were at considerable difficulty to keep solvent. They resorted to a number of measures to improve their operation as new technical developments permitted, though their basic technical features remained unchanged. More powerful locomotives, specially designed carriages and more heavily ballasted road-beds permitted greater speeds on streamlined trains. Lines were electrified, first in the vicinity of major cities, then more generally. Bit by bit, the oil-burning diesel engine replaced the steam locomotive. (Pl. 12a, 12b.)

In some regions the extension of the railway during the twentieth century was a means of opening new territory and of creating important transport links. The trans-Siberian railway completed in 1917 joined the centres of European Russia with its Pacific port. The Berlin-to-Baghdad railway, projected by Germany in the years before the first world war, was finally completed in 1940. The British vision of a through route from Cairo to Cape Town still lacked many links at mid-century, although there had been considerable railway construction in connection with the mine operations of the Rhodesias, the Congo and South Africa. Among the greatest additions to the world's railway mileage in the first half of the twentieth century was the network of lines which opened up Manchuria. Major railway developments in China continued under the Chinese People's Republic with the construction of a route westward into Sinkiang.

(a)

[*Pro Helvetia*

II   CIVIL ENGINEERING

    (a) *R. Maillart, concrete bridge on the Salginatobel, Canton Grisons, Switzerland, 1930*

    (b) *American turnpike, near Dallas, Texas*

(b)

[*Photo USIS*

[SNCF
(a)

(b)

12

TRANSPORT I

(a) *Express train*, 1905
(b) *'Trans-Europ-Express'*, 1961
(c) *The 'Metropolitain'*, *Paris*, 1938

[*Swiss Tourism*

(c)

[RATP

13   TRANSPORT II

    (a) *The S.S.* Lusitania, 31,550 *tons,* 1907
    (b) *The M.S.* Rotterdam, 38,650 *tons,* 1958
    (c) *The oil tanker* Sivella, 80,000 *tons,* 1963

(a)

14 TRANSPORT III

(a) *The Motor Club inaugural run to Brighton, June 9, 1907. (Photograph shows Miss Evie Greene and Mr Huntley Walker on a 6-cylinder)*

(b) *Austin Mini, early 1960's*

(b)

Railways thus continued to afford a means of opening new areas and providing an essential element in the industrial base for the underdeveloped areas in the twentieth century as they had done for the industrially advanced countries in the nineteenth century. Even in these regions, however, the aeroplane often preceded the locomotive and roads were as likely to be the penetrators as were railway lines. In some non-industrial areas which passed from animal transport directly to air and motor travel, it appeared unlikely that railways would ever be constructed.

A major aspect of the problem of railways in the twentieth century was that of the rates to be charged. Both where railways were government ventures and where they were private companies operating under government regulation as in the USA, and in Britain until nationalization in 1947, the rate structure was based upon a balanced load—i.e. a balance between long and short haul, between low-value heavy freight and high-value light shipments, and between small and large consignments. Under this system some items that were more profitable to carry balanced the less profitable, and bulky goods were transported at a cost which was not prohibitive.

Commercial road vehicles, initially without regulation, were under no compulsion to carry a balanced load. They could skim the cream, hauling the profitable items and leaving the railways to haul the less profitable ones. The railways, in turn, were not in a position to raise their rates on the remaining items in order to make their operation profitable, both because of regulation and because of the economic impact of such a move. This dilemma was at the heart of the rate-making difficulties confronting all railways as motor transport grew.

This problem presented itself in all industrial countries. Everywhere policy had to balance two considerations and to work out an effective compromise in the national interest. All governments recognized the importance of keeping the railways in vigorous operation, if for no other reason than that they were an indispensable part of the military structure, a strong reserve which could not be allowed to deteriorate. On the other hand the new and flexible motor transport had obvious advantages, which in the interest of the national economy should be encouraged and utilized. In the 1930s countries began to regulate their motor transport as they had their railways or they incorporated all rail, road and other transport into one single state-regulated system. Socialist economies sought a balanced use and development of their several means of transport through the application of their economic plans.

But railways were far from becoming obsolete in the course of the first half of the century even though motor, pipeline and air transport largely supplanted them for short hauls and in the carrying of passengers, small shipments, perishables and liquid fuels. They continued to be the most effective means of mass transport for large consignments and they remained a main form of transport, especially in countries with extensive continental territory. In 1955 the railways of the USSR carried more than four-fifths of the total freight transported. Even in the United States, with the world's most highly developed motor transport and road system, nearly half of all freight still travelled by rail.

V. WATER TRANSPORT

Ocean transport remained the chief means of overseas shipment, and ocean tonnage kept pace with the expansion of production throughout the world. Its vital importance to the life of all industrial countries was amply manifested during the two world wars, when the sinking of merchant shipping became one of the most crucial of military operations and the one on which much of the outcome depended. Although a steadily growing proportion of travellers crossed the oceans by air rather than by surface vessel, the total increase in international travel kept the number of ocean travellers growing, and freight continued to be sent almost wholly by surface, since only the most valuable and perishable cargo could bear the cost of shipment by air.

Inland waterways, which in many places had been the major means of moving heavy loads from one place to another before the advent of the railway, declined in importance with the growth of rail and motor transport. But the construction of canals as parts of comprehensive river development schemes gave inland water transport new prominence. Such canals formed important parts of the industrial development programmes of countries with large river systems, notably in the USSR, whose network of inland waterways was the longest in the world, in India and especially in the Chinese People's Republic. Improvement of port facilities increased the efficiency of the older inland waterways, notably in Europe and North America, and helped them to maintain their relative position among alternative means of transport.

The principal technical developments in water transport, after the original introduction of the steam vessel, had come in the late nineteenth century, when the compound steam engine and the steam turbine permitted a great increase in the speed, size and economy of ocean vessels. During the twentieth century, the substitution of oil for coal to produce steam and the introduction of the diesel engine increased the sailing range and economy of the vessels and freed space in the hull formerly occupied by the bulkier fuel, thus making it possible for a given vessel to carry more cargo. By the opening of the second world war virtually all naval vessels, ocean liners and most freighters either used oil as fuel for steam engines or were diesel-operated. Motor and diesel-electric vessels were widely used on inland waterways and high-speed vessels which employed the hydroplane principle to lift them partially out of the water were beginning to be introduced. (Pl. 13a, 13b, 13c.)

Among naval vessels the submarine represented the newest development of the period. First extensively developed in its modern form by the Germans as a means by which a largely land-locked power could challenge the supremacy of the British on the seas, the underwater vessel became part of the fleets of all naval powers in the period between the two wars. Through the years, the submarine's range, speed, ability to submerge rapidly and other aspects of manœuvrability were greatly enhanced. The submarine was the first type of vessel in which atomic fuel was successfully employed as a source of power. Among surface naval vessels the aircraft carrier represented the chief innovation. The battleship, once the queen of the fleet, proved vulnerable to submarine and air attack and by the end of the second world war had become largely obsolete.

For general civilian use the petrol or diesel engine in small craft played somewhat the same role as the internal-combustion engine in the motor car. The small marine engine transformed all types of fishing craft, from the one-man boat which made the rounds of fish or lobster traps to the trawlers which dragged the bottom with great nets. Pleasure boating took on many of the features of pleasure driving. With lightweight outboard motors which could be attached to small open boats, or with built-in engines in motor boats of all sizes, thousands of people went fishing, travelled the bays and shores and rivers, and enjoyed the sea air. When the British troops were driven to the beaches of Dunkirk after the fall of France in 1940, it was the little boats which poured out of British rivers and bays that effected their rescue and averted a complete disaster.

VI. RAPID TRANSIT

The enormous cities so characteristic of the twentieth century depended not only on transport from without but rapid transit within, for hundreds of thousands of people to travel to and from work or from place to place on business or pleasure.

At the turn of the century traffic within western cities was being carried by electric tramways, running on rails through the city streets and generally supplied with power by an overhead cable. Many of the largest cities—London, Paris, New York, Boston, Chicago—already recognized that surface tramways could provide neither the volume of transport nor the speed required by the growing city, and had started to construct elevated tracks and underground railways. The first section of the London Underground was opened in 1863, the Budapest underground railway, first of its kind on the European continent, was opened in 1896, that of Glasgow in 1895 and the Paris Metro and Boston subway in 1898. Chicago put a high-speed elevated electric railway into operation in 1895. New York, which came to exceed all other cities in the length of its underground and elevated rapid-transit system and the volume of passengers carried, ran its first underground train in 1904. As each major city grew in size, it constructed or extended its rapid-transit system. The construction of the Moscow underground in the 1920s called forth much national effort and enthusiasm, not only for its utilitarian purpose but as a symbol of the fact that Moscow had become a great modern city. The volume of traffic told the story of how the life of these cities was dependent on their rapid-transit services. The underground railway systems of New York, Paris, London and Moscow in the 1950s each carried average loads of two to five million passengers a day. (Pl. 12c.)

While electrically operated underground systems were being extended and carrying ever greater loads, surface street railways declined. Tracks in the middle of city streets interfered with other traffic; their extension to new areas as the city expanded was costly. From the 1920s on, the motor bus offered a much more flexible alternative. Paris abandoned its tramways in 1937; London trams were gradually replaced until they had disappeared by 1952.

With the steady increase in individual car ownership, private transport in the 1950s competed seriously with public surface travel, especially in the United States where private car operation was most general. In some cities, ironically, the very increase in mobility which the motor car brought to countless families and individuals reduced the mobility of others by making public transport unprofitable and leading to high costs and deterioration of service. Even where bus service was maintained as part of a unified municipal or state transport system operated in the public interest, traffic congestion resulting from the presence of private cars lowered the efficiency of all public surface transport.

VII. THE BICYCLE

Though the aeroplane brought the most dramatic change in the spatial relations among men, and motor transport entered most widely into the economic patterns and the personal lives of the people of the industrial countries, the humble bicycle remained an essential mode of transport in Europe and Asia up to the middle of the century. Easily tripling on level ground the speed at which a person could walk, while reducing the effort required, the bicycle enlarged the individual's range and gave him a flexible means of getting to work or to a shop, delivering a message, policing an area, visiting a friend or reaching a fishing stream. European workmen by the hundreds of thousands bicycled to work; farmers in many areas used bicycles to reach a shop, a distant field, a neighbour's home or a nearby town; families used these vehicles for Sunday outings, sometimes on lanes especially provided alongside the motor vehicle roadway. At mid-century the bicycle was still the most numerous class of vehicle on the roads of Britain, France, Germany, Holland, Italy, Belgium and Denmark.

In Asian countries the bicycle represented the first widespread application of mechanical principles to transport in areas where human beings supplied draught power. The bicycle cab or pedicab replaced the man-drawn rickshaw as the principal means of public transport in such cities as Djakarta, Singapore, Bangkok, Rangoon and Taipeh, and bicycles by the millions provided the principal alternative to foot-travel in India; bicycle manufacture rated as one of the key industries under that country's economic development plan.

With the development of the petrol motor, bicycles also were motorized. Heavy motor cycles, sometimes equipped with sidecars and having the essential qualities of small automobiles, were used for police-work and as a sports vehicle or means of getting to work. In the period after the second world war small auxiliary motors began to be used extensively on ordinary bicycles to increase their speed and ease of operation without essentially altering their character as simple, light, easily handled, easily stored, personal means of getting about.

By mid-century the bicycle had been virtually driven off the dangerous, high-speed, automobile-filled highways and streets of the United States and Canada and was used mainly for children's recreation. But it was still indispensable to many people in Europe, as the Italian film *Bicycle Thief* (1947) poignantly recorded, and it was the first mechanical possession and the first step in acquiring the mobility so characteristic of the modern age for people emerging from poverty or isolation in non-industrialized parts of the world.

VIII. THE SPACE AGE

By the late 1950s the 'air age' was beginning to yield to the 'space age'.

There had long been speculation as to whether life could and did exist elsewhere within the earth's solar system, or in the universe, with the planet Mars the principal candidate for such a habitat. A trip to the moon was a favourite fantasy; Jules Verne wrote *From the Earth to the Moon* in 1885 and one of the earliest motion pictures was Méliès' *A Trip to the Moon*. But when science fiction writers began to produce stories of space travel, and a few serious scientists began to insist that the concept was not impossible, the space age began to dawn. By 1957 it had become a reality.

As part of the Universal Geophysical Year 1957–58, the USA and the USSR both announced the intention to place man-made moons in orbit around the earth for scientific observation. That such a proposal could be made was the measure of transport advance. The proposal to place an earth satellite in orbit rested on the application of the rocket techniques developed in connection with the jet propulsion used in flight and by the German V2 rockets in the second world war. A rocket system which would travel the necessary distance to escape the earth's gravitational pull was an extension of the system which was filling the air with familiar jet-planes.

When the Russians placed the first *sputnik* in orbit on October 4, 1957, the sense that man had taken one of the biggest steps in human history electrified the world. When a few weeks later another *sputnik* travelled aloft with a live dog on board, the question became not whether but when man would be next.

In the following years a succession of United States and Soviet satellites and rockets, launched into space and returned to earth with experimental animals and scientific equipment or sending back radio and television pictures, provided much data on temperature, radioactivity and other conditions, and prepared the way for astronauts and cosmonauts to travel into space. (Pl. 3b.)

CHAPTER XI

COMMUNICATIONS

IN 1955 a person almost anywhere on the globe could send a telegram or speak by telephone to practically any other place, to ships at sea, trains or automobiles on land and planes in the air. He could hear messages broadcast from the Arctic or Antarctic regions or the Antipodes. Most people in North America, many in Europe, the USSR or Japan, and a rapidly growing number elsewhere, could view on television events hundreds and even thousands of miles away. The daily press offered stories and pictures received by teletype and telephoto. If a citizen visited his local airport he could see on the radar screen planes hidden by cloud or dark. Wherever these communication facilities existed, space and time had virtually been eliminated.

I. DEVELOPMENT OF MEDIA OF COMMUNICATION

These developments were foreshadowed before the end of the nineteenth century, for most of the basic elements that entered into the twentieth-century systems of communication had been discovered or tested experimentally and some were in extensive use. The telegraph, already in use in 1900 for half a century, linked major centres, not only over land where telegraph wires followed most rail routes and often extended beyond them, but by submarine cables across the Atlantic and between North and South America. The telephone, invented in 1876 by Alexander Graham Bell, had been generally introduced in the principal cities of Europe and North America, and in rural areas of Germany where it connected more than 800 rural post offices; by 1900 there were already 1,355,900 telephone sets installed in the United States. Marconi had received a patent for wireless telegraphy in 1896 and succeeded in sending a wireless signal across the English Channel in 1899 and from England to Newfoundland in 1901.

Experiments in the transmission of a visual image were being conducted in Germany, the US and France and, though the experiments did not reach a practical stage for many years, a scanning disc for transmitting pictures had been patented in Germany in 1884. Photography was well developed and devices both for taking and for projecting motion pictures had been introduced. Thomas A. Edison's 'kinetoscope' in which a series of pictures whirring past a peephole gave the impression of motion had been offered as an entertainment attraction in 1894; the Lumière brothers had designed a 'cinematoscope' and Thomas Armat's 'vitascope' had projected these pictures to a screen in 1895. A number of methods had been developed for recording sound by means of grooves cut in the surface of a cylinder or disc and reproduced through a needle which activated a diaphragm; Edison had received a patent in 1877 and by 1897 the manufacture of records had become a commercial success.

It required much research and development, however, to produce the modern telephone from the crude instrument which could carry the voice clearly only short distances, to change the wireless from a vehicle for transmitting dots and dashes into a medium for carrying the modulations of voice or musical instrument, and to bring the scanned picture or live event on to the television screen.

Many of the basic devices which were to permit the sounds and images not only to be transmitted but handled economically in great volume were also known or envisaged and had been put to use in telegraph and telephone systems. The essential problems were to connect the right sender with the right receiver, to carry many different messages simultaneously over a limited number of wires or air-waves, and to do this swiftly, accurately, if possible automatically, and without excessive cost.

At the opening of the century the manual telephone switchboard with cords to connect the calling and receiving lines was already in use, with multiple termini for each line to the appropriate socket in each operator's panel, signal lights to indicate that a line desired a call and busy signals to prevent two operators from plugging into the same line. Automatic switching, using the electromagnetic principle which continued to form the basis for automatic switching up to the 1950s, had been developed experimentally and put to limited commercial use in 1892. (Pl. 16a, 16b.)

Methods for carrying extra circuits on the same wires had also been developed. The 'phantom' or third circuit carried by two pairs of wires with each pair of wires serving as a side of the phantom circuit was worked out in the 1880s. The 'carrier' principle, which made it possible to use frequencies above the voice range to carry the voice signals, was applied to telephony by French inventors in the 1890s, although the principle was not put to commercial use until 1918. British scientists had studied the special transmission properties of the coaxial circuit, i.e. a copper tube with a single wire centrally supported within it.

The great technical improvements in communication came about gradually and steadily during the twentieth century. These developments lengthened tremendously the distances through which the voice could be transmitted clearly, improved the quality of transmission, permitted the transmission of visual images as well as sound, increased the number of messages that could be carried over a single route in a given time, provided increasingly elaborate interconnections among senders and receivers, made operations automatic and reduced cost.

While much of the development involved the refinement of the basic nineteenth-century inventions, one new invention was of revolutionary significance, the three-element electron or vacuum tube invented by Lee De Forest in 1906. This tube, by amplifying a very weak current, made it possible to reinforce telephonic impulses as they were carried over long distances, to magnify radio waves to audibility and to receive television and radar images and sonar echoes. By the 1950s a second revolutionary invention, the transistor, developed by W. J. Brattain and John Bardeen in 1948, was beginning to open yet another stage in the development of swift and economical communications. This tiny amplifier, using differences in atomic structure to create an electron current, performed the functions of the vacuum tube without heat and thus with only a hundred-thousandth of the power required by the latter. It permitted the construction of electronic apparatus of miniature size.

The various technical developments in the fields of communication were closely interrelated, whether they involved telegraphy, telephony or radio broadcasting, transmission by wire or air, or the reproduction and transmission of visual images or sound.

It was the vacuum tube which first effectively conquered the problem of distance. By 1914 the original De Forest tube had been improved to the point where it could be used for repeaters inserted at frequent intervals in a line to amplify the current and pass it over the next segment. The length of a wire circuit could thus be extended indefinitely, with no loss of volume. By this means a coast-to-coast telephone circuit across the United States was opened in 1915. Long-distance communication by air was established simultaneously. Transocean radiotelegraph service from San Francisco to Honolulu was inaugurated in 1912 and in 1915 listeners in Paris and Hawaii heard a voice speaking from Arlington, Virginia, USA.

There remained however the problem of distortion. As sound travels distortions may come in and be amplified by each repeater. The invention in 1927 of a device for reducing distortion known as the negative feedback was second in importance only to the vacuum tube itself in permitting voice or music to travel great distances without losing its original quality. Many other devices to suppress distortion contributed to the continuous improvement in the fidelity with which sound could be carried over great distances.

The revolution in communication came into full force in the 1920s. Radio broadcasting dates from 1920 when a Pittsburgh, USA, station broadcast the results of the presidential election. A commercial overseas radiotelephone was opened between Britain and the United States in 1927 followed within five years by services from Germany, Britain and the United States to South America, from Britain to Australia, and from the United States across the Pacific to Japan and the Dutch East Indies. Radiotelephone service to ships at sea was inaugurated in 1920 and became common not only on ocean liners but on many small vessels in coastal waters and on lakes and rivers. The first round-the-world telephone conversation was conducted in 1935. Radiophones became indispensable in both civilian and military aircraft.

The electrical transmission of visual images also reached the level of commercial use at the same time. By means of a light-sensitive electronic cell used to scan a picture and the transmission of the resulting electrical impulses, pictures were 'telephotoed' from one point to another by either wire or air. Pictures began to be sent across the Atlantic in 1924 and thereafter the world's press carried news pictures of distant events as promptly as the stories to which they referred. Successful experiments also established the feasibility of television. After considerable study and experiment in Great Britain, the United States and Germany, the basic patent on the iconoscope, or television camera tube, was issued in 1923. Television programmes were broadcast experimentally in these three countries from 1927 on, some for public reception in these countries and the USSR in the 1930s.

Later developments steadily improved and elaborated all these techniques. For radiotransmission, frequency modulation supplemented the older method of amplitude modulation in the 1930s. For both radio and wire transmission it became possible to utilize higher and higher frequencies, thus exploiting the potentialities of the transmission media much more fully. Television apparatus for both sending and receiving was entering commercial use on the eve of the second world war, and after the war television sets spread like wildfire not only in the USA, Canada and Great Britain, but in Europe, USSR, Japan; within ten years television was introduced in Australia, Latin American countries, Thailand, the Philippines, Algeria and Iraq, and colour transmission began.

Progressive improvements in vacuum tubes made more accurate, dependable and economical all the forms of communication which depended on this essential device. The tube's life was lengthened from six weeks to more than ten years and the power required to heat the filaments was reduced to one-tenth of that required in the early models. When the transistor began to replace the vacuum tube in the 1950s, the far greater durability and economy of this tiny instrument promised to make all types of long-distance communication still less costly and more sure.

II. EXPANSION IN THE USE OF COMMUNICATIONS MEDIA

The use of each new means of communication expanded at an astronomical rate. From the moment of its introduction the telephone grew by leaps and bounds. In the 1950s at least a dozen countries had over a million telephones each. In proportion to population the best-supplied countries were the United States with one telephone for every three persons, Sweden with one for every three and a half, and Canada and Switzerland with one for every four persons. Canada led in the amount of use made of the telephone system, with an average of 418 calls per person in 1954 as compared with 393 in the United States and 334 in Sweden. In 1954, 56 per cent of the world's 91,000,000 telephones were in the United States and the number was still growing rapidly, but the fastest rate of increase during the preceding five years had been in Asia and South America.

By 1953 international wire telephone circuits connected the European countries and many non-European countries or territories. Some 180 countries and dependencies were linked by point-to-point radiotelegraph channels and 110 were joined by radiotelephones. Telephone wires were laid under the Atlantic in 1956.

Radio broadcasting, inaugurated early in the 1920s in the United States, Great Britain and Germany, spread rapidly through Europe, the USSR, the British Commonwealth and Japan. By the late 1940s only a few remote islands and African territories lacked a local broadcasting service. In 1955 radio sets for the first time outnumbered copies of daily newspapers sold around the world; radios numbered an estimated 257,000,000 and newspapers 255,000,000. The greatest concentration of sets was in the United States, which had half of the world total or some 760 sets per 1,000 of the population, two and a quarter times the number of copies of the daily press. The number of radios also exceeded the copies of the daily press in Canada, Mexico, several Latin American and Caribbean areas, and in a number of African areas where literacy was low and newspapers scarce. European press circulation exceeded the number of radio sets except for Austria, Czechoslovakia and Hungary, as was also the case in most of the countries of Asia.

But there were over 215 sets per 1,000 people in Australia and New Zealand, 185 in Europe, 95 in the USSR, 60 in South America, 15 in Asia and 10 in Africa. Moreover, the number of sets was increasing rapidly in the less well-supplied areas of Africa, South America and Asia. The UN Conference on Freedom of Information in 1948 adopted a resolution saying that 'the possession of receiving sets is necessary to assure a really free flow of information and is in no way a luxury'.

Television's rate of growth was even more spectacular. In the decade after the second world war more than 30 countries put regular television service into operation, and by 1955 some 45,000,000 TV receiving sets were in use. Although four-fifths of these were still in the United States, TV services extended to nearly all parts of Great Britain, where there were 4,000,000 receivers, eight European countries participated in a programme exchange network known as Eurovision, the USSR was rapidly expanding the number of its stations and was regularly broadcasting all its first-run films to more than 700,000 receivers largely in clubs and centres, and Japan's stations and sets mushroomed from their start in 1953. TV was expanding more rapidly even than radio in Latin America and it was passing beyond the experimental stage in one country after another in every continent.

The spectacular increase in the volume of communication by telegraph, telephone, radio and television depended upon developments which permitted many messages to be carried simultaneously over the same route and which made their routing automatic. Phantom circuits increased the capacity of each four wires by 50 per cent, but carrier systems modulating the voice to a series of different higher frequencies were able to carry as many as sixteen simultaneous telephone conversations on a single pair of open wires and many more on cables. The coaxial circuits, introduced in Germany and the United States in the 1930s, used very much wider frequency bands, extending over as

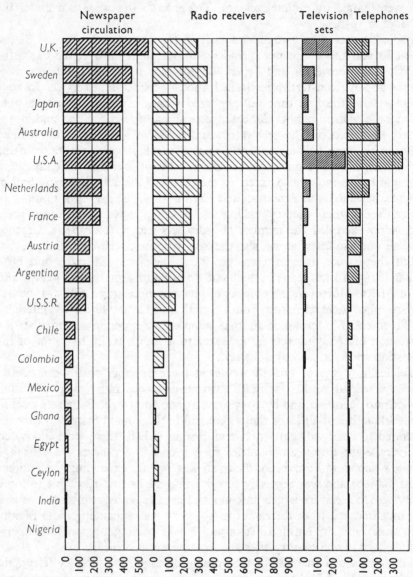

Number per 1,000 population

CHART XIV.   Press, Radio, Television, Telephone, Number per 1,000 Population. Selected Countries, 1958.

Source: *U.N. Statistical Yearbook,* 1960.

much as three megacycles (3,000,000 cycles) per second, and provided as many as 600 two-way voice channels on a pair of coaxials. Improved coaxials introduced in 1952 provided a frequency band of nearly eight megacycles and could carry 1,800 telephone channels or 64,800 one-way telegraph messages on a single pair. Microwave radio beams, travelling like a searchlight in a direct line-of-sight path, were used for voice transmission across the English Channel in the early 1930s. By 1951 a microwave radio-relay system beamed between a succession of high points across the United States provided 3,600 telephone channels in each direction. The hollow wave-guide conductor which would transmit wave bands up to thousands of megacycles was in an experimental stage by 1955.

The coming of television placed a heavy load on transmission facilities, for each television circuit required the equivalent of 600 telephone or tele-photo circuits. Coaxial circuits capable of transmitting 1,800 telephone con-versations simultaneously could, instead, carry three television circuits in each direction and the 3,600 circuit radio-relay beam could carry six. The demands of television stimulated the expansion of multi-channel facilities.

With these developments, the use of wire or air for transmission became almost interchangeable. Telephone calls were necessarily based on radio-transmission when made to or from moving vehicles, such as police cars, taxicabs, trains, ships or planes. But in spite of the existence of regular radio-telephone service across the Atlantic for nearly thirty years, the first trans-atlantic telephone cable, equipped at 40-mile intervals with vacuum-tube repeater-amplifiers designed to operate at the bottom of the sea for twenty years went into operation in 1956 and similar cables were being laid from the west coast of the United States to Alaska and Hawaii. Such cables were designed to avoid the atmospheric disturbances that sometimes interfered with communication by radiotelephone as well as to increase the number of channels. Of the eight complete transcontinental paths by which telephone messages could be carried or radio and television programmes relayed across the United States in 1954, four were principally open wire routes, two were wire cables, one was a coaxial cable and the eighth was a microwave relay. Many radio listeners in Europe, especially where atmospheric conditions often made radio reception poor, as in Switzerland, tuned in through a set attached to their telephone on programmes broadcast over the air, picked up and piped to their sets by wire. Wired reception was widely used in the USSR and eastern Europe.

The multiplication of communication channels and of the number of persons using them enormously complicated the problem of connecting the right sender with the right receiver and made the development of successful automatic switching imperative. Without automatic switching the US tele-phone system would have required half a million operatives to man the switchboards by the 1950s and other countries with a high *per capita* telephone service would have needed corresponding numbers. By the mid-1950s 77 per cent of the world's telephones were automatic as compared with 15 per cent in the 1920s, and most of the telegraph messages between major centres were handled automatically. While the bulk of automatic telephone switching was for local calls, direct long-distance dialling was rapidly joining local automatic operation.

A wide variety of switching mechanisms was developed and put into use in different countries, the most flexible and widely adopted being the cross-bar system. The objective in automatic switch design was to develop devices which would take an incoming message, determine quickly what circuits were open, make the connection and then return to position ready to serve the next call while the first was still going on. Automatic recording devices were also necessary wherever an individual charge had to be made for the call or message. Virtually all automatic switching systems continued to use electro-magnetic devices, although electronic devices could perform the same functions more rapidly. Because of their bulkiness, power consumption, tendency to wear out and less than complete reliability, vacuum tubes were not used in switching mechanisms. The transistor, however, had none of these disadvantages and could be used for instantaneous electronic selection comparable to that in an electronic computer.

The advance in technology and great expansion in volume brought spectacular reductions in the cost of communication, especially over long distances. It cost one-seventh as much to call from coast to coast across the United States in the 1950s as it had in the 1920s; in dollars of comparable value it cost less than a tenth. The reduction in cost was largely a product of the great multiplication in the number of circuits carried over the same medium, for the larger the number the lower the cost per circuit. Lower costs for the complicated equipment required at each end of a carrier system to transpose the voice to high frequencies and then to restore it to normal further contributed to general reductions in cost. So long as the terminal equipment was very costly, carrier systems with their multiple circuits could only be used for long distance. With lower terminal costs, carrier systems became practicable for short-distance and rural circuits and for inter-office trunk lines in metropolitan areas. The costs of radio and television receiving sets dropped with both mass production and technical improvements. In some places, receiving sets pre-tuned to a single or limited number of wavelengths were made and distributed at especially low cost in connection with radiodiffusion educational programmes or to permit the reception of official broadcasts.

III. USES OF COMMUNICATIONS MEDIA

The communications systems were put to a myriad of uses. In addition to placing the twentieth-century individual in contact with other individuals, on his own or their initiative, they exposed him to vast bodies of material brought to him for an endless range of purposes.

Communications media were as essential as machinery to the carrying on of a business. By telephone, customers placed orders and companies made sales and reports; managers received and issued instructions; headquarters offices could know at all times what was going on throughout an organization; a bank could compare a signature by telephoto; a factory manager could observe the works by closed-circuit television; a taxi-cab dispatcher could direct a fleet of cabs in response to calls; a spotting plane could guide fishermen to schools of fish. Every form of telegraph, telephone, radio and television was built into the structure and daily operation of every sort of business, government and military activity, and into the lives of people.

Besides serving constantly in the daily routine the media of communication provided an emergency resource of greatest importance. Police could be summoned to the scene of an accident or crime or could broadcast the description of a fugitive; a sheep farmer at a lonely Australian station could summon a doctor of the flying medical service; a ship in distress could call for aid. The ability to maintain communication made scientific bases practicable in the polar regions; arctic expeditions no longer vanished into silence, to emerge months later or fail to return.

By means of the rapid communications techniques a world-wide network for the collection and dissemination of news kept the people of the world constantly informed of what was happening everywhere. In addition the use of the mass communications systems to create and maintain a mass market subjected the twentieth-century individual to an endless stream of advertising especially in the countries where radio and television operated commercially.

The mass media also provided a channel for mass education, both when they were deliberately used to supplement the more usual forms of instruction and as the by-product of broadcasting for entertainment or other purposes. They placed a powerful instrument of propaganda in the hands of governments which chose to use their communications systems as instruments of control. They provided a large part of the entertainment which twentieth-century man came to enjoy and furnished the basis for vast new entertainment industries. They played their part too in the shaping of twentieth-century artistic expression, both by the instruments which they placed in the hands of producers and in the mass audiences which they reached.*

IV. COLLECTION AND DISSEMINATION OF NEWS

The public function most intimately bound up with the systems of communication and responsible for much of their expansion was the collection and dissemination of news. The instrumentalities for this purpose constituted

* For discussion of the communications media as sources of entertainment see Chapter XXVII, Leisure; for their educational role see Chapter XXVI, Education; in relation to the arts see Chapter XXXI, Literature and the Arts.

one of the most central, multi-faceted and powerful institutions in twentieth-century life.

1. *News channels*

The world's news travelled over telegraph and telephone networks, by international submarine cables linked to these networks and by radio communication systems, both point-to-point radio telegraph and telephone channels and radio broadcasts beamed to broad areas. News pictures were conveyed by telephoto and television.

Areas differed greatly, however, in the number of communications channels which were available, the cost of using them and the way in which their use was regulated. All of these factors affected the volume and kind of news originating in and reaching different parts of the world.

London was and remained the principal centre through which news flowed by reason of the early leadership assumed by Britain in laying down cable links, the wide connections with empire and commonwealth areas, low telegraph and cable rates, the extensive coverage of the British news-gathering agency, Reuter, and the use of London as the European distributing point by North American news services. American and French facilities and services were next in extent and range. The USSR maintained extensive internal and external facilities and an organization for both the collection and dissemination of news. Germany, whose international news service had been one of the oldest and best established at the opening of the century, lost its position as a news centre during the first world war.

In general the European and North American centres of population were much better equipped with facilities for the collection and dissemination of news than less industrially developed regions, although by mid-century very few areas were wholly lacking in wire or radiotelegraph or radiotelephone connections over which news could be transmitted to and from the outside world. Most of the modern cables that provided many circuits and could carry the voice, as well as most of the teleprinter and telephoto circuits, the extremely rapid, electronically operated telegraph equipment, and the principal radiotelegraph and radiotelephone connections, linked the major centres.

Many non-industrial areas remained without sufficient communications channels to permit an adequate dispatch and receipt of news. Limited telegraph systems equipped with slow hand-keys continued to offer the only wire link to a number of non-industrial areas. Up to the middle of the century such countries as Burma or Liberia had only one or two links with the outside world, although many of the less well-served countries were rapidly expanding their radiotelegraph and telephone services. During the period after the second world war several of the countries of Latin America and the Middle East increased their international links more than tenfold in the course of five years.

15   TRANSPORT IV

  (a) *Wright Brothers' aeroplane, Kitty Hawk, North Carolina, December 14, 1903*
  (b) *Jet airliner, Boeing 707, 1958*

(a) [*PTT Muse...*]

16 THE TELEPHONE

    (a) *Telephone exchange, Berlin, 1912*
    (b) *Automatic telephone exchange: Crossbar CP* 400, c. 1960

(b) [*Ericss...*]

Within each country collection and dissemination of news depended on internal communications networks which differed greatly in their adequacy. The major centres and many minor points in the UK, USA, European and Commonwealth countries were linked by teleprinter, telephone and radiotelegraph services. Most industrial countries depended on teleprinters for the transmission of a large proportion of their news, but the USSR relied chiefly on radiotelegraphy. Most other countries, as well as the vast majority of non self-governing territories, lacked adequate teleprinter services or other two-way means of transmitting news rapidly within the country. In the absence of such internal lines of communication, news sometimes did not penetrate beyond the capital city and most of what reached the outside world originated there.

The inadequacy of established international and internal channels was partly overcome by the direct-voice broadcasting of news to areas which lacked wire or point-to-point radio communication. Here again London remained the principal news centre. The British Broadcasting Corporation beamed news broadcasts overseas which any listener with a short-wave receiving set could hear; in the 1950s it was sending out these broadcasts in some 46 languages. News broadcasts from other sources, however, began to reach many areas after the second world war. Moscow radio sent out foreign broadcasts in 35 languages and radio-Peking was also heard beyond its national borders; the Voice of America broadcast in some 38 languages, the Italian radio in 34 and Vatican City in 25; radio-India used one of its 3 major transmission facilities for news broadcasts to Asia and Africa in a dozen languages; radio-Cairo reached parts of Africa and the Arab countries; broadcasts in a dozen or more languages also went out from France, Spain, Hungary, Czechoslovakia and Turkey, and in a smaller number of languages from Belgium, Bulgaria, Austria, the Netherlands, Canada, Israel and elsewhere. How widely these broadcasts were heard depended on reception facilities. Where receiving sets were few or where wired redistribution systems or sets pre-tuned to certain wavelengths were extensively used, foreign broadcasts could not penetrate to many listeners.

Within countries, radio news broadcasts supplemented other methods of news dissemination; they became the principal news channel where other communication facilities were inadequate, the press was not well developed or literacy was low. News broadcasts by the national radio service were picked up by the press, as in India where local papers depended on the radio-India broadcasts for much of the news which they printed. In many countries radio news was listened to in villages where no printed press existed. But although news broadcasting could disseminate news to places where facilities were otherwise inadequate, it could not solve the problem of news collection. Where two-way channels were lacking, news might flow in but it could not be gathered and sent out.

The content of news tended to be heavily weighted with material originating in the major centres. One of the problems which most concerned Indian journalists, for example, was how to develop a flow of news from neighbouring Asian countries instead of relying so heavily on the usual sources of foreign news which supplied a disproportionate amount of news from Europe. Not only the source but the point of view tended to be that of the established centres. The nature of the vast news-generating and distributing machinery meant, inevitably, that those who controlled it set their stamp upon the content, whether consciously or unconsciously. The international news services were especially important in this respect.

2. News agencies

The international collection and distribution of news was in the hands of a few great news services. At the opening of the century four of these agencies divided the world among them. Reuter of Great Britain gathered news originating in the British empire, the Far East and Egypt, and supplied these areas with news from abroad; Agence Havas of France covered the French empire and Latin America in the same way; Wolff of Germany supplied news to and from the rest of Europe; the Associated Press of the United States operated in North America. These four agencies, which had come into existence with the development of the telegraph and the commercial press in the middle of the nineteenth century, exchanged news by mutual agreement and redistributed it to the areas which they served.

The pattern of exclusive areas began to break down during the first world war when Reuter and the Associated Press invaded areas formerly served by Wolff and Havas, and it was completely destroyed in 1934 when the Associated Press refused to renew its agreement with Reuter on the ground that competition in supplying news to all areas would mean better service for all. At mid-century six world news services operated competitively: Reuter, Havas which was re-established in 1944 under the name Agence France-Presse, the Associated Press and two additional US services, United Press and International News Service which had been established in 1906 and 1907, and the Soviet news agency, Tass, set up in 1918 under the name Rosta. All or most of these services maintained offices in each of the major news centres around the world, such as London, New York, Washington, Paris, Rome, Berlin, Stockholm, Moscow, Istanbul, Tokyo, Hong Kong, Delhi, Manila, Cairo, Buenos Aires, Rio de Janeiro. Each agency, however, remained the principal provider of news to and from its area and in localities where the political or cultural influence of its country was strong. A few areas were served by only one of these services—parts of Africa by either Reuter or AFP, parts of Central and South America by the three American services, China, Outer Mongolia, North Korea and East Germany by Tass. Some combination of Reuter, AFP and one or more of the American services reached most places, with the addition of Tass in eastern and western Europe, the USA and some parts of Asia.

These news services maintained their own foreign bureaux and correspondents for the direct collection and distribution of news. In addition they had agreements with press agencies in most of the countries where they operated by which these agencies supplied news from their area and in some cases distributed to their member papers the news furnished by the international services.

After the first world war Reuter began to use radio to speed up the receipt and distribution, first of commercial information and then of general news, and other news agencies followed suit. By December 1929 continuous service of general news was being broadcast by Reuter to Europe and by Havas to South America and the Far East, and after 1934 by Reuter to the East and to Africa.

At mid-century Reuter was transmitting 90 per cent of its news by 'Globereuter' service on seven radio beams whose combined spread covered nearly the entire world. The other major news agencies made less extensive use of radio than Reuter. The United States agencies, however, expanded their use of radio after rates were reduced in 1946, the French agency became a large distributor of news by multiple-address radiotelegraph, and a number of other European and non-European countries utilized similar services. In some areas, however, no reception or distribution facilities for this type of service existed, sometimes as a matter of censorship and sometimes because the costs of reception made it unavailable to those who needed it most.

As the elaborate system of world news gathering and dissemination evolved, national press associations were formed in one country after another to serve or control their national press and to tie into the world network. In most European countries, the USA and Japan, national press organizations had been formed before the opening of the twentieth century. By mid-century they existed also in the principal Asian countries, several countries in Latin America, and the Sudan and the Gold Coast (Ghana) in Africa. In some countries, notably the United States, the national press associations were independent associations of newspapers; more generally, they were linked to the government or were official monopolies. In the many countries where the national press services received and distributed news from international agencies they determined the relative use made of one or another of the world sources.

3. Change in character and content of newspapers

With the spread of mass literacy the number, variety and circulation of the world's newspapers expanded until the circulation of daily papers in 1955 amounted to one-tenth of the total world population. Great Britain led in rate of newspaper circulation, with 6 papers sold daily for every 10 men, women and children in the country, followed by the Scandinavian countries, Australia and New Zealand, Japan, the USA and the other countries of western Europe. Newspaper growth was not limited to highly industrialized countries, however, but took place in areas where literacy was only beginning to spread. By 1955 the Gold Coast had 11 dailies with a total circulation of 75,000, 9 weeklies and a local news agency, and Nigeria had 13 dailies with a circulation of 92,000.

Newspapers ranged in tone from the staid reporting and modest headlines of *The Times* of London, its news discreetly hidden behind a front page of classified advertisements, to the screaming headlines and dramatic pictures of popular tabloids such as the *New York Daily News* and the lively sensationalism of the London *Daily Express*. Their editorial viewpoint reflected a range of political opinion. Though papers of all types flourished, the most spectacular growth was in those which offered a mass appeal by catering to the tastes of a broad body of readers. *The Times*, with 235,000 daily circulation, appealed to essentially the same educated public that it had reached in 1900, while the *Daily Express*, which Lord Beaverbrook had started to modernize in 1913, provided news and especially entertainment in 1950 to over 4,000,000 people, one-quarter of all Britain's avid newspaper readers.

The spread of mass literacy and education also changed the character of what constituted news. By the opening of the century the newspapers of the major cities were already losing their traditional character as purveyors of opinion and information on political, diplomatic, local and financial topics for a limited range of readers, and were starting to become sources of information on the multitude of subjects that the mass of readers regarded as news. In the following decades the news media, catering to wider publics for whom many assorted kinds of information were news, covered large new areas, of interest to both new readers and old.

As the century progressed the news came to reflect the tremendous expansion of industry; especially after the economic collapse of 1929, economic problems and the relationship between industry and government became central topics. It reflected, too, the growth of urban populations and related questions of ways of life in cities, the conflicts of labour and capital and of social and racial groups and new developments in education. Reporters presenting news of new discoveries in science made an effort to bridge the gulf between experts and laymen. News of sports, always a popular subject, occupied much space in the press of all countries; in the 1950s, for example, Agence France-Presse had nearly four times as many subscribers to its special racing news service as to its special stock exchange news. Closer world contacts made foreign peoples seem of more immediate concern to the ordinary individual.

Newspapers of all levels covered this wide new range of material. Papers which served a more educated public carried a substantial proportion of serious reporting on all of these subjects and increased their demands from the world news agencies for explanatory or background material on world events to supplement the spot news which had once been considered adequate. The papers which catered to a mass audience prided themselves on their succinct coverage of news and their treatment of cultural and scientific developments, but they carried less background material explaining world events and economic problems and filled their columns with more of the crime, sex and accident news and gossip which made a sensational appeal.

The cost of the collection and distribution of news was high, and grew higher as the areas of the world and the subjects to be covered became more numerous and complex. It took more and more subscribers to support a full-scale newspaper, and the press had therefore to serve the demands of many publics in order to survive. Even a large circulation, however, became an insufficient financial base, and in the countries where the press was privately owned it came increasingly to depend on advertising.

At mid-century advertising provided as much as 70 per cent of the income of the average newspaper in the United States. Advertisements occupied up to two-thirds of the space in some of the mass-circulation dailies in North and South America, more than half in some popular British Commonwealth journals, about a third in the popular journals of west Europe and 40 per cent in Japan. In the less popular journals of more limited circulation the proportions were lower.

The advertisements themselves were one form of news, as readers looked to them for information on what was available to buy and also for an indication of the changing tastes, fashions and standards of life of their society. The relation between circulation and advertising was reciprocal: a large circulation attracted advertising and permitted the charging of high advertising rates. The costs of newspaper publication thus tended to favour the papers which were able to achieve mass circulation, and pressed publishers in the direction of editorial policies and newspaper content which would attract and hold the widest range of readers.

The costs of transmitting news generally favoured the areas already best served. Telegraph and cable rates were usually lower in the industrial countries with ample facilities and a large volume of business than in countries with less adequate facilities and without mass use. Press rates reflected this difference, for they were ordinarily based on rates for commercial messages; for the countries acceding to the international agreement of 1949, they amounted to one-half. London enjoyed a special advantage, for British commercial rates were lower to most points than those of other countries, and a special press rate of a penny-a-word prevailed throughout the British Commonwealth after 1941. In general the rates from the less developed countries were so high as to discourage the transmission of full news reports.

In areas of low literacy and low newspaper circulation, in fact, the main problem was keeping the press alive at all, let alone supporting the costs of effective domestic and international news services. This was recognized as a world problem by international organizations, and was one of the central matters to which Unesco addressed itself. As new nations took their places in the international community and other non-European countries became increasingly active in world affairs, the need for adequate, balanced news services in these areas became acute. At the same time the industrial countries with full local news services needed greater knowledge of the areas where news facilities were poor.

In the effort to assist in the meeting of these problems Unesco conducted a world-wide survey of the press, radio, television and film facilities of each country, prepared manuals and offered scholarships for the professional training of journalists and of radio and film technicians, examined the legislation affecting the status of news media and the free flow of information and co-operated with the International Telecommunications Union in the latter's effort to improve the procedures and lower the costs of communication. It worked with the FAO to stimulate the production of newsprint and its equitable distribution, promoted international agreements for the free flow of information, and provided technical assistance to countries requesting help in developing their press and communications systems.

The difficulties encountered by the developing countries were further complicated by the shortage of newsprint. Canada and the USA, with less than 10 per cent of the world's population, consumed 70 per cent of the world's newsprint. Europe, with a substantially larger population and a higher percentage of newspaper readers, consumed only a third as much, while the volume of available newsprint was extremely limited in Asia, outside of Japan, and was negligible in Africa and the Middle East. By mid-century, the FAO had begun a long-term programme to open up new producing centres, in the hope that decentralized production would facilitate the provision of newsprint and help to provide paper in the areas where it was very scarce.

4. *Freedom of the press: news, propaganda*

Prior to the first world war the gathering and dissemination of news was carried on as a private enterprise. Individual papers were everywhere operated commercially or as the organ of an individual or political group, and the wire services were run as private ventures like Reuter or, like the Associated Press, as a co-operative undertaking by a number of papers. The press of the principal centres enjoyed and jealously maintained freedom from government censorship or restraints other than those generally imposed by laws of libel, fraud or obscenity.

During the first world war governments began to enter the news field. In total war, public attitudes were hardly less important than arms; propaganda and censorship became essential aspects of the war effort. The radio offered a new means of reaching many receivers and was used by various belligerent governments for propaganda purposes. When Germany was cut off from its regular news contacts with the rest of Europe the German government set up a radio service, Transocean News, in 1915 to bring the German view of events to the outside world. Trans-ocean broadcasts, picked up by German embassies or other outposts, were relayed to the local press in the countries where they were received. Other belligerent governments in one way or another enlisted their press facilities, and to a limited extent their radio, for the promotion of the war effort.

A politically motivated struggle to command the minds of men was thus added to what had been a commercially motivated contest for the provision of news. From the first world war onward the media of communication were used for both purposes. On the one hand the press of the liberal democratic countries and the news agencies which served them made objectivity and accuracy in news reporting their goal and they achieved a high level of competence in these respects. But where authoritarian forms of government prevailed, control of the flow of news and the use of news media to advance the objectives of the régime was everywhere a basic procedure. One of the first steps which dictators took to secure their power was to suppress the free press, as was evidenced in the famous example of the Argentine paper, *La Prensa*, suppressed by the dictator Juan Perón, and re-established immediately upon his fall. With alternative sources of information cut off, such governments used their news media to present a single official version of all important events.

The United Nations Universal Declaration of Human Rights declared: 'Everyone has the right to freedom of opinion and expression; this right includes freedom ... to seek, receive and impart information and ideas through any media and regardless of frontiers' (Art. 19). A United Nations conference on freedom of information held at Geneva in 1948 attempted to spell out, in a series of resolutions and draft conventions, the necessary conditions for the exercise of this right. It specified in principle the right of news personnel to have access to sources of information, to travel unhampered, to transmit their copy without censorship or delay and to have news material from all sources admitted on equal terms.

The basic strength of the free press came from the rank and file of newsmen who kept the great mass of news flowing. In order to cope with the swift methods of communication and the increasingly wide and complex fields of news, press and radio required a large body of highly competent reporters whose job it was, day in and day out, to cover the whole range of news, bringing to the smallest story or the biggest a workmanlike capacity to recognize a news event, pursue information relentlessly and present it clearly, correctly and simply.

As the content of news became more complex, newsmen needed more and more background in order to understand the significance of what they saw and heard. Some reporters specialized in particular fields such as science, economics or sports, or in particular regions, in order to be in a position to present news stories well-buttressed with soundly selected background data necessary to an understanding of the immediate event. Schools of journalism were established at university level to provide men and women with the broad education and professional training which their task increasingly required.

Although newspapers and radio were uneven in the quantity and quality of the news which they offered, they responded generally to the demands of a better-informed public with a better-informed press. At their best the free press and radio offered the reading and listening public the opportunity to become informed on an ever wider range of current developments.

At the same time the use of press and radio to manipulate readers and listeners and mould their opinions, attitudes and desires becomes a highly developed art. In sharp contrast to the goal of accuracy and objectivity in news reporting, propaganda sought to use all the devices suggested by ancient experience and modern psychology to focus attention, arouse emotions of fear, prejudice, anxiety or desire, and by slogan, symbol or other appeal to command an uncritical response. Adolf Hitler enunciated the concept of the 'big lie' which, by its very preposterousness, undermined reason, developed uncertainty and then led to acceptance. By such means governments sought to assure the allegiance of their people; political leaders endeavoured to influence their followers and as many of their opponents as they could; advertisers resorted to similar devices as they refined their techniques for stimulating the desires of potential purchasers and promoting sales. 'Public relations' became a recognized skill and experts were employed by businesses, organizations, agencies and public figures to arouse a favourable public response.

But although news reporting and propaganda were aimed at different, often opposite, objectives the line between them was not always clear. The way in which newspaper editors handled the news could hardly fail to affect attitudes and opinions of readers. Some news items were featured and others passed over; captions directed attention to particular points; the speech of one political candidate appeared in a more conspicuous place than that of his opponent; editorials, cartoons or signed commentaries highlighted points in the news and gave a slant to its meaning. Even the papers which laid greatest stress on objective news coverage, such as the London *Times*, *New York Times* or Manchester *Guardian*, were necessarily selective in what they printed. Reporters provided greater detail on the stories which they thought their paper would use.

The line between reporting and propaganda was also blurred in respect to the collection of news. From the first world war onwards governments began to maintain press bureaux to supply information and statements on public issues to the press. Private bodies that wished to make a favourable public impression, such as corporations, labour unions or other institutions, also set up press offices and gave out news. Government officials and others in power were often tempted to control the facts issued in terms of their notion of what was good for the people to know, or for the bargaining position of the nation or for their own position. This resulted on the one hand in a variety of forms of censorship, both informal and official, and on the other in constant efforts by responsible men of the press to uncover the needed facts and assure freedom in transmitting them.

During the second world war news reporting was far more extensive than during the first world war and the inter-war years, as radio, especially, was used to keep the people of the belligerent countries constantly informed of day-by-day, even hour-by-hour developments on the far-flung battle fronts and to penetrate behind enemy lines. The news broadcasts of the British Broadcasting Corporation reached the people of occupied European countries and bolstered their morale when other means of communication were cut off.

Propaganda also was greatly intensified. Belligerent countries set up agencies to engage in psychological warfare by sustaining the spirit of their own side and undermining that of their enemy, beaming radio programmes both to their own people and abroad and, especially in occupied areas, trying to prevent reception of foreign news by suppression of receiving sets or by 'jamming' the air with conflicting sounds. In the cold war which divided the world in the years after the second world war the importance of radio as an instrument of propaganda was evidenced by the extensive external programmes sent out by governments of all sides and by the measures taken to prevent reception from outside by means of jamming.

These opposing trends were reflected in the failure of the United Nations to reach an agreement as to the proper role of government in respect to the control of information. Fundamental differences of view prevented the General Assembly from adopting the conventions proposed by the 1948 conference on freedom of information.

On one side the countries with a tradition of press freedom took the position that the interests of society were best served by free access to the market-place of news and ideas, and that interference by government should be limited to the minimum required by decency and security. On the other hand the socialist countries, proceeding from their class understanding of the freedom of the press, adopted a stand which in their view permitted the pursuit of social goals by more realistic means. The USSR maintained that, in the words of Lenin, 'the freedom of the press is a delusion so long as capitalists commandeer the better printing establishments and the largest stores of papers and capital retains its power over the press'. It regarded publication facilities as elements of socialist property. Freedom of speech and of the press were, according to the Soviet delegate, 'guaranteed by the state upon the sole condition that they be utilized in accord with the interests of the toilers and to the end of strengthening the socialist social order' and were denied to the foes of socialism, and 'every sort of attempt on their part to utilize to the detriment of the state—that is to say, to the detriment of all the toilers—these freedoms granted to the toilers must be classified as a counter-revolutionary crime'.*

Both groups disapproved of the language proposed for the draft convention on freedom of information and for a code of ethics. The Soviet delegates

* *Freedom of Information* (United Nations Economic and Social Commission, 1953), p. 3.

objected on the ground that it failed to set forth positive obligations on the media of information to work for the cause of peace and to combat 'the remnants of fascism'; the delegates from free-press countries objected because it imposed some obligations and restrictions on the media of communication beyond the primary duty of the press to publish accurate information.

In addition many of the new countries and those with press services not fully developed felt that financial support from government was often necessary to assure an adequate flow of information, and that such support should be recognized as a public responsibility. Some also feared that the freedom enjoyed by correspondents from countries with highly developed information media might not always serve their best national interests, either in the view presented to the outside world or in the local repercussions of such reporters' stories. They recognized the world press as the vital avenue to world opinion and welcomed the chance to be heard; but they were also distrustful of the light in which they might be made to appear. This widespread attitude was expressed in Kwame Nkrumah's response to foreign reporters when he was elected to office in 1951 while still in prison: 'I promptly refused to have anything to do with them for I had long since discovered that such people rarely report you verbatim; they give their own interpretations, and the more lurid and sensational they can make these, the better they like it.'*

It was not clear whether the trends of this period in fact enlarged or diminished the freedom with which news and other information circulated through the world. Certainly the volume of such news and information increased enormously. With every expansion in facilities the volume of communication expanded. One measure of such growth was the fact that Reuter's news agency was sending out fifty-four times as many words of news per month at mid-century as it did before the second world war.

Although there had been few restrictions on travel and communication in the years before the first world war, the area within which information then flowed freely was actually limited to the industrially developed countries and to certain segments of the population. The views which found expression and coloured the most factual of reports were those of the representatives of the European and American powers, and of the prominent members of these societies. In the following years the scope of news coverage broadened tremendously, newsmen sought their stories in all areas and walks of life and voices that had been entirely unheard and places and people which were virtually unknown beyond their borders became familiar to all who read or heard the news.

Against this broadening of the scope and spread in the dissemination of news, however, must be set the barriers which came into being as a result of the world wars and the establishment of rigidly controlling states—

* Kwame Nkrumah, *Ghana, the Autobiography of Kwame Nkrumah* (Thomas Nelson & Sons, New York, 1957), p. 134

censorship, passport and visa requirements, exclusion or suppression of publications, limitation of radio licences and jamming of radio reception. The record of news censorship maintained by the Associated Press showed that many countries censored or controlled news at the source, and that a number each year suppressed or suspended domestic newspapers, banned foreign papers or barred foreign correspondents. In the years after the second world war the record showed no clear trend, as the relaxation of censorship in one country was often balanced by a tightening elsewhere.

V. OPERATION AND REGULATION OF RADIO AND TELEVISION

By the nature of the medium, radio and television transmission required control, for the air waves are limited and the uncontrolled emission of messages on whatever wave the sender might choose could only produce interference and complete chaos. The principles of freedom of the press which had grown up with the unregulated private development of newspapers were therefore more difficult to apply to the air. As soon as radio passed beyond the stage of experimental and amateur sending and was used for general broadcasts, all governments took some steps to regulate its use.

The first problem was a technical one—non-conflicting use of the several air channels. In 1903, only four years after Marconi's first successful overwater transmission, an international radiotelegraph conference met on the invitation of the German government to establish conditions for intercommunication among ships of different nationalities and between ships and shore installations. The convention drafted at that conference was signed three years later by representatives of twenty-seven countries. At the Washington radio conference in 1927 a comprehensive frequency allocation table was drawn up, and a list was compiled for the Madrid conference five years later showing for each frequency the date on which the International Telecommunications Union had received notice of its use, in order to determine priorities. When the International Telecommunications Union became a specialized agency of the United Nations in 1947 it established an International Frequency Registration Board with headquarters in Geneva. All major countries set up national systems of regulation which made it possible for the international conventions to be carried out.

With respect to the material sent out over the air, the radio and television systems of the world fell into two main groups, those conducted as commercial enterprises and those operated as public or semi-public agencies. The foreign broadcasts of all countries were supported and controlled directly by the government. For domestic broadcasts the commercial type of system prevailed in the USA and in most of the Latin American countries, while the public type characterized the systems of Europe, the USSR and much of the rest of the world; in the countries of the British Commonwealth, both private and public systems frequently existed side by side. In some

European countries the physical facilities were maintained as part of the state-operated post and telegraph system while the programming was carried on by one or more independent or semi-independent bodies. Technical features as well as policy tended to preclude a competitive pattern within these countries, for the multiplicity of political subdivisions, and the nearness of centres of population to each other required more limitation on the number of stations than was necessary in the large spaces of the US, Canada, Australia, the USSR or the countries of South America.

Some 97 per cent of United States radio and television stations were privately owned and received their entire revenue from advertising, excepting only a few stations used exclusively for educational purposes or operated by municipalities. They operated under licence from the government, which allocated the wavelength, authorized the strength and time of day of the transmission, required a minimum amount of broadcasting, obliged the station to provide a certain proportion of public service features without commercial sponsorship, and stipulated that if time were offered or provided to a political party or candidate equal time must be provided to opponents.

This system resulted in as many as 20 stations operating in some large cities. More than 3,000 radio and 400 television stations held licences for commercial broadcasting in 1955. On the principle that the public interest would be best served by maintaining competition, the number of stations which could be owned by the same company within a given area was limited, and although a large number of stations were linked to one or another of four nation-wide networks, local stations retained their autonomy and used only such network programmes as they chose. Programmes tended to be geared to popular taste, for the ability of the station to secure commercial sponsors and thereby to finance its programmes depended on the size of its listening audience.

A large proportion of radio and television time was devoted to advertising, which became a form of entertainment itself in order to hold the attention of the listener or viewer. Under this system the content of programmes and the rates charged to advertisers were not subject to regulation, beyond the limitations imposed by the general laws against libel and obscenity and the requirement of equal time for the presenting of opposing political views.

The most systematically and extensively developed of the semi-public agencies was the British Broadcasting Corporation, which served as an example, if not a direct model, for systems in a number of other countries. In its first form the BBC was a commercial company, formed at the suggestion of the Postmaster-General who asked the several private companies which had applied for licences to combine in a single organization. The shares of the company were held by manufacturers of radio sets and revenue was provided from taxes on the sale of receiving sets collected by the Post Office and turned over in part to the company.

When this source of funds proved inadequate, two parliamentary committees studied the problem and reached the conclusion that the state should exercise a closer degree of supervision over broadcasting because of its importance in political education and cultural exchanges and its influence on public opinion. While they did not favour a radio system directly operated by the state, they considered the system of free enterprise unsuitable because 'no company or body constituted on trade lines for the profit, direct or indirect, of those composing it can be regarded as adequate in view of the broader considerations now beginning to emerge'.* They therefore recommended a public corporation under the control of the Postmaster-General but enjoying the fullest possible liberty within limits clearly defined by royal charter.

The British Broadcasting Corporation operated on this basis from 1927 on, subject to review by Parliament at the time of the periodical renewals of its charter. It enjoyed a monopoly of radio broadcasting in Great Britain, receiving its support from an annual licence tax on all radio receiving sets in the country and allowing no advertising. It was fully responsible for its domestic programmes, except for the requirement that it broadcast summaries of parliamentary debates and communications from the government, with the privilege of announcing that such communications were broadcast by request of the governmental department concerned.

Under this system, and a variety of somewhat similar arrangements adopted by other European countries, the body which enjoyed a broadcasting monopoly was in a position to serve as an independent educational and cultural agency, under the overall supervision of the government. It was less dependent on public taste and under less pressure to provide entertainment than the commercially operated systems and was in a position to offer programmes geared to the tastes of different audiences instead of constantly seeking the maximum number of listeners.

State radio systems operated directly by the ministry of education or information and supported out of the public budget were general in the USSR, other communist countries and a number of Asian countries. In these systems the radio was used primarily for educational or propaganda purposes directly in line with the policies of the government.

Under all systems of regulation or administration, radio and television served a variety of purposes: the transmission of news, education, political propaganda, entertainment. Where they were commercially operated, they also were a major factor in creating and maintaining the mass market. The amount of time devoted to each purpose, however, varied with the type of broadcasting system.

The state-operated systems of the communist countries devoted most of the time to educational and scientific programmes, to official news and talks, relays of programmes from theatres and concert halls, and special courses of instruction for schools, farmers and industrial workers.

* Quoted in *Legislation for Press, Film and Radio* (Unesco, Paris, 1961), p. 158.

The French radio monopoly broadcast chiefly music and drama, in three programmes geared to different levels of taste. The BBC offered three distinct types of programmes designed to provide information, education and entertainment for audiences at different educational levels. American programmes, dictated by public taste and the desire of advertisers to attract large audiences, were primarily for entertainment.

All broadcasting systems devoted a substantial part of their time to news, which they generally secured from the same sources as the local press, i.e. the major wire services serving their areas. A few of the larger broadcasting systems—the principal American networks, the BBC, and others to a more limited extent—had their own correspondents in the major centres at home and abroad, and these constituted independent links in the gathering and dissemination of news.

VI. COMMUNICATIONS RESEARCH AND THEORY

The great importance of communications to all aspects of modern life led to study of the nature of communication, in its technical and psychological aspects, and to the development of a body of communications theory. At the technical level this involved such problems as the proportion of the sound waves set up by a voice which must be carried to the receiver for the quality of the voice to be conveyed, or the number of pictures per second required to give the appearance of smooth motion to the human eye. The information which a wire or radio circuit was called on to transmit was translated mathematically into common units so that the relative performance of different systems could be analysed in quantitative terms.

In the psychological area, studies of the number of items which a listener or viewer could grasp in a given period indicated that the capacity of the communications media to transmit oral messages or visual images exceeded the capacity of the listener or viewer to grasp what could be presented to him. Studies of the relative effectiveness of different media in communicating the same material to comparable groups of persons indicated that television could be more effective than either radio or printed page. Other studies investigated the kinds of stimulus which must reach the recipient in order to arrest his attention and to stand out from the background impressions of sight or sound or thought which he was constantly receiving. They explored the relation of effective communication to the *Gestalt* in the mind of the listener, to his motivation in receiving the message, and to the feedback of controls in response to signals already received which permitted or excluded further reception. Research in the technical and psychological areas contributed both to the technical efficiency of the media of communication and to their skilled use for purposes of education, administration, advertising, propaganda and entertainment, as well as for the transmission of information.

As the speed and complexity of modern life created demands for ever more rapid and complex communication, systems that exchanged and acted on information without human intervention began to perform a number of functions.

Most of the technical work in the field of communications up to the middle of the century was posited on the need to communicate to the human ear or eye—sounds to hear, pictures to see, print to read. At mid-century many of the principles and devices which had been developed with these objectives were being applied to communication between machines. The technical problems were essentially similar—to convert a message into a form which could be transmitted and to reconvert it at the receiving end into a form in which it conveyed the desired information to the receiver, whether in the same form that it went in or in some other form.

The most advanced development of automatic communication was in the military field, in such systems as those by which a missile seeking a target was spotted by radar which ordered up an interceptor, the missile dodged and the interceptor pursued—all under instructions from automatic communications devices. As the air became filled with jet planes travelling at or near supersonic speeds, pilots could not depend on their eyes and reactions to see and avoid an approaching plane even in a clear sky. By the late 1950s technical means were at hand to replace the observation and guidance of human pilot or ground control, by non-human observation, computation of courses and automatic instructions to automatic control devices on planes. Electronic brains to detect and direct planes in relation to each other were beginning to be used in military air protection systems, and were in prospect for general air traffic control as a necessary form of automation to avoid disaster in the air.

While these elaborate systems of non-human communication were only beginning to be used, or were available but not actually in operation, many less spectacular forms of non-human communication had become part of everyday life. Automatic telephone service took a dialled number, converted it into a hunting mechanism to find a series of open circuits until it located the desired number, reported back if the number was busy, and on long-distance calls informed an accounting machine that a call had come from the initiating number to the point of destination, and instructed the accounting machine to enter the correct charge to the correct account. An air-line clerk could determine immediately whether there was space on a given flight by inserting a card in a machine and receiving an automatic report from the central recording machine many miles away that all space was booked or that the flight was open. In the field of communication the age of the mechanical robot was already at hand.

VII. COMMUNICATIONS IN MODERN LIFE

The importance of communication as a factor in modern life could hardly be overestimated. Modern man found himself bombarded with information and impressions, constant, immediate, insistent and beyond his direct experience, which broke into his private world and made him part of a larger scene. Communication ran ahead of direct experience, constantly arousing new desires and new images. Mass communication played an incalculable part in giving to the peoples of the formerly isolated regions of the world the stimulus to seek social and political change, whether the ideas came by way of the radio, a motion picture or telegraphed news in the popular press.

The new media of communication gave power to new people—to the man in the village who could counter the authority of the headman with the authority of what he had heard over the air, or to the government or other agency which controlled the media and could use them as tools. It was natural that every revolutionary group after the 1920s should have made the radio station one of its first objectives.

Radio and television made it possible for central governments to communicate instantly with the remotest areas, to keep all parts of the nation fully informed and acting in concert and to evoke immediate response by telephone or telegraph to mass appeals from leaders. The ability of the Chinese leadership to communicate each new slogan or appeal for action to the entire vast country by radio contributed in no small measure to the extraordinary speed with which radical changes were introduced; the use of the television by the Cuban revolutionary leader, Fidel Castro, in 1959, brought such immediate nation-wide response that he was able to force the president of the republic to announce his resignation while the leader's same all-night television broadcast was still going on.

Through the media of mass communication, entertainment, knowledge, music and drama reached people by the millions with material which had been enjoyed only by hundreds or at most thousands of people in the past. They provided the means for the spread of the mass culture which replaced both the folk culture and the mass ignorance which had characterized large segments of the world's population. The quality of this culture was a matter of debate, but the role of the new media of communication in its creation and spread was beyond dispute. Together with mass production and mass transport, mass communication set the tone of twentieth-century life.

CHAPTER XII

MEANS OF DESTRUCTION

THE application of scientific knowledge to the means of destruction during the first half of the twentieth century radically changed the character of warfare and created threats to the very survival of mankind. In a succession of stages it transformed warfare from the specialized activity of a limited military group, first into the total mobilization of industrial resources to produce weapons which would overwhelm military objectives, then into the total involvement of entire industrial societies in the process of hurling concentrated, mechanized force against military or civilian targets anywhere on the globe, and finally into a scientific contest to develop weapons of annihilation and the means of delivering them to destroy the opponent's total society. At each stage the forces of destruction were increased many times, the complexity of organization was very greatly enhanced, the moral and political stability of the home front as well as the armed forces became a more critical factor, and dependence on scientific development became more complete.

I. METHODS OF WARFARE AT OPENING OF CENTURY

By the opening of the century weapons designed by the application of scientific technology had already given the industrialized nations an overwhelming advantage against the non-industrialized peoples and had provided a basis for the political and economic imperialism of the western powers. The machine-gun had given the unskilled foot soldier a formidable weapon and had stepped up the destructive power of a given fighting force. Navies were composed of armoured vessels and the development of new steels had strengthened the armour plating of battleships and increased the piercing power of naval guns. The submarine had made its appearance to challenge the surface vessel, using internal combustion for surface propulsion and electric power for sub-surface motion. Field artillery had attained considerable range and accuracy, firing fragmentation shells in place of the old cannon balls which only did damage if they hit their mark directly.

Although chemical warfare had not been employed, it seemed apparent that the rapid developments in chemistry in the last half of the nineteenth century would sooner or later find their way into weapons. It was clear too that, once flight became practicable, its potentialities were as great for military as for civilian use.

All these developments of technological warfare made it evident by the beginning of the twentieth century that a new era of destructiveness was at hand unless means could be found to curb the process of applying scientific technology to weapons of war or to restrain the use of such weapons.

In the first Hague Peace Conference in 1899 the powers there assembled attempted to prevent the application of chemistry and aviation to warfare declaring prohibitions on the launching of projectiles from balloons or by other similar new methods and on the use of projectiles to diffuse asphyxiating or deleterious gases. Efforts to limit the development and quantity of arms failed, however, and the second Hague Peace Conference in 1907 concentrated its effort on establishing substitutes for war as the means of settling international disputes, and on an elaboration of the rules for 'civilized' warfare designed to take account of the situations created by the new military technology.

Although new destructiveness was envisioned at the opening of the century, the revolution in warfare that was to effect a revolution in life was not foreseen.[1] Nor did warfare occupy the central position that it came to fill in the following years. Military activity was carried on by a limited group of military personnel in a limited geographical area, while civilian life remained relatively undisturbed. Force was accepted and employed as an instrument of national policy, and had been in virtually continuous use during the nineteenth century in brief local conflicts involving the maintenance, extension or clash of colonial authority, the unification of Italy and Germany, the fate of the Ottoman empire, Japan's bid for status as a first-class power, accessions to political power in Latin American countries, and conflicts between European powers that came to a head in the Crimean and Franco-Prussian wars. But only the American Civil War, by its intensity and scale and its utilization of new industrial means, had presaged the kind of warfare which was to mobilize total resources and involve whole peoples.[2] Few people at the opening of the century saw that the application of modern science and technology to warfare would within fifty years so increase man's power of destruction and disruption that it would threaten the survival of civilization and indeed of mankind itself.

In fact, in spite of the continuous presence of warfare during the nineteenth century and its use to effect a major shift in the relations among nations through the victory of Japan over China and Russia, there was a general tendency in the western world to regard warfare as an obsolete instrument, to assume that the world was entering a period in which war would play a lesser part while economic expansion held the centre of the stage, and to relegate military activity to a specialized corner. It was assumed, furthermore, that if war should, nevertheless, break out it would be carried on according to more 'civilized' rules. The two Hague conferences were an expression of the latter concept.

Yet at the same time world tensions were mounting and technical developments were making localization and regulation of the conduct of warfare less likely or possible.

In the face of efforts to establish means to settle international disputes without violence, notably the creation of the International Court of Arbitration at The Hague in 1907, the major powers engaged in an armaments race which further contributed to the rising tension. In this race the private armaments industry was the main source of new developments in military technology. Working to expand their markets and enhance their sales, the great armaments firms—Krupp in Germany, Vickers-Armstrong in Britain, Schneider-Creusot in France, Skoda in Austria and Putiloff in Russia—not only vied with each other in the design of weapons that would out-fire those of their competitors but increased their own sales whenever they could make obsolete one of their own products.

The armaments race took the form chiefly of adding weapons of improved design to the arsenals of each country, guns of greater velocity, naval craft with greater or more accurate fire-power or more armour or speed. These weapons were not expected to modify in any major way either strategy or tactics, much less to change the nature of warfare almost completely. They were simply fitted into the prevailing concepts of warfare—i.e. a vigorous attack on enemy forces with the forces at hand, defence or counter-offence, and a quick decision on the field of battle.

Although the armour of fighting forces had been vastly altered since the days of Napoleon and Lord Nelson, essential military concepts had changed little. The leading authorities on naval warfare, Admiral Mahan and Sir Julian Corbett, reached the conclusion that the ironclad steamship with heavy fire-power had not significantly altered naval warfare and that the lessons of the wars of the sailing ships still held good, though some other authorities held that such new types of weapons as torpedoes, mines and submarines had changed the character of war at sea. On land, railway and telegraph had merely expanded the field of strategy while modern rifles and artillery had intensified the tactical problems of defence, and conscription had increased the size of the forces involved. The enemy forces remained the sole target; even munitions plants were not deemed by the strategists to be military objectives. The potentiality of the aeroplane and of chemical warfare had been recognized, but the prohibitions laid down by the Hague Conference were expected to preclude their use.[3]

II. FIRST WORLD WAR: BEGINNING OF TOTAL WAR

The first world war drastically changed the nature of warfare. Within a few weeks the war settled into positional warfare in the trenches. The improved weapons—quick-firing field artillery, rifles and machine-guns—pinned down the enemy's forces and gave fire-power almost complete superiority over movement. The difficulties of supplying and directing the unprecedentedly large forces in the field contributed to the immobility. Traditional military skill was reduced to ineffectiveness.

The unexpected stalemate precipitated a general revolution in warfare which had been implicit in the development of modern industry. In place of the traditional clash of fighting forces, warfare became a clash of national resources. The traditional limited and marginal war efforts which drew on only a fragment of the nation's manpower and resources were replaced by the total mobilization of manpower and industrial potential. The new situation brought the new concept, 'total war'.[4]

In the effort to build up a sufficient concentration of forces to break the long, consolidated fronts in continuous contact with each other, belligerents mobilized their men to the utmost and some of their women. In order to meet the abrupt and unforeseen rise in the requirements for munitions, they were driven to expand their war production from a few specialized firms until they were mobilizing their full industrial and agricultural capacities. The military demand for manpower, colliding with the equally urgent demands for workers to produce munitions and to meet the minimum needs of civilian life, required a continuous, complex process of adjustment. Economic systems geared to peacetime competition had to be organized and co-ordinated for the common effort and measures had to be taken to prevent inflation. Emergency administrations with tens of thousands of staff workers had to be built up.

Total mobilization, furthermore, aroused and depended upon a sense of personal involvement throughout all classes and groups in the populations of the warring nations. Rationing made involvement general, while new mass media of communication and means of propaganda were used to whip up emotional identification. The civilian populations ceased to be bystanders; they became 'home fronts' backing up the fighting fronts.

The effort to break the stalemate by overwhelming the opponent with the sheer weight of military equipment was concentrated on relatively few items. Thousands of millions of rounds of ammunition for small arms were turned out, hundreds of millions of artillery shells, millions of rifles, hundreds of thousands of machine-guns and tens of thousands of pieces of field artillery. There were thousands of millions of sandbags and thousands of miles of barbed wire.

While these established items were being produced on a mass scale, new technical developments brought poison gas, the tank and the beginning use of the aeroplane.

The use of poison gas, which the Hague conventions had failed to forestall, seemed even more ominous than the growing intensity of fire-power in pointing to the possibility that the destructive potentials of modern technology might outrun the possibilities for protection. The tank was a direct product of the breakdown of the war of movement, and met the need for an armoured device which would enable men to get out of the trenches and stand up to machine-gun fire. Conceived by the British when the war was already in progress, the first tanks reached the battlefield two years after the start of the conflict. By the close of the war, the tank had become a major new offensive weapon for the Germans, but was still of secondary importance for the Allies.

Although a military potential had been envisaged for the aeroplane from the time of its invention, its use in the first world war was confined almost entirely to reconnaissance, including observations to help direct artillery fire, and fighter cover for observation planes. Raids on England by the obsolete and highly vulnerable Zeppelins had nuisance value rather than strategic importance. Toward the close of the war, the possibilities of using planes for bombing were just beginning to be explored. There was however no serious attempt to destroy the productive capacities of the enemy.

Compared with the most elaborate previous military operations, the new industrial-scientific warfare was extremely complex. The continuous front lines constituted immense networks of field fortifications, barbed-wire obstacles, observation posts, systems of communication, approach and supply. Here the men on the ground—infantry, engineers, artillerymen—struggled against the preponderance of material, of which the key elements were the machine-gun, field-gun and tank, supplemented by a whole arsenal of newly developed specialized weapons—hand grenades, trench mortars, steel helmets, barbed-wire cutters etc. Massed artillery, as many as 100–150 guns per mile, equipped with new scientific devices for spotting, ranging and co-ordination of fire, hammered enemy positions to shreds. Volume increased from half a million shells per day to one and finally to two million. The vast array was co-ordinated in gigantic, closely integrated and synchronized attack plans for a decisive strategic breakthrough which repeatedly failed because the very complexity resulted in some hitch which prevented the full exploitation of a break when it was opened up.[5]

The revolution in land warfare was not paralleled on the sea, for the traditional strategy of blockade remained essentially unchanged and, though the new mass-production methods of industrial mobilization could speed up the flow of minor weapons—guns, mines, depth-charges—they could not be applied to the supply of fighting ships. The effect of the sea warfare, however, was to increase the intensity and completeness of total war by the extent to which the blockade and counterblockade cut into the lives of the civilian population. Aware that military effectiveness now depended on the functioning of the industrial economies, both sides treated virtually everything as contraband and used blockade and counterblockade to starve industry of its raw materials and civilian populations of food and other necessities. Where this meant unrestricted submarine attack against merchant shipping, the fate of crews and passengers whom the submarine was in no position to rescue drove home dramatically the total character of the conflict. The fate of these civilians sharply foreshadowed the more complete total war in which civilian populations themselves, as well as armed forces and military installations, were to become major military targets.[6]

III. DEVELOPMENT OF MILITARY TECHNOLOGY

After the cessation of the first world war hostilities, the development of military technology slowed down in the face of rapid demobilization, a general revulsion against warfare as too destructive to be tolerable, the effort to prevent further resort to war through the formation of the League of Nations, and the direct attempt to check the naval arms race by the Washington Naval Conference of 1921. Nevertheless, the military establishments proceeded to digest what they had learned during the war and to improve both the new weapons and the new organization which the war had brought forth.

Industrial organization was most thoroughly assimilated. The military themselves took on many of the features of modern industrial society,* and each country formulated industrial mobilization plans, either as part of general economic planning, as in the Soviet Union, or as special industrial mobilization schemes devised by the military in unplanned economies, as in the United States.

The development of weapons proceeded more conservatively, and involved chiefly improved performance of existing types—increased rapidity of rifle and machine-gun fire, new methods of automatic direction and computation in naval and aircraft artillery, speedy and reliable tanks, submarines able to dive faster and deeper and to range farther, new types of torpedoes and mines and new aircraft, especially those able to operate over sea from land or carrier bases. But science was not as yet regarded as a field to be systematically explored for possible military application. The outstanding development, radar, which radically changed the strategy of sea and air warfare, was accepted by the military only after civilian scientists had repeatedly demonstrated its reliability and significance, although its sea counterpart, loran, was discovered by naval research scientists seeking to find a means of detecting submarines.

New and improved devices and weapons were fitted into the framework of strategy and tactics, but the process was still incomplete when the second world war broke out. Military transport was motorized, although the railways remained the most important means of moving large numbers of troops and supplies over land. Radio, together with improved long-distance telephone, extended the range of communications and permitted the tactical direction and co-ordination of forces, including tanks, planes and submarines. Once the stubborn opposition to tanks in most armies was overcome, the slow, almost blind tanks used individually in the first world war were transformed into powerful, concentrated forces by the development of systems for communication, control, fuelling and repair. The major use of planes by both sea and land forces was evolved in the face of resistance from the more conventionally minded military leaders and air defences were developed.

Although each aspect of the new mechanized warfare was worked out, the whole system of warfare was not reformulated in the light of the radical

* For the development of military institutions, see Chapter XXIV.

revolution which had taken place. The majority of military opinion envisaged warfare as a repetition of the 1914–18 deadlock which would be gradually overcome by the weight of material, and they directed their plans toward a maximum of forces.[7] A minority thought in terms of avoiding or overcoming deadlock by the use of small, concentrated, highly equipped and swift units. The developments of the inter-war years constituted a bundle of loosely co-ordinated, separate efforts. They were to experience as revolutionary a change in the course of the second world war as had the earlier system during the first.

IV. GLOBAL CONFLICT: SECOND WORLD WAR

The second world war was both global and total in a much more complete sense than the war of 1914–18. In this it reflected both those technical developments, including radio, radar and carrier-based and long-range planes, which immensely extended the range over which operations could be stretched, and the greatly increased ability of industrial societies to co-ordinate the use of their resources.

Whereas the technological developments of the first world war had made the defence almost impregnable until finally overwhelmed by sheer weight, the attack gained ascendancy in the second world war through more powerful weapons, more effective methods of direction and supply and greater mobility which made possible a virtually irresistible concentration of effort. The grand strategy of the second world war was to concentrate forces and supplies at any point on the world-wide theatre of operation.

At sea—and in its broadest dimension the second world war depended on control of the main lines of sea communication—this involved the greatly increased reach of naval forces through the use of air reconnaissance, radar and the aircraft carrier. The last replaced the battleship as the key naval vessel. Submarine warfare was carried on by ships that were no longer isolated attackers confined to coastal waters but centrally directed packs capable of roaming the seas and concentrating on targets as soon as they were sighted. In turn, the submarines were spotted and hunted down by air reconnaissance and special hunting groups.

On land the industrialized spearheads composed of tanks, motorized or airborne troops or tactical air forces used *blitzkrieg* tactics to break through at critical points and then, with vastly superior speed and range, to roll up entire opposing fronts manned by troop units many times the size of the attacking force. Where these tactics failed, it was at first largely because of breakdown in the supporting operations of repair or supply; later, defence in depth and fields of land-mines, together with massed artillery and defensive tank forces, provided a more mechanized version of the barbed wire and armoured defences of the first world war.

Air-power played a vital role, not only as a support to the older forms of warfare but as an independent force. It was not, however, decisive. Up to the last phase of the war its range was limited and its employment diffuse. In the course of the war the bomber range was extended from 500 to 1,500 miles and the value of the sharpest possible concentration of effort on crucial objectives was gradually recognized. But it was only in the final stages of the war that life in the countries which suffered the most severe aerial bombardment, Germany and Japan, was decisively disrupted; throughout most of the war industrial mobilization in all the warring countries proceeded with relatively little disorganization.

The character of industrial mobilization also changed markedly during the second world war. Instead of the mass production of a few key items, as in the first world war, the second conflict drew on virtually every phase of industry. The new engines of war—tanks, planes, radar equipment, bombsights etc.—were highly complex and delicate. War production involved an elaborate system for the mass production of several million items according to schedules and priorities that constantly shifted to incorporate new technical developments and the changing emphases of the war strategy. This was most strikingly evident in the United States, whose rate of munitions output by the end of the war equalled the combined production of both its allies and its enemies.

The tremendous output and the ability to meet changing requirements, such as the critical need for synthetic rubber, depended upon the organization and co-ordination of the whole industrial system through which mass-production methods were applied to the most complex instruments of war. At the opening of the war, for example, the United States had only a few hundred skilled lens grinders, but hundreds of thousands of bomb-sights and other optical instruments were needed. In a short time this highly skilled operation had been analysed into component elements each of which could be quickly learned, the few skilled men were assigned to inspection, instruction or final finishing, and bomb-sights or other instruments were rolling out by the thousand each day. At the opening of the war aircraft were virtually built to order. Very soon they were coming off the assembly lines along with mass-produced cars, lorries and tanks.

Most significantly of all, not merely technology and industrial organization but science itself was mobilized to contribute to the war effort. The most intense concentration of scientific work was directed both in Germany and among the Allies at developing the atom bomb, whose possibility had been glimpsed on the eve of the war with the first report in 1938 of the successful fission of the uranium atom. The final achievement of the bomb represented one of the largest and most highly focused scientific enterprises ever undertaken for any purpose.

Although the size and significance of the atomic project overshadowed all other scientific efforts, many of the latter were of major importance. In the young field of electronics the development of the magnetron permitting the advance from metre to centimetre radar was possibly decisive in combating the submarine, and the proximity fuse which was detonated on approaching its target revolutionized air combat and brought decisive air victories before the German forces knew what had hit them. The application of jet and rocket principles to planes and long-range missiles began to make anti-aircraft defences obsolete.

Secret research in the fields of chemical and biological warfare by all sides prepared for defence and retaliation if the enemy should use one or the other of these means. Much of this work remained unknown, as neither side ventured to let loose these potentials.

Medical research made possible rapid strides in the treatment of wounds, especially through the use of blood plasma, sulpha drugs and penicillin, with the result that, for example, the proportion of United States soldiers treated for wounds who died was reduced to half that of the first world war. Improvements in immunization and treatment of disease reduced mortality from other causes. The social as well as the physical and biological sciences were also enlisted as their knowledge of human behaviour was applied to the conduct of psychological warfare and the maintenance of national morale.

The second world war was a far more total war than its predecessor also in the involvement of the civilian population. In addition to the fuller incorporation of industry and science into war production and the greater regimentation of life through rationing, price and wage controls and the direction of labour, mass bombings, mass occupation of territory and the uprooting and displacement of millions of people all but obliterated the distinction between military and civilian fronts. Whereas in the first world war a division, sometimes bitter, had continued to exist between those who fought and those who remained at home, the man at the front in the later conflict often felt that he was as safe as, or safer than, his family exposed to a rain of bombs.

As the war progressed, saturation bombing became a major objective. The scientific race to develop an atomic bomb was not primarily for use against military personnel or equipment but against the nerve centres of the enemy's economy and, inevitably, the concentrations of population. The two atomic bombs, dropped at the close of the war on the Japanese centres of Hiroshima and Nagasaki, showed the total society to be now not simply the support for military instruments and an adjunct to military objectives but the central military objective itself.[8]

V. WARFARE OF SCIENCE AND PEOPLES: THE NUCLEAR AGE

The new nuclear weapons introduced an element so radical and decisive as to revolutionize all other aspects of warfare, and immensely to accelerate the pace of military development. Their destructive power was out of all proportion to anything known before. Bombs in the first world war averaged 50–100 lb; in the second they rose to the equivalent of 10 tons of T.N.T. The first atomic bombs boosted the destructive power two thousand times to an estimated equivalent of 20,000 tons of T.N.T. Within ten years the thermonuclear bomb had multiplied destructiveness one thousand times more, to two million times the power of the biggest pre-atomic bombs of the second world war.

Even beyond the immediate destruction by which, for example, an average ten-megaton hydrogen bomb could sear the heart of a city with a fireball four miles in diameter, was the lethal or damaging effect of the radioactive fall-out of particles sucked up into the atmosphere by the explosion. While the extent of the fall-out would depend on a variety of factors, and the seriousness of the genetic as well as the immediate effect was not wholly determinable, the area officially reported as affected by the thermonuclear test of March 1, 1954, was 7,000 square miles. The direction of the wind and other atmospheric conditions would determine how far this fall-out would extend its lethal influence and on whom it would descend.

Means to deliver nuclear projectiles kept pace with the development of the weapons themselves. The range of bombers rose in a decade from about 1,500 miles at the close of the second world war to 5–6,000 miles, bringing the world's main centres of power and industrial production within reach of each other. Long-range intercontinental missiles were being developed. The struggle for air supremacy became a struggle for the chance of survival.

In this nuclear phase of the twentieth-century revolution in warfare, scientific advance and the total organization of the life of the nations were the central elements. Military preparedness for total war virtually took the form of scientific development as countries or groups of countries sought to build up such superiority in weapons and means of delivery as to act as a deterrent against the use of these ultimate destroyers. The home fronts became principal fighting fronts, with cities, industrial centres and transport bottlenecks as major military targets and their survival a prime defence consideration and the indispensable basis for any effective retaliation.

For defence and survival, gigantic continent-wide networks of radar chains for early warning were constructed across the frozen Arctic and far out to sea. Elaborate systems of interception, relying increasingly on missiles with guidance or homing devices, were set up. Interception, however, needed to be virtually 100 per cent effective to provide protection against nuclear weapons, and the difficulties of intercepting missiles were very great.

Measures were taken in many countries to reorganize peacetime life against the threat of nuclear destruction and to establish emergency organizations for civil defence, more elaborate and flexible than those which functioned during the second world war. In countries dependent on sea-borne supplies like Great Britain, many small subsidiary ports were made ready in case main ports should be paralysed. The city of Stockholm prepared to carry on its life underground in shelters hewn out of the granite foundations. Government offices and business firms in a number of countries established alternative headquarters, set up succession lists of officials and executives, and micro-filmed and stored vital documents. Industrial mobilization plans were geared to substitutions and dispersal in case of disruption.

As ever swifter and more exacting weapons were produced, they placed new demands on the human beings who had to operate them. Science was also called on to determine the limits of human endurance and capacity to function under extremes of speed, heat, cold, altitude, pressure, sudden change and exposure to radiation.

In the decade following the second world war, the struggle for superiority in destructive weapons and means of delivering and intercepting them virtually constituted in itself a form of warfare. The intensity of the struggle, the size of the effort, and the extent of actual or potential involvement was greater than during the hostilities of the first world war and approached in everything except active destruction the situation during the second. The threat was far greater. Although it was recognized on all sides that all-out nuclear warfare could only result in making much of the globe uninhabitable, the struggle went on to build up more and more strength in order to prevent an opponent from securing a decisive advantage in striking power or defences.

Central to the new contest was the quest for speed and for the means of detection which would prevent surprise. It was military aircraft that broke the sound barrier and went on to higher and higher speed records. Long-distance missiles were still faster and were designed to travel from one conti-nent to another in a matter of minutes.

Against such speeds, observation posts located within national boundaries, or even in the reaches of the Arctic or the oceans, could hardly provide effective warning of a surprise blow. It therefore became necessary to seek means to bring and keep within view as large a segment of the globe as possible, including distant parts of the territories of potential opponents, in the hope of detecting in advance dangerous concentrations indicating the threat of aggression. Both manned and unmanned rocket devices containing radar and television equipment were designed to observe from high altitudes.

The next step was observation from space. The USSR and the United States placed earth satellites in orbit around the earth, equipped with instru-ments for various types of observation in connection with the International Geophysical Year, 1957–58. Though these earth satellites were designed for other than military purposes, much of the impetus to their development came from the military-scientific contest to which the revolution in warfare had brought the world by the middle of the twentieth century. Their possible contributions to military technology were well recognized.

While warfare was developing into a potential for unlimited destruction, the continued use of force in limited but intense struggles led to other develop-ments. In an effort to devise military instruments which would be usable and not merely deterrents, nuclear weapons were reduced in size to the point where they could be considered tactical weapons, though still immensely destructive

While the powers engaged in the race for supremacy in the capacity to inflict or resist annihilation, they also began to equip their armies with atomic artillery and to seek means of defence against relatively small-scale but inevitably devastating atomic attack.

In the remaining outposts of empire where colonial peoples resisted continued authority or in situations with the character of civil wars, as during the prolonged struggles in Indo-China and Algeria, weapons of massive destruction could not be used. Modern weapons did not equip armies to cope with guerrilla tactics.

The changed character of warfare was not solely the result of the changing technology of war. It was in part the expression of the changed character of the state. While total war was tending to make the state more total, the inclusive state was making war into an expression of the whole people.

As a total national effort, whether on the part of a democratic or an authoritarian state, war had to be pursued for complete victory and to inflict utter defeat. The psychology for total war was created by systematic whipping-up of hatred between nations. By the use of powerful devices for the control of opinion, the enemy was shown as wicked, inhuman, the destroyer of civilization—while each side saw itself as fighting in the cause of humanity, to safeguard civilization, to save a way of life.

War having thus been elevated to a struggle between light and darkness, compromise became difficult from the beginning and unconditional surrender with a dictated peace the unavoidable objective. The defeated enemy, moreover, was made to bear the burden of guilt as well as defeat. The war crimes trials in Germany and Japan which followed the second world war were a new phenomenon. At the close of the first world war the popular demand that the German Kaiser be tried for war guilt failed to find support among the governments of most of the victors; but after the second world war not only generals but diplomats, statesmen and others who had executed the national policy of their governments were tried before a court composed of their enemies.

The corollary of defining the struggle in terms of civilization and its opposite was to arouse in the victors a sense of responsibility for remaking the world and especially for reforming and re-educating the former enemy. The object of peace-making after the wars of the twentieth century was not, as in previous eras, to patch up the quarrels, transfer bits of territory and restore the system which had been shaken by war, but to reconstitute the world in the image of the victors. In the peace-making after the first world war both the traditional and the new attitudes were present, the representatives of the new forces seeking to reconstitute the world on the principle of self-determination of nations while representatives of the older view were more concerned with specific annexations and safeguards. The treaty structure which followed the war was an uneasy compromise between the ideas of reconstituting the world and the old policy of aggrandizing national interests.

After the second world war, the objective of remaking the world and re-educating the vanquished was clearly dominant in the occupation policies of the victorious governments in Germany, Japan and eastern Europe, though the victors had two quite different images in terms of which they sought to re-shape societies. Even the two minor wars of the mid-century, Korea and Indo-China, clearly demonstrated that modern war left no room for a peace settlement. At the close of each the only alternatives were division of the country or total submission of one side or the other to the way of life which the other sought to impose.

The impact of modern warfare on the life of mankind could hardly be exaggerated. Its terrible destructiveness was only the first aspect. The first world war was estimated to have cost the nations of Europe no less than 20,000,000 men, killed and disabled. The lost generation in Britain, France, Germany and Austria was a notable aspect of the inter-war years. In the second world war losses of military personnel alone amounted to one person in 22 of the population in the USSR, 25 in Germany, 46 in Japan, 150 in the UK and 200 in France and China. Civilian losses in some areas were much greater. Estimates of physical destruction could not be expressed in common units like lives; suffice it to recall that Japan's major cities were already gutted by bombs and fire before two of them were laid waste by atomic destruction, scorched earth tactics of retreating armies devastated western Russia, Burma and parts of China, saturation bombing and shelling left little but rubble in many parts of Germany, Italy, northern France and Britain, and broken dikes let the sea take over parts of Holland.

The indirect effects of total war were no less far-reaching. The nature of modern warfare tended to strengthen the large as against the small states, for only a major industrial nation could create and sustain a modern military establishment, and no small nation could stand against the forces of a large power. At the same time it became increasingly difficult for small nations, no matter where they were situated, to avoid involvement. With airlifts, neither Arctic ice nor desert sands offered the obstacles which they had in the past; the Canadian Arctic became a principal military frontier of North America. For long-range missiles there were no frontiers. However uninterested a small nation might be in a conflict among large powers, it might find itself at any moment in the path of the latter's military sweep. Military considerations thus tended to make small countries increasingly dependent on large, and to force countries together into blocs.

Modern warfare was no cheap game; it involved the entire financial re-sources of a state. Britain, the strongest financial power in the nineteenth century, was forced as a consequence of four years of the first world war not only to yield financial primacy to the United States but to repudiate her war debt. After the second world war it was only the huge financial resources of the USA through the Marshall Plan for aid in reconstruction that salvaged the economies of the European nations.

Modern war did much to determine the direction and shape of economic activity, not only during actual war when the economies of the belligerent countries were directly organized and oriented toward the war effort, but in non-war years when the burden of armaments continued to be great. This was strikingly evident in the planned economy of the USSR, which from the start included in its development plans the creation and maintenance of its military potential, and whose long-range plan to establish industrial centres in Siberia was accelerated by the invasion of its western region in the second world war. But war had major repercussions also on the unplanned economies of other industrial countries as well. It acted as a tremendous stimulus to production, especially outside the areas of destruction, bringing a great industrial spurt in the USA, of moderate extent in the first world war and of major proportions in the second. Even the economies of continental Europe and Britain, which were disrupted by destruction and disorganization, were stimulated by war demands to adopt new technology and to devise new forms of organization.

Political effects were no less crucial. The tendency for the functions and authority of the state to expand, a broad trend of the twentieth century, was greatly increased, and the authority of those in control was strengthened. Under the actuality or threat of war, democratic governments extended their authority in ways contrary to their traditional methods and principles, forced by a sense of urgency to take measures which appeared to be necessary for survival. The actuality or danger of war offered to authoritarian states additional possibilities for strengthening state control over the population.

Thus modern war and its echoes tended to make all states more authoritarian and to exact a greater measure of conformity from their citizens, lest divergence from the nationally established path or challenge to the wisdom of those in authority give aid and comfort to the assumed enemy. The tendency to insist on conformity was less marked in countries where traditional institutions for registering dissent were strong—in Britain, for example, where the loyal opposition had long been part of the structure of government. It was stronger in countries such as Germany where the tradition of authority was strong, or the USSR where dissent had, historically, been expressed through revolution. But everywhere the direction of trend was the same.

The impact of modern warfare on social structures was immense. Though the bases for many or most of the social changes which occurred during the first half of the twentieth century were present in the societies where they took place, the shock of war played a major part in loosening custom and breaking down existing structures. The demands of war and the total involvement of peoples placed individuals and groups in new positions from which they did not entirely retreat when more normal conditions returned. Wartime experience changed the relationships of classes, altered the role of women and gave new opportunities to minority groups. Especially in countries where there was a diversity of peoples and customs, the armed forces tended to act as a force for national solidarity and social integration. The conscript army was an equalizer, and the increasingly technical requirements which had to be met by military personnel resulted in the spread of a variety of types of knowledge through the population by the process of military training. As warfare became more scientific and science itself came to be part of the conflict, it raised the prestige of science in the public mind and emphasized scientific rather than humanistic education.

Finally, modern warfare entered the psychology of people, to distort their values. Historically, military virtues had always been associated with personal prowess and valour. Modern war left few opportunities for this type of conduct. When warfare meant not a contest of skill but the weight of destruction, it tended to dehumanize those who waged it—not merely the bomber whose target was a city full of people going about their daily life, but the total society, as it became inured to destruction, suffering and violence.

This effect may be seen in the changed attitude toward destruction between the two world wars. When the cathedral of Rheims suffered as a result of German bombardment during the first war, the moral conscience of the world was shocked. But in the second war, when the monastery of Monte Cassino was destroyed and the cathedrals at Cologne, Coventry, and many other churches and shrines suffered from air attack, the destruction was regarded as an unfortunate but necessary part of the total war. The climax was of course the atomic destruction of Hiroshima and Nagasaki. The exigencies of total war threatened all social values.

NOTES TO CHAPTER XII

1. Professor N. Talensky thinks it should be emphasized that although (as many leading sociologists agree) wars undoubtedly exert an influence upon the development of society, they have never occupied the central place in the society's life nor have they called forth the revolutionary changes in the people's mode of life.

2. It is incorrect to say, Gyula Raszszo writes, that only the American Civil War, by its intensity and scale and utilization of new industrial means, presaged modern warfare. In the Franco-Prussian war of 1870–71 the fighting was on just as great a scale, and modern military technology was employed just as widely, as in the American Civil War.

3. Gyula Raszszo points out that the account given of the military concepts prevalent at the beginning of the twentieth century is inaccurate. The authors devote too much attention to theories of naval strategy and overlook the revolutionary changes that took place in military science, one of which is connected with the name of Alfred von Schlieffen.

4. Professor N. Talensky thinks that at this point it is necessary to add that the essence of total war is the complete subordination of the whole life of the people and the economy of the belligerent state to the cause of preparing and waging war, with the application during the war of all possible means of terrorizing and destroying *en masse* the civilian population.

5. Gyula Raszszo writes that in general it is true to say that the strategy of the breakthrough failed, not because of its unparalleled 'complexity', but because there were not enough vehicles able to move at sufficient speed. After all, the second World War created conditions that were incomparably more complex, but during the course of the fighting there were quite a number of strategic breakthroughs: the point was that armies now possessed armament of adequate power and mobility.

6. Professor N. Talensky points out that during the first and second world wars the dominant principle was that the course and outcome of the war would be determined in the main by the destruction or annihilation of the armed forces of the enemy.

7. Gyula Raszszo writes that in his opinion it is incorrect to say that military opinion was for the most part conservative; this is true only with regard to French, British, and to a certain extent American military thinking. There can be no doubt that the requirements of modern military technology were completely taken into account by Soviet military science, and also in many respects by German and Italian military science (above all in the employment of tanks and aircraft).

8. Professor N. Talensky underlines that the dropping of the two atomic bombs on the Japanese cities of Hiroshima and Nagasaki was in no wise dictated by military necessity since the outcome of the war had by this time already been decided. See also: J. D. Bernal, *World Without War* (London, 1958); L. Pauling, *No More War* (N.Y., 1958).

SECTION THREE

DEVELOPMENT AND APPLICATION OF THE BIOLOGICAL SCIENCES

CHAPTER XIII

DEVELOPMENT OF THE BIOLOGICAL SCIENCES*

T HE outward character of biology became greatly altered during the first half of the twentieth century, so that its emphases seemed to differ markedly from those of its nineteenth-century counterpart; its fundamental concepts were less changed than might appear.

Evolution was the dominating concept in biology at the end of the nineteenth century. It has been said that all subsequent biology has been a commentary on the *Origin of Species*; this is true in so far as the concept that all organisms are genetically related to one another became so generally accepted by the twentieth century that it could never again be ignored.

There were other unifying concepts, however, which the biology of the twentieth century inherited from that of the nineteenth: the concept of protoplasm as a common living substance composing all organisms;[1] the theory that the protoplasm of all organisms is organized into cells; the proof that, under conditions currently prevailing on the earth, cells can be formed only from other cells and life can proceed only from other life; the concept that all organisms undergo an orderly process of differentiation during their development from the egg; finally, the concept expressed by Claude Bernard (1813–78) that life, no matter what it may be, manifests itself in processes which conform to the laws of physics and chemistry. All these nineteenth-century synthesizing doctrines aided in the unification of biological thought and its focus on the study of common problems and new techniques of investigation.

The major problems to which biologists directed their attention were evolution and inheritance, cell biology, the nature of the living substance, and the question of the origin of life. These problems will be seen to be not strictly separable from one another; evolving organisms are constructed of cells, and cells are made up of protoplasm, and protoplasm uses the same kinds of atoms and molecules as compose the inanimate world. During the nineteenth century each major concept acted as a unifying device in its own limited area. It remained for the twentieth century to redefine these concepts and work out their interrelationships on a biochemical and an evolutionary basis.

I. HEREDITY AND EVOLUTION

Although Darwin presented a theory to account for change in organisms, he could not elucidate to the full either the possible or the actual mechanisms of

* This chapter was prepared by Dr. Jane Oppenheimer.

inheritance of variations. It was Mendel who postulated an explanation for the phenomena of inheritance in studies which were neither understood nor widely known during the nineteenth century. They were, as has already been noted, rediscovered and at last taken into account in the year 1900. The study of Mendelian inheritance from then on became a central discipline of twentieth-century biology, though geneticists of the USSR, particularly after 1936, postulated quite different non-Mendelian mechanisms.

1. *The theory of the gene*[2]

Genes were first given their name by Wilhelm Johannsen (1857–1927) early in the twentieth century, but the theory of the gene was crystallized by T. H. Morgan (1866–1945) and his co-workers during the first third of the twentieth century, in a series of experimental studies for which Morgan received the Nobel prize in 1933.

The improvement in the glass industry during the nineteenth century had led to the manufacture of achromatic lenses which allowed more detailed observations than had hitherto been possible on minute bodies within the nucleus of the cell. Before the end of the century the use of these lenses had demonstrated that the nucleus may be the seat of heredity and had suggested that visible bodies within the nucleus, the chromosomes, carry the factors of heredity.

Specifically, biologists learned during the last quarter of the nineteenth century that the number of chromosomes is normally constant for all the cells of each species, and described the mechanism whereby the chromosomes are duplicated lengthwise at cell division, one of each of the two new members being distributed to each of the two new cells. They further discovered, by the end of the nineteenth century, that another special mechanism comes into play during the cell-divisions which produce the male and female reproductive cells (gametes) which will combine to form the new individual; as a result of this, only half the typical chromosome number for the species passes into an animal's egg or spermatozoon, so that when these reproductive cells combine to produce a new individual, the chromosome number characteristic of the species is restored, the new individual has the same number of chromosomes as had each of its parents, and the infant receives half of these from each parent. An important summary and synthesis of this work was published in 1900 by E. B. Wilson (1856–1939) in his book *The Cell in Inheritance and Development*.

Microscopic studies of chromosomes carried out in the first decade of the twentieth century showed that sex determination in higher animals could be explained on a chromosomal basis. Each ovum (female gamete) or spermatozoon (male gamete) contains a specific number of chromosomes, later called autosomes, and in addition may also contain an additional chromosome, visibly distinct from the rest, the so-called sex-chromosome. In some forms, such as grasshoppers, the sex chromosome carried in the ovum and always present in it is recognizable by its shape. Spermatozoa in this genus were shown to be of two kinds, one carrying the sex-chromosome and the other lacking it. If an ovum with its sex-chromosome is fertilized by a spermatozoon carrying another, the resultant organism is a female having two sex-chromosomes; the ova that she produces will necessarily have one sex-chromosome each. However, if an ovum containing a sex-chromosome is fertilized by a spermatozoon lacking it, the new organism has only one and becomes a male; half of its spermatozoa will receive the sex-chromosome and half will not.

Such studies gave an important visible clue to the fact that chromosomes might differ from each other in their specific hereditary functions, and the fact that the number of males and females in a species is approximately equal could be explained by random assortment and recombination of unitary elements of the cell, in this case sex-chromosomes, helping to determine sex. Thus a visible mechanism was described which assorted and recombined elements in exactly the way postulated by Mendel's hypothesis, and biologists soon recognized the chromosomes as the carriers of the genetic factors. It was found that many of the other chromosomes of various species could be recognized by their size and shape. In this way it became confirmed that the chromosomes are present in the adult nucleus in pairs, the two members of the pair being homologous, one member of each pair having been derived from each parent.

Morgan's work definitely showed that Mendel's factors—Johannsen's genes—are carried by the chromosomes. The principal contribution of Morgan and his co-workers was made by means of breeding experiments which could be related to what was known and what was still being learned microscopically about the chromosomes. Morgan found that the common fruitfly, *Drosophila melanogaster*, furnished ideal material for combined microscopic studies and breeding experiments. This species of fruitfly has a small number of chromosomes, four pairs, easily distinguished from one another by microscopic study. It breeds readily and quickly in the laboratory; and many of its genes undergo heritable change, either spontaneously or, as became apparent later, as a result of laboratory experiment, so that the results of the breeding experiments are easily detectable by simple examination of the flies.

In some of the early breeding experiments with *Drosophila*, Morgan and his co-workers observed, what had already in the first decade been suggested by William Bateson (1861–1926) and Reginald Punnett (1875–   ), that not all the factors they studied showed independent segregation and assortment, as would be expected from a strict application of Mendel's laws. In contrast, a number were inherited in groups. The chromosomes were known to assort independently of one another; and geneticists postulated that the factors associated with any one chromosome might tend to be linked together, independently of those associated with other chromosomes. If this interpretation was correct, *Drosophila melanogaster*, with its four pairs of chromosomes, should have four separate groups of associated factors, and scientists found that this was the case. It had been Mendel's good fortune to choose for his studies on peas characteristics each of whose hereditary factors was located on a separate chromosome.

During the preparation of the reproductive cells, homologous chromosomes, one received from each parent, twist around each other, and during this process they break and interchange sections carrying homologous genes. Such exchange was first postulated by Morgan and his group as the only possible explanation of the results of some of their breeding experiments; it was later verified through microscopic study by Curt Stern (1902–   ) in 1930. Breeding experiments further suggested that exchanges between two chromosomes can take place at any region of the chromosome. If the position of the gene could be located, then by studying the frequency of exchange of particular chromosome parts, as detected in appropriate breeding experiments, the relative positions of the factors on the chromosomes could be worked out. In this way, Morgan and his co-workers mapped the chromosomes by establishing the relative position on them of the genes. These then became conceived as unit factors arranged linearly on the chromosomes.

Biologists soon demonstrated with clarity that genes sometimes exercise their functions during development by being responsible for the production of specific enzymes. Enzymes are organic catalysts, primarily protein in constitution, which are produced only by organisms, and which accelerate and facilitate the accomplishment of chemical reactions in the organism. They are of the utmost importance in all cellular functions, and the relationship of gene-action to enzyme-production in ascomycete moulds (George Beadle, 1903– and Edward Tatum, 1909–   ) was one of the important discoveries responsible for the central position of genetics among twentieth-century biological disciplines. It became possible to relate the effects of particular genes to the production of enzymes and other specific chemical syntheses when work on genes was extended to the moulds, and also to bacteria, since these can be grown in simple solutions containing known chemical nutrients. Here the effects of particular genes could be related to the pathways of specific chemical syntheses.

Since the nineteenth century enzymes had been known to be highly specific with respect to the conditions under which they operate and to the reactions in which they take part. Their selectivity was first explained by the characteristic shape of the protein molecules which are among their principal constituents. In addition, many other situations in which biological processes are highly specific, including genetic ones, were considered to be explicable in terms of the selectivity of protein reactions. This hypothesis was reinforced by the known importance of proteins in many of the highly specific immunological reactions by which the body combats bacterial and some other diseases.

During the early twentieth century scientists began to attribute increasing importance to the substances called nucleic acids in connection with genetic action. These substances are able to self-replicate and to influence the manufacture of proteins (enzymes) with specific actions. While the nucleic acids had been discovered in the nineteenth century as important chemical constituents of nuclei, their chemical structure was established only in the twentieth; Albrecht Kossel (1853–1927) received a Nobel prize in 1910 for his part in its elucidation.

Biology had, in some of its phases, been dependent for its progress on previous findings in chemistry and physics or on their technological applications. This was particularly evident in the twentieth century when it became strongly dependent on elaborate physical instrumentation. The development of knowledge concerning the nucleic acids was a case in point. Through the use of ultra-violet spectrophotometry, Torbjörn Caspersson (1910–   ), around 1940, was able to study with great precision the amount of nucleic acids within cells, and this gave early evidence as to their function, particularly in connection with protein synthesis. Almost simultaneously Jean Brachet (1909–   ) worked out a new method of recognizing their presence in microscopic sections of tissues and thus of localizing them in various parts of the cell. He and Caspersson both emphasized their role in growth and reproduction.

Another of the clues to the importance of the nucleic acids in heredity was derived from a group of studies which at the outset seemed completely unrelated to the study of genes. These involved investigations of certain disease-producing agents, known since the nineteenth century as filterable viruses because they are so small that they pass through the filters used to strain bacteria from solutions during sterilization processes. Some of these viruses were shown during the 1930s to be nucleoprotein in nature, that is, to be made up of complexes of protein and nucleic acid. Some, such as that causing tobacco mosaic disease, could be crystallized, like inanimate matter, but could be reproduced only in living cells as a result of distorting the cell's own metabolism. They thus attracted great attention, as entities on the borderline between living and non-living matter.

A further important insight into the significance of nucleic acids in heredity was obtained in the 1930s from experiments in which it was shown that one strain of pneumococcus, a bacterium causing pneumonia, could be transformed into another strain by a chemical extract from the first strain which was later proved to consist almost exclusively of one type of nucleic acid, known as DNA (deoxyribonucleic acid). Later (1952) experiments with radioactive isotopes corroborated these results by showing that it was only the DNA in bacteriophage and similar viruses, and not its protein component, which entered host cells, there later operating to build its own characteristic protein. Many other types of experiments, notably quantitative studies on multi-cellular organisms indicating the relative constancy of DNA in the cells and its doubling or halving when chromosome numbers are doubled or halved, all supported the hypothesis that the DNA molecule is responsible for the self-copying and self-variation of living matter, and thus for heredity. (Pl. 5a.)

The DNA molecule was known to contain a number of different components. James D. Watson and F. H. C. Crick postulated in 1953 that it had a shape somewhat like that of a ladder with the uprights twisted spirally. The part of the molecule corresponding to the rungs, according to their model, is made up of nitrogen compounds which form complementary cross-links between the spiral parts of the molecule and assure its self-replication during self-division.

Scientists interested in applying mathematical communications theory to genetics postulated that the particular linear sequence of the different cross-links might act as coders of genetic information—in other words, genes. It appeared that DNA is the bearer of the specific genetic code, and that it is responsible for the formation of the various specific proteins in the body, via the intermediary of molecular templates composed of RNA (ribose nucleic acid).

Information theory as well as the results of some genetic experiments made it seem possible that within the DNA molecule the action of one group of cross-links might depend on that of its neighbour. According to this concept, genes might be groups of DNA cross-links, rather than relatively independent elements as Morgan's theory originally predicated. By the late 1950s, however, no one had fully demonstrated the exact relationship of the DNA molecule or its parts to the genes whose linear arrangement Morgan and his co-workers had demonstrated.

One advantage of the 1953 model was that it presented a possible explanation of how the DNA molecule, either in gene or virus, might be self-duplicated. An unexpected outcome of the studies on viruses was that some of them appeared to be similar to certain self-perpetuating particles, found in the protoplasm outside the cell nucleus and sometimes called plasmagenes, which seemed possible subsidiary agents in the mechanism of heredity. The study of the viruses thus made it appear that all control of heredity was not localized solely in the nucleus, as had been postulated at the beginning of the century. Since the evolution of life must have involved a stage in which molecules first became self-duplicating, genes, viruses and plasmagenes thus were brought close to the problem of the origin of life.[3]

Proof of the fact that a number of human attributes are controlled by specific nuclear genes separately or in combination—blood-groups, some kinds of colour-blindness, haemophilia—gave hope that a science of human breeding or eugenics might lead to the betterment of the human race. But the majority of thinkers viewed this possibility, though important, as distant of attainment, in view of the paucity of knowledge of human genetics and also in the light of the value judgments involved.[4] Nonetheless, eugenics became an active movement in the 1920s, and came to the fore again in Nazi racial policies. Later, pedigrees were drawn up indicating the inheritance of a number of human diseases or other abnormalities, and it was found possible to predict mathematically, in some cases with great accuracy, what the probable result of a given marriage would be. By the middle of the century a few advisory centres were set up where such probabilities were calculated and reported to applicants who requested them. A number of cases are definitely known where specific deleterious effects can be guarded against. Although genetic prophecy can prove very accurate, however, it is never certain since it depends on probability theory.

2. Variations and mutations

A large body of evidence accumulated during the twentieth century linked the groups of studies on Mendelian factors with Darwinian natural selection.

Darwin recognized the fact that the essential basis of natural selection is that organisms vary and much variation is heritable. He did not exactly take variations for granted, but he had no clear and adequate explanation of their origin. While he depreciated Lamarck's theory as a whole, he accepted on a number of occasions the inheritance of characters acquired as a result of changed 'conditions of life'.

Towards the end of the nineteenth century August Weismann (1834–1914) cut off the tails of rats at birth for many generations and found that the offspring were nevertheless born with tails as long as ever. He explained this, and the non-inheritance of other mutilations such as circumcision, by the theory of the germ-plasm (1885), which contrasted the ordinary body cells of the organism with the germ-cells which would later give rise to eggs or spermatozoa and hence contribute to the formation of a new individual. This theory maintained that changes in the body cells do not affect the factors bearing the hereditary characteristics in the germ-cells and that if the progeny differs from its parents the germ-cells themselves and not the body housing them must have been altered. It was highly influential in establishing a climate of opinion for the acceptance of Mendel's work in 1900. This theory received a tremendous amount of observational and experimental confirmation during the whole first half of the twentieth century and was generally held by geneticists everywhere, except in the USSR after the late 1930s where, under the leadership of T. D. Lysenko (1898–   ), an opposed view accepting the inheritance of acquired characters became for some time the official doctrine of biologists in that country.[5, 6]

Hugo de Vries, one of the three re-discoverers of Mendel's work in 1900, made an important discovery when, by studying the evening primrose (*Oenothera*), he found various 'sports', plants not resembling their parents, some of which bred true in their changed form. He concluded that variation in organisms is produced not gradually but by sudden jumps, and he defined the process responsible for such change as mutation (1901). In the light of Weismann's theory it was recognized that mutation affects the germ cells, and it was postulated that all heritable change in organisms results from mutation, though mutation as commonly understood is a result of different processes than had occurred in the material studied by de Vries. True mutation, the process which results in alteration of the hereditary material, involves intrinsic change in the substance or the pattern of the genetic constitution. What had been responsible for the effects observed by de Vries were occasional cross-overs in a very peculiar type of gene-complex.

There were thus found to be two sources of variation in organisms. One was based on the shuffling and recombination of the hereditary factors during the preparation and random combination of the germ-cells, the other on actual alterations of the factors by mutation. Mutations in some cases affect the genes themselves, producing different gene-alleles. In others they involve changes in the number of chromosomes or of chromosome sets, or changes in the arrangement of genes within the chromosome (inversions, translocations etc.).

The mutations studied by de Vries appeared to him to arise spontaneously, that is, the cause of the occurrence was not discovered until later, and subsequently many other apparently spontaneous mutations were observed. As mentioned above, the early work of Morgan and his co-workers on the fruitfly proved successful in part because the rate of spontaneous mutation in this animal is relatively high under laboratory conditions. Great impetus, however, was given to the further investigation of heredity when Hermann J. Muller (1890–   ) discovered in 1927, by a study involving a masterly mathematical analysis and equally masterly experimental methods, that the rate of mutation in the fruitfly might be appreciably increased by the use of X-rays. Later studies by a number of workers showed that the mutation rate could be increased, or new mutations produced, or both, depending on the treatment and the organism used, by other ionizing radiations, or by ultra-violet light, or by high temperature, or even through the application of certain chemicals. The nitrogen mustards prepared for use as poison gases were among the first of the chemical substances to be proved effective.

The discovery of artificial methods of inducing mutations was very valuable for the progress of genetics, but by the middle of the century it did not yet explain the causes of the so-called spontaneous mutations. Most mutations are gene mutations. After the discovery of the importance of DNA for the transmission of hereditary characteristics, it was postulated that mutations might affect the order in which some of the basic constituents of the DNA molecule, the cross-links, are arranged in sequence, or their detailed structure.

Scientists had not, by the middle of the twentieth century, found it possible to control the kind of mutation produced except to a very small extent. They had demonstrated that most mutations, spontaneous or induced, are harmful to the organism, but by selective breeding some of the advantageous ones, or combinations of them, were being put to the service of man, as in the increase of the frequency of egg laying in hens or the production of butter fat in cow's milk.

A vast amount of discussion as to the power of man to influence the production of mutations followed the first explosions of atomic and hydrogen bombs. Since ionizing radiations had been shown to be the most potent agents producing mutations in the laboratory, it became clear that the increase of such radiations as a result of bomb explosions was a potential danger with respect to health and normality, and to the perpetuation and further evolution not only of man but of all living creatures. Similar peril was seen to be inherent in the increase of exposure to ionizing radiations through excessive use of X-rays and other radiations in medicine and industry and through the peaceful uses of atomic energy if not properly safeguarded.

3. *The course of evolution*

The evolutionary effects of mutations were considered in the twentieth century to be mediated by selection. Organisms produce more young than can survive. They vary, and some variations are heritable. Therefore, on the average, more favourable ones will survive to reproduce. Darwin had taken one of his principal clues from an analogy between selection by the domestic breeder and that by nature. The discovery and analysis of mutations finally permitted the elucidation of the change studied by evolutionists in terms of the mutations studied by geneticists. The biologists of the first half of the twentieth century accepted the theory that natural selection acts, with results for the future, upon heritable change occurring through mutation as well as through recombination, and calculations were published in the 1940s indicating that what was known of the age of the earth and of the fossil history of organisms, together with what was known of rates of mutation, was compatible with this theory.[7]

There were many studies of the course of evolution and its operations. Three main trends came to be recognizable: (1) branching evolution leading to diversification, (2) upward evolution leading to improved adaptation and specialization, and (3) limiting evolution leading to stabilization of type. George Gaylord Simpson (1902–   ) was able to calculate rates of evolutionary change in different groups.

Darwin realized that selection by nature was a process involving populations; in fact one of the main ideas leading him toward the development of his theories was Malthus's generalization concerning the rate of increase of human populations relative to resources. The development of new concepts concerning evolutionary mechanisms provided another example of the dependence of twentieth-century biological progress on mathematical theory. R. A. Fisher, J. B. S. Haldane (1892–   ) and Sewall Wright (1889–   ) in the 1930s all developed, independently and nearly simultaneously, mathematical theories responsible for the beginning of a new branch of biological science, population genetics, which dealt with the heredity not of individuals but of groups. From this arose the concept of the gene-pool, or the totality of all the genes and their various alleles of all the organisms making up a population. This became a new frame of reference against which mutations were evaluated, and it became clear that those mutations in the gene-pool would be selected which would enable the population to reproduce most successfully under whatever conditions it existed in nature.

An important result of the concentration of attention on populations was a change in the basis of classification. From the time of Carolus Linnaeus (1707–78) through the greater part of the nineteenth century, biologists had considered the species the fundamental unit of biological classification, a fact which was recognized by Darwin when he chose the species as the focus of his own thinking. The criteria for the classification of organisms changed in a number of ways during the twentieth century. They were no longer limited to the visible characteristics of organisms or their parts as before; as advances were made in embryology, physiology, ecology, biochemistry and immunology, the criteria were extended to include data from more varied aspects of the life of organisms. In addition, under the influence of population genetics, species became defined as reproductive communities sharing actually or potentially a common gene-pool, and the probability of the selection of particular factors was analysed from a statistical point of view. Furthermore, since the mathematical studies suggested that selection in populations varies under different conditions, classification in particular and biology in general turned during the twentieth century to new dynamic studies of populations of organisms in relation to their wider environment.

4. Ecology[8]

Biologists have always had to be concerned in some way with the relationships of organisms to their surroundings, since it is a principal feature of living beings that they are in a continuous state of balanced interaction with such surroundings, including other organisms. Darwin fully appreciated the complexity of the relationships of various groups of organisms to each other and to their surroundings of inanimate nature, and wrote what remained one of the best accounts of the subject.

It was however largely within the twentieth century that the study of the relations between organisms and their environment became codified into the formal science of ecology. The subject acquired great practical importance when chemicals came to be employed extensively to eradicate pests or weeds, or predators were introduced to wipe out pests of a particular species, for these measures affected the balances of populations within an area. At the beginning of the century ecology was predominantly botanical. Henry Cowles (1869–1939), Frederick Clements (1874–1945) and Sir Edward Salisbury (1886–   ) were leaders of schools attempting to understand plant communities. Cowles made the first good studies of the succession of plants from first colonizers through dense forest; Clements made challenging generalizations about the climax which is the final, unchanging stage in succession; Salisbury used these and other results in interpreting British habitats. Plant ecology progressed but little beyond the work of these men. Perhaps the most striking improvement was the result of the expansion of forestry as a subject for research. Modern foresters understood something about the environmental conditions under which different trees flourish.

At the same time, investigators transplanted plants to new environments and so studied the genetic nature of these adaptations to different habitats.

Beginning seriously with studies by E. A. Birge (1851–1950) and Chauncey Juday (1871–1944), important work was carried out on organisms living in lakes. Since a lake is a smaller body of water than an ocean and more narrowly confined, it can be more easily studied as a whole. Limnology, the field of ecology dealing with lakes, made great progress not only in describing the chemical constitution of a lake, but also in analysing its change, becoming almost a study of the metabolism of lakes. This work led to studies on the land and in the ocean in which the names of species play little role, but the numbers of species and their rate of energy consumption are considered. In these studies, natural communities are considered as heat engines transforming energy, ultimately derived from the sun, into living matter. Thus much attention was paid in marine ecology to the conditions governing the abundance of plant plankton, on which all pelagic marine animals depend.

Two new approaches to ecology emerged from the late 1920s. One was centered about mathematical deductions from simple assumptions about the interactions of species. This is profitable because even simple interactions seem too complicated for the mind, unaided by mathematics, to grasp. Consequently, in the hands of Alfred Lotka (1880–1949) and Vito Volterra (1860–1940), some quite unexpected predictions were made from simple assumptions. These assumptions were thereby made testable. This work was the origin of the subject of cybernetics, which became popular in its own right. Subsequently, their work was made more general in the attempt to find necessary and sufficient conditions for populations to oscillate and for stable equilibria.

Coupled with the mathematical approach, laboratory studies of confined populations sought to test which of the mathematical models could be realized with real populations. G. F. Gause (1910–   ) was the most prominent of these laboratory investigators. He was able to show that animal populations are able to change in most of the ways suggested by the mathematicians.

A reaction, however, set in, questioning whether these population interactions, predicted by mathematicians and shown to be possible in laboratory experiments, actually play any part in nature. This reaction on the part of field investigators led to a reanalysis of the mathematical models and laboratory verifications.

Finally, relationships of organisms to one another in the field were investigated, not only as population-problems but in terms of behaviour patterns, in a branch of biological science known as animal behaviour or ethology.

5. Ethology: studies on animal behaviour

Darwin had considered sexual selection to be one mode of action through which natural selection operated. He postulated that the display patterns of male birds, for instance, in species in which the male is brightly coloured and the female drab, evolved as a result of the preference of female birds in that species for bright colour; that is, if two males were competing for a female's favour, according to Darwin's theory, she would choose the more brightly coloured for her mate, and thus the quality of brightness of colour would be passed on to her offspring. Many biologists saw two fallacies in this argument. First, a brightly coloured male might not necessarily have offspring all as brightly coloured as himself. Secondly, this concept was taken by some to attribute to the female bird the same aesthetic tastes and appreciations that characterized her human observers. The tendency to endow other animals with subjective reactions similar to those of man became known as anthropomorphism and was soon recognized as a principal hazard in the interpretation of animal behaviour. The ability to discriminate colour patterns, and in some cases to prefer them, can however be demonstrated on non-anthropomorphic grounds.

In the early part of the twentieth century Julian Huxley (1887–   ) observed and described the highly complicated and seemingly bizarre behaviour patterns indulged in by the male and female great crested grebe during the breeding season. In these diving birds the two potential or actual mates perform, as in a ritual or dance, a sequence of different actions. Many of these activities, such as diving, erecting the crest, lowering the head or spreading the wings, result in one bird presenting in turn strikingly different visual appearances to the other. Huxley's interpretation of such display as a factor in sexual selection was somewhat different from Darwin's. He considered that the display of one bird stimulated the opposite sex partner in a combination of emotional, nervous and biochemical ways.

This postulate permitted the analysis of animal behaviour in less anthropomorphic terms than had previously been practised. Further encouragement was given to the pursuit of such studies when Konrad Lorenz (1903–   ) named and analysed the phenomenon of imprinting, long familiar to farmers and other breeders of birds and barnyard animals. The reason that a duckling normally follows its mother is that she is the first organism of a certain size it sees when it hatches from its egg. Lorenz showed that if it sees for instance a crouching man before it sees a duck, it follows the man as it would have followed its mother; the duckling need only see the object for a short time in order to establish this pattern of behaviour.

Ways by which organisms give clues to one another in many aspects of their behaviour were studied subsequently in many countries and were incorporated in a sort of sociology of nature. One great significance of the development of ethology was that, at a time when much of biology was becoming narrowed to examination of parts of organisms by complicated laboratory instrumentation, it, like the new classification, encouraged many investigators to return to the study of the behaviour of the whole organism in its natural surroundings. Comparative studies of behaviour patterns in a number of related species proved especially rewarding. In other words, even in the twentieth century biologists were continuing to develop fundamental concepts through studies made without complicated equipment and carried out by techniques peculiar to biology.

Ethologists in some cases performed experiments simple in type, either in the field or in the laboratory. For example David Lack (1910–) confronted a male European robin, a bird which fights with other male robins during the breeding season, with both an isolated patch of red breast feathers and a complete stuffed juvenile robin which had no red breast, to ascertain which of these he would attack. Such studies led to the important concept of specific patterned 'sign-stimuli' acting as 'releasers' of specific patterns of activity. The acutal mechanisms within the robin culminating in the attack on the patch of red feathers could be inferred, but it was more difficult to explain other patterns of behaviour, such as the pulling up of grass by a sea-gull in the middle of a fight. Nonetheless, the study of such 'displacement activities' which occur when there is conflict between opposing drives showed promise of increased understanding of animal behaviour.

From the beginning of the century studies on instincts and learning in animals were performed by psychologists as well as by biologists. In studies of learning processes in rats, they discovered that if appropriately rewarded with food for correct performance or punished with slight discomfort, as for instance by a light electric shock, rats could quickly learn to follow mazes or perform other feats. These results indicated the importance of motivation as a factor in learning, at least in rats.

Other students of animal behaviour towards the middle of the twentieth century analysed particular behavioural mechanisms in other types of organisms. J. Z. Young (1907–), for instance, studying the behaviour of the octopus, observed its alterations after the removal or separation of particular parts of the nervous system, and studied the latter by some of the electrical methods first worked out for the study of mammalian brains. Ornithologists showed that in birds day migrants orient themselves with reference to the sun, night migrants with reference to the pattern of the constellations. Some brilliant and successful studies of animal behaviour were made on honeybees by Karl von Frisch (1886–) who discovered experimentally that bees know the direction to follow between hive and food through their ability to analyse the degree of polarization of light from the sky, and the distance between them through some internal nervous mechanism. He found also that they are able to communicate to other members of their community, by executing various movements in a dance, both the direction in which food might be found and its relative distance from the hive. This was a set of processes which to some biologists indicated that bees in their own way might have evolved the powers both to make abstractions and to symbolize them, abilities which had previously been considered the prerogative of man alone, though the symbolization was recognized as controlled genetically and not built up artificially as with human language.

6. *Biological and evolutionary aspects of human behaviour*

Much progress in the biological study of human behaviour was made possible after the end of the nineteenth century by great improvements in methods of operating on the nervous system. The functions of the mammalian and human nervous system became open to experimental investigation only after the perfection of the techniques of anaesthesia and asepsis extended the range and safety in surgery. In addition, such experimentation was facilitated by the increasingly mechanistic outlook and the new knowledge of man's position in the animal kingdom, which made it possible to study human behaviour by the same objective methods as that of other organisms.

Physiologists during the nineteenth century had carried out operations on the nerves entering and leaving the spinal cord in animals. Their results indicated that different sets of nerves are responsible for carrying sensory and motor impulses related to sensation on the one hand and to muscular activity on the other. At the beginning of the century, C. S. Sherrington (1857–1952), who received the Nobel prize in 1932, performed operations on animals which excluded the brain from its control over the spinal cord, and he thus was able to demonstrate the degree to which the spinal cord independently of the brain could co-ordinate complex and purposive actions, such as scratching. He interpreted his results in terms of the integrative action of the reflex pathways in the cord involving both sensory and motor components.

Knowledge of the reflex and its separate components actually dated back to the nineteenth century, but its significance was demonstrated by Sherrington's experimental studies, and the concept was to be responsible for a number of important later investigations directly related to human behaviour. Anatomists, who knew that the spinal cord receives and gives off separate sensory and motor components, localized these pathways within different regions of the cord. This made it possible to demonstrate comparable pathways in parts of the brain and thus to elucidate the function of its different parts. These pathways are not directly evident as a result of simple inspection or dissection of the human brain, which has a very much more complicated organization than the spinal cord. They were, however, worked out by comparison with brains of other simpler vertebrates and especially by comparison with embryonic brains of both simpler vertebrates and of man himself, where the relations are also more simplified. Thus, neurologists and neurophysiologists learned the functions and began to understand the interrelations of many of the groups of cells and bundles of nerve fibres within the human brain which had hitherto been only surmised as a result of studies on brain damage. These clinical results had often previously been difficult to interpret since most accidents and diseases may involve several adjacent parts of the brain rather than only a single one.

The cerebral cortex, or outer layer of the forebrain, is the part of the brain that is relatively larger in mammals than in other vertebrates and relatively larger in man than in other mammals. In man it consists of approximately

10,000,000,000 cells, three times as large as the human population of the globe. Surgical removal of parts of the cortex of the human brain also shed light on the functions of various parts of the brain with respect to sensation and movement. The greatest progress was made, however, when brain surgeons discovered that electrical stimulation of the brain surface could be carried out safely and painlessly in conscious patients. While the results of stimulating the part of the cortex controlling muscular activity could be observed as successfully on other mammals as in man, only man can describe to the surgeon his sensations when the parts of the cortex responsible for them have been stimulated. The results of electrical stimulation demonstrated the degree to which control over various activities is localized in the cortex.

Curiously enough, investigators showed that the particular part of the cortex, the prefrontal area, that is relatively largest in man as compared with other vertebrates, is singularly unresponsive to electrical stimulation. While many had postulated that, because of its size, it was the seat of the highest intellectual activity, its electrical stimulation not only did not give rise to the production of ideas, but did little else except for a few minor portions which are involved in the control of motor activity. In fact, surgeons did not find that stimulation of any part of the cortex caused thinking, although in epileptic patients stimulation of certain areas within the temporal lobe enabled the patient to recover detailed memories which had become unavailable to him. The brain surgeons found also that neither the prefrontal area nor any other particular part of the surface was responsible for the production of consciousness as such, long considered one of the higher functions of the human cortex. They found no particular area of the human cortex which when stimulated would awaken sleeping or otherwise unconscious patients.

Experiments on animals, however, led towards knowledge of some of the mechanisms with which consciousness is associated. These took advantage of the fact that the brain, like other parts of the organism, is characterized by changes in electrical potential. The electrical changes in the heart were studied by physicians using a technique made possible by the advances in physics which permitted detection, amplification and recording of the change in electrical potential of the heart muscle. Other studies by physiologists demonstrated that the nerve fibre conducts its impulse by means of the passage of a wave of electrochemical change. During the 1920s Hans Berger (1873-1941) discovered that changes in the electrical potential of the brain as a whole took the form of rhythmic waves which could be measured by electroencephalography, just as the electrical changes characteristic of the heart muscle had been measured by electrocardiography.

Although the details of the production of the electrical changes in the brain were not understood by the middle of the twentieth century, nevertheless much was learned from the study of the pattern of the waves, which differ in various parts of the brain and in different states of the organism. Most important, the study of electrical changes demonstrated the intimacy of the relations between the cortex and underlying parts; stimulation of the underlying parts changed the electrical wave patterns of the cortex. Physiologists thus learned that the cortex does not work alone in the control of behaviour, but in co-operation with deeper-lying brain parts. It is, for instance, the pathways between the prefrontal cortex, found to be largely unresponsive to electrical stimulation, and a particular underlying part, the thalamus, which are cut by the surgeons who perform frontal lobotomies to relieve the anxieties of some mentally disturbed patients. Furthermore, by means of the combined electrical stimulation of deep-lying parts of the brain in animals and study of the accompanying changes in electrical pattern of the cortex, it was discovered that particular areas deep within the brain, whose activities had not been adequately investigated before, are responsible for waking the brain and holding it in a state of attention.

Not all the studies on human and animal behaviour carried out during the twentieth century depended so exclusively as these on combined surgical, physiological and anatomical methods. Others of equally great significance supplemented these with different techniques. Among the most important and fruitful were the studies leading to the concept of the conditioned reflex for which Ivan Pavlov received the Nobel prize in 1904. Towards the middle of the century study of electronic circuits involving the feedback of information to control the circuit and the development of mathematical theories of communication led to the framing of analogies between the brain and computing machines. The principles of cybernetics provided a possible explanation of how much of man's highly complicated behaviour might be explained by the complexity of circuits in the cortex made up of almost ten thousand million nerve-cells, most of which have multiple connections.

Finally, by the middle of the twentieth century, the brain and its functions, like most other biological systems, became subject to chemical study. Drug action, in the case of opiates for instance, had been known from time immemorial to cause changes in mental activity. During the twentieth century physicians learned to produce changes in mental activity accompanied by less drastic physiological effects through the use of the tranquillizers. They administered chemical substances such as dilantin which in many patients were successful in the control of epileptic seizures. In addition, metabolic studies of the brain began to suggest correlations of the quantity of specific substances, for instance serotonin, with variations in mental function, and many physicians looked towards biochemistry for the diagnosis and cure of hitherto unexplained and intractable nervous and mental diseases, notably schizophrenia.

Advances in knowledge of brain structure and function were not unrelated to evolutionary studies. Some biologists have considered the specifically human mental capacities for intelligence, imagination and conceptual thinking to represent the highest achievement of evolution. In any case man, by means of the use of his mental capacities, has become the latest dominant type in evolution. It was generally agreed among biologists by the middle of the twentieth century that man was by then, and would continue in the future to be, responsible not only for his own destiny but also for that of the rest of earth's organisms.

II. CELL BIOLOGY

One of the principal unifying practices of twentieth-century biology was the explanation of physiological processes in terms of the actions of cells and cell systems. This followed the introduction of the functional outlook into biology through the development of physiological studies which was one of the chief features of late nineteenth-century biology.

Investigations on the nervous system, among many others, exemplify this tendency. Nineteenth-century physiology and surgery made the nervous system accessible to experimental investigation; studies on tropisms encouraged biologists to think of the operations of organisms and their parts as mechanical processes, and thus opened the way philosophically for new interpretations of behaviour, including that mediated by nervous action. The twentieth-century scientists analysed the functions of the nervous system not only by defining its cellular components according to anatomical and embryological criteria, but also by seeking to determine, through electrical and chemical studies, how each cell carries and transmits the nerve impulse to the next. Biologists of the nineteenth century had established the cell as the basic structural unit of the nervous system; those of the twentieth century analysed it as the functional one. Thus they replaced the static concept of the cell by a dynamic one, not only in connection with the nervous system but for all cells, whether these are parts of many-celled organisms or are one-celled organisms in their own right.

Twentieth-century biologists did not however abandon structural study of the cell when they embarked on their biochemical studies of its functional processes. In fact advances in the physical sciences were responsible for such improvement in instruments used for biological observation that many of the nineteenth-century observations on cell structure required almost completely new interpretation. (Pl. 4a, 5a, 5b.)

One of the important new instruments was the phase microscope, invented by F. Zernike (1896–   ), which employed a different system of optics and thereby made visible smaller changes in refractive index than did the conventional microscope. This proved of particular advantage for the study of living cells in tissue culture and independent unicellular organisms. In the 1950s an X-ray microscope was put on the market which showed great promise for the more detailed study of many-celled organisms of small dimensions. But in some ways most important was the introduction of the electron microscope, which permitted the examination of objects, though unfortunately not in the living state, up to a magnification of 100,000 to 200,000 times, in contrast to the magnifications of 1,000 to 1,500 times which were high for the conventional light microscope. By the middle of the century biologists had made a number of important discoveries through its use. They demonstrated that the animal cell membrane is far from the simple wall it had once been considered to be, as is likewise the nuclear membrane separating the nucleus from the rest of the cell. They showed the cytoplasm of the cell to be far more complex than hitherto postulated. They also showed that some of the particles included in the cytoplasm, especially the mitochondria, which are of interest because of their universal distribution in cells of the most varied types, are complicated structures with considerable organization in their own right.

Other advances in physical instrumentation, particularly the invention of the ultracentrifuge which separates broken cells into their constituents by whirling them at a rate of 6,000 or more revolutions per second, made possible the isolation of many kinds of intracellular particles. Biochemists, taking advantage of high-speed centrifugation, demonstrated that isolated mitochondria were the seat of some of the fundamental biochemical mechanisms used by cells to release energy for the life-processes, and biologists postulated which parts of the mitochondria, as known through electron microscopy, might be involved. Such studies made biologists much more conscious of the great complexity of cells.

1. *Differentiation in developing organisms*

Work along a number of lines was responsible for developing an understanding of the general mechanisms by which the organism as a whole and its constituent organs, tissues and cells, operate as units of function.

At the beginning of the twentieth century experimental embryologists, following along the way opened by Wilhelm Roux (1850–1924) and Hans Driesch (1867–1941), made particular innovations in the study of how embryos and their parts become differentiated. Their predecessors had established firmly, by descriptive methods, the concept of progressive differentiation. According to this principle, the fertilized egg in the many-celled organism passes through a series of processes, each one causally dependent on immediately preceding processes. This integrated chain of reactions is responsible for changing the apparently simple egg cell into the specialized and complicated adult whose component cells are structurally and functionally adapted for their special operations. Since, as Henri Milne-Edwards (1800–85) had already emphasized, the organized life of the organism depends on the division of labour among its cells as well as on their integration, the study of the chains of processes whereby these attain their final specialized and integrated state was viewed as one of the key problems of biology, and embryologists devised many new and original methods for its investigation.

Tissue culture, one of the most ingenious of these methods and also one of the most fruitful, was originally developed in order to clarify the exact mechanism of formation of the nerve fibre. It was one of the more curious ironies of biological history that when Schwann formulated the cell theory in the nineteenth century he imagined the nerve fibre, in the face of much evidence to the contrary, to be the product not of a single cell but of many. The controversy as to the precise origin of the fibre was settled only by the introduction in 1907 of the tissue culture method by Ross G. Harrison (1870–1959). Harrison, in order to confirm his belief that the nerve fibre is an integral part of the nerve-cell itself, produced by it and not added on to it by other cells, developed a simple technique whereby he removed from a frog embryo a young nerve-cell before any nerve fibre had been formed. He allowed the young nerve-cell to develop in clotted frog lymph in a microscope slide and he found that it formed a fibre itself in the absence of the other cells which Schwann had postulated as making it.

This simple experiment not only firmly established the nerve-cell as the structural and functional unit of the nervous system, but provided a method which for the first time permitted detailed studies of living cells under conditions controllable by the experimenter. For some years the new method was not so successfully exploited as it might have been. By the 1930s, however, embryologists began to use it effectively to examine the degree to which the early differentiation of cells is controlled by factors resident in the cells, as compared to factors in their environment. They showed that in some tissues and some organisms external factors are more important in influencing differentiation than in others; and that cell types are more susceptible to such influences at younger stages than at older ones.

By the middle of the century, when biologists had become more chemically minded, they took advantage of their ability to grow cells in an artificial environment of known chemical composition, and the method became of more value for the study of plant and animal growth and differentiation, normal and abnormal. It was used to grow cells in which viruses were propagated, and thereby contributed much not only to the theoretical understanding of virus reproduction but also to the control of virus diseases, for instance in the development of the Salk vaccine against poliomyelitis. Later, in the 1950s, experts were able to grow in tissue culture colonies or populations of human cells, each produced by cell division from a single isolated human cell, a technique which promised to provide much information not only concerning normal and abnormal growth of human cells but also as to the role played by mutation during continuous cell division in producing abnormalities of growth and development.

While the tissue-culture experiments enabled investigators to observe the differentiation of various types of cells under a wide variety of chemical conditions, they did not, at least at first, permit investigation of the stimuli which promote differentiation. This problem was approached in a different way. The studies on the fertilization of the egg which had been carried out during the previous centuries had established that it is normally the entrance of the spermatozoon into the egg which initiates the development of the latter. Investigators at the turn of the century discovered that some eggs could be activated to begin their development and differentiation, in the absence of the spermatozoon, as a result of various changes in the chemical and physical surroundings of the egg. This process was called artificial parthenogenesis, and early in the century biologists attempted to find out the exact mechanism of artificial parthenogenesis in animals. Different methods were used with success on different kinds of eggs—changes in temperature, changes in the salt concentration and constitution of the surroundings, changes in their acidity or alkalinity, and in some cases merely shaking or pricking the eggs. These experiments failed to isolate one factor common to them all, and the hope was soon destroyed that there might be a simple explanation of the parthenogenetic effect. Embryologists therefore finally became reconciled to the concept that the entrance of the sperm might be a trigger which set off a chain of reactions in the egg which could also be started by a number of other triggers which seemed to have little if anything in common.

The efforts to determine the mechanisms of fertilization, however, brought some important practical and theoretical advances. Animal breeders found that spermatozoa, even of mammals, could be frozen and chemically treated and stored for later use, and artificial insemination was employed with great success in the breeding of some domestic animals, cattle in particular. In a number of cases artificial insemination was used in human reproduction when sterility prevented normal conception.[9]

On the theoretical side one of the more fruitful results of the fertilization studies stemmed from consideration of the high degree of selectivity of the fertilization reaction, which normally prevents the egg of one species from being fertilized by the spermatozoon of another. Frank R. Lillie (1870–1947), during the first quarter of the century, postulated that this selectivity was controlled by the same kind of reaction which is responsible for the antigen-antibody relationship in immunization against disease, where antigen and antibody interact with great selectivity, presumably because of the shapes of their protein molecules. By the middle of the twentieth century embryologists were studying the possibility that the differentiation of embryonic cells might be controlled in part by the production within the embryo of substances acting like antigens, and such antigens were demonstrated to exist, for instance in the case of the lens of the eye.

Embryologists also used other methods to study differentiation as controlled by factors within cells and, in fact, to some degree its initiation. By the close of the nineteenth century they had begun to develop a technique for transplanting groups of cells from one embryo to another. Tissue-culture experiments deprived cells of their normal cellular surroundings in the embryo; grafting experiments gave cells new cellular environments by placing them in different parts of eggs. It thus became possible to study interactions between new and different combinations of cells and tissues.

By performing such experiments embryologists were able to demonstrate that in the eggs of some species one group of cells could influence another group of cells to differentiate in a manner they would not have done in the absence of the first group; this process was called embryonic induction.

Induction was first analysed, with particular brilliance, during the first third of the century by Hans Spemann (1869–1941). Spemann's first grafting experiments showed that a part of the salamander brain which later becomes the retina of the eye induces the skin lying over it to form a lens. When he transplanted flank skin over this part in a young embryo, the flank skin formed a lens. These experiments were the basis for the concept of induction. A few years later he showed that one part of the very early salamander embryo, if grafted to another salamander egg in the same stage of development, would induce the host to form a second embryo. This region he called the 'organizer'. If the organizer, which acts only during early embryonic development, was divided into two parts before cellular differentiation was completely under way, a single egg could be formed into two embryos rather than one. These results validated experimentally the concept of progressive differentiation according to which each step of development is causally related to the preceding step. Spemann was rewarded with a Nobel prize in 1936.

In the following years embryologists tried to discover the mechanisms by which induction occurs. This was also the period during which interest in biochemistry was burgeoning among biologists. When embryologists showed that dead organizer cells could induce new structures to form, and that even other killed cells from a great variety of organisms, such as guinea-pig liver or mouse kidney, could cause inductions in salamander eggs, they began to search for a particular organizer substance which might be common to all the kinds of cells that had been effective, dead or alive, in producing inductions.

They found, however, that many different chemical agents were successful in producing induction in living eggs or in tissue culture (digitonin—a protein, fatty acids, nucleic acids, a class of organic compounds called steroids, and a number of others). They finally admitted, therefore, that the organizer does not act through the production of a single simple organizing substance, but that various substances can somehow serve as physiological triggers. In the 1950s chemical embryologists were concentrating on the roles of proteins and nucleic acids in induction. Some preliminary but inconclusive attempts were made to ascertain by the use of radioactive isotopes whether such substances or their parts actually passed from inducing cells to those induced to differentiate. Other biologists attempted to discover, by the use of filter membranes with a minute pore of known size, if actual protoplasmic continuity between induced and inducing cells was necessary for induction, and presented some evidence that this might be so.

In fact, however, important genetic studies involving developmental interpretations had been begun long before embryologists were driven to an impasse by the chemical work on the organizer. Richard Goldschmidt (1878–1958) in his important work on sex differentiation in the gypsy moth had already in 1916 attributed great importance to the developmental actions of genes and had explained these functions quantitatively in terms of enzymes; Sewall Wright in the same year discussed the inheritance of coat-colour in the guinea-pig from a developmental point of view. But such contributions were sporadic, in part because little was yet known about the embryonic development of the organisms such as *Drosophila* that were best known genetically; and the genetics was not yet known of those best known embryologically, such as the amphibian and the echinoderm. By the middle of the century, however, combined embryological and genetic studies were being carried out on *Drosophila* (Donald Poulson, 1910–   ), Curt Stern, Conrad Waddington, 1910–   ), Ernst Hadorn, 1902–   ), on salamanders (Rufus Humphrey, 1892–   ), Victor Twitty, 1901–   ), on chickens (Walter Landauer, 1896–   ) and on mice (Leslie Dunn, 1893–   ).

Other developmental studies carried out during the first half of the century ran parallel to those on organizers and genes, but had not yet converged with these by mid-century. These involved the concepts of gradients and fields. Gradient theory implies that the form or pattern of differentiation is set by a system of gradients and fields involving metabolic differences of various sorts.

Polar differentiation of the egg was first discussed in the nineteenth century by Karl von Baer (1792–1876), and Driesch too was much interested in it. Boveri, through his interest in polarity, studied the stratification of visible substances in the egg and introduced the concept of the gradient to explain it in 1910. Very shortly after, in 1911, Charles Manning Child (1869–1954) used the term 'axial gradient' in connection with studies on regeneration, but later applied it to embryonic development. Child considered his metabolic gradients to have their basis in higher rates of oxidation at one pole. While more refined studies later in the century failed to confirm this, his work was of great importance in opening the way toward the metabolic and biochemical interpretations of development that were to become so popular later in the middle of the century.

The field concept encompassed both the axial gradient and organizer concepts. The first ideas responsible for this, though not the name, emanated from the work of Ross Harrison on the development of the amphibian limbs in 1918. In 1921 Hans Spemann considered that the organizer acted by producing a general field of organization; in later stages of development, fields of organization appear in relation to all the main organs, such as limbs.

Field theory was first generalized to cover a number of developmental phenomena by Paul Weiss (1898–   ) in 1926; eight years later Julian Huxley and Gavin De Beer (1899–   ) accounted for a number of developmental data on the basis of what they call gradient-fields, a combination of gradient and field theory. Huxley stressed the importance of gradient-fields in relation to the differential growth of organs and their parts; in molluscan shells such as snails', two growth-gradients operating at right angles determine the characteristic spiral form.

Another basic feature underlying differentiation, established by Waddington, was the channelling of the differentiation of particular organs along well-defined developmental pathways. These are biochemically self-regulating, so that it is difficult for the process to be deviated by environmental agencies and produce an abnormal result. Once the operational unit was identified, embryologists began to identify some of the biochemical and metabolic process involved.

The studies on induction were performed on developing animals. In plants some aspects of growth were more successfully demonstrated to be under the control of known chemical agents. The study of tropisms in the nineteenth century had indicated the degree to which plants were dependent on external stimuli for the direction of their growth, and the tropism theories postulated mechanisms whereby the sunflower turns towards the sun as a response to light and roots grow downward in response to gravity. Plant physiologists in the twentieth century further explained some of these phenomena in terms of the unequal growth of parts of cells, and showed, moreover, that such differential cell growth was caused by the action of specific chemical substances produced in other cells of the plant. These substances, the plant hormones or auxins, were not only chemically identified but were actually synthesized in the laboratory.

2. *Chemical integration: animal hormones*[10]

Before the existence of plant hormones was suspected, physicians and physiologists had demonstrated some actions of hormones in man and other animals. Animal hormones are defined as substances, made by special glands, which are liberated into the blood stream and act as chemical co-ordinators by affecting various other organs. Physiologists during the twentieth century showed that hormones are present and active not only in vertebrates but also in some invertebrates, where they control colour change, moulting and other processes; the same hormone sometimes acts on different tissues, and therefore produces different effects, in separate groups of animals. In many cases the hormones seemed also to act as triggers; in a very few cases their specific biochemical action became known.

These chemical agents came to be recognized as of the utmost importance in preserving the constancy of the internal environment in vertebrates and later in other higher animal types. Their significance was dramatized by the action of some hormones, for instance that of thyroxin, the hormone of the thyroid gland, in producing physiological changes both so drastic and so subtle that they affected even human personality. When such hormones as thyroxin were not only chemically identified but synthesized in the laboratory, the importance of chemical control in the co-ordination of even the most complex functions of complicated organisms was brought home to biologist and layman alike. This importance became still further appreciated when it was discovered that the nervous system also, the other great co-ordinator of body action, transmits its impulses, at least in some cases, through the release of specific chemical substances at nerve endings.[11]

3. *Biology of one-celled organisms*

The importance of biochemical control of cellular activity was recognized not only from considerations of chemical mechanisms controlling growth, regulation, heredity and other complex functions in many-celled organisms. It also became known from studies of one-celled organisms, especially protozoa and bacteria. Biologists were well aware that one-celled organisms are not necessarily simple cells because of being single cells. They recognized an amoeba, for instance, as in some ways very complicated since it can perform within one cell the various functions that are divided up among very different kinds of cells in many-celled organisms. However, since many one-celled organisms do not undergo complicated processes of progressive differentiation and since they multiply by simple division, they provide populations in which multiplication and reproduction can be studied in the absence of differentiation.

Furthermore, the techniques which medical bacteriologists had devised to grow disease-producing bacteria for clinical identification were readily modified to enable physiologists to study, by accurate quantitative procedures, which particular substances bacteria required for their nutrition and their growth.

Bacteriologists made a primary move towards recognition of the fundamental similarity of biochemical processes within organisms when they proved that bacteria require for growth some of the very same vitamins that experts had shown to be essential for the nutrition of many-celled animals and man. Bacteria had been shown to be able to live under a greater variety of chemical and physical environments than any other organism, some of them even in the complete absence of oxygen. When bacteriologists, studying their life processes, proved further that no matter what substances bacteria required for their nutriment, they all stored and expended energy by the same fundamental molecular mechanism as that utilized by all other organisms, they took another important step towards the concept of the biochemical unity of organisms which was to dominate so strikingly the biology of the middle years of the century.

III. THE NATURE AND ORIGIN OF LIVING MATTER

1. *Biochemical unity of organisms*

Thus studies which had begun with strictly biological interests converged by the middle of the century towards chemical studies which covered widely divergent groups of organisms. Breeding experiments, microscopic studies of cells, and chemical investigations of nucleic acids, for instance, all pointed to the fact that DNA acts as the hereditary material in viruses, in bacteria and in many-celled organisms. Likewise, studies on human nutrition and on bacterial growth showed that vitamins are necessary for the life of one-celled organisms and of man.

In the 1930s direct stimulus to biochemical interpretations of cellular differentiation and interaction came from the work of Joseph Needham (1900–   ) who focused attention on a particular class of compounds known as steroids —complex molecules, chemically closely related to each other—which he thought might be responsible for a number of processes related to growth, differentiation and reproduction. Some biologists at that time showed that the hormones responsible for the sexual characteristics of male and female vertebrates belonged to this class of compounds, and others demonstrated that the application of coal-tar products containing steroids could cause cancer if repeatedly applied to the skin of animals. Embryologists showed that some of the agents causing induction were steroids which also caused cancer when applied to the skin. Although it was later shown that a number of agents beside steroids can cause cancer and the steroids are not the only inducing substances in embryos, Needham's emphasis on the varied actions of this one group of compounds was among the important factors spurring the development of the concept of the biochemical unity of organisms.

Before biologists could focus their interest on biochemistry, however, they had first to develop more refined concepts than had been held in the nineteenth century concerning the nature of the living substance itself. The biologists of the nineteenth century defined protoplasm as the living substance, but by the end of the century had modified this concept. Late nineteenth-century physiologists and their followers in the twentieth century described the living system which constitutes cells as a colloidal system of the utmost complexity, and they learned many details of its physical and chemical properties. They studied the salts dissolved in it, its acidity or alkalinity, its electrical and its osmotic properties, its surface tension, and its dynamic relations to its surroundings in terms of physics and chemistry. In the twentieth century the use of the word protoplasm became an historical anachronism.[12]

Physiologists during the twentieth century studied the role of water, of the dissolved salts, ions, free radicals and electrons which participate in the life processes. They also showed that the substances known in the nineteenth century as essential foods in a balanced human diet are necessary constituents of all cells and are involved in the processes of molecular break-down and build-up whereby the cells obtain and use the energy for living.

Advances in organic chemistry during the nineteenth century had permitted chemists to obtain some knowledge of the structure of the complex molecules of proteins, fats and carbohydrates. The biologists of the twentieth century, through improved physical instrumentation, were able to learn much more of the structure of these compounds and the processes in which they are involved.

Particular progress was made in the study of the physical and chemical structure of protein molecules. In some cases the arrangement of their components was ascertained through X-ray diffraction studies; the contraction of a muscle fibre was shown, for instance, to depend on the change of shape of the protein molecule myosin. In addition, chemists and biochemists learned much of the chemical nature of proteins. This was important since the specific constitution of the protein molecule was supposed to be responsible for many of the highly selective properties of biological processes: for enzyme reactions, for instance, and for antibody-antigen reactions studied by immunology.

There was considerable evidence pointing to the fact that variety in the form and constitution of the protein molecule was responsible for much of the variety which distinguishes either one organism or its part from another, or one process within an organism from another. The biochemists contributed to an understanding of the basis of this variety when they were able to identify over twenty of the different amino-acids which are the components of proteins. Chemists who measured the molecular weight of proteins showed that the molecule might contain thousands of amino-acids; and biochemists believed that the various possible combinations of over twenty amino-acids and their various specific arrangements to form proteins might suffice to explain the bewildering diversity of living organisms and of vital processes. Some of them made an analogy to the number of words that might be made by different combinations of twenty letters forming an alphabet.

While organic chemists and biochemists of the late nineteenth and early twentieth century had postulated many processes whereby some of these various organic substances might be broken down in the organism and utilized in the production of energy for living, twentieth-century biochemists went far beyond them in gaining an exact understanding of the mechanisms involved. A number of lines of thought, starting out from widely divergent outlooks, contributed to the elucidation of the interrelated processes whereby energy in the cell is made available for the life processes in a mechanism common to all cells studied.

Otto Warburg (1883–   ), in the early years of the twentieth century, began the studies on the internal respiration of the cell for which he received the Nobel prize in 1931. In demonstrating that a change in combining capacity of the iron portion of an intracellular enzyme is responsible for oxygen transport within cells, he destroyed the old notion that foodstuffs are 'burned' in the organism by direct combination with molecular oxygen. Comparative biochemists found that the iron-bearing enzymes he studied, later called cytochromes, are present in all cells. From his time on, through the middle of the twentieth century, the nature of the oxidative energy-giving processes was a key problem investigated by biochemists.

Louis Pasteur (1822–95), in the 1850s, had been interested in the processes of fermentation by which cells are able to utilize energy for carrying on the life processes in the absence of oxygen. Warburg also was interested in fermentation; but the fact that the reactions occurring in fermentation and in true respiration are intimately allied, as part and parcel of the same general system of chemical reactions, was learned only as the outcome of entirely different series of studies.

Increased knowledge of enzyme action and structure, plus facilitation of the study of the transformation of one substance to another through the use of radioactive isotopes, permitted biochemists in the twentieth century to postulate a highly complicated system of interrelated chemical processes whereby carbohydrate is oxidized to produce energy, both in fermentation and respiration, through the combined action of Warburg's enzymes and of many others. The existence of a great many of the postulated enzymes, intermediate substances, and steps in the reaction was experimentally verified. The most important result of these investigations was the demonstration that the essential agent in the storage, transfer and release of energy within cells is a chemical bond holding together some of the atoms of a molecule called adenosine triphosphate, ATP for short, which is involved in the oxidation of glucose. ATP was later proved to be a principal provider of energy for all living processes in all organisms.

Biochemists discovered that a number of the vitamins and some of the hormones participated in this complex chemical system; they showed by using radioactive isotopes that the breakdown and synthesis of fats and proteins were also part of it. It was one phase of this series of reactions that was postulated as localized in a particular part of mitochondria. The proof of the universality of action of ATP in a system involving the breakdown and synthesis of the fundamental chemicals of the cell contributed strongly to the concept of biochemical unity of organisms, and was one more important step towards amplification of the evolution doctrine through the demonstration that all organisms share common biochemical mechanisms.

The study of ATP, however, involved only the investigation of energy transfer and utilization within the confines of the cell, not the ultimate mechanism by which energy is transferred from the environment into the cell. Different studies were performed to analyse photosynthesis, the process in plants by which all energy for life, originating in the sun, is transmitted to organisms which cannot create their own energy, but can only transform that which they receive from the sun.

Scientists had recognized the interdependence of plants and animals long before the nineteenth century, with respect to some of the life processes. Biologists of the nineteenth and twentieth centuries worked out in considerable detail the turnover of oxygen and of carbon and of nitrogen as exchanged between organisms, living and dead, and the soil and the waters and the atmosphere, in great cycles of synthesis and of generation and decay in which all plants, animals and bacteria participate.

Photosynthesis was known during the nineteenth century to involve the utilization by plants of carbon dioxide and water, and the production of oxygen; and it was known during the nineteenth century that by using the energy of sunlight plants are able to form carbohydrates. The exact methods by which the photosynthetic process is accomplished in plants were vigorously investigated during the twentieth century. Plant physiologists showed that, in the presence of added vitamins and enzymes, the chloroplasts, and even their parts, the grana, which contain the green substance chlorophyll—the primary agent in photosynthesis—can carry out the process when isolated from the cell. Many aspects of the long and complicated system of chemical processes whereby plants break down carbon dioxide and water to form oxygen and carbohydrate became known. But by the end of the 1950s the precise method by which light-energy is converted to chemical energy still remained to be discovered. Thus biologists still had before them the challenge of learning to understand the primary and essential first step in the formation of the basically important carbohydrate molecule which, through its energy-providing properties, together with ATP, furnishes all living organisms with their potential for living and evolving.

2. *The origin of life*

Pasteur in the nineteenth century showed that life is not spontaneously generated under the conditions currently prevailing on our planet. It has been a propensity, however, of biologists for centuries to speculate on the possibility of synthesizing or creating life. Goethe, when he wrote *Faust,* had Faust's apprentice Wagner make a homunculus in a little vial, in the antique alchemical manner, and had him say, 'What used to be organized we can now crystallize'. Extension of the evolutionary concept to include conjectures as to the origin of the solar system and the earth before life arose allowed twentieth-century biologists to speculate in a new way about the origin of life on the earth. Thought in this direction was greatly stimulated by the publication of a book entitled *The Origin of Life on the Earth* by Alexander Oparin (1894–   ) in 1936.

Many theories were expressed during subsequent years as to the origin of organic compounds from inorganic ones; as to the origin of amino-acids and their first syntheses into proteins; as to the origin of photosynthesis to provide energy for life; as to the origin of the self-duplicating molecule DNA and its possible significance as a forerunner of living organisms. These were all based on what could be surmised of the physical and chemical state of the earth and its atmosphere at the time that life was supposed to have arisen, and were all formulated, as indeed were all concepts of biological energetics by the middle of the twentieth century, in the light of the second law of thermodynamics.

Some biologists in the twentieth century tried to duplicate some of the postulated processes in the laboratory. One investigator, by applying an electric spark, synthesized amino-acids from methane (marsh gas) and ammonia in an atmosphere of water vapour. Another, through the application of heat, produced complex molecules called polypeptides, building blocks of proteins, from amino-acids. A third synthesized DNA outside the cell, only however in the presence of pre-existing DNA from the cell used as a primer in the reaction. Proteins themselves were not synthesized, nor was DNA in the absence of provided DNA.

Biologists were well aware that the performance in the laboratory of a few of the suggested steps by which life might originally have come into being was far from the creation of an organism in the sense that Faust's apprentice crystallized his little man. The experiments that were performed were, however, long steps forward. Biologists agreed that under certain conditions life would have originated on earth, and that once these conditions were changed it was unlikely to do so again as its precursors would be utilized and destroyed by existing organisms. The significance of the twentieth-century speculations concerning the origin of life was that they pointed up the degree to which the evolution concept had been extended to include the inanimate as well as the animate universe in a single interrelated whole. Thus, both new understanding of the similarity of biochemical pathways through which all organisms utilize energy for life, and growing knowledge of the basically similar chemical processes by which they all carry out self-propagating and change in the genetic sense, led twentieth-century biologists to a far deeper appreciation than had been formerly possible of the significance of the kinship of evolving organisms to each other and also of their relations to their simultaneously evolving environment.

NOTES TO CHAPTER XIII

1. The concept and theory of 'protoplasm', Academician Ivan Malek points out, were first formulated by the great Czech physiologist J. E. Purkyne (Purkinje) (1787–1869). He was one of the founders of cell theory.

2. To state that genes are responsible for the production of specific enzymes, writes Professor Ignat Emanuilov, it is necessary to proceed from the evidence that they do indeed exist and that they are subject to increase. But M. Demerec writes in his article 'What is a gene? Twenty years later' (*The American Naturalist*, 1955, Vol. 89, No. 844): 'up to the present time there do not exist any means, whether optical, physical, or chemical, for direct study of the gene'.

   From what is said on pages 359–60 it follows that the gene has now been replaced by the molecule DNA, which is stated to be responsible for the self-reproduction of living matter and for heredity. But the leading American geneticist C. C. Lindegren, in his article 'The Stability of the Gene', *Science* (1956), criticizes the theory of the gene. At the Tenth International Geneticists' Congress at Montreal, Canada (1958), in his paper, 'The Recombination of Complex Loops in the Yeast Saccharomyces', he states that one allele can be transformed into a completely different one through contact with maltose— and consequently not through the medium of DNA. In this case, we are told, the specific changes are carried out by specific substrates, and not by DNA. These examples show that representatives of the school of formal genetics themselves criticize the theory of the gene and attempt to substitute for it the molecule DNA, advancing its claims as the unique bearer of heredity.

3. It appears necessary to add, Doctor of Biological Sciences P. Henckel points out, that the harmony of the chromosome theory of heredity is undermined by recognition of the existence of plasmagenes, i.e. by the facts of transmission of hereditary characteristics through the protoplasm of the egg. Mendelian laws do not operate in the case of inter-specific or more distant hybridization, or of vegetative reproduction.

4. It should be stressed, Doctor of Biological Sciences P. Henckel persists, that the racists of Hitlerite Germany, in studying the mechanism of human heredity, not only drew reactionary anti-humane conclusions, but actually elaborated a whole system of measures of coercion aimed at 'improving' the so-called 'German race'.

5. Professor Ignat Emanuilov points out: The authors err in their statement that Weismann's theory was universally accepted during the first half of the twentieth century, and that only in the 1930's there appeared an opposed view regarding the inheritance of acquired characters, which for some time became the official doctrine of biologists in the Soviet Union. Already in 1907–9 the Bulgarian biologist M. Popov, in a number of experimental works, refuted Weismann's theory, and in particular the propositions that chromatin is the unique and exclusive bearer of heredity. 'Eibildung bei Paludina Vivipara und Chromidien bei Paludina und Hielix', *Arch. für mikr. Anat. und Entw. Geschichte*, Vol. 70 (1907), pp. 1–89); he showed that tetraploid chromosomes, which Weismann considered to be a specific feature of germ cells, are in certain circumstances to be found in somatic cells as well ('Über das Vorhandensein von Tetradenchromosomen in den Leberzellen von Paludina vivipara', *Biol. Ctrbl.*, Vol. 28 (1908) No. 17; pp. 555–87); that there are no physiological differences between germ and somatic cells, and that the processes of development and maturation of germ cells are common to all cells of the body ('Experimentelle Zellstudien', *Arch. Zellforschung*, Vol. I, No. 273 (1908); Vol. III, No. 1–2 (1909); Vol. IV, No. 1 (1909)).

6. Sir Julian Huxley calls attention to the fact that the process of 'genetic assimilation', discovered by C. H. Waddington, simulates the inheritance of the effects of environmental agencies, but actually depends on the selection of genetic variants which happen to favour changes in this direction.

7. Professor Vittorio Marcozzi finds the Author-Editors lacking in this chapter in consideration for the importance of Divine plan and Divine intervention, of the distinction between man and the rest of nature, or of what he calls the 'philosophical aspect'. Thus he asserts that 'some biologists maintain that evolution cannot be explained in terms of mutations and selection. Others, however, admit the validity of this mechanistic explanation in the field of micro-evolution, though they consider it incapable of explaining macro-evolution.' He states that 'some of the best psychologists' regard the view that bees 'might have evolved the powers both to make abstractions and to symbolize them' as 'anthropomorphic'. He is willing to apply the term 'consciousness' to animals as well as to man only in 'analogical senses'. To the statement of the Author-Editors that 'some biologists have considered the specifically human mental capacities for intelligence, imagination and conceptual thinking to represent the highest achievement of evolution' (page 370), he remarks that 'the problem here is not merely biological but predominantly philosophical'. When the Author-Editors discuss 'our knowledge of the chemical and physical aspects of life and of the structure of living matter', the commentator denies that this knowledge solves 'the problem of the nature of life. For this problem also possesses a philosophical aspect'. And where the Author-Editors discuss the origin and evolution of life, he states that this process 'cannot be explained simply by the play of accidental factors'. In raising these objections, Professor Marcozzi expresses the Catholic view that scientific problems are to be seen within the framework of belief in the power of a personal God and freedom of the human will.

A quite opposite view of the relations between science and religion is held by Sir Julian Huxley, for whom the findings of science themselves provide the terms in which religion for modern men must be formulated. According to Huxley: 'The supernatural hypothesis . . . appears to have reached the limits of its usefulness as an interpretation of the universe and of human destiny, and as a satisfactory basis for religion. It is no longer adequate to deal with the phenomena, as revealed by the advance of knowledge and discovery. . . .' He continues:

'Twentieth-century man, it is clear, needs a new organ for dealing with destiny, a new system of religious beliefs and attitudes adapted to the new situation in which his societies now have to exist, including the new knowledge which they have discovered and amassed. The radically new feature of the present situation may perhaps be stated thus: Earlier religions and belief-systems were largely adaptations to cope with man's ignorance and fears, with the result that they came to concern themselves primarily with stability of attitude. But the need today is for a belief-system adapted to cope with his knowledge and his creative possibilities; and this implies the capacity to meet and to inspire change. In other words, the primary function of earlier systems was of necessity to maintain social and spiritual morale in face of the unknown: and this they accomplished with a considerable measure of success. But the primary function of any system today must be to utilize all available knowledge in giving guidance and encouragement for the continuing adventure of human development' (*Knowledge, Morality and Destiny*, New York, 1960, pp. 257, 260). Huxley finds the answer in what he calls 'Evolutionary Humanism'.

For further discussion of the subject consult the following:

Theodosius Dobzhansky, *Mankind Evolving* (New Haven, 1962).

Sir Julian Huxley, *Religion Without Revelation* (New York, 1927; rev. ed., 1957).

Bernard Rensch, *Evolution Above the Species Level* (New York, 1960).

C. H. Waddington, *The Ethical Animal* (New York, 1960).

8. In connection with achievements in ecology, writes Imre Törö, Professor of Histology and Embryology, mention should also be made of biocoenosis, which established the methodology of future research in the natural sciences. So far as limnology is concerned, it is essential to refer to the existence of an important branch of modern biology, 'production biology' (a term coined by Hungarian hydrobiologists). It is concerned with research work that serves to increase the productivity of certain natural complexes such as lakes and forests, by examining geological factors, flora and fauna, and the relationships between them, and so to assist in the development of the economy and planned improvement of living standards.

9. Doctor of Biological Sciences P. Henckel points out that at this point mention should be made of the research carried out by I. I. Ivanov on the theory and technology of artificial insemination of mammals. It is widely used today in livestock-breeding.

10. Estimating the Section 'Animal Hormones' Academician Ivan Malek writes: The definition given here of hormones, and the description of their role in the life of an organism, are incomplete. It should be added that:

(1) At the present time hormones are known that are formed, not in particular glands, but in cells having other functions.

(2) Hormones exert an influence on other parts of the body, and their co-ordination of various processes.

(3) Among the functions subject to the action of hormones in invertebrates (insects, crustacea, amoeba, molluscs, and worms) that should be mentioned are growth and metamorphosis, which are two of the most important and best studied.

(4) Marked analogies have been discovered between the hormone system of vertebrates and that of the best studied groups of invertebrates (insects and crustacea).

In some cases something more than mere analogy is involved. This shows that the system of internal secretion is just as common and essential to animals as the nervous system, digestive system, etc.

11. Doctor of Biological Sciences P. Henckel points out that very little is said here about hormones in vertebrates. Mention should be made of the dependence of secondary sexual characteristics on hormones of the sex glands and experimental sex changes—of the work of Pezard, M. M. Zavadovsky, Witschi, and others. Neurosecretion, as a particular type of chemical interrelation, writes Academician Ivan Malek, has recently been described and carefully evaluated by the scientists E. and B. Schrarrer (1945–54). They describe it as an inner secretory function of certain nerve fibres, connected with the migration of granules of secretory substance from the axis cylinder (axon) of these cells to the spot where they are dissolved into the blood-stream.

At the present time neurosecretion is known to be a characteristic of all the main species of animals. In all of them it plays a role as an intermediary between the nervous system, charaterized by short but instantaneously arising interrelations and by responsiveness to external impulses, and the endocrine system, as a means of regulation that functions slowly, over a protracted period of time.

12. It appears necessary to add, writes Doctor of Biological Science P. Henckel, that the concept of the protoplasm as a static (microscopic or submicroscopic) entity was undermined at the beginning of the twentieth century by the experiments of A. G. Gurvich. He showed that intensive centrifugation of the eggs of amphibia and echinodermata, producing stratigraphy of the ooplasm, does not prevent mitotic division of the nucleus and granulation of the egg on account of the restitution of the ooplasm. In the 1930s Gurvich developed a 'physiological theory of the protoplasm', which he considered to be a complex of non-equiponderant molecular constellations sustained by exothermal chemical reactions of the metabolism.

CHAPTER XIV

FOOD AND AGRICULTURE

I. INTRODUCTION

THE interplay between advances in the biological sciences and their application to the promotion and preservation of life was, if anything, even closer and more immediate than was the case with developments in the physical sciences and their application to the control over material resources.

The world-wide concern with the promotion of agriculture and the improvement of health led to a tendency to put new knowledge to work as rapidly as possible to improve crops, save lives or prevent disease. In most countries the promotion of new knowledge of agriculture was undertaken as a positive government responsibility, and there was a vigorous exchange of information as knowledge flowed from the scientific laboratory and as it came back in the results of practical experiment in the field. The medical profession was eager for the new tools which advancing biological knowledge could supply and the results of medical experience and tests in practice constantly flowed back to the biologist, to provide him with data for his further research. Like the alert physician, the scientific-minded twentieth-century farmer was continually extending the range of knowledge through testing and experiment.

The application of the biological sciences, moreover, was generally less hedged about by barriers to the free flow of technical information than was sometimes the case in the physical sciences, where trade secrets, patents and considerations of military security stood in the way of the pooling of knowledge. With few exceptions agriculture and medicine were both open books, and the institutions related to them were oriented toward complete sharing of tested knowledge as it emerged.

New knowledge arising from the biological sciences had an immediacy to the lives of people which much of the knowledge of the physical sciences lacked. The modern individual could use a telephone, listen to a radio, ride in an aeroplane, turn an electric switch or drive a car with little or no knowledge of any of the scientific principles involved. Somebody else could do the scientific knowing and thinking for him. But the ordinary individual had to know at least a little of the principles upon which his own health practices depended, and some elementary ideas relating to nutrition. It was usually the farmer himself, and not a remote production manager, who had to make observations and decisions involving an understanding of some of the biological principles relating to growth and genetics.

The results of the application of physical science were more spectacular,

and these appeared to be the technological changes which most greatly transformed the life of mankind during these years. Yet the application of the
biological sciences may well have brought a more profound revolution in outlook and have been more responsible for the incorporation of a scientific
point of view into the minds of broad segments of mankind.

Application of scientific knowledge to the production of food during the
twentieth century, and to its preservation and distribution, enhanced the
capacity of the earth to feed its people and reduced the proportion of the
population required in agriculture and fishing in order to produce food for all.
These developments were most marked in the countries which combined
high population density with advanced scientific development, such as
western Europe and Japan, in the labour-scarce countries, especially the
USA, Canada, New Zealand and Australia, and in the USSR which reconstructed its agriculture with the application of scientific techniques. The
scientific approach to human nutrition focused world attention on nutritional
needs and led to measures designed to bring protective foods to vulnerable
groups in the population, to modify food habits and to redirect food production.

Yet although increases in agricultural productivity kept pace with productivity in industry in areas of most advanced agriculture, and even outstripped it during the second quarter of the century in the USA, for the world
as a whole productivity in agriculture remained relatively low.

During the first half of the twentieth century the gap in level of living
widened as between the two-thirds of the world's people that worked the land
and the one-third that depended on industry and related activities. This
situation led the Director of Agriculture of the United Nations Food and
Agriculture Organization (FAO) to characterize agriculture at mid-century
as a 'depressed industry' and to observe, 'it is science and technology which
form the basic pattern of modern human society, and if agriculture lags
behind in its application, it will lag behind in the social and economic status
of those occupied in it'.*

Destructive farming, grazing and lumbering practices in many parts of the
world, moreover, resulted in serious loss of soil productivity through erosion,
depletion and drought, destroyed wild life and greatly reduced areas remaining in a natural state. Such practices reflected carelessness with respect to
abundant land resources in some areas and pressure of population in others;
where new techniques were applied without regard for the ecological balance,
they too could have serious effects.

As these threats to the agricultural base came to be recognized, they
aroused a counter-movement for conservation of soil and forest resources and
measures for soil improvement designed to check the forces of destruction
and to build up the productivity of poor or depleted land.

During the twentieth century the majority of the world's people continued

* F. T. Wahlen, *Address to the 8th Session of the FAO Conference* (1955).

to be engaged in agriculture, as had been the situation since time immemorial. But a marked decline in the proportion of the population so engaged had already set in by the opening of the century, not only in the industrial countries of western Europe which depended on the agricultural resources of the Americas and Australasia for much of their grain and meat, but in these food-supplying regions as well. Throughout the nineteenth century, and in spite of the settlement of vast new lands, the proportion of the labour force of the United States engaged in agriculture had steadily declined; in 1900 it stood at only 37·5 per cent.

In the first half of the twentieth century the application of technology to agriculture sharply divided the countries of advanced agriculture from those which continued to follow ancient ways and widened the gulf between the traditional agricultural villager and the farmer in industrially developed countries. Only where agriculture was itself transformed by technology did the farmer share in and become part of the modern age. As he became a user of new knowledge, whether as a New Zealand cattle raiser, an American maize grower, a Dutch dairyman, the manager of a Soviet collective farm or member of an Israeli *kibbutz*, he entered the main stream of twentieth century life. In these countries agriculture and industry advanced hand in hand; industry was the basis of much new agricultural technology, while the presence of opportunities for employment in industry drew surplus labour from the land and created conditions which favoured measures to raise the productivity of those who remained.

The account of the application of new knowledge in the field of agriculture during these years must therefore be an account of agriculture in the advanced agricultural countries, notably the United States, Canada, New Zealand and Australia where productivity per worker in agriculture was highest; in Holland, Denmark and Japan which achieved high yields per acre; and in the USSR where the conversion of peasant farming to scientific agriculture by means of collectivization brought major improvements, though at mid-century rates of production were still well below those of the most advanced countries. And since institutional factors affected the application of knowledge to agriculture, it is necessary to consider such matters as land tenure, credit, the provision of information, and public measures to affect the economics of agriculture, as these facilitated technical advance or had the effect of reinforcing traditional methods.

Agricultural production during the twentieth century was carried on within the types of farm units traditional to different areas, or those created by more or less radical social changes during these years. In western Europe, North America and Australasia the unit was the family farm; large-scale plantations, cattle ranches and 'factories in the fields', as well as tiny holdings, were only minor elements. In these areas it was the owner-cultivator providing his own capital, labour and managerial skill who was the main agent for the application of scientific knowledge to agriculture, aided by research, information, technical advice and credit provided by government and co-operative agencies.

In eastern Europe, much of South America and most of Asia, most land was held in large estates worked by peasants, either as farm labourers or as holders of small plots under various forms of tenure, or it was divided into very small holdings worked independently. If agricultural technology reached these areas it was through the large landowner, for the peasants did not have access to new knowledge or the means to apply it. Only as major political and social changes broke down the system of *latifundia* did the agricultural populations in these regions share the new knowledge and its application. This was even more true of the traditional agricultural units of tribal Africa.

The USSR following the October revolution, and especially after the inauguration of the first five-year plan, converted the system of peasant agriculture on large estates which had existed under the tsars into a system of large socialist units. The people's democracies of eastern Europe took steps in the same direction in the decade after the second world war, while the Chinese People's Republic organized the peasants into agricultural communes.

Soviet state farms, *sovkozi*, which came to produce about a quarter of the agricultural output of the Soviet Union though numbering less than 10 per cent of all farms, served as examples, demonstrating the application of new agricultural techniques. Collective farms, *kolkhozi*, were unions of small peasants formed to conduct large-scale production on the basis of co-operative ownership of the means of production and the joint labour of members. Both state and collective farms were very large operations, state farms in the 1950s averaging as much as 25,000 acres and running up to 375,000 acres, while collective farms averaged around 5,000 acres and ran up to more than 60,000 acres. They were in marked contrast to the farms producing for market in the USA which averaged less than 350 acres. The large size enabled each farm to have its own agronomist, agricultural engineer, veterinary surgeon or other specialists, as well as central barns and storage facilities. Until the late 1950s, however, all machinery was supplied through state-operated machine-tractor stations.

The workers on state farms and the peasant members of collectives, numbering less than 100 households on the smaller units and more than 500 on the larger and averaging between 200 and 300 in most regions, composed one or more villages on each farm. With the food produced by each family on the small plot adjacent to its house, and a portion of the crop set aside annually for capital improvements, each farm was largely a self-sustaining community, with its own school, social centre, health service and other facilities. These were the units through which the fruits of scientific knowledge, supplied by the state, were applied to agriculture throughout the Soviet Union and the countries which adopted similar systems of socialized production.

During the first decade of the century efforts to increase yields and improve the quality of major crops through better knowledge of soils and the use of fertilizers and of improved strains were intensified in European countries and North America. The great period of exploitation of virgin land in the western hemisphere and Australasia was past. Though some new land was brought into cultivation, this was largely marginal grassland converted to grain culture through new techniques of dry farming. It had become apparent that major gains would have to be achieved on lands already in use.

The first world war stimulated food production and the development of agricultural technology, especially in the transatlantic areas undamaged by war, and laid the basis for a marked increase in agricultural productivity in the years between the wars. The use of improved types of farm tractors spread with great rapidity in North America after 1920, not only reducing the labour involved in farm operations but releasing for food crops land formerly required to support draught animals. In the Soviet Union tractors were introduced as a key element in the collectivization of Russian agriculture and its reconstitution on a scientific and technological basis. European countries whose production had been curtailed by war recovered and soon exceeded former levels, except in parts of eastern Europe where changes in land tenure reduced the output of some former cash crops. Although new lands were not a major source of expanded production in this period, more northerly lands were brought under cultivation in the USSR as new strains of grain were developed, some new lands were opened up in Argentina and Brazil, Italy and Holland reclaimed land through drainage, and arid lands were cultivated by means of irrigation in the United States, as well as in the Middle East and India.

The principal bases for the greatly increased yields in these years, measured both in yields per acre, which were high in Europe, and production per agricultural worker, most noteworthy in North America, were: the spread of mechanization, the application of genetics to the development of more productive and disease-resistant strains, the increased use of scientifically designed fertilizers, the use of improved fungicides and insecticides, improved methods of tillage, and scientific farm management. The production of livestock, milk and eggs was correspondingly increased by improvements in animal nutrition, selective breeding and disease control.

Prior to the second world war all of these developments were confined almost entirely to the prosperous, industrialized segments of the world, chiefly North America, Europe, Australasia, the USSR and Japan. It was the industrial potential of these countries, in fact, which made possible the widespread application of new knowledge to agriculture. Without a vigorous chemical industry to produce a large volume of each new insecticide, weedkiller or fertilizer, and implement producers to turn out agricultural equipment in quantity, the tremendous gains in agricultural productivity during these years could not have been made.

Elsewhere there was little change in ancient, traditional agricultural

methods and in the availability of food, although some European countries
initiated a small amount of agricultural research and development in areas
under their colonial administration and a start in the same direction was
made in the western hemisphere through the establishment of the Inter-
American Institute of Agricultural Sciences in Costa Rica. Famine remained
endemic in Asia and struck in China and India several times during the period.
In Africa the traditional subsistence agricultural economy was undermined in
some areas by the drawing off of men to the mines or by shifts from subsistence
to cash crops.

There thus developed in the inter-war years, outside the self-contained
economy of the USSR, a world pattern of countries where agriculture had
become so productive that markets were glutted with surpluses and others
with low rates of production whose people lived at precarious levels far
below the average consumer in the food-rich areas. The problem of agricultural surpluses in the countries of high technology was intensified in the 1930s
by the world-wide economic depression which reduced both domestic and
world markets, and by the tariff walls erected by European countries seeking
to make themselves more self-dependent against the threat of a second
world war. Countries experiencing such surpluses instituted various measures
to protect farmers' income from the effects of glutted markets. The problem
of endemic hunger in many parts of the world, however, was not yet a matter
of active world concern.

In the mid-thirties a new element entered the picture, which had major
influence on the direction of developments in the following years—the focusing of attention on the problem of nutrition. The new science of human
nutrition, which had been developing since the early years of the century,
was brought into public consciousness and public policy by a series of events:
the League of Nations appointed a Mixed Committee on Nutrition in 1935;
two publications attracted wide attention, Sir John Boyd Orr's *Food, Health
and Income* (1936) and the United States Department of Agriculture's *Diets
at Four Levels of Nutritive Value and Cost* (1933); the results of the dietary
surveys undertaken in several countries revealed the presence of extensive
under-nutrition and malnutrition even in countries with surplus food supplies.

During the second world war nutrition became the basis of agricultural
policy, most notably in Germany, Japan, Great Britain and Switzerland,
where nutritionally oriented production and rationing sustained the population under prolonged wartime stress and, in the case of Britain, even improved the nutritional level of segments of the population. After the war,
nutritional considerations entered into the agricultural policies of both
food-rich and food-poor countries.

In the decade after the war the position of the industrialized, scientific
farmer in Europe, America and the USSR was consolidated. The scientific
approach was applied with increasing effectiveness to problems of farm
management, over and beyond the separate component factors affecting

production. The agricultural entrepreneur who operated an economic-sized farm with the tools of modern science and technology, and likewise the members of collective farms, became as much a part of the modern world as their industrial counterparts.

This decade also saw widespread organized efforts to place in the hands of the peoples of underdeveloped areas the means to reconstruct their traditional food production, to reduce the backlog of malnutrition and to provide a basis for sustaining the coming generations. Technical assistance programmes of FAO, the United Nations and its other specialized agencies, the Organization of American States, individual countries and private welfare groups supplemented the national efforts of developing countries to improve their agricultural methods and raise their nutritional levels. In the people's republics of eastern Europe and China, this objective was sought with the technical co-operation of the USSR by means of the reconstruction of their agricultural economies mainly on a collective basis.

At mid-century world attention was focused on the problem of how to achieve and maintain a balance between food production and consumption at a level of health and vigour. Both in the areas of individual farming and in those of socialized agriculture it was widely recognized that this did not depend upon agriculture alone, but upon many aspects of economic life: industrial development to employ unused and unneeded agricultural workers, the provision of cheap and abundant power, the effective preservation, transport, storage and distribution of agricultural and food products, and the means of financing the highly capitalized modern farming operations. It depended on access by farmers to the kind of education and continuing sources of information which would enable them to understand and apply the growing body of scientific knowledge in the field.

The establishment of the United Nations Food and Agricultural Organization in 1945 provided an international organ for world food development. Its studies and reports and its programme of work were directed toward the application of agricultural technology on a world scale to the welfare of the world's farmers, to the effective elimination of hunger and to the promotion of good nutrition. Its creation as the first of the United Nations agencies reflected the sense of urgency with which the countries of the world had come to view the problems of food and agriculture by mid-century.

II. AGRICULTURE

1. Development of agricultural technology

Agricultural problems varied sharply in different areas but in one form or another they were present everywhere. For the underfed half of the world's population, especially in Asia, food production even in the years after the second world war was lagging behind in the race with population increase, though by mid-century the rate of lag was falling. In areas of advanced agricultural development, such as Denmark and Holland, scientific farming lay at the basis of the nation's prosperity and must be maintained. Countries such as Britain which had largely abandoned agriculture in favour of industry turned to scientific farming for national security.

CHART XV. Food Consumption *per capita*: Calories, Protein, Cereal, 1958 and pre-World War II in Selected Countries.

Source: *U.N. Statistical Yearbook*, 1960.

For the new lands of the Americas and Australasia, where extensive farming of virgin soil could no longer bring the rich returns of the previous century, science and technology had brought highly productive agriculture, but had left unsolved many problems of economic adjustment. The USSR, confident that its state and collective farms offered the most effective means of raising productivity, was still striving to bring the gains in agriculture up to those in industry. Israel's efforts to bring fertility to barren lands in the Middle East was one of the most determined of the widespread efforts to make arid lands productive. Africa's potentialities under modern methods of cultivation were only beginning to be explored at mid-century.

For mankind as a whole, the critical questions were: how could the productive capacity of the earth be conserved and enhanced rather than destroyed; how could the world's capacity for food production be developed and used to sustain the world's people; and what limits, even under favourable conditions of conservation, exploitation and distribution, would the earth's resources place on the optimum size of the world's rapidly growing population?

(a) *Agricultural technology at opening of the twentieth century*. At the beginning of the century a balanced system of productive agriculture existed in northern Europe and in some other areas of the temperate zone to which the European system of crop rotation had been extended. This system, developed in the late eighteenth and nineteenth centuries, involved the rotation of row crops, such as wheat, with grasses and legumes and the use of animal manure and chemical fertilizer. It had raised north European wheat yields from 6–10 bushels per acre, where they had stood from Roman times to the end of the eighteenth century, to 20–30 bushels by 1900, with corresponding increases in other crops and substantial increases in the production of milk and meat. It provided the framework for further increases of 30–50 per cent in European yields during the first half of the twentieth century, in spite of the setbacks resulting from two destructive wars. It also laid the basis for improvements which greatly increased productivity per farm worker. By mid-century it was still the only system of permanent agriculture that produced continually high yields while maintaining the fertility and integrity of the soil.

In the new lands of the western hemisphere and the south Pacific the foundation was being laid for a shift from extensive cultivation that exploited the plentiful soil to scientific methods of conserving soil and increasing production. In the United States agricultural experiment stations had been established in each state and a national soil survey to study and map the character of the soil had been inaugurated in 1899.

In Japan at the opening of the century a system of intensive rice cultivation on irrigated land was beginning to show the higher yields that were to make the Japanese system an example for neighbouring countries of Asia.

During the twentieth century many types of new knowledge revolutionized agricultural production in some areas and revealed immense possibilities for the rest of the world: knowledge of soils—their properties, structure and response to different methods of treatment; of genetics which made it possible to improve the strains of plants and animals; of nutrition which revealed the needs of plants, animals and humans and the means of satisfying these needs; of the physiology of plants, animals and humans which indicated both how to provide conditions favourable to healthy growth and how to destroy noxious weeds and pests and control disease; of chemistry as it permitted the development of countless fertilizers, pesticides and drugs; of engineering which produced mechanical equipment to supplement and replace human and animal labour.

From time to time a single development appeared to be of overriding importance, such as the use of DDT to free areas of potentially productive land from the malarial mosquito or the spectacular increase in yields from hybrid maize, or the saving of whole herds through elimination of rinderpest in Africa and Asia. But generally the agricultural achievements of the twentieth century were the result of a combination of interrelated measures. In the final analysis they depended on the conversion of the traditional cultivator who practised a routine craft into one who used new knowledge as it became available, evaluated its results according to scientific principles, and exercised sound judgment and skilful management at each step in the farming process.

(b) *Soil science and plant nutrition*. Basic to twentieth-century agricultural progress was the growing knowledge of the world's soils, and how to make and keep them productive. Soil science was not new; it had been inaugurated with the establishment of the Rothamsted Experimental Station in England in 1843 and with major Russian efforts in the 1870s to explore and analyse the Russian land-mass with its great range of climate and topography.

At the opening of the twentieth century the prevailing concept of soil was that which had been put forward by the German chemist, Justus von Liebig (1803–73), who regarded the soil as a sort of bank from which plants drew the chemical nutrients which had been placed there. Study and application focused on soil chemistry and the use of fertilizers. As the work of Russian scientists became better known, especially that of V. V. Dokuchayev (1846–1903) and his associates, the concept of soil shifted from that of a storage vault into which nutritious chemicals were inserted and withdrawn, to that of an immensely complex structure alive with micro-organisms and composed of many interacting layers whose character was determined by the original rock from which they were formed, time of formation, climate, vegetation and the configuration of the land. Soil science had to confront thousands of distinct kinds of soils, categorized by Russian soil scientists under a few main heads, and to determine how best to manage each.

The most pressing problem of soil management in many areas was how to check the destructive erosion which took an annual toll of millions of acres, especially in new lands where farmers 'mined' the soil. A general erosion survey in the United States in 1934 estimated that two-thirds of the land had lost more than a quarter of the original topsoil—some had lost all—and that half of the land in cultivation was being progressively depleted by the practices then in use. Books with such titles as *Our Plundered Planet* (by Fairfield Osborn, Boston, 1948) dramatized the problem created by open cultivation of steep hillsides, overgrazing and cutting of forests which destroyed the grass and trees that had held the soil and retained moisture, and the ploughing up of the dry prairies.

From the 1930s onward, prevention of erosion became a major defensive component in programmes for agricultural development, as many governments undertook intensive efforts to teach their farmers such soil conservation practices as contour-ploughing and maintenance of grass cover, and embarked on construction projects for upstream dams, reforestation of denuded hillsides, restrictions on overgrazing, and the planting of shelter belts to check wind and dust storms. By mid-century these steps had reduced but had not eliminated the erosion threat. The United States had not yet fully reversed the downward trend in soil fertility, while major losses continued in South America, Africa and elsewhere. In irrigated areas land was still being lost because of salt accumulation much faster than preventive and restorative measures and reclamation could counteract the process.

With progress in soil science, soil conservation shifted from the negative effort to prevent waste to positive attention to soil management.

Recognizing that many of the arable soils of the world are made better by good farming than they were in their natural state, soil scientists insisted that low fertility of the soil could no longer be accepted as automatically ruling out certain areas or condemning them to low productivity. They expressed the view that the technical possibilities for expanding the world's food supplies were very great, noting that 'the evidence from soil science leads to the belief that, given favourable social and institutional environments, the world has abundant resources for a dependable food supply under efficient soil conservation practices, based upon the soils that we have and the results being obtained by a fraction of the world's cultivators'.*

The techniques developed by soil scientists were based on the analysis of the entire profile of a particular soil to several feet in depth, noting its physical properties and chemical and bacterial content in relation to its location and climatic environment. Some forty major types of soil were identified, with subdivisions running into the thousands, and these were used for the construction of detailed soil maps and as a basis for advice to farmers as to how best to use their particular land. By mid-century the detailed mapping of the soils of the United States and of the USSR, which had been in process in both countries for fifty years, was far from complete. Elsewhere extensive

* Charles E. Kellogg, *Address before the Fifth International Congress of Soil Science* (Leopoldville, Belgian Congo, August 1954).

soil mapping had been carried out in Canada, Australia and New Zealand; considerable mapping had been done in Hungary, Portugal and Belgium, as well as in Great Britain and the Netherlands; soil mapping had been begun in parts of Africa, notably Southern Rhodesia, the Belgian Congo and British and French colonial areas. But nowhere had soils been fully mapped in detail.

Farmers of the temperate zones profited more during this period from the developments of soil science than did those of the tropics, although the latter had even greater need of a scientific basis for soil management under the rigours of tropical climates. Only a beginning had been made in systematic work on these soils at institutes of tropical agriculture in India, Indonesia, the Belgian Congo and Puerto Rico. Under the technical assistance pro-grammes of the FAO, the US and the Colombo plan, soil scientists were sent to some thirty countries during the ten years following the second world war.

The study of soils was paralleled by a growing knowledge of plant nutri-tion. Attention was first focused on the major nutrients needed for plant growth—nitrate, phosphorous and potassium—and the conditions under which they were found in the soil in a form which plants could use. Chemical or organic fertilizers were designed to provide these in the balance which the particular soil and the particular plants required. The effect of soil acidity on specific plants had long been recognized and the liming of acid soils was a generally accepted practice.

Even with adequate supplies of these basic substances, however, crops showed signs of malnutrition and set scientists searching for the causes. These investigations revealed that a variety of minerals such as iron, boron, manganese, copper, zinc, nickel, cobalt, are needed in minute quantities, and that the addition of these 'trace' elements to soils which were deficient in one or another mineral could bring spectacular results, such as those achieved on what had been thought to be uncultivable lands in Australia. The science of plant nutrition was carried to the point where plants could be grown in water, supplied with a complete set of chemical nutrients.

Biologists, meantime, identified the role played by various micro-organisms as they affect the nature of the soil and the ability of plants to derive nourishment from it. The discovery in 1888 that bacteria which grow on the roots of legumes enable these plants to take nitrogen from the air and then convert it into usable form in the soil had enhanced the importance of legumes in systems of crop rotation and led to much work on the develop-ment of types of legumes suitable for various climates, soils and purposes. Further understanding of the processes by which the decomposition of organic matter in the soil contributes to its chemical content and to its structure made it possible to use manures and composts more effectively. Some people in fact insisted on the exclusive use of organic material rather than chemical fertilizers to maintain soil fertility. Their view was not widely accepted in its most extreme form, but their insistence on the importance of soil structure and the presence of humus was a reminder that continuous productivity of the soil depends on more than the known array of inorganic chemical nutrients.

Emphasis on soil structure also led to studies of methods of ploughing and cultivating the soil other than those which happened to be traditional to a particular area, and resulted in the design of implements suited to the depth or manner of treatment needed. Chemists investigated the possibility of treating the structure of the soil chemically and experimented with chemicals that appeared to have some capacity to loosen clay soils and maintain the new structure for a period of years.

When careful studies of the most effective ways to use a wide variety of fertilizers were coupled with progressive knowledge of plant nutrition, they revealed that yields could be greatly increased if far larger quantities of chemicals were used than had been thought to be effective, and if they were applied at the right time, in properly prepared soil and in the most usable form. In the 1950s farmers in the United States were using more than five times as much fertilizer as they had used only twenty years before, and were applying much of it with the precision which agricultural science dictated.

Extensive use of chemical fertilizers was confined almost wholly to the agriculturally advanced countries. It was negligible in Asia, except Japan, in the Near East, except Egypt, in Africa and in most of Latin America. Commenting in 1954, the FAO reported that 'taking the world as a whole, we have only begun to use the potentialities inherent in the chemical fertilizer industry'.*

(c) *Plant genetics and growth.* While soil science and research into plant nutrition laid a basis for increased yields, plant geneticists were hard at work seeking improved strains of wheat, rice, maize and other major crops. In each of the agriculturally advanced countries a continual process of selection and testing singled out the strains best adapted for the particular climate, soil, moisture, resistance to disease, or other factor needed in a particular area. In the US in 1955, 70 per cent of the cultivated land was planted to improved varieties that had not been in existence twenty years before. Among major crops the proportion of new varieties was even higher, including 80 per cent of the wheat, 86 per cent of the maize, 92 per cent of the oats, 95 per cent of the cotton, and 98 per cent of the soya beans.

Although the results of plant breeding to secure better stocks penetrated more thoroughly in North America than in most other areas, improved strains of basic crops were developed, tested, multiplied, distributed and planted in western Europe, Japan, Egypt, the USSR and in some parts of Argentina, Brazil and Mexico. In the years after the second world war,

* W. H. Pawley and others (FAO), *Possibilities for Increasing the Supply of Food and Agricultural Products by Exploitation of New Areas and Increasing Yields*, paper presented to World Population Conference (Rome, 1954).

scientific plant breeding as a relatively low-cost means of increasing food supplies was taking hold in the newly developing countries, especially in parts of India, Indonesia, Ceylon and Formosa.

Plants were bred for many different factors, not only high yields but adaptation to longer or shorter growing periods, or to colder or warmer, wetter or drier conditions. Plants were bred with a view to ease of harvesting by machinery, as for example types of cotton that grew high on sturdy stalks and ripened simultaneously for harvesting by mechanical cotton pickers. From the first attempt in the US in 1895 to develop a strain of cotton resistant to a soil-borne wilt disease, crops threatened with extinction were saved by the development of disease-resistant varieties. These included, among others, wheat and other grains resistant to rust, sugar beets, sugar cane, tobacco and lettuce. For nearly every vegetable, strains were developed that withstood the most threatening disease to which they were subject. Development in the USSR of sunflower strains resistant to rust and mildew made this the major source of vegetable oil in the Soviet Union, after its production had been abandoned in the United States in favour of soya beans because of susceptibility to disease.

Breeding for specific factors in the environment had dramatic effects in extending the areas which could be cultivated. Marquis wheat, for example, based on a cross between a European and an Indian variety, opened up much of western Canada as a result of its earliness and yield. Breeding for resistance to drought greatly extended the limits of the wheat belt in Australia and North America. Efforts, especially in Canada and the USSR, to breed earlier maturing varieties of various crops continued to push northward the frontiers of cultivation and offered possibilities for bringing into use the lands of the northern zone.

Selective breeding and crossing of strains according to Mendelian principles in order to reinforce or introduce desired characteristics accounted for most of the advances attributable to plant breeding, but the most spectacular results were obtained through in-breeding and hybridization. Initial experiments in developing pure strains of maize by in-breeding in order to eliminate recessive characteristics, and then crossing these pure strains, were undertaken in the early years of the century by scientists engaged in genetics research. Their discovery that the first generation of certain hybrids showed 'hybrid vigour' vastly superior to that of either parent led to the development of hybrid maize and then to extension of the procedure to other species.

The practical implication of these experiments, which permitted much greater control of quality than open crossing, were quickly recognized and tested out in a number of agricultural experiment stations in the United States. By the 1920s supplies of hybrid seed were becoming available and American farmers were beginning to learn of its new possibilities. Once they started to use hybrid maize, they adopted it rapidly. In 1933 only one-tenth of 1 per cent (·001) of maize acreage in the US was planted with hybrid seed. Ten years later 51 per cent was so planted, and after another ten years, 87 per cent.

Following this experience, plant breeders extended the principle of inbreeding and hybridization to other out-crossing species and produced a number of successful hybrid strains of vegetables suitable to particular areas; animal breeders successfully applied the same principles to poultry. By mid-century the use of hybrid seed was still largely confined to North America and Europe, but was spreading as strains adapted to new localities were found, while the less complex process of seed selection, crossing, and multiplication of desirable strains was under way in many more of the agricultural regions of the world.

High yields from hybrid seed did not depend on the seed alone but on the combined effect of seed, fertilizer and method of tillage, for each of these factors reinforced the others and multiplied their effect. Hybrid maize showed only about 20 per cent higher yields when planted in the same manner as other maize; but experiments with methods of tillage showed that it could be planted much closer together and that it could make use of much more fertilizer. When scientifically developed methods of tillage and generous application of appropriate fertilizers were combined with superior hybrid seed, the result was not just a 20 per cent increase but a doubling and tripling of production, or even more.

Appraising the potentialities for increased food production, the FAO in 1954 concluded:

'Selection, which involves choosing the best of what already exists, and hybridization, which involves creation of new genetic combinations, offer tremendous opportunities for further increasing agricultural production. In the more advanced countries, further progress will probably come mainly from hybridization. But in underdeveloped countries . . . the scope for improvement by systematic collection, testing, purification and concentration on a limited number of varieties is usually substantial. The production of new varieties opens up great possibilities which have hardly been explored in most underdeveloped countries'.*

Beyond selective breeding and hybridization, plant scientists discovered ways to produce mutations in the genetic stock, by means of radiation and by the application of chemicals. Among the latter, colchicine was found to induce doubling of the chromosomes, thereby altering the character and generally enlarging the size of the plant and permitting new genetic combinations. Although these treatments were not used, prior to the middle of the century, to affect importantly the major food crops, their use in the breeding of flowers indicated latent possibilities. The growing understanding of the nature of genes and how they may be affected, moreover, presaged further development of controlled mutations in the future.

* W. H. Pawley and others, *op. cit.*

Discoveries with respect to hormones and chemicals which regulate growth in plants offered still another medium through which to control plant development. These regulators of plant growth proved effective in delaying or advancing the time of blossoming, as for example in enabling pineapple growers to have plants flowering and ripening in every month of the year instead of all at once; they could be used to keep fruit from dropping before it was fully ripe, or for inducing the formation of roots so that more plants and trees could be grown from cuttings; introduced into a plant's system, they could promote or distort its development or destroy it. By mid-century, the use of these plant regulators had revolutionized the process of weed control and had opened up new possibilities for adapting plant life to man's needs.

By the same period the availability of radioactive isotopes enormously aided research into plant nutrition and development. They made it possible to trace in detail the manner in which plants absorb and use nutrients and other products and to detect the effects of any substances with which plants come in contact. On the basis of such careful studies of plant physiology, ever more precise and effective methods of cultivation could be designed.

(d) *Plant diseases, weeds and pests.* Positive measures to produce good plants, suitable to many environments and requirements, were accompanied by systematic attacks on the elements which interfere with plant growth or survival—disease, weeds, insects and other pests.

The battle against plant diseases was fully joined during the twentieth century with the same vigour shown in the campaign for human and animal health. While plant geneticists were breeding strains resistant to the most menacing diseases, chemists produced a wide variety of substances with which to spray or dust plants, treat seeds before planting, and purify the soil to eliminate soilborne infections. The struggle against plant diseases was a continual one, as the very measures which provided better conditions for plant growth generally improved the environment for the organisms which attacked plants. On the other hand, treatment designed to eliminate noxious or disease-bearing entities from the soil could destroy needed organisms. Prior to the second world war a few basic chemicals were used to combat fungus and virus diseases. During and after the war a multitude of new organic chemicals proved vastly more effective than those in earlier use. In this period, too, antibiotics which controlled disease in human beings and animals were applied with effectiveness to plants as well.

New chemicals and other measures to control insect pests and eradicate weeds were even more revolutionary than those for the control of plant diseases. DDT, developed during the second world war and in use around the world by mid-century, was greeted as a miracle because it was the first substance to destroy a wide range of insects both by contact and when eaten, and it retained its lethal properties for a long time. Originally discovered by German and Swiss dye firms seeking chemical dyes that would deter moths from eating woollen cloths, this product was immediately applied to military uses such as the protection of troops against typhus and malaria through elimination of body lice and malarial mosquitoes, and was tested out as an agricultural pesticide. When it was made generally available to farmers at the close of the war, it quickly became the most widely used ingredient of sprays and dusts for many purposes. Some of its achievements in the field of agriculture were spectacular. It helped to double the yield of potatoes in the US by control of insects, and to bring under control many of the most destructive of the orchard and forest pests.

DDT and other insecticides, however, had serious limitations, for they often killed many predators of the pests as well as pests themselves, they destroyed other desirable organisms, they resulted in the survival of mutants which were resistant to the chemicals, and they were often injurious to man.

The effectiveness of DDT and other new chemicals was enhanced by simultaneous improvements in methods of applying them, notably the development of the aerosol. Sprays or dusts delivered with ordinary apparatus quickly fell to the ground and reached only limited targets; the aerosol, a fine mist which remains suspended in the air like fog, enabled much smaller quantities to reach the insects in a given area more thoroughly. While the aerosol was most useful for the disinfestation of an enclosed space, such as an aeroplane cabin or a barn, it also permitted the production of spray fogs which could be carried by air currents to envelop whole areas.

Mass attacks, meantime, were conducted by means of the aeroplane. Dusting of forest areas against destructive moths, of swampy regions against mosquitoes, and of fields and pastures against many specific pests not only protected the crops of individual farmers, but set up regional barriers to the spread of insects from one farm to another. Where such wholesale attacks were undertaken, there appeared to be good prospects for success in the unremitting war which all farmers must wage on insects and other pests.

DDT was by no means the only chemical to show marked success against pests; and fortunately so, for as soon as the insects susceptible to DDT poisoning were killed off, the hardy mutants which appeared to be immune to its effect multiplied. This called for new research to find products which the new strain of insects could not withstand, and for new techniques of application such as alternate use of different chemicals to catch the strains immune to one type. Extensive research was undertaken in an effort to determine the physiological mechanisms involved in order to be able to combat the resistant strains.

Pesticide research looked for poisons which could be economically administered, as well as be effective. This led to the finding of chemicals which could be fed to the plants themselves along with the fertilizer, making the plants toxic to the insects which tried to eat them. While this reduced the application of fertilizer and pesticide to a single operation, it could be used only when the result did not make the plant also toxic to its human or animal consumer. Other devices included the fumigation or poisoning of the soil to eliminate diseases, destructive organisms such as nematodes, the grubs of destructive worms, and weed seeds. Chemicals were even found which first killed weed seeds, nematodes and other plant enemies in the soil and subsequently broke down into substances which served as fertilizer at the time that the crop was planted.

Biological forces as well as chemicals were called into play in the attack on pests. Observing the balance in nature, scientists looked for the natural enemies of the insect pests in order to utilize them as allies. The possibilities of this approach had been demonstrated before the turn of the century, for example in the identification and importation into California in 1889 of the Australian ladybug to control the Icerya scale that was infesting the citrus trees.

The quest for such parasites or other natural enemies became a routine part of pest-control research. Biological warfare against insects and larger animal menaces also took the form of the spreading of disease. The extremely destructive Japanese beetle was brought under control by infesting the soil containing the beetle grubs with a milky disease. The rabbit disease, myxamatosis, brought the Australian rabbit population down to 10–20 per cent of its previous numbers within a few years, in spite of the survival of disease-resistant animals. Such diseases were, however, dangerous tools, for they could get out of hand, be transported to other areas, destroy more than was intended or by removing a predator permit another species to multiply to excess.

Weeds too were subjected to attack by chemical and biological means. Here the revolutionary discovery was that substances which regulate plant growth can be used to destroy weeds more completely and more selectively than chemicals which merely destroy foliage in order to deprive the plant of its oxygen. The most widely used of the new systemic poisons, 2-4D, when taken into a plant's system in sufficient quantity eventually destroys its whole structure. Since this substance affects only broad leafed plants (dicotyledons) and does not injure grains or grasses (monocotyledons) it can be used in the cultivation of maize, small grains and sugar cane. Similar substances and various cell-destroying chemicals were sought and found to work selectively in cotton fields and elsewhere. Insects were also used to attack certain weeds, among them the cactus moth and other insects used in Australia in the 1920s to clear many millions of acres of the prickly pear which had been spreading at the rate of a million acres a year.

The use of chemicals to control plant disease, insect pests and weeds was still by mid-century confined almost wholly to North America, western Europe, Australia and New Zealand, USSR, Japan and Egypt. On the situation at this time the FAO noted that 'the gap between knowledge and practice is probably greater than ever before, owing to particularly rapid scientific progress in recent years'.*

* W. H. Pawley and others, *op. cit.*

(e) *Livestock*. The application of science to the improvement of livestock followed the same general lines as for field crops: the application of genetic knowledge to animal breeding, knowledge of animal nutrition, the control of animal diseases and parasites, and the provision of a favourable environment for the animal's growth.

Selective breeding of livestock was not new in the twentieth century. The enclosure movement in England in the sixteenth century had facilitated the improvement of herds and the standardization of lines of sheep, while the breeding of horses was a traditional and highly skilled art among Arab peoples. In the twentieth century scientific breeding of livestock was based on studies of such factors as milk production by the progeny of proven sires, the rate at which animals put on weight in relation to the amount which they were fed, the configuration of meat animals, the quality of wool of sheep or the laying habits of hens.

Work along these lines in Europe, USSR, North America and Australasia bore fruit by the middle of the twentieth century in superior animals of every sort. By maintaining careful records of performance animal breeders, especially in the Netherlands, Denmark, UK, New Zealand, Switzerland and USA built up a body of data on which very careful selection of the desired factors could be made. The organization of dairy improvement associations in the United States using proven sires resulted in herds with an average milk production twice that of other dairy herds in that country. Even more spectacular results were achieved in Holland which at mid-century had the highest milk production per cow of any country in the world.

Improvement of both dairy and meat herds was greatly facilitated by development of means of artificial insemination. In the United States organizations for artificial insemination were set up in every county where dairy farms were numerous. There, in the USSR and in Europe, artificial insemination was used to produce thousands of progeny from a single selected sire. Methods of preserving the semen through quick freezing made it possible to reach herds at greater distances from the sires and thus to extend the influence of selective breeding to a much wider area. Strains of livestock that showed resistance to disease were also developed, such as Texas cattle crossed with Zebu which were resistant to cattle tick fever.

The results of livestock research were slower to become apparent and to be applied than in the case of plants because of the longer time between generations and the smaller number of progeny. By mid-century they were largely confined to the developed agricultural countries. It was apparent, moreover, that the countries which lacked a background of years of livestock research could not simply import into areas of difficult climatic and disease conditions stock which had proved to be highly productive in its native habitat. Beginnings had been made in these areas with the slow process of studying and selecting indigenous stock adapted to local conditions and cross-breeding it with animals from outside to develop superior local strains.

Development of animal nutrition paralleled animal breeding and included improvement of pastures, the use of balanced prepared feeds and provision of the vitamins that were as important to animals as to man. Work on animal and human nutrition went side by side, discoveries in one contributing to the other. Of special importance was the discovery of vitamin B12, known as the animal protein factor, which supplied most of the substances which vegetable protein failed to provide in animal feed or human food. In temperate areas of Europe, America, Australia, New Zealand and South Africa, superior grasses and legumes, together with fertilization of pastures, strip grazing, the mowing of fodder to avoid waste from trampling, and the use of grass silage enabled improved pastures to support many more animals.

Elimination of animal diseases, especially those which could strike with epidemic force, was of the utmost importance. Among the diseases brought under control were the foot-and-mouth disease of cattle, driven out of the United States in 1929, rapidly being brought under control through international efforts in the American republics and the object of intensive international control measures in Europe; swine fever against which pigs were protected by immunization, a treatment which had become virtually universal in the United States by mid-century; testing for and elimination of foci of infection of tuberculosis and brucellosis (contagious abortion) in cattle and goats, especially important because these diseases could be transmitted to humans in the milk; and several of the diseases, particularly Newcastle's disease and coccidiosis, which devastated flocks of poultry and impeded large scale raising of poultry until they were brought under control. The elimination of rinderpest in Africa and Asia, undertaken with the help of the FAO, was the indispensable first step toward improved livestock in these areas. The one animal disease of major proportions still remaining to be conquered at mid-century was that produced by the tsetse fly in Africa, but beginnings were being made in the breeding of cattle resistant to this disease, and extensive aerial spraying had cleared the tsetse fly from large areas.

Elimination of internal parasites, though less dramatic than control of epidemic diseases, made the difference between stunted growth and fast-gaining animals. Improved drugs were discovered and then mixed into the animals' normal feed to keep herds and flocks continually free of debilitating infestations. The accidental discovery that animals throve on feed that contained residues from the preparation of antibiotics opened yet another area of research with respect to animal feeding. The combination of highly nutritious feed, adequate supply of vitamins, control of parasites and the use of antibiotics led to such increases in animal growth that many pigs, beef cattle and chickens were going to market at lower ages and much higher weights than had been the case in the past. These improvements made it possible for animals to put on as much as 20 per cent more weight with the same amount of feed. The total effect of improved breeding, improved nutrition and the control of animal diseases increased the average production of livestock per breeding unit in the United States between 1920 and 1955 by 67 per cent.

Attention was also paid to the habits of animals in order to determine the environment in which they did best. Studies showed that animals ate more, gained weight faster, gave more milk or laid more eggs under specific conditions of light, water, heat, cold—even music. By controlling environmental conditions, farmers secured more meat, milk and eggs from a given herd or flock.

The difference between the developed and the less developed countries with respect to animal husbandry was perhaps even more marked than in the production of field crops. In most of the underdeveloped countries the livestock, fed on unimproved pasture or without the attempt to provide balanced feed, ate little more than enough to keep it alive, and did not consume much which could be converted into body growth and the making of meat, milk or eggs.

(f) *Farm mechanization.* While twentieth-century agriculture owed its greatest increase in yields to the application of biological and chemical knowledge, farm mechanization played a major role in North America, it was a cornerstone of the agricultural programme of the USSR, and after the second world war it became an essential part of farm development in Europe. Mechanical equipment drawn by animal power had been developed in the nineteenth century for such heavy and difficult processes as reaping, threshing and cultivating, and many new implements were developed in the twentieth century which could be drawn either by animals or by motor power. It was the substitution of tractors for animal power on the farms, however, which constituted the major element in twentieth-century farm mechanization; in addition, lorries and jeeps replaced animal-drawn vehicles for farm chores and transport to market.

The first tractors were large machines, suitable only for use on large acreages such as the huge wheatfields of the American prairies or the Russian steppes. Their cost was high, their operation clumsy, and they were beyond the reach of individual farmers who had operated their farms with a team of horses or bullocks. In the 1920s small tractors designed to have the flexibility of the work animal and be suitable for use on the small farm came on to the market, and their use spread widely from the 1930s onwards until animal power was driven from most of the small as well as the large North American farms.

Substitution of tractor for animal power not only increased the amount of work which the farmer could do but released much land from cultivation of feed crops for the work stock and made this land available for the production of food. By reducing the time required for sowing and harvesting, it lengthened the growing season and made possible the use of marginal land where the frost-free period was short or rainfall periodic. The tractor also provided the farmer with motor power which could do many things besides drag agricultural implements, and enabled him to perform quickly and alone many farm tasks which had required much time and labour.

In the years after the second world war, the number of tractors in use in Europe tripled as part of the effort to increase food production, and was especially high in the British Isles. The use of tractors had already reached substantial proportions in Australia, New Zealand and the USSR and was beginning to spread to Latin America. By mid-century, however, it had only begun to reach the Near and Far East. A rough picture of the extent of farm mechanization may be gained from the number of arable hectares per tractor, although the large, almost completely mechanized grain farms which made up a large proportion of the farming of North America, the USSR and Australia are hardly comparable to the smaller mixed farms more characteristic of western Europe and the rice cultivation of much of Asia. The ratios were roughly as follows:*

WORLD TRACTOR NUMBERS BY REGIONS[a]

Region	1938–39	1953	Arable area per tractor 1953 (hectares)[d]
Europe	275,000	1,414,000	104
North America	1,695,000	4,650,000	50
Latin America	35,000	189,000	470
Near East	5,000	52,000	1,200
Far East	—	20,000	8,500
Australasia	57,000	211,000	100
USSR[b]	524,000	969,000	230
TOTAL[c]	2,590,000	7,505,000	130

(a) Tractors of 8 h.p. or over included. Underestimates Europe where garden tractors most numerous.

(b) Stated in terms of tractor units of 15 h.p.: most farm tractors exceed 15 h.p.

(c) Omits some small countries in Near and Far East, dependent territories, China, Union of South Africa; add ca. 150,000 tractors to 1953 total to include these areas.

(d) 100 hectares = 247 acres.

The use of mechanical equipment on farms encountered major difficulties in areas where farms were small and farm operators poor. The high initial cost limited the use of equipment to relatively well-to-do farmers, co-operative groups, individuals who specialized in doing contract work with their equipment, or to the government which established machine pools or tractor stations. Where there was an abundance of labour, as in the Asian countries, the inducement to substitute machine for hand labour was negligible. Here the main advantage in using tractor power was to do the hard tasks which could not be done with the human or animal power available. In the monsoon areas tractors could break up the hard soil before the monsoon

* FAO, *The State of Food and Agriculture, 1955* (Rome, 1955), p. 61.

rains instead of waiting for the soil to be softened by the rains, and crops could thus be planted sooner. Similarly, the use of power at harvest time made it possible to get the crop off the land quickly and to prepare the soil for a subsequent planting. Tractors were also used to condition land which needed a drastic treatment. In India for example they served to break up land which had grown up to tough grass; once broken the newly conditioned land could be maintained by farmers with their traditional tools.

Two methods were used to introduce farm mechanization where conditions were relatively unfavourable—the establishment of farm machinery centres and the designing of small machines. The tractor stations where machines could be kept in repair were general up to 1958 for the collective farms of the USSR, and government tractor pools were beginning to be maintained in such countries as Ceylon, Indonesia, Burma, Turkey, Egypt and several Latin American countries, including Peru, Brazil, Cuba and Chile. Small, relatively low-cost equipment which could be used by the owner of a small plot and which he could afford to purchase was developed particularly in Japan. Japanese rice-threshing machines, for example, could be carried by hand to small plots, assembled to the engine which could be separately transported, and could then be carried on to another field or back to the barn when threshing was completed. The motor could then be used on another small piece of equipment, such as a machine for husking the paddy. In Europe the small garden tractor served similar purposes in the hands of small farmers.

The use of machinery on the farm required not only a vigorous farm-machinery industry but someone with a knowledge of mechanics to keep it in operation and make repairs. In countries where mechanical knowledge was general, the farmer himself became a mechanic, able to keep his equipment in running order and to make minor repairs. In addition a repair service industry grew up throughout farming areas. In non-mechanized regions, however, the attempt to introduce agricultural machinery ahead of the general familiarity with mechanical processes frequently resulted in the breakdown of the machinery, in the absence of anyone to take care of or repair it, and its prompt disuse. In an effort to avoid these wasteful results in areas where mechanical knowledge was not widespread, tractor pools were used as training centres. In some areas simple farm implements were introduced before the attempt was made to adopt more complex ones; an FAO technical consultant in the Near East, for example, started by introducing an adjustable blade on a hand scythe in order to teach farmers the use of a wrench and screw bolt.

On the fully mechanized farms of North America, Australia, New Zealand and western Europe, where mechanical power and electricity were available, power was applied to ploughing, planting, cultivating, fertilizing, harvesting, animal feeding, milking, pumping irrigation water, handling and transporting products and many other operations. Machines used for harvesting sugar cane on the highly mechanized sugar fields of Hawaii replaced the laborious process of cane cutting for thousands of workers. Aircraft were used for sowing and spraying and chemical weedkillers replaced the patient labour of men and women with hoes.

(g) *Farm management.* In order to use the fruits of scientific discovery through efficient farm management, the farmer of the mid-twentieth century needed to know many things: how to secure an analysis of his soil and to determine what crops and what fertilizer to use; what method of tillage was likely to give him the greatest yield; what chemicals to apply to pests and weeds and in what strengths; what amount of moisture and how best to apply it; how to feed, doctor and house his livestock; how to take care of his equipment and keep it in repair. He must be able to handle and plan the financing of the investment in the farm and its equipment and to understand markets and changes in market conditions. In short the twentieth-century farmer was called upon to understand and command the resources which science and technology had made available to him and to assume responsibility for using this knowledge with wise judgment.

Where family farms prevailed, the individual farmer not only had to master a wide range of skills but to plan intelligently, organize effectively and make decisions constantly in the light of new considerations. From being one of the most traditional of occupations, farming became one requiring the greatest alertness and readiness to change. These developments gave a great advantage to those farmers who were the most intelligent, well trained and best able to afford an experimental approach. They placed at an increasingly serious disadvantage the poor or ignorant farmer whose lands were insufficient for economic operation, who could not secure the capital to invest in improvements that would increase his yields, whose income was so low that he could not risk loss and therefore dared not try something new, or who lacked the necessary intelligence or opportunity to learn good farm management.

Where farming was carried on collectively, the main responsibility for farm management fell on the managers of state and collective farms, acting in accordance with directives provided by the state. It was thus concentrated in relatively few hands; in the USSR the total number of farms in 1958, 82,400, was less than 2 per cent the number of farms in the United States, and 4 per cent of US full-time commercial farms, although the area under crops was a third larger. Under the Soviet system of machine tractor stations where all the major equipment used by collective farms was held, management responsibility was shared by the directors of these stations, since they determined when and how the equipment would be used; after these stations were abolished in 1958 and the machinery distributed to the collective farms, full responsibility rested with the collective farm managers aided by boards composed of key members of the farm.

The change in the nature of farming had the effect of opening up an enormous gap between the scientific agriculture of the technically advanced countries and the traditional methods which generally prevailed in the rest of the world. For countries seeking economic development, the effort to raise agricultural productivity and income could involve changes as radical as those required by industrialization.

Modernization of traditional agriculture, however, encountered severe obstacles not only in the farmers' lack of knowledge and experience but in lack of capital and especially in the excessive numbers of persons on the land. To the extent that agricultural technology was labour-saving, its introduction displaced agricultural workers; but rural people were already leaving the land in most of the underdeveloped countries more rapidly than urban employment could absorb them. The initial effect of such methods was to create further unemployment.

Mechanization of agriculture in the manner of North America, western Europe or the USSR had much less to offer these areas initially than labour-intensive methods such as those used in Japan to achieve very high yields per acre. Improved seed, improved tillage methods, use of fertilizer, better methods of weed and pest control and the adaptation of small implements all presented possibilities for raising productivity without displacing undue numbers of farm workers and with a minimum of capital outlay. These were the kinds of improvements towards which many development programmes and technical assistance projects were directed in the effort to bring the advantages of modern agricultural science to farmers in the developing regions of the world. The Chinese People's Republic used these same methods in its vast modernization programme, which relied mainly on changes in organization and farming practices to raise yields.

2. *Adaptation and dissemination of agricultural knowledge*

The development, and especially the application, of agricultural knowledge required field testing under the varied conditions of soil, climate and topography with which farmers of different areas had to deal. Although much new knowledge came to agriculture from the scientific laboratory and basic principles had general validity, such knowledge only became usable when problems of application had been worked out in appropriate settings. Individual farmers however were rarely in a position to conduct systematic experiments.

(a) *Agricultural research*. Agricultural experiment stations where new knowledge was tested out under local conditions therefore became a central feature of the agricultural structure in most countries. The first such stations were established in the 1840s, at Rothamsted, England, Edinburgh, Scotland and Mockern, Germany. In the last quarter of the nineteenth century a network of experiment stations was set up in the United States, especially after 1887 when federal grants were provided to all state agricultural universities which maintained stations. By the 1950s the US government, in co-operation with the states, was conducting agricultural research in some 500 research locations throughout the country.

Each of the European countries established research centres for practical agricultural study, including such famous centres as Wageningen in Holland and Svalov in Sweden. Britain set up stations in different parts of the country under a programme initiated in 1909 and greatly extended the work during the second world war; it established agricultural experiment stations throughout its possessions as part of its colonial administration. The centre established by the Dutch in Java was one of the most extensive stations for research into tropical agriculture. In Russia the broad terrain and varied climate led to extensive field studies in the nineteenth century; under the Soviet régime the Lenin Academy of Agricultural Science, established in 1929, was conducting more than 150 of its own research institutions during the 1950s, covering various branches of agricultural science, and it directed the activities of agricultural science bodies, selection centres and experimental centres throughout the USSR.

(b) *Agricultural education.* Actual adoption of improved methods, however, depended upon their being known and understood by the farmers, and upon the latter's attitude towards the rationalization of agriculture and their readiness to depart from practices deeply rooted in tradition, folk ways and folk wisdom. The channels of education and communication through which agricultural knowledge flowed were essential to its use.

General education as it developed in the nineteenth century was strongly urban in content and orientation, not only in Europe and North America but wherever the British or continental European systems of education spread. Agricultural content was especially lacking in Britain. By the second quarter of the twentieth century, and especially after the second world war, agricultural materials were being included in basic education for rural areas much more generally than before. This tendency reflected the educational trend toward using direct experience as a source of teaching material; school gardens or poultry-raising offered an opportunity for learning by doing. Education for adults was also built around practical problems.

Specialized agricultural schools at the secondary level began to be established by European countries in the late nineteenth century, along with other types of technical schools for children who did not continue their academic education or leave school altogether; two schools in Hungary were among the first of these establishments. By the middle of the twentieth century such technical agriculture schools were universally a part of the educational structure wherever the European educational system prevailed. At the higher education level, faculties of agriculture or special agricultural institutes also offered professional training to agronomists or agricultural engineers.

In the United States, agricultural universities were set up in each of the states in consequence of a law in 1862 which made large grants of federally owned land to the states for the support of such institutions. In the early twentieth century states began to introduce agricultural subjects into their secondary-level high schools and in 1917 the federal government provided grants to the states for this and other vocational subjects, a noteworthy development in view of the fact that general education otherwise was wholly financed by states and localities.

Agricultural training in the USSR was greatly expanded after 1928, both at the higher and the secondary level, with the result that by 1957 the number of people with higher or secondary agricultural training who were working directly on farms was nearly 7·5 times as great as before the second world war.

Specialized agricultural institutions and special courses in regular schools provided formal channels for the transmission of agricultural knowledge. But in a field where knowledge was growing daily and its use depended on understanding and action by many thousands of independent farmers, it was not enough to provide technical instruction in schools and colleges. The new knowledge must reach the farming population directly and be accepted generally.

To meet this need a number of countries developed a distinct pattern for carrying new knowledge to the farmer and his family by means of agricultural extension services. The USA and Holland were among the countries which developed extension methods most fully and which provided models and personnel for the introduction of similar programmes elsewhere. By mid-century their methods had come to be widely accepted as a way to achieve the spread of scientific agriculture.

The US Agricultural Extension Service, established in 1913 and expanded rapidly under the stimulus of the first world war, operated through local agricultural agents who conducted demonstrations, advised farmers individually or collectively, conducted study groups or discussions, distributed literature or engaged in any form of education which would be effective among the farmers of a particular area. The programme was tied to the state agricultural universities and was supported by funds from federal and state governments and farm organizations. In the Netherlands separate extension services supported by the central government and linked to the appropriate research centre were organized for agriculture, horticulture, livestock and dairying. In the 1950s the agricultural extension service alone provided one local extension worker for every 400 farmers. In combination with a network of agricultural schools and courses at elementary, vocational and professional levels, which were attended by approximately half of all Dutch farmers, they helped to raise Dutch agriculture from a backward art at the beginning of the century to one of the most productive in the world by the 1950s. Extension services in Denmark were organized and administered by farmers' organizations with subsidies from the government.

Farm women too were encouraged through the efforts of extension home demonstration workers in the USA, Holland and elsewhere to take advantage of modern knowledge in the conduct of the farm home, in raising and preserving vegetables, in applying nutritional principles to the feeding of the family, in child care and in other aspects of family and rural life. In Canada and Britain Women's Institutes, established during the first world war to encourage rural women to make best use of available supplies in time of scarcity, stimulated village women to learn and share techniques of cooking, preserving, gardening and poultry raising, and encouraged handicrafts and popular arts.

Informal education of farm youth was also developed in a number of countries as part of the agricultural extension programme through clubs where boys and girls learned improved farming practices for themselves by engaging in projects such as raising an animal or a special crop. Known usually as 4-H clubs, their original name in the USA, or some variant such as 5-V clubs in Venezuela or 3-C clubs in Colombia, or Young Farmers in Ceylon, they did much to give rural youth a positive orientation toward the business of farming.

The core of all extension methods in countries where farms were individually operated was personal contact with the farmer. This was accompanied and supported by meetings and study clubs, through radio, films and press, and through demonstration plots and experimental farms where the farmer could judge new methods for himself.

Agricultural extension was unique at the time of its inauguration, for it meant carrying a public service directly to the people. As the idea of the welfare state emerged, the methods which the extension services had developed for dealing with people on their own terms and enlisting their interest and active participation spread not only to agricultural programmes of many other countries but to activities and services in other fields. By the 1950s agricultural extension programmes or their equivalent were general in Europe; they had been introduced, frequently with US technical assistance, in a number of Latin American countries. The FAO conducted regional training centres for agricultural extension, during the single year of 1953, in Beirut for the Near East, in Peru for Latin America and with Dutch and American collaboration, in the Netherlands for Europe. Agricultural extension activities were incorporated into the community development programmes of various countries as these programmes were established, notably in India, Pakistan and the Philippines.

In the Soviet Union, the latest developments in agricultural science were disseminated from the ministry of agriculture through the ministries of the several republics to the state and collective farms, where the farm's specialist in each field was responsible for digesting technical information and passing it on to his fellow workers so that they might put the new ideas into practice on the farm. Magazines dealing with the types of production in which each farm was engaged reached the libraries in the social centres of the collective and state farms, as did magazines of special interest to rural youth. The Communist party organization conveyed to the farms information relating to the national plan and the responsibilities of the farmers for their part in carrying it out.

The adoption of improved methods of farming depended in the last analysis on the attitudes of farmers. One of the most striking examples of the re-orientation of a farming population took place in Denmark in the last quarter of the nineteenth century, where a depressed agriculture was converted, through co-operative organization, cultural revival and application of scientific knowledge, into one of the most progressive in Europe. Even in the USA, which lacked the deep-rooted traditions of older agricultural societies, practical farmers spoke scornfully of 'book farming' and it was not until the second quarter of the twentieth century that scientific farming was fully accepted; but once it took hold it was pursued with enormous vigour. In the struggles of Europeans to stay alive during the second world war and to recover agricultural productivity after the war, most of the remaining resistance or indifference to agricultural rationalization was swept away in these areas. Great Britain went so far in its agricultural legislation of 1947 as to authorize the government to take away a farmer's land if he failed to practise 'good husbandry' and this provision of the law was in fact carried out.

Farm magazines played an important part in the development of a scientific attitude among farmers. In the USA magazines addressed to the working farmer, which were among the periodical publications with the largest circulation in the country, kept news of the latest scientific developments flowing into the farm home in a form which the farmer could understand and use. In these journals the commercial suppliers of the fertilizer, equipment, insecticides and other materials on which modern farming depended described their wares in terms of their contribution to the newest agricultural practices. Their advertising in the 1950s was addressed in technical terms to farmers who were presumed to have detailed knowledge of soil chemistry, plant and animal nutrition and methods of planting and cultivation, and who were expected to make their decisions in terms of careful calculation and rational consideration of alternative practices.

Practical changes in the conditions of rural life did much to alter the farmer's outlook. Roads and motor travel broke down his isolation; rural electrification not only provided power for farm tasks but conveniences for farm living—lights, electrically pumped water, household appliances; radio and television brought the outside world into the farm home; mail-order houses and chain stores serving rural areas made the same wide range of goods available to rural as to urban consumers; accessible motion pictures brought the same kind of entertainment to country as to town; improved rural schools and health services brought comparable facilities within the reach of farm families. By mid-century the farmer in countries of advanced agriculture enjoyed amenities similar to those of the town, and was exposed to many of the same currents which shaped the outlook of the urban dweller.

In all these ways a milieu for advanced agriculture was created, both in areas of individual and of socialized farming, in which the farmer was no longer governed by tradition and folk wisdom, but was brought into the stream of rational scientific thought. The most fundamental contrast between countries of advanced agriculture and those where agriculture followed traditional methods was in the atmosphere within which the farm operation was carried on.

Modernization of farming in underdeveloped areas involved a change in attitudes and milieu even more than changes of specific agricultural practices. It was towards this objective that much of the technical assistance in agriculture and many of the community development programmes of the 1950s were directed, as were also the radical changes of the socialist economies.

3. *Organization of agricultural production*

The application of scientific knowledge in the field of agriculture depended on the ways in which agricultural production was organized, its legal basis and economic potentialities, as well as on the progress of agricultural research and the dissemination of new knowledge.

(*a*) *Landholding and land use.* Basic to the structure of production were the size and nature of the farming unit and the system of land tenure on which they rested. In contrast to industry whose structure was largely determined by technology, the structure of agriculture in most areas was traditional.

With the exception of commercially organized plantations, which made up a small proportion of the world's farms, the size of the farm unit and the manner in which its lands were distributed were the product of historical accident, family size, inheritance laws or other factors which took little account of the optimum unit for a particular type of farming. The rationale for existing structures, if any could be recognized, was related to quite different technological conditions from those which developed during the twentieth century. The fragmented holdings in much of Europe, for example, had come down from the three-field system of cultivation of the mediaeval manor or village community, further subdivided by inheritance according to the principles of the Napoleonic Code; the 160-acre American farm had been acquired originally under the Homestead Act of 1862 which enabled settlers to claim homesteads of this size in hitherto unsettled areas. In these circumstances the farmer made what he could of his inherited farm, whatever its size, sometimes abandoning it for city employment if the latter were available and his lands inadequate, sometimes trying to acquire additional holdings by purchase or marriage where this was possible.

Systems of tenure in many parts of the world at the opening of the twentieth century were also unfavourable to agricultural progress. In western Europe, North America and Australasia, owner-cultivators enjoyed security of title; in Britain, where tenancy was general, cultivators were protected in their tenure so long as they practised good husbandry. But in most other regions land was held in large estates worked by those who did not own.

The bulk of the land in eastern Europe and Russia and some in western Europe was in the hands of formerly feudal landlords; in Latin America it was held in *latifundia* with many feudal characteristics, or in plantations worked by agricultural labour; it belonged to hereditary owner-rulers—sheikhs—in the Middle East; it was held by absentee landlords who collected quit-rents in India and other parts of Asia, or by operators of tea, cotton, rubber, coconut or other plantations.

In all these areas tenant cultivators had neither the means nor the incentive for improvement, for barely a subsistence income remained to them when they had satisfied their obligations to their landlords; they had no reserve out of which to make investment in fertilizer, equipment or soil-improving practices, and they had no assurance that the fruits of their extra effort would accrue to themselves; their holdings were generally too small to provide an adequate farm unit; in some areas obsolete systems of cropping were established by rigid custom or law. Absentee owners of large estates were often interested only in collecting their rents; other landlords frequently lacked the capital for modernization. Moreover, so long as they had at their disposal a plentiful supply of cheap rural labour which continued to eke out a living on the land for lack of alternative employment, there was little incentive to invest in equipment or adopt labour-saving practices.

There were of course progressive operators among the large landowners in all regions, and it was through them that new methods and new equipment were introduced into areas in India, for example, or in Latin America where the small proprietors were too small, poor or uneducated to undertake new ways. More generally, however, tenant-cultivators on large estates remained traditional in their methods and received incomes that were close to or even below the level of subsistence.

Owner-cultivators on excessively small holdings—*minifundia*—were generally to be found in the same regions where large holdings prevailed. Often they cultivated the hillier or rougher land while the large estates occupied the fertile valleys, though *minifundia* were characteristic of much irrigated rice land in the valleys of south-east Asia. Even if they had secure ownership, they had too little income, and many improved practices could not be applied to such small units. Labour-intensive practices in Japan and China, however, demonstrated the possibility of getting much more from small plots than farmers in areas such as India and Java were doing. In some places, notably parts of Latin America, south-east Asia and Africa, small farmers pursued a system of shifting cultivation, without acquiring title to the land which they cleared, cropped and then abandoned. Where systems of family tenure were traditional, as in Jamaica, British West Indies, uncertainty of title made it difficult for cultivators to take advantage of credit which was available only to those whose land titles were clear.

During the twentieth century land reform became a burning issue in many parts of the world.* By the middle of the century much land had passed out

* See Chapter XXX, Drives for Individual Freedom and Human Dignity: Peasants and farmers.

of the hands of former owners into those of the men who worked the land, and the large private landholder had become a diminishing type. The impetus for these reforms came generally from political pressures and social movements. Their effect on agricultural efficiency depended largely upon the size and organization of the resulting units in relation to the types of agriculture involved and on the technical and financial aid available to the cultivators.

Reforms directed most specifically toward agricultural improvement were those designed to consolidate fragmented holdings and to bring idle or unimproved land into cultivation by taxing it heavily, as in Britain, or exempting reclaimed land from taxation, as in Colombia, Mexico or Chile. Several European countries set up procedures for the consolidation of fragmented holdings, notably Switzerland, where the average farm in 1905 consisted of 14·3 plots and in 1950 still averaged 8·7. In France, where legislation to facilitate the consolidation of small holdings had been in effect since the close of the first world war and additional legislation which went into effect after the second world war greatly accelerated the process, the FAO reported in 1950 that half of the cultivated land was still in need of consolidation to make workable farm units. Spain, Holland, Belgium and Sweden were among the other countries adopting similar legislation. These countries had before them the unique example of Denmark which had consolidated most of its land into farms of economic size at the beginning of the nineteenth century and had prevented their subsequent break-up by law.

Where there were simply too many people on the land—the situation in many regions—measures designed to create economic farm units met insuperable difficulties. In the crowded area of western Ireland, legislation enacted in 1923 was used to a limited extent to resettle some farmers whose holdings were too small on unused land expropriated from large estates; their former lands were then added to the holdings of those who remained in the locality. But in the absence of alternative sources of employment the problem of *minifundia* remained unsolved and reforms which redistributed large holdings often left untouched the basic difficulty of insufficient land *per capita*.

Land reform movements in Latin America, eastern Europe and Asia demanded the transfer of ownership from large landlords to the tenant cultivators. The first such movement to be successful was in Mexico, where land for the peasants became a major objective of the revolution of 1910. In the course of the next thirty years about half of the cultivated land in the country was expropriated and transferred to villages under the *ejido* system traditional to the country. By this system, title to the land vested in the village and villagers received individual plots which they retained so long as they cultivated them. The reform freed the cultivators from debt-peonage to the landowners and improved the terms of employment of agricultural labour and of crop-sharing for tenants. It did not however provide peasants with economic-sized holdings or raise the level of agricultural productivity, for it gave *ejidal* rights to those who were actually on the land, regardless of their number. By 1945 the average *ejidal* holding was close to the minimum size for subsistence and even at that a quarter of those entitled to claim land as *ejiditarios* had not received a plot. Larger plots, improved credit and additional technical assistance in later years began to overcome some of these unfavourable factors.

In eastern Europe and Russia, where the feudal system remained essentially intact at the opening of the century in spite of the abolition of serfdom, the demand for redistribution of land was strong and there were frequent peasant riots or revolts. Lenin's promise of land to the cultivators brought the support of the peasants to the October revolution and acted as a stimulus to land distribution in neighbouring areas. One of the first steps taken by the new states of eastern Europe which came into existence after the first world war was to divide up large estates and vest title in the individual peasants. These measures, however, were carried through extensively only in Czechoslovakia and partially in Yugoslavia before the reaction against the new democratic governments led to the establishment of dictatorships and a halt to reform.

After the second world war the communist governments of the east European countries moved to redistribute the land with extreme rapidity. Division of the large estates in East Germany was completed in four months, in Hungary and Rumania in ten days. These measures were designed to eliminate the surviving feudal structure rather than to establish permanent peasant proprietorship, however, and they constituted a first step toward collectivization, the aim of agricultural policy in these countries. In Yugoslavia, widespread individual ownership resulting from both the earlier and later periods of land distribution was accompanied by a trend toward co-operative farming in some areas.

In the USSR the socialist transformation of agriculture was carried out on a gigantic scale with the organization of peasant farms into collectives, and the establishment of state farms as demonstration units. In the years after 1928 these types of agricultural organization almost completely replaced the individual family farm. While the immediate effect of this unprecedented experiment in the complete economic and social reconstruction of agriculture was to reduce output for the time being, the collective structure provided the means through which knowledge of improved agricultural practices could reach the peasants and productivity could thereby be increased. The Soviet state extended technical assistance and guidance to the collective farms, supplied them with modern machinery and introduced social and cultural facilities designed to eliminate much of the difference between the way of living in villages and towns. The Soviet collectives provided a model for the people's democracies of eastern Europe, where similar programmes were applied at varying rates and in different ways according to the situation of each country.

In the years after the second world war extensive changes in landholding were carried out throughout Asia and the Middle East. The chief effect of these reforms was to remove the absentee landlord as a rent collector—as he had been, for example, under the *zamindar* and related systems in India— and to leave existing cultivators in possession, subject to direct taxation by the state. The cultivator was thus relieved of some of his burdens, which had often been very high in relation to his output, but without change in the size of his holding or conditions of cultivation.

In addition, redistribution of large holdings was inaugurated in a number of countries. Such redistribution in Japan added to the holdings of more than half of the Japanese farm families, though the size of farms which resulted remained still very small. In India voluntary gifts of land were stimulated by a follower of Gandhi, Vinoba Bhave, at first to individual farmers (*bhoodan*) and then in the late 1950s to village units for co-operative agriculture (*gramdan*). Although some millions of acres were transferred under his stimulus, this movement was far from solving the difficult land problem.

The Chinese People's Republic undertook the most drastic reorganization of agriculture attempted by any country, adopting in the course of its first ten years successive measures, first to distribute land to the peasants, then to organize them into co-operatives, and finally to convert rural communities into people's communes in which both labour and consumption were organized on a communal basis.

In the Near East some expropriation of land for distribution to landless farmers became part of the policy of all countries in the area. Turkey adopted an ambitious programme of land distribution in 1945, but in the early stage of its operation it served mainly to provide a means of resettling large numbers of Turks repatriated from Bulgaria. The Egyptian agrarian reform law of 1952 set an upper limit of 84 hectares to the amount of land which any owner could continue to hold and called for the redistribution of the remainder. Similar legislation in Lebanon, Iran, Iraq and Syria looked toward the substitution of a measure of peasant proprietorship for the large estates which characterized the region. In Iran the Shah in 1951 set an example by the distribution of some of the crown lands. Only in Israel however was ownership by cultivators the rule, either through communal groups— *kibbutzim*—and co-operatives or, less frequently, by individual proprietors.

In the countries of Latin America other than Mexico, little headway was made in modifying the *latifundia* system except in Bolivia, where a comprehensive land redistribution programme was undertaken in 1952, and in Cuba where agrarian reform followed a successful revolution in 1959. The experience of Bolivia well illustrated the difficulties in attempting to lay a basis for efficient agriculture in areas where there were too many people on the land. In an effort to prevent a further lowering in the productivity of Bolivian agriculture and to achieve a division into sufficiently large units to permit the peasants who received land to make a decent living, the land reform law provided for the allocation of minimum-sized units, determined in relation to the quality of land and its appropriate use, and permitted the retention of somewhat larger units by those who were already using improved agricultural methods. Where there was insufficient land to provide an economic-sized unit for each cultivator then on the land, those who could not be supplied were to be resettled from the crowded highlands to the relatively undeveloped region of the lowland jungles.

It proved virtually impossible, however, to carry out this careful plan, for the peasants who were living and working on the land took possession and put such pressure on the local courts to confirm their titles that much land was subdivided into far too small plots. As for the plan to permit economic farms to operate with larger acreage, the peasants refused to accept this part of the measure; they moved on to such lands, and even the government itself was unable to hold some of the lands in its experimental farms against occupation and division by land-hungry peasants.

Similarly in Indonesia, peasants after independence occupied and destroyed forests which were essential to erosion control in their efforts to translate *merdeka*—freedom—into the possession of land.

Where large, private landholding survived, both in areas of advanced and of traditional agriculture, agricultural labour remained the most poorly paid and disadvantaged group. Wage levels in agriculture in 1950 were comparable to those in industry only in Australia and on the state farms of the USSR. Although the differential was substantially reduced between the 1930s and 1950s in most European areas, agricultural wages in the latter period were still less than half the average in industry in the USA, Italy, Japan and India, and in Mexico they were only 20 per cent of industrial wages in spite of land reform in that country. Measures to protect workers from exploitation comparable to those in industry—minimum wages, regulated hours, minimum conditions of work—were only slowly extended to agricultural workers.

In addition, plantation workers were often employed seasonally, generally for harvesting, and remained in a precarious condition for the rest of the year unless they had other sources of employment; when labour was performed by migratory workers who moved from crop to crop with the harvest season, their status might be even more insecure. A noteworthy attempt to convert plantation agriculture without losing the benefit of large scale operations was undertaken in Puerto Rico after 1942, where the lands of sugar estates in excess of a maximum of approximately 250 hectares were organized by the government into profit-sharing or 'proportional benefit' farms, operated as a unit for the benefit of the workers. Even under this system, however, the profits returned to the workers were not sufficient to carry them through the 'dead season' between harvests without other sources of income.

In many parts of the world, resettlement schemes were undertaken in an effort to take care of surplus rural populations. There were measures to resettle poor farmers from crowded Java on other islands in the Indonesian archipelago, notably Sumatra; Italian and Spanish peasants were settled on reclaimed land, Iraqis on land brought back into cultivation in the upper Tigris-Euphrates valley, and farmers from the Andean highlands in the unsettled plains or jungles of South America. These and many other schemes sought to cope with the ever-growing problem of the landless or impoverished peasantry, whose rate of increase, mounting with the spread of measures to preserve health, exceeded the ability of urban employment to absorb the rural surplus. On the whole, however, resettlement measures received only limited support and they offered a very minor solution to the great problem of excess population on the land.

Agricultural development thus depended upon the expansion of industrial employment as much as upon trends within agriculture itself. Small industries scattered through the country were part of the economic development policies of some countries, notably India and Puerto Rico, as they had been in the industrialization of Japan. Electricity and the internal-combustion engine made such industries possible, and atomic and solar energy might make them yet more feasible when these sources of energy should become generally available. But whether through rural industries which would supplement agricultural employment or by drawing off excess farm population to industrial centres, industrial expansion was a key to enabling agriculture to yield a living to producers comparable to that provided by industry.

At mid-century the world's agriculture was a long way from a pattern of organization which would make effective use of the great and growing body of agricultural knowledge.

(b) *Agricultural credit.* Second only to the problem of landholding was that of agricultural credit or other sources of capital. Most aspects of improved agriculture required additional capital and intensified the farmer's perennial problem of finding the resources with which to meet his costs of production during the crop year until his income came in with the harvest. The modern farmer needed funds to invest in equipment and improved livestock and for additional fertilizers, insecticides and selected seed.

The problem of agricultural credit was a reflection of the structure of the agrarian economy; it was neither new nor limited to particular types of farming. The moneylender with a stranglehold on farmers was traditional in the agricultural countries of eastern Europe and Asia. The American farmers' political demand for cheap money had been their historic response to their position as debtors. In the USSR the credits made available to collective and state farms through the banking institution were determined by the requirements of the national economic plan and the manner in which each farm fulfilled its goals.

Regular lending agencies in the free economies, accustomed to secure themselves against risk, normally charged rates of interest which made borrowing prohibitive for all but the wealthiest farmers, and the need to make special provisions for agricultural credit came to be recognized in a large number of countries. These took the form of co-operative credit associations, either standing alone or linked to a central credit institution maintained by the state, special agricultural banks with government support or subsidy, or direct provision of agricultural credit by the state. After the 1930s when depression pushed farmers to the wall at the very time that new technology was calling for additional capital, these facilities were greatly extended.

Even these special provisions, however, frequently failed to meet the needs of the poorer farmers. This was true in the countries of advanced agriculture such as the United States and Britain, and even more true of countries of low agricultural productivity such as most of the countries of Asia and much of Latin America. In India for example, where co-operative agricultural credit had been available for fifty years, only 3 per cent of the credit used by farmers was coming from this source in the 1950s and another 4 per cent from the state and other financial institutions; Indian cultivators continued to depend on private moneylenders, landlords or other individuals for 93 per cent of the credit they received.

To meet the needs of low-income farmers for whom even special agricultural credit facilities were not effective, a number of countries developed schemes for combining credit with technical aid. Small farmers who were regarded as bad financial risks by agricultural lending institutions could receive special loans on the condition that they accept technical help in planning and operating their farms. Such programmes of supervised credit, inaugurated in the USA, a number of Latin American countries and elsewhere, were designed to raise farm productivity and thereby enable the farmers to meet their obligations. In addition many countries after the depression of the 1930s provided direct subsidies to one or another aspect of their agriculture.

(c) *Agricultural processing and marketing.* Adequate facilities for the processing and marketing of agricultural products were also vital to the efficient operation of agriculture. In countries of advanced agriculture improved transport systems, including the extension of all-weather farm-to-market roads, motor vehicle and air transport, and new methods of processing and preserving foodstuffs, including quick freezing, broadened the farmer's market for perishable as well as for staple foods. In the market economies farm products entered a system of wholesale and retail distribution which became more elaborate with the extension of its scope. In the socialized economies state systems of procurement and distribution handled all except the small amounts which reached local markets.

In the market economies packaging became more elaborate, both to permit shipment and for sale through mounting numbers of self-service outlets where the package rather than a shop assistant acted as salesman. In order to make this form of marketing possible, standards of size, quality and nomenclature were developed, generally by government agencies, and laws were enacted requiring that certain information concerning the content appear on the labels of containers. Farmers whose product did not meet prevailing standards found themselves at a competitive disadvantage. For the protection of public health, inspection services were established for livestock slaughtering and other processing and buyers came to depend on these safeguards for assurance that the food which they bought was safe.

Increased processing, packaging and shipping made the commercial farmer and the consumer more dependent on the middleman. In order to reduce this dependence and to secure as large a proportion of the consumer's food money as possible, farmers in most of the agriculturally advanced countries formed co-operatives to market and often to process and package their products. Marketing co-operatives, especially strong in Denmark and Holland and very active in other countries of western Europe and North America, became extremely powerful and came virtually to control the marketing of particular products in their areas. In addition farmers formed co-operatives to purchase their seed, fertilizer, tractors and other supplies in order to lower their costs by performing the middleman's wholesale function for themselves. Direct co-operative action by farmers, however, could not protect them against the major economic pressures to which they were subject. Much of their organized effort was therefore directed toward political action to secure the intervention of government on their behalf.

Extensive processing and packaging had not become part of the agricultural economy of the USSR by the 1950s. Handling of farm products in their natural state was still the major problem in getting produce from field to consumer, for distances were great, storage facilities on the farms and at collection points not always sufficient and roads within and to the farms generally unimproved. Inter-*kolkhoz* enterprises, established to serve several collective farms, had as one of their main functions the improvement of roads and storage facilities.

In the underdeveloped countries the inability of the farmer to get his crop to market, waste and spoilage in the process and costly methods of handling were serious obstacles to the improvement of agriculture, the raising of farm income and the reduction of food costs. In addition, farmers often lacked access to essential supplies. In Asia and Africa and parts of Latin America numbers of agricultural villages or hamlets could not be reached by a wheeled vehicle; where roads existed they were often impassable in the rainy season. Storage facilities were inadequate and losses from rodents, vermin, weather or spoilage reduced by as much as a half the volume of produce shipped from the farm which finally reached the consumer. Town merchants often had farmers at their mercy when it came to price. Retail distribution was carried on inefficiently by a great multitude of small traders who made a meagre living selling foodstuffs.

Programmes for the improvement of agriculture in these countries focused on roads, transport, storage and handling facilities, as well as on the industries producing fertilizers, agricultural chemicals and low-cost equipment; some included measures to improve retail distribution. In India for example, village roads were among the most frequent projects undertaken as community development activities, and fertilizer manufacture was one of the basic industries designated by the first five-year plan as of such importance as to require government operation. The agricultural programmes of most of the Latin American countries included measures to improve storage and marketing, by co-operative effort or as a government service.

4. *Government measures to support farm income*

The crux of the farmer's economic problems in the countries of advanced agriculture and individual farms was twofold: the farmer remained a highly competitive producer of a product whose price he could not control, in an economy where an increasing proportion of non-agricultural prices were administered by corporations or, in the case of wage rates, by agreement between employers and labour unions; and, except in time of war or crop failure, farm production tended to outrun the market as improved techniques raised yields more rapidly than demand was augmented by increased population and rising incomes. The depression of the 1930s demonstrated how extremely vulnerable the agricultural segment had become to the impact of fluctuations in employment and prosperity in the rest of the economy. Prices for agricultural products collapsed, but the farmer's costs remained high, for the companies from which he purchased his equipment and supplies were in a position to hold prices up by cutting down on production. Fixed charges on his debt, moreover, continued regardless of his income.

Farmers who produced for export were particularly hard hit, as in Canada, Australia, Argentina and Brazil, when prices on world markets fell to a quarter of their pre-depression level while stocks of wheat, wool, meat and coffee continued to pile up unsold. Many farmers lost their farms to the banks to which they were mortgaged. United States farmers in some localities resorted to direct action to stop mortgage foreclosures; when a neighbour's farm was put up for sale to satisfy a mortgage debt, they assembled in force, intimidated any outsider who tried to bid, and bought the farm back for a few dollars.

In the face of this situation governments stepped in to protect their farmers from economic disaster. The measures adopted were various, and changed through the years, but in one way or another they provided for a buffer against extreme downward fluctuations in price and in some measure tried to assure farmers a market for their product. Notably in the United States these measures were associated with efforts to limit supply by restricting the acreage planted to particular crops—efforts which were continually undermined by increased yields on the acres which remained in cultivation.

Support measures generally took the form of guaranteeing the farmer a given level of prices, sometimes by government purchases at this price, sometimes by government loans on supplies held in storage against a future price rise, sometimes by estimating the probable size of a crop and fixing prices so as to sustain a given level of farm income. Some measures were linked to soil conservation, either by making conservation practices a condition for receiving benefit payments or by making it of direct advantage to farmers to engage in such practices. Farm support measures generally applied to specific crops, and were sometimes adjusted to trends in consumption—e.g. away from grains and to 'protective' foods such as milk, fruits, vegetables and meat as incomes rose; at other times they reflected the strength of the producing group and the place of the product in the economy rather than consumption trends or nutritional needs.

A number of countries set up programmes for feeding special groups in the population outside the regular commercial channels of food distribution, through school lunches, infant milk stations and welfare agencies, and they used these programmes for the disposal of surpluses which threatened to depress the market. Whatever the form, these economic measures substituted controlled markets for free markets within countries and involved governments heavily both in regulating and in providing financial backing to agriculture.

Public measures on behalf of agriculture were based on the developing study of agricultural economics pursued by agronomists seeking to understand the farmer's economic as well as his technical problems and economists who applied economic theory to the agricultural segment of the economy. They depended too on the development of statistical techniques for estimating crop yields, insect populations and the effects of weather conditions and for establishing the interrelations among the many factors which play upon production, farm management and the agricultural economy. As a field of study, agricultural economics grew out of a variety of interests followed during the nineteenth and early twentieth century in different European countries—farm management, credit, farm accountancy, agricultural co-operatives—and it reached very extensive proportions after 1920 in the United States and Canada, Australia and New Zealand. In 1929 an International Conference of Agricultural Economists was organized to link the organized societies of specialists in European countries, North America, Australasia and India. Through work in this field economic measures on behalf of agriculture came to be based on elaborate systems for reporting, estimating and forecasting farm production, income, demand, costs and related factors.

At the beginning of the second world war the surpluses accumulated in the USA and Canada provided the initial basis for wartime supplies. Thereafter agricultural production in these countries expanded enormously. Such expansion was encouraged by government guarantees that farm prices would be supported after the war and not be allowed to collapse as they had after the first world war when European agriculture recovered and huge supplies from North America were no longer needed. This expanded production helped to carry the allied countries through the war and to meet the immediate post-war situation of acute food shortage.

But within a few years, the major producing countries were back to a surplus position, as European farming not only recovered but underwent rapid modernization and European countries took steps to sustain the level of home production for reasons of national security. By the 1950s programmes of agricultural support, which had been inaugurated during the depression and used to stimulate agricultural production during the war, had become a sort of permanent crutch for agriculture. Agricultural technology constantly reduced the number of farmers required to meet the need for domestic consumption and export. But farmers continued to demand the economic protection which governments were committed to maintain and satisfactory measures had yet to be devised which would not depress farm income, would expand consumption, would encourage the withdrawal of surplus farmers to other occupations, and would avoid stimulating the production of crops already in greater supply than the market would absorb.

Food-importing countries such as Great Britain used many devices similar to those used by countries with agricultural surpluses, but with different objectives. Their agricultural programmes were designed in the interests of national security rather than to benefit the farm segment of the population for its own sake or because of the large contribution of agriculture to national income. They supported farm prices and farmers' incomes in order to make it worth the farmers' while to remain in agriculture; they adjusted taxation to stimulate modernization; they sometimes subsidized particular crops, placed quotas on foreign imports and otherwise sought to reduce dependence on outside sources for vital supplies.

By mid-century, agriculture was the most cared-for and protected segment of the economy in the technically advanced capitalist countries. Although many criticisms were levelled at the comprehensive programmes maintained by these countries, including various marketing schemes, subsidies, tax relief, price supports or other measures, these programmes had become so much a part of the world-wide move toward greater security and welfare that they appeared likely to continue to characterize the structure of world agriculture. At the same time the clear relation between city incomes and farm markets made it abundantly evident that the prosperity of agriculture not only contributed to but depended upon an expanding world economy.

In the socialized economies the level of support for agriculture was determined by the contribution expected from the agricultural sector to the total economy. In the early stages of the Soviet economy, agriculture was made to bear the major share of the cost of capital development; since the USSR was a predominantly agricultural country at the time of the October revolution, this was the main source from which national savings could come. The situation was similar in other socialist economies, especially the People's Republic of China. With the establishment of an industrial base, the USSR was in a position to draw resources for expansion from the industrial sector, while at the same time sustaining the rural segment at a higher level as its productivity rose.[1]

III. FORESTRY

Essentially the same body of basic knowledge was applied to the growing and harvesting of trees as to agricultural crops, but the nature of forests made the process of application different in many ways from that in agriculture.

For a number of reasons the application of scientific knowledge to forestry was largely a matter of public policy: the period of tree growth often extends beyond the life span of man; forest patterns are highly complex as compared with single agricultural crops and involve quite different problems of harvesting and handling; forests affect the maintenance of stable soil and water conditions beyond the immediate locality and the results of sound forest practices are primarily social, benefiting others than those who apply them.

The application of forest technology involved distinct problems in the widely differing forest regions of the world—the large northern forest areas of North America, Russia and Scandinavia, the cultivated forests, mainly in Europe, the tropical forests of South and Central America, southern Asia and Africa, and the regions where forest cover had been largely destroyed, especially in the Mediterranean, parts of China and some sections of the Andes.

The history of forestry in the twentieth century involves the extension of knowledge and of forest policies from the European centre where they had been developed. Knowledge was elaborated and intensified by observation and research into the specific conditions of more and more regions, notably in India, North America, South Africa, Australia and New Zealand, Chile and the USSR. Programmes and policies reflected, and in turn affected, the growing public appreciation of the necessity for forest conservation, the growing body of technical knowledge of forest management, and the technological improvements in methods of harvesting timber and utilizing forest products.

These developments took widely different forms under different conditions: where trees were still a surplus product of nature which man was engaged in reducing, as in parts of North and South America, south-east Asia, Africa and the USSR; in countries short of timber, such as Australia and South Africa; in areas, such as the Mediterranean littoral and much of China, where man had long ago destroyed the tree cover; in regions, notably in Europe, where a stable balance of wooded and open land had been worked out and was being maintained.

1. Emergence of scientific forestry

The scientific management of forests grew out of the effort to preserve woodlands as the habitat of wild life which could be hunted for food and sport. Feudal, royal or state forests had long been protected for this purpose, especially in central Europe, and before the nineteenth century some of the forest wardens entrusted with the care of these forest preserves had begun to observe the growth patterns of trees systematically and to develop systems of cutting which would provide the amount of sun or shade, space and nourishment which favoured the growth of particular species and would permit a forest to maintain itself through the years. In Russia the first experiments in the study, description, mapping and protection of forests had been undertaken in the time of Peter the Great.

In the first quarter of the nineteenth century schools devoted to scientific forest study and the training of foresters had been established in Germany, France and Russia. In these countries, and in the other European countries to which systematic forest management and forest training spread during the nineteenth century, state forests were brought under scientific management, a body of knowledge was built up relating to the growing habits of European tree species, standard cutting methods suitable to different conditions and purposes were worked out, and professional training supplied the personnel which carried the principles and practices of forest management to other parts of the world.

The principal development in the nineteenth century outside Europe had been in India and Burma, where the British government had begun to set aside certain of the teak forests as public reserves in the middle of the century and to develop a trained forest staff for their administration, and in Indonesia where the Dutch administration had brought the teak forests under regulation at the end of the century. A body of British foresters trained for the Indian service in France and Germany, and after 1885 in Britain, had developed techniques for the management of Indian and Burmese forests and supplied the personnel which at the turn of the century was beginning to extend scientific forestry to Malaya, Siam, East Africa and the West Indies. In the Asian areas main attention was focused on the commercially valuable teak, although systematic study of other Indian species was under way.

In North America towards the end of the nineteenth century the virgin forests which European settlers had regarded either as a bar to settlement or as an unlimited source of fuel and building material were beginning to become depleted and Americans were awakening to the need for conservation. The United States government had started to set aside lands as national forests in 1891 and had provided for their scientific management in 1897. The first American foresters had returned from training in Europe to join two or three German foresters in manning the new national forest service, administering the first scientifically managed private forest, and establishing in 1898 the first American school of forestry.

2. *Major developments in forestry practices in the twentieth century*

(a) *Sustained forestry.* The outstanding development in forestry in the twentieth century was the spread from Europe to other parts of the world of the principle that forests should be made continuously productive.

Forest management systems were the crux of sustained-yield forestry. European forestry evolved a series of alternative or complementary systems, such as the selective cutting of large trees, cutting of small growth to allow selected trees full use of space and nutrition, or complete cutting of stands where the species required sunlight for seeding in order to permit a new stand to take hold. These forest management systems, whose basic purpose was to perpetuate forest growth, were dependent for their applicability not only on the growth patterns of particular kinds of trees, but on the costs of operation, the uses to which forest products would be put, and on the related public policies to which forest management contributed, such as the protection of watersheds, grazing ranges, wild life or recreation areas.

The conditions upon which this body of knowledge and practice was based were specifically those of Europe: a moist, cool climate, a limited number of commercially valuable tree species, generally porous soils, ample but gentle rainfall offering a minimum threat of erosion, flood or drought, little serious danger from fire and a high demand for forest products together with an ample supply of manpower which made labour-using practices profitable and minimized waste.

Other regions of the world presented many conditions and problems which were wholly outside the European range of research and practice. Climate, soil, water supply, the contour of the land, the varieties and combinations of native trees and the possible uses of forest products all combined to define the problem of forest management differently for each forest area and to set the special terms for effective practice. Ingenious foresters applied the basic principles of scientific forestry to new situations; new bodies of data were developed through the slow process of observing the growth of local trees, the interactions among species and the results of different methods of treatment. As scientific forestry was extended to new areas, a wide variety of forest management practices were developed which were adapted to the combination of factors present in each region.

Sustained-yield forestry took hold slowly in tree-rich North America, but it gained momentum through the years. It spread gradually to other heavily forested regions, in Latin America, south Asia, Africa, Siberia, and to timber-scarce areas such as Britain. By the middle of the century a growing body of experience and knowledge, combined with a widespread movement for conservation, had brought acceptance of the principle, if not the practice, of continuously productive forestry throughout the world.

(b) *Forest plantations.* Sustained-yield forestry depends on the pre-existence of a forest area. The open steppes, the treeless prairie or veld and regions denuded of trees by over-felling require a different approach.

Forest nurseries where trees were grown for use in afforestation had been well established on the European continent and in Britain during the nineteenth century and were widely extended in many regions. In these nurseries experiments with seed beds made it possible to determine conditions of sun and moisture most favourable to initial survival and growth and to check these against knowledge gained by observations in the natural habitats. These studies made it possible to go beyond the practice of reproducing natural conditions and to select and breed strains which showed particularly rapid rates of growth or other special characteristics.

Forest plantations where these rapidly growing species of trees were scientifically planted and harvested were successfully established and their cultivation and management were developed to a high level, especially in South Africa, Australia, New Zealand and Chile. In South Africa nearly 2,000,000 acres of land were set out in forest plantations, some three-quarters under commercial operation and the remainder by the state. At mid-century plantation methods were spreading to many areas, as it began to appear that timber, pulpwood and pit-props might be produced more cheaply in man-made plantations on favourable sites than through natural regeneration in managed natural forests. Forest plantations were encouraged by state subsidy and by public operation in Britain, they were increasing in Scandinavian and other European countries and were becoming widespread in the United States.

(c) *Tree genetics.* Research in many places and under many conditions constantly added to the number of trees whose growth habits were known. In the course of these fifty years most of the major North American species were identified and their main characteristics studied, as were some five hundred or more potentially useful tropical trees in south Asia. Wherever forest services were established, local species were subjected to study; in addition expeditions from North American and European institutions made studies in areas such as parts of Latin America where such services were lacking.

Data remained inadequate in many regions, however. For the North American forests, where a single area often contained as many as thirty major species of trees, it was a mammoth task to determine not only the habits of each species but the ecology of the whole group and the possible response to many possible changes. Only time and long experiment could yield full data on the many growth complexes and their response to changes in the environment. For many tropical and semi-tropical forests, ranging from dense rain-forests and jungles to arid areas where trees could barely survive, scientific study was still in its infancy at mid-century. Attention was being extended, however, from a few commercially valuable species such as teak, mahogany and rubber to the growth and possible uses of unexploited types.

Beginnings were being made in the application of genetics to silviculture, especially in Sweden, Denmark and the United States. Experiments in selection and hybridization, which had been started in the 1930s, were bearing fruit, and work in tree breeding was expanding rapidly in many regions. Except in the growing of nursery stock little work had been done in the field of tree nutrition and fertilization under forest conditions.

(d) *Protection of forests against fire, disease and pests.* Protection of forests against fire, disease and pests was vital to forest conservation and management, especially under the conditions which prevailed in North America. The vast forest areas of Canada and the United States, often difficult of access and frequently dry, required methods of fire protection which had not been so necessary a part of European forest practice. By mid-century, however, fire protection was being actively promoted in European countries also.

Forest fire control was based on the principle that fires must be detected immediately and fought when they are small and manageable, they must be subjected to an all-out attack, and no area, public or private, can be exempt from protection. On this basis the United States and Canada developed elaborate systems of look-out stations, communications, and organizations to summon fire-fighters quickly and deliver them swiftly to their station, and a similar system was set up in the USSR. The introduction of the bulldozer in the 1930s provided fire-fighters with an important tool for opening up lanes in the path of the fire to prevent its spread; the fire services evolved techniques for dropping fire-fighters by parachute on the far side of a burning area; air patrols in time supplemented stationary lookouts, and helicopters made it possible to pick up the parachutists and transfer them to other areas.

Scientific studies of the conditions which produced fires led to the development of ratings of fire danger and permitted more effective use of the organization for constant vigil and swift attack. With the aid of such ratings, fire-susceptible areas were spotted in advance, personnel was alerted and concentrated in danger zones, and areas were closed to the public when fire danger became most acute. Fire itself became a protective tool, as studies of its use indicated when prescribed burning could safely and effectively be used to reduce the fire hazard from accumulated underbrush and at the same time could eliminate disease carriers and breeding grounds for pests and provide an improved seedbed for trees of certain types.

By mid-century approximately 70 per cent of the forest land of the United States—all the federal and state forest land and a large proportion of the privately owned—was under systematic fire protection, and on these lands the burned area was held down to about six-tenths of one per cent of the area protected. On the private lands which were outside the zones of protection the proportion of the area burned by destructive fire was estimated at twenty-five times that of the protected lands.

Techniques for the control of pests and disease were less well developed than those for the control of fire. Although the amount of destruction, especially from pests, was known to be high, control measures were rarely launched until a disease or infestation reached epidemic proportions. A few major compaigns were successful in bringing a particularly destructive blight or pest under control; for example, adequate measures were taken on the west coast of the United States (1910–34) to check the chestnut tree blight when it appeared there, after it had completely destroyed the chestnut trees on the east coast.

Towards the middle of the century some of the new weed and pest control chemicals from agriculture were being used experimentally in forests, including aerial spraying of DDT to combat leaf-eating pests. In addition, studies of the habits of pests and the kinds of growth likely to act as carriers of disease led to the development of forest practices designed to lessen the likelihood of their spread. The economical application of such practices, however, depended on carrying out the fire-control principle of early detection and all-out attack. At mid-century Canada was incorporating this principle into its forest protection programme by training its forest rangers to watch for and recognize signs of blight or infestation as well as fire, and to organize equivalent attacks on disease or pests, and the United States was beginning to follow suit.

(e) *Mechanization of forest operations.* The mechanization of logging operations, with the use of portable, motor-driven saws, bulldozers to clear logging roads, and motor transport to supplement streams, slides, logging railways and animal power, revolutionized lumbering. When hand methods were used, it was often profitable to bring out only the main trunks of the trees, leaving as much as 40–60 per cent of the wood behind, and the losses under traditional methods of transport were also high. Mechanized operations cut waste in logging and transport and reduced the labour required to a small fraction of that used before. Technical guidance in the introduction of logging machinery and in the maintenance and repair of logging equipment was one of the areas in which the FAO and the United States technical assistance programmes were called upon to provide aid, especially in Latin American and Asian countries.

Mechanization was applied much less widely and successfully to the planting and cultivation of trees than to their harvesting and processing. As compared with agriculture, silviculture continued to be a labour-using activity, especially under conditions of steep or rocky terrain.

(f) *Utilization of forest products.* Technical development in the uses of wood were also revolutionary. At the opening of the century, wood was used chiefly for fuel, for structural material in the form of solid boards or beams, for containers, for the manufacture of articles such as furniture and for the manufacture of paper from certain specific types. For most of these purposes, only good logs for sawn boards or pulp were used; the rest of the cut timber was discarded in the woods or burned as fuel in the mills.

By the middle of the century new chemical processes for reducing wood to pulp and for bleaching greatly extended the range of types suitable for paper making, and more elaborate processes for utilizing the cellulose content of wood from chips as well as from solid logs made it possible to use all sorts of bits which could be ground up and converted into pulp. For the production of synthetic rayon and many of the plastics, the cellulose content of wood was extracted and converted to a liquid which could be drawn into fibre or extruded in plastic sheets. The development of new, stronger and weather-resistant adhesives led to the substitution of plywood for solid wood in containers and wall panels, greatly reducing the amount of wood used and the space occupied by it for a given strength and purpose. As applied to containers for war material during the second world war these developments were credited with reducing the shipping space required by one-fifth, as well as providing better protection from damage in transit and a 10 per cent saving in lumber used.

Methods of preserving wood against decay and insect attack by impregnation with chemicals and oils made woods usable which had formerly been uneconomic because of their rapid deterioration and they prolonged the life of poles, piles, railway sleepers and posts. In a period of thirty years the amount of wood needed for the replacement of railway sleepers in the United States was reduced by 60 per cent as a result of new techniques of wood preservation and treatment. Still other uses resulted from the distillation of wood sugars, first for alcohol during the first world war and then to produce molasses for animal feed and, under conditions of sugar shortage in wartime Germany, for human food.

These technical developments in the utilization of forest products not only expanded the variety of trees which were commercially valuable but indicated the special properties of wood that were desirable. In some cases, these properties could be enhanced by one forest practice rather than another. At mid-century the relation between specific properties of wood and conditions of growth of some species was beginning to be sufficiently understood to serve as a partial guide to forest practices designed to yield the maximum proportion of the kind of wood desired.

(g) *Uses of forests to conserve water, soil and wild life.* Forests are not only a resource which can be scientifically managed in order to produce a sustained yield of a valuable crop; they are a means of conserving soil and water and providing a habitat for wild life. Interest in their conservation began to spread to various parts of the world in the last quarter of the nineteenth century, as people became aroused lest the ecological balance of nature be so upset as to bring unforeseen and dangerous consequences, lest species of life become extinct, and lest man in the future should no longer have the opportunity to know and enjoy nature in an unspoiled state.

In forest-rich North America public attention was directed first to the preservation of the remaining stands of virgin timber and of the wild life which inhabited the forests, and then to the relation of forests to flood and erosion control. One of the first American foresters, Gifford Pinchot (1865–1946), who did more than anyone else to arouse public consciousness and interest in forest conservation in the United States during the first quarter of the twentieth century, used pictures of treeless, eroded and flood-wrecked areas of China to dramatize the need to protect the forests before it should become too late. An International Conference for the Protection of Nature was held in 1913 in Switzerland and an international office was established in

Brussels in 1928. By the second quarter of the twentieth century conservation had become a world-wide issue as books bearing such titles as *Deserts on the March* (by Paul B. Sears, Oklahoma, 1935) warned of the dire consequences of continued neglect of the imperatives of conservation.

The issue was dramatized by a series of floods and dust storms in the 1930s in the drought-stricken dust bowl area of the central United States, where grass cover had been ploughed under and dry farming undertaken in response to the high farm prices of the first world war. Possible remedies were also dramatized in that country when the Tennessee Valley Authority was set up in 1933 to develop the whole of a great river valley by the application of forest and grassland practices, construction of dams, control of floods and the provision of electric power and navigation. The TVA fired the imagination of people in other countries who projected similar valley development programmes in which watershed protection through forest conservation and reforestation would form a vital part, such as the Snowy River project in Australia, the Damodar Valley project in India and extensive river development projects in the USSR and China.

Toward the middle of the century studies of the role of forests in conservation were extended to include the part played by forests as consumers as well as conservers of water. The flow of streams from areas where the forest was unbroken was compared with that from similar areas which had been partially cut, and as much as a third to a half as much additional water was found in some cases to enter streams from the opened slopes. Such planned cutting reduced water consumption by the trees themselves by lessening their number, and it permitted snow to reach the ground instead of evaporating from the tree tops. The concept of watershed management as opposed to mere protection was thus developed and ways were sought to balance the objective of flood and erosion control with that of maximum water supply in areas where rainfall was seasonal or scarce. In snow areas the development of windbreaks to induce drifting was undertaken in the effort to create snow reservoirs which would melt slowly and continue to deliver water after the undrifted snow had gone.

Wherever open grazing was practised the problem of range management was linked with the management of existing forests or with new planting. Goats which overgrazed whatever area they penetrated prevented the natural rejuvenation of forests by eating down new growth as it appeared. Especially in the Near East and along the slopes of the Andes, goat control was the *sine qua non* of forest management, reforestation, and watershed protection. Overstocking of ranges and uncontrolled grazing of cattle presented a similar problem of serious proportions in parts of the United States, India and Russia.

The most difficult problems of conservation arose where forest or grass cover had already been destroyed and remedial reforestation or afforestation was required. In the 1930s both the United States and the USSR launched large-scale programmes for the planting of shelter belts in their open plains in order to check wind erosion and perhaps to affect the climate of the areas. Both programmes were fairly successful in establishing stands of trees. Evidence as to the possible effect of these belts on climate, however, appeared to indicate that their effects were confined to the very immediate locality. The Russian programme to extend the planting of shelter belts for many hundreds of miles was continuing at mid-century.

Along the Mediterranean littoral, the Tigris–Euphrates valley, parts of India and much of China, where population had been dense for thousands of years, conditions were extremely unfavourable to reforestation. The tall cedars of Lebanon and their counterparts elsewhere had long since been cut, and much of the unprotected soil had washed, blown or leached away, leaving stony hillsides or spreading, windswept deserts and annual dangers from destructive floods. In these areas the beginnings of economic planning in newly established countries, supported by the momentum of the conservation movement and the stimulus and technical assistance of the United Nations Food and Agriculture Organization, set efforts in motion at mid-century to reverse the age-long process of physical deterioration.

Arid lands presented the most baffling, but some of the most important problems in reforestation. At mid-century no solution to the problem of dry land planting had yet been found, but research and practical efforts were being carried on in a number of areas, notably in the arid regions of India, the United States, the USSR, Australia, Israel and China.

3. *Forest policies and programmes*

Progress in the application of scientific forestry depended to a major degree on the adoption of national forest policies. Since the benefits of forest practices become apparent only after many years and do not accrue solely to the owner of the forest land, public measures were required to secure sound forest management. Most forest legislation applied principally to domains under public control, scientific practices were most widely introduced on public lands, and research and experiment were chiefly supported by public funds.

Forest policies and programmes took the form of the administration of state forest lands; regulation of designated areas to protect water sources, check erosion or preserve wild life; measures to protect private as well as public forests against hazards of fire or pests or to regulate or supervise their cutting; financial and technical aid to private individuals; and programmes to educate forest users and promote sound practices.

(a) *European programmes*. By the opening of the twentieth century most continental European countries had effective forest codes and administrative structures for controlling forest practices on state lands. A half to two-thirds of the forest lands in most European countries, however, were in private hands and a substantial proportion of the public domain belonged to municipalities, cantons or communes, sometimes only partially subject to national control.

European forest programmes in the twentieth century were largely designed to improve the practices in public forests and to extend productive forestry to as large a proportion as possible of the total forest area of the country in order to maintain forest resources at least at existing levels and to preserve their protective features. Most European countries strengthened their forest laws and intensified both administrative and promotional activities. They differed in the extent to which they brought private lands under control, from Switzerland, where all private and cantonal as well as national forests were placed under the surveillance of federal forest police in 1902 and nearly three-quarters of the forest lands were subject to strict cutting regulation by 1904, to France, where private lands constituting nearly two-thirds of all forests remained free from the restrictions of the forest code and the supervision of state foresters.

The two world wars had a profound effect on European forest programmes and policies, for they not only destroyed the forests which lay in the path of combat but stimulated excessive cutting to meet the heavy wartime demands for wood. In areas such as Germany where the combination of regulation of state forests and voluntary measures on many large private areas had established a balance between growth and extraction, cutting exceeded replacement during much of the period after the beginning of the first world war. By 1954 the forests of the German Federal Republic had been restored to a balanced yield. In the states of eastern Europe, which inherited their forest laws from the 1852 forest code of the Austro-Hungarian Empire, the need of a cash export crop in the inter-war years added to wartime destruction and demand to deplete the forest resources of these areas. Although these countries launched planned reforestation programmes after the second world war to regain self-sufficiency and a sustained output, the process of depletion appeared to be still continuing at mid-century.

The northern European countries adopted strong programmes for both regulation and promotion. They forbade the cutting of young forests except for thinning, and limited cutting of older growth to that which would maintain a sustained yield; they developed local commissions or boards to oversee such regulations and they formed co-operative organizations which employed foresters to provide technical guidance to local owners. The Netherlands required a licence for all cutting, but succeeded in bringing less than a quarter of its woodland under sustained-yield management. Britain, which was aroused to acute consciousness of its dangerous lack of wood when the first world war cut off imports, adopted its first effective forestry act in 1919, setting up a state forestry commission which took over the royal forests and planted a million acres by 1957. After the second world war the commission was given control over felling in private woods and inaugurated a system of 'dedication' under which the owners of private woods accepted supervision in return for financial grants.

(b) *North American programmes*. In the large forest areas of North America, which furnished a quarter of the world's commercial wood supply in the twentieth century, direct measures to restrain cutting were almost wholly confined to forest lands in the public domain. For the United States from 1891 on, successive legislative acts extended the authority of the federal government to retain or to acquire forest lands in order to conserve a national resource, for stream and watershed protection and finally without specific limitation; they also provided authorization and funds for forest protection and forest research. By 1955 national forests, together with forest lands similarly set aside by the states, amounted to a third of the forest land of the country, but they accounted for only 10 per cent of the timber which was cut annually.

The federal government exercised no direct control over cutting on private land but it extended fire protection (1911) and later, pest control (1947) to these areas, and after 1924 it co-operated with the states in providing free or cheap planting stock for conservation and shelter belts and it offered bonuses for various conservation practices. During the depression of the 1930s, unemployed youth, organized in a Civilian Conservation Corps, were set to work on conservation projects throughout the country. From 1937 on, a forest extension service similar to the agricultural extension service offered technical advice to farmers on the management of their woodlands and to owners of timber stands on mangement procedures appropriate to each area. A majority of the states revised their tax laws in order to encourage rather than to discourage good forest managment. Forest planting on private farm lands was stimulated by the distribution of low-cost trees from state forest nurseries to farmers at rapidly increasing rates which reached several million trees a year by the mid-1950s.

Much destructive cutting by small farmers and lumber companies continued. But the combination of conservation subsidies, technical advisory services, the supplying of trees to farmers at nominal cost and the recognition by commercial companies of the practical value of scientific forestry measures was bringing sound forest management to an increasing proportion of the forest lands of the United States.

In Canada all except 6 per cent of the vast forest area was publicly owned, three-quarters by the separate provinces, each of which had its own programme of administration and control. The provincial and national Crown lands were exploited chiefly under licences issued to private companies, and the principal method of control was to require the licensees to submit working plans before receiving the right to cut. Increasingly, licensees were required to maintain a sustained yield, but a number of the provinces in the 1940s and 1950s considered their forest policies inadequate and appointed commissions to review their programmes, while the national government in 1949 instituted a programme of aid to the provinces for forest management.

The eastern provinces, where most of the private forest land was located, established forest services to aid in the development of farm woodlands and one, Nova Scotia, took the first step to control private forests directly by enacting legislation after the second world war requiring permission to cut all trees under ten inches in diameter.

(c) *Forest programme of the* USSR. The forest programme of the USSR was one of the most ambitious. It was based on the forestry traditions of Europe, for German methods had been adopted for the administration of the tsar's forests, and the Leningrad Institute was one of the oldest forest research institutes in the world. Combined with these European traditions of forest management were vast forest resources and frontier conditions similar to those of North America. Forest policy in the USSR was directed toward the full development of timber resources and the wide use of forests for protection and conservation; forest projects were given high priority in respect to capital investment, machinery and equipment. Guided by research carried on in a dozen major and a multitude of lesser forest research institutes and experimental stations, and supplied with a large body of trained personnel by forestry schools which graduated several thousand foresters and forest technicians annually, Russian forest operations moved eastward to tap the relatively undeveloped resources of Siberia and to supply wood for the eastward moving industry and population of the USSR. The first large-scale pulp and paper mill in the Far East was established at Komsomolsk on the Amur river in 1942.

Large areas of forests were set aside as screens around health resorts and industrial centres, and forests on watersheds and river banks were designated as protection forests where cutting was restricted. In a gigantic fifteen-year undertaking to 'remake nature', the USSR launched in 1948 a project to erect a 5,000-mile forest barrier against hot south-east winds, to plant shelter belts around cultivated fields on some 12,000,000 acres of open land, to create some 44,000 ponds and reservoirs, and to build hydroelectric power and irrigation systems and a series of major canals. These measures were designed with the hope that they would convert a wide, treeless, wind-swept area of steppe and desert into a balanced green landscape, to modify the climate, to increase crop yields in the protected areas and to bring former desert areas into cultivation.

(d) *Programmes for tropical zones.* In most other parts of the world programmes of forest management and conservation were limited, but by mid-century nearly all countries maintained some form of forest regulation and service for their public domains and the development of forest resources was part of their plans for economic development. In most tropical and semi-tropical areas—south and south-east Asia, Central and South America and Africa—the situation was similar. Near centres of population forests were so depleted that even firewood was scarce; in less accessible regions forests were almost untouched and often unexplored.

The most elaborate programmes for tropical areas were those originally established by the British in India and Burma to manage the reserved forests under public authority and to regulate some additional protected areas. At the opening of the century 20 per cent of the reserved lands of India and Burma were being administered according to scientific principles; by 1933 three-quarters of such lands were under approved working plans. The Indian government after 1947 laid out a programme for reforestation to check the progressive deterioration of the soil in some areas, for the establishment of village woodlands, and for the continued management of public forests with a view to making use of a wider range of tropical trees. These programmes encountered severe technical and administrative problems arising from the character of the land to be reforested, for it was difficult to find suitable species and to devise planting patterns to withstand the severe climatic conditions while trees were becoming established. In addition the extreme shortage of fuel in densely populated areas made it difficult to protect plantings against depredation.

In other countries of south and south-east Asia, forest programmes were being directed toward the fuller use of forest resources and the protection of forests in inhabited areas against waste from the widespread practice of shifting agricultural cultivation.

Among the countries of Central and South America few effective forest policies were adopted until after the second world war. Mexico had begun to develop a reforestation programme in the early years of the century; Brazil and Chile enacted laws in the 1930s to regulate cutting but did little to enforce them. After the second world war most of these countries took steps to adopt or revise forest legislation, to establish or strengthen their forest services, to launch programmes of reforestation and to develop methods for exploiting their lowland jungles. The largest number of technical assistance projects by the forestry division of the FAO during these years were in Latin America.

In tropical Africa most of the forests remained unexploited except for limited and specific purposes, chiefly in east Africa. Some areas were reserved as preserves for big game. Only a beginning had been made by mid-century in developing techniques for sustained forestry, and in creating forest reserves which would prevent destruction prior to the development of sound practices.

(e) *Programmes for denuded areas.* Where forest cover had been most completely destroyed, as in China, the eastern Mediterranean and parts of the Andes, only drastic measures for reforestation under most difficult conditions could begin to undo the results of centuries of abuse.

In China interest in forest conservation and reforestation began after 1911, but it was not until 1938 that a national forest law was enacted, modelled on that of Japan, and a forest administration established, and only after 1949 that vigorous measures for forest reclamation were launched. The 1938 law gave the central government the power to establish areas as 'protection forests' which no one might cut or damage, to compensate the owners of such forests and to require persons who benefited from forestry work done by an owner to bear part of the cost. After 1949 an elaborate administrative organization was developed to administer the 'protection forests' and provincial forest lands, grant licences and supervise cutting on other land, and to organize and stimulate the reforestation of denuded areas. An immense tree-planting campaign was launched which stimulated farmers' organizations and especially youth groups to undertake projects for planting millions of trees. At mid-century the task of restoring tree-cover to China's vast bare regions overshadowed all other aspects of its forest programme.

In other treeless regions, South Africa developed extensive plantations, using entirely imported trees. Australia concentrated its efforts on the introduction of softwoods which could provide raw material for paper, on planting experiments in some of its dry regions and on measures to control the acute fire hazard. In the denuded areas of the eastern Mediterranean and the Middle East, forest programmes were in their infancy. Turkey had a well-organized forest service but had not yet checked abusive cutting on its remaining wooded areas. In most other countries of the area a bare beginning had been made by mid-century on the multiple and difficult problems of reforestation. Only in Israel, where tree planting became a symbol of the national effort to reclaim the land, had substantial headway been made toward reforestation in this region.

(f) *International co-operation in forestry and forest policies and programmes.* The inclusion of a forestry division in the United Nations Food and Agriculture Organization signalized the world-wide importance of forest development and its relation with food and agriculture. The aspects on which the FAO was called on to provide technical assistance during its first ten years indicated the needs of the different regions. The largest number of its projects were in the forest-rich areas of Latin America, where the aid sought was initially in the development of forest policy, drafting of forest laws and establishment of forest administrations; thereafter specific projects constituting parts of the countries' programmes for rational exploitation of their forest resources, such as settlement of the Amazon basin of Brazil or development of forest industries in Paraguay, received FAO assistance and led to the setting up of a regional research and training institute in Venezuela.

In the Near East, by contrast, the almost total absence of remaining forests led to requests for assistance in reforestation, grazing control, soil conservation practices and the training of foresters, and to plans for a regional training centre for the area in Iran. Most of the countries of south and south-east Asia inherited forest policies and services from the British and Dutch colonial administrations which had been concerned with the extraction of the valuable lumber crop, mainly teak, and requests from these countries were largely in relation to new uses for additional types of woods, and new techniques of logging, transport, drying and preservation. Some assistance was also requested from this area to improve forest practices and check indiscriminate burning where this method of clearing for shifting cultivation persisted.

4. *Forestry, forest policies and conservation at mid-century*

At mid-century the science of forestry was still in its infancy, in spite of its long history and rich development in Europe, because of the enormous regional differences between areas which required the repetition elsewhere of the kind of long-term observation, experience and experiment which had given European forestry its sound local base. The technology of wood utilization was in a stage of very rapid development which greatly increased the range of forest products which could be economically exploited.

The conservation movement had become world-wide; the International Union for the Preservation of Nature, organized in 1948 with the co-operation of Unesco, was composed of more than 150 national and international conservation organizations and official bodies in some thirty countries. In many areas, however, the movement was still not sufficiently strongly supported by individuals in their private behaviour and governments in their public programmes to reverse the trend toward the depletion of resources.

Forest conservation was part of a many-faceted struggle to retain the world's soil, water and renewable growth and to preserve them against the depredations of mankind. Sound forest practices generally required social as well as individual action, but they depended also upon the co-operation of individuals and their willingness to pursue long-range rather than only short-term goals and to consider the effects of their actions on others as well as themselves. It was the claim of scientific forestry that the social conscience and responsibility of a people could be measured by the way in which it handled its forests.*

IV. FISHERY

Fishing, too, received new impulse and took new shapes in response to the scientific and technological developments of the twentieth century. During the first half of the century the volume of fish production doubled. For the world as a whole, however, this meant little or no increase in the *per capita* amount of fish caught, for the expansion of fish production was roughly in proportion to the increase in world population during these years. But for those countries where fishing reflected an advanced technology and expanding economy, notably northern Europe, North America and Japan, it meant a large growth in volume and marked increase in the productivity of persons engaged in fishing. Toward the middle of the century fishing developed rapidly in several new areas, and its techniques began to be revolutionized in regions where traditional methods were being replaced by modern technology.

* See Franz Heske, 'Forestry in the Twentieth Century', *Journal of World History*, vol. v (1959), p. 748.

1. *Deep sea fishery*

(*a*) *Fishing methods.* The major expansion in fish production was made possible by the mechanization of fishing operations and technical developments in the processing and preservation of fish and fish products. The early steam trawlers, sent out by France in the 1870s and by Britain and Germany in the 1880s, presaged the substitution of motor power for sail and oar which became virtually complete in northern Europe, North America and the USSR by the second quarter of the twentieth century and was very extensive by mid-century in Japan. Powered trawlers, operated at first by steam and later also by diesel engines, could travel to distant fishing grounds. Equipped with otter boards which held open the mouth of the seine as it was dragged over the floor of the ocean, and with power hoists to raise the catch, these boats could haul in large quantities of fish in a short time. As their power and speed were increased—up to ten or even twelve knots by the middle of the century—and their design was improved, they could go farther, be more independent of weather conditions and bring back their catches in a shorter time.

Smaller fishing craft, too, were almost completely motorized in these countries by the middle of the century. Fishermen whose boats were powered by petrol engines could tend many more traps than those dependent on sail or oar, and they were less limited by weather and distance. Improved gear was also developed for small craft, such as the light Danish seine which was widely adopted in a number of countries.

In the years following the second world war, and especially after 1950, mechanization spread rapidly to new areas from the major producing countries to which it had hitherto been largely confined. In 1950, for example, only some 50 of the fishing boats in the Indian state of Bombay had engines; by 1955 there were more than 600. The fishing fleets of Hong Kong, Singapore, Ceylon and Indonesia were undergoing a similar motorization and even some of the Pacific islanders were substituting motor boats for outrigger canoes. Some of the smaller producing countries, such as the Philippines, the Union of South Africa and French Morocco, increased their output three to five times from before the war to the early 1950s, South American production doubled, and that of Angola increased nearly ninefold. The governments of economically developing countries frequently facilitated the process of technological change.

The use of electronic devices was second only in importance to the application of motor power and the design of fishing boats and gear. Electronic echo-sounders, or sonar, developed as aids to navigation and for the detection of submarines, were found to be of great value to fishermen in detecting schools of fish. At first used principally on ships engaged in fishery research and then by special scouting vessels such as those sent out by the Norwegian government in the 1940s to spot schools of cod and advise fishermen of their whereabouts, the echo-sounder came to be part of the equipment of many fishing vessels. Radio communication gave fishermen access to news of weather conditions and the whereabouts of fish; in some cases spotting planes circled near-shore fishing grounds to report the presence or absence of fish in the area.

Yet with all these technological improvements, fishing remained a hazardous occupation and an uncertain venture, and it continued to be carried on primarily by those who had followed the sea for generations.

(b) *Processing and preserving of fish and fish products.* Improved techniques for processing and preserving fish paralleled changes in catching methods. By mid-century a quarter of the fish taken from the seas and inland waters was canned, frozen or reduced to fish oil and meal, while half continued to be consumed fresh and a quarter was preserved by the traditional methods of salting, smoking and pickling.

Though fish canning had been developed in the nineteenth century, it was not until bacteriological studies in the twentieth century provided a basis for standard canning procedures that canned fish became a safe product. Canning industries, processing chiefly sardines, salmon and tuna, developed extensively and reached a high level of technical efficiency and automation not only in the major canning centres of the United States and Japan but in many other areas from South Africa to Siberia.

The development of quick freezing offered more revolutionary possibilities. Refrigeration with ice, both in the holds of vessels and for distributing fish to inland places within the temperate zone, was well developed at the opening of the century, but this method of preservation could keep fish in good condition for only short periods. Quick-freezing and low-temperature storage could preserve fish virtually fresh for months. These processes were developed in the 1920s after it was discovered that the rapid formation of crystals did not break down the cell structure as did the slower formation resulting from slow freezing, and that enzyme action in fish was halted only at very low temperatures, $-29°$ to $-31°$ C ($-20°$ to $-24°$ F). The United States was much the largest producer of frozen fish, but the method was used increasingly elsewhere, especially in Canada, Iceland, some parts of Europe and the USSR.

A growing proportion of the total fish catch was reduced to oil and fish meal; at mid-century the amount so used exceeded that which was preserved by canning and freezing. The fish meal and oil industry absorbed more than half of the African catch and nearly a quarter of the European and North American, and was the basis for rapid expansion in herring and pilchard fisheries in several areas. Its economic importance was considerable. By salvaging some of the wastes formerly discarded in cleaning and filleting the fish and by using the miscellaneous fish hauled in the nets, fishermen were able to realize a higher return from their total catch. As the value of the vitamins and minerals supplied by fish in all its forms came to be appreciated, methods of refining fish oils and of making fish meal palatable were developed, and products which had been thrown back into the sea or used as fertilizer were converted into animal feed and at mid-century were beginning to be used as human food.

These methods of processing, which involved using the fish in its fresh state rather than dried or salted, made it necessary to bring the fish to the processing point before its quality had had time to deteriorate. In spite of the greater speed of fishing vessels and improved methods of refrigeration in insulated holds, shore was too far away from some of the fishing grounds. Even the fish sold fresh in European markets was often too old to be offered as a first-class product by the time it reached the consumer; a survey in 1950 found this to be the case for half of the fish on sale.

Floating factories which accompanied fishing fleets and freezing equipment installed on fishing vessels were partial answers to this problem. The first of the whaling factory ships entered the Antarctic in 1904, and thereafter provided the means for processing most of the whales caught in that area. Floating salmon canneries accompanied Japanese fishing fleets in the north Pacific. The first of the United States factory ships for converting herring into meal and oil was put in operation in the 1920s, followed by others in that country and Norway. Towards the middle of the century freezing equipment began to be installed on some individual fishing vessels, and newly designed freezer-trawlers were being sent out by Britain, the United States, France, Germany and the Soviet Union.

The new fishing technology brought changes in the organization of the fishing industry, for large motorized vessels and complex gear involved heavy capital investment beyond the reach of most individual fishermen. In Great Britain, Germany, Japan, Canada, Portugal and the United States, a growing proportion of fishing operations was conducted by fishing companies which often combined catching, processing and marketing. Frequently they sent out fleets with 'mother ships'. Some mother ships, like most of the Portuguese, simply butchered and stored the fish caught by the smaller vessels. Others, such as the American tuna clippers which operated in the southern Pacific and elsewhere, were elaborately equipped with tanks for live bait, canning or freezing equipment, and sometimes even planes for spotting shoals of fish. In countries such as Norway and Iceland where much of the catch continued to be salted or dried, the individual skipper-owned vessel persisted to a greater extent. Fishermen's co-operatives were formed in a number of countries for marketing the catch and purchasing equipment and supplies.

(c) *Scientific knowledge of fish characteristics, habits and environment.* Throughout these years deep-sea fishing remained, as it had always been, a hunting activity. But during the period substantial headway was made in scientific efforts to discover the habits of different types of fish, to understand ocean and climatic conditions affecting their growth and migration, to determine the ecological balances among species and in relation to sources of nourishment and other aspects of the environment, and to evaluate the effects of fishing under various conditions on the supply of fish in future years. By mid-century these developments brought ocean fishing closer than it had ever been before to being an activity which sought to manage rather than merely to exploit the resources of the sea.

Scientific investigation into the characteristics and habits of certain species of fish was well under way by the opening of the twentieth century and continued to be carried on by constantly improved methods. Some of the more commercially valuable types, such as the Arctic herring and cod which made up nearly half of the total European catch, were studied by various means, including tracking with the aid of sonar sounders, until much was known about their breeding places and habits, their feeding grounds, their movements throughout the year, their relation to ocean currents and their place in the ecological balance of ocean life. Much research of this type was conducted aboard fishing vessels, or by special research ships equipped as fishing craft, and was based on the experience and observation of fishermen as well as of scientists. The USSR used a specially equipped submarine for this purpose.

Oceanographic research, aided by improved instruments for measuring and recording ocean temperatures and sampling water at various depths as well as for sounding and for exploring the ocean floor, threw light on the environments within which fish were found. Uniform procedures made it possible to derive more complete information from scattered observations, as was evidenced in the picture of environmental conditions in the North Sea secured in the late 1940s by simultaneous crossings of that sea according to a uniform plan by seven fishery research vessels from seven different nations.

Statistical analyses of numbers, ages and types of fish caught produced a growing body of knowledge which threw light on characteristics of the stock, and on factors, such as conditions affecting the young, which influenced the volume of fish in an area. This and other research provided an increasingly scientific basis for forecasting annual yields, for guiding fishermen to profitable fishing grounds and for protecting sources of supply. By mid-century a theory of fishing had been worked out covering such aspects as survival of young, growth, migration, natural mortality and mortality from fishing, and complex calculations were being made as to what fishing practices would maintain fishing grounds at productive levels.

(d) *Conservation of the resources of the sea.* In the course of these years it became apparent from a number of examples that fish in the sea were not an inexhaustible resource which could be pursued without thought of the effect of fishing on future supply. The danger of overfishing was dramatically apparent in the exhaustion of the halibut fishery off Greenland in the 1930s and the threat of extermination of the Antarctic whale. In the much-fished North Sea catches were exceptionally large and of improved quality after fishing had been interrupted by each of the two world wars. These experiences pointed to the need for measures to manage these fishing grounds in order to achieve the goal set forth by the United Nations International Technical Conference on the Conservation of the Living Resources of the Sea in 1955: 'to obtain the optimum sustainable yield so as to secure a maximum supply of food and other marine products'.

Many national governments, which had long been concerned with their fishing industries as training and recruiting grounds for sailors, inaugurated or extended programmes of research, information and, often, economic facilitation in line with their overall economic and development policies, and took steps to conserve the resources of their territorial waters. They joined internationally to increase the knowledge of the sea and to regulate some aspects of fishing on the high seas.

Formal international co-operation in marine research and conservation was inaugurated in 1899 with the establishment of the International Council for the Exploration of the Sea by the fishery nations of north-western Europe. International commissions were set up in 1923 and 1937 to regulate the amount of halibut and salmon respectively which could be caught each season in the north Pacific area and the time of year when fishing could be carried on. An international convention for regulating the meshes of nets and size limits of fish in the North Sea was adopted in a preliminary form in 1937 and made formal in 1954. Attempts to restrict Antarctic whaling began in 1931, and were intensified after the International Whaling Commission, formed in 1946, undertook to fix hunting seasons and catches and to supervise the catching and processing of whales.

After the second world war international commissions with regulatory functions or with the duty of formulating regulatory proposals for the approval of member governments were formed for the north and north-west Atlantic and for the north and south-east Pacific. The United Nations organized technical conferences on the conservation of marine resources in 1949 and 1955 and set its International Law Commission to work on problems involved in the use of international regulation to raise and sustain useful production from the sea.

When the Food and Agriculture Organization of the United Nations was established, it recognized the integral relation between fisheries and other sources of the world's food by including a fisheries division in its organization. The FAO sponsored fisheries councils for the Mediterranean and the Indo-Pacific regions, provided technical assistance in support of the development work of individual governments and launched a broad project for the thorough mapping of the world's resources, including the resources of the sea.

2. Inland fishery and fish culture

Fish taken from inland waters amounted at mid-century to some 18 per cent of the world's total fish catch and to as much as 30–40 per cent of the fish actually consumed as human food. Three-quarters of the freshwater fish production was in Asia. Fish were taken from lakes, ponds, rice paddies and other limited bodies of water under more nearly controlled conditions than were possible in deep-sea fisheries.

Regulation of freshwater fishing and public measures to sustain or improve the supply of fish were widespread, especially in Europe and North America. Programmes to control soil erosion which required the construction of ponds to impound waters also included the aspect of fish production. At the same time the dumping of industrial wastes which destroyed the fish in rivers became an increasingly serious problem in some areas. The conservation policies of countries in these regions were based on the results of continuous studies of fish habits, of how to maintain a balance between predacious and non-predacious species, of fish hatchery management and of sound procedures for stocking waters with young fish. These programmes were concerned to a considerable extent with maintaining fishing as a sport and only partly with freshwater fish as a source of food, except in the case of farm ponds.

In Asia, on the other hand, much freshwater fish was directly raised for food, especially in China, Japan, Cambodia, Indonesia, Thailand, Malaya, the Philippines and India, all of which areas had well-developed traditions of fish culture. In these countries and in other parts of the world fish culture was related with agriculture in a single complex. Swamp lands unsuitable for agriculture might be converted into productive areas by drainage and the development of fishponds, as had been done in Java, the Yangtze valley and along the Adriatic coast. Irrigation systems offered opportunities for fish culture, although they also presented problems such as the need to provide fish ladders at dams to permit some types of fish to reach their upstream spawning grounds. Fish culture might be combined with animal husbandry, as was done by the Chinese who used methods for draining animal waste into fishponds to fertilize the plankton on which the fish fed and to stimulate the growth of aquatic plants for animal fodder and grass for grazing along the margins of the ponds.

Because of the importance of fish as a source of protein in areas where nutritional levels were low and other sources scarce, research was conducted in many places into means of improving the efficiency of fish culture and raising output. Where it could be developed, fish culture offered possibilities for very much larger production of animal protein per acre than did animal husbandry. Fishpond culture, moreover, yielded much greater production per surface area of water than did fishing in natural water.

Fish farming in ricefields, long practised in Asian countries, was greatly developed during these years through experiments in fish types and culture methods. In Indonesia the practice of stocking the flooded ricefields with large numbers of fish, primarily with carp before the second world war and thereafter with particularly prolific types such as the African tilapia, led to high yields. The Japanese planted special strains of rice which flourished under conditions that were also favourable for fish, and they achieved an extremely productive, balanced rice-and-fish economy. In India the government encouraged fish culture in the ricefields by the free distribution of fish for stocking, when studies showed that the principal varieties of Indian carp grew faster in rice paddies than in ponds. Evidence from Indonesia, China, Japan and Malaya, moreover, indicated that fish culture, besides providing an additional source of income to the rice farmer, actually increased the yield of rice by from 6 to 15 per cent, since the fish ate weeds and insects injurious to the rice and fertilized the plants.

The development of fish culture was also closely related with measures of public health. As a means of purifying sewage, it was of major importance in countries such as China, where an estimated quarter to a third of all deaths were attributable to disease borne by night-soil used as manure, or in Java where sewage water was found to contain large quantities of typhoid bacteria. Purification of sewage water by means of sewage fishponds proved effective in rendering sewage water safe for irrigation while producing large yields of fish which could be safely eaten.

Recognition of the role played by mosquitoes in transmitting malaria, filariasis, yellow fever and dengue led to the development of cultural practices designed to eliminate this menace, and their application in many regions of infestation. The stocking of waters where mosquitoes breed with species of fish which feed on mosquito larvae and the rearing of plantfeeding species to keep ponds free of the vegetation in which mosquitoes breed were found to give the best guarantees of continuous improvement. Efforts to control the small snail which acts as host for the parasites causing bilharzia in Africa, South America and China led to successful experiments in East Africa and the Belgian Congo in stocking infested waters with plant-eating fish to control the food on which the herbivorous snails depend and with mollusc-eating species of fish to devour the snails directly. Biological control of disease vectors and carriers was still in its infancy at mid-century, but there were indications that research into fish species and culture methods would bring significant results for the sanitation of water areas.

V. NUTRITION

In the middle of the twentieth century, the British Ministry of Health declared that 'nutrition is the very essence and basis of national health'.* The dean of American nutritionists, Dr Henry C. Sherman, reviewing fifty years of scientific work in many laboratories, concluded that nutritional knowledge now made it possible to increase the health and efficiency even of those who were already healthy and efficient and to add extra years, not simply to old age but to the prime of life. He aptly titled his review *The Nutritional Improvement of Life* (New York, 1950).

* Quoted in Henry C. Sherman, *The Nutritional Improvement of Life* (New York, Columbia University Press, 1950), p. 8.

The science of nutrition on which these claims were based was a twentieth-century development, though it rested on many earlier studies in chemistry and physiology. From small efforts in the early years of the century it grew with great rapidity, gaining momentum and proliferating in many directions. By the 1930s the new knowledge was entering into public consciousness and public policy. The stimulus of the second world war with its pressures for survival brought further advances in both knowledge and public understanding.

As a body of scientific knowledge, nutrition was unique both in having a direct and immediate bearing on the life and welfare of each individual, and in depending for its application upon the conscious choice or established habit of all the people. That choice was limited by the individual's resources, and where these were insufficient to ward off hunger nutritional knowledge could not solve the basic problem, yet even at low dietary levels it could make a substantial difference. Although it provided an instrument for agricultural policy, medical practice and social welfare, its effective application required widespread understanding and acceptance by every family, not merely by the scientist and technician. As Dr Sherman expressed it, 'nutrition is everyone's adventure'.*

The groundwork for the twentieth-century science of nutrition was laid in the work of nineteenth-century European chemists and physiologists who identified major food components—proteins, fats, carbohydrates—studied processes of digestion and respiration, devised methods of measuring bodily intake and output of certain chemicals, and experimented on a variety of laboratory animals to establish conditions under which they could not survive. Feeding experiments on farm animals, undertaken in the agricultural experiment stations established in Britain, the United States and some of the European countries from the middle of the nineteenth century, set the pattern for many developments in which the quest for healthier and more productive animals threw light on the needs of healthier humans.

As the science of nutrition developed, it covered an ever-widening field. Starting with the overall problem of the conversion of food into energy, it brought into the focus of investigation the protein component, minerals and the newly discovered vitamins. By the 1930s knowledge of energy, proteins, minerals and vitamins was sufficient to provide a general guide to good nutritional practice, but a continuing process of discovery and refinement brought constant elaboration and revision of concepts and standards. New research techniques became possible through developments in many of the sciences, including electronic instruments for more exact measurement, techniques of microbiology which permitted the use of bacteria, moulds and other micro-organisms as subjects of study in place of animals with longer life-cycles, and the use of radioactive isotopes to trace the course of specific nutrients through the system.

* H. C. Sharman, *op. cit.*, p. 9.

1. *Food as a source of energy*

Food was first studied systematically as a source of energy. Beginning in the 1890s new laboratory methods for measuring the conversion of food into energy were used to determine the rate of conversion, the ability of the body to store energy, the manner in which it maintains energy levels and the effects of energy depletion. Out of these studies came a basis for calculating requirements in terms of calories—units of energy-giving food—in relation to body size and energy expenditure.

Calorie requirements had still not been fully explored by 1950, however, when the FAO undertook to formulate them in terms which would be applicable internationally. Requirements in relation to body weight for a 'representative' man and woman engaged in 'normal' activity and for children of different ages, all living in the temperate zone, could be stated on the basis of a substantial body of scientific evidence, as could the additional needs of women during pregnancy and lactation. But the increases or decreases indicated in the FAO standard to take account of older ages, hotter or colder climate and greater or less activity were based on much more fragmentary evidence.

In offering its guide the FAO noted that research was still needed to validate or modify its assumptions, including assumptions as to the constancy of the weight-calorie relationship in different areas and cultures and the decline of requirements in direct relation to age, warmer temperature and lesser activity, as well as the assumption that these are independent variables. It called attention to the need for more knowledge of the requirements of adolescents, of the effects of taking in the same total of calories but in different forms, and of what would constitute 'optimal' nutrition and not mere sufficiency.*

2. *Protein requirements*

Studies of the protein component of the human diet were initiated in the early years of the century in the attempt to establish the amount of protein needed and how far this might be reduced without damage. Subsequent investigations kept this question alive, and at mid-century it was still open to difference of opinion. The broad question of amount, however, had been replaced by the more important question of which of the several amino acids yielded by proteins were essential and in what quantities. Several of the amino acids had been isolated in the nineteenth century, but it was not until the 1930s that the importance of each was tested and the broad concept of protein requirement effectively broken down. This remained one of the most important and still incomplete areas of research. Although at least eight distinct amino acids had been identified as essential, and quantitative require-

* *Calorie Requirements: Report of the Committee on Calorie Requirements*, FAO Nutritional Studies no. 5 (Washington, D.C., June, 1950).

ments for some had been worked out, nutritional guides continued to state protein requirements as a whole.*

3. *Mineral requirements*

The importance of certain of the minerals was recognized in the nineteenth century, notably calcium for the formation of bone, iron for the treatment of anaemia and iodine to prevent goitre, but these and other inorganic substances were regarded as specific medicines to treat disease rather than as essential nutrients in normal life. In the early twentieth century specific studies of calcium requirements revealed their great importance for growing children and pregnant women and stimulated the consumption of milk. Infant milk stations, which had been established by philanthropic efforts in the poor districts of some cities as a means of relief and to reduce infant mortality, became centres for nutrition education where the need for adequate milk consumption was impressed upon the mother. Later studies of the calcium requirements of adults indicated the possible value of generous supplies of this mineral for adults as well as children, but at mid-century this was another of the open questions requiring further research. The mounting evidence of the value of milk as a source of other nutrients, however, led to a constant increase in its consumption and thereby to a tendency toward greater calcium intake.

When iron was recognized as an essential element, not merely as a therapeutic drug, and its presence in green vegetables was detected, a second major class of 'protective' foods, leafy vegetables, was brought to public attention even before the full value of green vegetables for other nutrients became known. Every child in the United States who attended the movies or read the comic strips became familiar with a comic character, Popeye the Sailor, who fortified himself with one of the leafy vegetables, spinach, before performing prodigious feats of strength, and spinach became a household byword as the symbol of a healthy diet.

The general need for iodine was established in 1921 by a mass experiment on school children in an area where goitre was endemic (Akron, Ohio), and thereafter the general practice of iodizing salt eliminated this once familiar evidence of dietary deficiency. Other minerals which were successively recognized as essential were generally found to be present in sufficient amounts if other dietary requirements were met, but the possible need for minute quantities of trace elements comparable to those found to be essential for plant nutrition focused research at mid-century on these less conspicuous but potentially vital minerals.

4. *Vitamins*

The revolutionary developments in nutrition in the twentieth century, however, involved the elusive substances which came to be known as vitamins

---

* *Recommended Dietary Allowances, Revised* 1953. National Academy of Sciences—National Research Council. Publication 302 (Washington, D.C., 1953).

and whose identity and specific effects were gradually and continually unfolded during these years.

Although the deficiency disease, scurvy, once the curse of sailors on long
trips, had been controlled for a hundred years by means of fresh fruit, the
reason for this success was not known. At the turn of the century, studies
in Indonesia by the Dutch scientists, Christien Eijkman (1858–1930) and
G. Grijns (1865–1944) and other studies in Japan, revealed that beriberi, a
deficiency disease prevalent among populations living on polished rice,
could be checked if the grain husks were also consumed. From these observations the idea began to develop that the lack of specific factors produced a
qualitative deficiency in the diet.

The existence of some substance or substances essential to normal growth
and the prevention of deficiency diseases was established in a Cambridge
University laboratory in 1906, and in 1912 the term 'vitamin', introduced by
the Polish chemist Casimir Funk (1884–   ), was adopted for this unknown
element. The vitamins turned out to be many different substances, each with
specific properties whose presence was essential to the health of the
organism. By mid-century fifteen or more groups of vitamins had been
identified and research was continuing to uncover elements not previously
detected.

Research into vitamins proceeded simultaneously along two lines; the
existence of each vitamin was inferred, its effects noted and its presence
in different foods was determined before it was physically isolated and
chemically identified. Although the principal vitamins were the subject of
intensive study, and their existence, general function and presence in certain
foods became a matter of public knowledge in the first quarter of the century,
they were not identified chemically until the 1930s. Once the chemical composition was known more precise experiments could be carried on and
synthetic vitamins could be administered therapeutically or used as a food
supplement to avoid dietary deficiences.

Initially the emphasis in vitamin research was on their role in the control of
acute deficiency diseases—scurvy (vitamin C, in citrus fruit), beriberi
(vitamin B_1, thiamine, in whole meal), pellagra (vitamin B_3, niacin, in milk,
greens), and rickets (vitamin D, in fish-liver oil, sunshine). The prevention of
nutritional disease continued to be a principal goal.

It soon became apparent, however, that vitamin inadequacy could reduce
efficiency long before it produced symptoms of disease and that some vitamins
might never show their lack in disease but only in poor growth and vigour.
The focus of much research shifted from how to prevent disease to how to
ensure positive health. Studies on many generations of rats, for example, all
maintained in health but fed diets with different quantities of vitamins, showed
statistically significant differences in many respects: rate and amount of
growth, age of maturity, fecundity, ability to rear healthy offspring, signs
of ageing, and longevity. Such experiments made it apparent that knowledge

of nutrition offered a tool which could be used to effect very marked modifications in the quality, vigour and length of life.

At mid-century knowledge of vitamins was sufficient to permit the formulation of a general guide to sound nutritional practices. Especially for the temperate zones where most of the research had been conducted, and in relation to dietary patterns prevalent in those areas, normal nutritional needs for the major vitamins had been established with sufficient authority to provide benchmarks for the housewife, mother, institutional director or public official responsible for rationing or agricultural planning, and to offer a basis for dietary surveys of population groups to evaluate the relation of existing dietary patterns to what would be presumed to be adequate levels. Yet much remained to be learned. Additional substances with specific nutritional effects were constantly being detected. Though much was known about minimum requirements, great uncertainty continued as to the optimal amounts, i.e. how much more than that needed for balance could advantageously be absorbed and with what results. Knowledge of nutritional needs under tropical conditions and in relation to diets found in those regions remained very incomplete.

5. Nutritional value of specific foods

Translation of nutritional principles into practice depended upon knowledge of how the necessary nutrients could be secured from particular foods. By the 1920s the major foods from which the principal nutrients could be derived had been recognized; as additional nutrients were identified they were generally found to be present in the same foods. Although some forty essential nutrients were known by mid-century and the search for more was continuing, practical programmes of nutritional improvement could be focused on relatively few elements, since foods which contained these could ordinarily be counted on to furnish sufficient amounts of the others. Emphasis on milk, green vegetables and fruits as protective foods continued, and the importance of adequate sources of protein was stressed. With later analysis of protein factors, however, crucial difference between those derived from animal and vegetable sources became apparent. In view of the needs of areas where land resources or dietary habits made the provision of animal protein most difficult intensive investigations into alternative sources were conducted. The protein supplied by soya beans and groundnuts was found to approximate that from animal sources and to contain properties which were lacking in grains. Fish culture also offered an important protein source in these areas.

In order to provide a guide which the housewife could follow, daily requirements were formulated in terms of foods which would furnish the necessary nutrients. In the United States, for example, daily servings from each of seven groups of foods were recommended. For other regions standard dietary patterns were necessarily adapted to different food preferences and to local food supplies.

6. *Use of nutrients by body*

Since nutrition is not simply a matter of nutrients but of their total role in the living organism it was essential to understand their interrelationship, possible factors which might impede their use, their effect on the dynamic balance of the body, and their relation to processes of growth, recuperation and degeneration and to disease or injury.

The interrelations among nutritional requirements led to immense complications in nutritional research, since not only the individual components but their many possible combinations had to be explored. As elements were more clearly identified it became possible to examine these interrelations more precisely. The dietary requirements of the vitamin niacin, necessary to prevent pellagra, for example, had to be modified when it was found that niacin could be formed from a specific amino acid if it was present in sufficient quantity. Certain substances present in some foods, moreover, were found to block the operation of particular vitamins and to create conditions of deficiency. On the other hand some of the antibiotics appeared to permit the organism to make fuller use of available nutrients and resulted in improvement in growth when fed to young animals.

The fundamental concept that a whole organism is more than the sum of its parts, furthermore, plagued all such research by calling into question the results of observations made with synthetic elements removed from their natural context. In practical application this led to a long conflict, still unresolved at mid-century, between those who thought that nutritional adequacy could be achieved by supplementing dietary deficiencies with a synthetic form of the specific nutrient known to be lacking, and those who held that since all the relationships could not be fully known and reproduced, only the use of natural vegetable and animal products could ensure that the interrelations provided by nature were being maintained. This difference in view found its most vigorous expression in the struggle at the time of the second world war over the use of whole-grain flour as against white flour enriched by the addition of the vitamins known to have been lost in the milling. Whatever the merits of the issue, the enrichment or fortification of bread flour, of margarine with vitamins A and D, milk with vitamin D, and salt with iodine proved a practical means of improving nutrition on a broad scale. Efforts to use similar methods for enriching milled rice, in view of the poorer keeping qualities of unmilled paddy and objections to its taste, met with greater difficulties because of the likelihood that the added substances would be lost in cooking. Fortification of widely used foods produced and distributed commercially continued however to offer one important shortcut to nutritional improvement.

As nutritional studies were extended from problems of preventing deficiency to possibilities for positive improvement they led to a revision of traditional assumptions about the fixity of bodily characteristics and such notions as that differences in size between upper- and lower-class populations reflected differences in racial origin. Studies of laboratory animals indicated that nutritional adequacy might differentiate individuals of common heredity and have the effect of raising what had been presumed to be hereditarily determined limits. Experimental feeding of numbers of children living in institutions in England and Scotland resulted in marked differences in physical and mental development, for which no genetic explanation was plausible, between those who received and those who lacked milk supplements to their diets. Such studies, combined with new insights into the dynamic processes of constant change and mutual adjustment of body constituents, revealed a much wider range of potentialities and much greater flexibility than had been assumed, and made nutrition appear as an instrument for positive human development. When the average height of second world war recruits in several countries was found to be well above that of the first world war, and similar evidence was reported in the United States for succeeding generations of university students, the possibility that improved nutrition might affect the characteristics of whole populations appeared to be more than an hypothesis. Experience with school lunch programmes indicated that the effects could be mental as well as physical.

A vital aspect of nutrition study related to the rate at which nutrients were used, the frequency with which they must be supplied, what resources the body could store and what capacity it had for recuperation when its needs had not been met. The early preoccupation with deficiency diseases and work on the needs of children for proper growth and development led directly to the question of how permanent was damage suffered in childhood or by reason of severe deficiency. While the need of a continuous supply of many elements was established, such far-reaching studies as *The Biology of Human Starvation* (by Ancel Keys and others, Minneapolis, 1950) revealed the human body's capacity for nutritional recuperation and the mechanisms by which this was brought about. Other studies of the effect on nutritional requirements of febrile diseases, surgery and shock, and of the relation of nutritional status to the healing of wounds and other regenerative processes made the manipulation of nutritional factors an important therapeutic tool in the hands of the medical profession.

Toward the middle of the century attention began to be focused on the role of nutrition in the process of ageing and the maintenance of the vigour of life. For the first time, in 1953, the revised edition of the *Recommended Dietary Allowances* issued by the National Research Council in the United States included a differential for age of adults, as the results of the first studies on the relation of diet to ageing began to become available. Nutritional research became an integral part of studies of chronic and degenerative diseases, notably heart disease, hypertension and cancer. Mounting evidence of a relation between certain body fats and certain conditions of the heart stimulated investigation into the role of fats and carbohydrates which had remained largely unexplored while the basic knowledge of vitamins, minerals and proteins was being developed. The National Research Council in 1953, however, continued to omit these substances from its table of recommended allowances, noting that the state of knowledge was still too limited to permit recommendations for either fats or carbohydrates.

7. Dissemination of nutritional knowledge

Application of nutritional knowledge in practice depended upon its widespread dissemination in a usable form, on the availability of necessary foods, and on food habits and the willingness of people to change their dietary patterns. Public policies played some part in raising nutritional levels, although in the last analysis nutrition rested on the daily actions of all the people.

By the 1920s, the new knowledge of nutrition was beginning to reach the public. Evidences of physical defects among military recruits in the first world war focused public attention on the problem of nutritional status as a factor in national health. The simultaneous discovery of vitamins pointed the direction for action. The child health movement quickly incorporated the new knowledge.

Nutrition-consciousness reached the public through the press, where the women's pages offered their readers information concerning the calorie content and nutritional values of recipes which they published and suggested ways to plan balanced meals. Advertisers of certain foods such as milk stressed their nutritional properties. When synthetic vitamins became available, their producers spared no effort in informing the public of their value. Knowledge of nutrition spread through educational channels. The first university professorship in nutrition in the United States was established in 1921 at Columbia University in New York, and the subject was introduced into the curricula of schools and colleges in the following years.

One of the major means of spreading knowledge and also of affecting nutritional levels directly was school feeding. From the middle of the nineteenth century the provision of school meals for destitute children and for those who by reason of distance from home would otherwise be unable to attend school had been a favourite form of private charity in many countries where the extension of elementary education was bringing poor and hungry children into the schools. In the 1920s these measures for the relief of hunger began to be converted into means of ensuring that all children should receive the right kind of food, since it had become clear that a large proportion of children suffered from improper diets even when they had enough to eat. The 'Oslo breakfast', designed in Norway to provide protective foods and to make up for likely deficiencies in home diets, became the prototype for school feeding programmes in many countries. Evidence from Oslo and elsewhere that the provision of such foods not only affected the children's health but their alertness and ability to learn made good nutrition a tool of education and increased the popularity of school feeding as a means of spreading nutritional knowledge and habits to the general public.

Countries differed considerably in the manner in which they used the school lunch device. The Netherlands for example, one of the first countries to make public provision for school meals for children who otherwise would be unable to attend school, considered school feeding as an encroachment on the normal domain of the family and provided only milk, using school lunches primarily for emergency situations or in cases of extreme need. Britain on the other hand made school milk and school lunches part of its general national health plan, available to all. In the United States a programme which started in the 1930s as a means of disposing of surplus agricultural products developed into a broad programme of federal aid in which schools and local jurisdictions received federal funds only if they met established nutritional standards and made meals available to all children, without cost to those who could not pay. In some countries, notably Israel, older children learned nutritional practices by preparing the school lunch. Elsewhere, as in Puerto Rico, the participation of mothers' groups in school meal preparation served as a means of introducing the mothers to the nutritional ideas on which the lunches were based.

School lunches, however, were only one of the many organized channels through which nutritional knowledge reached the public, especially mothers. Maternal and infant health services took advantage of the eagerness of mothers to accept new knowledge for the benefit of the child. Day nurseries, day care centres and kindergartens demonstrated the uses of milk, fish-liver oil and fruit juices. In a number of countries milk stations for infants and preschool children were supported by public funds and community effort. From the 1930s on, every mother who came in contact with virtually any programme of child health, education or recreation found herself exposed to ideas of sound nutrition and to pressures to conform.

The relatively small impairment of health in the countries most hard hit by the depression of the 1930s was attributed to the efforts of families, even on sharply reduced budgets, to include the protective foods whose importance they had learned. The publication by the United States Department of Agriculture in 1933 of *Diets at Four Levels of Nutritive Value and Cost* provided a guide which showed that, above a reasonable minimum income, an adequate diet could be provided at costs consistent with lower as well as higher income levels. Intensive nutrition campaigns during the second world war, which made good practices a patriotic duty, left a strong residue of nutrition-consciousness when wartime austerity was past.

8. *International concern with nutrition*

Nutrition was recognized as a matter of world concern with the establishment of the League of Nations Mixed Committee in 1935. When the United

Nations FAO was established in 1945, international efforts to develop world food supplies received a strong nutritional orientation. FAO's estimates of world food needs, and its technical assistance in relation to the world's food resources, were based upon the concept of food as nutrition; they directed attention and effort to the production and distribution of those foods most needed to raise or maintain nutritional levels. FAO's first world food survey in 1946 pointed out that in order to meet current standards for good nutritional status, world production of fruits and vegetables would have to be raised 163 per cent above pre-war levels, milk 100 per cent, pulses and nuts 80 per cent, as against only 12–34 per cent for sugar, cereals, tubers, fats and oils. In the light of the accumulated evidence that milk could make the most crucial difference in child health, the United Nations Emergency Children's Fund (UNICEF) devoted the major part of its programmes around the world to the provision of milk through direct distribution, the development of milk drying facilities, and educational programmes around its use.

At mid-century the science of nutrition and the application of nutritional knowledge were still far from their goals. Not only was there much to be learned concerning nutritional requirements and how they might be met, but in vast regions of the world existing knowledge was still poorly applied. In much of Asia and parts of Africa total food supplies failed to provide sufficient calories and proteins, and hunger remained widespread. Good nutrition on a mass scale depended on overall economic and social conditions as well as on education; poverty barred many from its benefits and ignorance or apathy barred many more, not only where supplies were scarce and poverty widespread but in countries where food was plentiful. Yet the application of the new knowledge had already brought spectacular results, people throughout the world were becoming aware of basic nutritional principles, and public policy was directed toward the goals of human health and vigour which the science of nutrition held out.

VI. INTERNATIONAL MEASURES FOR FOOD AND AGRICULTURE

The need for international action relating to both technical and economic aspects of food and agriculture had been recognized before the end of the nineteenth century. Specialists in many fields, chiefly from European countries, held international technical meetings, such as the first International Veterinary Congress in Hamburg in 1863, a Congress of European Forest Experiment Stations and Research Organizations at Namur in 1883, an Hydrographers' Congress on marine life in the Baltic and North Atlantic in 1893, and conferences on various phases of agriculture, horticulture, viticulture, pisciculture, dairying, plant and animal breeding, plant and animal diseases and meteorology. Economic aspects were first approached internationally in 1864 when Great Britain, France, the Netherlands and Belgium attempted unsuccessfully to control export subsidies for sugar by means of an international convention. The severe agricultural depression of the 1880s and 1890s led to the formation in 1889 of an International Commission of Agriculture to study ways to offset the inherent economic weaknesses of agriculture.

In 1905 a permanent intergovernmental organization, the International Institute of Agriculture, was established in Rome. Its initiator, David Lubin (1849–1919), recognized the farmers' disabilities in acquiring technical knowledge and their weak economic bargaining position, and was able to persuade governments that this situation could not be wholly amended by measures limited to single countries. The Institute initiated joint action by governments on such matters as pest and disease control; it laid the groundwork for viewing agriculture on a world-wide basis by securing the adoption of procedures which would permit the international compilation and comparison of agriculture data, such as standard nomenclature for classification of soils and standard weights and measures for reporting agricultural statistics; it instituted a number of yearbooks and monthly bulletins on agricultural legislation, agricultural statistics, forestry statistics, agricultural science and practice, agricultural economics and sociology, plant protection; it prepared technical monographs on many specific subjects. Since support for the International Institute of Agriculture was chiefly European, its materials and studies dealt mainly with this area and did not include the underdeveloped sectors of the world.

The work of the International Institute of Agriculture was focused on production. Prior to the 1930s there were no general statistics of food consumption and few family budget studies had been made; nutrition was still mainly a laboratory science. But when the League of Nations entered the agriculture picture in the 1930s it was through a concern with consumption— 'food' rather than 'agriculture'. The 1937 report of the League's Mixed Committee on the Problem of Nutrition showing the prevalance of malnutrition in economically advanced countries stimulated some twenty governments to set up national nutrition committees and to begin to formulate their national policies in relation to the consumption as well as the production of food. When the second world war converted surpluses into shortages, nutrition committees played a major part in the rationing of supplies in relation to nutritional needs, and international techniques were developed among the allied powers for allocating scarce food and raw materials.

The Food and Agriculture Organization was projected during the war at the Hot Springs (USA) conference in 1943 and created at Quebec, Canada, in 1945 as the first of the new United Nations' agencies. It drew its inspiration and basis of operation from three sources: the groundwork of information and co-operation built up by the International Institute of Agriculture; the League of Nations' concern with nutrition; and the wartime demonstration in Canada and the United States that the application of science could bring as spectacular results in agriculture as in industry, leading these countries to believe that their experience could be applied with dramatic effect to the remaking of agriculture in other parts of the world. The organization as set up included divisions of agriculture, forestry, fisheries and nutrition.

The objectives as stated in the preamble to the constitution of the Food and Agriculture Organization were:

raising levels of nutrition and standards of living . . . , securing improvements in the efficiency of the production and distribution of all food and agricultural products, bettering the condition of rural populations, and thus contributing toward an expanding world economy.

As the Canadian chairman of the first session of the FAO conference, Lester B. Pearson, pointed out, FAO was the first international organization to set out 'with so bold an aim as that of helping nations to achieve freedom from want'.

The first director-general, Sir John Boyd-Orr, envisaged the organization as providing a world-wide mechanism for enabling supplies which could be produced to reach people who needed them, and he proposed a world food board for this purpose. During the immediate post-war years when shortages were acute, an International Emergency Food Council performed such a function. But as European agriculture recovered and shortages quickly turned again into surpluses, the idea of a world food board was rejected, because of the difficulty of making surpluses available to hungry groups in other countries without disrupting the normal trade in agricultural products within the country and compounding difficulties in the international balance of payments.

The problem of hunger in the face of plenty appeared inseparable from the broader problem of poverty and low productivity in much of the world. National efforts to adjust agricultural production and sustain farm incomes, moreover, were in themselves obstacles to international measures with the same objectives.

Only in the case of dried milk was a means found through the work of the United Nations Emergency Children's Fund to make surplus supplies in large volume available to the world's undernourished children. For the rest, emergency grants in case of threatened famine or other disaster remained the main international machinery for directing surplus agricultural products to needs during the 1950s.

Nevertheless, the issue of the relation of the world's food-producing capacity to the world's food needs received increasing attention as very rapid rates of population growth in the decade after the second world war raised questions as to the adequacy of food supplies for the future. In the debate which went on during these years, the director-general of the FAO, Norris Dodd, stressed the possibilities for international effort which had not begun to be tapped. 'We will not give up to hunger . . .' he declared, 'until we have tried everything we can think of. We haven't done that yet even on a small scale, let alone all over the world, all together.'*

As the FAO developed its international programmes it veered more and more toward a type of activity which had not formed part of the international thinking in the field of agriculture in the earlier period, and which had not been at the centre of planning when the FAO was formed, namely technical assistance to underdeveloped areas to bring to them the techniques which had given the agriculturally advanced countries their high level of productivity.

The League of Nations Mixed Committee on Nutrition had included no one from Asia, the Near East or Africa among its twenty-one members and only one from Latin America. Neither the League nor the International Institute of Agriculture had been concerned with the low level of nutrition and low productivity of agriculture in underdeveloped areas. Participation in the formation of the FAO was somewhat broader than in its predecessor organizations, but it was not until after 1947, when numbers of newly established countries became members of the international organization, that the focus of international effort in the field of agriculture began to shift toward the underdeveloped sector of the world.

Pressure in the newly developing countries to speed up development and their requests for international aid in this process made technical assistance, by the mid-1950s, a principal function of the FAO. Considerable international assistance in food and agriculture also reached these countries through such other channels as the Colombo plan and the technical assistance programme of the USA.

The FAO was called upon to assist countries around the world in a great variety of ways. Some indication of the range of approaches and of the interests common to a number of countries may be found in the training institutes held on a regional basis for representatives from a number of countries, under FAO auspices, in the years 1950–55. Within this five-year period ten regional institutes were held on agricultural censuses and other statistics and five each on agricultural extension, fisheries and fish culture, forestry and forest products. Seminars on the formulation of development projects were held in three regions. Two institutes were conducted on rice culture and grading, on dairying, on pasture and range, on disease control, on nutrition and on co-operative organization and one each on land problems, agricultural credit, rural electrification and rural welfare. Two-fifths of these training programmes were held in Latin America, a quarter in Asia and a fifth in the Near East and Africa.

Extensive though these activities were, they made only a beginning towards resolving the long-standing and intractable problems of the world's food and agriculture. The momentum of technical progress, moreover, constantly tended to widen the gap between the technically advanced and the under-

* Quoted in P. Lamartine Yates, *So Bold an Aim* (FAO, Rome, 1955), p. 65.

developed areas. Reviewing the world state of food and agriculture in 1955, the FAO concluded: 'Continued advances in technical methods no less rapid and fundamental than those of the past decade may be expected in the years immediately ahead. But the extent to which they can be utilized will depend to an increasing extent on the success with which the economic and social problems of agriculture can be resolved.'*

NOTES TO CHAPTER XIV

1. Professors R. I. Stolper and A. M. Gurevich consider that the Author-Editors have not brought out sufficiently the difficulties which the Soviets have met in collectivizing agriculture and in achieving high levels of agricultural productivity where agriculture has been collectivized. Non-communist experts in agricultural economics and rural sociology maintain that this field of endeavour is not susceptible of the kinds of organization appropriate to industry and that the agricultural population cannot be transformed into the social type of the industrial proletariat. They argue that agriculture is a highly diversified occupation requiring the individual to make daily decisions based upon close observation of plants, animals, soil, weather, etc., to command a variety of knowledge and skills, to plan and manage a changing series of processes, to meet frequent emergencies, and to be responsible, under conditions which often defy close supervision, for tools, machinery, supplies, buildings, animals and harvested crops. Some farms producing a single crop such as grain or sugar may be operated after the manner of a grain or sugar factory; but diversified agriculture requires the kind of responsibility and attention that do not appear to be consistent with collectivization.

The evidence upon which these writers base their judgment is twofold: (1) the great success and productivity of family-type farming in such countries as Holland, Denmark, the United States, Canada, and New Zealand, and (2) the record of the Soviet Union's search for a way to transform peasant farming into state or collective farming while increasing the production of agriculture necessary for the success of the entire communist objective. The government's first efforts at thorough collectivization were met by peasant resistance—refusal to work on the collectivized farms, slaughter of animals and destruction of products which were to be delivered to the state. The policy of steering peasants into collectivism by establishing tractor stations where farm equipment was concentrated for cultivating the land in the large masses of the collectivized farms worked fairly well for crops which could use large machinery. Farm workers, i.e. ex-peasants, however, still found little satisfaction as an agricultural proletariat working upon a large-scale farm. In the 1930s the Soviet government permitted the peasants to have a small plot of land, a few animals and some poultry, which they and their families could tend while being employed as well on the collective farm. Within a short time the peasants were producing on their plots much of the food available to the consuming public. This system had two major defects from the Soviet point of view: it led the peasant to neglect work on the collective farm in favour of his private plot; it tended to preserve a sense of private property and thereby to obstruct the drive toward the objective of communism. Although critics have noted that Soviet agriculture has been exploited in order to provide the resources necessary for rapid industrialization, they maintain that this difficulty has not been the central one. They argue that until the Soviets recognize the essential difference between agriculture, which is dependent upon the forces of nature and requires the attention of individuals who can responsibly adjust to these forces, and industry, which is dependent upon manmade machines and requires individuals to operate and control these machines, they will continue to encounter difficulties with this aspect of the economy. These critics take as further evidence the repetition of the difficulties in countries that since World War II

* FAO, *The State of Food and Agriculture, 1955* (Rome, 1955), p. 132.

have come under communist control, where retreat into something comparable to Lenin's New Economic Policy has had to be made. The retreat means that a large measure of peasant farming has been permitted, although collective farming has been retained as the objective.

The following may be consulted:

Merle Fainsod, *Smolensk Under Soviet Rule* (New York, 1958).

Naum Jasny, *The Socialized Agriculture of the USSR: Plans and Performance* (Stanford, California, 1949).

Roy D. Laird, *The Evolution of Soviet Agricultural Policy in Theory and Practice with Special Reference to Developments after 1950* (Seattle, 1956).

Roy D. Laird, *Collective Farming in Russia : A Political Study of the Soviet Kolkhozy* (Lawrence, Kansas, 1958).

Roy D. Laird (ed.), *Soviet Agriculture and Peasant Affairs* (Lawrence, Kansas, 1963).

I. T. Sanders (ed.), *Collectivization of Agriculture in Eastern Europe* (Lexington, Ky., 1958)

D. W. Treadgold, *The Great Siberian Migration* (Princeton, 1957).

Nicholas P. Vakar, *Taproot of Soviet Society* (New York, 1962).

Lazar Volin, *A Survey of Soviet Russian Agriculture* (Washington, D.C., 1951).

The following standard works may also be consulted:

Alexander M. Baykov, *The Development of the Soviet Economic System* (New York, 1947).

Harry Schwartz, *Russia's Soviet Economy* (2nd ed., New York, 1954).

CHAPTER XV

HEALTH AND POPULATION

IN perhaps no other area did the application of knowledge during the twentieth century remake the life of mankind more dramatically than in the field of health. While the development of transport, communication and industry radically altered the conditions of life, the application of medical knowledge affected the maintenance and quality of life itself.

In the first half of the twentieth century measures for the protection of health, together with many other improvements in levels of living, nearly doubled the average life expectancy in the technically advanced countries within the space of two generations. The developments of these years all but removed from these countries the prospect of premature death from most of the diseases which had taken the heaviest toll throughout human history, leaving degenerative diseases, man-made hazards and mental illness the major threats to life and health. In the middle years of the century medical knowledge and health practices spread with great vigour to the non-industrialized countries, bringing an even more rapid reduction of mortality in those areas.

The dramatic change in the life expectancy and the health of the people of the world came in two principal directions: the control of communicable diseases which from time immemorial had taken periodic toll in mass epidemics, had constantly threatened the lives of children and had weakened or impaired the vigour of much of the population; and the enormously increased survival rate of the infants that were born.

I. MEDICAL KNOWLEDGE AND HEALTH PRACTICES AT THE OPENING OF THE TWENTIETH CENTURY

At the beginning of the twentieth century the groundwork had been laid for the spectacular reduction of mortality and morbidity that occurred during the next fifty years. Living germs transmitted from person to person, directly or indirectly, were known to be the immediate cause of the principal killing diseases, and during the last two decades of the nineteenth century bacteria producing most of the major diseases had been identified, mosquitoes and other animal vectors had been recognized, and the principle of immunization had been established. The micro-organisms responsible for such diseases as cholera, diphtheria, dysentery, gonorrhoea, meningitis, pneumonia, malaria, plague, tetanus and typhoid fever had been isolated and continuous search was leading toward the discovery of the disease germs for African sleeping sickness, whooping cough, syphilis and others. The mosquitoes which transmitted malaria and yellow fever had been detected in 1897 and 1900 and work was in progress leading to the identification of the tsetse fly as the carrier of African sleeping sickness and lice as hosts for typhus. The discovery of diphtheria antitoxin in 1890 stimulated the development of other immunizing serums.

Germ theory had been developed and provided the basis for public sanitation and personal hygiene. Antisepsis, widely introduced after the 1870s as a result of the work of Joseph L. Lister (1827–1912), had made possible safe surgery. It had made the hospital an institution for the protection of life and the treatment of disease instead of the centre of infection which it had so often

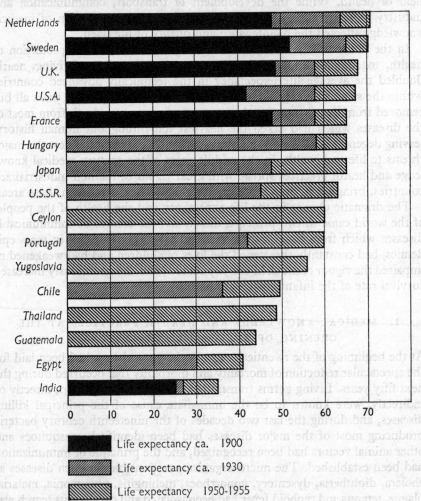

CHART XVI.   Life Expectancy at Birth for Males, 1950–55, and Increase since 1900, in Selected Countries.

Source: Woytinsky, *World Population and Production*, pp. 182–8; US *Statistical Abstracts*, 1961.

been prior to the last quarter of the nineteenth century. In the 1890s aseptic practices, designed to prevent the entrance of bacteria into the wound instead of merely combating them, had become the basis of surgical techniques. Basic tools essential for advancement in the treatment, diagnosis and prevention of disease were at hand, such as the X-ray and anaesthetics for surgery.

The concept of public health had been accepted and was reflected in the existence of municipal departments responsible for control of water supply, sewage and refuse disposal, for the maintenance of sanitary conditions in respect to food, housing, and public abattoirs and for quarantine and other measures against communicable disease. Voluntary public health bodies supported public health programmes and educational campaigns against particular threats to health, such as tuberculosis. The first university chair of social medicine was established in Berlin in 1902. The pattern of collaboration among the medical profession, research scientists, government and industry to combat threats to health had become established.

The groundwork had been laid too for a positive attack on the risks of birth and infancy with the establishment in the 1890s of pre-natal clinics and consultation bureaux for infant care. Medical services to school children had been inaugurated in some cities. Paediatrics was a well-developed field of medical specialization.

Several lines of inquiry were under way which were to bear important fruit in the course of the following years: efforts to discover bacteria-destroying drugs, to identify the internal secretions or hormones which maintain or upset the necessary chemical balance of the body, to understand the nature of allergy, and to discover the characteristics of the essential nutrients whose existence had been established experimentally but whose composition was unknown. Mental disorders had begun to be recognized by the public as well as the medical profession as a form of illness rather than punishment for sin, and their identity and origins were being sought.

The basis had also been laid for the fundamental scientific discoveries that were to bring success to these and other medical inquiries, in such developments as the studies of cell structure and pathology, and of metabolic and nutritional processes, some understanding of the nervous system, exploration of psychosomatic relationships, beginnings of blood chemistry and the rediscovery of Mendel's principles of genetics.

There was, moreover, strong institutional support for research in medicine, as well as in the basic natural sciences. University research had been well developed in Germany during the nineteenth century. The Pasteur Institute, established in Paris in 1888 with international subscriptions following Pasteur's successful preventive treatment against rabies, furnished the model for separate research institutes devoted to the isolation and study of disease-producing bacteria, the development of vaccines and sera, and a wide range of physiological and chemical investigations relating to disease.

Before the turn of the century institutions of this character had been established which continued to serve as major centres for medical discoveries and advances in medical science during the twentieth century: the Russian Institute of Experimental Medicine where Ivan Pavlov carried on his outstanding work in physiology; the British Institute of Preventive Medicine, later known as the Lister Institute, which served not only as a research centre in bacteriology, experimental pathology and biochemistry but as a diagnostic and public health laboratory for the city of London; the Institute for Infectious Diseases in Berlin under the direction of the pioneer bacteriologist, Robert Koch (1843–1910), who had identified the first of the human disease bacilli, anthrax; the Institute for Infectious Diseases in Japan established by Koch's associate Shibasaburo Kitasato (1856–1931), one of the discoverers of tetanus and diphtheria antitoxins and of the plague bacillus; the Institute of Experimental Therapy in Frankfurt, Germany, under another of Koch's associates, Paul Ehrlich (1854–1915), which became a centre for the development and standardization of immunizing vaccines and sera.

French scientists had established Pasteur institutes in Indo-China, Tunis, Algeria and Dakar, while British had founded the Haffkine Institute in Bombay, initially as a plague research laboratory, and an institute in Kuala Lumpur, Malaya, for research in malaria and beriberi. In Latin America, Mexico had set up a National Bacteriological Institute and Brazil had a Bacteriological Institute of Serum Therapy in Rio de Janeiro which later became world-famous as the Instituto Oswaldo Cruz. In the United States, Johns Hopkins University had been founded with the purpose of combining scientific research and teaching in the manner of the German universities and the City of New York had established a municipal bacteriological laboratory which was not only a pioneer in the practical application of bacteriology in the administration of public health but a centre of research in related fields.

At the opening of the century the scientific and institutional bases were thus laid for the strong advances in the prevention and treatment of disease which marked the first half of the twentieth century. Most importantly, health was coming increasingly to be regarded as a matter of science rather than of religion or superstition, and the 'healing art' was finding its basis in 'medical science'. Medicine was being reconstructed from the ground up by the application of the methods of the experimental sciences.

II. CONQUEST OF MAJOR DISEASES AND LENGTHENING OF THE LIFE SPAN IN TECHNICALLY ADVANCED COUNTRIES

In the technically advanced countries during the first half of the twentieth century, all the tendencies noted above were directed simultaneously and with intensified vigour against one after another of the major threats to health and survival. As each principal cause of death and disease was brought under control, the attack shifted to those which had been formerly overshadowed. First the pestilences were conquered, then one after another of the other major infections; infant deaths were lowered dramatically though a hard core of neo-natal fatalities continued to present a stubborn problem; maternal mortality was reduced more slowly but was finally nearly eliminated. When heart disease and cancer replaced pneumonia, tuberculosis and diarrhoea as the leading causes of death, they became the focus of concern and effort. As success was achieved in ensuring the health of the young, the health of older persons who made up an ever larger part of the population offered the new challenge. Finally, modern society itself brought its new hazards—road and industrial accidents, pollution of the air, radioactivity and the strains of modern life.

1. *Advances in medical science and development of public health*

The great strides in controlling disease and promoting healthy conditions of life were made possible by advances in medical knowledge, the extension of public health principles and practices, and the general economic improvement of the population.

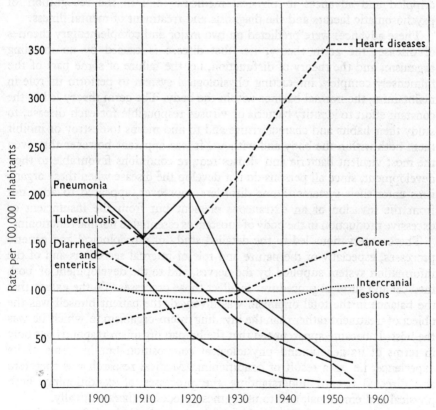

CHART XVII. Deaths in the USA from Principal Causes, 1900–1955.
Source: US Public Health Service, *Vital Statistics of the US.*

Building on the basis of the scientific developments in the previous centuries, medical science pushed forward vigorously; it swiftly incorporated new insights in the basic biological sciences as these were developed, and each advance found almost immediate application in medical practice. The intellectual climate of the twentieth century, the organization of the medical profession, and the public expectation with which medical services were sought all favoured the acceptance of new knowledge and its prompt use to save the lives and mitigate the suffering of mankind.

During these fifty years, medical science made spectacular advances along a number of lines: in the development of vaccines which could be used for immunization against a widening range of diseases; in chemotherapy, with the discovery of the sulpha drugs, the antibiotics, the antihistamines and many others; in endocrinology, with the identification and production of a number of hormones by which internal chemical balance could be maintained or restored; in nutrition; in the control of allergic reactions; in elaborate and delicate surgery, including techniques for the rehabilitation of maimed and crippled and advances in physical medicine; and in the recognition of psychosomatic factors and the diagnosis and treatment of mental illness.

These advances were predicted on two major and complementary theories of disease: the germ theory, i.e. that disease is caused by an invading organism, and the theory of disfunction, i.e. the failure of some part of the immensely complex, interacting physiological system to perform its role in maintaining the normal balance within the body. The germ theory led to the constant effort to identify bacteria or viruses responsible for each disease, to study their habits and characteristics and to find means to destroy or inhibit them both within the body and without. It was apparent however that even the most virulent bacteria and viruses require conditions favourable to their development, since all persons do not develop the disease when these organisms enter their systems. Some disorders, moreover, appeared to arise not from the invasion of an extraneous element but from the insufficient or excessive production in the body of substances essential to normal functioning.

These observations led to the detailed study of physiological and genetic processes, especially of the nature and role of internal secretions and of the information system supplied by the nerves, and to the development of both medical and surgical procedures to affect those processes. To the extent that the balance in the total organism was involved, the patient himself was the object of treatment rather than the invading micro-organism to which he was the host. It became apparent too that the human organism responds not only in terms of its genetic and physiological composition but in terms of its experience, i.e. as a result of conditioning. Medical research was therefore also directed toward understanding the processes of conditioning, both physical and emotional, and to using these processes therapeutically.

The incorporation of advances into medical practice depended upon a broad development of laboratory techniques and facilities, of specialized diagnostic tools using chemical, electrical, electronic and radiological devices, and of elaborately equipped hospitals to provide expert diagnosis and treatment facilities. It required a high degree of specialization in the medical professions, for with so vast a range of new and ever-changing knowledge the general practitioner could no longer be expected to keep abreast of all developments. It necessitated extensive means of communication through scientific and professional journals, professional organizations and other channels in order that new discoveries might become widely known. It relied upon the development of large-scale industries for the production of drugs, sera and medical equipment on a mass basis for mass use.

Military medicine was often in the vanguard of medical progress. The major wars of the period accelerated the development of medical techniques and their application in many fields, including extensive immunization, the use of new drugs such as penicillin and of life-saving substances such as blood plasma, and the perfection of new surgical techniques and prosthetic devices to permit the recovery and restoration of the physically damaged. Advances which were first registered in the much higher survival and rehabilitation rate of military personnel were later reflected in the health of the general population.

Public responsibility for some matters affecting health had long been traditional, but the public health movement which brought sanitation and health services to the masses of the people in the twentieth century originated in the efforts of civic-minded leaders in the mid-nineteenth century to reform the conditions of the poor. Edwin Chadwick (1800–90) in England and others elsewhere brought to public attention the unhealthy conditions under which the urban working population lived and the threat to the health of all which these conditions produced. Public health measures were undertaken in the second half of the nineteenth century as a part of the movement for better working conditions in factories, shorter hours, reduction of child labour, decent housing and improved living conditions in the slums.

Initially public health was conceived primarily as a matter of public sanitation, and municipal departments of sanitation constituted the core of the public health services. With the requirement that doctors report all cases of specific communicable diseases, immunization against smallpox and further elaboration of quarantine procedures at ports and in communities, public health agencies entered the direct effort to control epidemic diseases. Throughout the period under review, the control, prevention and eradication of communicable diseases remained at the heart of all public health programmes.

With the establishment of maternal and child health services the concept of public health was extended to include measures to prevent forms of illness or death which did not menace the public by reason of contagion. It was broadened still further to make positive health and not merely the prevention of disease a matter of public concern. By mid-century public health programmes were undertaking to ferret out incipient cases of chronic as well as contagious diseases, to rehabilitate those who were temporarily or permanently disabled by disease or accident and to make available to entire populations every type of protective and curative medical care.

In the last analysis, however, improvement in the economic situation, living conditions and nutrition of the masses of the people must be credited with much of the reduction in mortality and improvement in health. Health surveys repeatedly showed the incidence of all except the degenerative illnesses to be greater among lower economic levels in the population and in sections of cities characterized by congestion and bad housing. Inadequate diets not only meant deficiency diseases in extreme cases but general lack of resistance to such diseases as tuberculosis. Although medical science showed dramatic capacity to raise survival rates in underdeveloped countries in advance of substantial improvement in economic levels and living conditions, the advances achieved in the industrially developed countries during the years under review were intimately bound up with the rising levels of real income enjoyed by the people of these societies.

2. The control of communicable disease

(a) Major pestilences: plague, cholera, smallpox. The great and terrible scourges that had periodically descended upon mankind—plague, cholera, smallpox—had been almost wholly eliminated from western countries by the opening of the century and they were kept out by rigorous measures for quarantine and, in the case of smallpox, immunization. The principal uncontrolled scourge was influenza. The last epidemic of plague to reach Europe occurred around the turn of the century, but it brought no major outbreak and only occasional cases appeared thereafter. Cholera re-entered some of the European ports during the first world war, but the epidemics which had recurred in principal western cities during the nineteenth century were a thing of the past. There were small sporadic outbreaks of smallpox where vaccination was not general.

These diseases were excluded from the West, for the most part, by methods already well-established at the opening of the century. The western countries took the lead in international efforts to prevent their spread by world-wide measures for quarantine and the control of ports and airfields. At mid-century, however, points of infection still existed, especially in south Asia. Plague remained a threat in India, China and Indo-China, though its incidence was being gradually reduced, and sporadic outbreaks continued to occur in parts of Africa and of South America. Cholera, too, remained endemic in south Asia and China. Smallpox broke out from time to time in Asia, Africa and Latin America, and occasionally in Europe or North America.

So long as centres of infection remained, the struggle against these diseases had to go on, through world-wide co-operation to halt every sign of spread and to eliminate remaining sources of infection. When cholera broke out in

Egypt in 1947, supplies of serum were rushed from all over the world and every possible international measure was taken to isolate the epidemic as well as to bring it quickly to an end. The World Health Organization provided technical assistance to India in its intensive effort to control the spread of plague by wild rodents. The regional WHO committee for the European region in 1955 included in its agenda the need for preventive action against smallpox even in the absence of apparent risk. In a world of rapid transport and active travel, eternal vigilance was the price of effective protection.

(b) *Principal diseases borne by animal vectors: yellow fever, malaria, typhus and others.* At the opening of the century yellow fever remained a serious threat in many tropical regions, although it was ceasing to invade the temperate areas periodically as it had in the nineteenth century. Malaria was endemic in nearly all tropical and sub-tropical regions and made some areas virtually uninhabitable by reason of its prevalence. Though less lethal than yellow fever, it was a far more serious disease for mankind in its overall effects.

Discovery of some of the mosquito carriers of these diseases around the turn of the century opened the road to their control. Dramatic success in the control of yellow fever by eliminating the mosquito carrier was achieved during the building of the Panama canal after 1900, in an area where earlier attempts to build a canal had been given up in the face of high mortality from this and other diseases. While this success led to the suppression of yellow fever in most areas and its exclusion from urban centres, the hope that it could be completely eradicated had to be abandoned when it was discovered that yellow fever exists among jungle animals. Although the cycle of human patient and animal vector can be broken by preventing the person in an infectious state from being bitten by the carrier mosquito, the possibility remains that the disease may be transmitted to man from jungle animals by jungle mosquitoes. The danger of the recurrence of the disease could therefore not be eliminated in the parts of South and Central America and Africa where it remained endemic.

In malarial regions measures to drain swamps and spread oil on the breeding places of mosquitoes reduced the prevalence of malaria during the first four decades of the century, especially in those areas where the sources of infection were relatively few and where the incidence was not extremely high. Specific drugs, quinine and mepacrine (atabrine), offered a means of treatment and a measure of protection against the severity of the disease. In much of the tropics, however, in Central and South America, Africa and Asia, malaria continued to be ubiquitous and debilitating, deaths from it were numerous and few people in the population of low-lying areas escaped.

During the second world war discovery of the value of DDT, combined with the fact that troops were fighting all over the world in heavily infected malarial areas, led to a spectacular demonstration of what could be done to eradicate the disease. Drastic measures taken by military authorities in regions where troops were stationed, including the administration of mepacrine to prevent contraction of malaria and the elimination of the mosquito carrier, freed the troops from the danger of the disease. This demonstration of the effectiveness of thorough as against half-way measures led to the adoption of similar tactics by governments in many parts of the world.

Venezuela, where mortality rates from malaria were extremely high and large areas were considered uninhabitable because especially virulent forms of the disease was prevalent, formulated in 1945 the earliest national programme to eliminate malaria completely. Teams equipped with DDT spray visited village after village periodically, spraying all houses inside and out. By eliminating the carrier at the point where it would pick up the infection from an ill person or transmit it to another, this method checked the spread of the disease and reduced its sources. Although mosquitoes continued to breed away from the centres of population, these rarely carried the infection.

Similar measures were put into effect in other parts of the world. The results of these campaigns came rapidly. Italy, which had over 400,000 cases in 1945 had only five primary infections in 1955 and no malaria deaths since 1948. In Ceylon, where more than half the population suffered from malaria in 1940, only one case per 3,000 in the population was reported in 1956.

How long this method of control would remain effective, however, was an open question, for mosquitoes in some areas soon began to display immunity against the spray. In the face of this situation the World Health Organization in the mid-1950s gave malaria control top priority in its programme and determined to marshal all available resources in an effort to eradicate the disease, and thus destroy the sources of infection, before the resistant strains of mosquitoes could take over.

Typhus, transmitted by body lice, had long been a scourge of armies and poverty-stricken populations suffering from the disruptions of war, and it recurred in epidemic proportions in many areas. During the first world war the toll taken by typhus, particularly in eastern Europe, was second only to that of the influenza epidemic of 1918, and the heavy incidence of typhus in Russia during the years of revolution and civil war provided a powerful incentive for the rapid development of public health measures. Immunizing serum was used to protect the troops of western Europe and America in the first world war and more thoroughly for all military personnel in the second, reducing the danger of the spread of typhus from the areas where it continued endemic. There were severe epidemics in German concentration camps during the war, however, and a form known as scrub typhus, prevalent in Asia and the South Pacific, took a considerable toll before special measures were used to check it. When DDT became available it greatly facilitated the elimination of the lice, or in the case of scrub typhus the mites, which transmit the disease. At the close of the second world war the United Nations Relief and Rehabilitation Agency (UNRRA) was able to forestall the anticipated typhus epidemics by distributing quantities of DDT anti-louse powder to danger areas and administering it in the manner found effective in checking an incipient epidemic in Naples in 1943. In the following years prophylactic measures undertaken by the people's democracies of eastern Europe reduced the threat of new outbreaks in that area.

Other diseases carried by insects, both those such as dysentery or trachoma whose germs are merely transported by flies and those such as African sleeping sickness where the tsetse fly acts as host, yielded to a combined attack on the sources of infection, the means of access by the insect transmitter, and the insects themselves. The new insecticides supplemented the measures for public sanitation and personal hygiene which had already largely eliminated most of the insect-borne diseases from the technically advanced areas, and offered important new tools to reduce their prevalence in the regions where they remained widespread.

(c) *Water- and filth-borne diseases: typhoid, diarrhoea and enteritis.* At the opening of the century, typhoid fever was widespread and frequently fatal, even in the countries with relatively high standards of health and sanitation. The reduction of the incidence of this disease to an insignificant cause of death in northern Europe, North America and Australasia reflected the measures taken, city by city, to ensure a pure supply of water and milk and the proper disposal of sewage and refuse. These same measures played a major part in reducing the foremost cause of infant deaths, diarrhoea and enteritis, as well as offering protection against the reappearance of such water-borne pestilences as cholera. By the end of the first quarter of the century typhoid fever had been greatly reduced in most parts of these areas, and by the middle of the century, it had ceased to be a problem there, although it remained a serious disease in many parts of Latin America and eastern Europe, as well as in Asia and Africa.

In 1900 few cities could boast a pure, potable water supply or a safe supply of milk; by the middle of the century a pure water supply had become almost universal in cities and towns of the westernized areas, sanitary handling and pasteurization of milk were general, though by no means universal, and sewage disposal was fairly adequate. The change however did not come overnight. In the city of Chicago, for example, it required over seventy-five years to conquer typhoid fever. Steps to secure a pure water supply repeatedly proved inadequate to meet the conditions created by the growing population, pollution recurred, the incidence of typhoid jumped up, to be brought down again by new measures for control. Only when chlorination of water, and also pasteurization of milk, were finally made complete and thorough during the first world war was typhoid fever virtually eliminated from the city and its recurrence forestalled.

Other cities of Europe and America went through the same process at different times, some earlier and some later. Some had a readier source of pure water than others and a less difficult task of sewage disposal and were able to achieve control more easily. Some outgrew their facilities and faced recurrent crises in their control systems.

As in the case of diseases carried by animal vectors, the control of the water-borne diseases was a cumulative process. With the reduction in the diseases, foci of infection disappeared and the danger of contamination was thereby reduced. In time the goal of a physical environment free from these major health threats was achieved throughout most of the industrially developed world.

Sanitary measures to break the cycle of infestation were also the means of controlling the major diseases produced by internal parasites. Of these the most widespread and debilitating were ancylostomiasis (hookworm), transmitted through the skin from soil infected by the deposit of faeces, and schistosomiasis (bilharzia), whose parasite also enters through the skin from water in which its host, a snail, is present. Campaigns to eradicate these debilitating infestations, most characteristic of rural areas, took the form of systematic detection and treatment, installation of latrines, wearing of shoes, and in the case of bilharzia chemical treatment of irrigation waters and streams to destroy the snail hosts. Such measures reduced the parasitic infestations to a minor problem in the developed countries, but these remained as major causes of debilitation in many less developed areas.

While quarantine, attacks on animal vectors and public sanitation produced the major safeguards against the scourges which threatened the total population, immunization also played a part against some of these diseases, namely yellow fever, typhus, typhoid and cholera, and it played a major role in combating some of the contagious diseases of childhood.

(d) *Contagious diseases of childhood.* With the aid of immunization, the developed countries brought under control those contagious diseases of childhood which constituted the principal killers of young children above the age of infancy and, next to diarrhoea and enteritis, took the largest infant toll. Combined measures to quarantine, immunize and treat these diseases reduced their incidence and limited their severity.

The basic techniques for the development of immunizing vaccines against bacterial diseases were at hand at the opening of the century in the ability to isolate the bacteria, to cultivate them in the laboratory—*in vitro*—and to experiment with the development of vaccines which would cause the body to generate antibodies, or of sera containing antibodies generated in the body of an animal which would give temporary, passive immunity when transferred to the patient. Following the development of the diphtheria antitoxin, safe vaccines providing a measure of immunity for varying periods were developed for such important diseases as typhoid, typhus, cholera, tetanus, whooping cough and tuberculosis. Large-scale inoculation of British, American and German troops against typhoid proved effective in the first world war; thereafter this and other preventive inoculations became general for military personnel, travellers and persons working in areas where such protection might be necessary.

Immunization of large parts of the child population against diphtheria virtually eliminated this major threat to the life of young children. Though the disease continued to be fatal in a large proportion of cases, its incidence was so reduced in the years after the first world war that some cities where hundreds of children had died annually from this cause at the opening of the century went for years without reporting a single death. Immunization against whooping cough was introduced later than that for diphtheria, but by the middle of the century it was part of the routine protection for infants and young children.

The virus diseases, however, presented more difficult problems although two of the first diseases against which immunization was used, smallpox and rabies, are virus diseases and vaccines were gradually developed for other virus diseases including yellow fever. The viruses causing such diseases as poliomyelitis, measles and the common cold for a long time could not be cultivated outside the living host as could bacteria. For more than forty years efforts to isolate the poliomyelitis virus and to develop an immunizing serum were unsuccessful, but in 1955 these efforts were finally crowned with success when vaccine produced by Dr Jonas Salk (1914–) showed substantial capacity to protect against this dread disease and offered the hope of bringing it under control.

By this time methods had been developed for cultivating viruses in the laboratory using certain animal tissues, such as eggs or organ extracts, and a basis was laid for the production of vaccine against other viruses as these might be identified. With the memory of the influenza pandemic of 1918 in mind, much effort was directed toward the identification of the viruses which produce the many types of influenza, and vaccines against several types were developed in the 1940s. When in 1957 a type of influenza started to spread from Asia around the world, the virus was identified and an immunizing serum was immediately developed, though not with sufficient speed and in sufficient volume to prevent an epidemic.

Some of the most stubborn and elusive of the viruses, those causing common colds, continued at the middle of the century to baffle widespread efforts to track them down. Until such time as each of the disease-causing viruses could be identified, isolated and grown in tissue cultures, control of virus diseases through immunization remained remote and the medical profession was forced instead to rely on the maintenance of general health through good nutrition, building up general resistance in the patient's body and controlling side-effects by means of the new drugs, most of which were ineffective against the viruses themselves.

Measles, scarlet fever and other childhood menaces no longer offered the same threat primarily for these reasons, as well as by reason of an apparent decline in virulence. At mid-century only an estimated one out of every thousand cases of measles in the British Isles and the United States proved fatal, whereas in Mexico and Egypt reports indicated that as many as one out of every four or five cases of measles might still be ending in death.

(e) *Tuberculosis.* At the opening of the century tuberculosis was one of the chief causes of death in all western countries and was by far the principal killer of young adults. The tubercle bacillus had been identified by Robert Koch in 1882 and the manner of its transmission was understood. But no immunizing agent was known nor was the disease responsive to any known drug. The standard treatment was to transport the patient if possible to a climate thought to be more favourable to recovery; hence the location of sanatoriums in Switzerland and other mountain areas.

The attack on tuberculosis therefore had to take the form of organized efforts to prevent its spread by identifying cases before the infection was passed on to others, by modifying health habits so as to minimize the chance of either receiving or communicating the infection, and by building up resistance to the disease through improving the general level of nutrition and health. Such an attack necessarily involved more than the medical profession and public health officers, for it required the understanding and co-operation of the people themselves. The fight against tuberculosis thus became a major world-wide campaign of education and organization.

During the first half of the twentieth century the co-operative efforts of medical institutions, public health agencies and organized citizen groups drove down the death rate and the incidence of the disease in the industrially developed countries and finally began to bring a substantial reduction all over the world.

For treatment of the disease special sanatoriums were established which had the double advantage of isolating the patient to prevent contagion and of providing care. Systematic study of the disease by large numbers of specialists in many countries led to the conclusion that climate was less important than pure air and rest, to enable the body to build up strength to throw off the infection. Sanatoriums were therefore set up for local patients, bringing care within reach of those who could not afford to go to distant places, though the number of beds available was rarely sufficient. Even at local institutions, however, few patients could afford the cost of the long treatment generally required, and tuberculosis hospitals came to be widely supported by public health agencies and charitable bodies. The treatment itself was improved as methods were devised for collapsing a diseased lung to permit it to heal and as several types of chest surgery were perfected in the second quarter of the century.

The public health aspects of the disease were clearly recognized—as early as 1889 New York City had required doctors to report all cases of tuberculosis to the city health authorities—and most public health departments developed special programmes for tuberculosis control. One of the most important of such measures was the elimination of bovine tuberculosis as a source of infection to humans through pasteurization of milk and the eradication of infected cattle. The disease was virtually stamped out among cows in the United States and the Scandinavian countries, by slaughter of infected animals in the former country and segregation from breeding herds in the latter area, and elsewhere it was being continually reduced.

Effective tuberculosis control, however, required more than the isolation and treatment of cases which might come to the attention of doctors and health authorities, and the extension of public health measures. It depended upon the early detection of cases while treatment could still be effective and before the patient had had an opportunity to spread the disease to others. From the establishment of the first special tuberculosis dispensary, in Edinburgh in 1887, tuberculosis clinics undertook: to keep a close check on the recovered patient in order to detect signs of a new breakdown; to follow up the members of the family and others with whom the person had been in contact in order to detect those who might have contracted the disease; to seek to improve health practices and living conditions in the home in order to minimize the danger of contagion and to increase the resistance to disease of those exposed; and to conduct a general programme of education concerning the nature of tuberculosis and precautions to be taken against it.

X-ray photography made early diagnosis possible, and the tuberculin test of the skin gave an even earlier indication that the infection was present and might develop into the disease. In addition to the systematic follow-up of known contacts, mass chest X-ray surveys were undertaken in a number of cities and chest X-rays became standard procedure in routine physical examinations of food handlers, nurses, members of armed forces and other groups. Mass use of tuberculin tests on school children or on persons working in tuberculosis sanatoriums were used to identify persons in special need of watching. As the attack on tuberculosis succeeded in isolating and treating the more advanced cases, the emphasis shifted more and more to case-finding in the hope that early detection would both permit the disease to be arrested in the individual and prevent its spread.

At every stage in the anti-tuberculosis campaign a major role was played by citizen groups. Voluntary organizations to support the establishment of sanatoriums and arouse public concern were formed in the 1890s in Austria, Denmark and other European countries. In 1904 the National Association for the Study and Prevention of Tuberculosis in the United States focused the anti-tuberculosis movement on prevention and research, and this pattern was followed by citizen groups all over the world. Against no other disease was there so widespread a public campaign of health education and such broad and systematic financial support for study and treatment of the disease and rehabilitation of its victims.

From the 1920s on, and especially after the second world war, immunization began to play a part in tuberculosis control. A vaccine known as BCG developed at the Pasteur Institute in France became available in 1921, but its widespread use was delayed for some years, partly because an early batch of impure vaccine was known to have occasioned a number of deaths. By the years after the second world war, however, prejudice against the vaccine had been generally overcome, BCG was being administered on a mass scale to children in a number of countries and the World Health Organization was sponsoring a programme for its use where the incidence of tuberculosis was still high. In the Scandinavian countries new-born infants were being regularly inoculated with the vaccine before mother and baby left the hospital.

In 1944 the long quest for a drug that would be effective against tuberculosis met with success in the discovery of streptomycin by Selman A. Waksman (1888–   ). Immediately a broad test of the drug's use, alone and in combination with other drugs, was set up under the co-ordination of the United States Public Health Service, and the basic conditions for its effectiveness were quickly established. In a very few years drug therapy had partially replaced the long and costly methods of treatment wherever supplies were made available. Many cases, especially those diagnosed early, could be treated at clinics without requiring hospitalization.

By all these means and as a result of general improvements in living conditions, nutrition, sanitation and health habits, deaths from tuberculosis in the industrial countries were steadily and substantially reduced, though the incidence of the disease rose temporarily in Europe during and after the second world war, reflecting the malnutrition and deprivations suffered by large segments of the population. At mid-century the advanced countries were looking to drug treatment, immunization, general health education and systematic techniques for detecting tuberculosis in the population as bases for an all-out effort to eliminate the foci of infection and to bring this ancient 'white plague' finally under definitive control.

(*f*) *Control of disease by drug therapy.* In the public mind the new 'wonder drugs' were the most dramatic of the twentieth-century developments in medical science. As preservers of lives threatened by major forms of infection their reputation was richly deserved.

The pharmacological research and experimentation which finally led to the development of the antibiotic drugs rested on the theory that chemicals could be found which for one or another reason would destroy specific microorganisms without at the same time injuring the body. Advances in chemistry and in knowledge of the behaviour of bacteria in the last part of the nineteenth century had made the discovery of such chemicals appear probable. One or two such drugs had long been known, such as mercury for the treatment of syphilis and quinine for malaria. It was not however until 1910, when Paul Ehrlich discovered an arsenical substance for the treatment of syphilis known as salvarsan, that a systematic search for specific drugs was undertaken. Other arsenicals were tested against African sleeping sickness, since the germ of this disease was not unlike that of syphilis, and an effective compound, tryparsamide, was found in 1920.

With the exception of tryparsamide however, and of mepacrine found to be useful against malaria, efforts to find drugs which would act as specifics against disease germs scored few successes. Most of the chemicals which would kill bacteria in cultures outside the body either killed the animal or lost their effectiveness when they were introduced into the body. The opinion grew in medical circles that chemotherapy was not likely to offer important new means for controlling disease.

In spite of these failures, however, a group of chemists in the laboratories of the German I.G. Farben dye industry persisted in the search and in 1932 found a compound which showed some effects against streptococcal infection in mice. In the following year the first of the sulpha drugs, prontosil, was tested clinically on humans and showed cures in cases of streptococcal septicaemia which would otherwise have been fatal.

In 1935 the developer of prontosil, Gerhard Domagk (1895–   ), published the results of his animal studies and the rest of the world woke up to the importance of this discovery. French scientists quickly established the fact that other sulphonamides produce similar results. By 1938 the effectiveness of the sulpha compounds against pneumonia had been detected in Britain and the drug had been synthesized in Britain, the United States and Russia. Within the next three years other sulpha compounds were developed, including sulphadiazine which was used in large quantities to combat infections during the second world war, and sulphaguanidine which effectively prevented dysentery during the war among fighting troops around the world. The battery of sulpha drugs thus brought a wholly new approach, that of specific drug therapy, to the control of various bacterial infections, including one of the major killers, pneumonia. They shifted the focus of medical thinking from general measures strengthening the body's resistance to precise remedies effective against specific disease agents.

Meantime, the discovery of the first of the antibiotics, penicillin, laid the basis for even more powerful weapons against specific diseases. Although for centuries the Chinese had used moulds to treat infected surface wounds, and anti-bacterial action by some moulds had been noted by Russian scientists in the 1880s and American research workers before the first world war, it was largely by accident that the British bacteriologist, Alexander Fleming (1881–1955), in 1929 stumbled on a mould which showed the ability to destroy certain types of bacteria. For a decade, however, this discovery remained of only academic interest. The identification of the sulpha drugs and their synthesis and rapid introduction seemed to point in a different direction. It was only on the eve of the war that two other British scientists, Howard W. Florey (1898–   ) and Ernst B. Chain (1906–   ), investigating penicillin along with other antibiotic substances, demonstrated that even in very minute quantities penicillin could inhibit the growth of the deadly staphylococcus bacteria. In 1941 the first human tests were carried on in England on cases of staphylococcus and streptococcus infections which had been given up as hopeless.

When the effectiveness of the drug against these infections was established its tremendous importance for military use was immediately recognized, and the British scientists came to the United States to secure large-scale production. The supply was expanded rapidly. In 1942 the whole supply was sufficient to treat perhaps a hundred cases; by 1943 enough penicillin was being produced to provide all the armed forces of the United States and the western allies. For the next three years the military absorbed practically all that was produced and penicillin was not available to the civilian population, but when supplies were released immediately after the war it became the standard drug for the treatment of many types of infection all over the world.

Scientists, meantime, presuming that penicillin was only one of many similar substances which might have anti-bacterial effects, set out to discover other antibiotics, using a systematic method of inoculating soil, observing what antibiotics developed, and then testing their effects and determining their composition. Within the next dozen years some 200 antibiotic substances were identified which were effective against one or another type of bacteria, although only a few of the 200 proved to be practically useful. One of the most important was streptomycin, found to be potent against tuberculosis and other infections which were unaffected by penicillin. The first of the antibiotics to be produced synthetically, chloromycetin (chloramphenicol) identified in 1947, was especially potent against typhoid, typhus and other ricketsial infections. Aureomycin, identified in 1948, was the first of the 'broad-spectrum' antibiotics, found to be active against a wide range of bacteria and some of the large viruses.

The combination of the sulpha drugs and the antibiotics thus placed in the hands of the medical profession powerful tools which could directly combat a very wide range of specific infections and diseases. They made possible the survival of many of those wounded in war and could protect patients during and after difficult surgery. No longer was it necessary to depend largely on the body's own recuperative powers to fight off major infections; they could be attacked directly. Among the most spectacular results of the use of the new drugs were the reduction of venereal disease and of deaths from pneumonia.

The original specific against syphilis, salvarsan, brought only limited results as a means of controlling venereal disease, for it involved a long course of treatment, people were reluctant to seek treatment until the disease was well advanced, and the drug was ineffective against other types of veneral infection. The venereal diseases remained general and continually spreading in the population, with systematic control maintained only among military personnel and in ports.

The discovery of penicillin changed the picture. Not only syphilis but other types of venereal infection could be treated by means of large single doses of penicillin or a short course of rapid treatment. This afforded a wholly new approach, provided the basis for mass campaigns and offered the hope that such diseases might eventually be eradicated.

Even more impressive from the point of view of mortality was the successful treatment of pneumonia. In 1900 this was the leading cause of death in the United States. When the new sulpha drugs were found to be effective against the types of pneumonia which had been responsible for the high mortality rate, the death rate from this cause dropped until at mid-century it was only a fifth of what it had been fifty years before.

The use of the new drugs was limited, however, by the fact that in some patients they produced a bad and sometimes dangerous reaction. The use of antibiotics to suppress symptoms might mask underlying conditions and delay or prevent diagnosis and treatment of the disease. Moreover, new strains of bacteria or viruses constantly appeared which were resistant to some or all of the drugs; the development of immune strains of staphylococci in hospitals presented a new danger of hospital infections. Yet whatever their limitations and dangers, they brought a new era in the control of disease. It was the introduction of these new drugs after the second world war, together with immunization and the use of new chemicals to control animal vectors, which led to a reduction in death rates in the underdeveloped areas much more rapid than that which sanitation and the older forms of treatment had already brought to the industrially developed parts of the world.

3. *Reduction in infant and maternal mortality*

At the opening of the twentieth century infant death rates ranged from about one in ten in the countries with the lowest rates, such as Norway, Sweden and Australia, to about one in four in Russia and eastern Europe and one in three in much of Asia. By mid-century the rate in northern Europe, the USA, Australasia and the USSR had been brought down to less than one of every twenty babies born. In many areas of Asia, Africa and parts of Latin America where rates remained relatively high, they had dropped to the levels which had characterized many of the advanced industrial countries at the beginning of the century and were being rapidly brought in line with the new rates in the latter countries.

The sharp reduction in infant deaths reflected a combination of factors. The most direct point of attack was the improvement of conditions surrounding childbirth—hospital delivery under aseptic conditions, with medical attention available in case of complications, attendance of births by physicians, and training of midwives in antiseptic procedures for deliveries at home. The most important result of the hospitalization of births was to save the babies and mothers where complications were involved, and to avoid the danger of infection. By mid-century the age-old hazards of childbirth had been all but removed for mother and infant, especially after the anti-microbial drugs became available.

Of equal if not greater importance in reducing the death rate among infants were measures to protect the mother's health during pregnancy and to keep the baby healthy during its first year. At the opening of the century it was the rare mother who received medical care during pregnancy unless illness or obvious complications developed. With the determined attack on infant mortality, however, it became apparent that the state of the mother's health was a vital factor in the normal birth and sound condition of the baby. The first of the pre-natal clinics was established in Paris in 1890 and some others followed in the same decade. The Scandinavian countries and Hungary were among the countries which pioneered in the setting up of systematic maternal and child health services, but it was only in the 1920s that such clinics became general in most countries. They were a central feature of the health programme of the Soviet Union. By the middle of the century pre-natal care was routine throughout the West, although a very considerable number of mothers still did not receive such care sufficiently early in the pregnancy to detect the signs of a disorder at the time when it could be most effectively remedied.

Maternal and child health centres which offered pre-natal care to mothers generally provided well-baby clinics and post-natal maternal care. Some infant hygiene clinics were the outgrowth of infant milk stations for poor or undernourished babies; some originated as adjuncts to a maternity centre. Whatever their origin, clinics where babies were checked periodically and their mothers advised as to their care became a central feature of the public health services of most countries.

CHART XVIII.   Trends in Infant Mortality Rates, 1900–55. Selected Countries.
Rate per 1000 live Births.

Source: Woytinsky, *World Population and Production*, p. 167; *U.N. Statistical Yearbook*, 1960.

The advancing science of nutrition found its readiest application in the field of infant welfare. While adult food habits were often slow to change and to incorporate nutritional knowledge, far less resistance stood in the way of the scientific feeding of infants and of pregnant and nursing mothers. Wherever health services were extended and health education was widespread, infants in the families of rich and poor alike received the vitamins and other nutrients required to give them a good start in life.

General programmes of public health, sanitation and hygiene contributed perhaps as substantially to the reduction of infant mortality as did specific measures for maternal and child health. Infant deaths were also reduced, along with those of the rest of the population, by the control of communicable diseases and by the use of antibiotics against infections.

In the opening years of the century the principal causes of death among infants were diarrhoea and enteritis. In some countries these accounted for as much as a half of all deaths in childhood. In the United States they were the

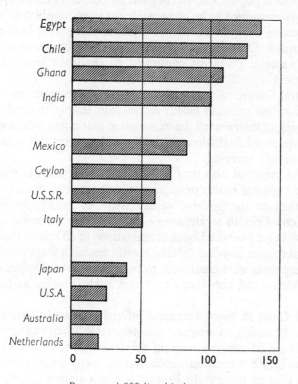

Rate per 1,000 live births

CHART XIX. Infant Mortality Rates, 1955. Selected Countries with High, Medium and Low Rates. Rate per 1,000 Live Births.

Source: *U.N. Demographic Yearbook*, 1960

third cause of death in the total population, exceeded only by pneumonia and tuberculosis. During the first half of the century this cause of infant deaths was almost eradicated in the advanced countries as a result of the general improvement in sanitation, specifically the protection of water and milk supplies. Sterilizing of milk used in bottle feeding and other care in the handling of infants' food supplemented public sanitation in protecting the infant population from these diseases. Growing health-consciousness was reflected in standards of personal hygiene and cleanliness in the home.

By the middle of the twentieth century deaths from diarrhoea and enteritis in the westernized areas amounted to less than 2 per cent of all deaths. The rate in the United States dropped from 143 deaths per 100,000 inhabitants at the opening of the century to 6 at the mid-century. In areas where general sanitation had not reached into many parts of the country, especially in hot climates, diarrhoea and enteritis remained the principal infant killers. In Egypt at mid-century for example, they were still responsible for a third of all deaths in the total population, and in parts of southern Europe, South America and Asia they continued to be responsible for large numbers of infant deaths.

Yet in spite of the great reduction in infant mortality a hard core of infant deaths remained. Deaths associated with prematurity, congenital conditions and other neonatal problems continued to challenge medical science and health practices.

The central feature of maternal and child health practices was that they were geared to maintaining health rather than simply to combating disease. At the opening of the century the expectation that many babies would die was part of a widespread fatalistic attitude. By mid-century this attitude had been almost completely reversed.

Infant and maternal care thus led the way in the shift of emphasis which characterized general health programmes in these years from care to prevention, and then to the positive enhancement of health. In line with this approach, school health services were introduced or extended in most countries to provide for periodic health examinations of all school children in order to detect and correct physical defects. Health teaching was introduced into the schools; campaigns were conducted to promote personal hygiene, immunization of children, and check-ups to detect such diseases as tuberculosis or syphilis.

The Red Cross in many countries offered courses in first-aid and home nursing. Public health nursing services were established or expanded with the double purpose of making nursing services available and of providing a channel for health education; such nurses were sometimes aptly named 'instructive visiting nurses'. In France, where a system of family allowances was established, those who administered the programme were trained as nurses as well as social workers and had the duty of carrying health education to the families they served. In Germany public health nurses visited the homes following the birth of each child. Health education and measures to promote good health became increasingly important aspects of public health programmes.

4. Chronic and degenerative diseases

The control of major communicable diseases and prevention of infant mortality left chronic and degenerative diseases, most especially heart and other circulatory diseases and cancer, as the principal causes of death. The lengthened span of life, following success in preserving the health of the young, brought the health problems of older people to the centre of the stage.

In the industrially advanced countries death rates from heart disease and cancer continued to mount absolutely as well as relatively, in the face of concerted efforts to trace their cause and of constantly improved techniques for diagnosis and treatment. It was an open question how far these diseases were produced or aggravated by the conditions of modern life—strain and anxiety, diet, atmospheric pollution, smoking—how far their incidence merely reflected the survival of persons who would formerly have succumbed to one of the traditional killers before these degenerative diseases had a chance to develop, and how far better methods of detection were bringing to light cases which would not have been recognized in the past. Whatever the source, their presence was very real and the further improvement in health and survival in the developed countries depended upon progress in their control. It was indicative of the role which these diseases had come to play in the advanced countries that in 1955 the World Health Organization inaugurated its first attempt to focus international co-operation on chronic disease by establishing a study group in the European region on the chronic degenerative diseases of the cardiovascular system. The WHO expected this inquiry to point the way to international co-operation on other important chronic diseases such as rheumatic conditions and cancer.

Chronic and degenerative diseases did not appear generally to arise, like communicable diseases, from the invasion of a micro-organism whose entrance could be prevented or which could be directly attacked by an immunizing agent or antibiotic drug. They appeared to reflect conditions of imbalance or malfunctioning arising within the body itself, and had therefore to be treated or forestalled by approaches which might involve the entire organism.

The attack on these still unconquered ills therefore required an immensely complex marshalling of medical knowledge and skills. It led to efforts: to recognize hereditary predispositions to certain forms of breakdown; to understand physiological processes as they involve the functioning and interrelation of all parts of the body; to identify the internal secretions of endocrine glands and extract or synthesize the hormones which they produce in order to be able to restore balance; and to understand the chemistry and behaviour of living cells and the effects of nutritional factors, physical stimuli and radiation.

Much progress in the understanding and control of diseases which reflected a chemical imbalance in the body was achieved during the second quarter of the century through advances in knowledge and use of hormones.

The need to understand the mechanisms which maintain in the body a constant internal environment and a chemical balance had been well recognized before the close of the nineteenth century. Physiologists were then studying the process of metabolism in relation to nutrition and the functioning of the central and sympathetic nervous systems as regulators. A number of scientists, especially in Switzerland where cretinism and goitre arising from thyroid deficiency were prevalent, were beginning to study the internal secretions by which certain glands supply the body with regulatory substances. During the first quarter of the twentieth century the principal glands of internal secretion were studied, some of the hormones which they secrete were identified, and their major functions were detected.

The first of the hormones to be identified, adrenalin, was isolated in 1901 and was synthesized and used in treatment before the first world war. Other hormones were isolated during this period, but it was not until the 1920s that insulin was extracted in a form that permitted its use to enable persons suffering from diabetes to function normally. A succession of hormones were identified, extracted and synthesized in the following decades and provided a means of influencing chemical balance and adjustment and an approach to the treatment of some of the chronic and degenerative diseases.

Once the hormones had been extracted and could be administered in differing volume, it became possible to observe their effects. Every general advance in physiology provided a fuller understanding of the processes to which the hormones contributed. Yet by mid-century an area of uncertainty still surrounded what was then known about most of the endocrine glands and their operation and, although hormones were being extensively used in medical practice for therapeutic purposes, their known or potential side-effects could present serious problems.

In spite of these limitations, however, advances in this branch of medical science were among the most important developments of the period and their significance was expected to increase markedly in the future. Their principal medical value was in relation to the chronic and degenerative diseases which arose from some disorder in the inner environment and normal functioning of the body. With an ageing population, checking the processes of degeneration through control of the mechanisms for normal balance offered the principal possibility for a further lengthening of the life span and, perhaps more importantly, for maintaining health and vigour through the later years. The hormones cortisone and ACTH discovered in 1949, for example, relieved the crippling and pain from one of the most prevalent of the degenerative conditions, rheumatoid arthritis.

Results achieved by horticulturalists during these years in the use of plant hormones, moreover, pointed to a wide potential in the human field. The successful use of plant hormones to modify, accelerate, enlarge and distort growth, to change the time of flowering, to induce a tree to hold or drop its leaves or fruit, revealed these substances as tools for the manipulation of living organisms. The use of sex hormones to affect human fertility and sterility and to alter secondary sex characteristics pointed in the same direction. This branch of medical science appeared to be placing in the hands of the medical profession instruments which might not only preserve and prolong but alter the character of life.

Yet although hormones played a role in the treatment of chronic diseases somewhat parallel to that played by the antibiotics in the treatment of infections, their use was less simple and direct, for instead of attacking a specific micro-organism they were called upon to affect the extremely delicate and complex interrelationships essential to the functioning of the total organism and its several organs. With the notable exception of insulin, whose use to control diabetes became well established and routine, and in some cases the use of sex hormones, most of the hormones were still being used tentatively and experimentally at mid-century for the treatment of functional disorders and the maintenance of health in maturity and old age.

Early detection coupled with treatment by surgery and radiotherapy remained the weapons available against cancer. In the effort to determine the factors producing malignancy and to discover some substance which might attack the diseased cells without destroying healthy tissue, research was pursued along many different lines, including the carcinogenic effects of chemical substances, radiation, physical damage and hormone action, the possibility of virus origins, the role of genetic factors. In view of the success achieved by medical science in other fields there was general hope that means to control cancer would also be found, and research was pressed forward with a sense of urgency on the chance of saving the lives immediately threatened. It appeared that success in this quest, and in relation to other forms of degeneration and malfunctioning, would depend in the final analysis on progress in understanding the life process itself.

Conditions causing debilitation or discomfort, as well as those leading to premature death, were the objects of intensive study and extensive treatment. Deficiency diseases and malnutrition were attacked by means of improved knowledge of nutrition and the identification and use of vitamins.* Recognition of the nature of allergic reactions in the first decades of the century laid a basis for relief of the discomfort suffered by large numbers of people, estimated at perhaps 3–5 per cent of the population, with allergies to certain substances. Such symptoms as asthma, hay fever and skin eruptions were brought under control by methods for identifying the offending substances, desensitizing the individual to them and, with the discovery of antihistamine drugs after 1945, by directly counteracting the allergic reaction.

One of the chronic conditions found to be most widespread in mass health surveys or the examination of draftees for military service was dental caries.

* See Chapter XIV, section on Nutrition.

Although dentistry was one of the oldest of professions and methods for treating dental decay and filling dental cavities were well developed by the opening of the century, the services of dentists were available to only a very limited segment of most populations.

In the early twentieth century emphasis began to be placed on the prevention of tooth decay, and the toothbrush became almost a symbol of advancing civilization. Following a demonstration programme to provide dental services for school children in an American city (Bridgeport, Connecticut, 1914–24), in which dental assistants were used to clean teeth and teach oral hygiene, dental hygiene became an auxiliary profession, dental hygienists received special training and people were encouraged to have their teeth cleaned professionally at regular intervals. Experiments with chemical treatment of children's teeth to protect them against decay brought substantial results and led to the addition of fluoride to public water supplies, although popular fear that fluoridation might be otherwise harmful delayed the adoption of this preventive measure in some places.

Dental clinics began to be extensively established, especially for school children, in the 1920s and 1930s. Buenos Aires, Argentina, in 1934 was one of the pioneer cities to set up municipal dental clinics providing all types of dental services to those unable to pay, and dental services free of charge were extended to the entire British population by the National Health Act in 1948. Dental care, however, remained one of the health areas in which provision of services and preventive measures were most unevenly developed.

5. Conditions requiring surgery

During the last quarter of the nineteenth century techniques of modern surgery had been established in the practice of asepsis and the effective use of anaesthetics. Spectacular new developments in surgery came less from improvement in the basic techniques to prevent infection and in the dexterity of the surgeon than from a greatly increased knowledge of the physiology of the body, the availability of new diagnostic instruments, the use of new types of anaesthetics and the use of antibiotics to prevent post-operative complications.

New knowledge of the chemistry and composition of the blood played a central part, for it made blood transfusion possible. Although the transfusion of blood had been practised occasionally for several hundred years, it did not constitute part of the technique of surgery at the end of the nineteenth century, primarily because of two factors: the disastrous consequences which had often followed the introduction of the blood of another individual and the difficulty of preventing the blood of the donor from coagulating before it was introduced into the circulatory system of the recipient.

During the first decade of the twentieth century the problem of coagulation was satisfactorily solved and the existence of blood types that are incompatible with each other was discovered by Karl Landsteiner (1868–1943). Once it was recognized that only blood of the same or of a related type may safely be transfused and the major blood types were known, transfusion became a safe and useful means of counteracting surgical shock and compensating for loss of blood in the surgical process. Transfusion techniques were sufficiently developed by the time of the first world war to be introduced into military surgery, especially in the medical services of the American armed forces where they were most extensively used.

In the following years blood transfusion became standard procedure in relation to many surgical operations, and improved methods of preserving whole blood were developed. Hospitals, the Red Cross, communities and the armed services maintained blood banks from voluntary donors in order to have blood of all types available instantly in case of emergency.

In the early years of the second world war a technique was developed for extracting the plasma from the blood, thus securing a product which did not deteriorate as did whole blood and which could be used indiscriminately since it did not contain the properties which differentiate the several blood types. While whole blood was more effective than plasma for some purposes, the use of plasma during the second world war was a major factor in reducing mortality from wounds. In the following decade efforts to find blood substitutes which could be synthesized and would not depend upon blood donations were pursued with some success, and substances were developed which could be used in place of blood in some cases.

The development of new anaesthetics and their careful use in relation to the physiology of the individual patient was the basis of some of the advances in surgery. Ether, which had been used as the principal anaesthetic since the nineteenth century, was supplemented or superseded by a variety of substances which produced different conditions of narcosis and which could be administered locally or by injection into the blood stream or spinal canal rather than through the respiratory system. These new anaesthetics, and new methods of administration, made new types of operations possible such as those in the thoracic cavity or upon the heart, and they could be used on patients whose system might not stand anaesthetics of the older type. The administration of anaesthetics adjusted to the patient's physiology and to the surgical procedure to be followed became a highly specialized field, so much so that a special diploma or degree for anaesthetists was established in 1935 in Great Britain and in 1936 in the United States.

In addition to depending on blood transfusion and carefully adjusted anaesthetics, the modern surgeon made use of the expanding knowledge of human physiology in a myriad of other ways. Much surgery came to have a physiological objective, to eliminate functional disturbances and not merely to correct an anatomical deformity or remove a diseased part. By severely lowering the temperature of the patient's body, physiological processes were slowed down to permit operations which would have been highly dangerous had these processes continued at their normal rate. Equipped with increased understanding of the functions performed by each part of each organ, surgeons learned how to keep the patient functioning by supporting the physiological activities of the body, such as normal blood pressure and fluid balance. Especially in difficult operations in the abdominal cavity, they used sulpha drugs and antibiotics to reduce internal sources of possible infection, for protection during the operation and to control post-operative complications. The new knowledge of nutrition enabled them to feed patients intravenously when they could not take nourishment in the normal manner, though the problem of reducing the necessary nutrients to a form in which they could be received directly into the blood stream presented continuing difficulties. Extended knowledge of the brain and nervous system provided a basis for the development of brain and nerve surgery, including the surgical treatment of such diseases as hypertension by operation on the sympathetic nervous system in order to relax the blood vessels. In all these delicate operations highly sensitive measuring and recording devices kept the surgeon informed as to the detailed condition of the patient throughout the operation.

During the second world war elaborate and highly refined surgical techniques were developed to rehabilitate the seriously injured. In conjunction with skilfully designed prosthetic devices, muscles which remained were often substituted for those which were gone and were taught to perform new functions. A large proportion of the people handicapped by war injury were thus enabled to function at a level undreamed of for persons who had suffered similar disabilities in the past. In the years after the war these techniques were applied to the rehabilitation of persons similarly injured on the roads or in other accidents of civilian life. Modern surgery and medical science made the helpless cripple a rare figure by the middle of the twentieth century, in spite of the many victims of war and of motor traffic.

6. *Hazards created by industrial society*

Developments in respect to life and health were not wholly one-sided during these years, however, for modern society brought with it new hazards of its own. Apart from the loss of life through vastly more destructive warfare than prior ages had imagined, and apart from the possible, but unverified, effect of the pace of modern living in increasing the incidence of some chronic diseases such as hypertension and heart conditions, many aspects of modern living produced dangers to life and health. Accidents were fourth in the causes of death in the United States at mid-century as compared with eighth fifty years before; a third of the accidental deaths were on the roads and approximately a fifth in industry. The toll of traffic deaths and injuries mounted everywhere as the number and speed of motor vehicles increased, in spite of regulations, safety education and improvements in the design of roads and vehicles.

Industrial hazards were gradually reduced through improvements in the design of industrial plants, more rigorous standards for factory inspection, and legal and economic pressures on employers to safeguard their workers' health and safety. New industrial processes, however, constantly added new menaces to those long familiar, especially those involving the use of radioactive substances, new chemical industries and other new substances. The International Labour Office, reviewing the range of industrial hazards in 1955, listed in its bulletin on *Occupational Health and Safety* hazards from chemical and other substances in a long list of industries, including mining and refining, the manufacture of insecticides, the manufacture and use of colours and paints, textile printing, the preservation of hides and wood, and the glass, rubber and pharmaceutical industries.

In some localities smoke, fumes and gases from industrial operations and motor traffic combined with atmospheric conditions to present serious health hazards. Occasional disasters dramatized this threat and some cities, such as Los Angeles, USA, learned to live with recurrent smog resulting from an atmospheric condition known as 'inversion' in which the fumes which are normally dissipated are trapped and blanket the area. The problem was of sufficient international importance to lead the World Health Organization to call a regional European conference on the subject of air pollution in 1957.

The coming of atomic fission brought a new and most serious threat to health in the form of radioactivity. Even before atomic power generators were placed in operation, the International Labour Office, the WHO and national health agencies were at work on means to protect workers in the multitude of plants where radioactive isotopes were being used, and in the transport of radioactive substances. The disposal of radioactive waste from atomic installations and the dangers of an accidental release of radioactive material presented grave problems to communities near such installations. The exact extent of the menace created by the testing of nuclear weapons was hotly debated during the 1950s, but the fact that all life had already been in some degree affected was acknowledged by all, and no official reassurances could conceal the fact that mankind was as yet without protection against this overwhelming danger.

As evidence of this new development in the field of health, the WHO in 1955 sponsored the first international training course for 'health physicists', a new category of professional workers made necessary by the health problems involved in reactors, radiochemical laboratories and the factories and laboratories using radioactive materials.

7. *Mental illness*

At the middle of the twentieth century two out of every five hospital beds in Europe and North America were occupied by mentally ill patients. It was estimated that one in every ten persons in the population of these countries would suffer in the course of his life from some mental disorder.

It was not possible to determine how far the vastly increased number of persons receiving treatment for mental illness reflected improved diagnosis, the mere fact that additional hospital facilities were available, increased numbers of old people in the population suffering from various forms of senility, the conditions of modern living which made it less feasible to leave some cases at large, or a tendency of more people to break down under the strains and anxieties of modern life. Certainly mental illness was much more widely recognized than it had been at an earlier time, though it was doubtful that its actual incidence was appreciably, if any, greater than in the days when the severely disturbed were thought to be 'crazy' or 'possessed' and the mildly ill were simply regarded as 'queer'. In any event general recognition of mental and emotional disorder as a form of illness was one of the outstanding twentieth-century developments in the field of health, and with the conquest of so many of the physical diseases the relative importance of mental illness increased.

Medical advances in the treatment of mental illness followed two major lines: techniques for bringing the psychotic patient back into contact with reality, and techniques for psychotherapy, including psychoanalysis based on a growing understanding of the processes of mental and emotional growth and adjustment. In addition, research into the possible physical and biochemical basis for mental and emotional disorders brought clues as to conditions which might be treated at the physical level.

On the organic side one form of mental illness, general paresis, was successfully traced to syphilis, and some other conditions appeared to be related to extreme malnutrition. Other efforts to link mental illness with focal infections, exposure to certain physiological stimuli, brain toxicity or type of body structure were less successful, but at mid-century the search for organic factors was being continued vigorously, especially by biochemists and neurologists. Frontal lobotomy brain surgery was introduced in the 1940s but observations as to the effect of the operation on the patient's personality led to a decline in popularity after a period in which it was in vogue. Various forms of chemotherapy were also attempted, some related to one or another of the physiological hypotheses that had been advanced.

Psychotherapy depended upon the ability of the therapist to establish contact with the patient, and various methods were developed to break through the patient's wall of unreality. These consisted chiefly in subjecting the patient to some form of severe shock, using insulin or electric current. In the mid-1950s new types of drugs known as tranquillizers began to replace shock as a means of quieting the patient's disturbance and allowing the physician to reach his consciousness. The patient's recovery, however, depended not upon shock or drug treatment but upon his psychological restoration, either with the direct psychotherapeutic assistance of the physician or by his own capacity for recuperation once the disturbing elements were held in check.

Prolonged psychoanalysis was extensively used to treat mild psychoneurosis and to some extent for intensive treatment of psychotic cases. More limited psychotherapy, based on psychoanalytic concepts, was included in most treatment of both psychoneurotic and psychotic patients. Group psychotherapy was coming to be used increasingly as the value of group experience for some patients came to be understood and the shortage of personnel made group treatment desirable.

Yet in spite of much effort and the return to normal living of a growing proportion of mental patients, medical science had a long way to go before it would be able to claim mastery in this field.

Much of the progress in dealing with mental health took the form of early diagnosis and psychotherapeutic treatment before mental disturbance should become far advanced. Child guidance clinics treated emotionally disturbed children. Mental illness occasioned by syphilis was brought under control as the incidence of that disease was reduced. Some types of breakdown, most notably alcoholism, were recognized as forms of mental illness and were made the object of special physical and psychotherapeutic treatment. Alcoholics were treated medically with the aid of a drug, disulphiram, which made the patient's body unable to tolerate alcohol; improved diagnostic techniques enabled the physician to distinguish the level and type of alcoholism and to provide the kind of psychotherapy most likely to be effective before the disease had produced a condition of apparently irreversible deterioration.

In all aspects of medicine the interrelation of psychic and bodily factors received increased attention. Psychosomatic medicine was far from new; it was in fact the basis of much of the traditional 'healing art' in all societies. But as a scientific concept, consciously and systematically applied to the understanding and treatment of specific conditions of ill health, it came to occupy a more and more important place in the second quarter of the twentieth century. Psychosomatic factors were presumed to be more involved in the chronic diseases such as hypertension than in those produced by infections, and their growing place in medical study and practice accompanied the rise in importance of these diseases.

In even broader perspective, psychosomatic medicine was only one aspect of the growing tendency to treat the patient as a whole rather than to treat only the disease. During the long struggle in the nineteenth and early twentieth centuries to conquer one specific threat after another, medical science and medical practice had sometimes tended to lose their traditional focus on the patient and to become disease-centred. But as the nature of the health problems changed and the emphasis shifted to the maintenance of positive health, the patient as a person again became the object of attention. With greater understanding of physiological processes and the chemistry of living cells, medical science tended to seek the basis of much pathology in general rather than specific causes and to provide treatment in terms of the body as a whole rather than a specific disease. In addition the social elements in the individual's life situation, which public health reformers had long stressed, received renewed attention as essential factors in health, and professional workers trained to analyse these factors and help patients to cope with them were increasingly included as parts of medical teams.

By mid-century medical science had thus moved into the wide field of the individual in relation to himself and his society, as it approached its new task of furthering the positive health of those whom it had saved from the killers of the past.

III. PROVISION OF MEDICAL CARE

1. *Development of the medical professions*

At the opening of the century medical education in all western countries combined both academic teaching to convey theoretical knowledge and hospital training to provide practical experience. British and continental European systems differed somewhat in their balance between theory and practice, as a number of British medical schools were directly attached to hospitals where there was more emphasis on training through bedside practice, while elsewhere medical faculties in universities placed somewhat greater emphasis on theoretical knowledge. Research in the basic sciences related to medicine was carried on by faculties of science or medicine or in special research institutes, while clinical and pathological research was generally a hospital activity. Latin American countries, Japan, Turkey and other areas which followed the lead of one or another European country tended to stress the academic aspect of training, while the British dominions, India, and other areas under British influence reflected the closer association of medical training with hospital practice found in Britain.

By 1900 second-class medical practitioners with substandard training had been largely eliminated in Europe, except Russia, but they continued in the United States where medical schools were insufficiently regulated and, in addition, a number of medical sects claimed to practise distinct types of medicine and maintained training institutions for their followers. Partly in response to public pressure, the medical profession in that country undertook drastic reforms in the decade 1910–20, eliminated substandard schools which lacked university affiliation and often a hospital base as well, and did away with second-class practitioners. In the resulting system medical schools were attached to universities, much of the training was provided through clinical experience in hospitals associated with universities as teaching hospitals, and clinical research was stimulated by the close relation between university and hospital.

Public health, which was an integral part of the German and British systems of training, was at first less generally included in the United States until after the first world war, when schools of public health were established at two leading universities; thereafter it received special emphasis in American training. In the USSR and the people's democracies of eastern Europe medical education, which had developed from a strong base of traditional European training, became largely oriented toward public health in line with the role of the physician in the health programmes of the socialist states, and the USSR after 1940 established special schools for organizing public health services.

By the second world war, the American system of medical education was at least on a par with the European, and after the war large numbers of persons from countries where training had been interrupted, facilities destroyed and scientific communication cut off by war, looked to the United States to help bring them up to date on medical progress. As a result of this interchange, features of training which had become part of the American system were introduced elsewhere.

As medical knowledge expanded and medical practice became more refined, both training and practice became highly specialized. In surgery alone as many as ten distinct specialities came to be recognized as the basis for special training, certification and professional organization. The resulting tendency was for an increasing proportion of medical practice to be carried on in hospitals where technical equipment and nursing services were available to facilitate and support the physician's work and for the disparity in available medical services to increase between those localities or groups in the population which had access to specialized services and those who must rely on the less intensive training and experience of the general practitioner.

For dentistry, regarded by some as a specialized form of medical practice and by others as an independent area of knowledge and professional skill, courses of training were developed, including clinical practice, comparable to those for medical practice. As the close relation between general health and dental health was recognized, training and practice in dentistry came to rest on a broader basis of general medical knowledge. In most places the supply of dentists remained far short of that needed to provide dental care according to modern standards.

All medical training was long and costly; that of the specialist was even more so. In nearly all countries, not alone those of meagre resources, provision of sufficient training facilities and the financing of the training for a sufficient number of doctors to serve the population became a critical problem. Responsibility for meeting the problem was generally assumed by governments, which provided subsidies to medical schools and stipends to medical students. In a number of countries students receiving government aid for their medical studies were required to practise in a rural area for the first two years after leaving school, a device adopted in an effort to overcome the disparity in medical service available to rural and urban residents.

The medical professions were strongly organized into national associations and into associations of specialists which originated in the last half of the nineteenth century and increased in number as new specialities developed. In co-operation with other national bodies such as hospital councils, they set professional standards and criteria for medical ethics. The organized profession played an especially large role in the licensing of practitioners in the English-speaking countries. In continental Europe and elsewhere standards for licensing were usually set by governments rather than by the organized profession. Where national professional bodies were powerful they tended to exert a conservative influence on the manner in which medical services were supplied.

The members of the medical profession functioned increasingly in teams with members of other professions, and depended on the work of nurses and laboratory technicians, on the availability of facilities for the care of patients in well-equipped hospitals and clinics, and on the preparation and dispensing of drugs by reliable pharmacists.

Nursing as a profession followed the pattern established by Florence Nightingale (1820–1910) who in the years after the Crimean war secured the establishment by hospitals of schools to train nursing instructors and visiting nurses to care for the sick poor. Because of the value to hospitals of the nursing service provided by students in training, however, schools tended to concentrate on the hospital rather than the public health aspects of their programme in Britain, the United States, the Commonwealth countries and the parts of Europe to which the 'Nightingale' movement spread.

The nursing profession organized itself in each country and was one of the first of the health professions to form an international body, the International Council of Nurses, established in 1899. A major purpose of the organization was to secure the passage of legislation regulating the practice of nursing, standardizing the nursing diploma, and requiring the diploma in order for a nurse to be 'registered'. The first such act was secured by the organized nurses of New Zealand in 1901.

Nursing schools were originally wholly connected with hospitals but gradually the nursing profession began to seek a university base, first for the training of teachers of nursing and then in the 1920s and 1930s to train nurses in broad fields of public health, for administrative responsibilities and for specialized services. At mid-century nursing retained its hospital base but much of the responsibility for public health programmes fell on nurses, who engaged in health education and often provided the full-time staff for services to which doctors acted mainly as consultants.

As nursing developed and spread, it played a special role in the changing position of women for it was one of the principal fields of employment entered by women at the point where they were beginning to seek work outside the home. The profession served this function for middle-class European women in its initial phase during the latter part of the nineteenth century, and again for the women of the developing countries in the course of the twentieth century.

In time of war or disaster and in the face of the great expansion of health services, trained nurses were repeatedly or constantly in short supply. Although the ratio of graduate nurses to the population was 217 per 100,000 in the United States in 1950 as compared with 16 per 100,000 in 1900, there was so great a shortage in 1950 that hospitals were understaffed and public health posts were unfilled. To meet this situation the Red Cross in many countries developed training courses for volunteer nurse's aides and organized their use, both to supplement regular nursing services and as nurse reserves for time of disaster.

The elaborate diagnostic and treatment techniques made possible by much of the new medical knowledge required a variety of technicians skilled in performing other specialized supporting services such as laboratory analysis and X-ray operation. The development of training, the establishment of standards and the organization of these sub-professional fields assured the physician or surgeon of performance on which he could rely. The compounding of drugs became a specialized function carried on by licensed pharmacists, druggists, chemists or apothecaries.

Much of the manufacture of drugs was taken over by large pharmaceutical firms, which not only produced pharmaceuticals in enormous quantities but carried on basic research, often in collaboration with medical schools and hospitals. In order to identify and standardize the great number of medical preparations and thus both to enable the physician to be sure of what he was prescribing and to protect the public from fraud, national governments adopted official pharmacopoeias in which drugs were specifically defined in terms of their ingredients and strength. By the mid-twentieth century, more than 30 countries had compiled a national pharmacopoeia, while other countries had adopted as official the one prepared by some other country.

In order to facilitate the international sale of drugs, and to serve the convenience of persons travelling from one area to another, steps began to be taken at the opening of the century to establish uniform standards internationally. Following the first international conference on the subject sponsored by the Belgian government in 1902, the Brussels agreement of 1906 proposed uniform nomenclature and standards of strength for many important drugs. The League of Nations set up a technical committee to draw up an international pharmacopoeia, and this work was completed by the World Health Organization, which published the International Pharmacopoeias in 1951 as a guide to encourage national governments to adopt uniform terms and standards.

2. Cost of medical care

As a result of the great advances in medical science, provision of medical care became an increasingly costly process. Elaborate diagnostic techniques through laboratory examinations, X-ray, and such devices as the electrocardiogram or the electroencephalogram could not be maintained by the individual physician but had to be supplied on a wider basis through hospitals, specialized diagnostic services or group medical practice. Treatment often involved expensive drugs, expensive surgery and expensive specialized care. The need to meet the cost of such services presented an acute problem in all countries; in some it was a cause for serious controversy.

Traditionally medical care had been received and paid for by those who could afford it, while the indigent sick had been cared for in publicly maintained almshouses or by religious orders or by private charity. In a few places, notably in Sweden and Norway, hospitals had been maintained as public institutions from their start in the early nineteenth century, and some medical care was offered by physicians on the public payroll. The more usual pattern, however, was that of the private physician and the privately endowed and operated hospital, except for such special types of institutions as mental hospitals, leper asylums and sometimes tuberculosis sanatoriums which were more generally maintained as public facilities. The private physician lived from fees paid for his services in the same manner as the lawyer, and his patients were those who could pay, except as he chose to treat poor patients without charge or for a nominal fee. Hospital services were paid for by the well-to-do, and those unable to pay were treated as charity patients.

This uneven system of care and payment was modified by the introduction of health insurance. Beginning with the German social insurance system of the 1880s, the insurance principle was widely adopted to spread the cost of medical care, chiefly for industrial workers whose earnings could be taxed to provide a fund out of which medical bills of all workers covered by insurance would be met. Health insurance became part of the social insurance system of nearly all industrial countries during the first half of the twentieth century, with the conspicuous exception of the United States where the organized medical profession resolutely fought its introduction on a broad scale and health insurance schemes remained voluntary or limited to particular groups.

Medical benefits were also generally included among the perquisites of various forms of employment, as for members of the armed services and their families, war veterans, the staffs of educational and other institutions, members of labour unions whose contracts called for health funds to be maintained by employers, certain classes of public employees. All these piecemeal methods, however, left medical care unevenly distributed, especially in case of major illness, and the burden of its cost fell heavily upon those not eligible for free service or not adequately covered by some form of insurance or other arrangement.

In the face of this situation many countries shifted a larger and larger proportion of the costs of medical care to the public treasury. State contributions to social insurance plans were increased to make broader coverage possible.

By the second quarter of the century the tendency was toward direct medical services supported by public funds and provided to certain categories of the population without charge. Public hospitals, clinics and medical consultation, available as a public service and not as an act of charity, offered a widening range of service not only to the poor but to the general public.

Some of the impetus for this trend came from the public health movement, for it became increasingly clear that it was impossible to maintain an effective programme of disease prevention unless treatment were also included. Public health programmes came to include aggressive measures to detect the presence of unrecognized or untreated disease in order to ensure early diagnosis and treatment and the elimination of foci of infection. Mass procedures were developed and campaigns launched to locate cases of tuberculosis, venereal disease, diabetes and cancer in whole populations, and statistical methods were designed for estimating the probable extent of various diseases on the basis of sample surveys. Standardized procedures for detection were developed—such as tuberculin and other tests for tuberculosis infection and periodic mass chest X-ray surveys, tests of urine sugar for diabetes, the Wassermann blood test for syphilis. Mass education campaigns taught people to recognize possible symptoms of cancer and to seek immediate diagnosis.

But unless it were possible to follow through with treatment when a programme of case-finding had been carried out or unless a programme for future prevention could follow treatment for a recurrable ailment, the broad objective of public health would not be served. Public health programmes thus expanded to incorporate treatment services along many lines.

Countries differed markedly in the extent to which they made the direct provision of medical care an integral part of their public health programmes. Differences reflected not only differences in economic resources and in institutional arrangements, but in judgment as to how to use medical resources effectively. Opponents of systems of prepaid or free medical service thought that it was necessary to retain the barrier of direct and immediate cost to the patient to prevent excessive and wasteful demands for medical service for minor causes by persons with hypochondriac tendencies. Supporters of the view that medical services should be fully available stressed the importance of early diagnosis and treatment and wished to encourage medical consultation at the appearance of first symptoms.

With the emphasis upon positive health, the European countries in the 1950s were beginning to explore the advantage of a family health consultant, to keep in touch with the family continuously, not merely for the treatment of illness which might develop but to promote the health of all the members of the family group. This was one of the newer developments to which the WHO through its regional organization lent support.

3. National programmes of health services

When the United Nations reviewed the development of health services around the world in the decade following the second world war it noted not only that such services had been extended to segments of the population not previously covered but that an increasing number of countries were adopting comprehensive health schemes. In such schemes preventive, curative and educational aspects were integrated into a single system of services provided directly by the government.

Great Britain went the whole way in shifting the financing of its health services from social insurance to tax support and in undertaking to provide comprehensive services to all on a national basis. The pattern for the British National Health Service was set by the experience during the second world war in making use of all available professional and hospital services under an integrated emergency medical service to care for civilian and military wounded and sick. The wartime measures systematized first-aid, out-patient and hospital services and distributed them so as to make them universally available.

The National Health Service, enacted in 1946 and put into effect in 1948, replaced a system in operation since 1911 under which insured workers, but not their families, were entitled to medical care. Under the new system the entire population was entitled to medical services, together with prescribed medicines or appliances, wholly at public expense. Doctors who agreed to work under the scheme were paid on a *per capita* basis for the number of persons on their rolls; hospitals and training centres received direct government support. Doctors continued to be free to offer private medical services for a fee, and patients were free to purchase such services outside the scheme if they so desired.

The comprehensive programme inaugurated in Chile in 1952 illustrated the manner in which a variety of approaches were made part of a single system involving all elements related to the problem. The Chilean National Health Service, responsible for all public health services and for the medical care of three-fourths of the population, incorporated the following previous programmes: the government's public health responsibilities, medical care and sickness benefits under the compulsory insurance programme covering workers and their families, a system of public hospitals originally developed by private philanthropy and increasingly supported by public funds, the national services to children, and a public research institute. The governing body included representatives of the medical profession, the university faculty of medicine, employers' associations and trade unions. The programme was administered through a decentralized system of health centres operating public health and medical care services, under medical officers assisted by a team of social workers and other health workers and advised by local councils.

The health programme of the Soviet Union was an integral part of the effort to develop the nation's resources—in this case its human resources. All medical services were provided free on a public health basis and preventive and treatment services were combined throughout the system.

Comprehensive coverage was achieved in urban areas by sectional doctors or hospital externes assigned to a neighbourhood where they not only responded to calls for service but maintained constant health surveillance of certain categories of people such as young children. Factories maintained health posts to provide emergency treatment, as well as to supervise sanitary conditions and conduct health education in the shop. Larger industrial establishments had medical departments offering clinic and hospital care and in some cases they maintained night sanatoriums where workers who were well enough to remain on the job received treatment and slept. Smaller factories depended upon health centres maintained by local hospitals. Special dispensaries for a wide range of diseases were attached to local hospitals, which also furnished in-patient specialized care. Maternal and child health services included pre-natal clinics where expectant mothers not only received care but also instruction in psychological attitudes and physical exercises designed to make possible painless births. In 1955, 92 per cent of all urban births occurred in maternity hospitals.

For the rural areas sectional hospitals with out-patient consultation served their respective areas, supplemented by maternity stations in each large village and maternity homes on many collective farms. Rural patients could take advantage of specialized services offered in regional and central city hospitals.

Special child health services were provided for each age level. The young children of working mothers received care in day nurseries in factories and on collective farms. Physical fitness programmes were conducted in schools and youth organizations. A network of rest homes provided healthy holidays for both children and workers.

Through programmes such as those of Britain, Chile, the Soviet Union, and similar plans in other countries, the economic barrier to medical care was reduced or eliminated in most of the economically developed countries, and the economically less developed areas were instituting similar programmes as fast as their national resources would permit.

IV. INTERNATIONAL CO-OPERATION IN THE FIELD OF HEALTH

Health was a matter of international as well as national concern, and the scope of health programmes broadened at this level as it did within countries. Early international health measures had been directed against the spread of pestilences, by means of quarantine conventions and agreements relating to the control of ports. As rapid travel brought all parts of the world closer together, control became more and more essential, for plane passengers could easily be carrying a recently contracted disease in the incubation stage. The League of Nations health office established international standards for immunization procedures and for the preparation of vaccines such as that for yellow fever. International trade in foodstuffs required standardized regulations relating to such matters as chemical residues from sprays or chemical additives to preserve the product. So long as foci of infection persisted anywhere in the world, the self-protection of all countries required their co-operation in campaigns for eradication.

The development and dissemination of medical knowledge, spread of public health practices and international attacks on specific diseases were greatly stimulated and promoted by the International Health Commission (later known as Health Division and Health Board) of the Rockefeller Foundation. From 1913 on, this privately supported foundation worked successively on one world-wide scourge after another, helping to discover, develop and demonstrate means of control and co-operating with governments in putting control programmes into effect. Its first attack was on hookworm, which debilitated millions of people in warm climates; the campaign for sanitary measures to check infestation by this internal parasite extended into fifty-two countries. In its intensified attack on yellow fever, begun in 1914, it dared to conceive of a world-wide campaign which would wipe the disease from the face of the earth—the first such imaginative approach to disease control, though one doomed to disappointment because of the reservoir of yellow fever among jungle animals.

Work on malaria control was extended from the United States to Venezuela in 1921, then to Brazil and then to many parts of the world, where the Foundation established training stations, offered fellowships to train for malaria control posts and aided governments in setting up programmes, which were particularly successful in Italy and Portugal. Basic work on typhus, rabies, yaws, tuberculosis, the snail-borne parasitic infestation schistosomiasis and other widespread and stubborn diseases laid the basis for control techniques; a combination of training programmes and co-operative work with governments helped to put controls into operation.

Recognizing that the success of public health measures depended upon the presence of trained personnel, the Foundation financed the establishment or expansion of schools of public health, first in the United States and then in many other places, as in São Paulo, Brazil, and Prague, Czechoslovakia. It also provided international fellowships for advanced study at these centres. By the 1950s the more than 3,000 men and women who had been trained in public health with the aid of these grants were occupying key health posts in nearly every part of the world. The existence of this corps of internationally trained people in public health was a major factor making possible the spread of health knowledge and practices at a revolutionary rate in the decade after the second world war.

Direct international co-operation in the field of health was carried on between individual countries and through professional organizations. The socialist countries of east Europe and the Soviet Union entered into annual agreements for co-operative programmes in medicine and public health designed to share advances in these fields and to take advantage of the extensive development of medical training and public health facilities in the USSR.

At the end of the second world war the United Nations Relief and Rehabilitation Administration (UNRRA) set up a Health Division to combat the menace of post-war epidemics, to restore health departments, provide medical supplies and train personnel. This was by far the largest international health organization the world had known; it was followed by the establishment of a permanent United Nations health agency, the World Health Organization, created in 1948.

In contrast to the health organization of the League of Nations, which had concerned itself mainly with controls in relation to international trade and travel and with the standardization of procedures, WHO engaged in direct assistance to countries for the development of their health services. The scope of its international aid included the development of public health services relating to sanitation, immunization, health education, hospital and clinic care, health statistics and reporting systems, health surveys, epidemiology; standardization of biological preparations; aid to medical research on specific problems; and the training of health personnel—doctors, nurses, sanitarians, auxiliary health workers.

International co-operation in the field of health also took the form of working together to cope with new problems. At mid-century the problems presented by the use of nuclear energy and danger from radiation were uppermost. A new phase in international health efforts was foreshadowed in the mid-1950s as WHO began to be concerned with what had become the major health problems of the developed countries—heart disease, cancer and other chronic ailments, and with measures designed to promote positive health.

V. EXTENSION OF MEDICAL KNOWLEDGE AND HEALTH PRACTICES TO UNDERDEVELOPED AREAS

Up to about the beginning of the second world war the application of medical science to the control of health was largely limited to the industrially developed countries. Elsewhere modern health practices were known and modern medicine was practised almost entirely in the major cities and among the Europeanized segments of the population, except for mission hospitals or missionary doctors.

In the years after the second world war, however, the picture changed drastically. As a central part of their movements for national development the non-industrial countries promoted national health programmes to spread medical knowledge throughout the population, reduce infant mortality, control communicable diseases and raise the general level of health. The most dramatic changes in health status during these years came in the underdeveloped areas. Death rates, and especially infant mortality rates, dropped in a decade as much as they had in western countries during fifty or more years. Deaths from diseases subjected to intensive campaigns dropped spectacularly. In Ceylon, for example, the general death rate fell from 22 per 1,000 in 1945 to 12·6 in 1950, largely as a result of an intensive campaign to control malaria.

1. *Reduction in mortality and control of major diseases*

The major health efforts in these areas followed the course which had brought health improvement in the western regions, but at an immensely accelerated pace and with the advantages of modern medical knowledge and the experience of the areas where many diseases had been brought under control. These countries directed their first and major attacks against the communicable diseases which remained their principal killers. Systematic measures were launched to eliminate pestilences where they were still endemic—plague and cholera in India, yellow fever in South and Central America, smallpox in all regions.

The governments of these countries sought and received the assistance of WHO in campaigns to eradicate yaws by the mass examination of whole populations and penicillin treatment of those found to be affected, in tuberculosis control, chiefly through mass programmes for vaccination of the child population with BCG vaccine, and in malaria control programmes to eradicate the disease and its carrier completely wherever this appeared possible and to introduce control measures where no efforts had been made in the past. In addition some countries sought assistance in controlling particular communicable diseases of importance in the area, such as trachoma in the eastern Mediterranean, leprosy in a number of countries and parasite infestations such as bilharzia and hookworm where these were a serious problem.

Maternal and child health services were second only to the control of communicable disease in the health programmes of many countries. In this field, the United Nations International Children's Emergency Fund (UNICEF) furnished very substantial aid, helping to train midwives, furnishing milk or stimulating its local production and providing specialists in child health to guide the development of local services and to train local personnel. WHO assisted in organizing such programmes and training needed personnel, both in countries such as Afghanistan where no such service had existed before and in places like India where services existed but extensive training and organization were required to extend them widely through the population.

In many areas improved health depended on better nutrition. Maternal and child health programmes stressed infant feeding, and UNICEF aid in supplying milk lent powerful support. In regions, especially in Africa, where the protein-deficiency disease generally known as *kwashiorkor* attacked many young children at the time when they were weaned, special efforts were made to overcome the inadequacy of the adult diet to which the child was shifted. General improvement in nutrition, however, was pressed with less vigour than attacks on communicable disease and was making slow headway against the hold of traditional food patterns.

For many of the underdeveloped countries environmental sanitation and basic health education were among the most essential needs, but practical difficulties and deeply ingrained habits presented serious obstacles. Whereas in the western areas general sanitary conditions had been achieved before direct control of many diseases by drugs or immunization became possible the situation was reversed in some of the underdeveloped countries. Environmental sanitation tended to lag behind while advanced techniques, such as BCG vaccination or treatment with penicillin, were being introduced. In the effort to strengthen programmes of sanitation and to stimulate their spread, WHO provided technical assistance in this field to the governments of several Asian and eastern Mediterranean countries, and the large number of fellowships which it offered to Africans in the 1950s were for this purpose.

In the development of health services and campaigns to combat disease underdeveloped countries were severely handicapped by shortage of personnel and inadequacy of training facilities. New medical schools were established in many countries, but they faced serious difficulties in maintaining adequate teaching staffs when the limited number of doctors and nurses were in great demand for direct medical practice and the administration of health agencies. International co-operation in medical and nursing education, and in training of laboratory technicians, helped to provide the manpower without which health programmes could not go forward.

WHO recognized that mass programmes for the improvement of health would have to be carried in large measure by auxiliary workers since no programme of professional training could be expected to provide sufficient professional personnel in the foreseeable future in regions of Africa and Asia where there were as few doctors as one per 50,000 of the population. It therefore undertook to suggest standards for such auxiliaries, to guide plans for training and to conduct experimental programmes to demonstrate their effective uses. One such WHO-aided demonstration programme, in El Salvador, set up a pattern of service which could be repeated throughout the country with the limited financial and other resources available. It included rural health posts manned by nurse-auxiliaries visited by a doctor periodically, village and town clinics with minimum essential facilities where much of the responsibility was carried by the public health nurses, and an area health centre where the doctors who attended the clinics and health posts were based, nurses and auxiliaries were trained, the sanitary inspector had his office and some hospital services were provided. Newly trained nurses and auxiliaries and young doctors assigned for public health experience were used to staff the demonstration area, while those who had already acquired experience within the area were transferred by the health department to establish similar health services in other parts of the country.

The importance of the social component in health was recognized in all these programmes. Medical social workers were frequently included in health teams, and even the restricted training given to auxiliary workers included instruction in some of the social factors which could be expected to affect the way in which health education would be received and the willingness to make use of health services or co-operate in health programmes. In general, while some popular resistance to modern health practices was encountered the eagerness to respond to life-saving measures was evident everywhere.

For underdeveloped areas the cost of medical care was an even more serious problem than in the developed areas. Because of the extreme poverty of the vast majority of the people and the high cost of modern medicine, most health services had to be provided through public funds. In some countries, particularly in South America, medical care for industrial and some agricultural workers, together with some care for their families, chiefly maternal and infant care, was developed through social insurance to which the employers contributed most of the funds, supplemented by grants from the state. Everywhere costs imposed a limitation on the expansion of services and gave special importance to preventive and mass protective measures rather than to facilities for individual care. The more immediate needs for rapid training and the development of services as quickly as possible tended to receive support in preference to the medical research and professional development essential to a high level of health services in the longer run.

The great problem facing these areas, along with the question of how heavily to invest their limited means in the costly provision of modern health services, was whether the development of their economy could keep pace with improvements in health, how far such improvements would themselves contribute to greater productivity, and whether their basic resources would be sufficient to sustain the lives which medical science would save.

2. *Replacement or incorporation of native medical traditions*

Some countries, notably India and China, possessed an ancient medical tradition unrelated to the scientific knowledge on which modern medical practice was based. Elsewhere, as in parts of Latin America, Africa and the Pacific, various types of medicine men, *curanderos* and witch doctors were the traditional practitioners of the healing art.

When western medicine first reached these areas, those whose practice was based on scientific knowledge scorned native medicine as superstitious and its practitioners as ignorant. Traditional medical systems persisted, however, into the mid-twentieth century. In India the Benares Hindu University maintained a school of Ayurvedic medicine in which professionals were trained in ancient techniques. In the Chinese People's Republic patients could choose a traditional or a modern doctor in many places. In many other areas, such as the region of the Andes, the West Indies or parts of Africa, people patronized both the modern doctor and the medicine man according to their ailment.

In the course of time some western-trained medical men revised their completely negative attitude toward these indigenous medical systems. Some of the traditional forms of treatment turned out to be sound by scientific standards. The discovery of penicillin, for example, validated the traditional Chinese practice of using certain natural moulds against infection in open wounds. A traditional Indian drug was found to be more effective in certain cases of hypertension than anything known in the West and was introduced into general medical use. Western-trained doctors practising in areas where a strong local medical tradition existed found it practical to use their diagnostic skills to determine the nature and gravity of the illness, and then to prescribe the familiar local drugs or other treatment if the case was not serious, reserving the limited supply of expensive modern drugs for cases where these appeared to be essential to recovery. In 1955 the Indian medical profession undertook a systematic analysis of the medication prescribed by the Ayurvedic system in order to ascertain the chemical properties and method of action of the traditional remedies and to make possible the incorporation of this knowledge into general medical practice.

Moreover, as western-educated doctors learned more about the importance of psychosomatic factors they came to realize that indigenous medical systems had often taken these elements effectively into account. Psychiatrists began to study the methods used by tribal witch doctors and to find evidence of procedures similar to their own, often at a highly sophisticated level.

Practitioners of traditional medicine, on their part, adopted many features of scientific medical practice. *Curanderos* added penicillin to their kits. Traditional midwives accepted training in aseptic procedures. At the Ayurvedic medical school of Benares Hindu University the surgery which was taught was the same as in other medical schools.

It appeared likely that the process of interchange, along with continued advances in scientific medical knowledge and the spread of medical services, would lead to amalgamation, just as the formerly rival systems in the West had already become a single system of world-wide medical practice.

3. *Impact of health practices: case example of Puerto Rico*

A vivid illustration of the process by which the application of health knowledge was remaking the societies of underdeveloped areas was furnished by the commonwealth of Puerto Rico.

At the opening of the century the island of Puerto Rico was typical of most of the tropical and subtropical regions of the globe, with a life expectancy of 36 years, an infant mortality rate of approximately 200 per 1,000 live births, all the familiar water-borne, insect-borne, infectious and contagious diseases, and a general death rate nearly double that of western Europe and North America at the time. In 1930 average life expectancy was still only 41 years. On the eve of the second world war the situation, though materially improved, remained that of a 'backward' area; life expectancy had advanced to 46 years and infant mortality had dropped to 113 per 1,000 births, but the leading causes of death were still diarrhoea and enteritis, tuberculosis, malaria and other communicable diseases.

By 1955 the death rate in Puerto Rico at most age levels was as low as that of the continental United States and many European countries, although the infant death rate still remained somewhat higher; the traditional killers had been brought under control and some virtually eliminated; deaths from tuberculosis had dropped from 260 per 100,000 in 1940 to 34 in 1955; no death from malaria was recorded in that year, only one from typhoid fever and a handful from childhood contagious diseases; the leading causes of death had become the same as those in the developed countries—heart disease and cancer. In fifteen years, average life expectancy had risen from 46 to 68 years.

The health record of Puerto Rico reflected the direct application of medical knowledge and the indirect effect of changing economic, social and educational conditions throughout the commonwealth.

At the opening of the century public health measures were directed primarily at the control of major contagious diseases, i.e. inspection of vessels in port and wholesale vaccination to combat smallpox. Medical care was provided efficiently to those who could pay, by private physicians trained abroad, located in the principal cities; the masses of people were served in an inferior manner by politically appointed municipal doctors whose cursory treatment and insanitary hospitals were the butt of prevailing jokes.

Systematic measures to reduce disease and promote health began to take shape in the 1920s with the beginnings of sanitary controls in the principal towns, the destruction of mosquito breeding places to reduce malaria, and the first maternal and child health dispensary, established by the Red Cross in 1921 and then taken over by the public authorities. In the mid-twenties the health department, following a visit of its commissioner to observe public health services in the continental United States, began to establish local public health units consisting generally of a maternal and child health clinic, clinics for venereal disease and tuberculosis, and a centre for health education. In the following decade such units were set up throughout the country and brought health services and health education within reach of people in all areas.

From 1940 on, Puerto Rico intensified its attack on health problems across a broad front. In that year it established a special venereal disease bureau, enlarged its maternal and infant health services, set up a programme for crippled children and organized a nutrition division in the health department. Medical social workers were added to health services in 1942, and in 1944 a special bureau of health education was created in a determined effort to reach the people. A special unit focused the attack on hookworm. Rapid treatment of venereal diseases with penicillin was started in 1945 and the use of DDT spray against malaria in rural areas the following year. Special divisions of the sanitary bureau were created to deal with industrial hygiene, rat control and the prevention of typhus, the contamination of water and disposal of industrial waste, and a drive for sanitary conditions in restaurants was launched. In 1949 mass vaccination with BCG vaccine was begun, and the following year treatment of tuberculosis with the new drugs was started experimentally. When in 1952 a new 800 bed tuberculosis sanatorium was opened, drug treatment of ambulatory patients had already started to replace bed-rest in sanatoriums as a preferred form of treatment, and the number of tuberculosis deaths and new cases had started to drop precipitately. Growing concern with chronic diseases was reflected in the establishment of a bureau for cancer control and the inauguration of a mental health programme in 1950.

In order to make more adequate care possible for all, the University of Puerto Rico established a medical school in 1941. The state provided a generous programme of scholarships for medical training, and the health department constructed a series of well-equipped district hospitals to supplement the inadequate care offered by the municipalities. In 1949 the department took the further step of bringing together in the first of its combined health centres the public health unit with its maternal and child health, venereal disease and tuberculosis clinics and health education programme, the municipal hospital and general medical consultation, the sanitary inspectors, vital statistics office, public health nursing service, child welfare and public assistance offices.

Eight years later, when such combined centres were in operation throughout the island, the local health centres began to be integrated with the district hospitals in a regional organization designed to make the best use of specialized facilities, to keep the personnel of the local centres at a high level of proficiency by making them part of a single regional staff, and to achieve a further co-ordination of preventive and treatment aspects. To provide the whole system with the highest professional and technical leadership, the fine new tuberculosis sanatorium, no longer needed for its original purpose, was converted into a medical centre which included medical research institutes and a teaching hospital for the university medical school.

The improvements in health during these fifteen years could not be attributed solely to the expansion of health services, for many other developments were changing the environment and contributing to general health. Aqueducts carried pure water to all urban areas and began to penetrate the rural zones; in some places clean supermarkets took the place of many of the often-insanitary little food stores; latrines constructed under the stimulus and inspection of sanitary officers reduced the spread of hookworm and bilharzia in rural areas; school lunch programmes and breakfasts for pre-school children raised the level of general nutrition. In the course of these years the average height and weight of students entering the university rose noticeably, and differences in size which had clearly distinguished lower- and upper-class children were no longer apparent.

Medical services developed under public auspices were offered to all people of limited means without charge. Well-to-do families continued to pay for the services of private physicians, either directly or through private hospital and medical insurance schemes. With the growth of a middle class able to meet some of the costs of medical care, the question of financing part of the general programme of health services on the basis of compulsory health insurance came under discussion.

The successful battle for health and survival brought to Puerto Rico the social consequences common to underdeveloped areas with rapidly declining death rates. The direct result in the vigour and productivity of the people could not be readily determined, but it must have been considerable. The effect upon the population balance was clear. In contrast to the developed countries where the slow reduction in mortality over a hundred years had been accompanied by a falling birth rate, death rates here dropped almost overnight, while birth rates showed relatively little change. By 1955 there were nearly five births in Puerto Rico for every death. Whereas the rate of natural increase during the first five years of the twentieth century had been 1·1 per cent per year, in the years 1950–54 it was 2·9 per cent and the birth rate was still nearly double that of most of the industrial countries. Heavy emigration drew off much of the increase, and enabled a vigorous national programme of industrialization to raise *per capita* income. But in a country which ranked in population density with Java and Japan, the achievement of a healthy population in less than a generation precipitated dramatically the problem of population balance which faced so many parts of the world.

VI. POPULATION

1. *Acceleration of population growth*

The great success of the attack on the causes of death brought a radically new population pattern to the world, for it produced a rate of population growth far greater than any which the world had ever experienced. In the mid-1950s the world's population was approximately 2,500 million; at the opening of the century, it had been approximately 1,500 million. Growing at the rates which characterized the 1950s, it would reach about 4,000 million by 1975 and 6,500 million by the year 2000, according to United Nations estimates. The rate of growth in the 1950s was nearly double that of the years from 1900 to 1950—1·6 per cent per year from 1951 to 1955 as against an average of 0·9 per cent for the half century. And the growth in the first fifty years of the century had already greatly exceeded any previous period; in the last half of the nineteenth century the rate had been only 0·6 per cent.

This tremendous burst of population growth was a new phenomenon in the life of mankind. Rough estimates place the world population at about 1,200 million in 1850, 750 million in 1750, 500 million in 1650 and perhaps 250 million at the opening of the Christian era. Throughout human history the population of the globe had grown unevenly, unsteadily and in different regions, expanding as men learned to command the earth's resources and cut back by pestilence, famine, violence or the disruption of established societies. Pressure of population had long been known in specific regions such as the valley of the Nile. Recurrent migrations of peoples had reflected the quest for living space.

But never before had the rate of increase begun to approach that of the mid-twentieth century and never before had the whole world faced the prospect of the filling up of open spaces, the crowding of ever-expanding cities, the pollution of streams, lakes and shores, and the need to expand the output of goods and services at an impressive rate even to maintain existing levels of living. And never before had the people of the world—the new millions born each year—needed so much material equipment, so much education and such a complexity of organization to enable them to function in the world into which they were born. Nor had any earlier age begun to match this in the technical resources for meeting these needs.

The high rate of population growth presented the world with a series of critical problems: competing demands for the use of resources—the claims of the 100,000 or more babies that were being born every day in the 1950s for food, shelter, care and training as against other claims, including those of industry for capital expansion; the prospective size of the world's population as for the first time in human history it became necessary to consider what practical limits the earth's total resources might place on the ability to sustain human life; and the effect of population growth on the interrelations among the world's peoples as it widened disparities in levels of living and set in motion pressures which could lead to conflict.

Even before the spectacular success of death control triggered the population boom of mid-century, population had been recognized as a world-wide problem calling for scientific study. An International Union for the Scientific Study of Population was formed in Paris in 1926, following the first World Population Congress in Geneva the preceding year. Health statisticians took the lead in this movement, joined by social scientists who were concerned with the economic and social aspects of population change, and by actuaries who needed a basis for estimating likely claims for life insurance benefits.

As governments all over the world improved their collection and publication of vital statistics and other population data, it became possible to make more systematic comparative studies. Recognizing the many influences on population growth, demographers analysed a multiplicity of factors affecting trends and developed demographic principles. These scientific studies laid a factual and analytical basis for the development of public policy when the dramatic tendencies of mid-century made population a national and international issue. The international importance of the problem was attested by the inclusion in the structure of the United Nations in 1945 of a special Population Commission, on a par with the commissions on Status of Women and Human Rights.

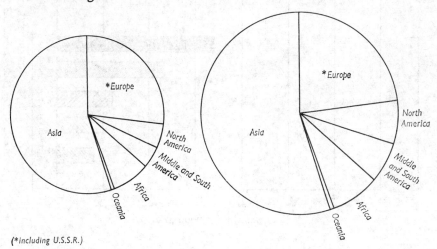

(*including U.S.S.R.)

CHART XX. World Population, 1900 and 1950. Percentage Distribution by Continents.
Source: UN, *Future Growth of World Population*, 1923.

CHART XXI.   Rate of Population Growth by Regions.

Source: U N, *The Determinants and Consequences of Population Trends*; *U.N. Statistical Yearbook*, 1960.

2. High rates of growth in underdeveloped areas

The rapid population growth of the mid-twentieth century came mainly in economically underdeveloped areas. In these regions high death rates had formerly balanced high rates of birth, so that population growth had tended to be slow or erratic, increases not infrequently alternating with decreases brought on by disasters. The Latin American countries had already begun to experience an acceleration in their rate of natural increase before the second world war, as mortality declined while birth rates remained high. In the years after the war the tendency was carried further in that region and was extended to large populations in Asia and to a lesser degree in Africa. The estimated annual increase in Latin America in the 1950–55 period was 2·4 per cent as compared with 1·9 per cent before the war. Even higher rates were recorded in some Latin American and Asian countries such as the Central American Republics and Ceylon.

The upsurge in population in the underdeveloped countries reflected mainly the application of mass methods for checking epidemics, controlling infectious diseases such as malaria and reducing infant mortality; it was not necessarily associated with any rise in the economic capacity or level of living of the peoples involved, and it therefore enhanced the economic and social difficulties faced by these countries.

The first problem faced by these countries, especially in areas where hunger was already endemic, was the relation between food supply and the number of mouths to be fed. This was a problem which had concerned European thinkers from the beginning of the nineteenth century and which had produced two general and opposing views, those of Thomas R. Malthus (1766–1834) and those of Karl Marx. Malthus held that population tends to outrun food supply, for, he thought, it increases geometrically while food increases only arithmetically; population therefore has to be checked by pestilence, war and famine unless controlled by the exercise of 'moral restraint'. Marx maintained that once men were freed from the hampering institutions of capitalism there would be no limits to the productivity which they could achieve and hence that population presents no problem in a socialist society.

The historic situation in the nineteenth and early twentieth centuries— improved technology and the opening of virgin lands—expanded both the food supply and the general economic base for larger populations; as a result the danger which Malthus stressed appeared not to be very real. Opportunities for emigration relieved the pressure in heavily populated areas such as Italy. Moreover, 'moral restraint' came into play and the birth rate dropped in Europe and North America so that the rate of increase remained well below that of expanding food supplies. Even so, aggressively expansionist countries such as Japan and Nazi Germany sought to justify their thrusts for territory by the claim that their populations needed living space.

The spurt of population in the underdeveloped countries raised anew the problem of whether population growth would outstrip food supply. Careful appraisals of possible food production, such as those by the geochemist Harrison Brown in *The Challenge of Man's Future* (1954) and by the British organization, Political and Economic Planning (PEP) in *World Population and Resources* (1955), reached the conclusion that double the existing world population could be fed if the best known techniques were applied to the land and waters then in use and to new areas which could be brought into cultivation. At the rate of increase then prevailing, a world population of that size would be reached in some fifty years. If radically new techniques should be developed and extensively used, such as the production of protein by the cultivation of algae or by chemical synthesis, food supplies might be sufficient for still larger populations.

But whatever might be the theoretical possibilities for feeding an enlarged world population, all the world's food production was not in reality available to those who needed it. While North American farmers found difficulty in marketing their surplus products, perhaps half of the world's people were living below a minimum nutritional level, many in a state of chronic hunger. In spite of vigorous programmes for increase in food production, *per capita* food consumption in Asia in 1955 outside the USSR was still below what it had been before the second world war. India struggled desperately to step up its output of food to get ahead of its population growth. China, committed to the Marxian view that socialist reconstruction of society could meet the needs of people in spite of population growth, took heroic steps to expand food production to feed its vast population and the fifteen or more million new mouths added each year.

The effect of population growth on economic development, however, involved more complex relationships than the equation between numbers of people and supplies of food. These relationships presented problems in socialist as well as capitalist economies, although socialist authorities regarded them as wholly soluble under their system. The need to use resources for capital formation in order to lay the basis for expanded production was competitive with the need to devote resources to education and housing. Different age structures affected the productive capacities and the consumption needs of a country. Any major change in population modified the internal balance of the society. Responsible leaders saw the need for measures which would keep population in line with other aspects of development in order to permit balanced growth.

A health official of one of the richer countries of South America, Venezuela, might have been analysing the problem in all the underdeveloped areas when he said of his own country in the late 1950s:

'Our successful campaign to reduce infant mortality has given us more problems. If we do not have adequate food supplies at reasonable prices and an understanding of nutrition, the babies we save may sicken or die of malnutrition before they reach school age; when they reach school age, there will not be enough schools, unless we can greatly expand our educational facilities; if they lack schools, they may become juvenile delinquents and present us with still other needs for services; if they reach working age without sufficient training, they will not earn enough to give their own children a good home—even if we manage to get enough housing built; and whether they will find jobs at all will depend on the rate at which we can expand our industry and improve our agriculture, and find the capital resources with which to do so. Unless we can move forward on all fronts at the same time, the saving of lives only puts us further behind.'*

The poorer the country and more limited the resources, the more difficult it was to meet simultaneously the needs of a rapidly growing population and of an economy which must be expanded still more rapidly. Even such a country as Brazil with vast untapped natural resources and the capacity ultimately to absorb a very much larger population found its efforts to achieve economic development and overcome its heritage of mass poverty complicated by its high rate of population increase. In India, where population pressure was already severe in many areas, national leaders recognized that unless the rate of population growth could be slowed there would be small chance of achieving the economic expansion which alone could lift the masses of the people out of hunger and poverty—yet India's rate of increase in the 1950s was not as high as that of many other underdeveloped areas.

On the positive side, reduction in mortality meant tremendous savings in the social cost of premature death, i.e. the cost to society of rearing children who failed to live long enough to repay the cost of their nurture through their own labour; even in the United States, with a relatively low death rate, the cost of premature death in 1950 was estimated at something like 3·5 per cent of the national income. But on the other hand the great increase in the number of children who survived placed a growing burden on the adult population, for it resulted in a higher ratio of dependent children to adults of working age than in countries with relatively stable populations. In Britain in 1950, for example, every ten adults of working age were supporting an average of five and a half children, whereas ten such adults in Brazil would have on the average more than eight children dependent on them.

Moreover, employment opportunities would have to expand as fast as young people reach the age to go to work. With annual rates of population increase of 2 and even 3 per cent, a corresponding rate of economic expansion would be required merely to prevent the economic situation from deteriorating. Yet even in the economically developed countries an annual rate of economic expansion exceeding 3 per cent over a long period was high. Any such rate of expansion required much capital to invest in industrial expansion; but

* Personal interview with Dr Espiritu Santos Mendoza.

in countries of low *per capita* income lack of capital was one of the most difficult obstacles to overcome.

The problem of sufficient capital formation was further intensified by the need of the increased population for housing. With people already seriously under-housed, the economically developing countries faced a most critical housing problem, for efforts to provide shelter for their additional families, even at prevailing low levels, competed for the limited supply of capital goods needed to expand economic production.

The difference in rate of population increase between the underdeveloped and industrially developed areas, moreover, tended to increase the disparity between the 'have' and the 'have-not' countries. At best the underdeveloped countries faced a difficult task in attempting to catch up with industrially developed areas whose capital, know-how and institutions gave them the basis for continued or accelerated economic growth. To the extent that the need to support and train a constantly expanding population acted as a drag on the developing countries while no corresponding drag held back the others, it stood in the way of their best efforts to close the gap that separated them from those who enjoyed an industrial head-start.

3. *Reduction in mortality and control of natality*

The drop in death rate in underdeveloped countries in the mid-twentieth century had a more disturbing effect than the corresponding drop which had occurred in the West, primarily because the decline came so rapidly and because there was not a corresponding drop in rate of birth.

In Europe and other western countries birth rates had fallen during the hundred years from 1850–1950 either at the same time that death rates were falling, as in France, or with some lag, as in Germany and England in the last quarter of the nineteenth century, and the process had continued over a long period. Methods for the control of natality were known and practised in western countries, more generally among families of higher economic and social levels and more education, but widely and increasingly by all levels in the population. Lowered birth rates were associated with urbanization, for fertility tended to decline further in large cities than in rural and small town areas. The birth rate also tended to fluctuate with economic conditions, falling to a low point in the depression of the 1930s.

Some signs began to appear that birth rates might eventually follow a similar course in the developing areas. In Puerto Rico the crude birth rate which had fluctuated around 40 per 1,000 for two decades dropped steadily in the 1950s to 34 in 1955 and 32·6 in 1956, though the latter rate was still higher than the rates which had prevailed in the United States and western Europe in 1900. But only in Japan, where drastic measures were undertaken after the second world war, was there a drop in natality comparable to the precipitate drop in mortality.

Spread of knowledge and the practice of birth control met with considerable

CHART XXII. Changing Birth Rates, 1900–55; trends in Selected Countries. Births per 1,000 Inhabitants.

Source: Woytinsky, *World Population and Production*, pp. 144, 149; *U.N. Statistical Yearbook*, 1960.

cultural resistance in many areas. Acceptance of children as an expression of the will of God was widespread, although in areas where a rationalist, scientific mentality and climate of opinion prevailed such an attitude ceased to be general. Some religious attitudes stood in the way. The Biblical admonition to 'be fruitful and multiply', the Muslim value attached to many sons, the traditional Chinese need for descendants to carry on respect for the ancestors and the religious connotation given by Hinduism to the act of creation all reinforced the natural desire of men and women for children. The principal opposition to the practice of contraception as such came from the Catholic Church, which categorically opposed any so-called artificial means and countenanced only abstinence and the 'rhythm' method to achieve family planning. In some predominantly Catholic areas other factors appeared to be at least equally important in determining the extent to which births would or would not be planned, and disparity in the sizes of Catholic and non-Catholic families was generally not great at comparable economic and cultural levels. Catholic teachings did however exert a strong influence on political developments in this field.

The one country where control of natality rapidly restored a degree of population balance once mortality had fallen was Japan in the years after the second world war. At the opening of the century the birth rate in Japan was somewhat, but not markedly, higher than in western Europe and the United States, and it was below that of Russia and eastern and southern Europe. It did not fall but even increased somewhat during the decades when birth rates were declining in western Europe and the United States from close to 30 per 1,000 to less than 20, or as low as 14·5 in Sweden and 17·1 in the United States in the 1930s. It remained high after the second world war while the death rate dropped to one of the lowest in the world as soon as it ceased to reflect the immediate effects of the war. As a result the population started to shoot upward at double its pre-war annual rate of increase. Then the birth rate began to drop sharply. From 34·3 per 1,000 in 1947 it fell to 19·4 in 1955.

The swift reduction in the Japanese birth rate was brought about primarily by resort to abortion, since contraception was not widely practised in the country. In 1953 an estimated one out of every three pregnancies ended in abortion. Speaking at the World Population Congress in 1954 representatives of Japan explained that although abortion was not a preferred method, it was nevertheless permitted and made medically safe in recognition of the need to keep the population within bounds until such time as the practice of contraception should become sufficiently general to maintain balance.

Other Asian countries recognized their population problem as serious and initiated efforts to bring it under control. India made population control part of its official policy and sought means to implement it as essential to the success of its five-year plans. It included family planning in its mass education campaign and in its village development programme, making it a part of the reorientation of village people toward the desire for a better life and the idea that improvement is possible. Pakistan showed similar concern. Although the Chinese People's Republic rejected the policy of population control, it made family planning a feature of its intensive public health programme in the interest of the health of mother and child.

But so long as the available means of contraception were costly and difficult to use, the chance that a rapid spread of knowledge would check rapid population growth seemed to be remote. Much medical research therefore was directed toward the quest for a cheap and simple method of preventing conception, experimenting with both chemicals and hormones. By the mid-1950s some progress had been reported. In the light of success along other lines, including the use of hormones to overcome sterility, it appeared probable that this problem also would yield to the onslaughts of medical science.

Yet simple means of birth control alone would not necessarily result in a slowing down of the rate of population growth. Personal attitudes and the stand taken by governments and religion played their part. Some national governments might be tempted to encourage population expansion for reasons of prestige and military strength even when economic and social considerations might dictate an opposite policy—witness the bachelor tax imposed by Mussolini in a country which had for generations supplied large numbers of emigrants because of pressure of population in the Italian peninsula. The position of the Catholic Church carried weight in the region of fastest population growth, Latin America.

On the basis of western experience up until the second world war it had been generally assumed that a rising level of living and increase in urbanization would have the effect of lowering the birth rate. By the 1930s such countries as France and Sweden were barely maintaining their population through natural increase.

After the war, however, birth rates rose and remained above their pre-war levels, especially in the United States and Canada where they were high enough to double the population of North America in fifty years, and in some European countries of very low rates, notably France. It thus appeared that although industrialization might result in reducing very high birth rates from over 40 per 1,000 to well below 30 as it had in the past, it could not be counted upon to bring the rate of population growth down to that which characterized Europe and North America in the first half of the twentieth century. The higher birth rates sustained in the industrial countries in the 1950s, in contrast to the drop which occurred following the peak after the first world war, suggested the possibility that once a high level of economic development had been maintained over a considerable period of time it might be reflected in a pattern of larger families than had seemed probable several decades before.

4. *Population as a world issue.*

The expectation of a more than doubled world population by the early years of the next century thus presented the problem of the kind of human society that was in prospect. If world population should double again in the succeeding fifty years, tendencies toward congestion would mount geometrically. Cities could be expected to double in size or multiply in number; roads would cover the landscape carrying their ever-mounting loads of traffic; fewer and fewer water sources could remain untapped; open areas and wild life would continue to disappear and patterns of life in most of the world would have to be adjusted to new population densities.

Even with no change in living levels the pressure on resources would be tremendous. But the modern world was committed to raising the levels of living of its people. Success would mean still more food, more housing, more traffic and more drain on other resources than would result from the mere doubling or quadrupling of numbers at the levels which formerly prevailed. Failure could only mean frustration for masses of people, with whatever the consequences might be in the nuclear age. The issue presented by such rapidly mounting numbers, moreover, was not merely the capacity of the earth to satisfy material wants; it was also the capacity of men so to order their lives that they could live together in such numbers on the globe. In the final analysis the issue was the quality of human life itself that would be possible and the opportunities for its fulfilment and enjoyment.

The question of population prospects and efforts at population control became a highly controversial one in the 1950s. Since the sharp change in rate of growth came mainly in the underdeveloped areas, it was easy to allege that concern expressed in the industrially advanced countries was no more than an effort to maintain the privileged position of these countries against the 'have-not' peoples whose mounting numbers they feared. The strong emotions aroused by the position on birth control reiterated by the Catholic Church made it difficult to treat the issue dispassionately wherever the influence of the Church was felt. Similarly the Marxian insistence that population could be no problem under socialism threw the issue into the arena of conflict between those who followed and those who rejected this doctrine. And the fact that 'population' was not a matter which could be dealt with directly since it resulted from the actions of millions of people in their private lives led other people to insist that the whole question lay beyond the reach of public policy.

Yet thoughtful people all around the world were recognizing at mid-century that the new phenomenon of rocketing population was a major factor affecting the kind of life that might be foreseen for mankind in the years ahead.[1]

NOTES TO CHAPTER XV

1. The analysis of the Author-Editors is queried by Mario Bendiscioli, Silvio Golzio, and Vincenzo Cappelletti, who assert that 'in dealing with problems related to the increase in population' the authors are 'solely concerned with a study of the trend in demographic development and the demographic factors on which it depends'. The Italian commentators state that greater emphasis should have been placed upon 'the complexity of the inter-dependence between the dynamics of population and other components of the socio-economic system'. They believe that the text 'is one-sided in the manner in which it poses the population problem: it sees the control of births as the only possible solution, and attributes any other views to unscientific political and religious motives'. They go on: 'It is incomplete in that it ignores, except for two very brief allusions, the marked increase in per capita real income ... during the last ten years in nearly all countries,' adding that 'This observation gains force if the recent results of research into the peaceful uses of atomic energy are taken into account. . . .' A somewhat similar view is expressed by Candidate of Medicine, Y. P. Lisitsyn, and Doctor of Medicine, B. Y. Smulevich:

'The whole discussion of the problem, based on neo-Malthusian theories, does not reflect the actual state of affairs. Soviet scientists maintain that the role of population growth as an economic factor is wholly subordinate to social-economic factors. . . . In socialist countries rapid population growth in no way interferes with the maximum satisfaction of the people's needs. On the contrary, it is a prerequisite of the further growth of pro-duction at accelerated rates and consequently of the improvement of public welfare.'

The Catholic position regarding population is defined in moral terms which regard certain forms of population control as sins against nature but which at the same time lay stress upon personal and social responsibility. The position with regard to birth control is defined in the encyclical *On Christian Marriage*, promulgated in 1930 by Pope Pius XI:

'But no reason, however grave, may be put forward by which anything intrinsically against nature may become conformable to nature and morally good. Since, therefore, the conjugal act is destined primarily by nature for the begetting of children, those who in exercising it deliberately frustrate its natural power and purpose sin against nature and commit a deed which is shameful and intrinsically vicious.'

In regard to the material means for sustaining a family, the encyclical places the responsi-bility first upon the parties to the marriage, then, if necessary, upon private charity and upon the state.

The Church does not directly oppose the idea of planning parenthood, Professor Emilio Pin explains; but it does condemn 'the motivations' and 'the means which are often linked to birth-control propaganda. These motivations and means are opposed by the Church as being selfish and immoral. If true social and moral reasons require limitation in the number of children, the Church does not oppose it, provided the means themselves are not immoral.' As a practical means the Church approves a so-called rhythm method of regulat-ing births.

Increasing attention has been directed in Catholic circles to the social problems resulting from irresponsible parenthood and from rates of population increase in excess of the rate of economic development needed to overcome the burden of extreme poverty. Catholic leadership has joined with non-Catholic in seeking means which are consistent with moral principles to strengthen and apply personal and social responsibility in this field.

On the subject of population, the following works may be used to supplement the text:

Horace Belshaw, *Population Growth and Levels of Consumption with Special Reference to Countries in Asia* (New York, 1956).

A. J. Coale and E. M. Hoover, *Population Growth and Economic Development in Low Income Countries* (Princeton, 1958).

Committee on Science and Public Policy, National Academy of Science, National Research Council, *The Growth of World Population* (Washington, D.C., 1963).

Sidney H. Coontz, *Population Theories and the Economic Interpretation* (London, 1957).

Robert Carter Cook, *Human Fertility: the Modern Dilemma* (New York, 1951).

Hope Tisdale Eldridge, *Population Policies: A Survey of Recent Developments* (Washington, 1954).

Richard Martin Fagley, *The Population Explosion and Christian Responsibility* (New York, 1960).

'The Interrelations of Demographic, Economic and Social Problems in Selected Under-developed Areas'—*Proceedings* of a Round Table at the Milbank Memorial Fund 1953 Annual Conference (New York, 1954).

John Charles Rock, *The Time Has Come* (New York, 1963).

Sir Edward John Russell, *World Population and World Food Supply* (London, 1954).

National Bureau of Economic Research, *Demographic and Economic Change in Developed Countries* (Princeton, 1960).

A. F. Zimmerman, *Overpopulation: A Study of Papal Teachings on the Problem with Special Reference to Japan* (Washington, D.C., 1957).

SECTION FOUR

APPLICATION OF KNOWLEDGE TO HUMAN BEHAVIOUR AND THE DEVELOPMENT OF THE SOCIAL SCIENCES

CHAPTER XVI

THE SCIENTIFIC APPROACH TO HUMAN BEHAVIOUR AND HUMAN RELATIONS

I. INTRODUCTION

At the beginning of the twentieth century the scientific method and attitude so effectively applied by western society to the physical world had scarcely begun to be applied to human behaviour and human relations. There was no body of already tested scientific data on human behaviour which could form the basis for a social technology comparable to the basic knowledge of physics, chemistry and biology from which the greater part of the twentieth-century material technology was derived. During the next fifty years this field became the object of vigorous scientific effort as the social or 'behavioural' sciences were developed and applied.

Although the simple faith in automatic human progress as the fruit of scientific and technological advance lost much of its hold, the first half of the twentieth century was characterized by an unprecedented range of efforts to use positive means to improve human living or to modify human life. Development of the social sciences was greatly stimulated by the search for scientific principles on which to base the social and economic programmes which became essential features of every modern state.[1]

The broad changes that were creating uncertainties, shaking values and making custom an insufficient guide to conduct called forth efforts to find a scientific and not merely an empirical basis for confronting old problems and meeting new ones. The direction of development in the social sciences was dictated not only by scientific curiosity applied to human behaviour and relationships but by the realities of rapid industrialization, mushrooming cities with their crowded slums, migrants and immigrants uprooted from their homes, recurrent economic crises, changing relations between social groups and among peoples, social breakdown reflected in mental illness, delinquency, crime and war.

There was, however, considerable resistance to conceiving of human behaviour as conforming to regularities discoverable by scientific methods, and consequent reluctance to accept as scientific the results of work in these fields. A strong drag of ignorance, inertia and practical difficulty prevented or delayed the use of the best knowledge that became available. Many people felt that man's behaviour was in fact already understood and that the scientific approach could add little or nothing to the vision of the poets, philosophers, religious leaders and elders. Or they insisted that individual variations rather than statistically recognizable regularities gave richness to life and should receive primary attention. They thought that the complexities of human life and the impossibility of subjecting it to laboratory experiment made it unsuitable for scientific investigation, and they rejected as over-simplifications the hypotheses adopted by social scientists. Some people hesitated to expose cherished attitudes and relationships to objective scrutiny and clung to familiar practices in the face of evidence which discredited their validity.

And even those who looked with greatest confidence upon the scientific study of human behaviour as a means of gaining new insights into mankind's problems recognized that such problems inescapably involve value judgments which are not scientific but rest in the last analysis on a philosophical, moral or cultural base.

In the early years of the century the main centres for the development of the social sciences were in Germany, both in the formulation of social theory and in broad-gauge studies of major social institutions drawn from a wide range of historical and contemporary sources. The Verein für Sozialpolitik offered vigorous leadership, and major writings in economics, sociology and political economy appeared in the many-volumed *Archiv für Sozialwissenschaft und Sozialpolitik*. In France the École Libre des Sciences Politiques was a centre for pioneer studies of political processes. The extensive work in geography carried on in Russia provided the basis for studies of the relation of man to his environment.

After the first world war, growth in these fields was especially extensive in the United States, with emphasis on the application of quantitative methods to the study of human behaviour in various fields—political, economic, social. In the second quarter of the century the social sciences enjoyed greater status in American universities, they were pursued by more people and they received more financial support than they did in Britain and continental Europe, except for history and archaeology which were associated with traditional classical and liberal education. Social science research establishments became numerous in the United States and were well supported by foundation grants or other funds.

Much study in the United States, however, involved the elaboration or experimental testing of theories evolved in Europe or pioneer studies conducted there. The latter included outstanding studies by British anthropologists in the Pacific and Africa, Danish studies of the community impact of local industries, French and Belgian studies of the sociological factors associated with religious observance, and various sociographic studies in the Netherlands, Germany and Austria, to mention only a few. Much work inaugurated in Germany was transferred to the United States with the mass exodus of German scholars during the Nazi régime.[2]

Yet in spite of the vigorous development of research in the social sciences during these years, one can point to few outstanding discoveries which were widely accepted and constituted the basis for further research and theoretical development. In contrast to the physical and biological sciences, the social sciences did not advance as a common field of study but remained a series of explorations, carried out within the framework of different national outlooks or preoccupations, different schools of thought and different individual assumptions. Although some work was of high quality and wide influence, an account of the social sciences in the twentieth century must be mainly an account of the major areas of systematic research and theoretical analysis rather than of universally accepted findings which modified the general course of knowledge and thought.

At the opening of the century a number of distinct subject and methodological areas were differentiating themselves from older fields of study. Psychology was not wholly detached from its two sources, biological science and philosophy, especially ethics and aesthetics. Sociology was asserting an identity apart from moral and political philosophy. Political science and economics were breaking down the unity of political economy, to focus on their respective areas. Anthropology included aspects that were to remain parts of the field—ethnology, linguistics, folklore and the study of physical types, and Edward B. Tylor (1832–1917) had introduced the concept of culture as the interrelated totality of man's material and non-material heritage that must be recognized as a whole for every society in order to understand the meaning of any specific institutions or techniques. History, which in former times had been written mainly by retired statesmen and churchmen, had become the work of professional historians who developed special methods to deal with the facts or interpretation of the past. Archaeology and pre-history tended more and more to become disciplines of their own, detached from history, although the object of study was the same: man in the past.

By the first quarter of the century each of the above fields had become established as a separate discipline with a specialized body of knowledge and set of theories and with specialized techniques of investigation. But as they extended their scope and refined their methodology they contributed to a growing core of common knowledge and common techniques which were beginning to convert a series of separate fields into something approaching a basic social science. By the middle of the century the principal areas in which knowledge of human behaviour was being developed were:

(1) The psychological processes by which the individual perceives, understands, reasons, judges and reacts; human motivation and human personality; individual differences: These were the areas explored by psychologists, following three principal and distinct approaches: one experimental, using laboratory methods to determine normal psychological processes and the means of detecting individual differences, one observational and statistical to test and study the incidence and interrelationship of differences, the third clinical, using the evidence of patients suffering from pathological conditions

to derive theories of human growth and development which could provide a basis for therapeutic treatment.

(2) The nature of culture, its distinctive forms, mechanisms, dynamic processes and reflection in social structure and individual personality; anthropology, 'the study of man', examined distinct cultures, at first wholly by means of studies of primitive societies, and then also in complex modern settings.

(3) Social structure and social processes, including social institutions, social roles, social stratification and mobility, the source and course of social change, and the operation and interaction of social groups in conflict, accommodation, integration and disintegration: sociologists sought understanding of these phenomena, principally through investigations of modern rather than primitive societies, and they built up a large body of factual evidence related thereto. In contrast to anthropologists, who focused on each unique culture and the totality of interacting factors and made it a matter of method to free themselves as far as possible from preconceptions in order to seek in the data themselves the particular meaning which the studied culture gave them, sociologists sought the basis for general social theory, they selected particular institutions such as the family or class stratification for intensive study, and they formulated a series of concepts and categories in terms of which to accumulate factual data and to analyse social phenomena.

(4) Economic behaviour: the field of economics, embraced factors which affected the operation of the economy as a whole. Economists devoted themselves to theoretical analysis, using hypothetical models and mathematical procedures, and to the accumulation through descriptive studies of a realistic picture of economic institutions and processes.

(5) Political institutions and behaviour: political science as a discipline was concerned with the theory of the state, description of political structures, analysis of political parties and other mechanisms, comparative legal systems and the growth of administrative law, and study of political behaviour. The subject of public administration was developed as a specialized field. In the main, political scientists confined their scope to political institutions, although great corporations, large labour unions and other organizations presented similar problems of structure, function, representation and the exercise of power.

(6) Man's life in the past: historical studies, which had become highly specialized during the nineteenth century in terms of different branches of human life, different periods of the past and different civilizations, nations or regions, expanded in three directions: study of the inexhaustible field of social and cultural history in its broadest sense; intensive investigation of parts of the world other than Europe; and more systematic theoretical exploration of what lies behind historical phenomena. History restricted itself, in line with its method of analysing and interpreting different texts, to those periods for which there were written documents; the past of which no written documents remain became the field of archaeologists and pre-historians who developed

and refined their own methods for interpreting physical remnants that were found by chance, and then for systematically exploring to discover and identify others.

Basic to the development of most of the social sciences was the application of statistical method. Nothing more distinguished the approach to the understanding of human behaviour in this period from that of earlier times than the marshalling and manipulation of quantitative evidence. The use of statistical methods was greatly facilitated by advances in mathematical statistics and the development of calculating and tabulating machines which made possible the rapid analysis of data. For important areas, however, especially those approached by way of anthropology and clinical psychology, statistical techniques though sometimes used were considered inappropriate to determine the unique combination of interacting elements which constituted the subject of study—a culture or a human personality.

Other methods also contributed importantly to social science development. Social surveys of living communities applied refined techniques to the observation and analysis of relationships. Archaeology, brought to a high level of technical proficiency, unlocked great store-houses of knowledge of past societies. Linguistics began to offer a valuable tool for the detection of attitudes and relationships. The study of blood types began to throw light on migrations and interrelations of peoples.

Although each of the social sciences developed its special techniques and brought them to bear on specific aspects of society, there was much interaction among them. Psychology and sociology began to bring together their separate approaches to social psychology as both came to recognize the inseparability of an individual's internal psychological processes from his social experience. The insights into human behaviour and motivation provided by psychology were used by anthropologists, sociologists and political scientists, though rarely by economists, to throw light on the ways in which the cultural setting affects their research and to scrutinize assumptions based on the norms of western society. The sociologists' analyses of social structure and group processes became part of the thinking in political science and were used, especially by British social anthropologists, in the study of primitive societies. Economics remained least affected by the other fields.

Many social problems, moreover, required the collaboration of specialists from several fields. The inter-disciplinary efforts needed to study such problems as juvenile delinquency, urbanism, the economic development of non-industrial countries or population trends had the effect of at least partially reintegrating the social sciences, though rarely could a team of specialists, each with his focus and vocabulary, achieve a degree of integration comparable to that of the individual creative scholar. To some scholars in each of the several fields, the development of a common social theory and method appeared within the range of possibility.

Directions of growth in the social sciences reflected the interests and concern of those who sought to use their results. The development of psychology was stimulated by continual pressure to provide practical tools to educators, doctors, advertisers or administrators and to help individuals to understand themselves, their children and their associates. Anthropology responded to the need to understand people of other cultures and the processes of cultural change, first on the part of colonial administrators and then by international agencies and by people of all sorts exposed to culture contacts and rapid social change. Although sociological theorists sought to understand the structure and functioning of society as a whole, much sociological study was focused on various forms of social breakdown in the effort to understand and cope with such social ills as crime, delinquency, family breakdown, urban slums, poverty and dependency. Economics was forced in new directions by the urgent need of governments to control their national economies during war, to find a way out of economic depression, to try to avoid post-war collapse and to achieve economic development. The tremendous increase in the power and responsibility of the state and the new instruments at its disposal provided a strong stimulus to the field of political science.

Viewed as a whole the social sciences passed through three stages of development in the first half of the twentieth century. The years prior to the first world war were a creative period when the major ideas that were to reorient social analysis were formulated and methods established by such dynamic thinkers as Émile Durkheim, Max Weber, Franz Boas and Sigmund Freud. In the inter-war period social science research was expanded and a large body of empirical studies gave the field a more solid foundation. By the second world war and the post-war years both theoretical and empirical approaches were becoming more closely related with practical application, though the social sciences were a long way from providing scientific bases for action comparable to those offered by the physical sciences.

II. NEW CONCEPTS: BEFORE THE FIRST WORLD WAR

By the opening of the twentieth century the ground for the development of the social sciences had been laid in a number of ways, not only by the comprehensive social theories of such nineteenth-century writers as John Stuart Mill, Auguste Comte and Karl Marx, but by a growing body of concrete materials derived from: the comparative study of law; the work of materialist and positivist philosophers with their emphasis on the study of concrete phenomena as a basis for positive social control; the increasingly full and precise observations of primitive societies recorded by colonial administrators, travellers and missionaries; the rigorous methodology of scientific history emanating from the German universities; and the extension of laboratory methods from biology to psychology. Raw data were being amassed through periodic census enumerations in the countries of western Europe and North

America, and the extensive information thus provided on the populations of these areas was being supplemented by vital statistics and morbidity data which were generally less complete. Statistics of international trade and finance were likewise generally compiled in these areas, and some labour statistics. In some areas under colonial administration, such as Indonesia and India, the collection of census and trade data was beginning to open up the possibility of studying quantitatively some aspects of the life of these regions.

The means were thus at hand for a noteworthy development in response to the aroused social conscience and the tendency to look to science for solutions which characterized these years.

1. New insight into human behaviour

The application of scientific method to determining the psychological nature of man first took the form of efforts to test in the laboratory the processes of perception and response to stimuli. The disciples of Wilhelm Wundt (1832–1920) carried to various parts of Europe and America the methods which he had developed in Leipzig in the last half of the nineteenth century for testing such things as an individual's ability to distinguish touch, smell or sound, or to register and recall words or sights.

These methods were based on the principle of isolating and focusing on the specific stimulus and the specific response. They depended heavily upon introspection by the person studied and his ability to report his experience accurately. They were rigorously limited to those stimulus–response reactions which could be produced and recorded under controlled conditions. The physics or physiology laboratory provided the model for the first psychological laboratories.

This approach held the field in the first decade of the twentieth century. It coincided with and helped to reinforce a mechanistic conception of human nature and human society bred of the mechanistic concepts developed in the western world since Descartes and Newton. It assumed that human behaviour could be reduced to a series of physical, chemical, organic or associational responses and that any other assumption was unscientific.

The most famous and far-reaching of the stimulus–response experiments were those conducted by the Russian scientist Ivan Pavlov, beginning in 1901. His brilliant and highly skilled experimental work not only greatly refined the field of physiological psychology at the time, but at mid-century still provided the basis for most of the psychological work in the USSR. Using a dog for his subject, he demonstrated experimentally the process of association, which he described as a conditioned reflex. The reflex was the response which automatically occurred when a familiar stimulus was repeated, in this instance a flow of saliva in response to food. Association meant that something associated with an original stimulus, in this instance a bell rung when the food was produced, could become so identified with that with which it was associated that it would produce the same response in the absence of the latter. The implications of his findings were obvious for education and other efforts to influence behaviour, as well as for the general problem of communication.

In the early years of the century much attention was directed toward the nature of memory and the process by which the individual learns. Some psychologists, such as E. L. Thorndike (1874–1949) and Robert M. Yerkes (1876–   ), used animal subjects and observed such processes as how rats learn to cope with a maze. Others used human subjects who were asked to repeat nonsense syllables or numbers. These experiments all assumed that the factors to be studied were discrete, separate phenomena which could be examined in and of themselves, without regard for their context.

The experimental approach called for continual efforts to perfect techniques of observation. Whereas early experimental work had relied heavily on the introspection of the subject, those who sought to give the study of human behaviour the same scientific precision as the study of natural phenomena placed increasing emphasis on ways to observe and interpret overt behaviour. Where animals were used as subjects it was obviously necessary to rely upon observation since the animals could not report their reactions or mental processes. A strong school of experimental psychologists, particularly that led by J. B. Watson (1878–   ) in the United States, insisted that the only data which had validity for psychological study were those derived from observation of behaviour. Some European psychologists, however, continued to use introspection as a tool of investigation.

The psychologists' attempt to investigate separate mental elements one by one was paralleled by the anthropologists' preoccupation with specific 'culture traits'—items of material culture, myths or kinship forms.

The anthropologists of the late nineteenth century had interpreted the random information about primitive peoples reported by travellers, missionaries, colonial administrators or traders in terms of the concept of evolution, assuming that they were viewing evidence of progressive stages of development from lower to higher cultural forms. Those of the early twentieth century discovered that the heterogeneity of primitive societies defied any neat ordering into a universal formula of stages of cultural development.

Confronted by endlessly varied customs and myths which appeared to be accidental and irrational in their combinations, some retreated from all effort to formulate general theories and concentrated on data-gathering, while others embraced a non-evolutionary interpretation based on the idea of the diffusion of culture traits from one area to another through contact and borrowing. Some of the diffusionists, such as Father Wilhelm Schmidt (1868–1954) in Austria, thought to establish three prehistoric centres of diffusion, or *Kulturkreise*. A British group led by G. Elliot Smith (1871–1937) attempted to trace everything back to a single centre, Egypt. Americans such as A. L. Kroeber (1876–1960) thought that similar traits were invented in many places and that they spread from their various points of origin like ripples from pebbles dropped in a pool. Whatever their theory, most students treated traits as independent entities whose wanderings could be traced or mapped without regard for either their human carriers or the total cultures of which they were a part.

The influence of Émile Durkheim in France and Franz Boas in the United States cut the ground from under the idea that human society could be understood from the piecemeal study of culture traits. Durkheim, drawing on a wide variety of ethnographic evidence, insisted that an institution must be seen in terms of the function which it performs in its society and cannot be understood out of context; the proper subject of study, he said, is systems, not traits. He held that value systems and ways of thinking are living realities experienced by man in society, that a social perspective is essential to an understanding of all aspects of human behaviour and that it is possible to find objective means to determine the nature of subjective phenomena. He not only exercised a major influence on the concepts and methods of sociology but stimulated work by European cultural historians as well. Boas insisted upon intensive and comprehensive study of the totality of a culture, with attention to the historical process which produced its pattern, the structural interrelationships among its institutions and customs, and the psychological unity which gave these institutions meaning. He initiated a line of anthropological studies with this orientation, especially in the United States.

Although the impact of Durkheim and Boas was not fully felt until the 1920s they laid the basis before the first world war for widespread recognition of the concept that only as the whole is perceived can its parts be understood.

A similar development in psychology, the *Gestalt* theory, dated from the same period though it, too, did not command widespread attention until after the first world war. *Gestalt* psychology was developed in Germany by Max Wertheimer (1880–1943), Wolfgang Köhler (1887–   ) and Kurt Koffka (1886–1941) and spread from there to western Europe, Britain and the United States. It established experimentally, and then applied to many fields, the concept of the structure or whole which determines what is perceived and how. The *Gestalt* psychologists pointed out that more is involved in hearing a melody than merely response to the separate notes, that a person will 'see' the complete outline of a familiar figure when only a few lines are drawn—in short, that what is perceived is a whole, not merely the sum of discrete parts.

This concept nct only reoriented much psychological investigation but it profoundly influenced the other social sciences. It set some students of linguistics on the study of meaning and not merely philological forms. It reinforced the anthropologists' use of the concept of culture by indicating a psychological mechanism through which culture could function at the level of each individual. It revolutionized many of the ideas about learning and communication and gave a new impetus and direction to research in both these fields.

On the ancient question of innate versus acquired qualities, the twentieth century inherited religious and philosophical concepts concerning man's moral nature ranging all the way from original sin to perfectability, and assumptions as to his original mental equipment ranging from innate ideas to a blank *tabula rasa*. Ideas varied concerning the nature and role of reason. The stimulus–response experimentalists assumed that stimuli came from outside and were responsible for setting in motion the mental processes of the individual. Such a view was challenged by those who insisted that human behaviour reflects inner drives and not merely external stimuli, whether these drives arise from the process of biological adjustment guided by mind as an active agent, as stressed by William James (1842–1910), or from innate instincts, as set forth by William McDougall (1871–1938), or from some kind of emotional impulse. McDougall's concept that human behaviour is purposive received wide acceptance even where his list of specific instincts was questioned or rejected.

McDougall also stressed the social implications of individual behaviour. His book, *Social Psychology*, which appeared in the same year (1908) as the first book by a sociologist on the same topic (E. A. Ross, *Social Psychology*), inaugurated this important field of study, approached from both psychology and sociology.

It was the work of Sigmund Freud during these years, however, which eventually had the greatest repercussions not only within the social sciences but on the public mind. Freud postulated that the individual is born with an unconscious reserve of primitive instincts, the 'id', which strives constantly to influence the developing awareness of self, the 'ego'. His emotional energy is identified with a particular source in the id, the 'libido', assumed to be a fixed quantity in any particular individual. It is derived in the first instance from the impulse to love and to obtain gratification through loving, but may be canalized into varied activities.

On this premise Freud built a theory of the psychosexual development of the child through successive stages: an infantile stage during which the child is preoccupied with his own body and secures gratification in relation to particular parts of it—first at the mouth in sucking, then the bowels in controlling elimination and then the sex organs. As the child becomes aware of another person besides himself, he fixes intense love on the mother, who is the source of gratification or frustration of his desires. He is jealous of whatever competes for the mother's affection, notably the father and, later, brothers and sisters. As he is taught to control his impulses, he experiences intense fear of parental disapproval. In time he incorporates into himself, as his 'superego', the norms to which he learns to conform.

These strains and conflicts which the child experiences through infancy, according to Freud, are so severe that he can only handle them by repressing, or banishing from consciousness, the more unpleasant experiences and the more strongly forbidden desires. By the age of five or six, he has normally thrust his emotional conflicts below the surface where they remain latent, ready to erupt in full force during adolescence. In this latter period emotional gratification is sought, first with members of the same and then with those of the opposite sex.

The individual who successfully handles the successive stages of emotional development from infancy to adolescence becomes a mature adult. Those who fail to cope with the pressures at one stage or another may have their emotional development arrested at this point, or may repress so much that is intolerable as to create an excessive unconscious drag on the conscious effort to function normally. These are the persons who exhibit immature or pathological personalities or suffer from various types of neuroses and psychoses. It was they who provided Freud with the clinical material out of which he built his theory, and for whom he evolved the method of treatment known as psycho-analysis. In applying this method the psychoanalyst helps the individual to bring up to the surface out of his subconscious the suppressed experiences in order that he may face them, understand their source and be freed from the hidden terror and sense of guilt which the suppressed thoughts and desires have built up within him.

The details of Freud's theory were the subject of lively disagreement and elaboration among his followers but, however supplemented or modified, they showed enormous vitality. Various followers of Freud elaborated his approach in their own way. Alfred Adler (1870–1937) held that the central drive was not for love, as Freud maintained, but for power; he attributed much behaviour to the unconscious sense of inadequacy and insecurity—the 'inferiority complex'—which might lead either to withdrawal or to compensatory aggressive and authoritarian conduct. Carl Jung (1875–   ) generalized Freud's concept of the libido into an *élan vital* not specifically sexual, and he saw the structure of the human personality as based upon antitheses of thinking and feeling, sensation and intuition, extroversion—predominant interest in objective experience—and introversion—preoccupation with the inner world of thought and fantasy. He thought that as one or the other of these contradictory tendencies dominates the individual's consciousness, the opposite is present in his unconscious. He thus sought to explain both the existence of apparently distinct personality types and their apparently para-doxical behaviour. Later followers called attention to ways in which Freud's interpretations reflected his own cultural environment and might, therefore, lack validity in other cultures, for he drew his theories from observation of the urban middle-class patients who came to his Vienna clinic in the decades before the first world war.

However much the specific content of Freud and his successors' theories were challenged, certain of his concepts were revolutionary in their impact on western thought: that all human behaviour is purposeful, not simply a res-ponse to external stimuli, albeit the individual is frequently unaware of what he is seeking to achieve by his conduct; that the processes of infancy and early childhood through which the individual learns to adjust his inner drives to the demands of society are crucial in the formation of his personality and the determination of his future behaviour; and that the individual, perpetually in a state of tension, resorts to a variety of mechanisms for handling his past experience and the life situations which confront him, including the repression or sublimation of forbidden drives and the reversion to infantile or irrational behaviour when the psychic situation becomes unmanageable or the tensions excessive.

The line of approach to the understanding of human behaviour which Freud and his successors opened up gave direction to a wide range of developments, except in the Soviet Union where his ideas were not accepted. Such developments came first in clinical and then in social and experimental psychology, in anthropology, sociology and political science and in the many applied fields relating to mental health, child rearing, juvenile delinquency, psychosomatic medicine, marriage counselling and even administration, advertising and religion. Coming at a time when the certainties of Newtonian physics had been shaken and the accepted social order in the West was about to be given a body blow by the first world war, Freudian and related concepts released thinking about human behaviour from many of the assumptions by which it had been bound, and provided fresh and dynamic hypotheses in terms of which to observe that behaviour. It focused attention on hidden motives for action and presented in an unfavourable light many attitudes and patterns of approved behaviour, especially, it appeared to many people, the taboos and conventions relating to sex. Although it aroused much fear and revolt among many whose values it threatened, it became an integral component of social thought in the succeeding years.[3, 4]

The other major psychological development of the pre-1914 period, the psychological test, had a pragmatic origin and application. Its purpose was to detect differences among individuals, initially in what was termed 'intelligence', or the ability to acquire knowledge. The tests rested on the theoretical assumption that there are innate qualities which can be tested, i.e. that the human organism is not wholly the product of the stimuli to which it is exposed. Beyond this basic assumption, the makers of tests followed the pragmatic procedure of looking for norms in the observed responses of the group rather than in any concept of normal development. The norm for a ten-year-old child was what most ten-year-olds were found to be able to do; the child of that age who could not do this was rated as below the average or norm; the one who could do what most ten-year-olds could not do was above this norm.

The tests, designed originally by Alfred Binet (1857–1911) and Thomas Simon (1873–   ) in France in 1908 and revised by Lewis M. Terman (1877–1956) in the United States in 1916, contained exercises which were found effective in sorting out the children of the groups used to build the tests, and they were scored so that the total result placed the tested child below or above the normal mark of 100. On the assumption that the 'intelligence' which was being tested was a permanent characteristic of the individual, the child should come out with the same I.Q. (intelligence quotient) if he were retested at a later age.

The first objective of such tests was to enable educators to identify children who were so subnormal that they could not profit from ordinary instruction, and in general to help teachers to appraise the capacity of their pupils. In the places where they were originally designed and among groups with comparable experience they served this purpose sufficiently well, so that they came to be widely used. In the course of time, however, it became apparent that the social experience of the individual could markedly affect his score, and that the tests were not valid instruments for comparing persons whose experience differed because of nationality, region, urban versus rural background, class or other social distinction. The content of the tests devised during the first part of the century strongly reflected the urban, middle-class culture of certain segments of western society.

Moreover, as the intelligence tests were used on a variety of subjects it became apparent that they depended heavily on the verbal facility of the person tested. Since they were designed to reflect generalized mental capacity and not merely verbal facility, this discovery led to the formulation of a variety of non-verbal tests, designed to avoid the distortion of verbalism and, hopefully, to provide tests less dependent on the individual's social experience. It came to be recognized also that the score achieved on any type of test which probed for innate capacity might be affected by the subject's emotional state and his reaction to the circumstances in which the test was given.

While the first tests were strictly for children, the possibility of testing individual differences appealed to those who had to evaluate the capacities of adults, and during the first world war such tests were used to sort out military recruits for work or training assignments. Thereafter a substantial proportion of psychologists devoted their efforts to designing and administering tests of a wide range of aptitudes and characteristics, in the hope that standard tests could be devised which would detect human qualities much as the tests evolved by natural scientists could determine properties of materials.

2. *Social processes and structures*

In the years before the first world war there were no developments of the other social sciences which had the far-reaching influence of those in psychology and anthropology. Sociological theory was elaborated, not only by Dürkheim but by a number of thinkers, particularly in Germany and Italy, who moved away from the dominant nineteenth-century theories contained in the positivism of Auguste Comte and the evolutionary social theory of Herbert Spencer, and who brought the assumptions of nineteenth-century western society under scrutiny. Among these Max Weber (1864–1920), in his comprehensive analysis of economics, politics, religion and the interrelations among institutions, insisted that a knowledge of the meaning of any activity was a prerequisite to establishing causal relationships and he stressed the role of values in moulding social behaviour, as for example in his thesis that the Protestant ethic, by its sanction of thrift and identification of spiritual salvation with economic success, provided the spirit of capitalism and thus was responsible for the latter's growth. Vilfredo Pareto (1847–1923) developed a cyclical theory of social change based on the alternation of strong leaders committed to positive ideals and cunning opportunists skilled in manipulation.

Techniques for the systematic observation of social life, however, were slow to be applied. Even the founders of American sociology, which later became heavily empirical, insisted on rigorous logic but not on rigorous observation. The new efforts to apply theory to practice or to test it by observation were mostly limited to problems of social breakdown such as those encountered in the field of penology, and to the social surveys which were undertaken to determine the need for local social services.

Some of the most significant developments in techniques of research during these years came in archaeology. Scientific methods of digging based on engineering principles, developed by A. H. Pitt-Rivers (1827–1900) in the late nineteenth century, were adapted by Flinders Petrie (1853–1942) to excavations in Egypt during the early years of the twentieth century, and further elaborated with the aid of a multiplicity of technical devices. These methods enabled the archaeologist to recover from artifacts of all sorts a picture of a past age, including something of its culture, the characteristics of its people and its social history.

Archaeological research brought to light during these years the ancient civilizations of Egypt and Mesopotamia, Crete and Asia Minor, of India, China and Indo-China, of the Maya in Central America and the Inca in Peru. Other techniques moved the frontiers of pre-history into an ever more remote past. It was not until the middle of the century, however, that new knowledge of radioactivity made it possible to date organic materials such as wood or grain brought to light through excavation and revealed that many evidences of early societies were older than had been assumed. This tremendous expansion of knowledge of past human societies was a prime factor in shaking many traditional concepts and in providing perspective on human development and on the rich diversity of human cultures.

A growing number of historians, too, were expanding the knowledge of the past by carrying their studies beyond the national history, mostly political and diplomatic, which had been the main interest of nineteenth-century historians, shifting their interest to economic history and then to various social or cultural aspects. Within each of these fields specializations developed around the history of agriculture, finance or business, of social orders and classes, of such institutions as law, religion or warfare. Each of these specialized fields, and others such as the history of literature and the arts, of technology and of science, developed its own methods and techniques to handle its own problems. Although historians thus became highly specialized in relation to period and area as well as subject-matter, they brought to light an ever-widening body of evidence on the life of the past.

The scope of historical study was further extended to include parts of the world to which critical historical scholarship had not been applied. Western scholars had been preoccupied with the history of western areas, while Asian countries had generally lacked a tradition of historical scholarship. As European scholars brought critical historical research as well as archaeological exploration to bear on Asian areas, they enabled these countries to reconstruct their past and develop an historically-based self-image, and they stimulated Asian scholars to develop and apply critical historical techniques themselves.

Political science emerged as an area for systematic study with its main content divided between description of political structures and theoretical discussion of political philosophy; techniques of administration and practical politics were learned on the job. Critical study of political processes and political structures was stimulated by evidences of malfunctioning such as revelations of graft and corruption in American municipal administration and the difficulty experienced by some continental European countries in their efforts to operate parliamentary systems. The pioneer work of André Siegfried, *Tableau politique de la France de l'ouest sous la troisième république* (1913) opened up the study of political attitudes. Marxist political thought was challenging liberalism and its influence was reflected in the prominence of socialists among European political scholars. Writers in several countries began to call attention to irrational elements in political behaviour. Social causes rather than moral or hereditary weakness were increasingly recognized as responsible for poverty and crime. But it was not until the 1920s and 1930s that systematic study was directed to the implications for political behaviour of newly developed understandings of motivation and social structure, or to political and administrative processes.

In spite of the fact that economic behaviour had long been the object of systematic theory and that the impact of technology was most direct in this area of living, the field of economics remained predominantly theoretical well into the twentieth century. Classical *laissez-faire* theory remained dominant, subject to efforts toward greater mathematical precision. According to this theory, 'economic man' was assumed to act rationally, in quest of profits if he was an entrepreneur and to avoid starvation if he was a worker. With this motivation, with legal instruments which assured the security of property rights, and with flexible prices in a free market, the economic system would operate automatically. It was believed to be fundamentally stable, for, according to 'Say's law', there could be no prolonged unemployment. The system was presumed to be progressive, for the quest for profits would lead inevitably to the improvement of product, lowering of price and a rising standard of living.

The whole economic structure and rationale was challenged fundamentally by the followers of Karl Marx, who maintained that, far from providing a stable equilibrium and progressively higher standards of life, the system inevitably would produce progressive poverty for the masses, insufficient markets for the products of industry, sharper and deeper depressions and ultimately collapse and revolution. In the years before the first world war however, and even up to 1930, there appeared to be enough face-value evidence to sustain the general assumptions of stability, progress and capacity for economic recovery and outside the Soviet Union the Marxist challenge did not deflect the main stream of economic thought.

Nevertheless, the Marxist hypothesis concerning the relation between forms of production and the whole range of social institutions in any society had a profound impact on many who did not become doctrinaire Marxists—sociologists, political scientists and historians as well as economists. Especially in Germany, Sweden and elsewhere in continental Europe, it acted as a stimulus to studies of concrete phenomena such as housing, taxation or tariffs, as well as labour, class structure and political behaviour.

Other attempts to test economic hypotheses by systematic observation took the form of broad historical studies by German scholars who undertook to derive laws of economic development from the comparative study of economic systems, and original work by a few students, such as Thorstein Veblen (1857-1929) in the United States, who scrutinized the characteristics and operation of specific economic institutions. Meantime, possibilities for more accurate and scientific study of economic behaviour were being created as data on a variety of subjects not heretofore recorded were systematically collected and published by governments and other bodies.

Prior to the first world war most of the serious study and analysis of human behaviour was conducted within the framework of western society and on the assumptions of the cultural norms of that society. There were outstanding exceptions, as in the work of Max Weber who studied the relation of religion to economic ethics and social life in Hinduism, Buddhism, Confucianism, Taoism and ancient Judaism in an effort to understand this relationship in Christian societies of the West. But rarely did anyone assume that civilized man might have something to learn from his primitive cousins, or that the study of primitive societies might affect the understanding of his own.

III. NEW METHODS AND MATERIALS: THE INTER-WAR YEARS

In the 1920s and 1930s the major disrupting events which destroyed the nineteenth- and early twentieth-century complacencies—war, revolution, depression and the challenge to western supremacy—created a milieu in which it began to appear as important to understand social behaviour as to determine the causes of disease. Anthropological studies, especially in the United States and Britain, began to challenge rather than, by assumption, to confirm prevailing concepts of human behaviour. Together with new concepts derived from *Gestalt* and Freudian psychology, they provided new tools of observation and analysis. At the same time concrete studies of social, political and economic behaviour and structure, conducted with the aid of new statistical techniques, provided a growing body of data for social study.

1. *New perspectives on culture*

Although Franz Boas had insisted as early as 1901 that the mind of primitive man was not different from or inferior to that of civilized man but that the same mental processes were merely applied to different conceptions of reality and to different experience, it was not until the 1920s that his findings received full attention and their implications were fully recognized. Influential scholars who maintained that primitive man was unable to think rationally, such as Lucien Lévy-Bruhl (1857–1939), continued to be widely read, especially in Europe.

By the 1920s the principle of cultural diversity as against cultural superiority was well established on the basis of field studies of living communities covering all aspects of their social life. Thenceforward the major anthropological effort was directed toward studies of total societies in a systematic attempt to discover their social structure or cultural configuration.

This work resulted in a large number of ethnographies of primitive societies, outstanding among which were those of Bronislaw Malinowski (1884–1942) (*Argonauts of the Western Pacific*, 1922) and A. R. Radcliffe-Brown (1881–1955) (*The Andaman Islanders*, 1922) and their followers in Britain, of Franz Boas and his disciples studying Indian tribes in the United States and in the South Seas, of Alfonso Caso (1896–   ) and his associates in Mexico, of Nicolaus Adriani (1865–1925), Albertus Kryut (1869–1949) and other Dutch scholars in Indonesia, of Russian ethnographers both before 1917 and under the Soviet régime, and of French scholars in Africa, Oceania and Latin America.

British scholars, such as Raymond Firth (1901–   ), Meyer Fortes (1906–   ) and others, calling themselves social anthropologists, generally focused on systems of kinship and other institutions which gave social, political and legal structure to primitive societies, and examined them in terms of the social functions which they performed and the social integration which they provided. They hoped that by thus limiting the field they might develop sharper concepts and more scientifically established general hypotheses than if they followed what they regarded as the 'grab-all' method of looking indiscriminately at all aspects of a culture.

Many American scholars, on the other hand, such as Edward Sapir (1884–1939), Ruth Benedict (1887–1948) and Margaret Mead (1901–   ), undertook to explore the psychological content of particular cultural integrations. Ruth Benedict's *Patterns of Culture* (1934) focused attention on the concept of culture as something more than an accumulation of customs—as the particular dynamic interrelation among the beliefs and practices of a society into which each new member is inducted and by which his behaviour and his personality are moulded. Margaret Mead's classic study, *Coming of Age in Samoa* (1928), undertaken to test how far the psychological phenomena of adolescence observed in western society are specific to western culture and how far they are universal phenomena, was one of a series of studies which tried to determine the limits within which cultural influences were effective and the method of their transmission.

Anthropological field studies which introduced people to ways of life of primitive communities provided a perspective on western society and had an effect on thought and attitudes far beyond this field of knowledge. The studies of child rearing and child development in the South Seas not only showed that the norms of western society did not hold universally, but indicated that some of the problems of child development which were recognized in western society were absent in the societies studied and thus called into question the former's standards and processes.

The concept of culture entered into the thinking of other social scientists and of the lay public. Comparative studies were undertaken of children in different cultures, and efforts were made by psychologists and anthropologists to develop tests or techniques of observation which would permit the study of common problems or characteristics across cultural lines. The psychiatrist, Dr Karen Horney (1885–   ), in *The Neurotic Personality of Our Time* (1937) insisted that the neuroses with which the psychiatrist deals are not independent of the individual's cultural milieu but are often precipitated by its pressures and expressed in its terms, and are susceptible of treatment only in relation to the culture which has shaped the individual's personality and has given him his system of values.

Social workers dealing with immigrants and rural–urban migrants became aware that they were confronted with cultural differences and consciously tried to avoid the tendency to judge their clients by the standards of the group to which they themselves belonged. Colonial administrators were increasingly conscious of their need to understand the cultural values of their subject peoples. Even an agency such as the United States Department of Agriculture, traditionally dedicated to technical improvements in crops and livestock, launched a series of cultural studies of distinct agricultural communities and attempted to develop a culture-area map of rural United States in order that its programmes of technical aid to farmers and agricultural improvement might be adjusted to the cultural differences among rural regions of the country.

The impact of anthropological studies was perhaps greatest in respect to the question of race difference. Throughout human history assumptions of racial superiority have reflected the ethnocentrism of virtually every society and power group, to whom the 'others' have been 'barbarians', 'natural slaves' or 'lesser breeds without the law'. At the opening of the twentieth century this universal tendency took the form of the concept of the 'white man's burden' associated with the political and technological supremacy of European peoples, and backed by the evolutionary concept of the survival or emergence of the superior race. While the white man who regarded himself as superior had to acknowledge the cultural richness of the ancient civilizations of China and India, and the obvious evidence of superior capacity on the part of the Asian Japanese to master and use the white man's technology, the white administrator, business man, tourist and missionary moved through his colonial dominions and spheres of influence with a sense not only of power but of racial superiority. To the colonial subject the white man's authority was often less offensive than his unconscious contempt.

The physical anthropologists at the beginning of the century, accepting the prevailing assumptions, investigated the relationship between physical characteristics and mental or personality traits. They found, however, that no relationship could be established between superior or inferior capacities and racial characteristics. On the other hand the evidence as to the differentiating effect of culture was clear and positive. Most anthropologists had concluded before 1920 that the concept of race as a determinant of the capacities of individuals or peoples had been discredited by the evidence.

In the 1920s their findings influenced the psychologists, some of whom had formerly given a racial interpretation to comparative scores on psychological tests. Tests given to American army personnel for the purpose of work assignment, for instance, had at first been seized upon as evidence of different capacities among groups with different racial and nationality backgrounds. Closer study of the results, however, had revealed that test scores were strongly affected by the individual's social and cultural experience; it was observed, for example, that average scores for Negroes from urban centres surpassed those of whites from some rural areas. By the time of the Nazi rise to power the racial theories upon which National Socialism rested were already at variance with scientific opinion throughout the world.

It required the changed power relationships among peoples, brought to a head by the second world war and the subsequent collapse of colonialism, fully to discredit assumptions of racial superiority. But the scientific denial of racial inequality worked as a leaven undermining the *status quo*, both between peoples and within racially heterogeneous populations in various parts of the world.

2. *Impact of Freudian and* Gestalt *psychology*

Comparable in pervasiveness and influence to the concepts derived from the study of primitive peoples were those derived from Freudian and *Gestalt* psychology. Clinical practice using psychoanalytical techniques provided a growing body of material, drawn from deeper levels of consciousness and the unconscious, with which to test the hypotheses of Freud and his followers as to the processes of human development. The wholesale emigration of scholars and professional men from Germany and Austria where these ideas and methods had originated and flourished gave a great impetus to their spread, especially in the United States.

In the effort to develop means to penetrate into the private world within which the individual lives and to discover the structure of his personality, clinical psychologists developed a series of projective tests, of which the most famous were the Rohrschach test devised in Switzerland and the thematic apperception test (TAT) devised in the United States.

From the work of psychologists and anthropologists there emerged the concept of 'personality' as the particular dynamic integration which each individual makes of his experience. This concept, broader, deeper and more comprehensive than the more limited concepts such as perception or consciousness with which psychologists had originally worked, became the focal idea for much of the work in the succeeding years.

The most dramatic general impact of Freud's thinking was to give a basis in scientific theory for the release of the subject of sex from the taboo on discussion under which it had been placed in western societies by the code of nineteenth-century morality. Although Freud's emphasis on the importance of the sexual drive in human development was only a part of his total system, it was this which focused public attention. While many other factors contributed to the change in sex *mores* in the years after the first world war, including changes in the position of women, weakening of religious sanctions and the revolt against traditional values, the rationale which Freud offered supported a freer attitude toward sex and provided a new set of terms in which to study and discuss it.

By the 1940s the subject of sex had become a field for systematic investigation with the application of social science research techniques. Going beyond the theoretical analysis of Freud and his followers and the popular works of Havelock Ellis (1859–1939), Alfred C. Kinsey (1894–1956) undertook to determine the actual practices of a statistically selected sample of men drawn from a cross-section of American society, and he followed it with a similar study of women. The results of these studies were widely read and discussed, and they brought into question many of the assumptions of conventional morality.

In the course of time Freudian concepts were applied to the growing fields of child study and juvenile delinquency. Research centres where studies were conducted on the development and behaviour of the very young child and child guidance clinics for children with emotional or behaviour problems both expanded rapidly during the 1920s. Initially the problems studied in these centres were defined pragmatically, but as the influence of Freudian ideas grew, both the child study and child guidance centres began to look at their material in Freudian terms. By the late 1930s evidence from these sources as well as from the clinics of practising psychiatrists and the experience of social workers was being used to test and refine Freud's hypotheses. All these sources tended to confirm the assumption that the earliest relationships which the infant establishes with a maternal figure are a vital factor in his personality formation and his relation to the world.

In the USSR, where Freudian thought was not accepted, corresponding studies were carried on in pedagogical institutes on hypotheses derived from the physiological and psychological studies of Pavlov and his followers and the application of Marxist–Leninist principles.

Freudian theory also focused attention on the problem of motivation. His concept of basic drives and the individual's need to handle feelings of fear, hate and guilt in the process of canalizing them into socially acceptable forms, provided a basis for interpreting actions whose purpose the individual himself often did not recognize. The concept that much behaviour is unconsciously purposeful was of practical importance to those who wished to influence action, and it offered a new tool with which to study various types of behaviour. It also was used to support tendencies toward irrationalism and anti-intellectualism.

Political behaviour was one of the areas to which the growing knowledge of motivation and the various techniques of social observation were applied. Especially in the United States, political scientists looked for evidence of the motivation which gave political leaders their drive for power, and tried to examine the corresponding motivations which led people to follow leadership of a particular type. Carrying further the approach to political realities initiated at the École Libre des Sciences Politiques, Charles Merriam (1874–1953) and his associates at the University of Chicago brought under scientific scrutiny the nature and structure of political parties, their formation and control, the basis of their hold on their members and their relation to the legislative and executive machinery of government. Harold Lasswell's (1902–) *Psychopathology and Politics* (1930) introduced psychoanalytic concepts into the study of political behaviour and deepened the study of political leadership. Voting behaviour was analysed statistically in the effort to determine what factors appeared to influence people to support a candidate or a party or not to vote at all.

Much effort was dedicated to the study of public opinion. Public opinion polls were conducted systematically, using refined sampling techniques to permit a determination of the views of large numbers from small scientifically selected groups. Studies were undertaken into the formation of public opinion and its modification, the spread of and resistance to propaganda, the question of whose opinion actually functions as 'public opinion', and the manner in which opinion actually affects political behaviour.

The processes of administration were subjected to systematic analysis in the effort to evolve general principles that could guide the multiplicity of new and expanded agencies set up to carry out the new functions which governments everywhere were taking on. Utilizing not only political concepts of structure and authority but concepts relating to motivation, communication and group interaction drawn from other fields, specialists sought a basis for converting administration from a personal art to a systematic set of standard processes and relationships, and established research and training centres through which to impart this approach. Yet in spite of extensive study, insight into political behaviour and political processes in varying circumstances remained super-ficial and limited.

When in the 1930s events in Nazi Germany revealed highly irrational political behaviour in what had been thought to be a predominantly rational society, attention was directed to the possible effect which the structure of the family and the early experience of the child might have on the kind of political behaviour that can be expected of adults. The concept of the 'authoritarian personality' was evolved and studied, and psychologists and political scientists joined to explore the question of whether such a personality could be expected to operate democratic institutions successfully. Some psychologists such as Erich Fromm (1900–   ) (*Escape from Freedom*, 1941) raised the further question as to whether free institutions place demands on individuals that are beyond their capacities and desires, and they thus forced political scientists to review their fundamental assumptions.

Economic conduct was the only major aspect of human behaviour not subjected to systematic scrutiny in the 1920s and 1930s in terms of the new understanding of human motivation and the concept of culture. Thorstein Veblen in the United States had attempted to introduce a recognition of various motivations into economic thinking, pointing to some of the motives affecting patterns of consumption (*Theory of the Leisure Class*, 1899) and to the conflict in motivation between the technician and the businessman (*The Engineers and the Price System*, 1921). The widely used Hawthorne studies of productivity* brought out the effect on a worker's output of his emotional state and personal concerns. But even the institutionalists who attempted to build up a descriptive picture of the actual operation of economic institutions gave little attention to the human element. The great majority of economists continued to base their theoretical analyses of the economic system on the assumption that man is governed by rational choice, although they were well aware that this did not accord with the new knowledge.

3. *Scrutiny of social institutions*

At the same time that new psychological insights and studies of primitive societies were enlarging the knowledge and understanding of human behaviour, several aspects of western social structure were being subjected to realistic description and analyses. In the 1920s and after, sociological studies based on direct observation greatly increased. A series of ecological studies of urban communities, most notably those conducted at the University of Chicago following the lead of Robert E. Park (1864–1944), delineated patterns of urban growth in relation to areas characterized by social break-down. Demographic studies of census data and vital statistics revealed some of the dynamics of population changes.

Total communities were studied for evidence of social structure and social processes, and efforts were made to document the processes of social change.

* See Chapter IX, p. 278.

The community study, which had been developed before the first world war as a simple social survey for planning welfare services, became a more refined tool for testing sociological hypotheses with respect to such questions as the structure and functioning of social class, the nature of social groups, the character of social institutions, the performance of social roles and the operation of social controls.

As agricultural agencies came increasingly to recognize the importance of social factors in the improvement and use of agricultural technology, rural sociology became an important field of study in countries of advanced agriculture. In eastern Europe studies of rural life in the 1930s were closely related to political movements for social reform on behalf of the peasantry. Problems of Hungarian villages were brought to light by the studies of a group of young writers who called themselves the 'March Front'. Research by students of sociology at the University of Bucharest led in the late 1930s to a short-lived programme requiring students completing their university or high school courses to work in villages and study peasant life for a year. Detailed studies of peasant life were also undertaken in Yugoslavia.

Immigrants and migrants provided evidence on some of the processes of acculturation, as in the major study by W. I. Thomas and Florian Znaniecki of *The Polish Peasant in Europe and America* (1918). A variety of other social groups were studied for details of social stratification and factors affecting social mobility. Anthropologists, too, began to apply the methods and concepts derived from their studies of primitive peoples to the scrutiny of non-primitive societies. This body of sociological and anthropological research brought considerable sophistication to thinking about the nature and problems of modern social life, although, as noted at the fourth World Sociological Congress in 1959, many sociologists tended to avoid broad generalizations and focused on the specific situations which they were studying.

The nature of economic institutions was also becoming increasingly familiar through a growing body of descriptive studies. Some of these showed that assumptions basic to economic theory did not accord with contemporary conditions. In the large and increasingly dominant corporation, ownership was found to be so divorced from control that the traditional concept of economic motive power, the private owner pursuing individual profit, did not hold. A high degree of price rigidity, rather than the price flexibility which in theory provided the mechanism for economic adjustment, was found to exist, apparently associated with the concentration of production in relatively few hands. A new group, the managers and other executives of business corporations, was seen to be emerging as the locus of much economic power. Some people saw them as a new 'class' and spoke of their rising power as a 'managerial revolution' (James Burnham, *The Managerial Revolution*, 1941). Marxists on the other hand insisted that in spite of the changes in capitalist society its nature and essence remained the same.

A body of knowledge was also being developed with respect to dynamic economic processes. Studies of national income—its total, its sources and its distribution—were undertaken in the major industrial countries in the 1920s and thereafter were kept current and made more comparable. Studies of consumer expenditure provided a basis for recording changes in the cost of living and for comparing patterns of spending at different income levels. Studies of economic interrelationships and growth produced formulae for estimating fluctuations in the demand for specific products under conditions of higher or lower national income, and the levels which would be required to maintain full employment.

Classical economic theory was further developed, chiefly in the work of Joan Robinson (1903–   ) in Britain and Edward Chamberlain (1899–   ) in the United States in respect to competition among the few, but in fundamentals it remained unchanged. Neither the studies of economic institutions nor those of dynamic economic relationships were incorporated into the theoretical structure. Nevertheless these studies provided a body of knowledge and techniques which could be drawn upon when the combination of economic disaster and fresh theory brought a reorientation of economic thought.

The world-wide economic collapse and depression of the 1930's shattered confidence in traditional *laissez-faire* economic theory. As a body, economists failed to predict the crash of 1929.[5] As crash lengthened into depression and unemployment spread, confidence that prosperity must be just around the corner in an automatically adjusting economy gave way to a determination to take a fresh look at the facts of economic life. Some found a ready answer in the Marxian analysis. More, unwilling to accept the idea that the free enterprise system was a complete failure and doubtful that even the evidence of the depression fully sustained Marx's hypotheses, looked further.

Major stimulus to the reorientation of economic thinking came from the Englishman, John Maynard Keynes (1883–1946). His challenging *Economic Consequences of the Peace* (1919) had arrested the attention of economists at the close of the first world war but it was his *General Theory of Employment, Interest and Money*, published in 1936, which focused thinking and offered a basis for policy.

Without departing from the two major premises of classical economic theory, price flexibility and market competition, Keynes maintained that the system was not necessarily self-correcting, and that equilibrium was possible at less than full employment—as the years of depression seemed to make fully evident. He held that the place to look for the disturbing factor was not in the behaviour of production, prices or interest rates, but in what was happening to consumption and to the balance between consumption and saving. He even offered a remedy—adjust the government's spending in relation to taxes so as to increase consumption when demand is insufficient to take off the market the goods produced.

While Keynes' theories were by no means universally accepted and led to lively and continuing controversy among professional economists, they helped to deal the *coup-de-grâce* to *laissez-faire* economics. Thus stimulated, economists and statesmen of the industrialized countries set out in search of possible controls which might be used to keep their economies functioning and growing and their people employed.[6]

All these tendencies, as well as the changed outlook of the natural sciences, were reflected in the study of history, enlarging its scope, modifying its methods and providing the historian with concepts which he could apply to the societies of the past. Historical students, especially those concerned with the modern period, began to make more use of the concepts and research techniques of the related social sciences and they could count on more systematic documentation with which to work. An ever growing body of statistical data made it possible to reconstruct in quantitative terms what might be only hinted by literary sources; archives were better organized and records more systematically deposited with a view to providing a basis for historical study, as in the war-documentation collections assembled and made available for research by governments in several countries.

In reaction against the specialization which broke up the undivided continuum of history into fragments, a number of historians developed cultural history as a field. Their concept of 'culture' was not the limited study of customs and usages which had constituted the nineteenth-century historian's version, but rather the comprehensive concept used by the anthropologist. The leading Belgian historian Henri Pirenne (1862–1935) tried to present in his *Histoire de Belgique* (7 vols., 1910–32) the political, economic, social and intellectual history of his country as one integral whole. The American historians Carl Becker (1873–1945) and Charles A. Beard (1874–1948) were part of a similar movement to develop a 'new history'.

Historians who sought to apply this new approach had to deal with complicated interrelations between the different fields of human activity—political, economic, social, intellectual, religious. In calling for an expanded view both in scope and geographical extent, the new history or cultural history thus placed heavy demands on the historian for, in addition to the interrelation among fields of activity, the interaction among civilizations became an inescapable part of his study. This required the European or American historian to have knowledge of Asian history and vice versa.

In contrast to the nineteenth-century historians who had taken for granted the values of their societies and, like their counterparts in the natural sciences, had concentrated on achieving scientific objectivity, a growing number of historians began to question the assumptions in terms of which they were viewing the past. Several German historians sought terms in which to evaluate whole periods of civilizations. In the footsteps of the Swiss historian, Jakob Burckhardt (1818–97), Karl Lamprecht (1856–1915) vehemently insisted on studying societies as cultural wholes and tried to characterize entire periods in psychological terms. Oswald Spengler (1880–1936) saw civilizations as independent organisms passing through cycles, and he identified the contemporary cycle of western civilization as a period of decline. The English historian Arnold J. Toynbee (1889–   ), making a somewhat similar assumption of a cyclical process, looked for causal factors which produced the dynamic and waning periods of great civilizations.

In general the concept of 'law', regularity and repetition was still a point of discussion among historians at mid-century. On the one hand there were many historians who rejected the existence of historical laws with the argument that historical phenomena differ essentially from both natural and sociological phenomena in that they are 'one-time events', as German thinkers at the turn of the century such as Heinrich Rickert (1863–1936), Georg Simmel (1858–1918) and Wilhelm Dilthey (1833–1911) phrased it. On the other hand there were those historians who either accepted the idea of historical laws or did not reject the idea in advance. These ranged from the orthodox Marxists, who pursued evidence to show that Marx had already found the correct societal laws, to scholars like Spengler and Toynbee who formulated their own historical laws. They included historians of various views, many with a more or less Marxian outlook, who neither accepted a predetermined system of laws nor designed their own but sought to place historical phenomena in some broad pattern of societal regularities.

These different opinions about the structure of history and the best way to analyse it brought the need for a special study of such problems as periods and rhythms in history, and the part played by the great individual on the one hand and the masses on the other. This field of study came to be known as theoretical history or as theory of history and it largely replaced what was formerly called philosophy of history, substituting theoretical analysis on the basis of the historical phenomena themselves for speculation about history on the basis of a *Weltanschauung*.

But however greatly historians differed in their opinions and formulations, the most eminent among them turned away from the extreme specialization that threatened to separate history from life. One of the first to do this was the French historian Henri Berr (1863–1954), who in 1900 founded his review *Synthèse de l'histoire* and tried to work out a synthetic view in the hundred volumes of *L'Évolution de l'humanité* of which he was for years the indefatigable editor. This work may be regarded as one of the first efforts to write what can properly be called world history.

Indeed, the writing of world history became possible only in the twentieth century, for the interrelations of regional histories came to be understood very much better during this period. The excavations at Arikamedu, for example, disclosed how close was the connection between the Roman empire and southern India in the first and second centuries AD. In the same manner the excavations in the deserts of central Asia showed the close relations of developments in India and China. Disclosure of the intimate contacts between the Hellenistic world and Asia through the silk route to China and through

Bactria to India told the same tale. In fact the historical work in the twentieth century showed regional developments to have been so interrelated at various periods as to leave no place for completely isolated regional history in any part of Asia or Europe. Interest in Africa's past was also aroused and work in this field was dispelling the idea that Africa had no history and was beginning to bring the history of that region into relation with that of other areas. The attention of historians was drawn to all these interrelationships of the past as the same parts of the world again became interrelated in the modern period.

4. *Social science in the Soviet Union*

The developments described above took place, in the main, outside the Soviet Union. Within the Soviet system social science took a different course, following three main lines. Ethnographic studies continued until the late 1920s to be linked to geography as they had been in the nineteenth century, and after the development of ethnology as a separate field they continued to explore the varied peoples of the Soviet Union in terms of human geography —man in relation to his environment and the origins and movements of peoples in relation to the characteristics of regions and areas. Soviet psychology rested squarely on the work of Ivan Pavlov, and thus on a physiological base. With some variation in emphasis through the years, it followed a continuous line of experimentation into the physical bases of behaviour and ways by which it may be conditioned. The general fields of history, economics and political science were pursued as an elaboration and application of Marxian principles. Phenomena were examined to find in them the dialectic relationships assumed to exist and to identify the historical materialist process. In this view economic history embraced much of what fell within other social science disciplines elsewhere. Soviet students rejected most sociology and cultural and social anthropology as being bourgeois, introducing false or irrelevant problems and assumptions, and in some cases having a 'racist' or a wrong political orientation.

Soviet social science was more directly focused on tasks of social engineering than was that of western Europe and America. Since the nation was engaged in a vast undertaking for conscious and directed social change, the social sciences were expected to yield instruments which could be used toward this end. Both natural and human geography provided knowledge essential to the development of the Russian land mass and the integration of its varied nationalities, while economic geography contributed directly to economic planning. Psychological studies had their direct value to education and to propaganda. The very extensive research and training in pedagogy applied Pavlovian psychology; the ideas of Freud and, except for a brief period in the 1920s, those of John Dewey and others who were influential in learning theory and education in other countries, were rejected as making bourgeois assumptions and applying bourgeois values. Training in social science was part of the preparation of Communist party workers for the development and use of propaganda.

The main fields of application were the many problems of economic organization and social direction which confronted Soviet planners and technicians. Much work was intensely practical for it was directed toward the solution of problems of planning, the operation of enterprises and the administration of agencies under the changing conditions of a socialist economy and communist state. At a more theoretical level it proceeded on the assumption that an historical materialistic process is at work and if it can be accurately detected it will be possible to line up forces effectively in its support. Even where dialectic relationships are not immediately evident, further study will be bound to reveal them. Marxist principles thus provided a common framework and set of analytical tools to all work in the field and a unified basis for interpreting and integrating results.

IV. NEW APPLICATIONS: DURING AND AFTER THE SECOND WORLD WAR

The second world war and the post-war problems of reconstruction and development gave a tremendous impetus to the expansion of the social sciences, first by calling for their application to pressing problems and then by making available funds and stimulus for work in many directions. Social scientists of all sorts were called upon to place their knowledge at the service of their respective countries for the conduct of war and the achievement of reconstruction and, in the years after the war, for international co-operation.

1. Stimulus to applied research

Much more elaborate devices for the testing of aptitudes than had been employed in the first world war were applied to the screening of military personnel and their assignment to proper functions; tests for the analysis of personality were also used. Psychological and psychiatric techniques were utilized for the assessment of morale and in the rehabilitation of neuro-psychiatric casualties. For the conduct of psychological warfare all sides enlisted their most skilled personnel in the task of undermining their opponents' will to fight and sustaining the spirit and motivation of their own people and their allies. Anthropologists were called on to analyse the culture of opponents and to recommend ways of dealing with them. The terms upon which hostilities were ended in the Pacific were reported to have been based on an anthropological evaluation of cultural factors, as well as military analyses of the strategic situation. In order to maintain functioning economies to sustain the war effort, economists were called on to develop techniques and principles of economic control. The rapid expansion of wartime administrations required the best knowledge and skill in this field.

The war experience and its aftermath intensified all the problems of social and personal breakdown which had engaged the attention of applied social scientists in the pre-war decades. Family disorganization, juvenile delinquency, displaced persons, problems of mental health and many kinds of social tensions challenged their knowledge and skills. The first director of the World Health Organization expressed the view that the world faced a race between the development of mature individuals able to function in the modern world, and the danger of being overwhelmed by the forces of destruction. The welfare state required the capacity to design sound programmes and institutions and to administer them well. The survival of predominantly capitalist economies clearly depended on their ability to prevent economic collapse.

Action along many lines was undertaken pragmatically, in response to need rather than on the basis of scientifically established knowledge or theory. But as social scientists tried to put their knowledge and techniques to work in all these areas, they found the opportunity to test in operation the body of knowledge which they had been building up and to expand it.

Under this stimulus both academic and clinical psychologists refined the techniques for psychological testing, opinion research and projective tests which they had evolved in the preceding years. Financial support from military and war veterans' service agencies drew a large proportion of psychologists into the clinical field and gave an important place to the problems that had been approached through methods of psychoanalysis or related techniques. A marked increase in the number of persons under treatment for mental illness tended further to reinforce this preoccupation. By 1950 some 50 per cent of the members of the American Psychological Association were at work in the clinical field, as against 10–15 per cent during the 1920s. Methods used by totalitarian régimes to break the will and 'brain-wash' political opponents and war captives gave rise to efforts to find principles which could be used in the training of military personnel to resist the effects of this scientifically-based assault on their integrity. The tremendous demands which supersonic planes and other modern weapons made on those who must operate them led to research into the conditions under which human beings could continue to function and exercise judgment. Evidence from this source as to the limits of psychological as well as physical strain added to basic psychological knowledge, as well as having practical implications for such matters as safety in civilian air travel and the management of personnel under less exacting conditions.

Anthropologists, called on both during the war and in the years which followed to analyse the cultures of enemies and others whom they could not study by their usual methods of first-hand investigation, developed techniques for using literary sources, testimony of emigrants and other available evidence. By these and more direct means they expanded the study of non-primitive societies which they had begun during the 1920s. In these years there appeared a large body of anthropological literature relating to France, Britain, Japan, the USSR, China, Germany, India, Norway, Rumania, a number of Latin American countries and the United States, some written by anthropologists of the countries studied and some by those from abroad. The United States material was so extensive that the anthropological journal *American Anthropologist* devoted an entire issue (December 1955) to 'The U.S.A. as Anthropologists See It'. Meanwhile programmes of technical assistance in relation to the economic development of non-industrial countries further stimulated the kind of anthropological study which would throw light on the possible conditions for industrialization and the cultural impact of technical change.

Indeed, in these years the problems involved in the impact of technological change on non-industrial areas virtually held the centre of the social science stage. The so-called industrial revolution had come to Europe and North America gradually and at a time when the field of human behaviour had not been brought within the scope of scientific inquiry. By contrast the introduction of modern technology into underdeveloped areas in this period became a conscious process and its social impact a matter of grave concern, both to the countries undergoing development and to the agencies which were trying to make their aid effective.

Faced with the likelihood that efforts to introduce agricultural and industrial changes would meet with resistance, fail to spread beyond their initial point of impact or produce cultural and social disorganization, governments and international agencies called on social scientists to provide guides based on knowledge gained from past experience.* Special institutes such as the Research Centre in Economic Development and Cultural Change at the University of Chicago brought together economists, anthropologists and specialists in other fields to carry on research. The social science division of Unesco made this topic one of the two main centres of its work and organized a special programme for the study of the social implications of technical progress. A review of the expanding horizons in social science research in 1953† found this problem to be one of two principal directions in which the field was developing.

Scarcely less central was the effort to apply and expand knowledge and understanding of personality development. Psychologists continued to test Freudian and other hypotheses in an effort to develop a dynamic theory of personality. Studies of personality structure were at the heart of continued efforts to understand types of juvenile delinquency or the nature of prejudice. Psychologists joined anthropologists in the effort to determine the effect of culture on personality. Culture–personality studies initiated by followers of Franz Boas and Edward Sapir in the United States used psychological tools, including projective techniques, to discover personality characteristics in

---

* See *Cultural Patterns and Technical Change:* A Manual prepared by the World Federation for Mental Health, ed. Margaret Mead (Paris, Unesco, 1953); *Human Factors in Technological Change; A Casebook* (New York, Russell Sage Foundation, 1952).

† F. Stuart Chapin, *Social Science Research: its Expanding Horizons* (Minneapolis, University of Minnesota Social Science Research Center, 1953).

different cultures. They attempted to determine the mechanisms of personality formation used by different societies. They made comparative studies of child-rearing practices as clues to differences in adult personality, and tried to study 'national character', i.e. the modal personality types produced by different cultures.

Although these studies remained controversial and not fully developed, they represented by the 1950s a substantial effort to bring a scientific approach to these crucial questions. Following earlier attempts to focus attention on the effect of bureaucracy on its members by such sociologists as Max Weber and Ludwig von Mises (1881–), writers in the 1950s identified characteristics of the 'bureaucratic personality' as seen in *The Organization Man* (by William H. Whyte, 1956), *Mass Persuasion* (by Robert Merton, 1956), or the 'other-directed' individual in *The Lonely Crowd* (by David Riesman, 1950).

The importance of the problem of personality was clearly indicated when the 1950 meeting of the decennial White House Conference on Children and Youth in the United States chose as its theme 'a healthy personality for every child' in contrast to earlier conferences which had dealt with legal protection of children, their economic well-being and welfare services on their behalf.

A constellation of problems under the broad head of 'communication' also assumed growing importance. One facet through which the problem was approached was language. The *Gestalt* concept had established the need to know what is in the mind of the hearer or reader in order for the speaker or writer to evoke the meaning which he wishes to convey. The study of linguistics along lines suggested by B. Whorf (1897–1941) and Edward Sapir was carried forward by anthropologists and psychologists who examined language as a reflection of the thought-structure, values and attitudes characteristic of a culture. The images and stereotypes in which people thought and expressed themselves offered a key to understanding a culture and to the kinds of communication taking place within it. Language was also examined in terms of those features of inflection, stress or gesture which are integral parts of oral communication and essential to its full use and understanding. The ever-increasing need for communication among people of different cultures using different languages and modes of speech made the whole problem an exceedingly pressing one. Efforts were being made to devise electronic translators which would automatically convert words from one language to another; but at the same time the body of evidence was growing that many elements enter into the complex process of conveying meaning.

The problem of meaning especially preoccupied one branch of the study of linguistics known as semantics. By examining the ways in which changes in meaning have come about and the varieties of meaning which a word or phrase may have in a given context, scholars in this field sought methods to achieve more precise identity of meaning between speaker and hearer, either by the choice of terms whose meaning is common to both or by establishing the sense in which each term is used at the time when it is employed. Such studies as *The Meaning of Meaning* by C. K. Ogden and I. A. Richards (1923) contributed to the development of theories of communication along two lines: the philosophical method of logical positivism and other forms of analytical philosophy, and the more popular consideration of communication in daily life.

A further approach to the subject of communication took the form of efforts to get at the essence of the idea or word or feeling that is being communicated —to discover its most elementary form. Communications engineers needed to know which of the sounds that enter into a word or sentence must be transmitted over telephone wire or radio wave if the meaning is to reach its destination and which sounds can be left out. The role of instincts in communication was studied in both humans and animals, by observations such as those to determine whether it is the shape of the mouth or some other aspect of expression that communicates a smile to an infant, or to identify the kind of shadow that tells a baby chicken when the shelter of the mother-bird's wing is at hand.

The extension of automation also had repercussions on communication research and theory. Automatic devices operate, in essence, by a system of signals; when a process reaches a certain point, say of temperature, distance or light, it sets off a signal which instructs a machine to stop, accelerate or turn, and this in turn may pass on other signals through endless complexities. Those engaged in communications research seized upon the concept of the automatic feedback, and directed attention to the built-in signals in the human mind which, like those in the automatic device, send back the messages which control the next thought or action. These and other approaches reflected a widespread recognition that communication was one of the central and imperfectly understood problems in all human relations.

Intensified study was also directed to the dynamics of small groups and the interrelations among groups, especially those involving group tensions. Interest in this area arose from the observation that in modern society the small group is the unit through which large organizations function, whether these be government agencies, corporations, labour unions or other associations. The individual—in school, on the job and in his social life—becomes a part of many such groups to which he must adjust and which affect his development; meantime the traditional groups of family, neighbourhood or occupation have lost or changed their traditional structure or role. The pioneer work of the refugee German, Kurt Lewin (1890–1947), in the late 1930s opened up for further study the question of the effect of democratic as against authoritarian leadership on the tensions among group members and the way in which the group as a whole performs.[7,8]

Political scientists added the concept of the 'group process' to that of 'line authority' in their efforts to evolve principles of administration and they studied the factors affecting the manner in which group decisions are reached and the way in which group participation is related to performance on the job. Educators and others concerned with children investigated the role of group experience in the development of behaviour and personality. Those concerned with abnormal behaviour experimented with the use of group situations for therapeutic purposes. Sociometric techniques were designed for the obser-vation and analysis of dynamic group relationships. All these approaches rested upon the assumption that the individual in industrial society cannot rely upon the role into which he is cast by birth or other circumstances, but must make and maintain his place through a variety of group relationships.

The interrelations among groups appeared as an equally pressing problem. Such insulation as had been provided in the past by distance or by clearly defined and commonly accepted status relationships was thoroughly worn away by technical and social changes. National, religious, class, racial, even age and sex groups confronted each other with immediacy and often conflict.[9] The problem of prejudice became a central concern to social psychologists who looked for its basis in personality structure, degrees of personal security or insecurity and types of social experience, as well as to sociologists who looked for its roots in social and economic structures and relationships. Unesco made the subject of tensions the centre of its first major social science effort.

In the field of political behaviour, two problems were of pressing importance in the post-war years: how to design international and semi-international entities which would redefine relationships among political units; and, in countries with democratic structures of government, how to make these institutions function effectively under conditions of modern technology. As governments took on many technically complex functions and intervened in a great many aspects of life, it became difficult to maintain a relationship of responsibility between an elected representative and his constituents. The interests of the constituents often were in conflict one with another on matters on which the representative was required to act. It was difficult for voters to be informed on the intricacies of technical problems or to find a means of expression when they were. In newly established states whose constitutions prescribed democratic machinery, the people lacked political experience and in addition were separated from the political leadership by a wide gulf of education. These problems were so charged with political emotion and so enmeshed in the struggle for power as to intensify the difficulties of subjecting them to systematic study.

For capitalist economists the major problem was how to maintain a high-level, expanding and stable economic system. The decade following the second world war provided a first test of whether enough economic understanding had been achieved to enable the capitalist countries to avoid a post-war depression. In the countries affected by the depression of the 1930s the recovery measures adopted prior to the outbreak of war had not wholly succeeded in eliminating unemployment. When the war ended, therefore, Marxian economists, and many others as well, confidently expected a slump. It was well recognized, however, that no government could afford to let depression descend upon its country or on countries with which it was intimately related. Even the United States, which maintained more strongly than most others a policy of keeping government intervention in economic affairs to the minimum, declared in its Employment Act of 1946 that the maintenance of full employment was a matter of public policy and government responsibility.

As the economy of the United States remained at a high though fluctuating level of operation and those of western Europe and Britain recovered and flourished, they provided an opportunity to refine and to test further the concepts and techniques evolved in the later years of the great depression of the 1930s. The most important of these techniques related to the use of fiscal and monetary policies to counterbalance economic fluctuations and procedures for arriving at quantitative estimates of economic relationships as a basis for some degree of economic planning. To what extent continued economic stability and growth was due to heavy military expenditures was a matter of dispute. But the experience of the 1950s made it appear that economic knowledge was at least beginning to yield techniques for maintaining in dynamic equilibrium an expanding industrial economy without the authoritarian direction of a centralized state.[10, 11]

The wartime experience in which the combined skills and resources of many specialists were brought together on common problems greatly strengthened the tendency toward integration, or at least co-operation, among the several social science disciplines. Many scholars prepared themselves in more than one field; virtually all research projects of any magnitude enlisted a team of different specialists; a series of interdisciplinary institutes were established to conduct studies of special areas, or to focus on major social problems such as the economic development of non-industrial countries, urbanism, population. The Social Science Research Council in the United States sponsored committees on which several disciplines were represented to explore needs for research on the frontiers of social science knowledge. The teams enlisted by international agencies for their projects were usually drawn from many fields as well as from many nations.

The stimulus of interdisciplinary research was reflected in renewed efforts to build a common social science. In the first half of the twentieth century there had been few efforts to build broad systems such as those which had characterized such nineteenth-century thinkers as Hegel, Comte and Herbert Spencer. Those who sought to apply scientific method to the study of human behaviour expanded the frontiers of knowledge piece by piece.

As the researches of different disciplines led to areas which were being explored by others, as concepts were borrowed and as techniques of research became common to several disciplines, scholars began to search for general system theory which would incorporate the findings of the several social sciences and provide a common basis for research. The quest for a common core preoccupied some scholars within each discipline, although others felt that the tendency to combine fields might interfere with the necessary task of refining the still very imperfect methods and theory of each.

2. Refinement of research techniques

Research techniques in use in these years were in general superior in each of the social science fields to those in vogue twenty or thirty years before. Loosely descriptive sociological studies had been replaced by more sharply focused inquiries. Refined techniques had been developed for sampling populations, evaluating statistical errors in the manipulation of data and analysing and correlating multiple factors. The research interview had been systematically tested and the relation between verbal response and both behaviour and attitude had been explored. Often with the aid of recording devices, techniques of participant observation and of action research had been refined. Scales had been devised for recording the intensity as well as the content of attitudes and opinions, and procedures were designed for detecting the nature and effectiveness of communication.

Observation and analysis were beginning to be used as a basis for prediction. While the opinion poll based on careful sampling did not prove to be a sufficiently accurate instrument to predict the results of a really close election, it demonstrated substantial usefulness for forecasting behaviour. Other techniques for the prediction of political behaviour were developed on the basis of past voting records. Statistical methods which had first been used to predict the production, consumption and prices of agricultural products in the United States proved valuable when used to forecast American elections.

Essentially similar methods provided means for the prediction of economic behaviour. Techniques of statistical correlation were applied to series of economic data in order to establish relationships and to make it possible to predict the reactions of some factors when others were changed. In conjunction with studies of national income, such studies provided a basis for economic planning and for tracing through the impact of specific monetary or fiscal policy or change in investment, consumption or production. They were indispensable tools in programmes designed to expand real income of both industrialized and non-industrialized countries. In the years following the second world war such techniques were applied by the economic development agencies of many countries, in evaluating requests for international assistance by the International Bank for Reconstruction and Development, and to provide information in the light of which business men could make their private decisions.

Efforts further to refine methodology took a variety of directions, and some basic differences, especially with respect to techniques of observation, were unresolved.

One division was basic. Most anthropologists, archaeologists, historians and clinical psychologists sought always, first of all, to observe and understand the unique event, culture or individual; experimental psychologists, sociologists and economists, on the other hand, aimed to abstract from the particular in order to establish general relationships. The first group sought to make the trained observer a more refined and sensitized instrument to detect meanings that would elude detection by other means; the second group depended mainly on the improved handling of quantitative data.

A second division was between those who sought means to isolate specific phenomena more precisely in order to subject them to rigorous scrutiny, and those who thought that the phenomenon to be studied was exactly the complex of interrelationships itself. The latter emphasis corresponded in part with interest in the unique situation, for anthropologists were among those who most distrusted generalizations based on treating items as independent, self-contained elements, preferring completeness of context to disembodied precision. Economists too, however, became increasingly absorbed in the search for means to express complex interrelationships in order to cope with the intricacies of economic planning.

A third division, which followed no line between disciplines, concerned the role of the observer. Should he seek maximum detachment and objectivity or should he consciously recognize the nature of his intervention on the theory that detachment is in fact impossible and that every effort to observe human behaviour distorts the behaviour itself, as for example when a poll to determine voting intentions creates the impression that one candidate will win and thereby changes the intentions it was designed to measure. Historians, who had been most insistent on letting facts speak for themselves, came to accept the idea that every historian necessarily brings to his study of the past the outlook and preoccupations of his own time; they differed in concluding that the only order in history is that which the individual historian imposes on the events he describes, or in hoping that by recognizing and acknowledging bias a measure of objectivity can nevertheless be achieved. In all fields there was a growing recognition that, perhaps as much as in nuclear physics, the process of observation so enters into the behaviour which is studied as to make the observation itself an inevitable part of the answer.

With respect to the handling of data, interest remained general in methods of sampling, correlation and probability analysis and the refinement of mathematical statistics. Those like the anthropologists who insisted that it was the combination of factors—the 'event'—rather than the separate items or traits that required observation and analysis looked to the newer branches of mathematics, such as topology, in the hope that they would supply techniques of analysis which probability principles alone failed to offer. The device of model making, most familiar in the field of economics, was adopted in other fields, and by those who were concerned with general theory. Models of hypothetical behaviour were designed on the basis of observed relationships and general principles, and were used to make predictions and to test such predictions of future behaviour by observations under controlled or uncontrolled conditions. The development of electronic computing devices opened up great possibilities for the handling of data by permitting the rapid analysis of complex interrelationships. With the aid of these devices matters such as the multiple factors affecting voting behaviour or the complex phenomena of juvenile delinquency were beginning to be subjected to analysis in the effort to detect the combination which had value for prediction.

3. *The social sciences at mid-century*

As it became increasingly clear, after two world wars and the development of ultimate means of destruction, that natural science in and of itself would not lead mankind along the path of progress which the nineteenth century had envisioned, the social sciences began to be looked to for aid in seeking solutions to the world's ills. The public showed ambivalence in an exaggerated confidence and an exaggerated distrust of what social science had to offer.

Social scientists themselves were not in agreement as to their potential role. While some thought that the application of social science knowledge and techniques in policy-making and administration held great promise for human welfare, others insisted that, like natural science, social science is neutral and that social scientists, equipped with knowledge but not necessarily with wisdom, can only inform and not guide.

In general, social scientists at mid-century were addressing themselves to urgent social problems, their services were in wide demand, and major funds both from governments and from foundations were being dedicated to expand the frontiers of knowledge in this field. The more modest among them agreed that they had developed a variety of techniques of investigation, increasingly refined, flexible and rigorous, which lent themselves to answering practical as well as theoretical questions, that they had amassed a growing fund of empirical facts which often had practical usefulness, and that they had gained increased sophistication about the variables or factors likely to be relevant to any given problem.

As compared with the fields of the natural sciences, however, knowledge of human behaviour was still very limited. Social scientists themselves were saying '. . . the social scientist knows more accurately than do other people the extent of our ignorance about man and human affairs. The social scientist is thus at the beginning of knowledge'.* The social sciences had not yet achieved a coherent body of theoretical generalization into which new research could be integrated, and through which new studies could be systematically related to previous research. Research continued to be carried on without reference to the work done by others; social scientists might disregard the findings or terminology of their fellow scientists with impunity, as no responsible natural

---

* F. Osborn, 'The social sciences in the service of man' in *The Social Sciences at Mid-century* (University of Minnesota Press, Minneapolis, 1952), p. 4.

scientist could do. Yet they had established, and gained widespread though not universal acceptance for, the idea that 'the behaviour of man, like the behaviour of materials, is characterized by certain uniformities and patterns that can be studied systematically'.* In so doing they had broken through the attitudes which had taken for granted existing forms and values and had made a start, however limited, toward understanding and coping with the processes of social change.

V. SOCIAL SCIENCE AND SOCIAL ACTION

As new knowledge of human behaviour was developed, it was unevenly applied. At times it was ignored while at other times the urgency with which social problems pressed for solution led to the application of very partial and untested knowledge and to frequent changes in technique.

In the main, social institutions evolved pragmatically in response to the practical need to cope with the problems which industrialization brought and under pressures from groups and strata of society which had formerly had no voice or political role. The rapidly changing conditions of urban industrial society required conscious steps to deal with many aspects of living, for which custom, folk knowledge, religious precept and family structure had largely provided in the past. The democratic spirit contributed a favourable milieu, for concern with the welfare of all the people required knowledge of their lives and systematic measures to meet their needs. Age-old conditions which had been taken for granted as normal aspects of life became 'problems' for twentieth-century man to solve or 'ills' to be remedied. Revolutionary societies undertook to redesign basic social relationships and to develop new men and women for a new age.

In these circumstances every resource of experience or knowledge was drawn upon by public agencies, organized groups and individuals, and the social sciences, whatever their limitations, were applied increasingly in virtually every realm of social life and human relations. They were carried into the home, to affect the processes of child rearing, home making and family planning and to protect and strengthen the family against the pressures of modern life. Control of the environment was attempted through the provision of city facilities and services, housing and measures designed to control urban growth, and by the extension of services and regulation to rural or semi-rural areas. Measures were adopted to treat, and if possible to prevent, the many forms of social breakdown which the impersonal, changing industrial societies threatened to produce, including provisions for security against the hazards of illness, incapacity, old age and the loss of the breadwinner, treatment of mentally and socially maladjusted individuals and the control of delinquency and crime. Knowledge of human behaviour was invoked in efforts to lessen

* C. Dollard, 'Strategy for advancing the social sciences' in *The Social Sciences at Mid-century*, p. 12.

tensions and facilitate interrelations among economic, racial and other divergent social groups, to promote economic stability and development, to improve communication, to exercise political influence and administrative direction and to market products through advertising.

New social professions arose and the scope of older professions was extended to incorporate new social knowledge. Professional services based on the application of social science knowledge became part of the institutional structure of industry, education, law enforcement and community life.

Behind all measures to apply social techniques lay the central problem of how social change actually does take place. Most study and effort at application outside the communist-dominated areas rested on the view that social change is necessarily a slow process in which old institutions, behaviour patterns and attitudes gradually adapt themselves to new situations; according to one widely held assumption, material changes take the lead, with social institutions showing a 'cultural lag'.

As countries tried to bring about a rapid transformation of their societies, however, there was a growing interest in examples of drastic social change which might throw light on how the social gap between advanced and backward areas might be quickly and effectively closed. Such examples were being studied on the hypothesis that a sudden and complete change involving the totality of interrelated factors, a sort of social mutation or break-through—as in the modernization of a primitive society or the complete remaking of a village by concerted effort—might be more effective than piecemeal changes each of which would tend to be dragged back toward old norms by the weight of other institutions. One school of thought insisted that partial transformations of non-industrial societies brought only disorganization and pauperization and that nothing short of complete remaking could save them from degradation.* In the Marxist–Leninist view revolutionary change involving the socialization of the means of production was the historically necessary basis for a transformation of society in which the fruits of science and technology would be used for the ultimate benefit of all.

The central problems at mid-century were twofold: would the social sciences provide sufficient understanding of human behaviour and adequate techniques for social action to meet the requirements of a highly mobile, interdependent world armed with great knowledge and power over physical and biological processes; and would knowledge of human behaviour be used to enhance or thwart human development?

Any attempt to trace the application of the social sciences during these years encounters the obvious difficulty that social changes are the product of many forces of which the conscious use of social theory and knowledge of

* For example: Margaret Mead, *New Lives for Old: Cultural Transformation—Manus, 1928–1953* (William Morrow & Co., New York, 1956); *Development of the Local Community of Nayarit* (United Nations, New York, 1954); Germaine Tillion, *Algeria; the Realities* (Knopf, New York, 1958).

social behaviour is only one small element. New knowledge of human development and behaviour was indeed consciously used in the rearing of children; but the experience, status and outlook of the young was more profoundly affected by broad changes in family life accompanying the growth of industry, cities, travel and communication, by the impact of war and revolution and by changing social values arising from cultural contact and social change. Efforts to deal scientifically with the urban environment played a minor role in the development of cities as compared with the pull of employment opportunities and the enterprise of merchants, realtors and purveyors of the myriad services which contribute to city life. Social science knowledge was perhaps most consciously applied in efforts to deal with social breakdown, for it was the need to cope with delinquency, crime, dependency and social disorganization which stimulated much of the research in the field. But here, too, practical measures based on custom and common sense continued to overshadow those which rested on tested observation and theory.

The three chapters which follow must therefore be read in conjunction with the chapters of Part II which examine the institutional changes resulting from the interaction of all the forces at work during these years, and also in relation to the chapters dealing with the physical and biological sciences, since the application of knowledge in these fields had, indirectly, a far more profound impact on social life than the direct application of the social sciences themselves.

NOTES TO CHAPTER XVI

1. Doctor of Philosophy V. Kolbanovsky says that the main stimulus that drove men to seek deeper knowledge of human life and more effective and systematic means of satisfying popular needs was the emergence on the political scene of new classes and social strata. As a consequence of this development a number of democratic measures were carried out, under the pressure of the popular masses, and new social forces arose to take part in social conflicts. Unfortunately bourgeois social science paid no attention to the methodology developed already in the middle of the nineteenth century by Marx and Engels for the scientific study of social problems (see note 10 to Chapter VI) and the vast material accumulated on such questions by Marxist-Leninists.

2. Doctor of Philosophy V. Kolbanovsky points out that the intensified interest in sociological research generally observable in the 1920s and 1930s, and the attempts made to intervene actively in economic and social matters with the aid of data provided by such studies, were to a very important extent stimulated by the deepening of social and economic contradictions in Western Europe and North America at this time. But only in the Soviet Union, which had established public ownership of the means of production and where men were armed with Marxist-Leninist theory, was it possible to establish genuinely comprehensive long-term planning of the economy of an entire country.

3. Professor E. N. Anderson states: The role of Sigmund Freud should be seen in two dimensions: (1) in his direct contribution to the development of psychoanalysis as a technique of scientific investigation and of clinical treatment, and (2) in his indirect influence on other behavioural sciences through the use of his theories, in their original or modified forms, as working hypotheses in these other fields. The Author-Editors have not distinguished clearly these two lines of influence. Creator of psychoanalysis as a scientific study, Freud inspired and trained practically all of the first generation of practitioners, whether Austrian, German, Swiss, French, British, or of other national origin. These followers spread into other countries from Vienna, and under the menace of Nazi persecution many emigrated to the New World, especially to the United States, fortified in their conviction about the power of the subconscious, the irrational, by the evidence of totalitarianism. The experience which they received as they moved or fled into other cultures, and which differed so much from that in Freud's pre-war Vienna, made many of the master's followers aware of the conditioning factor of culture upon the character of neuroses and led to the rejection of some of Freud's theories in favour of views deduced from the experience of new environments. The psychoanalytic school was divided into those who remained convinced of the validity of Freud's ideas and methods of analysis and therapy and those who developed their own modification of Freud or even new theories. Critics were found particularly in the United States, but European countries had and have distinguished representatives as well.

   With respect to the application of Freud's theories into other fields, there is scarcely a social science or a humanistic discipline which has not felt the stimulus of this thinker. Much of this adaptation of Freudism has been in the realm of speculation, much has been popularization, in both instances without the clinical control which Freud employed in his researches, but even this application has often been fruitful. One can scarcely conceive of studying political life under National Socialism, for example, without the use of Freud's basic views, and the abuse (or too easy generalization from too little knowledge) of Freud has not prevented essential research from being done in crossing psychoanalysis or psychiatry and anthropology, for example, as revealed in the works of Abram Kardiner and by others in Europe, in America and elsewhere.

   For further reading see:

Franz Alexander and Helen Ross (eds.), *The Impact of Freudian Psychology* (Chicago, 1952).

A. A. Brill, *Freud's Contribution to Psychiatry* (New York, Norton, 1962).

Erich Fromm, *Sigmund Freud's Mission: An Analysis of His Personality and Influence* (New York, 1959; Belmont Books, No. 51, 1963).

Sidney Hook (ed.), *Psychoanalysis, Scientific Method and Philosophy: A Symposium* (New York, Evergreen No. 261, 1960).

Ernest Jones, *Sigmund Freud. His Life and Work*. 3 vols. (London, 1953–57).
Abram Kardiner and Ralph Linton, *The Psychological Frontiers of Society* (New York, 1945).
Bruce Mazlish (ed.), *Psychoanalysis and History* (Englewood, N.J., 1963).
John Sutherland (ed.), *Psychoanalysis and Contemporary Thought* (New York, Evergreen No. 164, 1959).

4. Doctor of Philosophy V. Kolbanovsky notes that the account given here of the 'triumphant progress' of Freudian ideas in Western sociology is exaggerated, to say the least. The wholesale penetration of the social sciences by Freud in all its modifications and manifestations (Freud, Adler, Jung, Horney, Sullivan and others) is contested by a number of leading authorities. Some of them, such as H. Wells, Furst, and others, have subjected Freudian concepts to radical revision and have refuted their claim to provide a solution of clinical and social problems. Others, while accepting Freud's psychological and psychiatric ideas, have never taken seriously his essentially myth-making investigations in the field of social theory—as, for example, in the question of the origin of the family or totemism. It should be very strongly emphasized that the concept of psychoanalysis involves the extension to the sphere of social relations of data obtained from clinics for the treatment of nervous and psychiatric disorders, which are given a one-sided interpretation. As is well known, psychoanalysts regard broad social movements or manifestations of the class struggle as nothing other than a case of collective neurosis or mass hysteria, and outburst of unsublimated psychic energy from the depths of the subconscious which has not been directed in time into the proper channels.

The inner logic of such ideas is obvious: for if social phenomena are identical with those of the individual psyche, it is easy to show that many of their manifestations can be treated as pathological cases, as deviations from some conventional form. At this point one may recall the criticism made by the Russian physiologist I. P. Pavlov of the works of the German psychiatrist Ernst Kretschmer. Although it is unquestionably the case that E. Kretschmer's idea of characterology was based on much more solid material than the fanciful concepts of the psychoanalysts, I. P. Pavlov justly pointed out that it was not permissible to take clinical observations and apply them to the lives and activities of normal human beings. Still less permissible is it to take conclusions arrived at on the basis of clinical observations and apply them to the realm of social processes. For I. P. Pavlov's critique of E. Kretschmer's propositions, see I. P. Pavlov, 'Obshchie tipy vysshey nervnoy deyatelnosti zhivotnykh i cheloveka' (Types of Higher Nervous Activity Common to Animals and Man'). *Poslednie soobshcheniya po fiziologii i patologii vysshey nervnoy deyatelnosti* (Recent Communications on the Physiology and Pathology of Higher Nervous Activity), Communication III, 1935; *Pavlovskiye sredy* (Pavlov Discussions), Vol. III (Moscow-Leningrad, 1949).

5. Candidate of Juridical Sciences A. E. Bovin points out that the approach of the crisis of 1929, and its inevitability, were predicted by Marxists. Documentary proof of this is contained in the materials of the Fifteenth Congress of the VKP(b) (All-Union Communist Party (Bolsheviks)), Sixth Congress of the Comintern (1928) and Tenth Plenum of the Executive Committee of the Comintern in July 1929.

6. In the opinion of Doctor of Philosophy V. Kolbanovsky Keynes' ideas should be seen as an attempt to revive the authority of vulgar political economy in the new conditions of large-scale production and state-monopoly capitalism. As the experience of the last decades has shown, the measures put forward by Keynes have not given the capitalist economy security against shocks. Keynesian economics can temporarily conceal the traces of decline, but cannot prevent impending catastrophe.

7. Doctor of Philosophical Sciences V. Semenov thinks that including an individual in various 'small groups' does not detract from the necessity of analysing the social structure in terms of classes. The views set forth in the text are typical of those propounded by bourgeois sociologists anxious to prove that the conclusions of Marxism on the class structure of capitalist society are allegedly 'obsolete'.

The most widespread point of view among bourgeois sociologists studying developmental tendencies in the social structure is that in capitalist society class antagonism is disappearing on account of the 'social mobility' prevailing in that society. This concept of 'social mobility' proceeds from an anti-scientific treatment of the nature of classes, whereby class differences are ignored in favour of differences that are secondary and derivative. Bourgeois writers ignore the main criterion of class allegiance—relationship to the means of production—and thus deny the irreconcilable nature of class contradictions in capitalist society.

The term 'mobility', as applied to social life, is used very loosely by bourgeois scholars to refer to all manner of social displacements. They make a distinction between 'physical mobility' ('the movement of population elements . . . from one place to another') and 'social mobility' (the movement of individuals or groups from one social position to another in a constellation of social groups and strata) (see P. Sorokin, *Society, Culture and Personality*, New York and London, 1947, p. 405.) 'Social mobility' in turn is divided by bourgeois writers into 'horizontal' and 'vertical' mobility. 'Horizontal social mobility' is the transition of an individual or family from one social group to another at the same social level or stratum (see *ibid.*, pp. 398–9, 405). For example: a shorthand-typist leaving one insurance company for another, a worker leaving Ford for General Motors, an agronomist leaving one farm for another, and so on.

Such mobility does indeed take place in capitalist society, but of course it does not nullify class contradictions. So much is apparent to the bourgeois scholars themselves. Their attention is concentrated on 'vertical social mobility', by which they mean 'the shifting of an individual, family, or even larger group from one stratum to another in the pyramid of social stratification' (see J. O. Hertzler, *Society in Action: a Study of Basic Social Processes*, New York, 1954, p. 237). Bourgeois scholars list six 'channels' or 'elevators' of vertical social mobility 'which enable individuals to move up and down the social ladder': (1) 'economic institutions', i.e. the whole economic life of society; (2) the army; (3) the church; (4) various 'political institutions' (the state apparatus, the apparatus of the parties, the totality of political institutions and organizations); (5) 'the educational system'; (6) marriage.

But if such movement into the 'upper' strata through the so-called channels of mobility does indeed occur in capitalist countries, this only affects individuals and is not a law of social life. Such 'movements' cannot lead to the liquidation of classes, the class struggle, and the exploitation of man by man. Moreover, bourgeois ideologists frankly acknowledge that all these 'channels of vertical social mobility' (economic institutions, the educational system, etc.) are a sort of 'selective agencies' in the hands of the ruling class. 'These institutions', Hertzler writes unequivocally, 'also serve as sifters, testing and selecting, sorting and grading these persons of the population and distributing and locating them on the strata' (*ibid.*, p. 238). The reality of life under capitalism shows that no mass 'movement up' of working people takes place in fact. On the contrary, most of the working population are faced with a real threat of 'movement down', to ruin and poverty.

Even bourgeois investigators are compelled to admit this in one form or another. 'Hence, the difficulty of not only rising in the social scale but also of holding one's own becomes greater', writes Hertzler (*loc. cit.*).

What is actually taking place in capitalist society is a process whereby the population is moving in the main into the ranks of the proletariat. This not only does not lead to extinction of the class struggle, but on the contrary serves as one of the means for accentuating it further. The struggle of the workers, which increases in intensity from year to year, is the most eloquent proof of the falsity of the assertions made by bourgeois scholars to the effect that in capitalist society the class struggle 'is being eliminated'.

In these conditions any social theory which in one way or another seeks to by-pass the fundamental and decisive class division of society is scientifically worthless.

8. *The Author-Editors note that the data upon which sociologists in the United States and elsewhere base their theories with respect to social stratification include the trends in occupations, income distribution and relative earnings of industrial workers and professional persons in the United States which are shown in the Author-Editors' supplementary note 2 to Chapter V.*

9. In the opinion of Doctor of Philosophy V. Kolbanovsky among the social groups mentioned here the most important and fundamental are classes. See note 7 above.

10. As the fifteen years since the end of the second world war have shown, writes Doctor of Philosophy V. Kolbanovsky, the capitalist countries have only been able to ease their economic difficulties by engaging in increased production of armaments, and despite

this the USA has not succeeded in avoiding periodical declines in the level of business activity. Therefore the 'dynamic equilibrium' of the post-war years is extremely unstable, since it is founded not on 'economic knowledge' but on the expansion of the armaments industry. See note 9 to Chapter IX and note 1 to Chapter XXI.

11. *See the Author-Editors' supplementary note 2 to Chapter IX.*

12. In the opinion of Professor E. N. Anderson, the Author-Editors may be criticized for not including in this chapter a discussion of the efforts of economists to analyse stages of economic growth and to identify the factors responsible for this growth. Scholars have endeavoured since World War II to identify these stages, for economically under-developed countries have sought means to accelerate the rate of their development, and economically advanced countries and international agencies offering technical and finan-cial assistance to them have needed to know—in order to apply aid effectively—what are appropriate elements of growth.

The most discussed of the efforts to identify stages of economic growth has been the formulation of W. W. Rostow in *Stages of Economic Growth* (Cambridge, 1960), where he characterizes five stages: that of traditional society; that of the pre-conditions for take-off; that of the take-off; that of the drive to maturity; and that of the age of consumption. Although Rostow's analysis has been stimulating and fruitful in the search for criteria with which to compare the conditions and to gauge the needs of various countries of the world, the concept of 'The Take-Off into Self-Sustained Growth', for example (*Economic Journal*, March, 1956) has been subject to adverse criticism and to difference of opinion. One may consult:

W. W. Rostow (ed.), *The Economics of Take Off into Sustained Growth: Proceedings of a Conference Held by the International Economic Association* (London, 1964).

CHAPTER XVII

THE HOME

THE home, from its physical aspects and daily routines to its child-rearing functions, its human relations and its economic basis, became a field for scientific study, for the application of scientific knowledge and for the development of practices designed to enable it better to serve its functions under modern conditions.*

I. CHILD STUDY

The growing knowledge about the processes of learning and conditioning which came out of the psychological laboratories in the early years of the twentieth century led to a movement to bring a more scientific approach to the rearing of the child.

In all societies, child-rearing practices have constituted an important part of the body of knowledge handed on from generation to generation. Generally these practices have been learned by girls from their mothers in the home and absorbed from the conduct of adults toward children and the expectations to which children have learned to conform. In static societies these child-rearing practices have been a principal means for maintaining the patterns and values of the society and shaping the types of personality demanded by it. In most societies the child has occupied a secondary position as an immature or incomplete adult, a possession or a servant to be used by its parents, on the fringe of society—according to the adage that 'children should be seen but not heard'—and as something to receive the impress of the adult world. His physical care has been based upon folk practice and knowledge, and his emotional development taken for granted. His mental and moral training has been the principal object of conscious attention and educational theory.

In many western societies at the opening of the twentieth century the mental and moral aspects of child training were governed generally by the precepts and practices of the Church and by educational principles which had been modified from the time of the Renaissance by such philosophers and educators as Johann Comenius, John Locke, Jean Jacques Rousseau, Johann Pestalozzi and Friedrich Froebel. Theories of child rearing were based on varying assumptions as to the child's nature: that he was depraved and must be corrected from the start; that he was by nature good unless spoiled by society; or that he was a *tabula rasa* without innate tendencies on whose blank

* For changes in the family as an institution, see Chapter XXII, Social Institutions; for the development of education, see Chapter XXVI, Education; for maternal and child health, see Chapter XV, Health.

surface character and knowledge were to be imprinted. In other societies traditional ways of fitting the child to his family and his station in life were deeply ingrained and of long standing.

To these the twentieth-century approach to child rearing added: a new position for the child as a figure in his own right and a central rather than a peripheral member of society; recognition that in a rapidly changing society it is not enough to teach him to reproduce the pattern of behaviour of his ancestors—he must be equipped with the security, flexibility and knowledge which will permit him to make his own choices and to shape a new and different social order; and a new understanding of the processes of growth and development, especially of the emotional component which had been largely taken for granted or consciously ignored and now became a central factor.

Impetus for the conscious application of new knowledge to child rearing was strongest in those countries where the culture was most child-centred and the assumption of change most general. But in the course of this half-century a basic reorientation in the treatment of the child and in the concept of his role, and some modification of child-rearing practices in the light of modern knowledge, spread around the world. One of the first publications of the World Health Organization was in this field.* In many countries, children came to be considered as the instruments of a new day, especially in revolutionary societies during early stages of the revolution and in the developing countries at the point where they shifted psychologically from a static to a dynamic approach to social change.

The new ideas and attitude toward child rearing even reached and modified the culture of the most remote areas. In 1953 the anthropologist Margaret Mead returned to the Admiralty Islands in the south Pacific twenty-five years after she had gone there to study the culture of a people untouched by any of the major civilizations. When she had left there in 1928, they had beaten the death drums to sound her departure for a world which was to them 'stranger than the abode of their dead'. On her return, she was greeted by the school teacher and a local official who asked her to check a long set of rules for modern child-care, feeding, sleeping and discipline which they had written down as best they could from their memories of what they had been told and what they had seen the wives of Australian officials doing in the ports. Dr Mead reported:

'When I explained that my comments would be in terms of the latest thinking on the matter as developed in the International Seminar on Mental Health and Infant Development, held at Chichester, England, in 1952 under the auspices of the World Federation for Mental Health and the World Health Organization of the United Nations, *he understood what I was saying.*'†

* John Bowlby, *Maternal Care and Mental Health* (WHO Monograph Series, Geneva, 1951).

† Margaret Mead, *New Lives for Old*, p. 23.

In the early years of the century a protest against the traditional attitude toward the child was voiced by the Swedish feminist, Ellen Key (1849–1926). Her *The Century of the Child* (Barnits ärhundrade, 1900) was widely translated and heatedly discussed. Nine years later, when Maria Montessori (1870–1952) offered a positive training method based on her observation of the mental and emotional development of young children in the Casa dei Bambini in Rome (*Il metodo della pedagogia scientifica*, 1909), her ideas found acceptance in many quarters. She stressed the value of self-activity and individual work combined with community living and mutual help, and the importance of offering the child a stimulating environment to arouse and train the senses and elicit an active response.

Shortly before the first world war a movement for popular child study took shape with the formation of child-study associations and groups in a number of places. These associations focused their interest on the normal child rather than the child with abnormalities or in need of special care or protection; they were concerned with his total development as a person rather than with the problems of effective training with which educators were primarily concerned. Their aim was to study the implications of scientific findings for the care and formation of the child in the home and to impart to parents, through a broad programme of adult education, an understanding of the child and some of the precepts which such understanding implied.

Initially, material relating to learning and conditioning was the chief scientific source on which they drew, and they placed much emphasis on regularity and system in the child-training process. As detailed observations of child development were provided by work in various research centres, emphasis was placed on adjusting the demands made upon the child to his stage of development and readiness to respond.

When the influence of Freud began to spread, the implications of his findings for the child's emotional development came to occupy a central place. His emphasis on the relationships established by the child in earliest infancy gave central importance to the emotional security and response which the infant receives; the warmth and love of the parent and the child's sense of continuing well-being were seen as more essential to his total growth than the regularity of his toilet training and the strictness of his feeding schedule. It appeared also that parents could damage their children unintentionally by pressing them too soon to conform to norms of behaviour beyond their level.

Comparative studies by anthropologists of child-rearing practices in different societies also called into question some of the commonly accepted training techniques. By mid-century many of the concepts of child rearing which had reflected an attempt to apply scientific knowledge during the first quarter of the century had become outmoded and had been replaced by concepts based on later knowledge supplied by anthropology and psychology.

The change was interestingly reflected in the various editions of the widely distributed bulletin, *Infant Care*, published by the United States Children's

Bureau. The initial version, first published in 1914, stressed training aspects, with emphasis on regularity of the child's habits. But during the 1930s many of the precepts contained in the volume came into disfavour as placing the child under restraints and pressures which could do emotional damage, and they were recognized as doing more for the convenience of the parent than for the sound development of the child. In successive revisions in 1938 and during the 1940s and 1950s parents were encouraged to be more permissive and relaxed in dealing with their children, and some of the principles set forth were quite opposed to those of the earlier edition. Meantime, translations of the earlier rather than the later editions circulated in some places, notably in Latin America.

The channels through which child-rearing concepts entered the stream of common knowledge were many and various in different parts of the world. As it became apparent that the home alone could not always be counted on to prepare young people adequately for marriage and parenthood, schools began to include in their curricula both sex education and pre-marital education with respect to such matters as family life and child rearing, or to sponsor supplementary educational activities in these fields. Maternal and child health programmes were as much concerned with maternal education as with actual clinical treatment of mothers and young babies. The educational component of maternal and child health programmes, moreover, came to include the understanding of the child's emotional needs, in addition to hygiene and nutrition which were their original focus.

Studies of child development carried on by technical specialists through very careful observations provided the basis for a number of books designed to aid the parent in recognizing the normality of his child's behaviour and to guide his own handling of the child. The books of Dr Arnold Gesell of Yale University (*Infant and Child in the Culture of Today*, 1943) and Dr Benjamin Spock (*The Common Sense Book of Baby and Child Care*, 1946) became handbooks for thousands of parents. Doctors and educators wrote regular columns in newspapers to offer advice and to answer the questions of parents; magazines of all sorts—not alone women's magazines—featured articles relating to child development and adolescent behaviour; the theme became a familiar one on radio and television. In virtually all educational programmes directed primarily toward women, child care and child rearing were featured. Perhaps no other body of new knowledge was more eagerly sought or more widely disseminated in some form in most parts of the world.

The effect of all this was sometimes to make parents anxious lest they fail to do the right thing for their children. Their very effort to follow the latest guides and to behave as model parents sometimes produced such tension that their efforts were self-defeating. Critics of modern parents accused the latter of being afraid of their children and of failing to offer them the firmness and discipline which they needed and really desired. But few modern parents thought it practical to try to return to old ways under the conditions of new times, and most agreed with Mrs Sidonie Gruenberg, one of the founders of the child-study movement, who had insisted in 1913: 'We need not fall into the all-too-common error of placing common-sense and practical insight in opposition to the method of the scientists.'*

II. HOME ECONOMICS

Paralleling the child-study movement, and intertwined with it, were other lines of development which sought to apply the fruits of scientific study to home and family life. 'Home economics' or 'home science' became a professional and educational field, and recognition of the changing structure and functioning of the family under modern conditions led to educational and welfare programmes to promote family stability.

Home economics had its major development in the United States and Canada, and also in Australia, New Zealand and the Scandinavian countries. In most European countries housekeeping continued to be regarded as a technical skill and the term 'home economics' was only introduced as an Americanism after the second world war; nevertheless, the curricula of the training academies were expanded along similar lines. The approach developed by the professional home economists spread to a number of Latin American, Asian and African countries after the second world war and was adopted in these areas as a part of their efforts to reconstruct their traditional societies.

The conception which guided the development of the field of home economics in the United States was that formulated at the turn of the century by Ellen H. Richards (1842–1911), who saw the home as providing a nurturing environment for the child and a haven for adults, and as depending for support on the society of which it was a part and giving to society the fruits of family living. Although she was herself a food chemist, her main concern was with the social and spiritual aspects of the home and she saw the application of scientific knowledge to the physical needs and the mechanics of the home as helping to provide the health and leisure essential to good home life.

With this broad concept home economics teachers and professional practitioners drew from one field of science after another as new bodies of knowledge relevant to the home became available and new awarenesses of needs and possibilities dictated new emphases.

The first concern was with food, especially the feeding of infants and children. Knowledge of food chemistry, bacteriology and physiology was included in school instruction and in advice to mothers, and was marshalled in support of pure food laws and regulations to guard against the offering of unsafe or adulterated foods on the market. As knowledge of nutrition developed, home economists assumed much of the responsibility for its dissemination.

With the appearance on the market of new fabrics, other products made of

* Sidonie Gruenberg, *Your Child Today and Tomorrow* (J. R. Lippincott & Co., Philadelphia and London, 1913), p. 19.

new materials, laundering and cleansing substances and a variety of household appliances, home economists studied these products from the point of view of the user, both in order to give the home-maker sufficient knowledge to make good selections and to use and care for such products properly, and in order to advise producers on designs appropriate to home use. Industries soon began to employ home economists to demonstrate and sell their products as well as to aid in their production. Consumers organized to support testing agencies which could advise them on the comparative merits of competing items.

It was a small step from the selection of products for the home to concern over budgeting and the management of household finances. With increased numbers of women working, increased recreational attractions outside the home, and more leisure for the breadwinner to spend in the home or out, home management became a matter of the efficient use of time as well as money, and a considerable amount of research was carried on to determine how housewives actually performed their day-by-day tasks. These studies resulted in kitchens and home plans designed to save steps and efforts to bring to each of the household tasks the same kind of analysis and efficient arrangement as industry was applying to factory operations.

By the 1920s and 1930s findings in the fields of psychology and sociology began to be incorporated into home economics thinking and to shift the focus from the things used in the home to the people making up the family group. It was at this point that child-study became a central part of the home economics curriculum. Much attention was given to understanding the sociological changes which the modern family was undergoing and to redefining the roles of family members and the functions of the family group.

Largely for accidental reasons related to the establishment of colleges of agriculture in the United States, much of home economics came to be associated with agricultural education and advice. In Europe there were schools of agricultural domestic economy. Within the American agricultural extension service, home demonstration agents to aid and advise the farm woman on her home became the counterparts of the agronomists who advised the farmer on his crops, and similar services were provided elsewhere.

These services reached old-fashioned homes where food was raised and preserved and many productive household activities were carried on which were disappearing from city homes. Paradoxically, much of the energy of the home economics profession in the United States was devoted to the type of homemaking which was rapidly declining as the country became more urbanized year by year. But this very emphasis provided a basis for aid to underdeveloped areas, since many of the skills and techniques developed through rural extension programmes were helpful in the efforts of families in these predominantly rural regions to raise their levels of living. From the 1940s on, first in Latin America and then in other parts of the world, the field of home economics was one in which technical assistance was frequently sought and often effectively given. By the mid-1950s it was part of the agricultural exten-

(a)

17

THE URBAN
ENVIRONMENT I

(a) *Holborn, Kingsway,
    crossroads*, 1912
(b) *Fifth Avenue traffic,
    New York*, c. 1950

(b)

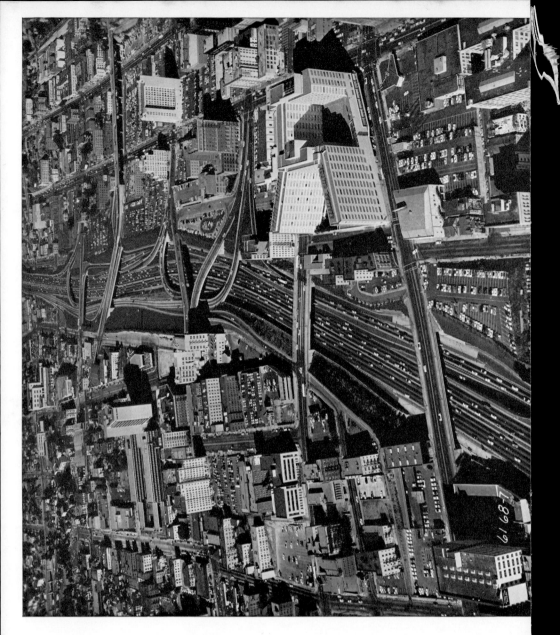

18   THE URBAN ENVIRONMENT II

The Harbour Freeway, Los Angeles, California, USA in the 1950's sion programmes of most Latin American countries, Japan, Korea, the Philippines, India, Thailand, Iraq and Liberia.

Other developments brought home economics subjects into general education at elementary, secondary and university levels. Colleges and universities added home economics departments or faculties until the field became an expected part of a university programme. In contrast to the agricultural home demonstration programmes, these university programmes generally gave a central place to sociological and psychological materials, and they led the trend away from preoccupation with household activities in the direction of child development, family living and human relations.

Home economics spread to other countries from this source also. Notably in India, Pakistan and the Philippines, university programmes in home economics, developed with technical assistance, gave an important place to child development, and they incorporated materials from the social sciences as well as from such fields as nutrition.

III. AIDS IN CHILD REARING

The Soviet Union experimented extensively with the collective upbringing of children and the results of this experience were available to other communist countries. Israel, also, used collective upbringing in its communal *kibbutzim*.

In the principal children's establishments of the USSR—crèches for children under three and kindergartens for those from three to seven—education in children's groups carried on by specially trained staff was combined with home training. Children divided into age groups followed programmes of physical and mental activities based on the latest data supplied by pedagogical science and designed to develop a sense of comradeship, independence of character and a necessary sense of discipline. For children of school age responsible social activities in school and the Young Pioneer children's organization continued the process of character training. Close contact between crèche, kindergarten or school and the parents through parents' committees, lectures on questions of child rearing and parents' universities aimed to combine collective and home upbringing.

In the United States also it came to be recognized that many children growing up in small urban families needed opportunities not furnished by the home to develop patterns of social behaviour and to learn to establish social relationships with others of their own age, and these considerations led to the establishment of nursery schools to supplement the functions of the home. Such nursery schools had two distinct origins and served two groups of children. In many places they were primarily for children of working mothers and they came into being as extensions of day nurseries established by welfare agencies to provide places where infants could be left during working hours. Under the influence of a growing awareness of the needs of the child, many day nurseries were converted from mere custodial institutions to nursery schools where trained workers used play techniques educationally to promote the child's development. At the other end of the scale, nursery schools were privately established in the United States and to some extent elsewhere by groups of families who were in a position to support such schools, sometimes co-operatively, for their own children.

In Europe kindergartens for children from three years up, often known as Froebel schools, were provided extensively by private and in some cases by public agencies. Day nurseries for the children of working mothers continued to be maintained by welfare organizations and by factories.

While the age at which children were enrolled in kindergartens varied and extended in some places to the age reserved for nursery schools in others, formal educational systems rarely included classes below the kindergarten level, and nursery schools remained an extension of the home rather than a part of early formal education. The nursery school movement spread in the 1920s and 1930s and continued to flourish thereafter. Home economics teachers recognized its value as a laboratory in which students could observe child behaviour and practise child care. By the 1940s no university home economics department in the United States considered itself complete without a nursery school, and nursery school laboratories were included in the university home economics programmes developed in the 1950s in India, Pakistan and other countries.

The importance of group association for the development of the child was also recognized since social participation in a small group offered the child means through which he might develop self-discipline and the ability to form new relationships, and had an important influence on the image of himself which he gradually built up. Conscious efforts were therefore made to provide opportunities for children to function in small groups—in nursery schools, in character-building organizations such as Boy Scouts and Girl Guides, settlement houses and youth groups.

In some countries the period of adolescence came to be recognized as a time when the child must make new emotional adjustments. Studies brought out the ambivalence of the adolescent in his struggle to achieve independence and the conflict between his impulse to resist parental supervision and authority and his need for parental reassurance and support. The desire to give the adolescent an opportunity to learn how to relate to members of the opposite sex was reflected in greater freedom of association between the sexes during adolescence than had usually been accepted in the past.

All these efforts to apply technical knowledge to the rearing of children and the functioning of family and home were designed not only to aid individual parents but as preventive measures against social breakdown. Evidence mounted that failure of the child to establish a meaningful relationship with parents or parent substitutes in infancy was basic to much later mental breakdown, juvenile delinquency, antisocial attitudes such as prejudice or sadism, and sometimes to a low I.Q. and poor academic performance. It thus became socially important to foster favourable conditions for child development, and all manner of policies were guided by this consideration, such as the modification of procedures in some maternity hospitals in order to place the child in the room with the mother rather than in a separate room for infants, or the use of foster homes in preference to institutional care for children deprived of their own homes.

In industrially developing countries programmes relating to child rearing and to the home were of importance in view of the social changes taking place in these countries. The single family home, in the western sense, was a new institution in the areas where the joint family was beginning to give way. As the smaller family unit replaced the larger, it faced many new situations in establishing a different type of home. The centres which sought to make the fruits of scientific knowledge available to the home were part of the effort to facilitate this aspect of social change.

Comparative studies of child rearing in various cultures and their relation to the types of adult personality which these cultures tended to produce focused attention on the problem of what kinds of personalities can survive and flourish in modern society, and they raised the question as to whether current practices were well designed to produce individuals of such types. It began to appear doubtful whether persons who did not develop independence, the ability to make their own choices, and the capacity to tolerate the independence of others could be expected to function effectively under modern urban conditions and to make democratic institutions work. All this had a direct bearing on broad issues of economic and social development. For it called into question the idea that modern economic organization or democratic political institutions could be imposed by people on themselves, through the drafting of a plan or a constitution or the establishment of administrative procedures, without regard to the kinds of people their child-rearing systems were producing.

CHAPTER XVIII

THE ENVIRONMENT

I N the twentieth century an ever-increasing proportion of the world's people lived in urban communities. The extraordinary expansion in the size and increase in the number of the world's cities was in fact a major twentieth-century phenomenon. Both the opportunities offered by modern urban living and the problems created by the concentration of population challenged the knowledge, ingenuity, and capacity for organization of social scientists, engineers, administrators and responsible citizens.

As cities grew in size and complexity, the disparity between their ways of life and traditional rural manners of living increased. But at the same time urban influences extended more and more widely, penetrating through many channels into rural communities to modify the outlook and habits and to break down the isolation of rural people.

I. CITIES

Cities were by no means exclusively the product of industrialization; they long had served, and continued to serve, as commercial or administrative centres. The cities which set their stamp upon the life of the period, however, were primarily those which accompanied the growth of industry and were made possible by industrial technology. In the western countries, the industrial city became the focus of economic life and the milieu which not only established the way of life of its residents but modified many aspects of rural living as well. In Asia, Africa and much of Latin America large cities oriented toward the economies of the industrialized countries developed as enclaves within, and sometimes detached from, their surrounding areas. With the political and economic reorientation of these areas, they became the centres of national life.

Both in the industrialized and non-industrialized countries it was the large, metropolitan centre that grew most spectacularly in the first half of the twentieth century. In 1900, 5·5 per cent of the world's population lived in cities of 100,000 or over; by 1950 the proportion had increased to 13·1 per cent. In absolute numbers the increase was from 89 to 314 million. More than 100 million people, amounting to 4 per cent of the world's population, lived in the forty-nine cities with over a million inhabitants. In 1900 there had been only eleven such cities. Great metropolises such as London, New York, Tokyo and Shanghai had five to eight million inhabitants. In a period of ten to fifteen years São Paulo, Brazil, increased 50 per cent, while Lima, Peru and Djakarta, Indonesia, tripled. Examples could be multiplied. The sheer size of these mammoth cities required a very high degree of economic, political and social organization and the mobilization of immense physical resources to meet the daily needs of such large numbers of people. The development and maintenance of urban facilities and services on a mass scale was one of the major achievements of the age. At the same time the continual expansion of the great metropolitan cities constantly created new and difficult problems and often thwarted efforts to meet old ones.

Most of the industrial cities of the nineteenth century had experienced an uncontrolled and haphazard development. Industries dependent upon water power, steam and mechanical operations had drawn working populations and subsidiary or related industries to central locations where power was available. Private ownership of land, speculative building and the play of competitive forces had determined land use. With a few outstanding exceptions, such as the city of Amsterdam whose growth had been planned and controlled, it was only after severe congestion and insanitary conditions had developed that citizens and governments were aroused to action in the attempt to remedy existing evils and prevent their recurrence. In the face of continued growth such efforts often took the form of a rearguard struggle to prevent the situation from becoming worse. Newer industrial cities which grew up during the twentieth century rarely escaped some of these same difficulties in spite of measures for regulation and planning.

When industrial development began to reach the predominantly agricultural countries, especially after the second world war, the resulting urban growth had features which distinguished it from that of the older industrial areas. European and North American cities had grown through the pull of employment opportunities at a rate which corresponded more or less to the rate of industrial development, while empty lands overseas had offered an alternative recourse to Europe's excess peasant populations. Many Asian, Latin American and African cities, however, were filled with rural migrants who came to the city not only because there was employment for them, but often because they could not secure a livelihood from the land under existing conditions of land tenure and agricultural technology; some came as refugees from areas of political turmoil or banditry, or were lured by a vision of city life.

These cities had fewer resources with which to provide urban services than had European and American cities at any time. Yet the growth of population of the large cities of Asia from 1900 to 1950 amounted to 450 per cent as compared with 160 per cent for the large cities of Europe and America during the same period and the peak of 250 per cent for large cities in Europe from 1850 to 1900. Rates of growth in some of the large cities of the USSR and Africa were even higher.

Efforts to deal with the needs of various types of urban communities led to the development of a considerable body of systematic knowledge, tested experience and formulated principles derived chiefly from work in the western cities. At mid-century the booming cities of the newly industrializing countries were becoming the object of joint study by technicians from older and newer industrial areas and the problems of urbanization in these regions were a focal point in the United Nations' study of the world social situation and an object of its technical assistance programme. Virtually everywhere, however, action fell short of established goals.

The major physical and social aspects of the large city involved: the basic physical necessities of water supply, disposal of wastes and transport facilities; housing; land use, both in the centre and on the fringes of the urban area; provision of services for the safety, order, welfare, education and cultural development of inhabitants; city administration; social organization and citizen responsibility.

1. *Physical facilities*

(a) *Water*. As soon as population reached a density which made private wells unsafe and insufficient, the need for water became acute. This involved two problems: finding and tapping adequate sources of supply, and such purification as might be necessary to protect the population from diseases carried by contaminated water such as cholera, typhoid and dysentery. Purification by means of filtration through sand or other substance had been introduced into the public water systems of a number of European and American cities during the nineteenth century. At the opening of the twentieth century, however, many of the large cities did not have safe water supplies and epidemics of water-borne diseases were frequent.

In the first quarter of the century vigorous public health efforts to eliminate epidemic diseases led most European and American cities to ensure the purity of their water supply. Chlorination, first used on a large scale to check a typhoid epidemic in Lincoln, England, in 1905, offered a cheap and effective method for treating even badly polluted water, and remained the most commonly used process, although other chemicals were employed in some water systems. By mid-century the need to ensure pure water had become so thoroughly accepted in North America, Britain and much of western Europe that supplies had generally been made safe in smaller towns as well as in large cities, and water-borne diseases had been eliminated in these urban areas. In most other places pure water remained a major city problem.

For many cities it was easier to meet the problem of purity than that of supply. As cities expanded they outgrew their sources of supply and reached far into their hinterlands, tapping lakes and damming streams as much as a hundred or more miles away. With rising living standards and the installation of modern plumbing, *per capita* consumption of water increased sharply, taxing still further the available supply. Large quantities of water were also required in the operations of many industries. *Per capita* consumption was less than 5 gallons a day in poor areas where supplies were short or had to be carried, about 20 gallons a day in small, non-industrial communities in

Britain or the United States, 50 gallons in large commercial British cities and 100–200 gallons in North American metropolitan centres.

By the middle of the twentieth century many cities were approaching the limit of their water resources with no new source available. In heavily urbanized regions such as the British Isles, north-eastern United States and western Europe, cities competed for remaining water resources or were unable to extend their range without running into some other city's source. The competition was especially acute in relatively arid areas. Some cities were forced to supplement their clear water from lakes or streams with polluted river water which could only be used after treatment and heavy chlorination. One of the few remaining untapped sources was the ocean. It appeared that the future of some of the major urban areas near the sea would depend on the success of the search for an economical method of removing the salt from sea water. Most of the Asian cities, except in Japan, had hardly begun to try to provide an adequate supply.

(b) *Disposal of waste.* The problems of waste disposal were only second in importance to those of water supply. Sewage systems of western countries used water to carry off the wastes either directly into a river, lake or the sea or through a treatment plant where bacterial action and sedimentation reduced and collected the solid matter, made it suitable for fertilizer and left the water relatively clean. Because of the high cost of installing and maintaining an adequate sewage treatment plant, many cities dumped untreated wastes into rivers or the sea, polluting sources of water supply for cities downstream or making beaches unfit for use.

Disposal of industrial wastes created a special problem, for these often consisted of noxious chemicals, gases or other dangerous or unpleasant substances which contaminated the atmosphere and seriously polluted the areas where they were dumped. City ordinances requiring the use of devices to minimize the amount of smoke released into the air helped to reduce the pall that hung over industrial cities, blackening the home and filling the lungs with soot. Yet Birmingham, England, which enacted its first smoke control regulation in 1817, was still struggling with the smoke problem in the 1950s.

The more serious problem of atmospheric pollution from gases released by factories and by heavy motor traffic in city streets also remained unsolved and the nature of the problem was insufficiently understood. From time to time the danger was dramatized by a disaster when a particular atmospheric condition prevented noxious gases from being carried away. Such disasters in the Meuse valley, France in 1930, Donora, Pennsylvania, USA in 1948 and Poza Rica, Mexico in 1950, made hundreds of persons ill and many died. Less dramatic episodes were reflected in irregularities in the mortality rates of London and other cities. But in spite of extensive research in several countries and various attempts at control, a number of industrial cities continued to be beset from time to time by smog or other forms of irritating fumes.

Chemical wastes from industry dumped into sewage disposal systems often destroyed the bacteria on which the effectiveness of the system depended and made the solids which remained after treatment unsuitable for use as fertilizer. Chemical detergents which were increasingly used in place of soap also prevented the proper functioning of the systems. How to dispose of radioactive wastes from atomic installations was the latest and potentially the most serious of the disposal problems confronting industrial communities at the middle of the century.

Most Asian cities did not install water-borne sewage systems, or only provided such systems for a limited sector. They depended chiefly on the manual collection of night-soil, which in the case of China and Japan was the principal source of fertilizer and an essential element in the rural economy and rural–urban balance. In the groups of huts which formed the slums of Asian cities around the periphery and within the city area, lack of any satisfactory disposal system constituted a continual health menace. Construction of a sewer in Peking in the 1950s was of such importance as to be the theme of a play, *The Dragon Whisker Drain*, by one of China's leading writers, Lao Shê.

(c) *Transport*. Without adequate transport facilities no large city could function, for workers must reach their places of employment, and supplies essential for daily living must enter the city and be distributed to shops and homes. The paving and upkeep of streets was a prime charge on municipal budgets. Public transport was provided in every city by trams or buses and in most of the largest by some form of rapid transit, usually an underground or elevated electric railway. With the widespread use of automobiles, private motor transport supplemented public services and at times virtually supplanted them when it reduced the number of users of public transport below an economic level of operation.

The efficiency and cost of transport affected the shape of city growth, and this in turn brought additional transport needs. The industrial cities originally were centred around the source of power or the transport system upon which their economic activity depended, and their growth was governed by strong centripetal tendencies, as the advantages of being close to subsidiary industries reinforced the advantages of being close to power sources. With the development of electric power which freed industry from dependence on the mechanical transmission of power from its source, of telephone communication which made proximity not necessary for communication, and of motor transport which freed both goods and workers from dependence on rail or water transport, the strength of these centripetal tendencies was weakened. The costs and inconveniences of central location—especially high land values and the traffic congestion which choked the streets—exerted a counter-push toward the outskirts.

The spreading suburbs where families moved to enjoy space and single-family dwellings added to the problem of transport as increasing numbers of commuters travelled long distances and often encountered traffic delays between home and work. Streams of cars became a constant menace to life and limb. Cities undertook exhaustive studies of traffic patterns, established elaborate systems of traffic control, and adopted a variety of devices such as one-way streets, express highways into and around cities and exclusion of through-traffic from residential areas. In spite of all efforts, however, traffic congestion continued to grow. At mid-century no major city had as yet solved its traffic problems or found a means to prevent them from becoming worse. (Pl. 17a, 17b, 18.)

2. Housing

In nearly all parts of the world in the twentieth century large proportions of the urban population were housed below accepted standards of health, safety and decency. The industrial cities of Europe and America inherited a grave problem of bad and insufficient housing from the process of rapid industrialization and urban growth which took place during the nineteenth century. Other countries developed the same problem in an even more acute form as they later experienced the same process. The problem was complicated by the financial need to spread the cost of a building over the years of its use, and by questions of legal rights and economic valuation of urban land. It was intensified as rising standards of what constituted a decent and sanitary home for a worker's family called for the provision of more ample and costly dwellings and made even less tolerable the old type of dark cramped quarters.

First in Europe, then in North America and the USSR, and finally in the developing areas of Latin America, Asia and Africa, governments intervened to attempt to meet the housing needs of their working populations. By the latter half of the nineteenth century it had already become apparent that they could not ignore the dangers to health and safety which the worst of their city housing offered. Public health reports in Britain, the United States and elsewhere had brought to public attention the insanitary conditions of the typical workers' quarters where a single room constituted a home, ventilation and sunlight were often lacking and beds were frequently used successively by workers on day and night shifts. Before the close of the century regulatory laws had been passed in a number of countries, including Britain, the Scandinavian countries, Germany and several of the states in the USA.

These laws introduced the concept which provided the definition of the housing problem and the dynamic for efforts to deal with it in the succeeding years—the concept of minimum standards for decent, safe and sanitary housing which it was a public responsibility to maintain. They provided for minimum standards of safety in the use of building materials, for sanitary inspection, for the right of municipalities to require landlords to repair or destroy grossly dangerous or unsuitable structures, and in some cases for excluding from residential neighbourhoods industries whose wastes polluted the surroundings.

Regulatory measures became more widespread and were greatly elaborated in the course of the twentieth century but they did nothing to stimulate the building of new homes within the reach of workers' incomes, and thus left the basic problem of housing shortage unmet. In fact the higher standards which they required made it increasingly difficult to build dwellings which workers could afford. Moreover, so long as a shortage of decent housing existed, condemnation and destruction of slum dwellings merely pushed families into other already overcrowded or deteriorated areas.

In the early years of the twentieth century civic leaders in Europe perceived that positive steps to facilitate housing construction and to lower housing costs would have to be taken. Denmark in 1887 and Sweden, Belgium and Great Britain in the 1890s had paved the way with government aid in the form of cheap loans to co-operative building societies and other forms of government assistance to builders of low-cost housing, and some housing construction by local government had been undertaken. The Dutch in 1901 enacted comprehensive legislation for housing and town planning which was still a model for such legislation fifty years later. Prior to the first world war, some large-scale projects for middle-income families in European cities were constructed with government aid by co-operatives and other non-profit organizations, and some encouragement to the building of workers' homes was provided by other forms of public contribution. These measures were, however, limited and scattered. In Great Britain less than 10 per cent of the local authorities took advantage of the cheap loans for municipal housing or the power to acquire land on advantageous terms for workers' housing which had been authorized by law.

In the decade following the first world war European governments stepped up their housing activity sharply in an attempt to remedy the shortage which lack of home building during the war had made much worse, and to close the gap between the cost of housing and the rents which workers could afford to pay. Large numbers of workers' homes were built by local authorities, and more extensive assistance was offered to co-operatives, non-profit corporations and individuals in such forms as loans, subsidies, the provision of municipal land and relief from taxes.

By such means some 4,000,000 workers' dwellings were constructed in Europe before these efforts were brought to a halt by the economic depression, the rise of the Nazis to power in Germany and Austria, and the shift of the European economies to a war basis. The workers' houses built during these years with one or another form of public aid housed from 10 to 22 per cent of the populations of the cities where such construction was undertaken.

The houses or flats thus provided often permitted a radical change in the living standards of workers. The new quarters met and even exceeded minimum standards of space, ventilation, light and sanitation, they were located away from the danger, noise and fumes of traffic arteries and industrial plants, and they were commonly provided with play space for children and community facilities for adults. They expressed the growing conception of the worker as a citizen entitled to a decent way of life, and they expanded the community's expectation as to what urban living could and should offer.

Yet notable though this achievement was, it left the European housing problem basically unsolved and in most countries failed to prevent the situation from deteriorating. New migrants continued to enter the cities and new urban families to be formed faster than new homes were built. The UN Economic Commission for Europe estimated that on the eve of the second world war there had been an accumulated deficit of over 12,000,000 houses. It noted that in the inter-war years 'Europe never built enough housing for the current needs of new families and for the replacement of dwellings obsolete because of age' and that 'slum conditions and community blight were . . . growing worse and more widespread'.*

The USA and Canada did not accept the construction of sufficient housing as a public responsibility until long after the principle had been well established in other industrialized countries, though their municipalities and states had enacted regulatory measures, and the control of neighbourhoods by means of zoning had become widespread after its introduction in 1916. The need seemed less apparent in these countries where real estate was a favourite form of speculative investment for people of small means as well as large, confidence in private enterprise was strong, and the worst slums were generally occupied by the latest immigrants who moved to better quarters after a few years. Not until the 1930s did the United States embark on a programme to facilitate the financing of private building by means of government mortgage insurance and loans, and to provide subsidized public housing for low-income families to replace their slum homes.

Soviet Russia recognized housing as a problem of critical importance and included measures to deal with it at each stage of national development. The first step, immediately after the October revolution, was to make sure that existing housing was fully used. Housing for rent and large mansions were nationalized and all space not fully occupied was used for the homeless and those housed in cellars or other unsuitable shelter. During the following decade a considerable volume of housing was built or made more habitable, some by government building some by state-aided co-operative societies. The rate of building in these years was, however, limited by the inefficiency of the building industry, material shortages and the concentration of effort on the development of heavy industry.

In the series of five-year plans from 1928 on, housing received a significant and growing place. The first five-year plan called for more than a doubling of the public investment in housing and for measures to begin to modernize the building industry. Each of the succeeding plans provided for a sharp increase in volume. On the eve of the second world war the total supply of housing had been increased by some 40 per cent since the mid-1920s. Nevertheless, the concentration of productive resources on basic industrial development under these plans entailed certain sacrifices in consumption, and housing

* UN Economic Commission for Europe, *The European Housing Problem—A Preliminary Review* (UN, E/ECE.110, 1 October, 1949).

competed directly with heavy industry for materials and workers. The gap was therefore not bridged between the supply of housing and the size of the urban population, which more than doubled during these years. Though the quality of much workers' housing was improved by more modern construction, homelessness was eliminated and tenants were protected in their occupancy, the rationed space enjoyed by most workers remained below the accepted sanitary housing standards.

At the close of the second world war it was apparent that far more drastic measures than had hitherto been contemplated by even the most ambitious of the European governments would be necessary to reconstruct the devastated areas, keep pace with growing demands and make a dent on the backlog of accumulated deficiency. The Economic Commission for Europe noted that even if pre-war rates of housing construction were doubled, it would take an average of twenty-two years for the European countries to come abreast of their housing needs. It was apparent too that home building for low-income urban families had ceased to attract profit-making private investment, since current building costs would require prohibitive rents, equal to about a third of a European worker's income. The European governments accordingly expanded their programmes of construction or financial aid as fast as their financial resources permitted.

The British followed the system of municipally constructed housing for all except upper-income families while the Scandinavian pattern was to provide government aid to co-operative, trade union or other non-speculative groups, sometimes including a rent subsidy for the benefit of lower-income families. Dutch housing followed both systems. Though in most countries legislation continued to provide encouragement to private builders, the great bulk of European home building for urban workers in the decade after the second world war was by public authorities or by non-profit agencies under government supervision. In spite of these enlarged efforts, however, most countries failed to keep pace with the current needs of their growing populations and deficits continued to increase.

In the United States a high level of general prosperity and generous public assistance in such forms as mortage insurance, loans to war veterans, and other special aids stimulated widespread private building activity, especially in the suburban areas surrounding all major cities. The result was to meet a much larger proportion of the desire for home ownership than had been met there or elsewhere in the past. New housing, however, still was beyond the reach of many low-income families. Public housing programmes were small and were limited to families whose incomes were well below the level for which private interests could be expected to build decent homes at current costs. Numbers of urban families continued to exist in crowded dilapidated slums, particularly those whose inability to find and afford suitable accommodation was intensified by size of family, instability of employment or racial discrimination; some were reluctant to leave familiar surroundings for a new environment.

When Canada enacted national housing legislation in 1954, the range of methods which it provided reflected the accumulated experience of other countries. These included: government provision of insurance for mortgage loans and loans for home improvement; guarantee of a minimum income from rent to builders of certain types of rental housing; low-interest housing loans from public or other regulated sources to municipalities, co-operatives or other non-speculative groups; public construction of housing; rent subsidies for low-income families; and grants to municipalities for slum clearance and the redevelopment of urban areas.

The USSR, with a third of its already insufficient urban dwellings destroyed by war, made a drastic effort to replace the loss and to catch up with mounting needs. Even during the war the government carried on a large-scale building programme to provide housing for the populations evacuated to the east and other workers in the new industrial cities beyond the Urals, and for the restoration of shelter in the western areas as rapidly as they were liberated. A central state committee on architecture was established in 1943 to supervise and co-ordinate the rehousing programme and special factories were set up for the mass manufacture of standardized houses and other building materials. In the 1946–50 five-year plan for the rehabilitation and development of the national economy, housing was assigned 14·5 per cent of total capital investment as compared with 10·5 per cent under the last pre-war plan. In accordance with this schedule the loss through wartime destruction was more than made up in urban areas, but the growth in urban population of some 30 per cent in the 1940–50 decade kept ahead of the rate of new construction. The succeeding five-year plan attempted to produce housing faster than the rate of urban population growth by raising the output and lowering the costs of the construction industry through mechanization and the development of new materials, designs and methods of assembly, and by seeking devices for carrying on construction during the winter. After 1955 the rate of housing construction rose very sharply, reaching more than double the 1955 volume by 1958.[1]

As the underdeveloped areas plunged into the process of accelerated industrialization after the second world war, all the housing problems which had beset the industrialized countries burst upon them in exaggerated form. Levels of income were lower in relation to the cost of building than they had been at any time in Europe or America. The numbers involved and the rate of urban growth exceeded those with which most of the older industrial cities had had to deal at any one time. A larger proportion of the total population was unable to secure or afford decent accommodation; in major Indian cities, for example, not only the vast majority of the working class but 50 per cent of the middle-class families lived in single rooms. Capital resources, building materials and skills were extremely scarce. At the same time the public conscience was already aroused against conditions which earlier generations would have accepted as the natural lot of the poor.

In the face of overwhelming odds governments in Latin America, Asia and Africa set up special agencies and cast about for new solutions beyond those which European countries had tried. They first followed the European lead in undertaking construction by public agencies or through publicly established mortgage banks. Some programmes were of spectacular size, such as a Bombay development housing 20,000 people where a few months before there had been only mud flats. But even these barely touched the need of a growing city like Bombay, where at least 2,000,000 of its 3,000,000 inhabitants slept in one-room airless *chawls* or under low shelters made of scraps of cardboard, sacking and tin, or on the pavement. In most of the underdeveloped countries government-built housing was occupied by government workers or other middle-class families with sufficient income to pay an economic rent. Few governments were able to provide the subsidies which would have been required to enable the vast majority of urban workers to enjoy decent housing.

In the search for less costly ways to meet the most essential needs governments devised various means to utilize the occupant's own labour to build his shelter, especially in tropical areas where less substantial construction would provide more adequate shelter than in colder climates. Around the fringes of Latin American and Asian cities, squatters built shacks on hillsides, in gullies, along roadsides, in fields. Often they occupied public land from which it was difficult to evict those who had nowhere else to go. 'Pirate' suburbs sprang up overnight beyond the limits set for the extension of water, sewage and roads.

Unable to prevent this growth, governments attempted to give it shape by setting aside land equipped with minimum facilities, where families were permitted to construct their homes. The most elaborate of these 'land and utilities' projects consisted of individual water and sanitary units and cement floors, spaced on small plots; others provided central water, sanitary and laundry facilities for a group of plots where houses could be put up; some offered only streets, a public source of water and materials for sanitary latrines. Some urban communities adapted from rural areas programmes of 'aided self-help' housing whereby groups of families, organized to work co-operatively, joined in the building of each others' houses under the guidance of a public agency which supplied plans, instructions for the making of building blocks and other materials, and technical supervision of the project. Such plans, which originated for rural housing in the Caribbean area and were developed for large-scale urban housing in Chile, were taken up in a number of regions, including other Latin American countries. They generally included a system of loans or subsidies to enable the occupants to purchase the materials, as well as municipal provision of water, sewage and electricity.

While these programmes were welcomed, not only because they offered a practical approach to certain types of housing but because of the education and the stimulus to responsible effort and co-operation which they provided, they could not offer even a remote solution to the housing problem in cities such as Singapore, where the official standard of overcrowding was defined as five or more persons per room, or Hong Kong, where housing for Chinese refugees took the form of one-room dwellings in six-storey buildings, with an average of five 'persons' per room—children counted as $\frac{1}{2}$ person—and a population density of 2,500–3,000 persons per acre.

In the effort to break out of the vicious housing circle in which both the industrialized and industrializing countries were caught, attention was directed to improvement in methods of home building. The Economic Commission for Europe noted in 1951 that the costs of building were a cause of concern, since in most countries there was no evidence of a significant increase in the productivity of the building industry.

During the twentieth century the building industry everywhere lagged behind other industries in technological development; it lacked the organization or orientation to engage in the kind of research that brought revolutionary advances in other fields, and the cost of housing in consequence remained high relative to workers' wages and the prices of other products. An indication of the meaning of this difference in technological development may be seen in the comparison of the automobile and building industries in the United States. Although the building industry of that country was one of the most mechanized and highly developed in the world, it was estimated that, if a 1950 American automobile costing $1,700 had been made with as little change in technology since 1910 as the building industry had shown in those forty years, the car would have cost $60,000.

Such a comparison gives an exaggerated view, for the production of housing differs in its nature from that of automobiles, and it was relatively more advanced in 1910. But factors limiting progress in building were real. Specialization of function in the building industry continued to be based on a series of independent craft activities which had to be co-ordinated rather than on a division of labour within a single process, as in factory production. The economic possibilities of mechanization, standardization of parts, factory production and the reorganization of construction methods were often resisted or ignored by tightly organized building labour, jealous of its craft prerogatives, by architects and engineers trained to design and plan in terms of existing techniques, and by builders who were often small local entrepreneurs.

The need for basic and systematic research was recognized by the British after the first world war, but their building research station, established in 1921, remained the only such national research organization until the second world war, when one European country after another began to establish national building research organizations. An International Council for Building Research and Documentation was formed at the initiative of the United Nations Economic Commission for Europe in 1949 and some forty national organizations, public and private, became members when it held its first general assembly in 1953.

Efforts to bring some of the economies of organized mass production into the building industry took two forms: factory prefabrication of parts of houses, to be assembled on the site; and application of the principles of assembly-line production to the building process at the site itself.

Prefabrication of frame structures was developed in the early years of the century in areas, especially North America, where wood was a common building material, but these proved suitable primarily for small buildings, warm climates and temporary use. In the inter-war period considerable experimentation was carried on by manufacturers in the use of new and lighter materials such as aluminium sheathing or composition board and with new methods of insulation. After the second world war the USSR concentrated on the development of prefabricated wall panels, roofs, floors and other structures of reinforced concrete in its determined effort to mechanize its construction industry, and experiments along similar lines with special types of concrete and other materials continued in other countries.

Mass-assembly at the site itself was more widespread than factory prefabrication, except in the Soviet Union, and more successful in holding down costs; in the United States it brought a high degree of rationalization into the building of large housing projects. Where a large number of houses or blocks of apartments were built simultaneously, the project was set up as a single operation, with materials delivered or produced on the site and crews of workers executing successive parts of the job with the timing and precision of a factory assembly line. Economies of such site-assembly methods were increased by the development of standard units which could be used flexibly in different multiples and combinations in designing the house, and which could be fabricated on a mass-production basis.

Further efforts to reduce building costs, especially in the industrially under-developed countries, took the form of experiments with the use of low-cost local building materials, such as various forms of stabilized earth, tile or treated bamboo. Where space and transport facilities permitted the building of small houses rather than multi-storey apartments, economical construction of this sort offered a possibility for improving the living conditions of the pavement dwellers and the residents of shacks or cubicles without involving costs which neither the occupants nor the municipalities could afford.

In spite of widespread efforts to meet the urban housing problem there remained a paucity of knowledge as to the actual needs and desires of families of different types in varying circumstances and cultural settings. Some types of city dwellers, moreover, were persistently overlooked, notably the large numbers of persons who were permanently or temporarily unattached, and the special needs of others, such as old people, were only beginning to be considered in the planning and construction of housing facilities.

Although the most distinctive architectural school of the twentieth century, the functionalists, insisted that the house should be designed as a 'machine for living', systematic studies of family living in relation to housing design were few. An international review of such research up to 1953* found some limited

* United Nations, *Housing and Town and Country Planning Bulletin*, no. 8 (1953).

studies being carried on in the Scandinavian countries, the Netherlands, Britain and the United States; only occasionally, notably in Norway and the United States, were the results of such research used to introduce changes in design and then to study the effects of such changes systematically. The volume of research into social aspects of housing was however growing. In the Latin American countries it received special impetus from the work of the Inter-American Housing Center located in Bogotá, Colombia.

A guide to needed research provided by one of the leading experts in the field of housing in 1953 listed a few of the unanswered social questions in housing and town planning as follows:

(1) the effect of the kind of urban environment being produced, or capable of being produced, on social organizations, human relations and emerging trends in social values and attitudes;

(2) what people would want if they knew the full range of possibilities and all the practical limitations, and how such knowledge could be conveyed and desires expressed;

(3) why people move and how their habits are affected by change from old to new environments;

(4) whether the desire for home ownership is a desire for ownership *per se*, or for an opportunity to live at ground level;

(5) what are the effects of various policies for selecting tenants for large housing projects and of the relation between manager and tenants;

(6) what are the relative advantages of apartments which can be provided, as in Sweden, with services to aid housewife and children, as against the single-family house and garden which is the basis for housing developments in Britain;

(7) in designing houses, what is the comparative importance of space and equipment, and how is the appropriate design affected by the available community facilities; how in fact have the facilities which have been supplied in housing developments been used;

(8) what is the social effect of segregating groups of families on the basis of economic level, size, type, age-group or ethnic identity, as a result of the cost or design of buildings or selection of occupants, as against housing designed to bring into the same neighbourhood a mixture of families of different types and circumstances;

(9) who uses neighbourhood and who central city facilities, and in what respects is the neighbourhood principle a valid conception for planning; in the light of high rates of mobility, should the attempt be made to create environments which will induce people to settle down;

(10) what variety of homes are needed by different kinds of households; are housing standards too low or too rigid ?*

* Catherine Bauer, 'Social Questions in Housing and Community Planning', *Journal of Social Issues*, vol. vii, nos. 1 and 2 (1951).

Although, as this partial list of unanswered questions revealed, much was yet to be learned with respect to the social aspects of urban housing, it was beginning to be recognized that urban housing involved not merely financial and physical problems but the social structure of city life, and that this aspect required as systematic study as the techniques of construction. The author of the above list of questions concluded by noting: 'What we failed to recognize was that the powerful tools employed for civic development and home production *also* predetermine social structure to such an extent that there is little room left for free personal choice or flexible adjustment' and that 'the most hopeful and ingenious innovations have often been wasted, because no one tested them to see how they really worked'.

It was indicative of the growing awareness of these social implications that the Inter-American Housing Center, established under the technical assistance programme of the Organization of American States at Bogotá in 1951, included social workers as well as engineers, architects and lawyers in its group of trainees from the housing administrations of the Latin American countries, and that these specialists studied and worked as a team on the critical housing problems of their region.

3. *Land use and city planning*

The uses to which urban land was put determined the location and type of housing, the character of neighbourhoods, the shape of the city and the pattern of physical growth. Control over urban land use was the principal device by which attempts were made to guide these developments in the public interest. In the course of the twentieth century restrictions were placed in most large communities on such use, and many cities adopted positive plans and programmes for the development of sectors of the city or the entire area.

Within whatever limits were set by national or local measures for control, cities tended to follow a common pattern of development. Industry and commerce crowded toward the centre in order to take advantage of convenience, transport facilities, labour supply and, until electricity became general, sources of power. Factories clustered around rail and water termini, or formed industrial nuclei, or satellite towns on the periphery. Residential sections ringed the central district or occupied higher ground above a waterside rail and dock area.

As the city grew, business and industry pressed outward against the residential area, and rising land values and changing neighbourhoods drove occupants to seek pleasanter surroundings further out. A new residential area was constructed while part of the old was replaced by business and the rest became a slum where old single-family homes were cut up, room by room, into quarters for workers' families, or were replaced by tenement houses into which workers' families were tightly packed. As the city continued to grow, new residential sections repeated the fate of the old, when industry, business and slums penetrated into these districts.

With the coming of rapid transit systems and then the motor car to link people with their places of work, the city spread its suburbs farther and farther into the surrounding countryside. In time some of the central slum areas began to be reclaimed and reconstructed, chiefly with high-rent, multi-storey apartments for those who could afford to shorten the long journey to work and did not feel the need of the space and greenery which suburban living offered. Slum dwellers displaced in this process either crowded into the remaining central slums or took the opposite course to the extreme fringe where land values had not yet risen so high as to be completely out of their reach and where they often formed colonies of squatters, shack-towns or edge-of-town slums.

Meantime, suburbia continued to grow and to widen—in fingers along traffic arteries and rapid-transit routes, in spotty developments where a land-owner chose to build a group of houses on his farm or home site, by incor-porating into the metropolitan community what had once been neighbouring villages or towns, or in a solid front that spread the city circumference to wider and wider limits. The suburban sprawl produced growing traffic congestion as more and more thousands travelled daily between centrally located places of work and suburban homes. Commercial establishments set up branches in outlying areas, large suburban shopping centres began to draw trade from centrally located stores, central land values declined and the city found itself with a spreading fringe and decaying core. Around the outskirts was a sort of no-man's-land between city and country. Farms went out of cultivation as speculators bought up land ahead of the city's advance or rising land values brought taxes that farmers could not pay. Until the spreading city encom-passed the area, land was often left untended, covered with squatters' shacks, spottily developed with isolated suburban units, scarred by roads and dumps and continually in a process of transition. (Pl. 19a, 19b.)

The nature of measures to control or guide this urban growth differed according to historic circumstances and urban traditions in different parts of the world. Those cities of northern Europe that had a tradition of strong local government, civic pride and orderly control frequently dating from the Middle Ages, and which often owned much of the surrounding land, never experienced the chaotic growth or faced the necessity for drastic remedial action comparable to that faced by cities in many other regions. As the impact of industrialization brought new problems, these cities adopted measures designed to permit orderly development. Sweden in 1874 enacted a law requiring every city to have plans regulating the layout of residential sections as well as streets, market places and public squares. Frankfurt, Germany, in 1891 introduced the idea of zoning. The Dutch housing and town planning legislation of 1901 included comprehensive provisions for the control of land use.

In Britain and North America on the other hand, and in much of the rest of Europe, industrial cities grew up in a climate of *laissez-faire*. Here private landowners determined the use to which urban land would be put during the period of the city's growth. Decisions as to what to build and where were dictated by the entrepreneurial decisions of individual owners, real estate dealers and speculative builders. Municipal improvements, such as streets and public utilities, followed where profit-seeking enterprise led. Once these had been laid out, the pattern of the city was more or less fixed, and replanning of built-up areas became difficult or impossible. (Pl. 45a.)

The British were the first to seek to apply social remedies to the conditions created by uncontrolled urban growth. By the middle of the nineteenth century their major industrial cities, such as Birmingham, were already awakening to the fact that their open spaces had disappeared. In the 1870s British municipalities received authority from Parliament to condemn buildings which constituted a menace to health and to require their improvement or destruction. This was the first attack on the worst of the urban slums. Building regulations also limited the kinds of construction permitted in certain areas. American cities began to follow suit, including in their regulations limits on the proportion of an urban lot which could be covered by a residential building. By the end of the nineteenth century the principle was becoming clearly established that owners of urban land could use their property only within limits set by the public interest.

Elsewhere other traditional approaches to city development prevailed. The cities of Latin America, laid out in the manner prescribed by royal order in the sixteenth century, preserved and beautified their central plazas and frequently repeated the pattern with smaller plazas in other parts of the city. For the rest their growth was unsystematic and uncontrolled. France too had a tradition of central beautification dating from the mid-nineteenth century when Napoleon III commissioned Georges Haussmann (1809–91) to open up the heart of Paris. Other cities such as Vienna, Brussels and Berlin followed the example of Paris by cutting wide boulevards through congested slums and adorning the centre of the city with parks. Apart from these measures, France, Italy and other parts of southern and eastern Europe adopted neither the orderly development established in Sweden and Holland nor the remedial approach of Britain. Asian cities were generally a compound of palaces, temples or gardens laid out by and for past rulers, adaptations of European standards introduced by colonial powers into areas occupied by Europeans, and unlimited land coverage with intense crowding in the rest of the city.

The USSR substituted for the pattern of unregulated growth in tsarist Russia the planned development of new towns and the replanning of old cities. Here and in the other communist countries state ownership of land and central control of financial resources made it possible to approach these problems with less regard for the relation between the cost of supplying housing and the ability of the tenants to pay, and without the need to deal with private owners of the land. Housing was generally regarded as one of the public social services and the policy was to make living quarters available to workers at costs of no more than 5 per cent of their earnings.

In the course of the twentieth century regulation of urban land use was greatly extended in all countries and a common set of devices were applied, with differences arising from historic patterns of landholding and forms of control. In countries where landholding had been widely dispersed in small units, such as France, Belgium and the USA, a strong feeling that individual ownership was in the public interest tended to keep public intervention to a minimum. Where landholding had historically been concentrated, as in the United Kingdom, there was greater readiness to regard land as affected with a public interest and to accept broad measures governing its use. In Russia the complete absence of control prior to the first world war was replaced by the elimination of all private ownership of urban land under the Soviet régime.

Though countries differed in the manner in which they compensated owners for the loss of property rights, the general trend was to follow the distinction explicitly stated for Great Britain by Mr Justice Uthwatt in the report on which the comprehensive Town and Country Planning Act of 1944 was based.* Where the state actually took property, it would have to pay compensation to the owner since the state had no right to requisition property without compensation. Where the state by regulation limited the use which an owner could make of his property, it would be under no obligation to pay compensation although the owner might suffer a financial loss, since the right to use the property in the prohibited manner was not taken over by the state but destroyed as contrary to the public interest.

The use of building regulations which specified minimum standards of construction for buildings in certain areas, one of the oldest methods of controlling land development, was widespread and the scope of such regulations was enlarged. Building codes were usually adopted city by city, though in some countries such as Japan they were enacted on a national basis. Although building codes were necessary as defensive measures against unsafe construction, they sometimes had the effect of delaying technological development and the use of new materials, they tended to increase building costs and at best they served only to prevent the worst uses of land under regulation.

Broader control was provided by means of zoning, which designated certain areas as residential, commercial or industrial and specified the types of housing, e.g. single- or multi-family dwellings, and kinds of business or industrial activity permitted within them, as well as such matters as height of buildings and percentage of land to be covered. Zoning ordinances were adopted by German cities at the end of the nineteenth century and became the most widely used device in the United States and Canada after 1916. Similar results were obtained by town planning laws in some European countries. Zoning was only beginning to be adopted by the Latin American cities toward the middle of the twentieth century.

While zoning regulations provided an indispensable tool to prevent the

* *Final Report: Expert Committee on Compensation and Betterment* (H.M. Stationery Office, London, 1942), pp. 19–20.

further misuse of land, they could not undo the damage already done since they only applied to future construction and use. Moreover, zoning of specific neighbourhoods in a piecemeal fashion might not result in an orderly pattern unless it was combined with some procedure for the overall planning of the entire city. This was evidenced in the spotty development of many of 2,000 or more towns and cities in the United States which employed the zoning device.

The regulation of land subdivision on the outskirts of cities became increasingly important as cities spread outward and the suburban population grew. Many countries adopted regulations requiring the approval of plans for new subdivisions before the owner or builder was authorized to proceed with construction. Such plans prescribed the layout of streets and open spaces, access to through traffic and protection from it, the location and types of utilities, houses, shopping centres and public buildings. Subdivision regulation was often seriously hampered, however, by the fact that many cities lacked jurisdiction over land outside their municipal limits to which the city population was spreading. In 1953 one-third of the population of metropolitan Toronto, Canada, for example, lived in suburbs beyond the Toronto municipal limits. As in the case of zoning, moreover, subdivision control gave effective direction to city growth only where it was combined with overall planning.

Measures to clear away slums, particularly those located near the heart of the city, were undertaken by many European cities in the first quarter of the twentieth century, in the United States in the 1930s and in other countries after the second world war. Such measures generally took the form of the acquisition of slum land by the municipality, destruction of existing dwellings and the rebuilding of the area by public effort or its dedication to parks or other public uses. Slum clearance too encountered basic difficulties. The high value of the land occupied by slums, the cost of new building and the reduction of population in overcrowded areas made it impossible for most of the original slum dwellers to return to the area unless aided by rent subsidies. Slum clearance projects were costly to the government, although there was good evidence in many places that the costs would more than be made up in reduced requirements for police, fire, hospital and other expenses arising from the crowded, unhealthy and disorganized life of the slums. As displaced families moved into other sections of the city, the clearing of one slum area only worsened the conditions in others. So long as the basic problem of providing enough housing for the growing population remained unsolved, slum clearance was only a rearguard action against urban blight.

Acquisition by municipalities of vacant land, and control over the time and manner of its use, came to be the most important aspect of the land-use policy of many of the countries which had gone farthest in the effort to guide and control city growth. The city of Stockholm, Sweden, for example, began to acquire large tracts of lands both within and outside the city in 1904 and by 1950 owned more than half of the land within the city limits and an almost equal amount outside. Land reserves were acquired by municipalities to be used at the time and in the manner called for by an overall city plan in a number of countries, including the Scandinavian countries, Britain, Germany, Austria, Turkey and some countries of Latin America.

Cities in several countries adopted a variety of other devices, such as differential taxation to penalize or encourage the use of land for particular purposes, rent controls, various measures to reduce the value of centrally located land and make possible its less dense use, and reparcelling of land where ownership patterns interfered with sound development.

In the years after the second world war it appeared that all these piecemeal efforts would not rescue the decayed centres of the overgrown cities. Broad plans for the redevelopment of whole sections of cities were undertaken, with enabling legislation permitting municipalities to acquire land, lower its appraised value, demolish existing structures and replan and reconstruct the area, aided in some cases by national subsidies. Such programmes for urban redevelopment were put into effect in the rebuilding of British and continental European cities shattered during the second world war, as well as in un-damaged cities of the United States, Canada and some parts of Latin America. But urban redevelopment too came up against the continuing shortage of decent housing for ever-growing city populations and plans were repeatedly thwarted by the unsolved problem of where families could go who were dis-placed in the process. Where speedy reconstruction or the need to keep down costs were major considerations, moreover, the advantage of using existing utilities and streets laid out according to old patterns hampered the more rational use of space.

Attempts to create communities in the outlying areas which would provide the conditions for healthy and satisfying living dated from the opening of the century, when the garden city movement, launched by Ebenezer Howard (1850–1928) in 1898 (*Tomorrow: A Peaceful Path to Real Reform*), led to the building of Britain's first garden city, Letchworth, in 1903. While Howard's idea had been to divert population from large urban centres by creating new, self-contained communities of some 30,000 people, garden cities became in fact dormitory suburbs. In other countries planning of garden suburbs became part of the general city plan, as in Sweden, where residential communities situated at the stations on the suburban railway were carefully planned to contain a balanced supply of different types of housing, shops, schools and other facilities, and a layout which offered convenience, safety from traffic and access to green areas.

Overall planning for the development of the total city spread during the twentieth century from the well-ordered cities of northern Europe to many parts of the world. Britain adopted its first Town Planning Act in 1909. The first official city plan in the United States was prepared by the city of Hartford, Connecticut in 1907, and twenty years later city planning commissions were at work in some 400 United States communities. The broad-gauged Moscow city plan of 1936 greatly stimulated the planning and replanning of Russian cities; the second five-year plan called for the reconstruction of some 400 cities, and the city plans developed as part of this programme later provided the basis for rebuilding many cities destroyed during the second world war. In 1937 Germany set up machinery for the general planning of towns. The establishment in that year of the International Federation for Housing and Town Planning with headquarters at The Hague evidenced the widespread interest in the field.

The scope of most of the city planning bodies was first confined to the layout of roads, streets and parks and the placing of public buildings and utilities. In some countries or communities planning was still in this stage at the middle of the century. Most planning bodies, however, extended their scope to include the location of residential, industrial and commercial activities and the provision of community services.

Initially planning agencies tended to prepare master plans with the idea that these would serve as a permanent guide to the city's development. But constantly changing conditions made it apparent that planning would have to be a continuous process of evaluation and re-evaluation and that the function of the body entrusted with the task must be to offer continuous leadership rather than a single proposal. Furthermore, the complexity of the task, the variety of factors and interests needing to be considered and the dependence of any plan for its execution on co-operation or acquiescence by the public led to the establishment of advisory bodies and the participation of professional and civic groups in the planning process.

Where, as was usually the case, the local municipality was the planning unit, the need to plan for territory outside the city limits led to a partial breakdown of planning efforts in some places, co-operative planning by adjacent jurisdictions in others, and in some to the intervention of the national government. By the middle of the twentieth century sufficient powers had been created by law in most countries to permit cities to carry out their plans. But here again practical difficulties arising from the growth of the urban population repeatedly prevented execution.

At the heart of the city planning process lay two closely related issues which remained unresolved up to the middle of the twentieth century: whether to allow high density of land use by constructing multi-storey apartment buildings or to spread out the population more thinly in single-family homes; and whether to plan for an ever-expanding metropolis or to use the tools of planning and control to develop a multitude of smaller cities rather than a few gigantic metropolitan areas.

The issue of low-density versus apartment building arose out of the differing practices in Britain and on the European continent, and alternate conceptions of the desirable use of space. As British towns grew they spread out over wide areas, and even the poorest housing was generally at ground level with some space for a garden. The principles laid down by British planners, who considered private space for the family outside the dwelling as an essential part of satisfactory housing, was a density of no more than 24–30 families per hectare (10–12 per acre). On the European continent, however, central areas were built up with apartment buildings. Although the housing and planning programmes of these countries sought to reduce extreme densities, they contemplated the continued use of multi-family dwellings. The Swiss-French architect Le Corbusier was a leading exponent of the view that better living could be provided more economically by multi-storey structures equipped with centrally operated conveniences, surrounded by open areas available for common use, than by giving each family a private little plot and burdening it with the costs and inconveniences of maintaining a single dwelling. The issue was complicated by the problems of transport and traffic congestion and by those relating to the encroachment of the cities on the surrounding agricultural land. (Pl. 45b.)

The issue of metropolitanism versus smaller cities was even more difficult to resolve. Experience left little doubt that most of the problems of urban living which appeared nearly insoluble in the large metropolis assumed more manageable proportions in small cities. The costs of providing small cities with municipal facilities, transport, housing and space for decent living were generally only a fraction of those involved in providing equivalent facilities in metropolitan centres. On the other hand large numbers were necessary to make a wide variety of services economical. Opinions differed on the social effect of metropolitan living. One major school, following the pioneer British city planner Sir Patrick Geddes (1854–1932) and such architects as the American Frank Lloyd Wright (1869–1959), maintained that the huge metropolis was in and of itself an inhuman institution. They held that the evils of noise, congestion, traffic, tension and impersonality, even more than considerations of cost, should dictate policies designed to check metropolitan growth. Others however saw positive human values in the rich complexity of the metropolis.

In spite of the logic of the case for small cities and the persuasiveness of those who urged the dispersal of industry and population among cities of moderate size, the trend toward metropolitanism continued unabated throughout the period. Much industry continued to seek metropolitan areas rather than smaller centres, drawn by a combination of factors which outweighed the disadvantages of high land costs and the delays from traffic congestion; as noted by the Regional Plan of New York in 1922, the relevant question was not why any industry tried to locate near the centre of a metropolis but what prevented it from doing so. The attractions of the metropolitan communities as centres of cultural activities, as well as their role as expanding administrative centres, contributed further to the unchecked growth of the largest cities.

The very process of coping with the city's problems often stimulated still more growth. Once traffic congestion, overcrowding or inadequacy of facilities had developed, it was almost impossible for planning agencies not to recommend measures to relieve the unsatisfactory conditions. Express highways or improved rapid transit to carry workers to and from work, new housing to lessen congestion, public utilities and social services to meet needs for water, sanitation, education and welfare all became imperatives which city administrations and planning agencies could not ignore. Yet in meeting these needs they made it possible for still more people to come into the city, occupy its houses and enjoy its facilities and services. Furthermore, the most powerful interests in the city were often those which stood to gain from continued expansion and they were reluctant to support steps to limit the process. At mid-century the metropolitan drift was still unchecked.

Two countries, Russia and Great Britain, made determined efforts to restrain metropolitan growth and to create new moderate-sized industrial towns.

Town planning in the USSR went along with general economic planning and was accomplished by the use of three principal means of control: ownership of urban land by the state, location of industry as determined by official plans, and the allocation of capital funds for construction as part of the overall capital budget of the country. In line with the development of industry and especially the opening up of the Asian areas and the eastward shift of population, town planning focused on the building of workers' settlements and new industrial cities. Some 200 new cities were built before the second world war and another 67 during the war.

Each town was planned as a distinct unit with due regard for its natural environment, its functions and its national culture and heritage, and with ample provision for parks, green belts and community facilities such as schools, nurseries, hospitals and cultural centres. Its central core was designed to give an impressive appearance and to provide a focus for the life of the community. Care was exercised to avoid too great contrasts between the central and suburban areas and to preserve standardization of design. These cities were planned with the objective of limiting their growth, generally to a population of less than 500,000.

At the time of the third five-year plan the policy was adopted of permitting no new industrial construction in large cities and of distributing medium- and small-sized enterprises to small communities. This policy was subsequently modified however on the ground that with modern facilities for transport it is more economical to concentrate the production of many types of finished products in a single centre. Instead of seeking to create cities of optimum size, urban planning looked toward large cities surrounded by suburbs, satellite towns and urbanized rural regions, so organized as to provide for appropriate specialization of function. The development of these large urbanized areas, together with the continuing development of small cities and new regions to supply raw materials and semi-finished goods, was envisaged as a rational pattern for an industrialized society and as a means of merging city and country and reducing the distinctions between urban and rural life.

Great Britain made a bold effort after the second world war to transcend the limitations of earlier planning measures. The comprehensive nation-wide programme adopted under the Town and Country Planning Act enacted during the war combined the principle of municipal responsibility with national supervision, financial aid and direct action. Initiative for local plans came from the municipalities, which used a planning procedure involving the active participation of citizen groups. The city of Birmingham for example prepared its development plan in 1952 on the basis of recommendations by twenty-one citizens' committees and eleven public bodies. The national government approved local plans or secured their modification in the light of the plans of other communities, it provided a measure of financial aid in carrying them out, it exercised the necessary controls over the surrounding country and it undertook directly the planning and establishment of new towns to relieve some of the pressure of population on the old. Plans called for the reduction of population density in the congested central areas and the systematic provision for facilities and services according to accepted standards.

In order to check the outward spread, prevent the blighting of rural areas and the loss of good arable land by the penetration of city fringes, and to ensure access to the country by the city dwellers, areas surrounding cities were designated as green belts in which land was restricted to agricultural use and urban construction prohibited. This was an important step, for little attention had generally been given in Britain or elsewhere to the relationship between city and surrounding countryside. Those responsible for city development had rarely been concerned with the effect of city expansion on nearby agriculture, while those interested in agriculture and rural life had limited their attention to the areas which continued to be farmed, while the no-man's-land between city and farm lay outside the scope of both.

A vital part of the overall British plan called for the creation of a series of new towns, outside metropolitan areas, designed and constructed by the national government to accommodate groups of relatively small industries and populations of approximately 50,000. These new towns were indispensable elements in the overall plan if the other objectives were to be achieved and the metropolitan cities prevented from spreading out in an ever-wider circle. The 1952 planning commission of the city of Birmingham, for example, calculated that there would be an overspill of 60,000 by 1971 if the plans were carried out for reducing the central density and for the orderly development of the city up to the edge of the green belt. The new towns were successful in attracting industry and population, but it was still not clear in the mid-1950s whether they would be developed fast enough to check the growth of metropolitan areas. (Pl. 20a.)

As Asian governments attempted to bring under control their booming metropolises, they found their situation even more difficult than that of the older industrialized areas. Asian cities were generally composed of a relatively small area where local *élites* and European residents patterned their living on the cities of the West, while the bulk of the population lived in neighbour-hoods which closely resembled rural villages in manner of living, social organi-zation and often in types of dwelling. The extreme poverty of the population and the high rate of its increase presented insuperable problems to munici-palities with their very limited resources and to the national treasuries subject to heavy demands for investment in economic development. With perhaps as much as 85 per cent of the population of Asian cities unable to afford decent housing constructed according to the most austere standards, most of the methods employed in the West appeared doomed to failure. To many it seemed that development of smaller cities was even more essential to the solution of urban problems in this region than in the West and it was the professed policy of most governments to encourage decentralization of industry and to attempt to check the flow from rural to urban areas by improving the conditions of rural life.

The representatives of the Asian countries attending the United Nations seminar on urbanization in Asia and the Far East at Bangkok, Thailand, in August 1956 concluded that a regional approach was essential to permit planning in terms of the interrelation between urban and rural areas and among communities within a region and to relate community planning to national development. They noted however that for their area the state of knowledge was so limited with respect to the many factors involved in indus-trial location, productivity, the development of a stable and efficient labour force, and the creation of the kind of environment conducive to economic and social growth that no positive guides were available. They expressed their confidence that 'it would be possible to find solutions which would mitigate the problems of urbanization, and to bring the fruits of modern technical and administrative progress to an ever-increasing number of people in Asia and the Far East',* but they stressed the urgency of the problems and the necessity for continued research and the co-ordination of activities in these fields. They noted, particularly, that urban development was not a problem in and of itself but was inextricably bound up with economic planning and productivity, education, health, housing and social organization. (Pl. 20b.)

4. Community services

The provision of services for the safety and protection of inhabitants, the education and welfare of citizens, the enjoyment of leisure and the cultivation of the arts were as essential to urban life as were water, housing or regulation of the use of land. These services became more elaborate, technical and costly as the size and complexity of the area to be served increased and standards of adequacy rose.

The organization, training and equipping of a police force became a specialized field, with its body of literature, professional associations, corps of

* *Conclusions of Joint UN-Unesco Seminar on Urbanization in the ECAFE Region, Bangkok, August 8–18, 1956. (Unesco/SS/Conf. URB./W/21, ref. 2, 31 October, 1956.)*

experts and inter-city and international technical consultation. Police often were trained in special academies in the use of scientific methods for the detection of crime, methods of directing and controlling traffic, and in the application of psychological principles to the handling of delinquency, group conflict and threats of disorder. Police departments of large cities were supplied with extensive equipment for communication, motor transportation, and laboratory analysis of evidence. Fire departments were equipped with elaborate mechanical equipment, municipal water systems provided high-pressure hydrants and a trained corps of men were maintained constantly on the alert. The cost of police and fire services, generally carried by the municipality, averaged 15 per cent of the budgets of US cities. When the motor car made it possible for persons committing a crime to escape beyond the jurisdiction of the municipal police, and road travel required policing, state, provincial or national governments set up police forces to supplement those of the localities.

Radically higher standards for every sort of welfare and cultural service, based on new knowledge and new understanding of need, involved increased expenditure and more technical operation. The bare school room equipped with little more than blackboard, benches and slates was replaced by the modern school plant, complete with workshops, laboratories, library and playing field; the isolation hospital for contagious diseases was replaced by specialized hospitals and clinics with the most up-to-date equipment for diagnosis, treatment and surgery. Libraries, museums, art galleries, recreation facilities were expected to meet the needs of young and old. Though high productivity in industrialized countries provided an economic basis for these extended services, their cost and complexity presented a constant problem of financing and an intricate task of planning and administration. In the countries of low productivity, standards and expectations of what cities should provide were far out of line with resources to support them.

5. Municipal administration

In the face of mounting problems and expanding responsibilities city administration became an increasingly difficult task which called for development of new administrative techniques. As the functions performed became more numerous and technical, city officials found themselves ill equipped for their responsibilities. City management became a specialized professional field and city managers trained in engineering, finance and administration were employed by increasing numbers of cities and smaller communities to bring to municipal operations many of the management methods that had been developed by business corporations.

Cities tended constantly to outgrow their administrative structure and financial resources. Tax rates and methods of financing geared to the support of more limited services failed to yield sufficient revenue. The situation was often complicated by the fact that municipal boundaries did not necessarily correspond with the metropolitan area to which the city's population spread and municipal governments lacked jurisdiction over their suburban residents. These in turn came under rural or semi-rural authorities who had relatively little experience in providing the facilities and services required by urban dwellers and were often controlled by older residents who regarded the people from the expanding city as an intrusion into their way of life and a burden on their limited financial resources.

Various methods were employed in the effort to overcome the inadequacy of municipal organization. In some countries new jurisdictions were created such as water districts, school districts, port, bridge or highway authorities each with its own geographical area and jurisdiction over the particular problem for which it was formed. Where these special authorities were granted power to borrow money and exercise eminent domain, they threatened to overshadow the municipal government itself. National or provincial governments frequently came to the assistance of local units by making grants for the provision of specific services such as education or welfare. In some instances an attempt to bring order out of the administrative chaos was made by the creation of a metropolitan jurisdiction as in the London County Council which had been in existence since 1888, or the municipality of Metropolitan Toronto, Canada, which united the central city and twelve suburban municipalities in 1953.

6. Citizen responsibility

Efforts to make cities satisfying places for human living involved fundamental problems of social relationships and the citizens' sense of responsibility. In the industrial city the individual's life was fragmented into a number of separate pieces: his work, his residence, his religious observance, his associations for purposes of friendship, recreation or interest took him to different places and required him to form a part of a series of different groups. In contrast to his village counterpart whose role was defined by his status, the urban individual had to establish himself in each new set of relationships. He had to define his own role and secure acceptance and recognition, although class, sex, race, religion, length of residence, occupation or education might set limits within which he made his choices and adjustments. In much of his life the city dweller was anonymous: a worker, a tenant, a customer, a passenger. He moved about impersonally and alone, among thousands of people whom he did not know and, not knowing, often did not see. The cloak of anonymity gave him freedom in his choice of conduct but tended to release him from the sense of responsibility for his acts and his environment. The sociologists applied the term 'anomie' to this characteristic of the industrial city. The great mobility of many urban dwellers left them with few roots.

Suburban living in turn brought its own set of social problems. The people of suburbia lived in a semi-insulated locale where they were not related to their neighbours functionally since most depended on the distant city for their livelihood, and where they often were exposed only to a small, relatively homogeneous fragment of the complex which made up the city. They were neither integral parts of a social, cultural and economic whole as were residents of villages or small towns, nor were they residents of the heterogeneous, anonymous central city where people rubbed elbows continuously with many different kinds and conditions or urban dwellers and where the evidences of the complexity of modern industrial life were constantly in view. Suburban residence moreover created a division in the focus of interest between the employed members of the family whose life was largely oriented to the central city and the non-employed members, chiefly the mothers and children, whose lives were lived in and oriented toward the place of residence.

The loss of the sense of belonging and of the responsibility which went with being a member of a small group appeared to many to be a factor at the root of chaotic conditions in industrial cities. Believing that people could not be expected to act responsibly except in relation to a relatively small unit, social workers and city planners in a number of cities and countries tried to develop some sort of neighbourhood structure through which the lost sense of belonging and responsibility would be restored.

Efforts at revitalization by way of the neighbourhood took a number of forms. The settlement house movement, inaugurated in London by the establishment of Toynbee Hall in 1884, brought groups of social workers to live in slum areas where they offered neighbourly friendship, facilities for recreation and adult education, and leadership in efforts to secure sanitation, public health services and better housing. The settlement movement spread to the United States and some cities of Europe, especially in France and the Netherlands, and grew markedly in the first decade of the twentieth century. Then it lost its vitality, as welfare services were extended, slum dwellers moved and the kind of neighbourliness envisaged by the pioneer settlement workers came to seem unreal.

The idea of neighbourhood organization around the public school as a centre for adult education, recreation, public discussion and democratic participation was popular during the same period, especially in the United States; in later years the principal application of the idea was in the community school programme of the Philippines. During the first and especially during the second world war the block or neighbourhood unit provided a basis for organizing civil defence in a number of countries. In the depression of the 1930s several American cities set up neighbourhood councils as a means of combating juvenile delinquency. British public housing projects were commonly equipped with community buildings designed to serve as neighbourhood centres, as were some projects in the United States, the Scandinavian countries and a few places in Latin America.

Yet few enduring successes could be recorded for the attempts to use the urban neighbourhood to bring new vitality into the older industrial cities and responsible participation to its citizens. After more than fifty years of experi-

FIG. 3. Chandigarh, Punjab (Le Corbusier, 1951): the layout of the city.

The area of 16 square miles, for a population of from 150,000 to 500,000, comprises four functional zones; the administrative services of the State of Punjab, an academic, a commercial, and an industrial centre. The several residential sectors are of 800 by 1200 metres each. *(Courtesy of Dr N. S. Lamba, Chandigarh*

19 THE URBAN ENVIRONMENT III

    (a) *Paris suburbs: Collective housing and individual homes*
    (b) *Paris suburbs: Sarcelles, collective housing*

(a)

20   THE URBAN ENVIRONMENT IV

    (a) *Maquette of Crawley New Town, Sussex, England*
    (b) *Chandigarh, Punjab: Residential sector*

(b)

Open Space   Commercial

FIG. 4. Chandigarh, Punjab (Le Corbusier, 1951): the layout of a residential sector.

Accommodating from 5,000 to 15,000 persons, each sector is a self-contained unit providing shops, recreational facilities, health centres, community centres, nursery and junior schools. Outer roads are left free for motor traffic while the sectors are connected by a system of pedestrian and cycle tracks. The linear shopping areas along the south side of High Street and the compact groups of from 150 to 200 houses were designed to suit local climatic conditions. [*Courtesy of Dr N. S. Lamba, Chandigarh.*

ment, the total impact on the character of urban life had been negligible. Some people in fact doubted the validity of the neighbourhood concept in relation to urban living, raising the question whether the ability of the city dweller to join with those who shared common interests might not be a sounder basis than the local neighbourhood for social relations in the metropolitan community.

In the Asian cities, where neighbourhoods often resembled villages, it remained to be seen how these units would function as their members became more fully a part of the industrial complex which was developing. A few Asian and Latin American cities in their attempts to cope with their boundless problems experimented with ways to combine the limited resources of the municipal or national government with the efforts of people on their own behalf. Impressed by the success of co-operation and self-help in the community development programmes at work in villages, they began to apply similar methods in urban communities as well.

The problem of how to bring responsibility, participation and wholeness to the lives of city residents was a persistent challenge to all concerned with the quality of life in the urban environment.[2]

II. THE RURAL ENVIRONMENT

While an increasing proportion of the people everywhere were adapting themselves to conditions of city life, the great majority of the world's people continued to live in rural areas. Yet the same influences were tending to urbanize the countryside and to reduce the differences between urban and rural life. Wherever roads broke down isolation, radios brought programmes originating in urban centres, electricity made possible some of the conveniences of urban living, schools and health services reached rural areas and larger proportions of farmers were drawn into the market economy, the self-contained isolation of the peasant village or rural hamlet tended to disappear.

The pattern of change varied greatly from area to area. In Japan general electrification, roads and universal education in rural areas, together with intensive cultivation of plots on the outskirts of towns and cities, blurred the line between urban and rural life. The USSR pursued a deliberate policy of minimizing the differences between rural and urban living by introducing into the collective and state farms as much as possible of the technology, education, health services and cultural activities that characterized urban life. Throughout western Europe and in much of North America the widening influence of metropolitan areas touched more and more rural communities, making them into appendages of urban centres. North American farmers, on electrified farms and with access to town by highway, shared the tastes and much of the manner of living of their urban counterparts.

Under these influences, many of the institutions of rural society lost their vitality. With entertainment available at the cinema in the nearest town or over the air, the social gatherings of village groups—around the church, lodge, family, co-operative or other unit—lost some of their exclusive role as providers of recreation. When the voice of a national leader was heard directly by radio, that of the village elder lost some of its exclusive authority. Exposed to other manners by way of the cinema, visits to town or the sight of town people in the village or on the roads, traditional village customs lost some of their sanction. Distinctive modes of dress tended to disappear.

The spread of literacy opened the door to new knowledge and ideas which not only changed agricultural practices but altered patterns of rural living and attitudes associated with them. Where rural life was radically reorganized through the introduction of collective farming, or in the case of China the establishment of communes, a new set of rural institutions was established with a new locus of authority and prestige. Elsewhere the tendency was to undermine the old rural institutions without substituting new ones specifically related to rural life.

The rural communities least affected by the changes of these years were the peasant villages of Asia and the Near East. Here too, however, the ancient patterns of village life were disturbed as bit by bit the same influences which were modifying rural life in the more industrialized countries penetrated to these areas. Even the rural communities in tribal areas of the western hemisphere, Africa, Asia and the Pacific were touched, as their men were drawn off for work on commercial plantations or in mines or industry.

The process of change was consciously speeded up and efforts made to guide it in many areas. Most countries with advanced agriculture established advisory and educational extension services which went beyond advice on the improvement of agricultural practices to advise on farm living and the sponsorship of youth groups and groups of men and women interested in improving aspects of rural life. After the second world war the central governments of most of the new states sought to stimulate villages to modify their way of life in accordance with standards and concepts of sanitation and health, nutrition, education, construction, the application of technology and participation in political activity formulated by those with an urban outlook on life, and they took steps to create new urbanized units in rural areas with which village life could be integrated.

NOTES TO CHAPTER XVIII

1. A special resolution on housing construction adopted in the USSR in 1957, provided for 'the liquidation of the country's housing shortage' within 10 to 12 years. This decision is being successfully put into effect. Between 1957 and 1962 in the Soviet Union there were built 12 million urban apartments and more than 3·8 million rural homes. During the past ten years 108 million persons (approximately half of the population) have moved into new homes and improved their living conditions.

('O razvitii zhilishchnogo stroitelstva v SSSR. Postanovleniye Tsk KPSS i Soveta Ministrov SSSR' ('On the development of housing construction in the USSR. Resolution of the CC of the CPSU and the Council of Ministers of the USSR'), *Pravda*, August 2, 1957; *Bolshaya Sovetskaya Entsiklopediya. Ezhegodnik, 1963*, p. 80; *Pravda*, June 20, 1964.)

2. Professor M. J. Wise regrets that 'the authors are constrained to generalize about cities and the similarities of their problems'. Being 'especially interested in the differences between cities', he notes that 'as between countries there exist great contrasts in city problems and in city size, form and function. Even within a small country, such as ours [Great Britain], it is difficult to generalize for there are major contrasts between the problems of, say, London and those of, say, Glasgow or Blackburn'. Professor E. N. Anderson observes that, without attempting to expand upon all the implications of Professor Wise's criticism, one may emphasize an aspect which would seem to be essential for understanding the city. This is its aesthetic dimension, the extent to which and the ways in which the city creates a personality for itself by the aesthetic use of its geographic setting and by the beauty of its centres, public buildings, parks, homes, and other features which impress character upon the entire urban life. Studies have been made which show that in the eyes of residents a city may be as amorphous and centreless as a pancake, as ugly and drab as a mill town or urban slum; in short, unattractive in spite of the presence of wealth. Character and reputation of a city may depend upon relatively few city landmarks, for example upon a cluster of public buildings and a square or park, which can be recalled as symbolizing the city. When visitors ask what to see, citizens can refer to these monuments with pride as embodying the best achievements of the city. Elsewhere distinguishing features may pervade the whole community, for example in aesthetically designed and well-kept homes, parks and tree-lined streets, in cleanliness, colour, pleasant neighbourhood facilities, and other evidences of the citizen's concern for and enjoyment of his surroundings. Other cities may have other means of individualizing themselves; in all cases some qualities of beauty or distinction must be present, in forms which can be identified by the citizens with themselves and in which they can share pride of achievement.

The conception can be extended beyond the city to the region: phenomena of nature, Victoria Falls, the Nile river, Fuji mountain and the like, were and continue to be objects of pride. In recent decades they must share appeal with man-made pieces of gigantic architecture or sculpture—Boulder and Aswan dams, radio towers, airports, and the numerous other manufactured manifestations of aesthetic as well as scientific and engineering genius that constitute the great works of art of our age. They are the twentieth century's Pyramids, Gothic cathedrals, Greek and Buddhist temples, the work of co-operative activity, of individuals representing many diverse skills and many forms of aesthetic expression, and made possible by the material participation of millions of taxpayers and stockowners. They have public character, they reveal grandeur, they transcend the individual and the momentary, to impress those who see them by their union of beauty and public service. It is in this way that beauty achieves a democratic character and both city and region assume aesthetic validity.

For further reading the following may be consulted:

A. J. Brown and Howard M. Sherrard, *Town and Country Planning* (Melbourne and Cambridge, 1951).

Frederick Gibberd, *Town Design* (rev. ed., New York, 1962).

Sigfried Giedion, *Space, Time and Architecture* (Cambridge, Mass., 1959, 3rd ed.).

Julian H. Levi, *Municipal and Institutional Relations within Boston* (Chicago, 1963).

Kevin Lynch, *Image of the City* (Cambridge, Mass., 1960).

Kevin Lynch, *Site Planning* (Cambridge, Mass., 1962).

Lewis Mumford, *The City in History* (New York, 1961).

CHAPTER XIX

TREATMENT AND PREVENTION OF SOCIAL BREAKDOWN AND PROVISION OF SOCIAL SERVICES

I. GROWTH OF SOCIAL SERVICES

SOCIAL programmes, undertaken initially in order to treat or prevent social breakdown, expanded tremendously, first in the industrially developed countries and then in those in process of industrialization. The programmes were made necessary by industrialization and urbanization and were specifically directed toward meeting conditions arising out of these twin processes. As the growth of industry and the migration to cities broke down social patterns of pre-industrial societies, the need for substitutes for older sources of welfare and security became apparent. At the same time industrialization provided the resources to support services which a less productive economy, more fully devoted to subsistence, could not afford. In the process it set stand· ards toward which even the newly developing countries, for all their lack of resources, were forced to strive.

The development of social services moreover reflected the conviction that the community must assume positive responsibility for the social and economic welfare of the people. The United Nations Universal Declaration of Human Rights included a series of social 'rights' which clearly identify thir document as a product of the mid-twentieth century, in contrast to earlies documents which had proclaimed political and civil rights. Although the enumerated social rights were far from being made a reality during these years, their expression symbolized their world-wide acceptance as objectives to which societies were committed.

The major social services to meet the needs of all the people for health, education, housing and recreation are discussed in other chapters.* The present chapter is limited to the services and programmes designed to intervene where social breakdown threatens or has occurred, either to protect or to treat the individual or to protect society. As the need for such services became ever more apparent the social sciences were called on to provide a more scientific basis for them than the pragmatic approach in terms of which they had operated in the past.

Every society has had some system of care for its dependent, displaced and delinquent members—for the stranger, the orphan, the sick and disabled, the

* See Chapters XV, Health and Population; XXVI, Education; XVIII, The Environment; XXVII, Use of Leisure.

aged, the penniless, the felon—through the extended family system, institutions maintained by religious bodies, mutual aid within occupational fraternities, obligations of feudal landlords or other superiors, or the responsibility of the local community. The problem of the twentieth century was to develop systems appropriate to the conditions of industrial society.

In the industrial countries of Great Britain, the United States, the British Commonwealth and parts of northern Europe, the basic pattern of public responsibility for those in distress had been inherited or adapted from the Elizabethan Poor Laws of the early seventeenth century: local responsibility, maintenance of public institutions for the mentally ill, the indigent sick, orphans and the aged, and work relief for the destitute able-bodied. The 'means test' restricted public aid or support to those without other resources. With the development of industry the means test had been coupled with the principle that the level of assistance must be kept well below that of wages in order to make sure that those able to work would not choose idle dependency over industrious labour. This system of social assistance rested on the assumption that the individual had a moral obligation to work, that poverty and dependency were a reflection of personal inadequacy and that the successful and well-to-do were morally superior to their poorer fellows and had a responsibility to correct their weakness as well as to succour them in need. These assumptions were sanctioned by Protestant religious convictions which, as the German sociologist Max Weber pointed out in *The Protestant Ethic and the Spirit of Capitalism* (1904–5), gave capitalist economic development much of its drive.

In areas dominated by Catholic attitudes charity continued to be regarded as an act of piety enjoined by religious duty on the giver, and most social assistance took the form of benefactions by individuals and institutions sponsored and manned by religious orders.

By the opening of the twentieth century the conviction had grown that much of the poverty and misery from which the needy suffered arose from factors beyond their control, and that blame and responsibility rested on society rather than the individual. It had become apparent that industrial societies with their systems of individual wage-earning limited to the period of actual employment did not offer the cushions against the normal hazards of life provided in an agrarian society by the pooled resources of an extended family.

Measures had been enacted in industrial countries to reform the basic conditions of the labouring classes—such as long hours, bad housing, inadequate sanitation, child labour and the labour of women in hazardous tasks. Public concern had been aroused over the plight of dependent groups, especially children herded in almshouses, and over the inhuman treatment accorded to the insane; and programmes had been initiated for providing children with special institutions or placing them in foster homes and for treating the insane as mentally ill persons rather than as evilly possessed subhumans.

The idea of rehabilitation had begun to replace that of relief or punishment in the work of some of the friendly visitors who hoped that the families in need whom they helped might become self-supporting and self-respecting, and in the movement for prison reform. The German programmes in the 1880s for insuring industrial workers against sickness and accident had established the principle that risks should be spread through society, not carried by the individual worker, had introduced the method of social insurance and had laid the basis for the social security systems that spread over the world in the twentieth century.

Although the comprehensive scope which the social services were to assume was hardly foreshadowed at the beginning of the twentieth century, the way had been opened for development of the concept of the welfare state and for the changes in principles, techniques and focus of responsibility which it involved.

Half a century later, when the United Nations undertook a world-wide review of programmes of social development* it found all types of programmes in the process of rapid extension in countries and territories at all levels of economic development and with all manner of political structures. Such programmes were similar in scope and objectives, regardless of the type of government or degree of economic development, although their forms differed as a result of their historic background and the structure of the society of which they were a part. The field of social welfare was one in which technical assistance was earnestly sought and in which international and national agencies worked to make available the best knowledge and the best social techniques and to stimulate their extension.

In countries with a long tradition of private philanthropy and a heritage of institutions established before the social attitudes of the mid-twentieth century had developed, the programmes which emerged combined both public and private responsibilities. The twentieth-century trend, however, was towards an extension of the area of public concern, as was evidenced in Britain and the Scandinavian countries which had some of the oldest and richest traditions of private welfare effort and yet developed some of the fullest public programmes. In the communist states which achieved rapid industrialization, social programmes were included as part of the total structure of economic and social administration by the state.

In the newly industrializing countries of Latin America and Asia, whose private welfare services were generally limited in scope and highly personal, strong pressures developed for public measures to meet overwhelming problems of mass need. These countries faced a dilmema that had not beset the older industrial countries, which had undertaken broad social welfare programmes only after they had already developed the economic potential to support them. In the social climate of mid-twentieth century they could not delay their welfare efforts or adopt as goals for their people more limited con-

* *International Survey of Programmes of Social Development,* 1955.

cepts of human dignity and well-being than those which other nations had accepted, yet their economic means were limited and their resources strained. Although they generally devoted a smaller proportion of their national budgets to social programmes than did the industrialized countries, they were doing far more than the latter had done at a corresponding stage of industrialization. Some, such as Chile whose welfare services developed hand in hand with the growth of industry, built up comprehensive programmes and became pioneers and leaders in the welfare field.

Though all programmes had much in common, countries differed markedly in the extent to which they applied new knowledge, in the emphasis of their programmes, their choice of methods and the comprehensiveness and generosity of their approach to social needs. The Scandinavian countries were among the most consistent and self-conscious in developing an overall approach to welfare on every front and in constantly revising all types of ·programmes and institutions in line with the growing potentialities of their economies and with expanding concepts of needs and services.

New Zealand was outstanding in its general programme of social assistance through which it incorporated into a single comprehensive system of aid to all, in all types of contingencies, what many other countries administered as a multitude of fragmentary benefits. Britain after the second world war put together a number of different programmes which had grown through the years, to form a 'cradle to grave' system of economic protection against risks and to provide health and some welfare services. The United States pioneered in individualizing many services and expanding their scope, but programmes were applied unevenly and reflected great differences in local resources and ideas.

The USSR and other communist countries included the provision of social security against risk as a basic condition of life and labour and they provided a range of pensions, benefits and services which supplemented and reinforced what workers received through wages. Israel drew on the best available knowledge and experience in designing and operating the social services which from the start were an integral part of this welfare state.

The newly developing countries, faced with mass problems of economic and social inadequacy, instituted programmes of community development which stimulated whole villages to undertake self-help activities designed to raise their levels of living. At the same time they made such efforts as their resources permitted to provide for special groups such as destitute children, the blind or crippled, and to apply to these efforts new techniques which were consistent with the conditions of their society.

All programmes of social welfare, whether in industrially advanced or newly industrializing countries, showed common trends. All brought a growing understanding of human needs and potentialities to the protection, care and rehabilitation of the major groups needing aid—dependent children, juvenile delinquents and adult offenders, the handicapped, the mentally ill, the aged. All combined, in some form, both scientific knowledge and the philosophies and value systems of their society and all were carried out by persons equipped with some combination of professional training and dedication to the service of their fellow-men.

The trends which are noted below characterized the development of welfare services and policies around the world. Actual provisions for care, treatment and prevention, however, remained far below prevailing standards and accepted policies. Almost universally, limited funds and a shortage of adequately trained personnel hampered the development of services; attitudes of indifference or rejection of those in need and ignorance of sound approaches to social problems often persisted in spite of public policy and growing knowledge. Model programmes were sometimes confined to the principal centres or special institutions.

Yet however great the gap between principles and practice, the emergence of universally accepted criteria and a common, positive approach to the welfare of those in need and common trends in methods adopted was one of the most distinctive features of the twentieth century.

II. PROTECTION, CARE AND REHABILITATION OF DEPENDENT GROUPS

1. *Dependent and neglected children*

Children deprived of adequate parental care have always presented a problem of community responsibility wherever they could not be absorbed into an extended family group. In the twentieth century measures for the protection, care and welfare of dependent, neglected, handicapped and delinquent children became central features of the welfare programme of every country.

The need for such measures was intensified by many factors in urban industrial life. The extended family was no longer generally at hand to assume responsibility when something happened to the immediate family. Although the number of orphans was reduced by lowered death rates of parents, especially by the decrease in maternal mortality, family breakdown and desertion by the breadwinner continued to leave many children without support or care. The number of children born out of wedlock remained a large and growing problem in many areas. Wars and population displacements left large numbers of children homeless.

Traditional methods of providing for dependent children by binding them out as servants or apprentices or by herding them into local almshouses along with other public charges were generally discredited by the opening of the twentieth century. In most countries, specialized asylums for orphans had been established by religious bodies, fraternal organizations, individual charity and public agencies. Organizations had been formed to protect children against abuse and to promote standards for their care, and children's institutions had been brought under licensing or other supervision by the state. Some children were supported by the state in foster homes, selected and supervised by a public agency.

The extensive child welfare programmes developed in the following years, although differing in comprehensiveness and in detail, showed common trends which reflected an increasingly sympathetic attitude toward children, a growing body of knowledge of their needs and much international consultation and co-operation on their behalf.

These programmes recognized the central importance to the child of its own home and tried to maintain the home or to provide the nearest approximation to it, especially for very young children. All evidence showed the extreme importance of providing a mother figure during the infant's earliest development; studies of babies cared for in institutions revealed serious retardation in mental as well as in emotional development even where physical conditions were entirely satisfactory.*

The principle that no child should be taken from his home for economic reasons alone was clearly established in the early years of the century and was incorporated in the declaration of the White House Conference on the Care of Dependent Children in 1909 and by the Pan American Child Congress in 1919. It led to the inauguration of mothers' or widows' pension schemes to enable mothers to remain in the home in order to look after their children, and the inclusion of survivors' benefits in systems of social insurance.

Mothers' pensions were provided between 1911 and 1913 by New Zealand and eighteen of the states of the United States and by Canada and the Scandinavian countries during the first world war. The German social insurance scheme added survivors' benefits in 1911 and these were included in the social insurance of Great Britain and other continental European countries after the first world war.

In the second quarter of the twentieth century most industrialized countries extended insurance or assistance benefits to cover virtually all children deprived of paternal support; some included housekeeping aids to mothers in case of illness in order that young children could remain constantly in the home. Provisions for the daytime care of children of working mothers were also widespread. They were general in the Soviet Union, both crèches for young children and after-school centres for older ones. In some Latin American countries large employers were required by law to provide day-care facilities. Elsewhere such facilities were maintained by welfare agencies, industries or local public bodies if the need was apparent.

The use of substitute homes for children without homes of their own was accepted by most well-developed child welfare programmes as the most desirable practice, in preference to institutional care. Welfare agencies endeavoured to recruit and supervise foster homes where children were boarded at public expense. Initially these agencies were primarily concerned with the ability of the foster home to provide for the child's physical health and care,

---

* See John Bowlby, *Maternal Care and Mental Health*, op. cit.

but as it became apparent that the emotional quality of the home was even more important to the child than its physical aspects, they gave primary attention to attitudes and relationships in the homes in which children were placed.

It was not easy, however, to ensure responsibility on the part of foster parents and to make certain that they were not taking in children in order to use them as servants. The latter practice was sufficiently serious in some countries to make the United Nations include it in its study of forms of slavery which still persisted in 1951. In some countries the inauguration of foster home placement was delayed and institutions maintained, contrary to the general trend, because no satisfactory machinery for supervision had been developed. In some, the local culture made it very difficult for families to give the foster child the feeling of belonging which was the rationale of the foster home system. Especially for older children, institutions continued to be an important means of providing for those who lacked parental care.

Institutions, in turn, were redesigned in order to approximate conditions of home life. Barrack-like dormitories were discarded wherever possible in favour of a group of cottages, and the rigid classification into age and sex groups tended to be replaced in some of the most modern institutions by the more normal grouping of children of different ages and sexes. Institutions ceased to be regarded merely as means of providing custodial care and were recognized as possible treatment agencies; specialized institutions were designed to meet the needs of children with special problems and to provide kinds of care which could not be provided or were not needed on a large scale. The Soviet Union, whose initial major problem of child welfare was to provide for the large number of homeless children left in the wake of the civil war, developed special children's colonies and homes where children received schooling and labour training as well as care.

Twentieth-century child welfare programmes rested on a concept that the child has rights which society should protect and that he should not be the one to bear the burden of circumstances such as illegitimacy or poverty which are beyond his control. Legislation with respect to children born out of wedlock and provisions for legitimization, establishing paternity and adoption reflected the general trend toward the protection of the interests of the child.

Family law was revised in most countries so as to reduce the distinction between the rights and status of children born out of wedlock and those born to married couples, although some countries such as Spain and Portugal retained laws which gave legal protection to legitimate children only, while a few such as Cuba eliminated legal difference altogether. Legislation tended to strengthen legal means to establish paternity and to exact the responsibilities of parenthood. It sought to remove social stigma from the child by such procedures as eliminating identification of illegitimacy from birth certificates, and to ensure that children born out of wedlock would not be excluded from such social benefits as family allowances, social assistance to dependent children, survivors' insurance or the allotments to dependents of military personnel.

Adoption as developed during the twentieth century was designed primarily as a means of providing a child with a home and parents, and of protecting the child, its natural parents and its adoptive parents against unregulated traffic in infants by unscrupulous persons. Where, as under the Roman law, adoption had been designed primarily as a means by which an individual could secure an heir, or where it was hedged about by restrictions aimed at protecting the interests of members of the family in family property, laws were modified in the interest of the adopted child. While some countries continued to make no provision for legal adoption and others excluded the adopted child from inheritance, the United States, most European countries, Great Britain after 1926, and several of the countries of Latin America established the machinery for incorporating adopted children into a family on a basis identical with that of children born to the family. The legal procedure, entrusted in most instances to the juvenile or family court, generally required a joint petition by both adopting parents, unconditional release by natural parents, careful investigation of the adoptive home by an authorized welfare agency, physical and mental examination of the child and often a probationary period before the adoption decree could become final.

The concept of children's rights which society was under obligation to safeguard and promote grew broader and encompassed emotional needs for security, affection and identification. The most complete formal statement was contained in the Children's Charter adopted by the White House Conference on Child Health and Protection in 1930, generally regarded as the children's 'bill of rights'. It proclaimed 'for every child' the right to spiritual and moral training, understanding and the guarding of his personality as his most precious right; a home, and the love and security which a home provides; for the child who must receive foster care, the nearest substitute for his own home; health protection at birth through pre-natal, natal and post-natal care of his mother, and from his birth to adolescence; a safe and wholesome home and school; a community which recognizes and plans for his needs, protecting him against physical and moral dangers, educating him to guard against accidents, and providing for his recreational, cultural and social needs; education which develops his individual abilities and prepares him for life, for a vocation, for parenthood and for citizenship; for the physically or mentally handicapped child, such care and training as will enable him to become an asset to society rather than a liability; for the child in conflict with society, the right to be dealt with intelligently as society's charge, not society's outcast; the right to grow up in a family with adequate and stable income and to be protected against labour that stunts growth, limits education and denies the right of comradeship, of play and of joy; for every rural child, as satisfactory school, health and other services as for the city child.

There was perhaps no other field of social welfare in which international co-operation was more readily forthcoming and in which there was a freer exchange of experience and agreement on principles. In the 1950s the United

Nations children's agency, UNICEF, was co-operating with the governments of some ninety-five countries and territories in direct assistance to meet emergency needs and in the development of child welfare programmes in the effort to extend the rights of the Children's Charter to 'all the world's children'.

Yet gaps were everywhere apparent betweeen accepted standards or aims and actual practice. Few places enjoyed a range of facilities which would permit those in charge of dependent children to place them in relation to their particular needs. Suitable homes for foster care or adoption were often lacking. Institutions administered by underpaid and under-trained staff on inadequate public payrolls, by religious orders with rigid practices or by other agencies without adequate staff, equipment or understanding were still far more numerous than those which reflected the best understanding of children and the principles to which most communities were committed.

2. The juvenile delinquent

The Children's Charter asserted the right of the child who was in conflict with society to be 'dealt with intelligently as society's charge, not society's outcast'. In the twentieth century the number of children regarded as delinquent increased markedly in many places and juvenile delinquency came to be considered one of the most serious and central problems of the times.

In line with changing attitudes the juvenile delinquent ceased to be an offender needing punishment and became a child needing help. New understanding of behaviour brought new procedures and institutions for his treatment. Research into the causes of delinquency, however, revealed complex and deep-seated social and psychological factors which often baffled efforts at treatment and prevention.

Under all legal systems, the very young child—under seven in the Roman law and codes derived therefrom—was assumed to be incapable of committing a 'crime' because of his inability to distinguish between right and wrong. Older children were either presumed to be less accountable for their acts than adults, or subject to less severe punishment for the same offence, but up to the close of the nineteenth century they were regarded in some degree as guilty of criminal behaviour if they violated a law applicable to adults.

The juvenile court, first introduced experimentally in Illinois in the United States in 1899, offered a new approach and a new concept. This type of court was not a judicial body which established the child's guilt and meted out punishment; it was a protective agency to determine the reason for his behaviour and to help him to conform to socially required norms. The court's action was based on a thorough social and psychological investigation of the child and its procedure was informal and private.

As the juvenile court system spread throughout the countries of Europe and to other parts of the world, it gradually introduced the principles and procedures of social investigation and treatment in place of judgment and punishment. Yet by mid-century the transformation was far from complete. Vestiges of criminal procedure remained in the practice of many juvenile courts in the United States which continued to charge the child with a specific offence and establish the facts of his 'guilt', although the Standard Juvenile Court Act issued as a model by the United States Children's Bureau in 1949 set forth the principle that no guilt should be involved but rather that 'it should be established whether a child, because of his ascertained acts, condition or environment is in need of the care and protection of the State'. An element of 'guilt' remained in the British and most continental European practices, although it was largely eliminated in Belgium. Under the stimulus of the Inter-American Institute for the Protection of Childhood the trend in the Latin American countries was to discard the term 'delinquency' altogether, and one country after another transferred its juvenile courts and related agencies from the jurisdiction of its justice department to its department of welfare or to a children's agency.

Application of the concept of treatment rather than punishment depended not only on the court but on related agencies—the police, the detention institutions and the agencies which investigated the child, diagnosed his problems and supervised his activities.

The attitude and practice of the police was of prime importance, since the child's behaviour was most likely to come first to their attention. Since most police training and procedures were not designed to produce an understanding attitude toward children in trouble, police departments in some cities, including parts of the United States, the United Kingdom, the British Commonwealth, the Netherlands and some Latin American countries, instituted separate specially trained juvenile squads. The duties of these officers assigned to work with children sometimes included supervision of playgrounds and the organization of recreation activities such as boys' clubs, in an effort to promote a positive relationship between young people and those in authority.

Institutions for the detention of juvenile delinquents were greatly modified in form and procedure. Reformatories had been initially established in the nineteenth century in order to separate young offenders from adult criminals housed in jails and prisons. They resembled prisons, however, in their bars and barrack-like structures, and their procedures were largely impersonal and based on the assumption that lack of discipline and respect for authority were characteristics of the delinquent which the institution should endeavour to overcome.

In line with changing concepts these institutions were reoriented from places of detention to treatment centres and were given other names such as 'training schools'. As new understanding of the delinquent child made it apparent that he usually needed the opportunity to be responsible for his actions, to belong to a group, to establish personal relations and to develop his capacities, the locked, regimented, uniformed barracks life was recognized as unlikely to provide an effective form of treatment. The model juvenile institutions in all countries came to be designed without bars or walls and to consist of cottages where each child could be a member of a small group.

Supervision of the delinquent child was provided by some form of probation system. In Britain the probation system which had been occasionally used under the common law was made general in 1907; on the Continent the French and Belgian form of conditional suspension of punishment was generally adopted. These and similar systems became integral parts of juvenile court procedure, and the most frequently used form of treatment in most courts was to place the child under the supervision of a probation officer. Even where the child was placed in an institution a probation officer often had responsibility for following his progress there and supervising his return to home and community when he was released.

The soundness of the juvenile court's action and the effectiveness of treatment depended upon the adequacy with which the child's case was investigated and his problems diagnosed. Such investigation and diagnosis was variously performed by the juvenile police, a welfare agency or by the juvenile court itself, which often came to include a corps of social workers and a psychiatric clinic.

A mounting body of research revealed the necessity for distinguishing between children whose mental and emotional development was normal but whose social circumstances resulted in anti-social behaviour and those whose behaviour was rooted in mental deficiency or emotional disorder. Studies of social factors presumed to be linked with delinquency readily established positive correlations between delinquent behaviour and such conditions as poverty, broken homes, neighbourhood disintegration and the coexistence of cultural sub-groups in marginal areas, and they showed the problem to be intensified where rural migrants or immigrants found their traditional values and authority no longer supported in a strange and confusing urban milieu. Yet not all who suffered from these social disadvantages became delinquent and a disturbingly large and growing number of delinquents came from ostensibly favourable conditions. Research was therefore focused increasingly on the individual child in the effort to determine the complex of factors which entered into the formation of his personality and motivated his behaviour. By mid-century there was world-wide recognition of juvenile delinquency as a problem in mental health; the first monograph issued by the World Health Organization dealt with *Psychiatric Aspects of Juvenile Delinquency* (by Lucien Bovet, Geneva, 1951).

All studies pointed to the conclusion that delinquent behaviour was a symptom of the child's efforts to resolve his own problems, and that in seeking to treat the disease and not merely the symptom it was essential to identify what it was that the behaviour expressed. For the large majority of delinquent children whose unacceptable behaviour grew out of a social situation, treatment involved the provision of a social environment in which the child could fulfil his needs within the framework and values of adult society. For the few who suffered from severe personality disorders, only the most highly skilled psychiatric treatment could hope to repair the personality damage which had been suffered. The best equipped and most progressive of the courts and the diagnostic and treatment agencies in each country were guided by these considerations in their approach to the ever-mounting volume of juvenile delinquency which continued to be a disturbing feature of the social changes of these years.

But the best equipped and most progressive courts and institutions remained the exception rather than the rule. Lack of sufficient trained personnel for investigation and supervision hampered the work of a large proportion of the juvenile courts. Probation officers were generally insufficient in number and inadequately trained. Many older types of institutions for juvenile offenders continued to operate and to perpetuate outworn procedures long after these had been discarded in principle. Means of early detection of delinquent tendencies and effective prevention were even more limited than adequate courts and institutions.

Surveying the world situation for the World Health Organization in 1951, Dr Lucien Bovet found only hesitant beginnings in the selection and training of staffs for work with juvenile delinquents along modern lines. Such outstanding experiments as the training centre at Amersfoort, Netherlands, were very few, some types of training were only to be found in the United Kingdom and the United States, and the vast majority of staffs of juvenile institutions in Europe and the United States lacked the necessary technical knowledge and emotional stability to make these institutions effective instruments for the treatment of the delinquent child.

3. *The adult offender*

The treatment of adult offenders followed somewhat the same course as that for juvenile delinquents, although the concept of criminality and procedures for establishing guilt remained. Developments in this field were chiefly in the reform of prisons and the modification of sentences.

In the latter part of the nineteenth century a movement for prison reform attacked the concept of prisons as purely custodial institutions, to protect society against further threats from those who had been put away and to punish offenders by cutting them off from normal life. The purpose of imprisonment began to be seen as rehabilitation, and the prison as a means to re-educate the offender and prepare him for return to the community. The reformatory at Elmira, New York, established in 1869 to receive youthful and first offenders, pioneered in this approach. Instead of being herded in idleness, prisoners learned trades and engaged in useful work during their stay in the institution.

The concept of rehabilitation carried with it implications for the length of the sentence. If the object of incarceration was to give the offender an opportunity to readjust to normal life, the length of his sentence should be related to the success of the rehabilitation process rather than the offence for which he was committed. The system of parole was designed to carry out this idea. If the prisoner showed evidence by his behaviour and progress in the institution that he was ready to return to society, he might be released conditionally under the supervision of a parole officer for the remainder of the term for which he was committed. The parole officer or other agent had the further responsibility of helping the released prisoner to adjust to normal life.

Twentieth-century developments in the treatment of adult offenders elaborated the concepts and procedures for rehabilitation which the prison reform movement of the late nineteenth century had established. The developments followed a common pattern although countries varied from those where trends were apparent only in a few steps taken by an exceptional institution to those where the entire penal system was characterized by the new approach.

Refined techniques for screening prisoners by means of psychological and social study were used to differentiate the ones more likely to respond to positive programmes of rehabilitation. In some countries, notably France, prisoners committed for a term of two or more years were sent first to an institution where they could be studied and observed before being assigned to the penal institution judged most suitable for their treatment.

With the objective of preparing the prisoner for return to community life the historic policy of cutting him off from normal contact by imprisonment was replaced by one of maintaining as much continuing relation with the community as possible. Prisoners in advanced institutions, particularly in the Scandinavian countries, worked for pay, frequently for employers outside the institution on terms consistent with prevailing wages and often arranged by the prisoner himself. Their earnings were devoted, under different systems, to payment for their board in the institution, support of their families, restitution in connection with the offence for which they were committed, or were placed in a fund which would tide them over the period of readjustment upon their release. They might receive furloughs to visit their homes periodically, or spend the latter part of their stay merely sleeping at the prison while they enjoyed the facilities of the community for work and recreation during the day.

Opportunities to develop responsible behaviour were provided through the internal organization of the prison on a self-governing basis and in the educational responsibilities carried by some prisoners on behalf of others to whom they taught literacy or trades. Through the co-operation of outside educational institutions prisoners could take advantage of correspondence courses. In some countries camps or farm colonies where prisoners could have their families living with them were established experimentally. Fixed sentences were replaced by indeterminate sentences subject to administrative decision or determination by a parole board as to whether the prisoner should be longer detained or had shown such response to treatment as to be ready for release.

These developments in procedure were accompanied by constant study at many different levels in the attempt to gain understanding of the variety of factors entering into criminal behaviour. In general such studies followed lines similar to those developed in the study of juvenile delinquency. They attempted to distinguish between those whose behaviour arose from essentially psychological causes and those where social factors predominated; they sought to provide specialized treatment for the former, and to use both the experience in the institution and the manner of return to the community to attempt to cope with the latter. Success of measures for the rehabilitation of offenders required the sympathetic co-operation of members of the family and community. A major part of all programmes for prisoner rehabilitation included measures to modify public attitudes and to work with families and neighbours toward acceptance of the released prisoner and support for his own efforts at rehabilitation.

Measures to improve the treatment of adult offenders, however, were constantly undermined by high rates of crime which tended to reflect growing urbanization, the strains and disorders of wars and depression and the new mobility provided by the automobile. Since modern individualized practices in prison treatment could only be used with relatively small numbers, the mounting numbers of inmates, crowding of prisons and shortages of personnel impeded their application. In most countries scientific technology was far more systematically applied to the detection of crime than were the best known practices to its treatment or prevention.

4. *The disabled and handicapped*

Persons suffering from physical and mental handicaps, either from birth or as the result of injury or illness, constituted a substantial proportion of the population of every country. Programmes for these handicapped groups aimed to make them able to function as fully as possible in normal society.

Child welfare services generally included special provisons for blind, deaf, crippled and mentally defective children. As far as possible they were kept in their own homes and were provided with services to remove or compensate for their handicap, to help them to grow as nearly as possible like and with normal children, and to enable them to function at their highest capacity. Improved techniques for the training of deaf-mutes and blind, orthopedic surgery, prosthetic devices and retraining of the muscles of cripples, accompanied by help in the psychological adjustment to the handicap, ensured to an increasing proportion of such children the opportunity to live fully as participating members of society. Mentally defective children who appeared to be too severely handicapped to have the prospect of becoming self-sustaining were cared for in special institutions, but these agencies, too, developed techniques for training according to the degree of disability, with the object of returning to the community some who would formerly have been considered hopeless.

The extraordinary career of the blind deaf-mute, Helen Keller (1880–), who learned to communicate with others and wrote, travelled and spoke throughout the world, offered an inspiration and stimulus to efforts in many countries. Specialized personnel was trained to utilize new techniques as they were developed. Electronic devices permitted the development of a variety of hearing aids which removed the bar of deafness from many with very limited hearing. Sight conservation programmes involving special classes in school, special glasses, treatment and sometimes surgery, aided the visually handicapped; together with measures to eliminate such diseases as trachoma and congenital syphilis, they helped to reduce the incidence of blindness. Libraries included sections devoted to books printed in Braille, the raised type invented in France in 1834, and to 'talking books' on gramophone records. Organized programmes for training guide dogs gave many blind persons mobility and independence. Programmes of economic aid to the blind or disabled made it possible for them to live in their own homes and largely eliminated the need for institutional care.

Rehabilitation of handicapped adults received a great stimulus from the impact of the wars, especially the second world war, both because of the programmes developed for disabled war veterans and because the extremely heavy demands for labour in wartime forced the use of handicapped persons who would not normally have been employed, and revealed their capacities for useful work. In most of the European countries legislation required employers to include in their work force a certain proportion of disabled persons, sometimes specifically war-disabled, ranging from 2 to 10 per cent of their employees. Elsewhere, especially in North America, Sweden and New Zealand, employers were encouraged to follow a similar course voluntarily by public appeals and by the work of special placement officers attached to employment services.

During and after the second world war the physical restoration of injured and maimed persons was developed to the point of becoming a medical speciality for which special training was offered in a number of medical schools in the United States and a special diploma in the United Kingdom and Canada. For the maimed, research in Germany, the United Kingdom and the United States resulted in the perfection of very delicately adjusted devices and methods of training the wearer in their use.

Psychological adjustment and vocational retraining or guidance proved of equal importance with physical restoration in enabling the physically handicapped to shorten their hospital stay and to become able to work and take care of themselves. A combination of job analysis to determine the actual demands on the worker made by specific jobs, and the careful determination of the handicapped person's capacities through the use of psychological and physical tests and through observation of his performance under simulated work conditions in diagnostic or training centres, provided the basis for vocational counselling and guided the individual to appropriate training and job placement.

For the most severely limited, who could not work under normal conditons, private organizations in a number of countries conducted sheltered workshops or provided work to individuals in their homes. The USSR maintained a wide network of technical vocational boarding homes and specialized secondary schools to train handicapped or disabled persons and to place them in employment in accordance with their condition.

All these measures combined to lessen the isolation of the handicapped and the waste of their energies.

5. The mentally ill

The new understanding of mental illness, together with the growing number of persons recognized as mentally ill, stimulated preventive efforts and programmes designed to restore such persons to normal life.

The mental health movement sought to establish among the general public concepts of mental health and illness based on the best available knowledge, to encourage the application of mental health principles in daily life, to support the establishment of facilities in the community and encourage their use by those needing psychiatric attention, and to create an atmosphere which would facilitate the return of recovered patients to community life and their sympathetic acceptance by employers, family and associates.

The mental health movement received a strong stimulus from the publication in the United States in 1908 of the autobiography of a mental patient who had recovered after experiencing harsh and brutal treatment in three different types of mental institutions.* The revelations of this book, and the tireless efforts of its author to arouse public interest and understanding, led to the formation of a National Mental Hygiene Committee in the United States in 1909, similar committees in states and local communities and the International Committee for Mental Hygiene in 1930. The concept of 'mental hygiene' brought out into the open, for public discussion and recognition as a problem of health, what had long been regarded as something dark and evil.

The first effect of the mental hygiene movement was to speed the conversion of 'insane asylums', where those presumed to be permanently unfit for society were herded, into 'mental hospitals' where ill persons were treated with the hope of returning them to society. Public exposures of conditions in these institutions brought enlarged appropriations for their support and professional direction to their administration.

Along with efforts to improve mental institutions went the establishment and great expansion of community mental health facilities for diagnosis, treatment and prevention. Chief among these were child guidance centres. Following early experiments before the first world war child guidance clinics were established in the 1920s in a number of places, many of them stimulated by grants from an American foundation, the Commonwealth Fund. These clinics were at first closely associated with efforts to understand and cope with

* Clifford W. Beers, *A Mind That Found Itself* (Longmans, Green & Co., New York, 1908).

juvenile delinquency; most children were referred by juvenile courts and the clinics dealt primarily with overt behaviour problems. Later emphasis was on the detection of early symptoms of maladjustment before the child's difficulties should reach a point where he would become a court case. Child guidance clinics were introduced into schools and made part of general community health services and teachers and parents were alerted to recognize in the silent, withdrawn child one who might be as much in need of help as the aggressive child whose behaviour earned attention.

Community clinics for adults and psychiatric services outside mental hospitals developed more slowly than mental health services for children, except for the psychoanalytical treatment of private patients able to pay the very high costs of such service in the major cities of Europe and America. Impetus to the extension of psychiatric services for adults came from the military services. In an effort to avoid a repetition of the experience of the first world war, in which large numbers suffered what was then known as 'shell shock', the armed services in the second world war attempted to screen recruits in order to eliminate those who appeared likely to break down under combat strain. On this basis more than 10 per cent of those called up by the United States army, for example, were rejected because of neuropsychiatric disorders; nevertheless, approximately a million of those accepted for military service were hospitalized for such disorders during the war.

In the face of this evidence of the widespread incidence of neuropsychiatric difficulties, psychiatric services began to be introduced into a wide variety of settings. Some large employers started to offer such services to their personnel, universities added psychiatric clinics to their student health services, psychiatric services were introduced into the more modern prisons and special clinics were established for alcoholics as chronic alcoholism came to be recognized as a symptom of mental disorder.

The shift in the approach to alcoholism was one of the major fruits of the mental health movement. Excessive use of alcohol, beyond that tolerated by social custom, had long been a recognized problem. Among the social reformers of the nineteenth and early twentieth centuries in Europe and North America, none were more vigorous than the leaders of the temperance movement who conducted a broad attack on the 'demon' drink. Their approach was a moral and punitive one—admonish the worker who wasted his weekly wage by getting drunk on Saturday night, withhold charity from his family unless he reformed, put him in jail for drunkenness, close the saloons that placed temptation in his way and forbid the sale of intoxicating liquor. These efforts reached a climax in the complete prohibition of alcoholic beverages in Norway in 1916 and Finland and the United States in 1919, with disastrous results, especially in the last country, in the development of illegal traffic but little success in coping with the problem of alcoholism.

Although in the early years of the century alcoholism was beginning to be seen as a problem of health and not simply of morals, the Health Committee of the League of Nations, in 1928, found public awareness of this insufficient to lead it to undertake an active programme in the field. In the 1930s, however, alcoholism came to be recognized increasingly as a means of escape from intolerable psychic strains with which the individual could not cope, and the alcoholic was seen as a person in need of psychotherapy rather than repression.

Following establishment of the first experimental alcoholic clinic at Yale University in the United States in 1940, special clinics for alcoholics were set up by mental hygiene agencies in several countries or were attached to general hospitals. In some circumstances these were closely linked with the penal system, attendance at the clinic being offered to an alcoholic prisoner as an alternative to a jail sentence, but since the effectiveness of clinical treatment was presumed to depend upon the co-operation of the patient, treatment was not generally compulsory. The World Health Organization in 1950 established a committee on alcoholism as a sub-committee of its Expert Committee on Mental Health, to stimulate research into stages and types of alcoholism and to encourage national health services to make the prevention and treatment of alcoholism an essential part of their public health programmes.

Spontaneously formed groups of former alcoholics themselves undertook to provide social support for the alcoholic who was striving to free himself from the need for this manner of escape from reality. Under the organizational name of 'Alcoholics Anonymous', established in the United States in 1932 and extending to other countries, many such groups helped to provide members with the social recognition and self-esteem which they needed and mutual support in their efforts at rehabilitation.

Efforts at prevention of mental illness took the form mainly of educational programmes and the dissemination of information through the public press, magazine literature, radio programmes and films. Films designed to disclose factors leading to mental disorder and to acquaint the viewer with methods of treatment were developed in Canada and elsewhere, and were used as the basis of discussion by parents, teachers, trade unions, churches and other groups. On the whole these programmes reached principally the better educated and younger members of the community, and by the 1950s the views toward mental health held by this segment of the population were generally in accord with those held by experts. Some programmes of mental health education were introduced into schools on an experimental basis. Participants in a Unesco-sponsored conference on Education and Mental Health in 1952 found programmes worthy of note in Denmark, Canada and the United States which attempted, through direct discussion of human relations or the infusion of such materials through the school curriculum, to give children some understanding of their own and other people's motives and to help them to grapple with their emotional problems as they arose rather than to repress them.*

Nearly everywhere, however, shortages of facilities and personnel stood in the way of adequate treatment and care for the mentally ill. Children's clinics

* W. D. Wall, *Education and Mental Health* (Unesco, Paris, 1955), p. 294.

frequently limited their services to diagnosis in the effort to single out those needing intensive treatment and to offer such help as the diagnostic process alone could render to the parents of children whose difficulties were not deep-seated; but even on this basis waiting lists for treatment were long and involved delays of many months. The extreme shortage of personnel—psychiatrists, psychiatric nurses and social workers, occupational therapists, special teachers for emotionally disturbed children, psychiatrically oriented hospital attendants—was accentuated by the concentration of such specialists in a few centres, such as Vienna, New York and other major cities. Large areas lacked any professional psychiatric worker, even in the United States where interest in mental health reached its height during these years and the number of psychiatrists was substantially increased by German and Austrian refugees in the 1930s.

In spite of reforms few public mental institutions in any country were able to offer care and treatment commensurate with the level of knowledge and understanding. Although the brutality which had been a feature of most mental institutions prior to the twentieth century largely disappeared, neglect remained, for in understaffed and overcrowded hospitals, where one psychiatrist might be responsible for as many as 500 to 1,000 patients, there was little opportunity for careful treatment leading to rehabilitation. It was estimated in the mid-1950s that as many as 10 per cent of all the patients in mental hospitals in the United States would be discharged if hospital personnel were sufficient to handle their problems and other community facilities were adequate.

Rehabilitation of the mentally ill, moreover, continued to be hampered by community attitudes and by the absence of other types of community services. Families continued to reject members whom mental hospitals thought ready for discharge and employers often hesitated to give them work. Where hospitals encountered such attitudes and could find no foster home to receive a patient in the absence of a suitable or willing family, they were forced to keep patients who did not need continued hospital treatment. Lack of such services as nursing homes for old people not requiring psychiatric care prevented the discharge of others.

At mid-century the attack on mental illness was being intensified from all directions. The third International Mental Health Congress, held in London in 1948, led to the formation of the World Federation for Mental Health and the World Health Organization established a mental health section dedicated to the effort to bring about wider recognition and application of principles of mental health.

All the programmes which served the physically or mentally handicapped or the physically or mentally ill were guided by a common principle—that the individual's remaining capacities, whatever they might be, rather than his lacks, were the necessary basis for his rehabilitation and functioning. By exploiting these positive factors society could gain an asset rather than being burdened by a liability, and individuals could enjoy satisfaction and self-esteem. Much of the research, organization, training of personnel and interpretation to the public was oriented toward ways to recognize such positive capacities and to work with them.

6. *The aged*

In the twentieth century, for the first time in history, a large proportion of the population in industrially developed countries lived to old age. At the mortality rates of earlier times, and those which still prevailed up to the middle of the twentieth century in many areas, only a small minority of those born reached late maturity or old age. In the twentieth century the average life expectancy at birth in the industrialized countries increased by some twenty years and at mid-century it exceeded 65 in most such countries.

In 1900, there were only three countries, Sweden, France and Norway, where more than 7 per cent of the people were over 65. In 1950, those over 65 constituted from 7 to 12 per cent of the population of nearly all of the European countries as well as Canada, the United States and Australia. In New Zealand it exceeded 15 per cent.

The great increase in the number of old people and in their proportion in the population coincided with economic and social changes which disturbed their customary status and role, their means of livelihood and their prestige.

The rapidly changing urban-industrial society placed the older person at a disadvantage. It put a premium on the qualities of adaptability and alertness, more often found in younger workers; it tended to make obsolete many learned skills; it drew a sharp line between the fully employed and the unemployed, leaving little room for the tapering off of economic activity and the adjustment of tasks to waning strength which kept the ageing rural worker usefully engaged. Older people were left outside the small family of parents and children instead of enjoying the respect and often authority that came with age under the large or joint family system. The rapidity of social change made old people no longer the repositories of knowledge and wisdom but more often the holders of obsolete ideas and standards. Small city dwellings and the world-wide shortage of urban housing crowded them out of living space.

In these circumstances the growing number of aged people constituted a burden of economic dependency as they were forced into retirement and as a series of severe inflations reduced the value of their savings and pensions. Their presence created a potential source of strain, both on themselves as they tried to hang on or to adjust to retirement in a work-centred society where to be employed was to belong, and on younger people who feared that their own advancement would be blocked or that unduly conservative policies would be sustained. Although the problem of the aged was only one among many social problems created by the spread of the urban-industrial way of life, it was of growing magnitude and became the focus of more and more conscious attention and professional effort during the period.

The first aspect to receive attention was economic—the needy aged without employment or means of support. Nearly every government in the world took some steps toward meeting the problem of income for the aged. Some twenty countries adopted special programmes of public assistance to aged persons in need, nearly fifty included old age benefits in their programmes of social insurance, and a few, notably Canada, New Zealand, Holland, Norway and Sweden, provided pensions to all citizens who reached a certain age.

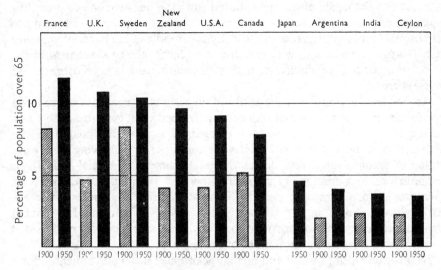

CHART XXIII.   Percentage of Population over 65, 1900 and 1950.
Selected Countries
Source: UN, *The Aging of Populations*, 1956.

A growing proportion of all old people in the industrialized countries received one or another of these benefits; where social insurance programmes were expanded to include additional categories of workers, a still larger proportion of younger people expected to receive benefits when they reached the age of eligibility. At mid-century somewhat less than half of the people over 65 in Great Britain and the United States were receiving insurance benefits or assistance grants, while virtually all British workers below that age and more than 85 per cent of Americans were covered by social insurance and could expect to draw benefits in the future. USSR state pensions covered all factory and office workers and servicemen, together with their families, while collective farms set aside a portion of their crops each year to provide a pension fund for their members.

In addition to general social security coverage, special pensions were paid in most countries to a number of groups such as government workers, military personnel and teachers, and were provided by industries for their employees as a result of collective agreements or voluntary action. Most people in industrialized countries were able to look forward to a continuing income after retirement from work and to freedom from dependence on their children for minimum support.

Toward the middle of the century, however, it became apparent that income was only one of the needs of aged people and that a multitude of other social and health problems required solution if the growing body of older people were not to constitute a drag on industrialized societies. At the same time the approach to the needs of the aged shifted from the negative one of providing income and care for those who were on the shelf, to a positive effort 'to add life to years, not merely years to life'.* By the middle of the twentieth century there was a strong and growing movement to enable the aged segment of the population to live productively, and with health, comfort, enjoyment and self-esteem.

At this time gerontology, the study of all aspects of ageing, emerged as a specialized field of professional endeavour. In medicine, geriatrics, the study of the diseases of ageing, had been recognized as a special field since the publication of the first textbook on the subject in 1914.† Following the organization of gerontological societies or the establishment of special councils or commissions in a number of countries, the first International Congress of Gerontologists was held in Belgium in 1950, followed by successive international conferences in the United States, Great Britain and Italy and a Pan-American conference in Mexico in 1955. The approach was many-sided and involved members of a number of professions.

In the interest of physical and mental health and social adjustment, efforts were concentrated on prevention of chronic illness and premature senility and on the physical and social rehabilitation of many whose years of usefulness and self-maintenance appeared to be over. Elderly people were absorbing an increasing proportion of the time of physicians as evidenced by the British experience under the National Health scheme, where patients over 65 averaged 40 per cent more medical consultations per year than adults below that age. Numbers of beds in general hospitals and mental institutions were occupied by chronically ill old people who did not need complete hospital care. To meet this situation a variety of measures were instituted to make it possible for old people not in need of hospital care to avoid hospitalization.

The traditional means of caring for the aged outside the family group was in old people's homes, and almost every country, whether industrially developed or not, had some such institutions housing from 2 to 7 per cent of their older people. In line with trends in the care of other groups, institutions which gave only a minimum of custodial care came to be regarded as unsatisfactory. There was a general movement to reduce the numbers of old people

---

* See Lord Basil William Amulree, *Adding Life to Years* (London, 1951).

† I. L. Nascher, *Geriatrics: The Diseases of Old Age and Their Treatment* (Blakiston's Son & Co., Philadelphia, 1914).

needing to go to an institution and to raise the standards of service for those requiring such care.

Some countries developed large well-equipped centres such as the Old People's Town in Copenhagen, with its own hospital, assembly hall and church, manned by a staff of 500 to look after its 1,600 residents. The USSR maintained special homes with workshops, social amenities and medical services. In some places, notably in Great Britain and the United States, the trend was toward small specialized nursing or boarding homes less isolated from the rest of the community.

Principal efforts, however, were directed toward making it possible for old people to live in homes of their own and to continue to function as actively as their strength would permit.

Hospitals in Great Britain and the United States were beginning to develop programmes of home care as an extension of their regular service. On the basis of the great success achieved during and after the second world war in the rehabilitation of very severely handicapped military personnel, physical rehabilitation and retraining was undertaken for many civilians, including aged persons, whose situations had seemed hopeless.

Housing was a difficult problem for older people who either had no family with whom they could live or for whom there was no room in their children's small apartment or house; a 1954 British study of persons over 70 found 43 per cent with no members of their family alive, no contact with family members or only a very weak or poor relationship. Housing projects for independent old people began to be constructed in a number of countries, initially in Norway, Sweden, Denmark, Britain, Holland and Canada. At first these were separate blocks of flats, but later they were built as integral parts of housing developments for a cross-section of the population in order that the aged might not be segregated from the community. In addition various housekeeping services such as prepared meals sent in to aged persons who could not cook for themselves, and laundry, mending and other forms of home-help were established and expanded rapidly, especially in Great Britain and the Netherlands.

Opportunities for earning at least a partial income were provided by the sheltered workshops and work for the home-bound established through voluntary organizations in many countries. Advisory services to help aged people to know the possibilities for retraining, employment, housing, recreation or medical care were provided in connection with most pension or other schemes for financial aid and by other social agencies.

By these measures and through the specialized research and attention of doctors, psychologists, sociologists, social workers, psychiatrists, educators and others, and through a shift in community attitudes, a beginning was being made at mid-century to transform what was regarded as the 'problem' of the aged into positive efforts to enhance the potentialities of this large and growing sector of the population.

III. ECONOMIC AID TO FAMILIES

In addition to making provision for various dependent groups, industrial countries took steps to equalize the situation of children growing up in families of different size. Under conditions of modern urban living the economic burdens carried by families in the rearing of their young came to be recognized as heavy, especially for large families. In agricultural societies additional children were often economic assets because of their ability to contribute at an early age to the productive work on which the family's living depended. Under urban conditions they were a liability, particularly since child labour laws restricted their employment.

In order to assist families in meeting their economic obligations countries in many parts of the world enacted legislation which took account of the differential economic needs of large families as compared with those which had few children or none. Such measures were not designed to replace income lost by reason of one hazard or another, as were social security benefits, but rather to supplement the regular family income. When the United Nations made a survey of *Economic Measures in Favor of the Family* in 1952, it found that such measures had come to make up the skeleton of a special scheme within the sphere of social welfare. In spite of the haphazard manner in which many of these measures had been introduced and the fact that some were organically connected with social insurance, some with assistance programmes and some were independent measures, taken as a whole they established a distinct principle: differential economic benefits for families of different sizes.

The most general of these measures were family allowances which added to the level of family income in relation to the number of children. These had been established by 1950 in some form in most industrial countries with the exception of the United States. Family allowances developed in different ways in different countries. In France and some other countries of continental Europe they were introduced by employers as a means of resisting labour's demands for a general raise in wages. When applied on an individual plant basis, however, a wage differential in favour of the heads of large families worked hardship because it made it economically advantageous to the employer to take on persons without dependents to do the same work for less pay. In order to avoid this dilemma industry funds were pooled and the wage supplements were paid out of the common pool so that the individual worker did not cost the individual firm more because he received an allowance.

Elsewhere, notably in the Scandinavian countries, family allowance plans were introduced in the 1930s because of concern over the low birth rate in urban areas, and were paid out of the public treasury, not industry funds. The Canadian scheme was inaugurated at the close of the second world war, primarily on the initiative of the business community which feared a post-war economic slump and saw the steady though small increments provided by the family allowance as a means of sustaining buying power and thus contributing to the stability of the economy.

Whatever the circumstances of their introduction, allowances were generally available to families without a means test, though the additional income which they represented was usually cancelled through progressive taxation above a certain income level; in no instance were they sufficiently large to provide for maintenance. In some countries grants were paid for all children while in others they began with the second or third child. In the USSR monthly grants for children from birth to the age of five began with the third child and increased with the size of the family; unmarried mothers received a grant at the birth of the first and every succeeding child. Some countries continued payments until the child reached sixteen; they differed in whether they maintained the size of the grant at a uniform rate or modified it upward or downward with the age of the child and the number in the family.

Virtually every country which collected an income tax allowed a tax deduction for each dependent. A few countries had special benefits such as marriage grants and birth premiums to facilitate the setting up of new families and help to defray the additional costs of pregnancy and birth.

In addition to measures of direct financial supplement or tax relief, some countries made special provision for food, housing and other necessities in such a way that direct expenditures were unnecessary or the family with a number of children had to spend less for the equivalent goods and services than others. Illustrative of such measures were special meals for school children, vegetable garden allotments on the outskirts of towns, larger dwellings for large families at lower cost as in Sweden, or priority in the allocation of new housing as in the USSR, rent allowances, rebates on gas and electricity, provision of certain types of clothing. Special concessions with respect to fares for children or families travelling together were quite common, including in some countries provisions to make it possible for families to take holidays or engage in recreation together; Sweden even provided holiday allowances for housewives and free holiday transport for housewives and children. These measures lessened the economic disadvantages for the child in a large family as compared with a small family of similar occupational status.

IV.   PRINCIPLES AND METHODS OF SOCIAL WELFARE

Underlying the measures to deal with dependency and to promote social welfare in all fields ran a common set of evolving principles and common tendencies in the choice of methods employed.

1. *Respect for the individual and confidence in his potentialities*

Twentieth-century social services were based on a fundamental attitude toward the individual: respect for him as a person and the belief that he had within himself potentialities for development and responsible action. In traditional liberal and democratic societies this meant the application of the central principle of such societies to elements in the population who had in actual fact been denied or only grudgingly accorded this dignity. In traditionally authoritarian and stratified societies such an assumption was part of the revolution in outlook which was taking place. In communist societies it reflected the assumption that the individual could and must function as a rational component of society and would respond to education and persuasion, though the need to maintain the social fabric intact might require a resort to punishment or exclusion as a temporary device. The development of this attitude toward the individual, and its infusion into public consciousness, into legislation and into the practice of those entrusted with carrying out social measures gave welfare programmes their most basic significance.

Social work practice recognized the individual's strong qualities, whatever his limitations might be, depended on his co-operation on his own behalf, had faith in him and in his ability to use his positive capacities and helped him to respect himself. This fundamental approach completely reversed the punitive and morally superior attitude with which charity had often been offered. Observing the beginning of this shift at the opening of the century, one of the founders of the social work profession in the United States, Mary Richmond, commented: 'In nothing does the change seem so marked as in our willingness to cooperate with the poor themselves and with their neighbours.'* In the following years the changed attitude came to be based not alone on the changing social and moral climate but also on a practical understanding of human psychology and motivation which indicated that only through his own active participation could the individual make full use of whatever services were offered, achieve his own rehabilitation or prevent his own distress.

In line with this attitude, the distinction between the general population and those who were the recipients of public aid was broken down. The 'poor', the 'needy', the 'dependent', the 'insane', the 'criminal' or 'delinquent', the 'aged', the 'illegitimate', not only came to be regarded as citizens with rights, feelings and dignity but to be treated by methods which as far as possible enabled them to retain their status and participate in the life of the community.

2. Changing focus of social programmes

The content and focus of social programmes shifted by successive stages from mere relief of distress, custodial care or punishment to measures for positive welfare. The first stage was the introduction of the idea of treatment and rehabilitation, which provided the foundation for the juvenile court and the reform of juvenile and penal institutions, for the conversion of mental institutions from custodial agencies to treatment centres, and for the services of social workers as counsellors in family welfare agencies, public assistance offices, clinics and hospitals. Along with the emphasis on treatment went a growing trend toward prevention rather than cure. Social insurance against

* *Charities*, vii (September, 1901), p. 191.

the major hazards likely to cause poverty and dependency—accident, illness, old age, disablement, death—became a characteristic feature of modern states; measures such as economic aid to larger families and parent education and counselling were adopted to prevent family breakdown; programmes to deal with juvenile delinquency focused on the detection of early symptoms of maladjustment.

As preventive measures were extended it became apparent that a negative approach was insufficient, and social programmes took on a positive orientation, well evidenced by the shift in focus of the decennial White House conferences on children in the US from 'the care of dependent children' in 1909 to 'a healthy personality for every child' in 1950. Services for all the people increasingly replaced programmes for dependent or insured groups, as comprehensive health programmes replaced limited health insurance and medical care for the indigent, public education was broadened and public facilities for recreation were extended.

The scope of social programmes broadened in every direction—in the hazards against which protection was provided, the range of people enjoying community services and the types of problems to which community resources were devoted. Most especially they came to include non-material as well as material needs.

By the middle of the twentieth century those responsible for social welfare in industrial countries were greatly concerned with the psychological strains of industrial society, for they were coming to recognize that the psychological effects of industrialization were cumulative. The older industrial societies were still heavily burdened by the psychological results of the poverty, indignity, social disorganization, crowded living and abuse of children which had characterized the earlier stages of their economic growth. Persons who had been raised in homes which could not give them the security of a stable society had in their turn been unable to provide their own children with the stability necessary to adjust to constant change. In spite of improved conditions, moreover, there remained an unresolved conflict between the stable, rational and responsible behaviour expected of the individual as a parent and citizen and the conduct required of him as an industrial worker, engaged in impermanent work under outside direction, faced with constant threats to his status from technological change and occupying an assigned role which tended to decline with advancing age.

The central social problems of industrially developed countries came to lie in the area of human relations, human satisfactions and human dignity.

3. Changes in structure and design

These basic changes in the character of welfare services were paralleled by changes in structure, auspices, techniques and the locus of responsibility. The same methods continued to be used: private philanthropy, public assistance, social insurance, establishment of minimum labour and living standards by law, and the direct provision of public services; but they changed in relative importance and in the part played by each in total welfare developments.

Private philanthropy lost its central role and its capricious and paternalistic character even in the countries where it was most widely developed and continued to flourish. Although often not subject to the same standards of impartiality as public services, private agencies generally came to occupy a specified place in an integrated and planned community effort, supplementing broad public services by meeting special needs, providing an opportunity for experimentation or serving special groups.

Public assistance largely replaced private philanthropy as a source of economic aid. At the same time it ceased to be granted as a benevolence and became a matter of right. Those who met legally established criteria of eligibility were entitled to aid, and the public assistance laws of the second quarter of the century generally confirmed this right by providing for appeal in case relief was denied.

While public aid took the place of private philanthropy, assistance based on evidence of need was in turn largely replaced by social insurance and preventive measures. In most countries assistance was retained as a supplement to these more comprehensive programmes. Some of the countries with the broadest welfare programmes such as New Zealand, however, chose to use generous social assistance for many contingencies in preference to contributory social insurance.

The most widespread expansion came in the development of social insurance systems which had only begun to spread from their German origins at the opening of the twentieth century and which were established in some form in virtually every country in the world by the 1950s. These systems generally began with small programmes covering limited groups of industrial workers and few hazards and were expanded until in some industrial countries they embraced virtually the entire working population in industry, agriculture, trade and services and included all types of risk. By 1956, 71 countries had adopted insurance programmes against work accidents, 49 provided for the maintenance of income during old age or after the earner's disablement or death, 45 countries, including every industrialized country except the United States, had health and maternity insurance to cover medical costs and usually to provide income during illness. The famous Beveridge Report in Britain, published in 1942,* which set the goal for that country as protection 'from the cradle to the grave', completely abandoned the old poor relief concept that the threat of near starvation is necessary to force people to work, and substituted the opposite assumption that insecurity is not an effective or necessary goad but tends to make people less able and less inclined to function at their best.

Social insurance systems varied in their method of financing and the relation of benefits to contributions. Benefit payments were most frequently related to

* Sir William Beveridge, *Social Insurance and Allied Services* (November 20, 1942).

the amount which the recipient had been earning, thus giving larger benefits to those whose wages were higher, though some systems provided for benefits at a flat rate or adjusted to need. Contributions were generally collected from employers and workers as a proportion of the worker's wage, partly as a means of securing the funds out of which benefits could be paid and partly to establish a claim of right on the part of the beneficiary. The state also contributed to some schemes, and there was a tendency for the state's share to increase as benefit levels were raised and more groups in the population were covered. Some countries abandoned contributions in favour of a pension out of tax funds, as did Canada, on the ground that all who reached the age of 65 after residing in the country for twenty or more years could be presumed to have contributed sufficiently to the nation's resources to be entitled to benefits. Benefits in the USSR were paid out of funds contributed by state enterprises without deductions from workers' wages, although the size of the benefit was related to wages and number of working years, adjusted upward in case of injury received in industry or military service; with the growth in national revenue the general level of social security benefits increased.

The device of using minimum standards set by law to place a floor under the working and living conditions of the people was also widely extended. The scope of labour legislation was broadened until it provided an elaborate framework of minimum wages, limitation of hours, minimum conditions of health and safety, minimum age of employment and a wide range of other conditions which industry was required to meet in order to be allowed to operate. Regulations designed to assure minimum living conditions took the form of expanded public health laws, food and drug inspection, and minimum standards of safety, space, sanitation and ventilation of housing.

The direct provision of public services as a method of meeting needs tended to reach its greatest extension in those countries committed to a socialist pattern of society and to be used less generally elsewhere. Nevertheless, the number and range of publicly provided social services grew apace in virtually all countries as one after another of the services which had been offered to dependent groups as charity were provided at public expense for the whole population. In some countries with a strong non-socialist orientation, such as the United States, a well-established tradition of public services in certain areas, such as education, libraries, recreation or public health, provided the basis for expansion in these areas, while non-traditional fields such as housing or medical care lagged behind. Elsewhere, as in many Latin American countries, the absence of any services except those publicly provided and the large proportion of the population too poor to take advantage of facilities on any other basis made for the extension of public services on pragmatic grounds rather than because of principle.

As the newly industrializing countries adopted welfare programmes they attempted to use the forms which had become established elsewhere. With few exceptions they introduced some sort of social insurance, set minimum conditions through labour legislation and committed themselves to provide a variety of direct public services and sometimes a measure of financial assistance to those in need.

It was an evidence of the strength of the trends in these directions that legislation often went far beyond the ability of the country to finance or man the programmes which it established on any but a very limited scale or to enforce standards beyond a few key places or groups. Meantime, the benefactions of wealthy individuals, the patronage of political or social leaders, and the services of dedicated groups continued to provide many of the pioneer and fragmentary services which were actually available in these countries. India, for example, estimated that it had some 10,000 private charities when it set up a Central Social Welfare Board in 1953 to assist and co-ordinate their activities.* There were however facilities for only something like 3,000 out of perhaps two million blind, scarcely any provisions to aid an estimated seven million crippled, only four institutions in the entire country for mentally defective children and virtually no psychiatric services for children.

The problem of designing welfare programmes for underdeveloped areas was thus a twofold task of dealing at the same time with the mass problem of poverty, ill health and ignorance and the special problems of particular disadvantaged groups. In the western industrialized countries, welfare services were primarily needed by a relatively small portion of the population that fell below the general level of adequacy which most families could maintain under normal circumstances, or were unable to make a social adjustment in industrial society. In the underdeveloped countries, where the general level of living was below minimum standards of adequacy, the problem was not merely to help the laggards but to raise the majority through broad measures affecting the health, nutrition and productivity of the general population.

In these circumstances one after another of the underdeveloped countries adopted what came to be known as 'community development' programmes whose essential purpose was to mobilize the initiative of people on their own behalf and to make limited supplies and specialized personnel available where people were ready to make use of them and to supplement them by their own efforts. The community development programmes were primarily addressed to the villages and aimed to stimulate the rural populations to better their own lot. The design of the programmes varied but most of them made use of some sort of 'village worker' who knew how to work with villagers, and who was able to tap the technical resources provided by existing social programmes and sometimes to teach certain skills. In some countries their work was supplemented by that of welfare aides whose activity was primarily with the women and children. Up to the middle of the 1950s community development programmes had not been effectively developed on any large scale to meet the problems of cities and towns, though they were seen to offer possibilities.

* *Social Welfare in India* (The Planning Commission, Government of India, New Delhi, 1955).

4. *Locus of social responsibility*

The development of social programmes involved a redefinition of the respective responsibilities of the individual, family, employer, local community and the state. In spite of the general shift to social responsibility, the principle of direct individual responsibility was retained in contributory social insurance plans, in fees for services adjusted to ability to pay and in the level of eligibility for public assistance which marked the line between the responsibility of the individual and of the state. Family responsibility was retained in the frequent requirement that legally responsible relatives, if able to do so, must provide support and care, but the list of relatives whom the law tried to hold responsible was generally reduced to the immediate group of parents and children. Where families failed to meet their obligations, as in cases of desertion or failure to support children born out of wedlock, state responsibility toward the child tended to outweigh the legal responsibility of the parent and public aid was extended to children born out of wedlock or abandoned by their fathers.

Countries differed considerably in the extent to which they required employers to bear costs relating to the welfare of their workers and made protection against the hazards of workers' lives a charge against industry, but the tendency was away from the concept that industry's only obligation was to pay for time actually worked or goods actually produced, and towards a broader view of employers' responsibilities.

Employers were held responsible for far more of the costs of their workers' livelihood than in the early days of industrial development when factories used pauper children from the almshouses. Workmen's compensation laws generally made employers wholly responsible for the cost of compulsory insurance against work accidents. In most systems of social insurance against illness, disability, old age and death, employers shared responsibility with workers and the state. Under some of the early family allowance programmes the extra burden of supporting large families was charged against industry, but later systems placed the burden on the state.

In the USSR many services were provided to workers through the factory, including maternity benefits and day care for the children of working mothers, health clinics, restaurants and housing, and these were charged as expenses of the industry. Elsewhere exceptional employers established welfare services or built factory villages but in some countries labour unions opposed these as a form of paternalism and insisted that industry should put the money into wages and leave the responsibility for social services to the state. Some labour unions through collective bargaining secured contributions from employers to welfare and pension funds providing health and hospital services, retirement and other benefits for their members. Newly industrializing countries, such as India and a number of Latin American countries, tended to make industry carry many of the costs of providing security and social services to their workers.

The strongest tendency was to place major responsibility on the state and to increase the share carried by central governments as against local units of government. Local responsibility which had characterized most of the European and North American systems was replaced or supplemented by the participation of central governments to support a national minimum standard, although actual administration frequently remained in local hands. In most countries social services and benefits came to be provided by a combination of centrally administered systems, grant-in-aid from central to local governments to supplement local resources and equalize services, compulsory insurance based on contributions from the individual, industry and the state, and a variety of voluntary efforts.

5. *The social professions*

To carry out social measures and to apply the growing body of knowledge of human behaviour, new social professions were developed and the scope of older professions was expanded by the incorporation of knowledge from social science fields. The training of doctors and nurses was broadened to include social aspects,* as was that of many teachers. Social work itself became a distinct profession. A number of quasi-professional activities were identified and several types of sub-professional or auxiliary workers were trained to supplement the professionals.

Social work as a profession was non-existent in 1900. The process of rendering aid to those in need had hitherto appeared to require no special knowledge or technique; a generous spirit or sense of duty sufficed. At the turn of the century the first formal training course was offered in New York and similar programmes were inaugurated shortly thereafter in Belgium and France. This step reflected the new idea that the effectiveness of welfare services depended upon the application of sound knowledge and the use of consciously developed techniques.

In the course of the next fifty years the profession of social work grew and spread from western Europe and the United States to more and more parts of the world. When the first International Conference of Social Work was held in 1928, a total of 111 institutions were offering professional training in most countries of western Europe, in North American and in one of the Latin American countries, Chile. In the succeeding decades schools of social work were founded in most of the Latin American countries and in India, Australia, New Zealand, South Africa, Egypt, China and Japan. A United Nations review in 1950 found 373 institutions in 46 countries; five years later the number exceeded 600.

Social workers generally assumed primary professional responsibility for services relating to economic aid, the welfare of dependent children and the social adjustment of the family and they supplemented the work of doctors, judges of juvenile courts, directors of correctional institutions and teachers; in some places they were used in industry to help workers who were new to

* See Chapter XV, Health and Population.

the ways of factory production, wage earning and city life to meet their problems of adjustment. The widespread need for trained workers in these fields led the United Nations Social Commission to give priority to the promotion of social work training through international fellowships for observation and study, the provision of social welfare advisory services and direct aid in the establishment of new schools for the training of social workers.

In the industrially underdeveloped countries the number of professionally trained workers was generally sufficient only to plan and guide programmes and to train and supervise non-professional personnel. To staff the mass services these countries experimented with ways of training large numbers of sub-professional workers to offer a minimum of service or to act as intermediaries between the professional workers and the people to be served. In a number of countries, such as India, Pakistan, Puerto Rico, Colombia, Brazil, programmes were established for the training of multi-purpose workers, village aides or auxiliary personnel in specialized fields such as nutrition, nursing or child care. The United Nations regarded the development of auxiliary-type workers as a prime requisite in the welfare fields and organized regional conferences on the subject in Asia, the Middle East and Latin America in the early 1950s.

6. Social welfare techniques at mid-century

When the United Nations in 1952 undertook a survey of methods of rendering social assistance with a view to determining whether there existed sufficent consensus to formulate standard recommendations to countries planning or replanning their programmes, it found common trends in principle but only a limited area of agreement in application.* The countries studied, Australia, Denmark, Egypt, France, Japan, the United Kingdom and the United States, chosen to represent all the principal systems that had been developed, used similar methods differently or in different combinations. Definitions of 'need' varied widely; although the general tendency was to broaden the concept from survival to health, and thence to the maintenance of dignity as human beings, there was no scientifically determined definition of 'need'. Governments recognized that the best defence against effects of unemployment was the maintenance of full employment, but there was as yet little information or understanding with respect to the relation between economic programmes to promote full employment and programmes of social insurance and assistance designed to prevent or relieve need.

The development of social welfare in the five northern European countries which were leaders in the field, Norway, Sweden, Denmark, Iceland, Finland, epitomized the trends of these years. There social welfare policy was gradually transformed from its traditional function of aid to those in need into a policy of social planning, centring around programmes for full and productive

* *Methods of Administering Assistance to the Needy:* Study by the Secretary General of Programs in Seven Countries (UN Department of Social Affairs, New York, 1952).

employment, family welfare and housing, prophylactic health and rehabilitation of handicapped persons. In principle the community assumed main responsibility for ensuring a decent minimum standard in fields of vital importance to the life of every citizen, at a modest level but increasing with advancement in national wealth and social thinking. Ever broader responsibilities were assumed by the state, but voluntary co-operative efforts and local initiative were also retained.

In these countries social measures increasingly took the form of public services and facilities at the disposal of the entire population. Although feelings of humanitarianism and social justice continued as driving forces for many social innovations, the main motive for these developments, according to the study sponsored by the welfare ministers of the five countries,* was the rational conviction that many improvements in living conditions for the whole or greater part of the population could best be obtained through community action. The cost of the comprehensive welfare programmes of these countries, exclusive of education and housing, amounted to from 8 to 11 per cent of national income as compared with 1 to 2 per cent for corresponding services at the opening of the century. Other countries with advanced social programmes, such as Great Britain and New Zealand, were also spending an estimated 10 per cent of their national income for similar services. The well-developed social programmes of these countries marked the direction in which other countries were moving.

Yet in spite of noteworthy developments the best available knowledge from the social and biological sciences was rarely fully and systematically applied and wide gaps in knowledge remained to keep the provision of welfare services an essentially pragmatic activity. Though there was much agreement in principle and acceptance of common approaches and standards, there was still little tested evidence of the effectiveness of various forms of social treatment and prevention. A large body of research threw light on the nature of many social problems. Agencies responsible for the administering of social security programmes and for providing social services set up what came to be called 'operational research' as an integral part of their administration in an effort to know how the programmes were being used and to provide a basis for making them more useful. Yet up to the middle of the century few well-tested techniques had been devised for evaluating social welfare programmes in terms which went beyond such elementary facts as survival and the incidence of detected illness and crime. Tests were yet to be evolved which could accurately determine how far and under what conditions specific programmes and methods of carrying them out prevented social breakdown, achieved successful and enduring rehabilitation and contributed to positive individual and social health and the maintenance of human dignity.

* *Freedom and Welfare: Social Patterns in the Northern Countries of Europe*, ed. George R. Nelson and others. (Ministries of Social Affairs of Denmark, Finland, Iceland, Norway and Sweden, 1953.)

PART TWO

THE TRANSFORMATION OF SOCIETIES

CHAPTER XX

MAJOR CHANGES IN CONCEPTS
AND IDEAS

I INTRODUCTION

THE application of scientific knowledge in many spheres of life was interwoven with the impact of ideas concerning the nature of human society and man's place in it, and with changing values which reflected social change and guided social action.

In general terms the twentieth century was an age both of great optimism and of great uncertainty. Optimism arose from the new sense of previously unimagined possibilities which science and technology brought and which the changing structure of power and changing social institutions were opening up to many people. Uncertainty reflected the fact that the spread of science and technology threatened established positions and destroyed established ways, and that inherited value systems and philosophical constructs were inadequate to the conditions of the new age. In these years no sphere of life remained unassailed by questions and doubts, no traditional system of thought stood unchallenged.

In the West the schematic philosophies of the past, together with the materialistic positivism of Auguste Comte, John Stuart Mill and Herbert Spencer, lost popularity and the Aristotelian logic on which these schemes had been erected was itself not free from attack. The twentieth-century study of the subconscious and its influence on human personality affected the continued acceptance of much of the philosophical thinking of the past. As knowledge expanded with great rapidity, covering every field and changing basic conceptions of time and space, of the nature of matter and of the universe, of society and of man's place in it, the redefinition of philosophical postulates and new philosophical interpretations proved most difficult to achieve.

In the non-European world the traditional assumptions on which the social order was based were everywhere subjected to heavy criticism. As profound social changes undermined traditional institutions and relationships, the formulations which sanctioned them lost much of their force. In China denunciation of the familial system of life was one of the expressions of the revolutionary drive which produced the New Tide Movement of 1917. In the thirty years of struggle which followed, the hold of Confucian ethics as the basis for social relations was so weakened as to permit the general displacement of Confucian by Marxian principles when the communists came to power in 1949. Japan throughout the period struggled to reconcile traditional values and those imported from the West or to find an accommodation between them. This struggle assumed special intensity after the second world war under the shadow of defeat and occupation. The challenge to the traditional conceptions of Indian society was perhaps even more fundamental, for Hindu society had identified its hierarchical system of castes, sub-castes and untouchables and many of its social customs with religion. As all these were attacked and finally were changed by legislation in the period after 1947, most of the social doctrines of the Hindus were either discarded or modified under the influence of ideas which had their origin in the West.

Nor were such developments confined to Asia for their counterpart was to be seen in Africa, which had remained practically outside world currents throughout the nineteenth century. In the twentieth century the outlook which underlay the traditional pattern of tribal life broke down under the European impact and by the middle of the century African life was undergoing a radical reconstruction.

Though this was an age of uncertainty and no dominant set of ideas could be said to have guided the life of mankind as a whole, it is possible to distinguish certain beliefs, doctrines and concepts as having found general acceptance, and, in any case, as moving large sections of mankind in their social, political and economic relationships. These may be examined in terms of changes in generally held concepts of man's relation to society, to his past and future, and to nature, his view of his gods and his concept of himself, and may also be viewed in terms of the efforts of philosophical thinkers to organize the experience and observations of mankind during these years.

II. MAN'S RELATION TO SOCIETY

First among the central ideas of the twentieth century were two that were often in conflict, the idea of nationalism and the concept of the unity of mankind. Nationalism as such was not an idea which originated in the twentieth century but this century was the first to witness its spread to nearly all peoples. Its influence on the outlook of peoples and the interrelations among them was overwhelmingly great, as has been pointed out in discussing the impact of nationalism on the flow of political events.* But no less far-reaching and even more distinctive of the twentieth century was the growing view of mankind as one.

In previous ages, though many religions stressed the brotherhood of man, the unity of mankind was not a generally accepted belief. The obvious differences among peoples in physical appearance, material advancement and other aspects of culture stood in the way of a general acceptance of the idea that mankind is one. In the period when Europe dominated most of the world the

* See Chapter II: The Impact of Nationalism and Trend toward International Cooperation.

majority of Europeans and other people of the white races felt that the unity of mankind was a myth. Nor was this idea confined to Europeans. Practically every people believed that they were different and superior, in some sense the chosen of God, or simply *the* people.

It was not without a struggle that the idea of the unity of mankind came to be accepted—at least in a general sense—by the middle of the century. The concept of the master *Herrenvolk* was proclaimed by Nazi doctrine, it continued to receive official approval in portions of the African continent and it survived among reactionary groups in old-established societies. But by the period after the second world war the unity of mankind had become one of the leading ideas of the time.

This idea was a motivating force in many of the more significant activities of the twentieth century: the effort to raise the economic, cultural and physical standards of backward communities; acknowledgement in principle of a general level of rights and privileges for all, as expressed in the United Nations Universal Declaration of Human Rights; the sustained endeavour to eliminate avoidable diseases to which many areas were subject; the administration of trust territories under international supervision. Though no one could claim that all peoples had achieved equality of opportunity, the striking fact of the twentieth century in comparison with previous ages of history was the world-wide commitment to the principle.

Not alone with regard to peoples in different stages of development, but within each nation itself the sense of unity was achieved only in the twentieth century. Even in countries such as Britain, France and the United States it was only in the decade following the first world war, and then incompletely, that the sense of equal entitlement was extended to members of the working class, women, racial minorities, and that the unity of the nation as a single community came to be more fully achieved.

In the countries of Asia the lack of unity within the state was even more pronounced, whether it took the form of the persistence of feudal relationships in Japan, of the almost complete lack of facilities for education, economic betterment or elementary medical care for the masses of the people in China, of India's elaborate system of castes and its 40,000,000 untouchables without primary social rights, or of secluded women and the secondary status of non-believers in Islamic countries. The idea of the totality of the people of a state enjoying equal privileges began to assert itself in Asia in the period following the first world war, at a time when the working classes of western Europe attained political power and the October revolution proclaimed faith in a classless society. One of the most significant aspects of the national struggle in India, Burma, Pakistan, Ceylon and Indonesia in those years was the affirmation of national solidarity by acceptance of the principle that internal inequalities should be abolished.

The communist states embodied the principle of the unity of mankind in the concept that the total population shares in the work of the community and enjoys its benefits. In the initial period of social reorganization the capitalist and landowner classes were to be subordinated to the dictatorship of the proletariat or in case of active resistance eliminated; but eventually the unity of the classless society would be achieved.

A second major idea of the twentieth century stemmed from this doctrine of the unity of mankind: recognition that the welfare of all is the concern of all. In the nineteenth century humanitarians were moved by the sufferings of people everywhere but there was no general recognition that poverty, illness, ignorance and the absence of opportunities in many parts of the world were matters of concern to the world as a whole. If people in Venezuela suffered from malaria, if yellow fever and sleeping sickness took their toll in Africa, if large areas of the world were exposed to chronic famines, these were regarded as the fate of the people involved; except as an occasional expression of charity or in time of disaster, the world in general did not accept responsibility for such a state of affairs.

By the middle of the twentieth century the numerous international organizations set up under the auspices of the United Nations bore ample witness to a changed viewpoint and to the widespread acceptance of the idea that the prosperity and welfare of the world is indivisible and is a common responsibility.

Another consequence of the concept of the brotherhood of mankind was the concept of non-violence as a mode of action in human relations. Non-violence was not a new principle; the Buddha preached it and it was part of Christ's teaching. But it had remained a religious doctrine, cherished and preached by idealists and saints, considered too impracticable in the realm of politics. In the twentieth century Mahatma Gandhi transformed non-violence from a purely religious doctrine into a force in politics, first in his struggle with the South African government in the early years of the century and then in the thirty-year fight which he led for the freedom of India.

In Gandhi's conception non-violence alone could successfully resist the use of violence, for if violence were met by violence it could only lead to destruction. His definition of non-violence was not merely a denial of physical force but a determination not to injure anyone, even those who were using violence, and he relied on strict adherence to truth and on moral force which could not be fought by the essentially amoral method of violence. Although the only widespread use of non-violence as a political method came in India, its success there brought it into the realm of practical, operating ideas and it began to be used to a small extent elsewhere. In the face of the ever-mounting destructiveness which the scientific age made possible it began to be seen as an alternative means of effecting political and social change.[1]

Also special to the twentieth century was the broad acceptance of cultural difference. In the prevalent nineteenth-century view Europe represented the final pattern of culture; civilization had originated with the Greeks and had been inherited through the Romans by modern Europe. The predominance that the West enjoyed in industrial, economic and political spheres gave a verisimilitude to the belief that other civilizations were either immature forms, stunted growths or lower organizations of society.

The view of European civilization as the final pattern of life was undermined from many directions. Archaeological research revealed that civilization did not in fact originate in Greece but that great cultures had been in existence in the Nile, Euphrates and Indus valleys, in China and in South and Central America long before Greece emerged as a centre of civilization; that other civilizations of the world, some of which, like the Chinese and the Indian, claimed continuity with the past, had not only produced cultural forms of abiding value but had contributed their share to the growth of science and to the advancement of thought.

The study of cultural anthropology not only brought a new understanding of the life of pre-industrial people in terms of their own cultural patterns and values, but demonstrated how closely many of the cherished conceptions and habits in civilized societies have their counterparts in primitive life. The twentieth century came to accept the idea that cultures differ in their value systems and cannot be simply dismissed as 'backward' or 'queer'. Modern European society came to be seen not as the inevitable outcome of a rigid process of progress which would automatically and inevitably lead to similar developments elsewhere, but as the product of a particular combination of circumstances; not as a model for all but only as one civilization among others.[2]

The twentieth century was further especially notable for the emphasis it placed on economic and social values as against the purely individual and primarily political values which found their apogee in western society in the nineteenth century. By the opening of the century challenges were coming from a number of quarters to *laissez-faire* individualism and its assumptions that the function of government was to assure the individual his natural and inalienable right to be free, that economic prosperity would result from individual effort and that social welfare should be left to the conscience of individuals. A growing body of opinion saw the untrammelled freedom of the individual as a form of social anarchy leading to the oppression of the weak by the strong and exploitation of the poor by the rich; it held that the freedom of the individual could have meaning for the people as a whole only when they enjoyed a measure of economic security and effective social safeguards.

From the mid-nineteenth century the doctrine of socialism emphasized the importance of collective rather than individual values. The trade union movement substituted collective action for the idea of a free market where the worker could sell and the employer could buy labour according to the law of supply and demand. The Catholic Church, which had consistently opposed the idea of the absolute right of the individual, asserted in the papal encyclical *Rerum novarum* (1891) the principle of social justice as a guide to economic relationships.[3,4] But it was only in the twentieth century that trade unionism and collective bargaining were fully recognized, that the social obligation of the state to look after the welfare of the people and tax the rich differentially for this purpose came to be accepted, and that socialist doctrines were put into practice over large areas of the earth.

The economic and social values of the twentieth century were exemplified in the idea of planning. The conscious organization of production on a planned basis was a natural development of socialist activity, and the communist formulation of successive five-year plans which provided for continuing control of economic development at all stages constituted the most elaborate system of planned economy.

But the idea of planning was by no means confined to the Soviet Union and other communist countries where it was combined with collective ownership of the means of production and the full authority to put plans into action. The Tennessee Valley Authority in the United States was the prototype for the planned development of river valleys in many countries. Town planning was carried to great lengths in the British Town and Country Planning Act of 1945 and welfare planning in that country's Beveridge report of 1942, both implemented after the second world war. From the time of the great depression of the 1930s many countries introduced some measure of planning into the direction of their agricultural production and into the use of fiscal and monetary policy for the maintenance of full employment. And most underdeveloped countries in the decade after the second world war approached their task of national development by means of some form of economic planning; the provision of financial aid by international agencies and from other sources was in fact made in terms of such plans.

The twentieth-century concept of planning—of a conscious, collective design for the actions of individuals—seemed to be in a sense the very antithesis of the nineteenth-century elevation of individual freedom to a central value. It was however not incompatible with the changed concept of freedom which came to prevail.

The Atlantic Charter of August 1941 declared among the 'four freedoms' two which expressed the new concepts of the twentieth century, 'freedom from want' and 'freedom from fear'. The twentieth-century view of individual freedom may be defined as the right of each individual to a healthy life, to a share in the goods of the world, to opportunities for education, to social protection against hazards beyond his control, and the opportunity to work as the fulfilment of his social obligation. The idea of individual freedom was no longer simply the right to do what one pleases within the law; it was the conception of being a member of a free society committed to the welfare of all.

This twentieth-century concept of individual freedom rested on a view of the welfare of society as not being a thing apart from the welfare of the individuals that constitute it. The idea was not new for it had often found expression by religious leaders and others in many cultures; it was a seventeenth-century English poet, John Donne, who wrote the oft-quoted lines,

'No man is an island . . . And therefore never send to know for whom the bell tolls; It tolls for *thee*.' But in the twentieth century the idea became the rationale for much collective action.

The organization of trade unions for example limited the freedom of the individual to bargain, but the purpose of collective bargaining was higher wages and better labour conditions, and therewith a greater degree of freedom for those involved. In the same manner planning by the state which controlled the sowing of crops interfered with the freedom of the individual farmer but its objective was to secure the economic interests of the farmers themselves. Every major social institution was seen to limit the individual's freedom in the interests of his own wider freedom. One of the major problems of the twentieth century was how this concept could be realized without destroying individual initiative, impairing the liberty of action essential to human dignity and the development of human potentiality and without imposing a burden of bureaucracy upon society beyond its usefulness as a necessary instrument for achieving common objectives.

Changed concepts of man in relation to society also modified basic ideas concerning the family, the principal institution by means of which the status and role of the individual in virtually all societies had been defined.

The concept of the extended responsibility of the community for the positive welfare of all its members, expressed through the responsibility of the state for education, health and various forms of social security, narrowed the area and lightened the weight of responsibility carried by the family. Not only were parents no longer wholly responsible for the education and health of their children; they could not reject the requirements which the state imposed. The state relieved children of much of the burden of support for aged parents and lifted from families at least part of the economic burden of illness.

At the same time the individualization of economic roles and the concept of each individual as a unit of society in his or her own right undermined the hierarchical structure within the family. As extended to women, it redefined the relations between husband and wife. The concept of the child as a person in his own right, not merely a chattel of his parents or an undeveloped adult, profoundly affected parent-child relations and the child's place in society; under conditions of rapid social change, the child came to be looked upon as the instrument of a new day.

The family itself, freed of much of its responsibility, with its hierarchical structure undermined and its members integrated by work or other activity into other social units, ceased to be the all-embracing and enduring foundation of the social order. In greater or less degree it tended to become a small personal group where mutual obligations within the group rested upon contract rather than sacrament and the possibility of dissolution through divorce was widely accepted. The family tended to become a planned unit, and the idea of birth control and family planning gained acceptance in ever-broader layers of society, even where clerical opposition continued; some countries stimulated family planning as a matter of public policy.

The changed concept of the family was most dramatic where such ancient, comprehensive institutions as the Confucian family system or the Hindu joint family were modified in practice or their legal basis was destroyed by legislation. The actual reduction in family functions and development of new patterns of relations among family members went farthest in industrial countries where women had the opportunity to be financially independent. The Soviet Union dissolved the institution of the bourgeois family almost completely in the initial process of social reconstruction and then restored 'a socialist form of home'.[5] The Catholic Church remained unshaken in its conception of marriage as sacramental and indissoluble and in its emphasis on the family as the central institution of human society, but even its great and pervasive influence did not prevent the penetration of other ideas into predominantly Catholic countries. Whatever the form of the family or degree of its modification, the reduced position of the family as an economic unit and basis of social organization was one of the features of the twentieth century.

On the whole it may be stated without exaggeration that man's relationship to society by the middle of the twentieth century was governed by many ideas which would have been considered revolutionary or impracticable in virtually every society in the nineteenth century.

III. MAN'S RELATION TO HIS PAST AND FUTURE

Changing viewpoints toward man's relations with his fellow men extended to new concepts of his own past and possible future. The study of history was extended immeasurably both in time and space. Pre-history opened up the vision of man's movement towards civilization through various ages of technical advancement; archaeology made available the history of great civilizations in different parts of the world—in the Nile valley, in Babylonia, in the Indus valley, in China, in America—giving humanity a better idea of its own past. The story of African peoples was being slowly unravelled.

As these stories unfolded, man's ideas in regard to humanity itself changed. They were no longer so directly centred on special regions to which each section attached special value, but embraced the whole perspective of human experience.

This great expansion in knowledge of the past, coupled with a new attitude toward man's efforts to control his destiny, brought a twofold response. On the one hand it created a certain humility arising from a recognition that the civilization in which man is living may also decay and die, and that there may be growing, unnoticed, forces which may ultimately destroy all that men have painfully built up, as was the case in previous civilizations in the world. On the other hand it offered the hope that increased knowledge of the past might enable man to shape the course of human evolution in a manner which would provide for continuous renovation without allowing the structure to break down. In either case it led to efforts to view the present age as a period in human history and to envisage the processes of human development in terms which could provide a new basis for interpreting contemporary events. It made unsatisfactory the various major formulations which had come down from previous times—the concept of all human life as merely a prelude to eternity,[6] or the view of society as essentially timeless and unchanging, or the vision of endless progress toward inherent perfection or through social evolution.

The great popularity of books such as Oswald Spengler's *Decline of the West* (1918–22) and Arnold Toynbee's *Study of History* (1934–54) were symptomatic of the effort to understand the present in the light of the past. Spengler, in whose view civilization attains maturity only when it has ceased to grow, held that western civilization had already passed its meridian and started on its career of disintegration. According to Toynbee, each of the twenty-six civilizations that preceded the present one lost its impetus after a certain period of activity and achievement, and he saw no reason to think that it would be otherwise in respect to western civilization, though he did not deny in theory the possibility of rejuvenation through a revival in religion. Walter Prescott Webb (*The Great Frontier*, 1952) sought to prove that the conditions which produced and had sustained western civilization since the great voyages of discovery—the untapped wealth of nearly 20,000,000 square miles of fabulously rich land—had ceased to exist and that western civilization consequently had begun to break down. The Marxian view saw the historical process as a dialectic one centring on the forms of material production and leading inevitably to a permanent classless society.

Whatever formulation he might accept, twentieth-century man saw himself as part of an historical process stretching farther into antiquity than his predecessors had imagined and embracing all parts of the human race.

As for the future, this too came to be conceived in terms of the whole of humanity. The rapidity with which scientific discovery and social change altered the life of mankind during these years opened up limitless vistas both for good and for ill—not just for a family, a nation or a people but for mankind as a whole.

For the first time in history the means were at hand to abolish poverty, hunger, disease and other major ills that had beset mankind through the ages. It became possible to think in terms of a society based on plenty, and people throughout the world did indeed come to think in these terms, not nostalgically as of a 'golden age', but realistically as a goal to be achieved. One of the most revolutionary ideas that moved men in the twentieth century was that poverty and misery were not the necessary condition of their children and their children's children.

But against this new optimism loomed growing apprehensions about the future of civilization and of mankind arising from the capacity for destruction which men had developed and were developing. The instruments of violence used in the first world war would have seemed apocalyptic to anyone in a previous age and sufficient to destroy civilization. But compared to what was at the disposal of powerful nations in the second world war, the fire-power of weapons, the aerial bombs, poison gas and underseas craft available to the combatants in the first war were child's play. When the first atom bomb was finally exploded in 1945 it seemed at the time to be the ultimate force of destruction, but it was quickly dwarfed by the far more terrible hydrogen bomb. When men realized that radioactive fall-out from atomic and hydrogen explosions could so pollute the atmosphere as to destroy life on earth, they were forced to think in terms of man's new power to put an end to the human race. Violence shadowed man's destiny; the vision of the apocalypse was of a possible man-made reality.

IV. MAN AND NATURE

The idea which penetrated most widely and about which there was nevertheless great ambivalence was the belief that science could find solutions to human problems. The advance of scientific knowledge and its utilization for human betterment was so great that its potentialities seemed unlimited. In the perspective of what had already been achieved and the accelerating rate at which scientific knowledge was being applied to affect the daily life of people, an endless vista seemed to open before it of achievements capable of solving the problems which faced humanity.

Yet faith in the omnipotence of science was not untinged with doubt and fear. In Europe the simple faith shared by many during the nineteenth century that science would automatically bring human progress was shaken by the destructive uses to which it was put during these years and the evident failure of mankind to develop the social and political arrangements which would ensure that its application would be beneficent. Even the peaceful application of science—to transport and communication, the production of food and the prolongation of life—seemed to some people to bring as many problems as it solved. While science was being accepted ever more widely as holding answers to human problems and human needs, its supremacy was being called into question by some who had put their faith in it in the early phases of its application.

It is to be noted, however, that doubts came principally from certain intellectuals and from people who feared that the progress of science would rob them of their privileged place in the world. They came, mainly in Europe, from those whose personal position rested on the continuance of traditional values, or who could not find or accept a place for themselves in the emerging society, or whose world position depended on continuation of the virtual monopoly of scientific advance by the countries where scientific techniques had first been mastered. Except for Mahatma Gandhi whose attack on industrialism was designed as a political weapon against British imperialism, questions as to the desirability of scientific advance did not come generally from the underdeveloped countries. These recognized that their future depended upon technical progress and the scientific education of their people, though they might denounce western culture as materialistic and reassert traditional spiritual values. Nor did the doubts come from the social classes in the industrially advanced countries that were the beneficiaries of increased productivity and of the improvement in housing, health and levels of living which the scientific age was bringing.

The revolutionary developments in the realm of physical sciences changed man's ideas of his relations to nature in a fundamental manner. This was a cumulative process which had been at work in western society since the seventeenth century and had been greatly accelerated by the scientific and technological achievements of the nineteenth. But only in the twentieth century did men acquire a sense of almost unlimited control over nature, and the spread of an aggressive attitude towards nature to large segments of mankind was a phenomenon of the period.

The general idea in most societies in the past was that nature was simply there, unalterably conditioning man's life; in the face of its overwhelming power he could not seek to bend it in any major degree to his requirements but must adjust himself to it. But man in the twentieth century became more and more aggressive in regard to nature, determined to force its secrets, to exploit its resources and to subdue its more dangerous effects. Could not new materials be created by man's power better than those which nature provides? Could not artificial insemination produce better species? If rainfall was irregular, could not clouds be induced to yield their waters? If heat was too great for man's comfort, could not air be conditioned to a normal temperature? And need man remain earthbound while outer space invited his exploration? Clearly, man's vision of himself in relation to what were conceived as the permanent features of nature changed greatly during these fifty years.

The challenge of man to nature brought a radical change in man's attitude toward fate. In the past every major calamity—drought, famine, epidemic and other avoidable misfortune—had been attributed to fate over which man had no control and against which it was unprofitable to struggle. As men came to know that things which used to be attributed to fate can be fought by human measures, the idea of fate retreated into the background. It remained in many minds, too ingrained a conception to be totally displaced, and it retained a potent influence on human behaviour. But its range became more and more restricted. The change in attitude toward fate was most noticeable in the countries of Asia where the doctrine of fate had great hold. One of the major results was a mounting demand in all these areas for the betterment of social conditions, especially in the matter of health.

Yet while the aggressive attitude toward nature gave man greater confidence in his powers and boundless hope, it raised moral problems that were by no means insignificant. If man himself possessed the means to remedy or prevent human ills, he would be forced to accept responsibility for his failure to do so; since he could no longer dismiss misfortune as the work of fate, he was burdened with a new sense of guilt for his failure to use his new powers effectively.

Man's command over nature moreover confronted him with a new source of uncertainty over the purpose of human life. So long as man accepted his lot as determined by a supreme moral law with divine sanction, he could feel that he was serving a supreme purpose by living a moral life. The elevation of man in relation to nature gave him a great sense of his own power but no source of moral authority for its use.

With each new discovery and invention other and greater dangers to humanity seemed to show themselves, and man was assailed by doubts over the results of his own mastery. The prospects of atomic energy opened out to man like a new and unsuspected paradise, but with it many dangers manifested themselves, even apart from the possibility of the deliberate use of this new power for destruction. Men were beginning to ask whether there is a purpose in life or whether humanity is merely moving forward blindly impelled by its own restless intelligence. What moral principles, what obligation of man to his fellow beings, could guide him in the use of his new powers? How, with these powers, could he choose the path which would lead to the welfare of mankind?

V. MAN'S VIEW OF HIS GODS

These questions were closely related to the place of religion in men's lives. All the basic concepts of religion, such as soul, salvation, efficacy of prayer, came under question, not merely as before by agnostics and atheists but by ordinary men and women who found it difficult to reconcile what science was telling them with their inherited beliefs. Consequently man's view of his gods also underwent a noticeable change.

A major fact of the twentieth century was that a third of the world lived under a system whose basic philosophy had no place for God. According to Marxist–Leninist doctrine dialectical materialism and a materialistic interpretation of history are incompatible with the conception of God; in a communist society religion, whose social role is that of an 'opiate of the people', will eventually disappear. With so large a proportion of the world's people in communist states it may be said that the conception of God lost its universality in the twentieth century.

Even in the rest of the world men's idea of God was modified during the same period, or the concept of God was rejected as a mere projection of man's own drive to transcend the limits of his being. As anthropology made clear the tendency of people to create gods in their own image, many people found it no longer possible to conceive of God in anthropomorphic terms or as a Being who might interfere with normal functioning of natural laws or demand special sacrifices as a proof of loyalty.

Yet though twentieth-century man tended to reject intellectually the cruder forms of anthropomorphism, many people continued to hold to revised versions of earlier formulae. They found ways to retain a personally satisfying structure of faith—by giving a symbolic meaning to what had been believed as a literal truth, by identifying human purposes with those of God rather than expecting God's intercession in response to prayer, or by re-interpreting the concepts of lesser deities or saints through which the sense of the divine was made personal.

A major change in most communities was a weakening of the sense of sin and a narrowing of the segment of the population within which it kept its hold on the minds of men. The conception of sin as an offence against the commandments of God was historically of utmost importance in most societies, not only as a source of moral principle but as a measure of social protection. But growing disbelief in some of the tenets which provided strong religious sanction, such as the doctrine of hell and the day of judgment which once had great reality to masses of mankind, made the conception of sin less potent than it was before. The study of anthropology showed that, while many common values underlie cultural differences, what is considered sin in one society may even be regarded as a virtue in another. The scientific concept of relativity seemed to imply a denial of absolute values. ✳ As the doctrine of sin depends on finality of judgment it lost much of its authority over the minds of twentieth-century men.

In the face of mounting disbelief, changing concepts and a weakening sense of sin, two trends were evident within the major religions, one to redefine man's relation to the supernatural in terms consistent with modern thought, the other to reassert in uncompromising terms the truth of estab-lished dogma. Reformed Hinduism, after shedding much of its social trap-pings, provided a basis for reconciling scientific thought with basic religious beliefs. In the Buddhist countries there were attempts to reinterpret the *Dharma* in terms of modern thought. Some Christian thought went far in a similar direction. On the other hand, the Catholic Church reasserted the absolute truth of its dogma and in the world of Islam the Quran remained the source of final truth.

The changes in man's view of his gods was perhaps greater in outward form than in inner sense. In spite of the great advance of science much of man's belief in supernatural power continued to be part of the mentality of non-communist countries. Even in communist countries where those in authority rejected the idea of God absolutely it appeared that a certain proportion of the people continued to adhere to one or another religious faith and to seek the solaces of religion.

[handwritten: all vices anthropology is apology for relativity entering our schools]

VI. MAN'S VIEW OF HIMSELF

Man's view of himself as it was emerging at mid-century reflected his changing sense of his relation with society, with nature and with God. In most
parts of the world, and widely through many levels of society, men saw
themselves possessed of or reaching for new powers and opportunities. They
saw themselves as standing on the threshold of a new era whose features
could only be glimpsed, but whose prospects were both exhilarating and
terrifying.

Throughout the world men had the sense of being cast loose from old
moorings to make their way through uncharted seas. For some this meant a
great adventure, for others a bewildering threat. Modern man found himself
in a situation full of paradox. The more he mastered his environment, the
more helpless he felt before forces some of which he himself had loosed.
The more aware he became of the world beyond his immediate ken the less
able he was to cope directly with much that affected his daily life. The more
that new knowledge undermined old certainties and new social forces
changed old institutions, the more he felt the need for some source of security
to take the place of those which he had lost.

Perhaps no feature was more characteristic of modern man's outlook and
view of himself—whether in a Malayan or a Mexican village, an African
'location' in Johannesburg, or the main street of Chicago, Brussels or Tokyo—
than his ambivalence toward himself and toward what was happening to his
life and the life about him. Except for those who were deeply committed to
one orthodoxy or another, the ambivalence of twentieth-century man was
both a reflection of and a factor in the transformation of his societies during
these years.

VII. MAIN LINES OF PHILOSOPHICAL THOUGHT

The crises of these years were reflected in the varied efforts of philosophical
thinkers to reformulate philosophical conceptions so as to include new
knowledge, encompass new experience and sharpen the tools of language and
logic. The distinctive outlooks of twentieth-century man and of his changing
societies found expression in formal and systematic thought as well as in
public attitudes and opinions.

In the West the efforts of philosophers produced a wide range of views,
and at the same time much interchange and even mutual influence of seemingly opposite tendencies. The period was one of lively and fruitful philosophical activity, though no common systems of thought emerged and though
there was a broad division between those who pursued the philosophical
implications of modern science and those who turned away from science to
seek the answer to their philosophical questions by other, non-rational
methods.

After the collapse of Hegelian idealism in the 1860s scientific positivism had become the dominant philosophical idea in the West. Whereas Hegel saw the universe as a reflection of a World Spirit or Absolute Idea, developing and unfolding itself through history in complex dialectic ways, the scientific positivists focused on external reality, approached through the natural sciences. They saw in the ever-extended application of scientific method the highest form of human activity, the only path to truth, however limited it might be, and the key to principles which could guide action. Both systems rested on the rationalist assumption that man through his reason could know and grasp the full meaning of the universe, although Hegel and his followers rejected the Aristotelian logic of the eighteenth-century Enlightenment and substituted a more complex logic of opposites within which a fundamental unity finally asserts itself through the dialectical process of thesis, antithesis and synthesis.

Neither the system-building of the Hegelian idealists nor the materialism and certainty of the positivists could remain unshaken by the discovery of limitations in the system of Newtonian physics, the undermining of traditional mathematics and, in time, the substitution of probability for rigid causality. Nor did the assumptions of rationality and automatic progress survive the crisis of the first world war and the revelations of Freudian psychology.

The Hegelian view that reality could be comprehended in terms of an Absolute Idea lost ground steadily, though it continued influential among some British thinkers in the early years of the century and Kant's idealism lived on in centres in Germany at Baden and Marburg even after the first world war. Its leading and most influential exponent was the prolific historian-philosopher Benedetto Croce (1866–1952), who explored the realms of aesthetics, logic, economics and ethics in his *Philosophy of Spirit* (1902–17), and saw in the unique unfolding of human history the expression of a purpose with which men could align themselves. For him the direction was toward greater human freedom, and he thus became the voice of Italian liberalism. But the effort to find a universal, transcendent Idea lost its appeal for most twentieth-century thinkers, and idealism declined from one of the dominant forms of philosophical speculation in the mid-nineteenth century to one of the forms least representative of twentieth-century thought.

Positivist thought showed a much stronger development, although in its materialistic and mechanistic form it also suffered an almost complete collapse and although in the course of time it became more and more limited in its focus and in the kinds of philosophical problems which it sought to solve. In the early years of the century it gave rise to the vigorous and influential thought of William James, John Dewey (1859–1952) and their fellow pragmatists and instrumentalists. These thinkers insisted that the only meaning of any term and the only reality of any object lies in what it can and will do, and that this in turn can only be determined by scientific test. Ideas have no validity in and of themselves, but only as they express an observable, verifiable reality; their importance lies in their results, in what happens to the person who acts on the basis of them.

In this view neither absolute origins nor ultimate finalities have any relevance; the reality lies in the process, where means and ends are one, where change is central and where conduct can be purposeful. Applying this approach to the whole range of human problems—biological, political, social—Dewey developed a comprehensive view of how human beings, using to the full their potentialities and guided by intelligence equipped with scientific method, could modify their environment and make life progressively better. In breadth of scope, acceptance of change and uncertainty, and orientation toward positive action, the pragmatic view and instrumental method of thought had far-reaching influence, especially in the field of education.

In the following decades scientific humanists such as Julian Huxley carried the philosophical implications of science still further. They saw man still in the process of evolution, only beginning to use his powers to create the conditions which would permit the fullest development of his potentialities. In this view the flowering of the individual is seen as an end in itself; but since man is an infinitely complex, many-sided creature whose individual fulfilment cannot be realized apart from nature and society, he must use his knowledge and intelligence to develop the type of environment and culture which will continually open the way to new and fuller realizations of his inherent possibilities. The application of scientific method to all fields of human endeavour could provide a means of cultural evolution.

Other positivist philosophers, however, focused their attention more narrowly on the sharpening of analytical tools rather than on broad social issues. The logical positivists of the mid-century abandoned all effort to build systems of philosophical thought in favour of the attempt to know accurately and to communicate precisely the elements of thought and observation out of which systems might some day be built. They concentrated on an analysis of language, symbols and meaning, moving ever farther away from those who sought in philosophical thought either a metaphysical view or a basis for values and guide to action, or both.*

In reaction against both main lines of nineteenth-century philosophical thought, idealism and positivism, and their whole rationalistic way of thinking, some of the most influential and popular philosophers of the twentieth century insisted on the primacy of man's non-rational faculties—his intuition, direct apprehension of phenomena, and awareness of inner experience. They rejected the nineteenth-century scientific approach for its materialism and mechanistic outlook and the new scientific view for its dependence on statistical probability, its concern with mass phenomena and its inability to shed light on the individual, unique case. They were concerned with life and with man, and more particularly with the individual, in the face of the mechanization of life in industrial society and the impersonal preoccupations of science.

* See Chapter VII, Mathematics and Logic.

The effort to approach reality through direct non-rational experience took a variety of forms. Henri Bergson (1859–1941), the most influential and popular of French philosophers in the first quarter of the century, insisted that intuition could penetrate to the core of reality which the intellectual pursuits of science could only surround as with a shell, and he maintained that the will could shape this reality creatively. Like his contemporary, Benedetto Croce, Bergson was an apostle of freedom, but not as the unfolding of the universal Idea; he saw it as the achievement of men motivated by an *élan vital* and changing through time in a process of creative evolution. The German 'phenomenologist' Edmund Husserl (1859–1938) focused his attention on what he called 'phenomena', i.e. the structures perceived by an observer, as when the structure of a cube seen from different angles appears different. He thought that the effort to examine these phenomena could fruitfully be applied to the inner perception of self. Even so scientifically oriented a philosopher as Alfred North Whitehead, co-author with Bertrand Russell of the classic statement of mathematical logic *Principia Mathematica* (1911), insisted in his later years that the body of scientific and logical thought is a superstructure built upon fundamentally intuitive beliefs and ideas.

By the second quarter of the century the approaches which assumed a fundamental irrationality in life came to be loosely called existentialism. The view that man must come to terms with the irrational and the absurd was not new; its exponents claimed as forerunners the nineteenth-century Danish philosopher, Sören A. Kierkegaard (1813–55), the German Friedrich W. Nietzsche (1844–1900) and the Russian novelist Fyodor Dostoevsky (1821–81). It was most systematically expounded by the German philosopher, Martin Heidegger (1889–   ), it became most widely known through the work of the French novelist and playwright, Jean Paul Sartre (1905–   ), and it was given a religious emphasis by the French Catholic, Gabriel Marcel (1889–   ), and the German Protestant, Karl Jaspers (1883–   ). The existentialist view had its greatest popularity on the European continent in the middle years of the twentieth-century, where it met the needs of people who had experienced the physical and moral destruction of the second world war—fascism, resistance, concentration camps, death, defeat. But it spread to many areas—to Britain, to Latin America, to Japan and to the United States.

In the existentialist view, existence itself—without reason, without purpose or direction, without a great Idea—is the only reality; this man must accept, and out of this he must make his life through constant choice. As he looks into himself the individual changes the very self which he tries to understand; by his own conduct and the exercise of his will he determines who and what he is. He has freedom to choose but this is a freedom which is imposed upon him, to which he is 'condemned'. Life is thus a risky enterprise, for by existing man risks his existence. In this view man cannot be passive, he cannot be concerned only to know and understand; he is forced by the very nature of his existence to commit himself, to act.

But there is no logic or system inherent in existence which guides such choice and such action; hence this view led to no common set of principles or beliefs. It led some of its exponents to agnosticism or atheism and others to various religious conclusions and commitments; it was used to justify National Socialism, as in the case of the writings of Heidegger, and to motivate the French resistance to Nazi occupation as in the case of Sartre. In its most positive form it gave a stimulus to action in the face of the collapse of traditional values and the revolutionary fluidity of twentieth-century life, it stimulated direct self-understanding without pretence or the intervention of protective rationalizations, and it led to the effort to establish communication with others not through precision in the use of language or other symbols which the logical positivists sought, but by entering intuitively and imaginatively into the existence of others. As such it promoted human relations and human understanding. At its most negative it detached the individual from systematic and organized life and thought, turned him in on himself in self-centred egoism, and produced 'disengagement' with life rather than the 'engagement' which was the core of the positive expression of the existentialist attitude.

Thus the main lines of philosophical thought in the West in these years led away from the certainties of the past and failed to formulate new systems of ideas which gave order to new experience. Yet in spite of their diversity and contradictions they were marked by some common characteristics which distinguished them from the philosophical systems and analysis of preceding centuries.

Philosophers of all schools tended to view reality, truth, the relation between subject and object, the nature of knowledge, awareness and being, in complex and interrelated terms which made obsolete the sharp distinction between the external object and the thinking subject which had preoccupied many philosophers in the past. Although some followed lines suggested by science while others denied the value of science as a source of philosophical knowledge, there was a widespread acceptance of the idea that simple rationalism is insufficient and that man has the capacity to achieve awareness and understanding through direct experience as well as through logical processes. There was a tendency away from the quest for a single 'truth' toward a pluralistic acceptance of the possibility of many kinds and apprehensions of truths. Attention was focused on process, on 'becoming', rather than on origins, ends or changeless forms—on events in a space-time continuum. Except for those who limited their efforts to refining the tools of analysis, the human person was central—his awareness of self, his relation to others and the implications for his action. Although twentieth-century philosophical thought was pursued by highly specialized thinkers using refined and elaborate techniques of analysis, the flow of communication cut across rigid lines and the ideas which emerged had a fluidity which offered fresh, undogmatic approaches, though no universally accepted response, to the challenges of the times.

Yet along with the ideas which reflected the uncertainties that philosophers and laymen both shared, two major orthodoxies remained intact and continued to offer a degree of certainty to their adherents: the assumptions and beliefs of the Roman Catholic Church, elaborated philosophically with the revival of Thomistic thinking: and the dialectical materialism of Marx and Engels as elaborated by Lenin to provide a body of doctrine and method of thought in the USSR, the people's democracies and the Chinese People's Republic.

The orthodoxy of the Roman Catholic Church continued to rest on the reality of the spiritual world and its primacy over the temporal. In the face of both scientific and social developments which brought doubts to many minds, the Church, broadly and in detail, reaffirmed its dogma. In the form of a revival of the philosophy of St Thomas Aquinas it offered a traditional philosophical as well as religious approach to the understanding of life in the modern age.

Interest in the thought of the great mediaeval philosopher had been reawakened by the encyclical *Aeterni Patris* of Pope Leo XIII in 1879 and by the establishment of a chair of Thomism at the University of Louvain, Belgium, in 1882. Thereafter Thomist studies grew in a number of European centres and interest spread throughout the Catholic educational and scholarly world. Subsequent Popes repeatedly prescribed that the Angelic Doctor should be studied, taught and his method followed.

In its assumptions and methods neo-Thomist philosophy retained essentially the same view of life and reality that St Thomas had expressed in the thirteenth century. As reinvigorated and pursued primarily but not exclusively in Catholic circles, it followed two main lines: the application of Thomist methods to the new materials of twentieth-century thought and experience, and the refinement of these methods in the light of historical and analytical studies of St Thomas's writings.

Neo-Thomist thought continued to use the rigorous formal logic of the schoolmen. It accepted the reality of things perceived directly through the senses and grasped intellectually through rational judgment, and it also accepted the reality of things which could not be perceived but could be inferred intellectually by applying the principles of causality and of non-contradiction—principles which could not be proved but which were known through intellectual insight. In the metaphysical Thomist view all things which exist need not be material; in fact all real events and actions cannot be explained by the laws and properties of material bodies. Actions such as thinking and willing depend on operative potencies different from material powers.

The keystone in the Gothic arch of Thomist metaphysics is the demonstration of the existence of a Supreme Being. In this view the existence and actions of things in this universe cannot be fully explained by secondary causes alone; although it is possible to account for a given event in nature by finding its proximate cause in nature, it is not possible to give an ultimate account of the whole system of natural things and events by reference to other natural causes. The only possible ultimate explanation of why the universe exists and works lies beyond the universe itself, in a first cause, God.

Man in Thomist philosophy is understood as a composite of both material and immaterial being, possessed of an immaterial soul as well as a material body. The parents, it is reasoned, who produce the individual's body cannot produce his soul since their own souls, being immaterial, are indivisible; the individual's soul must therefore be created by God, and since there is no known way in which such an immaterial thing may come to an end it must be immortal.

This view of man provides a basis for ethics and a concept of society. Man is seen as responsible for those acts which are under the control of his reason and will. It follows rationally that the good or moral use of man's power to act is related to the purpose and end of human life, and this can be defined in no other terms than the perfect good, that is, God. The attainment of such an end is reserved for a future life. Acts which are morally bad are those which work against the nature and powers of the individual, whether the self or others. Rules of moral behaviour are conceived as precepts of natural moral law because they grow out of the application of natural reasoning to the data of natural human experience.

Social life also is seen as essential to man's nature and the family as the simplest natural society, resulting not from contract but from the natural tendency to reproduce, love and care for offspring and promote the common good. Thomists insisted on the natural character and origin of the family and opposed whatever threatens its integrity as this kind of unit. Since the family is too small to provide for all man's social needs, civil society is also seen as natural rather than contractual, though the specific forms of the state may vary so long as they do not deny the basic, spiritual purpose of human life, the natural moral law and the natural social unit, the family. On the spiritual side the Church is the corresponding ecclesiastical society devoted to man's future life.

This general view was taught in all Catholic institutions, it was elaborated in thousands of universities and centres of Catholic studies, it was the subject of hundreds of learned articles annually and the basis for specialized Thomist journals which numbered no less than twenty-five in the 1950s, as well as for Thomist organizations and for international Thomist congresses. In terms of numbers it appeared that from the time of the first world war onwards no other philosophical group had so many thinkers in its ranks or so many centres of study at its disposal.

Dialectical materialism, which furnished the framework for all thought and the theoretical and philosophical justification for all action in the Soviet Union and other communist states, was at the opposite pole from the metaphysical system of the neo-Thomists. This system of thought was grounded in the basic doctrine and method of analysis developed by Karl Marx and Friedrich Engels in the mid-nineteenth century. Marx's system of thought was designed not merely to interpret the world but to change it, to be intensely practical in terms of historical necessity.

In his view the essential nature of man lies in his capacity for spontaneous productivity; his true activity is his labour which encompasses his total being and in which he transforms both himself and nature outside himself. Since he realizes his conscious being not through thought but through productivity, it is not consciousness that determines life but social life which determines consciousness. This principle extends not only to the forms of production which give life its basic shape but to the superstructure of economics, law, morality and religion. So viewed, the law and morality of bourgeois society can be recognized as merely the expressions of that society without autonomous character of their own.

Following Hegel's dialectical method of analysis, though rejecting his idealism as the purest form of bourgeois ideology, Marx saw the process of nature, of thought and of history as a dialectical one; reality consists of opposites, of theses that engender their own antitheses, which nevertheless contain a fundamental unity; in time this unity or synthesis comes to the fore to replace the old antithesis. He saw in bourgeois society an antithesis between the forces of productivity and the relations involved in production, for the ownership of the means of production gave the capitalist the power to exploit the workers and to prevent the use of their full and many-sided productive capacities; the synthesis could only be brought about in a society in which the private ownership of the means of production has been abolished and social ownership has taken its place.

In Marx's view the class of the proletariat was destined to play the historic role of overthrowing bourgeois society and thus carrying out the inevitable dialectical historical process. Lenin converted the doctrine of dialectical historical materialism into a practical instrument of revolution; under the guidance of a professional revolutionary group, using the method of dialectical analysis to penetrate to an understanding of the forces of society, revolution would be carried out by a close-knit minority with the tacit approval of a majority of the people. He maintained that the revolutionary will of the Communist party must be able to transcend the economic situation and make the contradiction between economic reality and political power in Russia into a positive, active factor through the method of 'democratic centralism'.

Josef Stalin subsequently carried the analysis forward to the conception that the revolutionary dialectic could be carried out and the synthesis of a classless society achieved within a single country, the USSR. By 1950 he believed that socialism had been realized in the Soviet Union and that communism could come under the leadership of the party without a further revolution, since the major contradictions between the forces of productivity and the relations involved in production had been done away with by the socialization of the means of production; the situation was no longer dominated by the antithesis, which Lenin had utilized as an active force, but by the synthesis which was emerging in the society of the USSR.

These concepts provided a unifying view of life to which all aspects and activities could be referred. The materialistic assumption, the dialectical method, historical necessity, the basic concept that ideas are the product of social experience and their function is to modify that experience in the direction of rational organization of production and full development of human capacities for physical and intellectual productivity, the method of democratic centralism—this core of the doctrine provided consistent terms in which to approach the development of technology, literary and artistic expression, political structure and social organization, the individual's view of himself and the direction of public policy.

The currents of thought which flowed in the West penetrated to the non-European world, bringing new ideas, shaking traditional certainties and stimulating a rescrutiny of concepts and values which had been taken for granted for many centuries. Scientific inquiry by both western and eastern scholars was directed toward the philosophical thought of the East and stimulated the republication of Buddhist, Hindu, Confucian and other texts, their critical study and the consideration of their implications for modern life.* Scientific attitudes and principles, both in their nineteenth- and in their twentieth-century forms, and various western philosophical lines of thought, including pragmatism, dialectical materialism and existentialism, entered the thought of the East through western-educated writers and leaders. No less than in the West, traditional structures of ideas were broken down under the general impact of new experience and new thought, without the immediate substitution of alternative, integrating points of view.

The principal orthodoxy of the East which remained firm was that of Islam. Though it had no central church to interpret doctrine with infallibility or to provide channels for administration and communication, and only the pilgrimage to Mecca and the traditional studies in the great mosques furnished a machinery for maintaining a common interpretation among many and varied peoples, the revealed Book, the prescribed prayers and the rules of daily life kept doctrine and attitudes intact. Yet the finality and comprehensiveness of the Quran still left much room for uncertainty in the area of social organization and conduct and the philosophical ideas of the West had their students and followers in Islamic areas also.

Most of the interaction between eastern and western thought was onesided, the impact of ideas originating in the West upon the thought of the East. The development in the West of non-rational philosophies during these years, however, began to provide a possible bridge to the philosophical thought of the East which had always stressed the use of non-rational faculties to penetrate to the essence of reality and had exacted a profound commitment

* See Chapter XXV, Religion.

in action. These tendencies, together with the new respect engendered by the rise of eastern nations to equality of political status, brought a growing interest in the philosophical thought of the East. Through the middle of the century, however, the gap remained wide as far as any real penetration of eastern thought into the West was concerned. It was indeed a rare westerner who was prepared to submit himself to the discipline which easterners associated with the sort of insight, self-penetration and wisdom which was part of their tradition and which the westerner, too, could only hope to experience from within.

NOTES TO CHAPTER XX

1. In the opinion of Soviet commentators, Gandhi's theory of 'non-violence' is not a new progressive method of effecting political and social changes, with the prospect of development in future. It is a backward moral-religious doctrine, which did the cause of Indian emancipation more harm than good, since it drove the national-liberation movement along the road of conciliation and concessions on matters of principle to British imperialism. It is characteristic that the Indian National Congress never applied the tactics of non-violence without reservations and ultimately renounced them. And even Gandhi himself did not remain true to this idea until the end. The theory of non-violence, which Gandhi tried to push through the Indian Congress as a practical basis for the policy of the Indian state, was a continual source of conflict within Congress and led to numerous political crises. J. Nehru writes: 'when Gandhiji raised in 1940 the question of non-violence in relation to the war and the future of free India, the Congress working Committee had to face the issue squarely. They made it clear to him that they were unable to go as far as he wanted them to go, and could not possibly commit India or the Congress to future applications of this principle in the external domain. . . . In December 1941, however, the same crisis took shape again when Gandhiji insisted on complete non-violence. Again there was a split and public disagreement, and the president of Congress, Maulana Abul Kalam Azad, and others were unable to accept Gandhiji's view. It became clear that the Congress as a whole, including some of the faithful followers of Gandhiji, disagreed with him in this matter. . . . At no other time was this issue raised by Gandhiji in Congress. . . . In later months, leading up to August 1942, Gandhiji's nationalism and intense desire for freedom made him even agree to Congress participation in the war if India could function as a free country. . . . In the conflict between the principle of non-violence which had become his very life-blood and meaning of existence, and India's freedom which was a dominating and consuming passion for him, the scales inclined towards the latter.' (Jawaharlal Nehru, *The Discovery of India*, New York, 1946, pp. 454, 455.) Thus, as this eminent Indian leader testifies, the principle of non-violence and the struggle for the liberation of his country from the colonial yoke were constantly in irreconcilable contradiction. There is not the slightest reason to place any hope in the principle of non-violence as a new progressive method of effecting political change.

   See J. Nehru, *op. cit.*, R. P. Dutt, *The Crisis of Britain and the British Empire* (London, 1957).

2. Academician N. Konrad points out that the 'particular combination of circumstances' on which European culture was actually based was itself a natural link in the chain of developments giving rise to world culture. In the Marxist–Leninist view, the general line of the history of mankind is expressed in the steady development and constant perfecting of progress. Despite all manner of retrogression, zigzags, and 'backward leaps', society proceeds along an upward course. One of the most important features of this objective law governing social progress is the historical continuity existing in the development of

culture. The essence of this continuity, a necessary prerequisite for the development of culture, is an unbreakable organic unity between, on the one hand, the heritage of the past, the cultural values accumulated by past generations, i.e. traditions, and on the other hand the critical analysis and creative re-working of those cultural values, i.e. innovations. The culture of any social-historical formation is the logical product of the very essence of that formation, of the processes and phenomena conditioned by its mode of production. The mode of producing material values determines the social, political and spiritual processes of the life of society as a whole, as well as the transition from one social order, and its culture, to another, higher social order, and the culture to which it gives birth. Culture must be seen as an historical phenomenon, as something in the process of development. Historical continuity in the development of material production is the basis of historical continuity in the development of material and spiritual culture. What is called 'European culture' was a continuation of the culture of the peoples of the Ancient Orient, elements of which can be clearly traced in the 'spiritual life' of the European peoples. And 'European culture' in turn is now being superseded by a genuine 'world culture', which is forming before our eyes with the appearance of a new socialist mode of production. (See (1) N. I. Konrad, 'Zametki o smysle istorii' (Notes on the Content of History), *Vestnik istorii mirovoy kultury*, 1961, No. 2, pp. 3–30; (2) E. A. Baller, 'Problema preemstvennosti v razvitii kultury' ('The Problem of Continuity in Cultural Development'), *Vestnik istorii mirovoy kultury*, 1961, No. 5, pp. 14–29).

3. The most widely known formulations of the Catholic position in regard to social justice and to private property in modern times were made by Pope Leo XIII in the encyclical *Rerum Novarum* (1891), and especially in the two recent encyclicals by Pope John XXIII *Mater et Magistra* (1961) and *Pacem in Terris* (1963).

Pope Pius IX, in the encyclical *Quadragesimo Anno* (1931), elaborated upon the statements in the earlier encyclical concerning the relation between social justice and private property in the words:

'First, let it be made clear beyond all doubt that neither Leo XIII, nor those theologians who have taught under the guidance and direction of the Church, have ever denied or called in question the twofold aspect of ownership, which is individual or social accordingly as it regards individuals or concerns the common good. Their unanimous contention has always been that the right to own private property has been given to man by nature or rather by the Creator Himself, not only in order that individuals may be able to provide for their own needs and those of their families, but also that by means of it, the goods which the Creator has destined for the human race may truly serve this purpose. Now these ends cannot be secured unless some definite and stable order is maintained....

'It follows from the twofold character of ownership, which We have termed individual and social, that men must take into account in this matter not only their own advantage but also the common good. To define in detail these duties, when the need occurs and when the natural law does not do so, is the function of the government.... It is plain, however, that the State may not discharge this duty in an arbitrary manner.'

Apart from discussion of practical problems of social justice contained in many of the references cited in the bibliographies of the volume, the reader will gain fundamental insight into the subject from Friedmann's analysis of the development of law in accordance with the changes in twentieth-century society, particularly in Western countries. *Cf.* W. Friedmann, *Law in a Changing Society* (Berkeley & Los Angeles, 1959).

4. Soviet scholars claim that it is wrong to present the Catholic Church as a defender of the rights of society against individualism. The basis of Catholicism is the doctrine of the autocratic powers and absolute prerogatives of the head of the Church—the Pope, in regard to whom individuals, peoples, and society as a whole either have no rights at all or are placed in an extremely subordinate position. Catholicism has been and still is opposed on principle to popular sovereignty—the basis of political justice (see *Konstitutsionnye Akty Gosudarstva-gorod Vatikan* (Constitutional Documents of Vatican City), arts. 1, 3, 4, 7 and others).

As far as 'social justice' is concerned, for which the Catholic Church is said to be striving, it is in fact extremely unjust, for private ownership of the means of production, the basis of every kind of social injustice, has always been and still remains the supreme symbol of the Catholic faith. In the Papal Encyclical *Mater et Magistra* (1961), as in a number of other Catholic documents, private property is considered as an irreplaceable element in a properly-ordered and productive society. Despite its demagogic phrases about 'socialization' and 'public ownership', this Papal Encyclical is, from its first syllable to its last, an attempt to give an ideological defence of the institution of private property. *Mater et Magistra* calls for the immutable rights of private property to be preserved at any price. Only such rights, it is said, can ensure the independence of the individual from the omnipotence of society and the state. In the view of John XXIII such rights provide a guarantee of freedom as well as an incentive to preserve it.

See: (1) Yu. Aseyev, 'Novoye izlozhenie sotsialnoy doktriny katolitsizma' ('A New Statement of Catholic Social Doctrine') *Mirovaya ekonomika i mezhdunarodnye otnosheniya* (World Economics and International Relations) (1961), No. 11, pp. 47–56; (2) L. Gallico, 'Razryv mezhdu vatikanskoy ideologiye i sotsialnoy deystvitelnostyu' ('The Gap between Vatican Ideology and Social Reality'), in *World Marxist Review* (Prague, 1961), No. 12, pp. 38–45.

5. Candidate of Juridical Sciences A. Bovin points out that in the Soviet Union no one specifically 'dissolved' the institution of the bourgeois family. The bourgeois family, with its inequality for women, did indeed collapse in the course of the socialist reforms that were carried out. However, the institution of the new socialist family, based on the full economic, and political equality of both parties, has always been encouraged and supported in the Soviet Union, as is shown by the whole history of legislation on family matters in the USSR.

See G. M. Sverdlov, *Sovetskoye semeynoye pravo* (Soviet Family Law), (Moscow, 1958).

6. Father Emilio Pin comments that: 'According to Christian thinking the idea that human life is a prelude to eternity, far from lessening the importance of life on earth, enhances it. It gives an eternal value to the efforts made by man to bring justice and love between men.' This view is elaborated in the Encyclicals referred to above and in many others. It has stimulated the writings of a great number of volumes treating sociology and other subjects in the social sciences, as well as the sciences and humanities from the Catholic point of view.

The following titles may be consulted for further study:

J. Y. Calvez, *Eglise et société économique* (Paris, 1961–63), 2 vols.

Cyril C. Clump, *A Catholic's Guide to Social and Political Action* (Oxford, 1955).

J. F. Cronin, *Catholic Social Principles: the Social Teachings of the Catholic Church Applied to American Economic Life* (Milwaukee, 1955).

J. F. Cronin, *Social Principles and Economic Life* (Milwaukee, 1959).

T. J. Harte, *Papal Social Principles* (Milwaukee, 1956).

Jacques Maritain, *Man and the State* (Chicago, 1951).

Melvin J. Williams, *Catholic Social Thought: Its Approach to Contemporary Problems* (New York, 1950).

CHAPTER XXI

ECONOMIC INSTITUTIONS

THE economic life of the world during the twentieth century was lived within two distinct sets of institutions and relationships.

A large and growing segment, involving a fifth to a quarter of the world's people at the opening of the century and perhaps a third or more by the middle, formed part of the world-wide commercial economy composed of industrial production, agriculture carried on for sale beyond the immediate family or neighbourhood, the trade through which these products were distributed and the transport, communication, construction and services related to these processes.

Outside this interrelated commercial economy, though increasingly affected by it, were the self-contained village and subsistence economies within which a large part of the world's rural people lived out their lives. There the cycle of most production and consumption was local and immediate. Although the few items which entered the subsistence economies from outside were sometimes of crucial importance—salt, essential tools—and some local produce or work had to enter into the commercial economy to pay for these necessities, the bulk of economic activity was carried on locally for local use.

At the opening of the century the subsistence economies, which took a number of different forms, were subject in varying degrees to the impact of the commercial economy. The more accessible of the Indian villages, whose traditional economy had been based on an elaborate system of mutual responsibilities, had already begun to be invaded by products from British factories which displaced local crafts, and in some areas subsistence agriculture had been replaced by commercial crops such as indigo or tea. The communal tribal villages of Africa at that time had barely begun to send their men to work in mines opened by Europeans. The groups of specialized villages in the valleys of Mexico, the nomadic herdsmen of central Asia and Iran, the subsistence farmers of the isolated mountain areas of Europe and the Americas and the shifting cultivators in parts of Latin America and South-East Asia all lived very largely to themselves.

In the course of the twentieth century the commercial economy expanded and penetrated further and further into the subsistence areas. Roads opened up isolated regions, radio communication brought awareness of life outside the village, more workers were drawn from the subsistence areas to work in industry, industrial activity in the form of mines and factories was established in new localities. Yet at mid-century the dual pattern still remained in large parts of Asia, Africa and Latin America. Where the subsistence economies were touched by the commercial economy they were more likely to be passively subjected to its impact than to become active participants in it, although vigorous efforts for economic development in the non-industrial countries were tending to draw them actively into the broader stream of economic life.

The village-subsistence economies were traditional and static, except as the pressure of population or depletion of the soil brought a deterioration of their condition or they were ravaged by famine or pestilence, flood or other disaster. Only where they came under the impact of the commercial economy were their structure and development materially changed. The commercial economy on the other hand was highly dynamic, not only growing and spreading, but developing new institutions or adapting old and undergoing many alterations during this period.

At the opening of the twentieth century the commercial economy was a single world economy, interrelated in all its parts, carried on through a common set of institutions. Although each industrial country had its unique features, these did not radically differ one from the other, and the mechanisms for international trade based on the gold standard linked not only industrial countries but industrialized segments of non-industrial areas. In the latter those engaged in production and trade came within the common commercial framework, either because this framework had been accepted as a basis for trade and industry by the country, as in the Latin American countries, or by virtue of colonial rule in the areas under the dominion of European powers, or through treaties establishing these conditions within independent nations, such as the treaties of extraterritoriality in China or Turkey.

In the twentieth century the unity of the world economy was broken and two separate economic systems were created by the establishment of a communist state in the USSR and the later incorporation of eastern Europe and China within this sphere. The interrelated capitalist economies and the economies of communist countries, as they developed along separate lines, had many common features, for they shared a common technology which influenced the direction of development, and they grew from a common base which was the historical starting point for many features of both systems. But the features which reflected the difference between communist and capitalist approaches brought two distinct patterns of development, and factors inherent in these developments, as well as in the political relations between communist and non-communist countries, so greatly reduced the economic interrelations between the two economic spheres that by mid-century each had come to be, at least for the time being, largely self-contained.

The common base in technological development has already been discussed. In the pages which follow the common base in the world economy of the early twentieth century will be reviewed, followed by a discussion of the divergent developments of the capitalist and socialist economies and of the patterns of economic development that were taking shape in newly industrializing societies, both in the form of mixed economies and under communist direction.* [1, 2]

I. THE COMMON BASE:
THE WORLD ECONOMY OF THE EARLY TWENTIETH CENTURY

The world economy of the early twentieth century was composed of private profit-seeking enterprises bound together and organized into a functioning whole by the operations of the competitive market. In principle, competition was unrestrained; in practice powerful monopolies dominated some fields and public utilities were coming to be regulated or operated by the state.

As an organizing force the market encouraged the production of those things which were in demand and discouraged those which were not; prices were established through the process of buying and selling and reflected supply and demand; producers decided whether they could operate profitably at the prices which the market offered and adjusted their production accordingly; a drop or an increase in price stimulated or reduced demand. The essence of the market mechanism as the organizer of the world commercial economy was flexible prices.

The market economy depended on money transactions and required a reliable money supply for its operations. This was provided in each country in the form of gold or silver, notes issued by governments and backed by their credit, and money created by banks under the regulation of their respective governments, either through the issue of bank notes or by loans which took the form of the creation of bank deposits. The stability of each country's currency was effected by government regulations as to the conditions for the issue of government notes and the conduct of banking; the relation among national currencies was automatically regulated by the flow of gold upon which the currencies of practically all the commercial countries were based.

The capital for industrial expansion was secured through capital markets which made funds available for the purchase of the machines, buildings and other physical capital required for industrial production. A network of financial institutions gathered up the savings of individuals and routed them to industry; banks and other private lending agencies received deposits and loaned them to business, investment houses marketed the securities of corporations, and stock exchanges or other security markets offered places where shares of stock changed hands. These capital markets, operating under national regulations designed to prevent fraud, provided a channel for the investment of foreign as well as domestic savings in the capital formation of a particular country. Capital moved freely, both nationally and internationally, to exploit natural resources and to take advantage of a cheap or skilled labour supply.

* For the technological aspects of these developments, see Chapter IX, Industrial Production; Chapter X, Transport; Chapter XI, Communication; Chapter XIV, Food and Agriculture.

The market for labour, as for goods and for capital, was open and free and operated by means of the wage system. Within limits set by inertia, high wages drew labour to the places and industries where it was needed. A mobile labour force, not only within the industrial countries but immigrating in large numbers to centres of industrial employment, especially in North America, was 'hired and fired' through the mechanism of the free market. Traditional relationships of paternalistic responsibility between master and apprentice had been quite thoroughly replaced by the cash nexus between the worker and his employer.

In order to route the products of industry to the distant markets where they would reach their consumers, a system of marketing institutions had been developed which included wholesale and retail selling, transport by sea, rail and horse-drawn vehicle, storage facilities, insurance in transit and the advertising of products.

The driving force in the commercial economy was provided by business enterprise. With few exceptions this was in the hands of private individuals or corporations, motivated by private profit or, in the case of traditional business castes or special merchant groups in Asia, by customary sanctions. Entrepreneurs were guaranteed in the enjoyment of their profits by the support for private property provided by the laws of the commercial countries; elsewhere they were protected by colonial rule, extraterritoriality and custom. In the industrial countries business success carried with it power and varying degrees of prestige, depending on the surviving strength of the landed aristocracy. Where no such aristocracy had ever existed, as in North America and Australasia, the successful businessman had no rival. 'Economic man' was assumed to act rationally in quest of profits and therefore to improve production to meet competition in the market.

The framework for enterprise was provided by government in the form of law, regulation, and government activity. A body of commercial law established rights of property, enforcement of contracts, conditions of incorporation, relations between agents and principals, stockholders and corporation, buyers and sellers, debtors and creditors. Although the details differed from country to country, especially as between those whose legal system stemmed from the Roman law via the Napoleonic Code and those based on Anglo-Saxon common law, the basic features of commercial law were common to all areas to which the commercial economy extended.

Regulations established by governments varied more than the basic legal framework, but they generally included the establishment and maintenance of standards for money and for weights and measures, regulation of the rates charged by public utilities such as railways, grain warehouses, or gas and electric supply companies, safety codes for building construction and the use of hazardous products, some protection of labour, especially the labour of children and of women in dangerous trades. Countries differed in the extent to which they attempted by law to preserve competition, as in the United

States, or to permit the formation of cartels, as in Germany, and in their acceptance of labour unions and the substitution of collective bargaining for the individual contract between employer and worker.

The economic activity of government itself was small, though it varied from country to country. In addition to military establishments and the post office, which were universally operated by governments, several European countries operated central banks, the British government operated the telephone and telegraph system, the government of Germany operated the railways, while government operations in the United States were limited largely to municipal services such as water-works and sometimes gas and electric utilities and rapid-transit systems. The expenditures for government services covered a limited range of activities for the maintenance of order and sanitation, fire protection, relief of the poor and provision of education, and they were supported out of taxes, chiefly collected in the form of tariffs and excises, which represented a very small proportion of the national income.

International trade was carried on between the enterprises of industrial countries which exchanged their respective products, and between those of industrial and non-industrial countries as industrial products flowed out and foodstuffs, raw materials and luxury products were received in return. Tariff barriers limited the entrance into some countries of products which competed with local industry. Tariff policies were, however, designed for revenue or for the protection of specific home industries, not to regulate the general volume of trade; the flow of gold, in exchange for imports which exceeded exports and as a return on capital invested abroad, was the standard mechanism for adjusting the international balance of trade.

The world economy had been subject to fluctuations in which high levels of economic activity were followed by more or less severe declines in production accompanied by unemployment, business failures and the collapse of markets for goods. There were prolonged depressions in the 1870s and 1890s and a sharp recession in 1907. While the circumstances which appeared to initiate each period of depression had differed—the aftermath of war, a speculative failure, a gold panic—there was widespread belief that such periodic swings between prosperity and depression were inherent in the system, and they were referred to as business cycles.

In classical economic theory they were assumed to be not only temporary but self-correcting phenomena; a boom which carried prices too high or raised the level of production beyond the ability of the market to absorb the output would be automatically corrected by a recession, while at the bottom of a depression business would recover and employment would rise when prices and wages had fallen sufficiently to make production again profitable in the light of potential demand. Each new period of prosperity was expected to carry the economy to a generally higher level before another peak would be reached at which the corrective of recession would again become necessary.

This had indeed been the case, as over the years the system had provided a rising level of living to a growing segment of the population.

In the Marxist–Leninist theory, however, these periodic depressions with accompanying unemployment were held to be an evidence of the fatal weakness of the capitalist system; they were bound to become more and more severe, producing progressive misery and widening inequality in income, and would ultimately lead to the downfall of the system, though that day might be postponed by resort to imperialistic exploitation of weaker economies to bolster economies which could not sustain a profitable market at home.

II. THE DEVELOPMENT OF CAPITALIST AND SOCIALIST ECONOMIES IN THE TWENTIETH CENTURY

1. *The capitalist economy of the United States and other advanced capitalist countries*[3, 4]

The capitalist economies developed from the base of the early twentieth-century world economy and remained part of a common system, although many new controls intervened to modify the free flow of goods, labour and capital both within industrial countries and in world markets. As these economies evolved they took on features which had not been part of the capitalist system in its earlier forms.

Many of these features were especially pronounced in the United States, and the economy of that country will therefore be used to illustrate major trends among the advanced capitalist economies during these years, although there were significant differences between it and some of the other capitalist economies.

(a) *Mass production and mass consumption.* [5, 6, 7] The central feature of the American economy was mass production and mass consumption. By elaborating the devices which the factory system of the nineteenth century had foreshadowed, mass production achieved low costs for great quantities of goods.

The pattern of mass production varied among industries. In some industries such as clothing or textiles the economies of mass production could be achieved with relatively small volume. In others such as automobiles, where an efficient production line came to require a market for some 100,000 cars of an essentially identical model, only a large domestic or foreign market could sustain mass production and only large companies could expect to function successfully.

Mass production would have been of little value without a mass market. It was the presence of a large common domestic market, unhampered by tariff barriers or by significant differences in tastes and ways of living, that accentuated the tendency of the American economy to exploit the possibilities of mass production. While much of the product of nineteenth-century industry, like most goods entering into trade and commerce in the past, had gone to satisfy the wants of a small segment of the population, the unique feature of the twentieth-century economy was production for mass consumption.

The American economy came to depend to a major degree on the purchasing power of the masses of the people, which in turn was made possible by rising productivity from mass-production techniques. The resulting wages and salaries, together with the multitude of available goods, produced a pattern of mass consumption in which what had been the luxuries of the few and the distinguishing features of middle-class life became part of the standard of living of the many. In the mid-1950s, for example, nearly three-quarters of American families had cars, telephones and television sets, and nine out of ten had radios and refrigerators.

The great expansion in consumption came in things beyond the bare essentials for survival, especially in durable goods such as household appliances and automobiles. As these were introduced into the consumer's budget they were accompanied by methods of financing which recognized their character as a form of capital. Instalment selling and hire-purchase plans extended to automobiles and refrigerators the principle of payment during use which had previously been limited to the purchase of housing with the aid of a home mortgage.

The mass of consumers who provided the market for the products of industry also provided much of the capital for its continuing expansion. An increasing proportion of the investment funds which entered industry came from the higher earnings of wage and salaried workers. Individual workers invested in corporate stocks through employee-purchase plans, and provided loan funds through the banks and savings and loan associations where their savings were deposited and through life-insurance funds; labour unions built up large treasuries and special pension or benefit funds which became large sources for investment. At the same time mounting taxes reduced the pool of upper-income savings from which capital had been principally derived in the past. The net result was a shift in the segment of the population upon whose savings the expansion of industry depended.

These tendencies were present in varying degrees in all the developed capitalist economies. Smaller countries which lacked a large domestic market tended to develop mass production in industries where mass techniques were effective on relatively low volume or for simple articles, or else to concentrate on special items for export. Sweden for example gained the advantages of mass production by making special products for export, such as ball-bearings and telephone equipment, thus commanding a large market for mass-produced items which could not be sold in sufficient volume at home. They also made very simple and inexpensive articles for domestic use which met the needs of the lower paid workers in order to tap the home market at its largest extent.

Mass consumption was most marked in the United States, but the trend was everywhere increasingly apparent. And it was the advantages of a domestic mass market which led the European countries in the middle of the twentieth century to take steps toward the creation of a common market on the European continent.

(b) *Large-scale organization.* Mass production and distribution brought about large-scale organization and were made possible by it. Large organizations—corporations, labour unions, government structures—grew in dimension and in relative importance in the capitalist economies. Their presence and growing dominance shifted the character of the economy more and more away from market organization and towards the substitution of administration for the traditional market forces.

For business operations the form of enterprise which gained ascendancy in the United States was the large corporation, a great industrial unit which employed many thousands of people, used the savings of many thousands of shareholders—its nominal owners—served hundreds of thousands of customers and controlled assets and did business amounting to many millions of dollars.

The large corporation was not a new phenomenon; by 1890 it had been sufficiently prominent to lead to the passage of anti-trust legislation designed to preserve competition and prevent monopolistic aggregations of economic power. The distinguishing feature of twentieth-century development was the growth in both size and importance of such corporations. As they became the prevailing form of business enterprise they had an increasing impact on the functioning of the economy by reason of their ability to control their own prices and production.

The 200 largest corporations in the United States, leaving aside the banks and other financial institutions, controlled by the 1930s some three-fifths of the assets of all non-financial corporations and roughly half of all industrial wealth. In the field of manufacturing 100 corporations in 1935 employed a fifth of all manufacturing labour and their products amounted to a third of the value of all manufactured goods. The leading corporations remained at least as dominant in later years. More striking and significant for the development of economic institutions was the extent to which they dominated specific industries—notably the great industries on which the industrial system rested, including steel, oil, automobiles, electrical manufacture, copper refining, aluminium, chemicals, rayon, as well as railways and public utilities. Service activities, agriculture, a substantial proportion of trade and many minor industries, however, were largely outside the sphere of corporate control.

The large corporation was chiefly to be found in those industries where the amount of capital investment per worker was greatest. The accelerated trend toward automation which required heavy capital investment further strengthened the position of the larger corporations. The trend was evident in the automobile industry, where one after another of the smaller companies dropped out or were merged with larger units until the industry was almost completely dominated by a very few very large concerns. The extent of concentration in the market may be seen by the list of industries in which 70 per cent or more of the output was produced by the four largest companies. From the 1930s on, these included, among the large industries, motor vehicles, cigarettes, rubber tyres, tin cans, rayon, together with the makers of a host of lesser products such as typewriters, sewing machines, electric light bulbs, chewing gum, breakfast cereals.

Large corporations also entered the field of distribution to provide mass outlets for mass-produced products. The 200 largest non-financial corporations in 1930 included two mail-order houses, two 'five and ten cent' stores, two department stores, a grocery chain and a chain of drug stores. Chain grocery and drug stores expanded greatly thereafter. These mass-distribution agencies, and also the special sales outlets for mass-produced shoes, ready-made clothing, automobiles or automobile accessories, served primarily as mass outlets for mass-produced goods, instead of performing the retailers' traditional role as intermediaries between the wants of consumers and the range of goods offered by producers.

The large corporations grew in size, with no apparent limit to the enterprise which could be operated as a single structure. The largest of them for example, the American Telephone and Telegraph Company, in 1956 had 787,000 employees, 1,492,000 stockholders, and assets of 11,100 million dollars. In 1900 this corporation was already among the large American enterprises; it then had some 37,000 employees and 10,000 stockholders.

Corporations grew in size by various means. The traditional method was to seek new capital funds through the investment market. Increasingly, however, the large corporations grew by the reinvestment of their own earnings, distributing only a fraction of their profits to stockholders. They also grew by exchanging their stock for that of smaller concerns in order to absorb or control them. The corporations themselves, rather than the investing public or the bankers, thus tended to determine where expansion would take place.

From the 1920s on they relied increasingly upon research to guide their growth and development. Following the lead of some of the pioneers such as the electrical manufacturing and telephone companies, they sought out the best scientific talent and offered resources and considerable freedom for study and experiment. By mid-century no large company was without its research arm, the sums spent on corporate research mounted annually and much of the invention and innovation of the period emerged from this source.

The large corporation was a continuing body with a legal personality, 'owned' by many stockholders who had neither direct knowledge of nor control over the affairs of the enterprise. It was governed by a board of directors, technically elected by the stockholders and representing them but in fact self-perpetuating. In the large corporation control was separated from ownership. Where stockholdings were so widely dispersed that no individual or small group owned a majority or even a substantial minority of shares, as was generally the situation in these companies, control rested in the hands of management; a few large shareholders might exercise influence by virtue of their general position and prestige rather than through a voting majority of the company's stock. In some cases the bankers who handled the corporation's financing were in a position to affect its policy, but the larger corporations tended to remove themselves more and more from bankers' control by using their accumulated earnings to finance expansion instead of distributing all earnings as dividends and then seeking new funds through loans or the sale of stock.[8]

Persons with a financial interest in corporate stock came to include a large proportion of the population. Although large stockholdings continued to be held by a limited group of persons with means, millions of small owners held a few shares each. In 1955 more than 8,000,000 people in the United States owned corporate stock directly, about a third of them from families whose income placed them in the lower half of the population. Many millions more had invested indirectly by placing their savings in an investment trust, savings and loan association, insurance company or trade union welfare fund, which in turn held stock in many different corporations and enabled the small investor to diversify his risk.

This widespread ownership gave the people at large a stake in the prosperity of the corporations but it did not involve them actively, except in the rare instances when an outside interest or rival faction challenged the existing control of a corporation and the votes of the small shareholders were solicited by both sides.

The men who ran the large corporations achieved their positions primarily, and increasingly, by rising through the industrial bureaucracy. They entered the structure as technicians or engineers concerned with production, as salesmen involved with promotion, as lawyers handling the multitude of legal relations in which the corporation became involved, in the personnel department responsible for employment policies and labour relations, or as part of the financial machinery of the enterprise. Though in the 1950s they were still likely to have come from families of moderately good incomes, an increasing proportion were coming from families of labourers or white-collar workers, family connections were less likely to have been responsible for their initial job than fifty or even twenty-five years before, and their advancement was no more rapid whether they were from a rich or a poor family.

As each corporation became a sort of small empire in itself, management tended to come from within the same organization, though sometimes a successful sales manager, production director or other executive was brought from one corporation to another. Twenty-two per cent of the chief executives of large corporations in 1950 had had no business experience outside their own company as compared with only 7 per cent in 1900; in the earlier year three-fifths (62 per cent) had had entrepreneurial experience as against less than one-fifth (17 per cent) in 1950.* Once part of the corporate structure, they might be shifted from one locality to another, like civil servants or military personnel, and the road to advancement frequently led from one department to another or through a series of branch plants and finally to the central office.

Each corporate bureaucracy developed its means of training its promising young men and giving them experience for future responsibility, its methods of seeking to command the loyalty and devotion of its members and to build an *esprit de corps* and of arousing the interest of the wives and families in order to reinforce an executive's devotion to his job and the welfare of the company. Since the objective of these efforts was the success of the corporation rather than the profit of any individual, power, prestige and advancement came to play a larger part than simple profit in the motivation of corporate management, although generous executive salaries and bonus systems based on corporate profits kept direct economic motivation very much alive, and high corporate earnings were the mark of success.

This new group of industrial managers came to replace more and more the representatives of the shareholders in the government of the corporation. In 1950 they composed half or more of the membership of the boards of directors of one-third of the large corporations; for 8 per cent of the companies they made up the entire board. The trend for management to occupy a position where no stockholder, banker or other outsider was influential enough to contest its direction of the corporation led some people to see management as taking over business. Other students of corporate structure thought that such a concept exaggerated the role of this group, but there was no question that the corporation manager was coming to be the main prototype of the successful businessman of the mid-twentieth century.

The large corporation contributed to the rootlessness of urban–industrial communities and made many of them dependent on decisions and events wholly outside their control. It often had plants in a number of different localities, sometimes because these were favourable for various distinct operations, or because the company had acquired the properties of smaller enterprises, or as a result of the extension of the corporation's activities into new areas. Decisions affecting these plants were made in terms of the enterprise as a whole, not the effect on the local community, since the large corporation rarely had substantial investments in local real estate, banks, stores or services which would be affected by what happened to its local plant. It could abandon plants containing obsolete equipment, build new plants in other localities, shift work from one plant to another in order to combat labour demands, move from areas where power rates were higher to more favourable sites, or shift to places which had advantages from the point of view of raw materials, transport or markets. Where the plants of large corporations constituted the principal source of employment in a community, whole

---

* Mabel Newcomer, *The Big Business Executive* (New York, 1955); W. Lloyd Warner and James Abegglen, *Big Business Leaders in America* (New York, 1955).

communities were subject to the decisions of corporate managements which had no direct stake in the community's welfare. Corporations frequently adopted policies of contributing to the physical and civic development of the communities where they operated, but this did not minimize community dependence on decisions in which the people of the locality took no part.

The separate corporations did not stand as completely independent units but tended to be part of a larger corporate community. Many of the large corporations were linked by interlocking directorates, with directors of one corporation sitting on the board of another, or they formed loose groupings of corporations with mutual interests. Bankers on the boards of several companies whose finances they handled used their influence as board members to make the policies of each contribute to the development of the others, as for instance in insisting that the site for a new manufacturing plant should be located on a railway with which they were also connected. Two or more companies frequently joined to establish a new concern for the manufacture of something which both companies needed, as when several oil companies set up a company to manufacture the chemicals which they all used. A common climate of opinion and norms of behaviour for the corporate group grew out of the use of common accounting firms and legal counsel, the activities of the financial agencies engaged in supplying funds and marketing and trading securities, and from personal contacts at lunch, on the golf links or at social gatherings.

In other capitalist countries large corporations played an essentially similar role and took on essentially the same characteristics, sometimes but not always in a less pronounced form. They were somewhat less dominant where co-operative enterprise was extensive as in Sweden, or where a larger proportion of economic activity was carried on by government. In Europe they often formed cartels to divide up the market—a practice legally prohibited in the United States. Some, such as the giant Unilever, were international in organization as well as in operation.

Yet although the large corporation flourished everywhere and became the dominant form of American business enterprise, small business did not disappear during these years. The individual entrepreneur conducting a small venture for direct private profit remained the principal economic unit in agriculture, in much retail trade, in the service industries and in many manufacturing activities.

The great bulk of commercial agriculture in the United States was conducted on family farms. Although a few crops, mainly cotton and sugar, were produced on large plantations, even the largest of the plantation enterprises were responsible for so small a proportion of total production of the particular crop that they did not occupy the kind of controlling position that characterized the industrial corporation.

In the field of distribution a multitude of individually operated retail establishments continued to function in communities or neighbourhoods too small to support mass outlets and in larger communities where some customers were willing to pay for additional retail services which chain stores, mail-order houses and other mass distributors failed to supply.

Small manufacturers survived chiefly in the making of speciality items, the development of new products and in supplying specific small mass-produced articles which either required little capital and relatively small volume in order to gain the advantages of mass production, or which constituted parts to be used by large manufacturers. Many thousands of new enterprises were started each year by individuals or groups who saw a chance for a profit in some new or old line of production. In the 1950s new manufacturing enterprises were being set up at the rate of about 25,000 a year; in addition, new enterprises in construction, trade, service and other non-manufacturing activities averaged 325,000 annually. Some of these efforts failed and old enterprises were discontinued for one reason or another almost as frequently as new ones were started. But many survived, some to remain small, others to grow to considerable proportions and in time to become large-scale enterprises themselves. There was no tendency either for the number of new enterprises to diminish or for fewer small enterprises to continue to function.

Ninety per cent of all manufacturing establishments continued to employ less than 100 workers, and the numbers of such establishments, not always of course operated by an independent company, was more than a third greater in 1954 than it had been twenty-five years before—264,000 as compared with 193,000. Small establishments were to be found in nearly every type of industry.

The existence of an economy of mass production and consumption itself favoured the survival of small enterprise. As the masses of the people acquired higher incomes and more leisure they had more scope for expenditure on things other than basic necessities—on entertainment, sport or hobbies, on things to decorate the home and to embellish its surroundings, on extra clothing, special foods, travel, enjoyment of the arts. Basic products, especially those involving heavy industry, offered little scope for small enterprise, for they were controlled by the large corporations and they required much capital and large expenditures on advertising to reach the mass market. Small enterprise survived as an integral part of the basic industries mainly in the specialized manufacture of machinery and in the mass manufacture of special parts to be used in the machine processes. But the speciality fields remained open and attracted the efforts of ambitious entrepreneurs who took advantage of the growing capacity of consumers to diversify their purchases.

The small enterprise had another advantage which contributed to its survival, its adaptability. It could adopt innovations without undergoing the high cost of revamping an elaborate production process or the delays of bureaucratic decision-making. Although small companies did not have the resources which enabled large corporations to maintain research laboratories, they were less hampered in putting new methods into practice since they did not have such heavy investments in existing processes.

The flexibility of the economy was thus maintained in two ways: by the research and development activities of the large corporations, and by the small companies whose multiplicity, adaptability and ability to enter new fields favoured innovation. The latter in fact exercised a certain pressure to keep the big corporations alert and to prevent their strong economic position from leading to stagnation.

The continuing vitality of small enterprise was even more marked in capitalist countries other than the United States. Notably in France, small enterprises depending on high levels of engineering and other technical skills kept the French tradition of speciality production very much alive.

The growth and power of large business organization were met by large-scale organization of labour. Until the 1930s most American labour organizations were craft unions which flourished especially in industries where small enterprise prevailed, while the large corporations successfully resisted the organization of their workers.

Thereafter collective bargaining was established in principle in the mass-production industries and was achieved in practice by the time of the second world war, although resistance on the part of some employers and in some industries was not dead. Collective contracts, negotiated with large corporations for all their operations and, increasingly, for entire industries, set wages and working conditions for one, two or as much as five years.

The large labour organizations had their own bureaucratic structures, much like those of the corporations. In form they were democratic, with elected officers; in practice the extent to which the structure functioned democratically varied markedly from one union to another.

The position of the union leader had certain unique features, for he was at one and the same time an elected head, a bargaining agent and a recruiter of union members. So long as he was successful in securing the union's demands the membership had little inclination to risk replacing him with someone who might achieve less. There was consequently almost as strong a tendency for the existing union leadership to remain in control of the mass unions as for the existing management to remain in control of the corporations. In some unions, in fact, there was little pretence of offering a choice to the members, and a fight for a change in control of a union tended to become as rare and dramatic as a fight for a change in control of a major corporation.

In addition to acting as bargaining agent for their members, labour unions shared responsibility for carrying out collective contracts. The structure of the corporation and plant was matched by the organization of the workers, with shop stewards to match the foremen and local union officers or business agents to match the higher levels of management. Under the terms of the collective contract, grievance machinery was ordinarily established to handle any question of the failure to carry out the terms of the contract, and union representatives dealt with their opposite numbers at whatever level the matter had to be settled. After the second world war labour unions also came to play an important part in community life. As representatives of large segments of the population they were in a position to give or withhold both approval and financial support for civic and welfare projects.

The tendency for labour organizations to become large bureaucratic structures and to participate in the administration of industry was even more marked in other capitalist countries. In some European countries they participated in the administration of certain social benefits or in plant decisions relating to some aspects of production and were sometimes included in boards of directors.

(c) *Government intervention.* The growing power of large economic organizations brought increased intervention in the public interest by the only body with sufficient strength and scope to match corporate power, the central government. Government intervened to regulate the conduct of corporate business in order to prevent fraud against the stockholder, the competitor or the buyer, to prevent the abuse of a monopoly position and to protect labour.

From the early years of the century, the individual American states, and later the federal government (1934), enacted laws to shield investors against fraud. They stipulated the information which must be disclosed to prospective investors when shares of stock or bonds were offered for sale and in the reports of corporate earnings which must be made public. Other laws offered some protection to the buyer, although they only modified to a limited extent the principle of *caveat emptor*—let the buyer beware—which was the accepted legal basis for commercial transactions in general. They required that packaged foods, drugs and cosmetics bear information as to the contents and forbade false or misleading advertising (1906, 1938). Legislation outlawing unfair competitive practices attempted to give the honest producer a chance to compete with the unscrupulous (1912). Checks on the exercise of monopoly power took the form of public utility regulation, laws against combinations in restraint of trade (1890, 1914), limitations on the formation of holding companies to control competing corporations (1935) and the establishment of government enterprise as a yardstick, i.e. a basis for determining whether the costs on which utilities asked approval for their rates were reasonable (1934).

Labour legislation covered hours of work, minimum wages, conditions of safety, child labour and the right of workers to form unions, strike, picket peacefully, and to bargain collectively through representatives of their own choosing (1935, 1938). Social security legislation required contributions from employers for the protection of workers against lack of income (1935).

The government thus provided a framework for the conduct of economic activity which sought to make it serve the public interest. Administrative agencies established to carry out the provisions of this legislation developed a large body of administrative law and procedure relating to the conduct of economic life which went far beyond the principles of commercial law that had provided the legal basis for economic activity at the opening of the century.

The manner in which governments intervened to regulate their respective economies differed from country to country, but the scope and general character covered essentially the same fields and evolved in an essentially similar manner. So also did the direct participation by government in economic activity. Other capitalist countries were more inclined toward government operation than was the United States, especially Britain in the years after the second world war when the Labour party was in power, but the difference among countries was one of degree. Even the reluctant governments undertook hydroelectric and atomic energy developments, built a network of roads, expanded health, education and other services and enlarged their military establishments. The countries which were more inclined to extend government operations entered the same fields of energy production, transport, services and military establishments and left the majority of manufacturing activities in corporate or private hands.

(d) *Breakdown of market mechanism.* The dominant role which came to be played by large organization—the corporation, the labour union and government enterprise—brought a basic change in the character of the American economy and other developed capitalist economies by undermining the market mechanism. The market as an overall regulator was not formally superseded by any alternative structure, as it was in the communist countries by the adoption of central planning. But administration replaced bargaining in many areas and as a result the functioning of the free market was impaired where it continued to serve as the regulator of economic activity.

The market mechanism had depended on adjustment by means of flexible prices. The large corporation which dominated its industry or faced a limited number of competitors set its own price in terms of its costs and the effect which it expected its price policy to have on the market. It fixed its prices for a period of time, revising them only when it deemed a revision to be in its interest. Instead of adjusting to demand by raising or lowering price, it adjusted by increasing or decreasing production, since it was in a position to hold its price and to vary its output. Wages likewise were fixed through collective contracts for periods of time and were as little subject to change in response to fluctuation in the market as were prices; if anything they became even more rigid as labour unions sought security and stability for their members and pressed for contracts extending over longer periods.

In these circumstances the corporation tried to sell as many cars or cigarettes or tons of steel as it could at its established price by capturing as large a share of the market as possible and by expanding the demand for its particular product. This meant high-pressure advertising and the use of brand names and other distinguishing marks to identify the product of the particular company in order that the customer might know and demand it. Mass advertising served the necessary purpose of bringing the products of mass industry to the attention of distant consumers; in the presence of administered prices it took on the additional function of pressing sales, a function which had been accomplished by price adjustment under more competitive conditions.

The importance of this development was not its novelty, but its extent. Industrial concerns making products which could be identified, or supplying local markets where there were few if any competitors, had long set their prices and given their products a distinguishing name; but in the early years of the century these formed only a small part of total output. At that time agricultural products and raw materials, whose prices conformed to market conditions and fluctuated with supply and demand, accounted for a large proportion of the goods which entered into trade, and many manufactured products such as common cotton cloth were made by many producers and were sold without distinction as to their source. What gave the administered prices of the twentieth century their profound impact upon the operation of the economy was the greatly increased proportion of all economic activity represented by industry and, within the industrial sector, by those economic units which were in a position to establish their prices.

The effect of price and wage administration was greatly to increase the instability of the economy. Economic depressions had plagued the industrial economies from their early years, but none had been so severe as the depression of the 1930s. In the economic collapse of these years the prices of manufactured goods produced by large American corporations which dominated their industries, such as automobiles, steel, electrical and farm equipment, fell only a small amount, and wages in these industries remained relatively stable; production, however, dropped as much as 80 per cent, creating tremendous unemployment.

In the face of falling demand, corporations clung to their prices and laid off their workers, uncertain that a lowering of price would increase sales, and preferring the safer road of limited output at a profit to the risk of expanded output at a possible loss. Corporations in other countries followed a similar course, except as they were prevented from doing so by dependence on prices in the world market. Labour unions for their part hung on to their wage structure to protect those of their members who were still employed, preferring to guard what they could control, though it meant loss of membership and protected only the workers who retained their jobs.

Meanwhile in the agriculture sector price flexibility prevailed and the farmer faced declining markets and declining prices. Unable to control his prices his only recourse was to keep up or increase his production in the hope of making something, however little, from the sale of his produce. While industrial workers were idle, farmers worked harder than ever for little or no returns. The fact that the agricultural sector of the economy continued to operate on the basis of the free market may be credited with saving the industrial countries from starvation during the depression, for food continued to be produced and was sold for what it would bring; but it did not save the farmer from bankruptcy and often foreclosure of the mortgage on his farm.

(e) *Measures for economic stability*. Faced with the evidence that the historic mechanism of adjustment had broken down so severely as to endanger the whole society, governments intervened with measures designed to achieve economic recovery and to maintain economic stability.

In the United States these measures included an effort to rescue agriculture by means of a programme to support farm prices, in part by limiting the production of major crops. In order to reduce speculation in the stock market, which had brought heavy losses to many investors, requirements were raised as to the proportion of each purchase which must be in the form of cash. Expanded programmes of public works were undertaken to provide employment to the unemployed. Extensions of unemployment insurance, economic assistance and other social security measures helped to maintain incomes.

As these and other measures were undertaken in the effort to bring economic recovery, it became clear that the government would have to assume positive responsibility for maintaining economic stability once full employment was obtained. In the Employment Act of 1946 the Congress of the United States declared it to be the continuing policy and responsibility of the federal government to promote maximum employment, production and purchasing power by all practical means and placed responsibility directly upon the highest executive and legislative authorities. European governments made similar commitments.

By the middle of the century a wide range of stabilizing devices existed to counteract the threat of economic instability. Some of these were structural and acted as built-in stabilizers. Agricultural price supports, restraints on stock-market speculation and expanded social insurance and assistance programmes, once introduced to combat depression, became permanent features of the economy; high progressive tax rates on individual incomes and corporate earnings provided for an automatic drop in tax collections when incomes fell. Increased general government expenditures for expanded services and for the civil and military establishments, however, did not respond automatically to business fluctuations.

A number of other factors increased the likelihood that the actions of both business and government would contribute to stability. Information on which business, labour and government could plan and act was being collected in a more extensive and systematic fashion, including data covering prices, living costs, employment, unemployment, wages, earnings, investment and money supply. The spread of automation involving large capital investment made uninterrupted high-level production more vital to success, and the recourse of reduced production to maintain profits became less feasible.

Governments had the means to control the money supply so as to permit the creation of additional money when needed, and to adjust fiscal policy in order to expand purchasing power either by increased government spending or decreased taxes or both. For control over the money supply, the United States government strengthened the central financial institution, the federal reserve system, and entrusted it with responsibility and power to keep the money in the country at a volume to sustain a high level of production and employment. Although many government expenditures could not be postponed or expanded to help stabilize economic activity, spending for public works such as roads, public buildings, harbour improvements or parks could be increased if a depression threatened, construction of hydroelectric or other major projects could be speeded up and there was some flexibility in the operation of government services. At the same time tax rates could be reduced and additional purchasing power could be provided by financing expanded government expenditures through borrowing from the banks rather than by withdrawing spending power from the public in the form of taxes. The reverse procedure might be used to check inflation when this arose from excessive demand.

The measures undertaken by other capitalist countries, either their built-in stabilizers or those designed to counteract tendencies toward depression, differed in detail and were affected by the relative independence of the national economy or its dependence on foreign trade. But all were designed to sustain demand when it threatened to drop and thus to prevent a reduction in production from creating serious unemployment and setting in motion a downward spiral which could not be counted on to reverse itself. All involved control over the volume of money and the use of government fiscal policy. Adjustment of government spending could be an even more potent device in European countries than in the United States, for government expenditures in the 1950s amounted to a third of national income in Great Britain and to a quarter in France and Sweden as compared with a fifth in the United States.

At mid-century it had not yet been established whether these controls would in fact be applied with the necessary skill and judgment and whether they would be effective against depression if put to a severe test, for they faced no such real test in the years after the second world war. During the 1950s the United States economy experienced several small recessions which slowed its rate of growth and occasioned some unemployment. The European economies grew steadily and rapidly after their post-war recovery. In any case it was clear that no government was prepared to allow a major depression to descend upon its people as it had in the past, and all were prepared to take the positive measures which they thought would be effective in preserving stability and sustaining a high level of economic activity.

(f) *Adjustment of international economic relations.* As countries controlled their internal currencies and took measures to combat unemployment and to guard against its recurrence, the mechanism of international trade had to be rebuilt. In the presence of these internal controls, the traditional means of international economic adjustment no longer sufficed and the free market forces were partially replaced by devices to manage the flow of trade, monetary payments and capital.

During the first world war the measures taken by the several countries to finance war activity had completely disrupted the pre-war relationship among the currencies of the industrial countries. The resulting disparities were so great that the attempt to restore the old pattern seemed out of the question, and countries abandoned the effort to return to the international gold standard. Although they retained gold as a means of paying for imports which exceeded their exports, they adopted managed currencies whose quantity was not proportionately affected by the flow of gold in or out of the country. The depression of the 1930s brought a tendency for countries to seek to make their economies more self-sufficient in order to insulate them from fluctuations taking place in other countries. This trend toward autarchy was most marked in the countries which were also engaged in a vigorous military build-up, Nazi Germany and Japan, but even Britain abandoned its traditional free trade policy, raised tariffs and worked out a plan of empire preference.

The impact of the second world war further shifted the relations among the economies of the industrial countries and left them at the close of the war even further than they had been at the end of the first world war from the possibility of using the traditional free flow of gold as a mechanism of adjustment. Countries retained their wartime powers to set quotas on imports and exports, to restrict the spending of their currencies abroad and to limit capital movements, using these powers to prevent their internal programmes for economic reconstruction and stabilization from being undermined by an adverse balance of payments.

As new international economic relationships emerged and new techniques for international economic adjustment were developed in the period following the second world war, these unilateral protective controls were gradually relaxed, though they did not wholly disappear. The new techniques consisted in the establishment of the International Monetary Fund and the International Bank for Reconstruction and Development and in a series of intergovernmental arrangements involving economic aid, mutual exchange and the creation of common economic communities of interest.

The International Monetary Fund was set up in 1945 as a mechanism for adjusting imbalances in international payments that might arise. For this purpose it was given authority to work out with the countries concerned the relationships among their several currencies, and it was provided with funds to assist in maintaining the relationships which were established. The Fund maintained a pool of the currencies of member countries and was thus in a position to lend the currency of one country to another in order to tide a country over a temporary inability to meet its international payments without exhausting its reserves of gold and deposits in foreign banks.

The International Bank facilitated the international flow of capital by lending to governments the funds deposited with it by member countries and those secured from private sources through the sale of its bonds; later, plans were made for the provision of risk capital through international channels.

The capital funds required for the reconstruction of the European economies proved too large to be supplied through any mechanism which required their repayment. To meet this situation the United States established what was known as the Marshall Plan for intergovernmental economic aid and collaborated with the European countries in the rebuilding of their economies. These countries, in turn, found their historic separateness an obstacle to their respective efforts to regain the economic position from which wartime destruction and the loss of colonial possessions had dislodged them and to restore a basis for the full employment and rising living standards of their people. Step by step they drew their economies closer together through a series of mutual adjustments in trade, quotas, tariffs and monetary relationships, through the establishment of the European Coal and Iron Community to develop these basic industries for the continent as a whole, and, finally, in 1957, through the agreement to create a Common European Market and a common means, Euratom, for exploiting the economic potentials of atomic energy. By these measures the European economies, restored to vigour, began to be reoriented toward the economic potentials of a common European domestic economy.

In the economic relations between the industrialized and the non-industrial countries, governmental action to provide economic aid and to direct the flow of capital was added to the old pattern of profit-seeking foreign investment. Private oil and mining companies continued to invest in overseas ventures and manufacturing companies established branch plants to assemble automobiles, produce synthetic fibres or process local foods. But the position and role of these enterprises were altered as the developing countries erected barriers to the foreign exploitation of their resources and made positive efforts to bring foreign funds into their development plans. Capital-supplying countries supported these efforts through United Nations technical aid and loans by the International Bank, and through assistance and loan programmes of the United States and countries co-operating through the Colombo Plan.

(g) *The capitalist ethic.* [9, 10] Although the institutions of the capitalist economies underwent major changes during these years, many of the basic drives that sustained early industrial development continued to operate in the capitalist industrial countries. The 'capitalist ethic' continued to sanction and give dignity to work, the quest for material success and the accumulation of wealth, and to condenm idleness, waste and indifference to material goals. In the United States, as well as in other countries such as Germany, the Netherlands, Sweden and Great Britain where capitalist economies were highly developed, it not only permeated the business community but entered the viewpoint of the farmer, or of the mechanic who looked for an opportunity to set up his own enterprise, or of the professional man who was expected to combine economic success with the performing of his professional service. Although the desire for security was intensified by the great depression, and drives within the industrial bureaucracies were often for power or prestige rather than simply for personal profit, the capitalist societies continued to regard the undertaking and conduct of profit-seeking enterprise as normal behaviour, and to accord respect and prestige to those who were successful in it.

The imperatives of this ethic were modified in form by changes in economic structure and social conditions. The American business community generally accepted the concept that profit could best be sought by producing and selling a large volume with a small margin on each unit rather than by a large mark-up on each of a small number of units. Elsewhere this principle was somewhat less generally accepted, especially where, as in France, there was a tradition of quality production for a limited market. High wages linked with high productivity were recognized as the source of a mass market. The goal of consumption, a high standard of living, became central for labour and for all segments of the public. Thrift and saving for its own sake lost some of its virtue as the notion spread that spending keeps the wheels of industry turning and as social measures provided minimum economic security. Much saving was invested in durable goods for current use rather than put away against a rainy day. Advertising played on every sort of desire and emotion in the process of stimulating consumption.

Goals of consumption themselves took new shapes as the economy became more productive. They were no longer expressed in terms of survival but in terms of sharing the fruits of modern industry. Many of the patterns of consumption which had distinguished the middle and upper classes from the lower no longer set them apart. The masses of the people ate much the same nourishing food, wore clothes in the street which made them virtually indistinguishable from all but the most elegant of the well-to-do, lived in houses which had many of the same comforts and household conveniences, drove similar cars, travelled and enjoyed holidays, sports and cinemas and had gardens, cameras or other hobbies. The levelling effect of high consumption patterns was most marked in the United States but it was at work in all the advanced capitalist economies.

Although couched in material terms, the goal of a high standard of living which motivated individuals and received the sanction of society had more than a material meaning. For it meant acceptance of the concept that poverty was unnecessary and that man by his efforts had achieved the means to conquer this ancient enemy. It carried the idea that to free man from material want was to free the human spirit and release human potentialities. And it meant that this freedom and release was not the privilege of the few but the birthright of all.

In this vision, the productivity of industry and the social institutions for the common welfare combined to create the conditions for a life of greater human dignity and satisfaction. This concept was expressed in a study of freedom and welfare in the five Scandinavian countries, sponsored by the welfare ministers of these states: 'The living standard of any nation depends primarily upon the volume of goods and services which it produces. Social benefits, whatever their description may be, are part of this living standard. . . . The goal pursued by the Northern peoples is simple. They want to make their countries a place worth living in for free men and women. . . . To realize this goal requires work and increased productivity; and it requires cooperation in a spirit of practical solidarity.'*

In the words of Britain's Labour prime minister, Clement Attlee, 'the new privileged class is everywhere in the perambulators'. Its members were the new generation of children born into societies which had achieved the means, adopted the determination and developed the institutions to offer material well-being to all their people.

2. *The socialist economy of the* USSR *and other communist countries*

The economic system of the USSR represented the first attempt to build a modern economy in a communist state. It provided an example which other states under communist control could follow in the development of their economic structures.

Only the most general principles for the design of such an economic structure were provided by Marxist theory. Marx described in detail what he considered the weaknesses and evils of the capitalist system and made it clear that a socialist economy would eliminate these features, most especially private ownership of the means of production and repeated economic crises. But on detailed guide-lines for alternative forms of organization Marx was silent. He regarded the new social–economic formation as having two phases, the first and lower phase being socialism and the second and higher phase complete communism. He saw the state as a necessary instrument during the first phase and expected it to wither away in the higher phase with the development of a communist society.

Marx lived in a time when most industrial activity was carried on in relatively small enterprises and he formulated his general expectations in terms of the direct control of production by workers. Lenin, confronted with large and complex economic units, thought of the economy as functioning like a single centralized economic enterprise. His major theoretical contribution to the development of the Soviet economy was his concept of the socialist state as the main instrument of the working class in building a national economy based on socialization of the main means of production. He conceived of the Party as the revolutionary spearhead which should not only assume disciplined direction of the seizure of power, but should continue to play the same role in the organization and operation of the socialist society. In assigning the Party this role, he entrusted it with political and economic generalship and expected that it would be able to work out the structure and operation of the economic system. Moreover, he believed that the modernization of industry was the indispensable condition to achieve socialism,

* *Freedom and Welfare, op. cit.,* pp. 517, 521.

expressing this view in his oft-quoted dictum 'electricity plus soviets equal socialism'.

(a) *Condition of the Russian economy*. The structure built by Lenin and his associates in the early years of the Soviet state and the devices which they created were pragmatically designed to meet the situations with which they had to cope. These situations were difficult and exacting. The country's economy was broken by the destruction and disorganization of the first world war, the Revolution, and the years of intervention and civil war. As a result of these catastrophes the output of large-scale industry in 1920 was scarcely one-seventh of the pre-revolutionary rate and the level of national income was reduced to little more than a third; the burden of homeless, ill, orphaned, uprooted and unemployed was tremendous. The pressing task of putting the pieces together was the first which confronted the Soviet leaders as they sought a way to build a viable economy, and it required six or seven years to accomplish this task after the end of the civil war and intervention.

The second condition faced throughout the forty years following the October revolution was the constant expectation of war. Communist doctrine, and the experience of intervention during the civil war, taught that the capitalist world would not permit a communist society to grow in peace. Although after Lenin's death in 1924 leadership passed to the faction led by Stalin who thought it possible to build socialism in one state without its being sustained by world revolution, the belief persisted that such a state must be prepared to withstand attack from its inevitable enemies. By definition the communist state under these conditions must be a defence state, and the socialist economy must be a defence economy, while it developed the basis for expansion and met the minimum needs of the population. The Nazi invasion of June 1941 justified the expectation of attack and the second world war repeated on a huge scale the destruction of the first. Loss of the main industrial areas to invading armies forced the removal of industry to the east beyond the Urals and required an intense effort to make up the loss and to rebuild the destroyed area as rapidly as possible after the war. Continuing international tension in the period following the second world war kept military defence a major aspect of the economy.

The institutions of the Soviet economy were thus designed under conditions of two major periods of disaster and reconstruction and a continual state of fear and expectation of the need for military defence. The need to establish an industrial base as advanced as that of major capitalist countries to enable the communist system to compete with the capitalist was reinforced by the overriding importance of defence.

Defence, in turn, was seen in relation to Russia's experience of repeated military defeat by more industrially advanced countries, by Sweden in the eighteenth century, France in 1812, Britain and France in the Crimean war of the 1850s, by newly industrialized Japan in 1905, by the invading German armies in the first world war. It meant not merely a strong military establishment but the industrial potential to sustain modern warfare. The drive to expand heavy industry rapidly and at all costs reflected the conviction that only thus could the defence needs of the régime be met and survival be ensured. The development of heavy industry was also urgently needed to provide agriculture with modern machinery and to modernize the light industries, food processing and transport.

The natural conditions upon which the Soviet economy rested were the enormous and varied resources of the great Russian land-mass, many still unexplored, and the rigorous Russian climate, excessively cold in moist regions to the north and excessively dry in many warm areas. These provided the potential and set some of the limits for economic development.

When the communist régime came to power the economy was predominantly agricultural—about 80 per cent of the population was still engaged in agriculture—but the industrial segment had been growing very rapidly in the previous fifty years and included large enterprises. From 1861 on, the tsarist government had taken a variety of measures to encourage industrial expansion: railway construction had opened up the country and linked European Russia with the Pacific; the Donbas-Krivoy Rog coal and iron complex had been developed; Baku oil resources had been brought into production. During several periods between 1885 and 1913 the rate of industrial growth in Russia had exceeded the current rate in the United States, Britain or Germany; from 1890 to 1900 the annual rate of expansion in industrial production had reached an estimated 8 per cent. Russia's relatively late start, however, meant that the extent of industrialization, even before the destruction of the first world war and the civil war, was much less than that of the major industrial countries.

A large proportion of the industrial expansion under the tsars, notably in mining, chemical, metal fabrication, woodworking and textile industries, had been achieved with foreign capital. Half of all the capital in Russian joint-stock companies in 1900 was from foreign sources, about 90 per cent French, British, German and Belgian, while loans from France, Holland and elsewhere had financed much of the railway construction. The vast natural resources of the country had made tsarist Russia an attractive field for foreign investment. A great deal of the machinery and equipment came from abroad, and numbers of foreign technicians supplemented the competent but small group of Russians trained in high-quality Russian technical institutes or abroad. After the October revolution a large part of the organizational, financial and technical resources which had contributed to pre-Soviet industrial expansion was thus not available to facilitate continued growth.

The labour force consisted of a large body of peasants, many of whom were underemployed and therefore available for transfer to industry, and an industrial proletariat of which an estimated 20 per cent retained rural roots and worked part of the year in agriculture while the majority had become permanent urban workers.

From the time of the emancipation of the serfs in the 1860s until 1905 the majority of the peasants had been collectively responsible through their communes (*mir*) for redemption payments entitling them to the lands released to them on emancipation. They were thus held more or less closely within communal groups and were subject to communally established planting patterns. Under the Stolypin reforms of 1906 redemption payments were no longer exacted and individual peasants could demand their share of the land, to cultivate according to their own design or to sell. By 1915 more than half of the peasant households held their land in hereditary tenure, but only a tenth of them cultivated land which had been consolidated into independent farms. The vast majority of all peasants were engaged in subsistence farming by primitive methods, they were in debt to landowners and even if they acquired title to land they often lost it. They generally farmed in collective groups, whether they owned strips individually or worked land which still belonged to the village community. There was profound discontent among the peasants and a constant struggle for land. Industrial workers for their part had repeatedly been subjected to repressive measures against the formation of unions and efforts to improve working conditions.

Both peasants and urban workers were generally uneducated. Three-quarters of the total population over 9 years of age was illiterate; among women only about one out of ten could read and write. A large number of independent artisans, who provided many of the consumer goods especially in rural villages, possessed craft skills. A few able members of the lower classes, including some of the revolutionary leaders, had been able to enter the system of higher and technical education which served primarily the members of the upper classes. The Soviet economic leaders thus had available an under-employed and undertrained agricultural labour force, accustomed to restraint and collective responsibility, from which had already been recruited a smaller but considerable body of industrial workers.

(b) *Initial steps in socialization.* In the initial stages, the period of war communism, 1918–21, when the main problem was to meet the emergency and to bring some kind of order out of chaos, the state acted rapidly to nationalize land, banking, industrial enterprises, wholesale and retail trade, and most urban housing, as well as continuing to control former state enterprises such as railways and communications systems. Grain was requisitioned to feed the urban population. In the factories, works councils guided by Party members began to direct production. The Supreme Economic Council, created in 1917, was at first mainly engaged in trouble-shooting—breaking bottlenecks as they arose in order to keep the factories somehow supplied with materials and equipment; thereafter it began to devote itself to the work of directing national enterprises.

Production however declined disastrously in the face of continuous warfare and inexperience in economic administration. The system of requisitioning affected grain production unfavourably. With the end of civil war and intervention it appeared to Lenin and his associates in 1921 that individual incentives, especially for the peasantry, would have to be employed for the time being in order to achieve the momentum for expansion and to allow time for planning processes to be developed to the point where they could effectively guide the economy. The New Economic Policy (N.E.P.) therefore introduced a considerably lighter tax in kind, permitted private trade and allowed peasants to sell a substantial proportion of their produce.

During the next seven years these relaxations of the principle of socialist production and distribution served as a stimulus to the agricultural production needed to feed the growing urban industrial population and for export to purchase machinery essential to industrial expansion until Russia's own machine-making capacity could be increased. The N.E.P. however was never regarded as part of a permanent structure but only as a temporary device. As soon as the rehabilitation of the national economy began to bring an increase in the production of commodities and in state and co-operative trade, private traders were subjected to unfavourable taxes, difficulties in securing supplies and transport and intensified competition from the expanding net-work of state stores and wholesale agencies. By 1928 the share of retail trade in the hands of private traders had been reduced from approximately 72 to 22 per cent; in 1932 private trading by merchants was forbidden.

At the same time that the N.E.P. was inaugurated the first large-scale attempts at planning were undertaken, in recognition of the fact that the crucial problem of permanent economic organization was how to substitute planning for the free market which acted as the regulator of capitalist econo-mies. In February 1921 the State Planning Commission (later renamed State Planning Committee) or Gosplan was set up. A special commission had already been created to make a comprehensive proposal for the development of electricity. The electric development plan as adopted in December 1920 not only called for the construction over a ten- to fifteen-year period of some thirty electric power stations, but set output goals for coal, iron ore, pig iron, steel and other basic products. It was subsequently incorporated into the first five-year plan when the latter was formulated.

By 1928 the planning mechanism had been developed to the point where it could serve as the major instrument of economic policy and direction. The first five-year plan, developed under a directive of the fifteenth Congress of the Communist party, December 1927, came into effect in September 1928. The planning system involved both the design of a plan and its execution, with mechanisms for checking the conformity of practice to the plan as laid down and measures to bring the execution into line when goals were not being met.

(c) *Collectivization of agriculture.* In such a system all major areas of the economy needed to be subject to unified direction. The backward, scattered, individual peasant households which under the N.E.P. remained outside centralized control were out of line with the growing, concentrated industry. The lack of centralization in agriculture and the very low marketable surplus offered a threat to the success of the programme and led to the determination to undertake the remaking of agriculture by uniting individual small households into co-operative collective farms. The first five-year plan called for a large increase, from 2·7 to 17·3 per cent, in the proportion of farming to be carried on by collectives or state farms. During the following years, an intensive drive to liquidate the class of individual capitalistic farmers known as *kulaks* brought agriculture within the system of control much more rapidly than the plan had envisaged. By 1931 two-thirds of the crop land and more than half of the people engaged in agriculture had been brought within the system of collective and state farms; by 1936 collectivization of agriculture was very nearly complete.

The cost of this operation was so high both in terms of production and in loss of life that the government took steps to slow it down temporarily, and to check the pressure of over-zealous Party workers and poor peasants impatient for land. Peasants who resisted collectivization often slaughtered their livestock, cutting both draught animals and other livestock by more than half; the famine which resulted and the rigours of expulsion and work camps claimed over a million lives. It was, however, considered essential to the overall structure of an economy organized and operated through the mechanism of central planning.[11]

(d) *Development of planning mechanism and techniques.* The development of the planning mechanism, its continuous extension into more and more details of economic life, and the elaboration of devices for control and adjustment of the enormous and endlessly complex economy of the Soviet Union was a feat of economic organization hitherto unparalleled in the history of mankind. The disappearance of private property in the means of production did not remove any of the basic problems of administration and co-ordination of enterprise, of relating cost to return, of securing supply and of co-ordinating the volume and flow of production so that the output of myriads of products would be in balance and the output of a piece of machinery would not be held up for lack of a screw or switch or other necessary part.

The first five-year plan, 1928–32, covered in practice only some fifty industries as compared with more than twice that number covered in much greater detail by the second five-year plan. Its method was to set a series of minimum targets which industries were to meet, or if possible to exceed, within the prescribed period. By setting targets for the most crucial industries and by designating some of these as 'leading links', it established a set of priorities in the supply of fuel and raw materials and in financing. If certain industries lagged behind but the leading links met or exceeded prescribed goals, the main objectives of the plan would not be vitiated. It was triumphantly announced that the plan had been fulfilled ahead of schedule in gross production on the basis of over-fulfilment of goals for items such as machinery and electrical equipment, although a number of other products fell short of the objectives set.

Successive plans expanded the number of industries covered—branches of transport, agriculture and trade—and the detail with which sub-targets as well as major goals were spelled out. By the fifth five-year plan, applying to the period 1951–55, the technique had been so fully elaborated that the total plan covered in considerable detail virtually all parts of the economy and culture and approached a balanced programme calling for the meeting of exact goals, or co-ordinated acceleration, rather than spotty overfulfilment of parts.

In the development of planning techniques two approaches initially vied for favour. One group of planners favoured a method which projected past performance into the future in terms of what might prudently be expected to happen, and set modest and 'realistic' goals. This method did not envisage high tempos. The alternative approach was to set goals in relation to the needs of the Soviet state, however difficult of achievement they might seem, and then to marshal every possible resource and every possible effort to overcome difficulties in growth and to reach the objective.

By the time of the first five-year plan the second approach had received the approval of the Party leadership as a revolutionary, progressive approach; those who advocated the more conservative procedure had been removed from an active role in the planning process, and the Russian economy was mobilized for the priority task of developing heavy industry and of creating an expanding base which would provide the military potential and permit a future expansion in consumer goods and food.

During the dictatorship of Stalin nothing and nobody was allowed to stand in the way of what Stalin regarded as the only course which would meet the political conditions of these years.[12] Those who advocated an alternative course became 'enemies of the State'. If something had to be given up somewhere in the economic programme and plan, on the fulfilment of which the country's independence and life depended, it was given up. This generally meant cutting the production of consumer goods and services, except for those such as education and public health which were essential to provide the literate, well-trained and efficient labour force which industrial development and cultural progress required.

The planning process was headed by the State Planning Committee which drew up not only the periodic five-year plans but annual, more detailed plans adjusted in the light of the progress toward fulfilment of the overall plan. From the time of its formation the Gosplan gradually built up a technical staff, not only at the centre but for geographic subdivisions and for separate industries and branches of production. A reporting system headed by a central statistical administration was also established in order to provide the essential tools for designing a plan and observing its execution. In time every industry and geographical area down to the smallest unit developed its planning mechanism, some as part of the Gosplan organization, others under one of the many ministries, others as a part of the party machinery.

National plans were formulated through a continual process of interaction and negotiation between the higher and lower authorities, those at lower levels commenting on goals proposed from above and offering counterproposals. Every effort was made to encourage lower units to offer to fulfil higher goals than those originally proposed. Final decisions taken by the higher authority became the required objectives for all. Frequent reports on fulfilment, made from lower to higher units and reaching the statistical administration, were designed to provide a continuous record of progress and to make it possible to detect and avert impending difficulties. In crucial industries details of plans were sometimes revised from month to month or more frequently in the effort to meet contingencies that might arise.

(e) *Organization and administration.* The administrative structure for conducting the various segments of the economy in line with the plans consisted of ministries at the top and enterprises at the bottom. Some major enterprises were directly responsible to a ministry; many were linked in combines or trusts which in turn were responsible to a ministry. The number of ministries and their scope varied from time to time as policy alternated between consolidating functions in a few ministries and distributing them on a more specialized basis. Under the central ministries the major heavy industries were directed on a nation-wide basis without regard to the administrative political divisions of the country; other industries, such as building materials, cotton or timber and paper, were conducted by union–republic ministries, with major direct responsibility resting in the hands of the ministries of the separate republics, co-ordinated by the corresponding central ministry. In 1957 the decision was taken to decentralize a larger proportion of the responsibility carried by the central ministries and to place it in the hands of agencies of the component geographical units—local councils of national economy.

The structure of economic administration was integrated with the overall administration of the state. At the highest level the Council of Ministers and its Presidium directed both the economy and all other state activity. For the union–republic industries, ministries of the several republics working with the corresponding central ministry carried responsibility within their area. Throughout all levels of the economy, as in all other areas of Soviet life, the Communist party acted as a spearhead to organize and take the lead, ever alert for the fulfilment of objectives. At the centre the Presidium of the Central Committee of the Communist Party and the party congresses established or accepted the goals. Party organs down to the factory and trade-union level assumed responsibility for watching and stimulating the execution of the plans.

Organs of both state and Party at all levels functioned as mechanisms of control, to keep track of development and to hold responsible those who might fall behind. The Gosplan through its representatives throughout the country kept constant check; the Ministry of Finance, through the State Bank and also through the tax collection officials, kept a check on the financial aspects; the Communist party, through its production departments directly subordinate to the Central Committee of the party and through party units at every level down to the factory cell, made special investigations or kept a running record of success or failure in meeting prescribed levels of output.

Trade unions after 1930 had as their main function helping to achieve production goals. During the 1920s there were differences of opinion as to the proper function of trade unions, Leon Trotsky insisting that they were properly arms of the proletariat state for achieving common economic objectives while the head of the trade unions, Mikhail Tomsky, maintained that their function was to represent the workers *vis-à-vis* the state, their employer. Lenin termed the trade unions 'the school of government, the school of communism' but insisted that they should not assume direct functions of government. In 1930 at the sixteenth Congress of the Communist party, the view represented by Tomsky was officially held to be a carry-over of trade-unionist thinking, appropriate to employer–worker relations under capitalism rather than to the conditions of a communist society, and the unions were made responsible for stimulating their members to reach production goals, organizing shock brigades and otherwise sustaining a high level of worker effort, discipline, competence and conformity to party policy and programme.

The ministries, trusts and enterprises constituted, necessarily, huge and complex bureaucracies. Major enterprises and trusts were comparable to the largest of the American or European corporations in size and complexity of structure; the ministries responsible for groups of trusts and enterprises were of course far larger. The immediate and continual problems of economic organization were thus the problems inherent in the structure and functioning of all bureaucracies.

Within the general framework of planning and direction each enterprise had a semi-independent status and identity. Although it was a government entity it operated under a separate charter, not unlike government corporations in non-communist countries. Its operations were expected to show at least the 'planned profit', except where an essential enterprise was planned to operate at a loss with the aid of a government subsidy. The enterprise's account at the State Bank, consisting of whatever capital funds were provided for it under the plan and a revolving fund for current operations, served as a device for financial recording and accounting. Relationships between enterprises were conducted as between independent buyers and sellers, within the physical limits set by the allocation of materials and the assigned quotas and goals, and with the wages, prices and turnover tax rates fixed by the control bodies. Each enterprise was required to achieve a financial as well as a physical balance and to meet its production goals within a framework set by fixed prices and wages and by the physical programme for related enterprises.

Up to the mid-1950s the primary instruments of planning were the physical goals and quotas; adjustments in prices were used to facilitate the realization of these physical objectives but were not in themselves the main means of controlling output. Wholesale prices for use between enterprises were set at a level calculated to encourage the production of needed commodities and to put pressure on enterprise managers to reduce costs. They were based on the costs which the planning agency considered reasonable, average or attainable for the entire industry, plus a planned profit. Sometimes they were set for regional segments of an industry where costs might differ, as for example between high and low-cost coal- or oil-producing areas. Managers of enterprises whose costs exceeded those calculated by the planners were thus under pressure to lower their costs.

Prices of some products were set below reasonable costs in order to stimulate other industries for which they constituted raw materials, as for example low prices set for metals and other materials essential to the machinery industry during the early 1930s, and reduction in the price of building materials in order to lower building costs in 1950. Where prices were held down for the benefit of other industries, losses were made up by government subsidy. When a broad revision of many industrial prices and freight rates was put through in 1949–50, the stated principles on which the new prices were based were: to enable enterprises, practically, to operate profitably according to plan and to avoid the need for subsidies; to stimulate output of deficit or especially necessary products and simultaneously limit their consumption in production; to discourage unnecessary transport, use rolling-stock efficiently, encourage water transport and enable railways to operate without loss.

(*f*) *Capital formation.* From the beginning the aim of the Soviet system was a self-contained economy independent of the capitalist world. The vast Russian territory with its rich natural resources provided the physical basis for such development, and high priority was immediately given to geological exploration and prospecting in order to discover the unexplored mineral wealth on which a major industrial development could be based. Until Russian heavy industry could be developed, however, much foreign equipment was needed in order to speed up the exploitation of these resources and to lay the basis for self-contained growth. The extremely rapid industrial development of the late 1920s and the 1930s was greatly facilitated by the use of equipment and techniques developed abroad.

Little foreign capital, however, was available to finance imports of mining machinery, electric generators and other equipment, although in the 1920s some foreign companies received concessions to operate mining or manufacturing concerns. A communist state dedicated to the elimination of private ownership in the means of production was hardly in a position to attract extensive foreign investment, even if it had wished to do so. Some foreign credits helped slightly to finance machinery imports, but these debts were liquidated by 1938. Most imports were purchased with the major product available for export, grain. In the early 1930s grain was also exported, even from famine areas, to purchase large numbers of tractors to provide the basis for collectivized agriculture and to replace the horses which had been slaughtered by peasants resisting collectivization.

In the absence of foreign sources the capital for industrial expansion came from the Russian people in the form of restraints on consumption. The major source was a turnover tax levied on all goods at the point where they changed hands. Roughly three-fifths of all the state revenue for financing both economic development and governmental administration was generally provided by this tax. The biggest part of this, amounting to more than two-thirds in 1939, was paid through the several ministries responsible for agriculture and food, and thus came largely from the peasants. It was reflected in the wide difference between the low prices paid to farmers for grain and the high prices charged to urban consumers for food. Most of the remainder was paid on other consumer goods. In addition to the turnover tax a share of the profits of each enterprise was allocated to the state investment fund. Some 10 per cent of the state budget came from this source and additional amounts from state loans and direct taxes on the population. These taxes and loans furnished the capital for industrial expansion.

Emphasis on fixed capital creation and the development of heavy industry and military resources set physical limits on the amount of goods available for consumption, as for example urban housing which remained in very short supply throughout these forty years, and other consumer goods which because of their low priority often fell below their production goals. Restraints on consumption offered a feasible method of securing the capital needed for expansion because they were accompanied by effective incentives and controls.

(g) *Incentives*.[13] The motivations relied upon for the operation of the Soviet economy were a combination of rewards and threats, of positive stimuli, both material and non-material, and of direct controls. The full impact of the state's instruments of propaganda was brought to bear to give prestige, emotional satisfaction and recognition to those who overfulfilled their quotas or otherwise demonstrated co-operation with economic objectives. Posters, wall newspapers, radio appeals and slogans exhorted the workers; publicly posted records permitted comparison and stimulated competition among them; public recognition through the awarding of prizes and titles of commendation, as well as the fundamental attitudes which the entire educational system was designed to build up, provided stimuli for the kind of effort required to keep the economy functioning and growing.

More tangible rewards took the form for managers of advancement through the bureaucratic hierarchy, and perquisites of office such as comfortable homes or cars in a society where these remained scarce. For workers they consisted in piece rates or other forms of incentive pay to stimulate and reward superior effort and to encourage workers to seek additional training in order to qualify for higher paid employment. A director's fund, consisting of a small percentage of planned profits and a larger proportion of profits over the planned amount, was set aside in each enterprise for extra expansion of plant and construction of workers' housing and for special bonuses or other recognition of outstanding workers. The increased pay and prestige received by the

Stakhanovites who exceeded production norms encouraged workers to increase their productivity.

Positive incentives, which played the main role in increasing the productivity of labour, were supplemented by a system of sanctions—demotion, transfer to an undesirable locality, or more severe penalties for those whose failure was judged to constitute sabotage—applied to negligent workers who violated decisions and orders of organs of the state. The security police were expected to detect this as well as all other forms of suspected disloyalty or failure to support the aims and objectives of the state. Direct restraints took the form of limitations on the right of workers to leave their employment, for which they required permission of the manager of the enterprise in the years 1940 to 1956. A large proportion of the youth were drafted into the labour reserve which was established in 1940, given technical training and assigned to specific industries and tasks. Other graduates from technical or other schools were placed in employment where they were needed, with little choice of where they would work. Finally, those who resisted the state provided a supply of forced labour for the most distasteful tasks in remote areas or under exceptionally harsh conditions.

In difficult situations the balance of motivations might lead to conduct which sometimes impeded the progress of the economy rather than promoted it. Some managers who felt themselves too much pressed and feared the consequence of failure to meet what seemed to them to be unrealistic objectives, might resort to hoarding of material or workers and other wasteful practices by which they sought to protect themselves against the danger of being unable to fulfil their quotas. Where some of an enterprise's products could be more profitably produced than others, managers were tempted to shift the proportion of production in favour of these, though the needs of the economy might call for a larger proportion of the less profitable items. There was a temptation to cut quality, especially on consumer goods which enjoyed a low priority and for which it was often difficult to secure the necessary materials. Examples of such practices were reported and discussed from time to time in the press. But the preponderance of evidence indicated that in the industrial sector the positive motivations which were invoked were successful in identifying the efforts of the great majority of the people with the requirements of rapid economic development.

In the agricultural sector the response was less satisfactory. Agricultural productivity was increased sufficiently to permit the recruitment from the rural areas of a large labour force for industrial expansion. Up to the mid-1950s, however, the expansion in agricultural production over the level of 1913 only slightly exceeded the increase in population. Agricultural production, especially livestock, received severe setbacks during wars and the period of collectivization. The problem of guiding and supervising many thousands of scattered units, even when organized as collectives, of providing the necessary incentives and of integrating the whole with the rest of the economy proved one of the most stubborn problems in the organization of the Soviet economy.

Various devices were adopted from time to time in the effort to meet this situation: peasants were allowed to cultivate personal plots in addition to participating in collective farm operations; selected urban workers were sent to collective farms to impart their drive and enthusiasm toward meeting goals. Major scientific efforts were made to expand production. Scientists developed strains of grain which would mature in colder areas with shorter growing seasons. Artificial insemination was extensively used to improve the quality of the livestock. Shelter belts of trees were planted to protect farms on the steppes from hot drying winds. Ambitious projects were launched to irrigate desert regions or to extend grazing areas by providing water for stock.

In spite of these efforts production data disclosed after the death of Stalin revealed a continued failure of agriculture to advance. New efforts to raise agricultural production were then launched by offering better rewards and increased responsibilities to collective farmers and by a vast programme to bring under cultivation virgin lands in the east. All these measures were designed to overcome the obstacles presented by the unfavourable Russian climate, and to raise the volume and efficiency of agricultural production to a point where it could offer an improved level of living to the people of the USSR and could continue to provide a supply of workers to the ever-growing industrial segment of the economy.

The centrally directed economy developed by the USSR demonstrated its strength and flexibility by its rapid industrial growth and its recuperative power following the tremendous losses during the second world war. The balance in the economy differed markedly however from that which characterized other countries which had undergone industrialization, including the deliberately industrialized economy of Japan. The direction of major resources into heavy industry and military equipment resulted in a much larger proportion of all economic activity in these sectors as compared with those producing consumer goods, and in a level of general consumption in most lines below that of countries with a similar *per capita* level of overall economic activity, though substantial resources were devoted to the provision of social services which supplemented private consumption.

It provided however a broad and strong basis for expansion of all sorts, as was evidenced in the late 1950s when the Soviet Union announced its intention of surpassing the advanced capitalist economies in the production of consumer goods. The output of food products was increased, together with many other items of consumption, and wages and pensions were raised, enabling workers to take advantage of these available supplies. At the same time the USSR expanded its export of capital goods to eastern Europe and China and to the newly developing countries of Asia and Africa.

With the exception of Yugoslavia which followed its own line of socialist experimentation, the Soviet economic structure provided the general pattern of economic organization for the countries of eastern Europe after 1945, and Soviet experience provided a guide for much of their economic activity.[14] Within a relatively short period, and with less need for experiment than the Soviet economy had experienced during the 1920s, these countries rapidly nationalized their industries and reduced the private area of trade and handicraft to an insignificant proportion of their total economy. Collectivization of agriculture was established as an objective. The nature and functions of trade unions were defined in terms which corresponded to their role in the USSR. Techniques of planning were introduced with the refinements which had been developed in the Soviet Union.

In contrast to the USSR, however, these east-European countries were not self-contained as the Soviet economy had been in very large measure from the start, but were linked among themselves and with the economy of the USSR. The areas which had been enemy territory during the second world war—East Germany, Hungary, Rumania, and to a lesser extent Bulgaria—paid substantial reparations in the years after the war in forms which assisted in the rebuilding of the Soviet economy and modified the productive capacity of the countries themselves. The Soviet government also took over German assets in these countries and directly operated the economic units which they represented. These enterprises, together with technical aid contracts, agency agreements and a growing number of joint enterprises in which the USSR became a part owner, linked the economies of the east European countries with the Russian. Joint planning was facilitated in specific fields by such bodies as the organization for railway co-operation. Imports and exports were governed by a series of trade agreements between each country and the USSR and among countries, especially Poland, Czechoslovakia and East Germany, which had formerly traded extensively with western Europe.

At the same time each country developed a national plan looking towards a high degree of self-sufficiency. During the first decade of their existence as communist states, two tendencies thus appeared, one to expand the economy of each country as a unit and the other to develop the combined communist area of Russia and eastern Europe as an interrelated whole.[15, 16]

The Yugoslav economy, after the break in 1948 between Yugoslavia and the USSR, developed along quite different lines and outside the interrelated structure of the economies of the USSR and her east European neighbours. Convinced that their form was truly 'socialist', the Yugoslavs based their economic design on social ownership of the means of production and control by those directly engaged in each productive enterprise.

In place of central operational planning, Yugoslavia used the central planning process only to allocate major investment funds between the central government, the governments of the constituent republics, and the pool of funds available to separate enterprises; to establish broad priorities and guidelines for the use of these funds; and to direct those segments of the economy, such as transport and utilities, which were under central government operation. Direct control over enterprises, which competed in domestic and international markets in much the same manner as capitalist firms, rested in the hands of workers' councils with powers similar to those of a corporate board of directors over production, prices, borrowing and disposal of earnings remaining after payment of taxes.

The socialist economy of Yugoslavia thus shared with other socialist economies social ownership of the means of production and a measure of economic planning, and with the capitalist economies a high degree of enterprise initiative, competition and the separation of ownership from control as in the large capitalist corporations. As such it offered an alternative system which was of interest to some of the newly developing countries as they sought economic forms appropriate to their situations and needs.

III. THE ECONOMIES OF THE NEWLY DEVELOPING COUNTRIES

In the years after the second world war economic development became a central objective of the countries emerging from colonial rule or semi-colonial status, and much of the thinking and activity of international bodies was couched in terms of the problems of assisting newly developing countries in their efforts to catch up.

The concept of economic development was not sharply defined but, as used for example by the International Bank for Reconstruction and Development, it meant an advance in national and *per capita* income, increased industrial and agricultural production and productive capacity, increased productivity of labour and a rising level of living for the people in the present or the future. Measures to promote economic development were adopted as people and governments became convinced that positive, constructive steps could hasten the process and as they feared that, without such efforts, levels of living would deteriorate in countries with low productivity and rapidly growing populations.

1. *The mixed economy of India and other non-communist countries*

In undertaking programmes of economic development, countries outside the communist-dominated areas devised a variety of mixed-economy systems in which free enterprise and central direction, private initiative and public responsibility, were variously combined. The mixed economy of India, which drew freely on the thinking and experience of both capitalist and communist countries, afforded a laboratory in which measures to achieve economic development under democratic guidance were being tested and worked out.

For 150 years the colonial economy of India had been shaped to the needs of Great Britain. This had meant the development of those economic activities which furnished raw materials for British industry, such as jute, cotton or indigo, or which supplied the British market with tropical products such as tea. It had meant that the flow of commerce, the transport system and the structure of trade and finance had been oriented toward the port cities. And it had meant the inclusion of the Indian economy within the free trade area and thus its exposure to the impact of European industrialism when machine-made goods entered the Indian market.

In these circumstances India had experienced the successive destruction of once flourishing handicrafts as European imports replaced many local urban industries that supplied the upper-class market. Even the village industries had suffered as imported kerosene replaced locally crushed oils, metal products competed with those locally forged and, above all, machine-spun yarn and machine-made cloth undercut the products of village spindles and looms. Even some of the new industries developed locally by Europeans had been destroyed in their turn, such as the extensive indigo production which collapsed with the development of chemical dyes in Europe at the end of the nineteenth century.

At the time of independence the Indian economy was predominantly agricultural. Roughly three-quarters of the labour force were engaged in agriculture and half the national income came from this source. Perhaps a third of the cultivated land was in large estates, raising commercial crops such as cotton, jute, tea, coconuts. The remainder, mostly in tiny holdings farmed by primitive methods, provided peasants with a bare subsistence, often at a level of permanent hunger. Throughout the period of British rule there had been a tendency to substitute commercial for subsistence crops whenever improvements in transport made it possible to send produce to market, in order to meet the taxes or rents required of the cultivators.

Yields for food crops were generally low, less than half those of Japan and for the staple food, rice, less than a third. Cultivation methods rather than poor soil were generally responsible but irregular rainfall was a major hazard outside the irrigated areas. If the monsoon failed the historic result had always been famine, against which the famine relief system developed by the British had provided only a partial defence. The death toll from the Bengal famine of 1943 amounted to some 1,500,000 lives. During the latter part of the nineteenth century the area of land under cultivation had been substantially expanded, helping to balance some of the depressing and dislocating effects of other economic developments. In the twentieth century, however, little expansion of cultivated land took place and there was a tendency toward subdivision into excessively small plots as a means of sustaining, at successively lower levels, the rural population for whom other outlets were not available.

The Indian agricultural village had, historically, been almost wholly self-sufficient, isolated by lack of roads and organized by a system in which the village craftsmen and the untouchables performed the functions needed by the village as hereditary obligations in exchange for subsistence provided in kind by the farmers whom they served. As factory-made goods gradually seeped into the village and farmers turned to cash crops, the hereditary system of mutual exchange was undermined, though it survived in part in less accessible areas. The village had also been self-governing, but under British administration village self-rule had broken down, as the judicial and revenue functions of the village councils (*panchayats*) were taken over by district judges and administrative officers.

Though the Indian economy was predominantly agricultural there had been substantial industrial development, particularly in the cotton textile and jute industries which employed three-quarters of the factory workers. Although the free trade policy had tended to push the Indian economy towards supplying raw materials rather than towards manufacture, and taxes on Indian-made cloth to prevent its competing with British were not abolished until 1926, the cotton textile industry had surpassed that of Britain by the time of the second world war and was second only to that of the United States. First developed by British firms, the industry had been expanded by Indian capital from the 1870s on. At the time of independence most of the mills were in Indian hands. The jute industry, composed of large mills employing an average of over 2,500 workers, remained in European hands until the establishment of the first Indian mill in 1921, but by independence nearly half the mills were Indian-owned. The nucleus of an iron and steel industry was present in the large steel works built by Indian capital from 1907 on, drawing on India's ample resources of iron ore and coal. Mining, however, especially coal, remained largely in the hands of British companies.

The labour supply consisted of a mass of rural people, distributed through more than a half-million villages, a large proportion underemployed by reason of the smallness of their holdings or the decline of their crafts. Except for agriculture in which all castes participated, both village and urban occupations were linked to caste and were hereditary, but factory and general labour in the urban areas was performed by people of various castes who sought escape from rural poverty in the industrial and service occupations of the city. Such workers came to the cities faster than jobs developed and much faster than housing was constructed. Urban unemployment became chronic, as was underemployment in the villages, and the pavement population of Indian cities mounted into the millions. Among Bombay's pavement dwellers many had jobs, as did those who camped beside roads or on vacant land under low improvised shelters of tin, cardboard or gunnybags, but many had neither jobs nor homes. After partition the number was augmented by millions of refugees.

Until about 1920 the population of India showed little increase. High birth rates were offset by high death rates and were cancelled periodically by famine and epidemic. Deaths numbering many millions from famine in the 1870s, famine and plague in the 1890s and the influenza epidemic of 1918 held the population down to its mid-nineteenth century level. Emigration of plantation labour within the British empire—to Fiji, Malaya, Ceylon, Burma, Africa and the West Indies—also had drawn off some workers, though not in very large numbers. After 1920, major epidemics and famine were brought under control, the changed political situation made large-scale emigration no longer even a minor alternative to unemployment, and the population increased more or less steadily at an annual rate of something over 1 per cent. Although this was not as high a rate of natural increase as that of many other economically underdeveloped areas in the second quarter of the twentieth century, an increase of some 4,000,000 a year was a substantial number for the Indian economy to absorb. In the decade after independence the rate rose to some 8,000,000.

Transport was provided by an extensive railway system, exceeded in mileage only by the railways of the United States, the USSR and Canada, with workshops capable of producing most of the rolling stock and keeping it in repair. Originally constructed and operated by private British companies whose profits were guaranteed by the British government of India, the railways were taken over and operated directly by the government after the 1920s. Railway lines and trunk roads, however, were designed for military purposes and foreign trade not for internal communication, and thus ran to the ports and frontiers rather than providing an interconnecting network throughout the country. Foreign and coastwise shipping travelled almost wholly in British bottoms, except that carried by sailing craft; the only Indian shipping enterprise was established after 1921.

Indian industry came to depend increasingly on Indian capital and Indian management in spite of the economic ties to Britain. The proportion of the factory workers in European-owned establishments dropped from a half to a third, from before the first world war to the eve of the second. Indian trade, moreover, became less and less concentrated on Britain. The percentage of India's imports coming from Britain dropped from a height of 80 per cent in the 1870s to 31 per cent on the eve of the second world war, in part as a result of the Indian nationalist movement to boycott British goods. Exports to Britain dropped from half to less than a quarter before 1932, when the proportion was raised somewhat under the Ottawa agreement which gave a preference to British empire products and which was applied to India over the opposition of the Indian legislative assembly.

The structure of economic organization was compounded of an Indian core and a superstructure of English institutions and practices. The Indian core was provided by the *banyas* or merchant castes, or by merchant communities such as the Marwaris, which carried on trade, banking and moneylending as an hereditary calling. Up to the time of independence, the principal Indian commercial and industrial enterprises which were not in the hands of Europeans were in the hands of these Hindu castes or of the non-Hindu Parsees.

British institutions and practices relating to trade, commerce, industry and banking were introduced into India with only a few adaptations required by local conditions. Except for personal law relating to family relationships and inheritance, which continued to follow Hindu and Muslim practices, British civil and commercial law and legal procedures were applied in their entirety. These recognized ownership in real estate and in tangible and intangible property, regulated contracts and defined agency and trust relationships. The joint-stock company with its concept of limited liability was superimposed on the Indian pattern of family enterprise. European firms in India operated on the joint-stock principle and Indians not only invested in them but formed joint-stock companies of their own.

Banking operations and currency control were well developed. Foreign trade was financed almost wholly through British-operated exchange banks. Four of the five large banks which together did about half the domestic banking business were Indian institutions. A reserve bank, established in 1935, exercised control over the lending operations of member banks, regulated the formation of new banks and exacted standards of banking safety from their member institutions. For more than a hundred years a single currency had been in use for commercial transactions throughout the many political divisions of the country.

The financial principles and legal system introduced by the British had strengthened the Indian class of merchants and moneylenders, who from pre-British times had conducted elaborate and large-scale financial operations. Enforceable contracts which carried the legal right to take possession of property to satisfy unpaid debts brought land into the hands of moneylenders when peasants defaulted on their mortgages. They contributed to the break-up of the joint family by enabling creditors to claim a portion of the joint estate in satisfaction of a debt incurred by a member of the family group.

A unique feature of the Indian economic structure was the managing agency system. In the days before rapid communication British companies had found it impossible to manage their Indian enterprises by long-distance from Britain, and had placed the management in the hands of agents who operated the companies for the owner, reserving a commission for themselves. At first the managing agencies were British firms, but during the twentieth century many Indian firms were formed, often on a family basis. Managing agencies, which frequently took on a number of concerns on a permanent or long-term basis, came to command great wealth and power and to provide much of the initiative for economic expansion. The system furnished a useful device for separating the functions of management from beneficial ownership, but such agencies could become powerful vested interests whose activity would not necessarily correspond with the interests of society.

The policy of the British government of India, in line with *laissez-faire* principles, had been non-intervention in economic affairs beyond the maintenance of a stable currency and other conditions favourable to trade. Not until 1921 was an Indian fiscal commission appointed which recommended a policy of protection to selected Indian industries. Approximately half of the government of India revenues went to the support of the Indian army, which served as the Asian arm of the British army. Although this army was supported by India, it was used outside the borders of India no less than nineteen times between 1838 and 1920. In addition to the army and the civil administration, public funds were used in the operation of railways, irrigation and communication systems and royal teak forests, in some hydroelectric schemes started after 1921 and for limited programmes of education and public health, mainly for the higher levels of education in urban areas, for the control of epidemics and for famine relief.

The government of India was little affected by the changes in economic and political thought that marked Britain's own transition to a welfare state. Indian leaders educated in Britain, however, became imbued with these ideas and sought to apply them to their emerging nation. The Indian National Congress attacked the policy of *laissez-faire* and called for positive measures to promote economic development. Impressed by the adoption of planning in the USSR, it created a planning commission under the chairmanship of Jawaharlal Nehru in 1937 to bring this approach into the preparations for the future Indian state.

The Indian government after independence faced the double economic task of reorienting a colonial economy to domestic needs and developing a more productive economy which could lift the Indian people from extreme poverty to a level of living closer to that of more prosperous and developed countries. It confronted these long-run needs while having to cope with emergency problems arising from partition, integration of the multitude of Indian states, and the threat of famine from floods and droughts during the first years of the régime.

The Indian constitution provided the democratic framework within which the processes of economic development were to be worked out, and set forth the economic objectives of the Indian state (Article 39):

> To ensure the right of the citizens, men and women equally, to an adequate means of livelihood; to ensure the distribution of ownership and control of material resources of the community as best to subserve the common good; and to prevent concentration of wealth and means of production to the common detriment.

The state thus took on positive responsibility for economic welfare, on the assumption that this responsibility could be carried out through democratic procedures.

Three years after independence the Indian government created a planning commission to give attention to the broad problems of economic development and the permanent structure of the Indian economy. The commission adopted the approach of setting up goals by means of successive five-year plans, the first covering the years 1951–56, the second designed for 1956–61. In the formulation of the plans the democratic principle of open discussion was fully applied. Divergent economic views were aired, alternative priorities proposed and differing judgments expressed as to how fast the economy could grow.

In the course of these discussions, objectives were clarified: to increase the real income of the people sufficiently rapidly to maintain stability in the society and to match popular demand; to achieve what the leaders termed a 'socialist pattern of society', which meant that extremes of wealth would be reduced, centres of private power would be eliminated or not allowed to develop, and the machinery of the state would be used for such economic purposes as might be appropriate in a democratic system; to seek balanced economic development, which should minimize the vulnerability of the economy to outside influences but not seek autarchy; and to provide for such defence expenditures as the political situation might require, with the assumption that in time these could be made less necessary.

India possessed ample resources of water power, minerals and soil to sustain a developed economy, though little of the water power had been harnessed, much of the mineral wealth was unexplored and much of the soil had been depleted by exhausting methods of cultivation. Its major problems lay elsewhere, in the realms of public attitudes, economic leadership and technical know-how.

The first necessary condition for economic development was the desire for change. In the days before the western impact, Indian society like other Asian societies had been essentially static; it assumed continuity as a central principle of life rather than change. The joint family was a static institution; its members came and went but the family itself remained. Hereditary status and relationships defined the destiny of each; religious ritual punctuated the cyclical events of life. Even the reformers of the nineteenth century had insisted that they were not calling for change but only for a restoration of a state from which society had strayed.

During the years of British rule the idea of change became part of the outlook and thought of the western-educated middle class. It was confined to the educated *élite*, however, until Mahatma Gandhi aroused the masses of the people with his call for the regeneration of Indian society and resistance to the British *raj*. But though his crusade loosened the hold of custom and raised the eyes of the villagers to new potentialities, its economic expression was couched in terms of a return to the spinning wheel. The first question which confronted the Indian leadership after independence was how extensively the acceptance of change could be aroused at the village level and canalized into productive effort.

The leadership itself, while imbued with the principle of change and eager for economic development, had little of the experience, training and habits which characterized the economic leadership in the West. Their western education had been overwhelmingly literary and theoretical rather than technical. They came predominantly from the Brahmin and other upper castes for whom money-making had not been an acceptable career. They had however engaged in management and administration. The problem of developing the necessary economic leadership thus involved modifying traditional attitudes toward economic enterprise among higher castes, or designing an economic structure which would use their managerial ability without requiring them to develop a profit-seeking or money-making motivation. The alternative was to continue to depend primarily on the Parsees, Marwaris and members of the former merchant castes to come forward with sufficient enterprise to create the momentum needed for the whole economy.

The lack of sufficient technically trained personnel reflected the fact that the British, while encouraging the highest literary and theoretical education for the Indian *élite*, had provided technical training chiefly for the lower ranks on the railways, irrigation projects, civil service and army, filling the higher posts with British personnel. While India was better off than areas such as Burma and Ceylon where virtually no technical training reached the local population, the number of technically trained Indians was far below the needs of a developing economy. There were outstanding mathematicians and physicists but limited numbers of trained and experienced engineers, except in the field of irrigation.

Emphasis on theoretical training, moreover, had associated prestige with intellectual as against practical activity, confirming the traditional attitude of the Indian upper castes in this respect, and it had offered a powerful impediment to the development of technicians who would not hesitate to soil their hands in the course of their jobs. In the traditionally status-conscious society of India, the problem of technical know-how was thus not only to train a sufficient number of technicians but so to modify the prestige structure as to overcome traditional negative attitudes toward all but intellectual work.

The first and second five-year plans provided guide-lines for government activity. They did not attempt to cover the entire economy. Since government in India was responsible for only some 8 per cent of the national income, in contrast to some 20 per cent in the United States and considerably more in a number of the capitalist countries of Europe, plans for government action were far from a comprehensive plan for the total of Indian economic activity. Rather, they were plans as to how government could use its instrumentalities to further economic objectives and stimulate growth in the private as well as in the public sector of the economy.

The government's instrumentalities were of five main sorts: its own operations in providing services such as education, constructing public works such as hydroelectric dams, operating enterprises such as railways, and developing basic industries such as shipbuilding, fertilizer production, machine tools, atomic energy; promotional activities, as in stimulating village efforts and reviving responsible village councils through a community development programme or encouraging hand-produced textiles by a special price subsidy; providing a legal framework for the activities of individuals through protection of property, labour legislation or such measures as the abolition of caste; direct restrictions on permitted activity, through licences for certain types of equipment or construction, prohibition of certain types of manufacture such as cloths reserved for hand-looms, or control of foreign exchange; and coercion, primarily through the use of the taxing power or, in some of the states, by the compulsory redistribution of land.

Execution of proposals contained in the plans was left to the appropriate department of government, co-ordinated through the cabinet under the prime minister and responsible to the Indian parliament. Planning thus became a means of co-ordinating and focusing the separate efforts of government agencies and the private efforts of individuals, both through promotion and regulation and by providing goals to which private as well as public agencies could aspire and efforts could be directed.

The first five-year plan focused primarily on agriculture, the basis of the Indian economy, with two major and related objectives, to stimulate the villages to pursue their own development and to improve agricultural techniques in order to provide a better economic base of village and national life. A large-scale community development programme reached 125,000 villages during the first five-year plan. It proved even more effective than had been expected in motivating villagers to accept change: once the interest and initiative of the villages were aroused, their demands for technical and other help in development projects threatened to outrun the ability of the government to make good its offers of aid. Helped by favourable monsoons the campaign for improved cultivation of rice stimulated a sufficient increase in agricultural production to reduce the need for food imports and thus to release foreign exchange for the purchase of steel and industrial equipment.

The first five-year plan also included measures to increase the production of chemical fertilizers and for hydroelectric flood control and irrigation projects designed to regulate the water supply and permit two or three crops on land yielding only one crop under the system of drought and monsoon. The programme thus looked toward the revitalizing of agriculture within the existing framework, with improved techniques, improved communication and irrigation where needed. It recognized the need for changes in landholding to overcome the evils of absentee landlordism and the fragmentation of land into too small plots, but left this matter to be worked out by the separate states, either through legislation or through the voluntary surrender of lands by large holders. The latter programme, initiated by a follower of Gandhi, Vinoba Bhave, resulted in the voluntary redistribution of a considerable amount of land in the 1950s, at first by dividing donated land among peasants, later by giving it to the village for co-operative cultivation.

The second five-year plan was more concerned with the development of industry than was the first. When it was published in tentative form, its stated purpose was 'rapid industrialization, with particular emphasis on the development of basic industries', but after a year of public discussion, the final plan made the development of industry only one part of a balanced programme 'to rebuild rural India, to lay the foundations of industrial progress, and to secure to the greatest extent feasible opportunities for weaker and underprivileged sections of our people and the balanced development of all parts of the country'. While the necessity and opportunity for the development of heavy industry was recognized, it did not dominate planning in these years.

The first two plans thus steered a middle course between two diametrically opposed views held by segments of the population. One group, basing its position on Gandhi's opposition to modern industry in the form experienced under British rule, wanted a policy of return to handicrafts and an effort to avoid industrialization. The opposite extreme was represented by those who saw in rapid industrialization the only hope for overcoming India's widespread poverty and proposed that every sacrifice be made toward that goal.

The counsel which prevailed in the first decade after independence followed neither of these lines, but sought both to strengthen the villages and to lay the foundation for industrialization. The second five-year plan expanded the community development programme, with the aim of reaching all 600,000 villages; it called for the enlargement of fertilizer, hydroelectric and irrigation projects and added two special schemes to strengthen the village and town economies. As a temporary measure, to fill the gap while the groundwork for industrialization was being laid, the hand-weaving of cloth was to be encouraged, and to a lesser extent the spinning of yarn. The objective was to provide employment to a large underemployed class of workers and to increase the supply of consumer goods without the necessity for capital investment to expand machine spinning and weaving. With a more permanent objective, small machine industries were to be promoted in villages and towns, either to produce for local consumption, or to make small articles for sale or as parts to be used in manufacture. The aim was to create a dispersed pattern of industrialization rather than to uproot people from their homes, in the hope of avoiding the creation of huge cities, such as Bombay, where industry had been concentrated in the past and where urban growth rapidly outstripped the ability of the municipality to cope with the housing and other needs of an expanding population.

At the same time the major increases in governmental expenditures called for by the second five-year plan were for industry and mining. While the total plan somewhat more than doubled the outlays included in the first plan, those for mining and industry were increased eightfold. Capital expenditure to enlarge the steel industry accounted for a large part.

The second five-year plan called for the expansion of the public sector of the economy beyond the public utilities to which government operations had been largely confined in the past. In so doing it began to define the respective roles of the public and private sectors and to shape a mixed economy that would aim toward a 'socialist pattern of society'. The policy of state operation of basic industries, such as mining, steel, atomic energy and machine tools, was adopted. Some of these were to be developed wholly by state enterprise and others through a combination of public and private enterprise, with the public sector assuming increased responsibility.

This policy reflected the thought that private industry would not expand with sufficient rapidity and, more importantly, that since these industries hold the key in industrialized societies, the concentration of economic power in private hands could best be avoided if government assumed responsibility in these crucial areas. The approach was a flexible one, however, and in the initial phase the steel industry was expanded under both private and public auspices. Where an important activity, such as shipping, was in the hands of powerful European companies, the government entered the field in the expectation that no private Indian enterprise would be strong enough to compete.

The problems of attitudes, economic leadership and technical adequacy remained central. Technical training was stepped up sharply, both through foreign study by large numbers of Indian students and through emphasis on facilities for technical training in the programme of educational expansion. In the meantime persons with special technical skills were brought from abroad for temporary jobs, either directly by the government or enterprises, or through the technical assistance programmes of international and national governmental agencies.

Motivation appeared less of a problem at the village level than many had assumed. But in the industrial sector there were problems of economic leadership. The merchant and industrial castes and communities which had furnished the private initiative in the past could be counted upon to continue to do so, and it would not be difficult to make conditions more favourable than they had been under British rule. But the Indian state wished neither to favour nor to depend upon any single group or groups. The agency system permitted a partial solution of this problem, if it could be prevented from creating vested interests, for it disassociated management from investment and enabled a wider group to participate in the management process. But one of the reasons for looking to public enterprise, and to co-operative organization in the private sector, was the opportunity which these forms of organization presented to use the talents of those whose traditional attitudes made them more likely to perform successfully as administrators or managers than as entrepreneurs.

Some outside observers thought that the ability of India to develop an expanding and vigorous economy would require the adoption of many attitudes associated with enterprise in the West. In the absence of the desire to take risks and invest for gain, the necessary drive would, they thought, not be generated. Others thought that motivations different from those to which the western world was accustomed might prove effective under conditions of Indian life, such as the desire to achieve non-material objectives, the motivation of disinterested service to society which was central to the Hindu revival and to which Gandhi gave great currency, or the readiness to follow a leadership which could inspire and show the way. In the initial stages the spirit of nationalism certainly played a role, as well as the sense of being on trial in competition with communist China to prove that economic development could be achieved by democratic means.

The most pressing problem was whether the Indian economy could achieve a rate of growth sufficiently rapid to keep ahead of population increase, to reduce unemployment, to improve the economic situation in villages and towns and prevent rural–urban migration from exceeding the expansion of opportunity in urban areas, and to maintain social stability in the face of the inevitable impatience engendered by high national hopes. The crux of this problem appeared to lie in the rate of investment which could be generated. The second five-year plan was presented to the public with a substantial gap between the expenditures called for and the visible means of securing the required funds. Loans or other financing from abroad were implied, and these proved essential in the event. But the principal need was for new sources of revenue at home. The government took over the life insurance companies and launched a campaign to encourage small savings. Even the full amount of the plan, however, called for a rate of investment below that of most developed countries. But this was more than the Indian economy had sustained in the past.

The crucial question was whether a country of low *per capita* income such as India, which had renounced the centralized methods and coercive techniques of the communist states, could engender through democratic means the level of investment needed for economic growth.[17]

Other countries of Asia, Africa and Latin America which faced the problems of economic development also sought to meet them with mixed economies in which state effort and private enterprise both played a part. The patterns which were evolving at mid-century differed in different regions and countries and were affected by many factors—by the balance of resources and population, the economic history and structure of the country and the orientation of the government. The problems of economic development in the oil-rich kingdoms of the Middle East were very different from those of the crowded valley of the Nile, or from the rice economy of Thailand, or the countries on the high plateau of the Andes. Countries which had experienced colonial exploitation from abroad, as in much of Asia and Africa, were in a different situation from those whose economy was mainly dominated by a local wealthy class, as in much of Latin America, or which had experienced a social revolution, as in Mexico. In some, land was held in *latifundia*, in others by peasant proprietors. Yet in one way or another virtually every underdeveloped country sought to use the conscious intervention of government to accelerate economic growth, and the economic institutions which it developed combined features of different economic systems.

These countries attempted to use the technique of economic planning in some way. In Latin American countries, where the tradition of private enterprise was strong, programmes of economic planning were at first limited to special projects for valley development such as the valley of the Cauca in

Colombia, or for agricultural improvement, or for foreign credits and control of international trade. Most Asian countries adopted some variant of the five-year plan. Some, such as Burma, formulated elaborate goals although effective means of working toward the goals remained to be developed. Others, such as Iraq, concentrated on plans for major public works, such as dams and irrigation projects, and the investment of government revenues which were already in sight. The planning mechanism devised by the commonwealth of Puerto Rico used a continuous process of replanning each year for the next six years ahead, instead of setting a five-year goal and then starting a new plan for the next five-year period. It also sought to combine central planning with local initiative by reserving a portion of the public funds covered by the plan for allocation in response to local interest and effort, rather than according to established priorities.

These countries in greater or less degree included social measures as part of their economic plans. Some, such as Puerto Rico, started with planning for physical construction and gradually included planning for social services as well. Others, like India, included social components from the start. Opinions differed widely as to the proper relationship between expenditures to promote social well-being and those which were more strictly economic in intent. In one view, social expenditures competed with economic and were a luxury which could only be afforded when the economic base had been expanded and national income increased. An alternative view insisted that expenditures for such things as health and education were sound economic investments, for they increased the productivity of the population and removed the costly burdens of dependency, ineffectiveness and early death. Where they resulted in an increase in the population more rapid than the rate of economic expansion, however, they could threaten to cancel out the gains, unless they helped to lay the basis for a future spurt in economic growth.

The conscious effort to accelerate economic development on the part of countries containing a large proportion of the world's people was unique in the history of the world. So too was the technological and political situation within which these efforts were being made. A leading international economist, Gunnar Myrdal of Sweden, reviewing the situation in 1956, concluded that the developing countries should not assume that the economic thinking formulated in the older industrialized countries necessarily had relevance for them. In the light of the new situation of the mid-twentieth century the process of industrialization might bring very different experiences from those which the previously developed countries had known.*

2. The socialist economy of the Chinese People's Republic

While India and most other formerly colonial or industrially underdeveloped countries were pursuing their goal of economic development by means

* Gunnar Myrdal, *An International Economy: Problems and Prospects* (New York, 1956), p. 313.

of mixed economies which retained much of the framework of their existing society, the Chinese People's Republic launched the most drastic movement for industrialization undertaken by any country at any time, by means of a total transformation of Chinese society.

When the communist régime came to power in 1949, the Chinese economy was not only largely undeveloped industrially, with much of what existed in foreign hands or oriented to foreign treaty ports or foreign-concession railways; it was in a state of chaos and disruption as the result of decades of civil wars and Japanese invasion and of the patterns of corruption which had come to operate all along the line under these conditions. In 1949 agricultural production was only about 75 per cent of what it had been during the 1930s, light industry about two-thirds and heavy industry only 30 per cent of former levels.

The Chinese economy was basically agricultural, producing primarily for subsistence, although the principal exports, such as tea and silk, were agricultural products. It provided a bare subsistence to the peasant population; rice and other food grains were imported into most areas, few districts raised a surplus, and famine threatened constantly and occurred periodically. Yet traditional Chinese agricultural techniques were highly developed. Chinese rice yields per acre were double those of India, but only two-thirds as great as the Japanese.

Such industry as existed was mainly light industry, chiefly textiles; only the beginnings of steel and related heavy industry had been made by the Japanese in Manchuria. The natural resources of the country remained largely unexplored. They were presumed to be adequate for a substantial industrial development, but the question remained largely speculative until after 1949. Inadequate transport facilities presented a serious obstacle to economic development. Goods were mainly shipped by water via rivers and canals, but river flows were uncontrolled, floods were periodic and many of the canals had fallen into disrepair. There was no general network of railways, only a few small systems leading to principal ports in the east. Roads were even less adequate, such as existed being mainly unpaved.

The reconstruction of the Chinese economy was carried out by means of the intensive utilization of China's major resource, her great manpower which had been only very partially employed under previous conditions. The labour of peasants in off seasons and of those who could be released by a more rational organization of agricultural production, the labour of women, the labour which could be made available by substituting other means of transport for the carrying pole, even the labour of children who could be mobilized for communal tasks and of older women who could release the more able-bodied by caring for children—these were the major resources which the communist leadership undertook to organize into an effective instrument for remaking the Chinese economy.

In organizing these resources for an effort designed to industrialize the country with unprecedented speed, the Chinese leadership undertook to apply Marxist–Leninist principles with pragmatic flexibility, in the light of Chinese conditions, and to make the most of the prior experience of other countries. In particular China drew upon the experience of the USSR in developing techniques of planning and of large-scale operations, as well as on some of the experience of Japan in achieving economic expansion with a minimum of capital. It carried on its massive reconstruction in an atmosphere of intense nationalism and patriotism, as the nation threw off a century of weakness and humiliation at the hands of western and Japanese imperialism, and it thus had available an emotional resource of great magnitude to focus common effort and maintain the feverish pace set by those in command.

In its first three years, the communist régime restored the chaotic and shattered Chinese economy to productive levels well above those which had been achieved in the past. It organized the country administratively under effective centralized direction and control and rooted out the graft and corruption that had debilitated economic life. It reoriented the economy in its foreign relations toward the Soviet Union and the rest of the communist bloc.

Thereafter it used the technique of formulating five-year plans with ambitious targets which were repeatedly revised upward, as stimuli to bursts of national effort brought overfulfilment at earlier dates. In 1956 it projected a twelve-year plan for agrarian development, comprising agricultural production, industrialization of the countryside and improvement in the farmers' way of life, to be financed principally from local sources and to be carried out side by side with the centrally financed five-year plans.

Developments were in two main areas, the transformation of the agricultural economy upon which some 80 per cent of the people depended and the creation of a base for industrial development, in heavy industry, transport, mining and the construction of physical plant and machinery.

The transformation of Chinese agriculture in the first decade was the most crucial element in the change-over, and both the drastic nature and the relative smoothness of the process made the experience of China unique. Mao Tse-tung had made the peasantry the core of the revolution, not merely one of its supporters, and he had promised them land. First in the north-west area during the war and then in the country as a whole, land was distributed to the poor peasants with small holdings or none who made up 70 per cent of the peasant population. Party cadres and committees in each village classified the peasants and assigned the available land, with a minimum of resistance from the landlords and rich peasants and with the support of the middle peasants who were generally undisturbed in their holdings.

No sooner had the land been distributed, however, than a campaign was launched to encourage the voluntary formation of co-operatives among the peasants whose holdings were small and generally scattered. By 1953 some 40 per cent of the peasants had already become members of agricultural co-operatives or mutual aid teams. The next step was to convert these co-operative associations into collective farms similar to those of the USSR with common operation and common administration. In marked contrast to the USSR and eastern Europe, Chinese peasants showed little resistance to the rapid liquidation of private ownership in land. By 1957 Chinese agriculture was almost completely collectivized.

At this point, the Chinese leadership took a further jump which carried the process of collectivization beyond that which the USSR or any other social-ized state had attempted, the conversion of groups of villages and collective farms into communes. Again reorganization of the rural economy proceeded with fantastic speed. In a matter of months whole provinces reported the communalization of their rural society, with administrative centralization, common eating halls, work brigades and the direct provision by the commune of the necessities of life for the members. After the initial rush to establish communes during 1958 there was a momentary period of relaxation; some individual cultivation of garden plots and sale of produce from them was permitted, and use of eating halls, nurseries and other collective facilities was made voluntary but strongly encouraged. The basis had been laid, however, for a fully communalized rural society and for the management of rural pro-duction in a manner which permitted the maximum organization of the labour force for work in the commune, for the assignment of task forces to large-scale construction projects elsewhere, or for removal of groups to settle new lands, extend rail lines or develop industrial, mining or oil centres.

Thus in ten short years the ancient peasant economy of China was converted into a highly organized structure. The aim was to raise production, not only to reduce the threat of famine, but to provide the exports with which to purchase machinery and equipment abroad while the foundations for domestic machinery production were being laid. This transformation, in contrast to the Russian, was accomplished virtually without mechanization. Improved ploughs and other simple equipment were distributed to some communes and collectivation permitted the fuller use of the available animal power to replace some manual labour. But the very substantial increases in agricultural pro-duction achieved during these years did not result from the establishment of tractor stations or any other form of mechanization. The main factors, in addition to the better organization of production on larger units instead of fragmented plots and the opening of some new lands, came from the same sources as those which Japan had found effective—seed selection, irrigation and more intensive measures for pest control and fertilization.

The industrial and commercial segments of the economy, like the agri-cultural, were converted from private to state enterprise gradually but rapidly, and with a minimum of resistance. Large-scale industry and trade had been mainly in the hands of Japanese and other foreigners or of the ruling clique of the Kuomintang and was readily taken over. The smaller factory-owners, handicraftsmen and merchants were offered inducements and persuasion to join co-operatives or to turn their businesses over to the government in return for a fixed payment on their investment. As it became increasingly difficult and unprofitable to operate independently, most entrepreneurs found it advisable to turn over their business to the state, often themselves staying on as managers. Here too the process of socialization was completed within a short period and without substantial resistance.

Thus, although in the initial stages it appeared that China might be evolving an economy that would retain some individualistic and capitalistic features, this apparent conservatism was in fact a means to a more rapid and complete socialization, centralization and communalization than any other country had hitherto attempted.

Restoration, extension and improvement of the transport system was the first essential for industrial development, as well as for national unification and administration. Millions of workers, mainly peasants in slack periods, but also some urban workers, intellectuals and soldiers, tackled the tremendous tasks of restoring the old canal and irrigation systems, constructing new waterways, rebuilding and extending the inadequate railways, laying out and surfacing a road system, and beginning the long process of damming and taming China's great, fierce rivers. Again the major resource was manpower, organized to function under central direction. Although earth-moving and other equipment from the USSR and east Europe was used on some of the projects, men and women with shovels and baskets dug most of the canals, laid up the dikes and roadways, levelled and ballasted the railway tracks and worked on the dams.

In line with the objective of laying the basis for industrial expansion, main energies were directed toward the build-up of heavy industry and of the electricity and fuel resources on which such industry depends. Coal mining was expanded rapidly, oil resources in Kansu and Sinkiang were probed and then exploited with the construction of more than a thousand miles of railway and the recruiting of hundreds of thousands of workers for this new frontier. The Anshan area became the centre of a rapidly expanding iron and steel complex. When in 1958 steel working capacity ran ahead of iron supplies, a nation-wide campaign to melt down scrap in backyard furnaces, and in some areas to dig and smelt local ore, made it possible to maintain the breakneck pace of expansion and gave people throughout the country the sense of participating in laying the industrial foundations of the new China.

Although most technology was pre-industrial at the time of the communist take-over, and much of it remained so during the first decade of development, the leadership was determined to place China as rapidly as possible in the front ranks scientifically, and to take full advantage of the scientific developments which had been made throughout the world. Very highly qualified Chinese scientists who had been trained in Europe, the US and the USSR, although relatively few in number, formed a nucleus which was supplemented by several thousand scientific and technical advisers from Russia, by Chinese sent to Moscow for training, and then by the graduates of the technical and research centres established in the country. Although at one end of the scale the campaign for technical improvement took such elementary forms as substituting the wheelbarrow or bullock cart for the carrying pole, at the other end it involved an atomic reactor, and Chinese factories were turning out jet planes.

The stated goal of national efforts was to make China a great industrial nation, moving immediately into the front ranks in scientific development and achievement, surpassing other industrial countries as rapidly as possible, starting with Britain and reaching ultimately a level of production commensurate with China's immense population and large resources.

The results of these efforts, measured in terms of production, were noteworthy. With due allowances for over-optimism and inaccuracies in reporting, including a substantial downward revision in the figures previously announced by the régime in 1959, the rate of economic expansion achieved in the course of ten years exceeded that of other countries in comparable stages of industrial development—Britain in the early nineteenth century, the United States, Germany and Japan in the late nineteenth century, the USSR after the October revolution. It substantially exceeded the rate of economic growth achieved by India or any of the other newly developing Asian countries during these same years.

In terms of consumption, the increases in production were not reflected in levels of living, for they were devoted to laying the basis for expansion in heavy industry rather than to the satisfaction of consumer wants. The extension of education and health services, the improvement in sanitary conditions and in facilities for child care, and greater probability that a minimum of food would be available for the many who had lived under the recurrent threat of starvation must be reckoned as net additions to living standards. But the great efforts called forth from the people during these years were for the sake of the future, not for material benefits in the present.

The Chinese economy was operated under central direction. Ministries, with their provincial and local subdivisions, were responsible for their respective segments of the economy. The party structure, with its cadres at every level, provided the direct stimulus for carrying out plans and directives and for reporting results. The methods of planning, administration and party control which had been tested in the USSR were put into operation. Radio communication provided a means of reaching and mobilizing the entire country immediately with each new phase of the programme and each new appeal for common action, a resource which the Soviet Union had not had at its disposal to the same degree in the early stages of its organization and development.

No aspect of Chinese life remained unaffected by the organization of the Chinese people into a vast instrument of production which could be focused at will on national objectives. Old institutions were discarded and new ones created; the authority of the family was replaced by that of the Party; women's subordination was replaced by equality of status and work outside the home, with institutional provision of meals and child care to relieve the women of former responsibilities; young people were raised to positions of trust and authority; age-old social distinctions were eroded by requiring intellectuals to do manual labour.

The skilful leaders of the Party and the state during these years followed a policy of using persuasion and stimulus to achieve results with as little resort to direct coercion as possible. Alternately heightening the pressures for achievement and relaxing them when they appeared to be creating too great a strain or to have served their purpose—as in the prescription that all should have eight hours of sleep when pressures to achieve new production goals appeared to be producing fatigue—or relaxing controls only to tighten them again, as when the 'hundred flowers' period during which criticism was encouraged was followed by stern measures against those who had gone too far, choosing successive slogans, such as the 'great leap forward', to focus the people's mind and spirit, and offering an outlet for pent-up animosities in hatred of 'western imperialists', especially the United States, they kept up the momentum during these years. But whatever devices were used to arouse public co-operation, to mobilize and canalize the latent vitality of the people and to make the Chinese economy function with increasing productiveness, the structure of control was complete. Nowhere in the world was there so thorough a regimentation of the life of a whole people potentially in the institutional structure developed during this decade, and actually in the daily routines of communal life.

NOTES TO CHAPTER XXI

1. Professor A. A. Zvorikine points out that international comparison of economic indicators is as complex a matter as it is important. The differences in the national statistical methods used make it difficult to compare such general indicators as national wealth, product, and income, etc., which give a highly compressed notion of the countries compared. If such indicators are to be compared properly, their economic basis has to be closely investigated, and special methods of comparison elaborated. In the Soviet Union, considerable methodological work is being done on this problem, and numerous calculations are being made on comparative data for a large number of basic economic and cultural indicators of socialist and capitalist countries. Some of the results of this work can be found in such publications as 'The Scientific Conference on the Methodology of Comparing Basic Economic Indicators in the USSR and the USA', *Vyestnik statistiki* (1963), No. 6, pp. 29–73; 'Statistical Law Patterns. Indexing Methods of Analysis. International Comparison of Statistical Indicators', *Uchonie zapiski po statistiki*, USSR Academy of Sciences, Department of Economic Sciences (Moscow, 1963).

    Significant errors are made in American statistics in defining the indicators for the distribution of the national income, particularly in respect of the share distributed among the workers. The comparison of the living standards of the workers cannot be confined to wages alone: it must take into account pensions, benefits, allowances, free education and medical treatment, the length of paid holidays, and other advantages and payments from public funds; the existence or absence of unemployment, the life-span, birth and death rates, the population growth, the spending pattern of the workers, and other such factors.

One or other statistical method is capable either of disclosing a long list of phenomena, or of presenting a distorted picture. This explains why statistical centres of the government and of business and trade unions in capitalist countries, while often working parallel and selecting data on the same problem, arrive at quite different conclusions. In the United States, for instance, the cost of living in the period from 1939 to 1961, according to the official Labour Bureau statistics, rose by 115·2 per cent, while the figure of the Heller Commission (University of California) for the budgets of working families was 210·4 per cent, and the index produced by the methods of the electricians' union gave 239·4 per cent (see, A. I. Katz, *Polozheniye proletariata S.Sh.A. pri imperialismye* [Moscow, 1962], p. 197).

The use of an indicator such as the average income per head of the population in capitalist countries in which the incomes of workers and employers are mixed, gives a false impression as to the prosperity of the mass, whereas the distribution of families according to the level of the annual income reveals the true material situation of the classes and social groups.

A comparison of the distribution of the mass of personal income among families and single people in the United States for almost half a century gives the following results:

NUMBER OF FAMILIES AND INDIVIDUALS WITH THE LOWEST INCOMES, EXPRESSED AS PERCENTAGES OF ALL PERSONAL INCOMES EARNED IN THE USA in 1910–1959

Families and Individuals with the Lowest Incomes

Year	less than 10%	10–20%	20–30%	30–40%	40–50%	50–60%	less than 40%	less than 60%
	Figures supplied by the National Industrial Conference Board							
1910	3·4	4·9	5·5	6·0	7·0	8·0	19·8	34·8
1918	2·4	4·4	5·7	6·9	7·2	7·7	19·4	34·3
1921	2·0	3·2	4·6	5·9	6·5	7·4	15·7	29·6
1929	1·8	3·6	4·6	5·5	6·5	7·9	15·5	29·9
1934	2·1	3·8	5·3	6·2	7·3	8·2	17·4	32·9
1937	1·0	2·6	4·4	6·0	7·2	8·5	14·0	29·7
	Figures based on a selective survey carried out by the Federal Reserve System							
1947	1·0	3·0	4·0	6·0	7·0	9·0	14·0	30·0
1950	1·0	3·0	5·0	6·0	8·0	9·0	15·0	32·0
1953	1·0	3·0	5·0	6·0	8·0	9·0	15·0	32·0
1956	1·0	3·0	5·0	6·0	8·0	9·0	15·0	32·0
1957	1·0	3·0	4·0	6·0	8·0	9·0	14·0	31·0
1958	1·0	3·0	5·0	6·0	8·0	9·0	15·0	32·0
	Department of Commerce figures							
1944	4·9*	10·9*			16·2*		15·8	32·0
1947	5·0	11·0			16·0		16·0	32·0
1950	4·8	10·9			16·1		15·7	31·8
1953	4·9	11·3			16·6		16·2	32·8
1956	4·8	11·3			16·3		16·1	32·4
1957	4·7	11·1			16·3		15·8	32·1
1958	4·6	10·9			16·2		15·5	31·7
1959	4·5	10·9			16·2		15·4	31·6

* Data for groups including 20 per cent families and individuals.

Source: A. I. Katz, *Polozheniye proletariata S.Sh.A. pri imperialismye* (Moscow, 1962), p. 108; National Industrial Conference Board (NICB), *Enterprise and Social Progress* (New York, 1939), p. 125; Federal Reserve *Bulletin*, 'us Income and Output' (1958), p. 161; and *Survey of Current Business* (July, 1961).

In the tables there are three groups of data which differ not only in respect of the criteria used in determining the incomes, but also in respect of the nature of the statistical material used as a basis for them. The summary series from 1910 to 1937 was compiled at different times by a number of authors using different methods, chiefly based on data for a given period, on wages distribution and fiscal statistics. The results (from 1910, see W. King, *The Wealth and Income of the People of the United States* [New York, 1923]; from 1918, F. Macauley, *Income in the United States* [New York, 1923]; from 1921–29, M. Leven, H. Moulton, and C. Warburton, *America's Capacity to Consume* [Washington, 1934]; and from 1934–37, the National Industrial Conference Board) are compared in varying degrees with the work of the National Industrial Conference Board, which is the scientific organization of the National Association of Industrialists. The data of the Federal Reserve System present the results of an annual selective survey, while the material of the Department of Commerce is made up of the totals of the synthetic calculations, based partly on information from fiscal statistics and correlated with summary calculations for the national income. However, in spite of the overall differences, the data on the distribution of the mass of personal income between groups of families and individuals with the lowest incomes, display on the whole a striking resemblance in respect of the scale and constancy of the trend, which is better than a mutual check. The approximate conclusion is that the share of 40 per cent of families and individuals with the lowest incomes in the general mass of personal income, fell from 19·8 per cent in 1910 to 15·5 per in 1929 and 14 per cent in 1937, and was then 14 to 16 per cent in the period from 1947 to 1959. The share of 60 per cent of the families and individuals with the lowest incomes accordingly dropped from 34·8 to 29·9 and 29·7 per cent, and was equal to 31–32 per cent in the period from 1947 to 1959. With regard to the lowest paid 10 per cent of families and individuals, their share in the overall mass of personal incomes fell catastrophically from 3·4 per cent in 1910 to 1 per cent in the 1950's, while the share of the next 10 per cent fell from 4·9 per cent to 3 per cent in the same period.

Without needing any other comment, these figures demonstrate the significant deepening of the chasm between the incomes of the rich and the poor in capitalist America in the last fifty years, the process of relative impoverishment to a great extent affecting precisely the most impoverished sectors of the proletarian population.

Cf. also notes 5 and 13 *infra*, by A. A. Zvorikine.

2. *The Author-Editors have included few comparative economic statistics in the text because of the difficulty of making meaningful comparisons. The United Nations have assembled some comparative figures for recent years (see Author-Editors' supplementary notes 3 to Chapter III and 2 to Chapter IX), but they point to the differences in the bases for the national figures and urge caution in the use of the tables.*

Different results will be obtained from the choice of different indicators. A comparison of trends in agricultural production and productivity in the U S A and the U S S R, for example, yields quite different results from the corresponding industrial comparisons. Industrial comparisons will vary according to the indicator, e.g., value added by manufacture, persons engaged, man-hours worked, and agricultural comparisons will vary according to product, or productivity per hectare or per worker or per man-hour. The period chosen for comparison also greatly affects the results. For a general discussion of the problems of Soviet–United States economic comparisons, the reader is referred to: Joint Economic Committee of the Congress of the United States, Comparisons of the United States and Soviet Economies *(Washington, D.C., 1959), Part I, pp. 1–30, and illustrations of these difficulties throughout the studies in this publication.*

Unemployment data are misleading when they do not take into account hidden unemployment in the form of excess numbers of workers on the land or large numbers of persons engaged in petty trade on too small a scale to yield an adequate income. Comparative wage data are affected by the presence of supplementary benefits. Countries in different stages of economic development show differing patterns, notably where major effort is directed toward laying an industrial base through the development of heavy industry, electrification, etc., as compared to those where greater emphasis is placed on consumer goods and services. Relative rates of growth will be affected by the relative size of the base from which growth is calculated. Fiscal data will reflect differences in the extent of government participation in economic life and the proportion of the gross national product which involves the government. Countries use different categories in their economic statistics or include different elements in similarly named categories, and apply different statistical procedures.

The following data are added to give a more complete picture of the economy of the United States. These data are internally consistent, but their use for comparative purposes, like the use of data relating to other countries, should be guided by awareness of the complicating factors listed above. See also the Author-Editors' supplementary Note 3 to Chapter III for data on occupations, income distribution, and earnings of industrial and professional workers, and Note 7 below for data on labour productivity, earnings, and hours of work.

NATIONAL PRODUCTION AND PERSONAL INCOME IN THE UNITED STATES

	Gross National Product		Per Capita Disposable Income (1)			
	Current dollars (1000 millions)	Constant dollars (1963)	Current dollars	Constant dollars (1963)	Index of Industrial Production (1957–59=100)	Index of Agricultural Production (1957–59=100)
1929	104·4	214·2	682	1254	38·4	62
1930	91·1	194·6	604	1162	32·0	61
1931	76·3	180·3	514	1110	26·5	66
1932	58·5	153·8	390	953	20·7	64
1933	56·0	149·9	364	923	24·4	59
1934	65·0	164·2	411	979	26·6	51
1935	72·5	179·8	458	1067	30·7	61
1936	82·7	204·9	516	1193	36·3	55
1937	90·8	215·6	551	1224	39·7	69
1938	85·2	206·3	506	1152	31·4	67
1939	91·1	223·2	537	1235	38·3	68
1940	100·6	242·0	576	1309	43·9	70
1941	125·8	281·8	697	1483	56·4	73
1942	159·1	323·2	871	1659	69·3	82
1943	192·5	364·4	976	1704	82·9	80
1944	211·4	391·1	1061	1756	81·7	83
1945	213·6	383·1	1075	1717	70·5	81
1946	210·7	332·0	1136	1680	59·5	84
1947	234·3	331·3	1180	1578	65·7	81
1948	259·4	344·4	1291	1632	68·4	88
1949	258·1	345·5	1272	1622	64·7	87
1950	284·6	374·0	1369	1720	74·9	86
1951	329·0	404·9	1475	1737	81·3	89
1952	347·0	420·8	1521	1756	84·3	92
1953	365·4	440·1	1582	1806	91·3	93
1954	363·1	431·4	1582	1790	85·8	93
1955	397·5	464·9	1660	1870	96·6	96
1956	419·2	474·7	1741	1928	99·9	97
1957	442·8	483·9	1803	1941	100·7	95
1958	444·5	476·7	1825	1928	93·7	102
1959	482·7	508·4	1904	1987	105·6	103
1960	502·6	521·3	1937	1993	108·7	106
1961	518·2	531·2	1983	2028	109·8	107
1962	554·9	563·6	2060	2087	118·3	108
1963	585·0	585·0	2127	2127	124·3	112

Source: Economic Report of the President, *1964,* and Board of Governors of the Federal Reserve System.

(1) *Income received by individuals after taxes.*

DISTRIBUTION OF INCOME PRODUCED BY AMERICAN CORPORATIONS

(in 1000 millions of dollars)

| | | Income Produced by Corporations | | Distribution of Corporate-produced Income after Corporate Taxes | | | | | |
| | | | | to Labour | | | to Capital | | |
	Total	Corporate Taxes	Income After Taxes	Wages and Salaries	Supple-ments	Percent to Labour	Interest	Profits	Percent to Capital
1947	104·7	11·3	93·4	77·3	3·9	86·9	0·6	11·6	13·1
1948	120·4	12·5	107·9	85·9	4·1	83·4	·3	17·5	16·6
1949	115·5	10·4	105·1	83·4	4·4	83·5	·4	17·0	16·5
1950	132·3	17·9	114·4	91·7	5·7	85·1	·2	16·8	14·9
1951	153·3	22·4	130·9	106·2	7·1	86·5	·3	17·3	13·5
1952	158·5	19·5	139·0	114·1	7·5	87·5	·3	17·1	12·5
1953	169·0	20·2	148·8	124·2	8·2	89·0	·4	16·0	11·0
1954	163·3	17·2	146·1	121·9	8·5	89·2	·5	15·1	10·8
1955	184·2	21·8	162·4	132·5	9·7	87·5	·5	19·8	12·5
1956	195·2	21·2	174·0	143·8	10·9	88·9	·3	19·0	11·1
1957	202·9	20·9	182·0	150·6	12·2	89·4	·4	18·8	10·6
1958	195·8	18·6	177·2	147·4	12·1	90·0	1·0	16·8	10·0
1959	220·8	23·2	197·6	160·4	14·1	88·3	·9	22·2	11·7
1960	227·4	22·3	205·1	167·5	15·6	89·2	·6	21·4	10·8
1961	230·0	22·0	208·0	169·7	16·0	89·2	·9	21·3	10·8

Source: *U.S. Department of Commerce,* Survey of Current Business, *November 1962, and* Economic Report of the President, *1964.*

ECONOMIC CHARACTERISTICS OF UNITED STATES AGRICULTURE

| | Farm Population as per cent of total Population | Index of Farm Output (1947–49= 100) | Index of Farm Output per Man-hour (1947–49= 100) (1) | Tenure of Farm Operators (per cent) | | | | Level of Living Index of Farm Operator Families (1945= 100) (2) |
				Full Owner	Part Owner	Manager	Tenant	
1900	39·3	56	—	55·8	8·0	1·0	35·2	—
1905	—	—	—	—	—	—	—	—
1910	34·9	61	45	52·8	9·3	·9	37·0	—
1915	32·4	68	49	—	—	—	—	—
1920	30·1	70	49	52·2	8·7	1·0	38·1	—
1925	27·0	70	49	—	—	—	—	—
1930	24·9	72	53	46·3	10·5	·9	42·3	—
1935	25·3	72	57	—	—	—	—	—
1940	23·2	83	67	50·5	10·2	·6	38·7	79
1945	18·1	96	84	56·3	11·3	·7	31·7	100
1950	16·6	100	112	57·5	15·3	·4	26·8 (3)	122
1955	13·6	112	149	57·4	18·2	·4	24·0 (4)	143
1960	11·4	129	205	57·1	21·9	·5	20·5	—

Source: *U.S. Department of Commerce,* Historical Statistics of the United States *and* Statistical Abstract of the United States, *1961; U.S. Census Technical Paper, No. 3, Farm Population, 1880–1950.*

(1) These figures differ somewhat from those given in Note 7, below, 'Labour Productivity',

by reason of slight differences in the composition and weighting of the indexes by the reporting agencies.

(2) Index based on per cent of farms with electricity, telephones, and automobiles, and average value of products sold or traded. Figure for 1955 is average of 1954 and 1956. In 1956, the percentage of farm families having the following was:

	per cent
Electricity	94
Telephone	52
Automobile	74
Running water	64
Mechanical refrigeration	90
Television	53

(3) Figures for 1954.
(4) Figures for 1959.

SOCIAL WELFARE PAYMENTS UNDER PUBLIC PROGRAMMES IN THE UNITED STATES, 1935–60

(in 1000 millions of dollars)

	Social Insurance	Public Aid	Health and Medical	Other Welfare	Veterans' Benefits	Education	Public Housing	Total	% Gross National Product	% All Government Expenditures
1935	0·4	3·0	0·5	0·1	0·5	2·2	—	6·7	9·8	51·2
1940	1·2	3·6	·7	·1	·5	2·8	·004	9·0	9·3	48·6
1945	1·4	1·0	1·9	·2	·9	3·4	·01	8·9	4·2	8·2
1950	4·8	2·5	2·3	·4	6·5	6·5	·01	23·0	8·7	36·3
1955	9·9	3·0	2·9	·6	4·4	11·3	·09	32·0	8·5	31·7
1960	19·3	4·1	4·3	1·2	5·1	18·2	·2	52·3	10·6	37·5

Source: US Department of Commerce, Statistical Abstract of the United States, 1963.

3. Academician E. S. Varga points out: The capitalist society of our times is the same imperialism that existed at the beginning of the twentieth century; its inherent inner laws of development have not changed. Under the conditions of contemporary capitalism there are incomparably greater opportunities than there were at the beginning of the century for the concentration of production and capital in the hands of monopolies, and particularly for the financial oligarchy to dispose of the capital of others. The monopolies and the financial oligarchy have become much stronger.

At the beginning of the century a factory with one thousand workers was considered a large-scale enterprise. Nowadays a factory with one thousand workers is considered a medium-sized enterprise. A large capitalist enterprise today is one which has at least 10,000 to 20,000 workers and employees. At the beginning of the century a concern with shares worth one hundred million dollars was regarded as one of the largest. Today the Standard Oil group has shares of which the total value amounts to approximately ten million dollars, while the American Telephone and Telegraph Company has shares worth eight million dollars. Share values of several million dollars are also possessed by Royal Dutch Shell, United States Steel, and many other monopolies. At the beginning of the century monopolies had already become the decisive force in the imperialist countries. But they were by no means so powerful as they are at the present time when, for example, three companies control the market for aluminium and automobiles in the USA. (E. S. Varga, Kapitalizm XX veka (Twentieth-century Capitalism), Moscow, Gospolitizdat, 1961, pp. 99–100).

Academician D. Kosev writes: The authors' view is based on the assumption that the difference between the firms of the late nineteenth century and the monopolies of the present day is purely one of quantity, that a monopoly is simply a concern that is larger in size. But in proceeding from this assumption they are in effect unable to give a qualitative analysis of twentieth-century economic phenomena (we have in mind the economy of the non-socialist countries). The authors constantly hover around this question, or give it relatively superficial treatment, in connection with the concentration of production (isolated from the concentration of property), but fail to point out what is qualitatively new about monopolies. In this instance the authors refrain even from calling things by their proper names, preferring to speak of 'large-scale organizations'. It can scarcely be considered right to avoid economic categories that have become firmly established in writings on economic theory, and to refrain from a full explanation of what these categories actually imply.

In this connection it may be added that in Marxist works the term 'capitalist monopoly' implies such a high concentration of capital and production that, within certain limits, it is possible to fix prices systematically, obtain a super profit, and secure economic and political supremacy.

4. *The Author-Editors have avoided the use of the term 'monopoly' for two reasons: because of the different senses in which the term is used, and because, in the sense used in classical economic literature, the significant developments of the period in the capitalist and mixed economies do not involve monopoly and the elimination of competition as such but rather the presence of large-scale enterprise with consequent changes in the character of competition and other economic relationships.*

In classical economic literature, the term 'monopoly' is applied to a single producer in an industry, especially where no other industry produces a close substitute for his product, or a single seller in a market (cf. Paul A. Samuelson, Economics: An Introductory Analysis, *5th ed., New York, 1961, p. 518). Large enterprises in industries where there are a few major producers, such as the principal American automobile manufacturers, steel corporations, or oil companies, do not qualify as 'monopolies' by this definition. Public utilities, such as telephone or electric companies, which are granted exclusive franchises for a given area and are consequently subject to government regulation, constitute 'regulated monopolies'. Government enterprises such as postal services are 'government monopolies'. In Marxist literature, the term 'monopoly' is used in a much more general sense to apply to private enterprises which are large enough or so strategically placed as to exercise considerable power over the means of production.*

5. Professor A. A. Zvorikine thinks that in certain countries and in certain historical periods the workers manage to secure for themselves a certain improvement in welfare standards, but on the whole capitalism places them in an increasingly disadvantageous position so far as their share in the growing social income is concerned. As a result of improvements in technology, there occurs a growth of the organic composition of capital, i.e. in the total sum of capital; the share of the fixed capital expended on means of production relatively increases, but the share of the variable capital, expended on labour power, decreases.

Thus, according to official American statistics, the share of the wages paid to workers in production, expressed as a percentage of the value of the products of manufacturing industry, is steadily declining. In 1937 it amounted to 40·2 per cent, but in 1958 to 36·7 per cent. This trend becomes particularly striking when one compares it with the tendency for the profits earned by capitalist concerns to grow: after making allowance for taxes, these rose from 4·7 milliard dollars in 1937 to 18·9 milliard dollars in 1958. The declining share of the total national income received by the working class means that the number of the workers declines in relation to the total population, that there is growing unemployment, that there is an increase in the number of dependants per wage-earner, that the worker increases his labour productivity, and much else, which puts the worker at a disadvantage *vis-à-vis* the employers.

As a clear example of the way in which the workers are losing their gains in regard to a minimum subsistence wage, we may take the 1930s, when an exceptionally grave crisis broke out in the USA. According to data of the US Department of Labour, the nominal weekly wage of workers engaged in manufacturing industry in 1938 was 11 per cent lower than it had been in 1929—and that in conditions of growing unemployment. Official statistics show that the number of unemployed between 1930 and 1940 did not drop below 7·7 million, and that between 1932–35 and 1938 it rose to more than 10 million.

Nor does the growth of productivity of labour, as a result of technical progress and automation, improve the position of the working class. For this growth is turned to the interests of the employers. Thus, according to American statistics, labour productivity in manufacturing industry rose by 25·8 per cent between 1953 and 1959. If we take the nominal wage of workers in manufacturing industry, we find that it rose by 21·4 per cent per worker. It would appear, therefore, that the employers are sharing with the workers the extra income gained by mechanization and automation. But if we check this with the price index we find that the real income per worker during this period increased only by 12·3 per cent. If we take the index of real wages and the index of labour productivity and compare them, we find that the 'relative position' of the worker is constantly worsening. Thus, if 1935 is 100, for the first quarter of 1959 the figure would be 39·3 per cent.

There is a growing disproportion between changing minimal needs required to reproduce labour power and the extent to which these needs are satisfied. The minimum limits of wages under capitalism are fixed by the cost of the means of subsistence necessary to enable the worker and his family to survive and to reproduce labour power, i.e., to raise and educate his children in accordance with the requirements of production. The minimum cost of labour power and the wages that determine living standards are not a constant quantity: they vary from one country or period of history to another. The deterioration of the condition of the proletariat also manifests itself in the direct lowering of living standards below the level historically necessary for a particular country and a particular period. In the monthly bulletin, *Labour's Economic Review*, published by AFL-CIO, it was pointed out that in the middle of 1960 seven million American citizens were living from hand-outs. Furthermore, over 35 million people had such low incomes that they were unable to maintain 'an American standard of decency'. This Bulletin also stated that more than 20 per cent of Americans, i.e., over 40 million, did not have the opportunity to satisfy their growing subsistence needs. They 'still live at a substandard income level today'. (*The Handbook of Basic Economic Statistics*, Vol. XIV, No. 1, January 1960, p. 24; No. 4, April 1960, pp. 94, 101–2; *Economic Notes*, May 1959, p. 2; *Labour Economic Review*, Vol. V, No. 8, August 1960, pp. 45, 47.)

For a more detailed study, cf. J. Kuczynski, *Die Geschichte der Lage der Arbeiter unter dem Kapitalismus*, t. 1, Berlin, Acad. Verb., 1960—see the material describing the twentieth century; *Labour Fact Book*, prepared by the Labour Research Association, 1–15 (N.Y., Inter. Publ. 1931–61); A. I. Katz, *Polozheniye proletariata S Sh A pri imperializmy* (The Condition of the Proletariat in the USA under Imperialism) (Moscow, USSR, Academy of Sciences, 1962).

6. Professor E. N. Anderson notes that non-Marxist economists and policy makers in non-communist countries regard a certain amount of temporary unemployment as necessary to a society in which workers may leave or change their jobs and employers are free to expand or contract the number and kind of their employees. They contrast this attitude with the economic system of socialist societies. There is difference of opinion among economists in capitalistic countries as to the volume of temporary unemployment necessary for flexibility. Practices also differ among countries as to the amount and the nature of assistance which should be given to facilitate re-employment. Sweden, for example, has demonstrated the ability to maintain flexibility with a very low rate of unemployment, less than 1 per cent in recent years, and has gone further than most countries in measures to facilitate labour mobility. In the United States 2 per cent has been assumed generally to be a probable minimum, and some economists have regarded a higher figure as normal. It is widely agreed that some form of unemployment compensation should be available to workers who have become unemployed involuntarily during the period required for them to find new employment. The cost for this is regarded as a proper one upon industry, and employers are taxed to support unemployment benefits schemes.

The kind of unemployment which represents the flexibility of a free economy is regarded as distinct from massive unemployment accompanying economic depression, such as occurred in the 1930s. Scholars and statesmen in capitalist countries generally agree about the means of preventing massive unemployment flowing from a major economic depression. The governments of these countries since World War II have assumed responsibility for assuring that such condition will not recur and have adopted policies toward prevention. The economic stability of European and American economies during these years is considered evidence of the soundness of such policies. Although there have been fluctuations in economic activity during this time, especially in the United States, small recessions have shown no signs of becoming deep depressions; the rate of expansion has soon been resumed.

Disagreement with respect to both theory and practice within capitalistic economies focuses upon the complex interrelations among employment, productivity, income distribution, consumption, investment and price stability, and on the means of achieving economic growth while avoiding serious inflation. Variations among capitalist economies in the 1950s are cited as indicating the complexity of the technical problems involved and the fact that these problems have not been fully solved; several European countries, for example, have had minimal unemployment; the Japanese economy has shown an exceedingly rapid rate of growth; in the United States, however, productivity has outstripped general economic growth, with the result that the rate of increase in production has exceeded that of employment, and unemployment has persisted at a level above that which reflects flexibility in the economy.

With increase in automation a further problem has begun to appear, the simultaneous existence of labour shortages and unemployment because the kinds of new jobs which are developing call increasingly for education, and the displaced workers lack the necessary education and training to fill available jobs.

Literature on the subject is voluminous; only a few works will be cited:

Sir William H. Beveridge, *Full Employment in a Free Society* (London, 1944).

Douglas Hague (ed.), *Stability and Progress in the World Economy: The First Congress of the International Economic Association* (London, 1958).

Daniel Hamburg, *Economic Growth and Instability* (New York, 1956).

Income, Employment and Public Policy: Essays in Honour of Alvin H. Hansen (New York, 1948).

Money, Trade and Economic Growth: In Honour of John H. Williams (New York, 1951).

Bertil Ohlin, *The Problem of Employment Stabilization* (New York, 1949).

United Nations, Report of a Group of Experts, *National and International Measures for Full Employment* (New York, 1949).

7. *The Author-Editors would like to supplement the text with the following table:*

LABOUR PRODUCTIVITY, REAL EARNINGS, AND HOURS OF WORK IN THE UNITED STATES, 1899–1963

		Index of Output per Man-Hour (1929=100)		Average Real Weekly Earnings in Manufacturing Industries (1963 prices) $	Average Weekly Hours of Work in Manufacturing Industries
	Total Private Employment	Agriculture (1)	Non-agricultural Industries		
1899	54·7	87·9	52·8	—	—
1904	58·5	89·4	—	—	—
1909	65·6	88·1	64·7	—	51·0
1914	64·7	92·7	—	33·16	49·4
1919	79·0	88·4	79·7	38·60	46·3
1924	91·7	90·0	—	42·35	43·7
1929	100·0	100·0	100·0	44·23	44·2
1934	104·5	101·0	—	41·65	34·6
1939	122·2	119·5	(116·4) (2)	52·07	37·7
1944	152·6	134·0	—	79·48	45·2
1949	162·7	165·9	156·3	69·25	39·1
1954	195·4	232·7	179·7	80·38	39·6
1959	225·0	289·9	203·9	92·81	40·3
1963	254·6	362·4	227·7	99·38	40·4

Source: U.S. Department of Commerce, Bureau of the Census, Historical Statistics of the United States, Colonial Times to 1957; *US Department of Labor,* Employment and Earnings Statistics for the United States, 1909–1962; Economic Report of the President, 1964.

(*1*) *These figures differ somewhat from those given in Note 2 above, 'Economic Characteristics of United States Agriculture' by reason of slight differences in the composition and weighting of the indexes by the reporting agencies.*

(*2*) *Figure for 1937.*

8. The Author-Editors stress the point that within the large corporation, the separation of ownership from control is to be distinguished from the separation of ownership from management. The latter has long been a familiar phenomenon in the form of the absentee landlord whose bailiff or manager is subject to his orders, or the owner of a business who hires a manager, or the owner of the majority of the stock in a corporation who controls the corporation and its management by voting his stock.

Separation of ownership from control occurs when no one owns a sufficient proportion of the stock of a corporation to exercise control by virtue of such ownership. This is typically the case in the large corporation in the USA and elsewhere, where the capitalization is so great and the number of shares so large that no single stockholder owns more than a small fraction of the total. In the US Steel Corporation in 1957, for example, the largest stockholder owned less than two-tenths of 1 per cent of the outstanding stock and all the members of the Board of Directors and principal officers in combination owned only approximately two-tenths of 1 per cent.

Although individual holdings, in and of themselves, may represent considerable wealth, they do not represent control. The latter resides in the self-perpetuating board of directors which can maintain itself in power indefinitely by means of the proxy system under which it uses company funds to solicit the proxy vote of shareholders. Only a shareholder or group of shareholders in a position to spend very large sums of money to solicit proxies from thousands of shareholders for a rival slate of officers can hope to unseat an established management. On the basis of the experience of large American corporations, a company management could not anticipate such a challenge on the average more frequently than once in 200 years. (See Joseph A. Livingston, The American Stockholder, Philadelphia, 1958.) This independence of corporate management from those who own beneficial shares in the corporation breaks up the attributes of property—the right to receive benefits and the power to determine use—and thus introduces a new set of relationships unknown to traditional economic theory, either classical or Marxian. (See Adolf A. Berle, jr., and Gardiner C. Means, The Modern Corporation and Private Property, New York, 1933; Adolf A. Berle, jr., Power Without Property, New York, 1959; Gardiner C. Means, Pricing Power and the Public Interest, New York, 1962.)

The divorce of control from ownership is not confined to capitalist countries and their large corporations. Yugoslavia has sought to apply this principle in its version of a socialist society by distinguishing between ownership which is social and control which is vested, without ownership, in the workers' council of each enterprise. In the view of Yugoslav economists and outside observers, this is one of the features which distinguish Yugoslav socialism from that of the Soviet Union where ownership of the means of production is assumed to carry control and the state operates, directly or through subsidiary organs, the enterprises which it owns. (See Calvin B. Hoover, The Economy, Liberty and the State, New York, 1950; George W. Hoffman and Fred W. Neal, Yugoslavia and the New Communism, New York, 1962.)

9. Professor E. N. Anderson thinks that the Author-Editors have not made it sufficiently clear that the capitalist ethic is not an isolated phenomenon but an integral part of a social outlook and value system which pervades democratic societies. Its basis is the belief that multiple centres of decision-making contribute to the health of society and constitute the soundest condition for stability, flexibility and progress, as well as for the development of creative and responsible individuals. According to this fundamental belief as applied to the economic sphere, the value of initiative, creativity and responsible judgment on the part of all types of entrepreneurs at all levels far outweighs the economic waste which may arise from overlapping or unco-ordinated efforts. Furthermore, since the same qualities of individual responsibility and widespread decision-making are of the essence of political democracy, they are part of the very fabric of the society.

With the growing complexity of modern life, these basic principles encounter problems of application in both the economic and political spheres, which have led to the development of large-scale institutions and kinds of regulation that depart from earlier and simpler forms of economic enterprise and political participation. The paramount considerations remain the same, however, and such forms of economic planning and extensions of political administration as are introduced are designed, not to substitute authority for responsibility, but to provide a framework within which initiative can be exercised and the pluralistic concept of multiple centres of decision-making can find effective expression.

For a theoretical discussion and for an analysis of concrete examples the reader may consult the following:

Walter Eucken, *The Foundations of Economics: History and Theory in the Analysis of Economic Reality* (London, 1950).

Walter Eucken, *This Unsuccessful Age, or the Pains of Economic Progress* (New York, 1952).

Frank Knight, *The Economic Order and Religion* (New York, London, 1945).

Frank Knight, *The Ethics of Competition and Other Essays* (New York, London, 1935).

Milton Friedman, *Capitalism and Freedom, Essays in Economic and Social Philosophy* (New York, London, 1947).

10. Academician E. Varga writes: The Soviet scientists' point of view is quite different from the authors' as far as the question of capitalist ethics is concerned. The main stimulus of the capitalist production is the pursuit for the highest possible profits, rising exploitation, and bitter competition. These factors form anti-social ethics of capitalism, justifying the aspiration for enrichment by any means, including unscrupulousness, duplicity, and the cult of force.

11. Soviet historians cannot agree with the appraisal of collectivization given by the authors of this chapter. Lately a profound study has been made in the USSR of the processes of collectivization, and the results of this study have been briefly set forth in the recently published *History of the CPSU* (2nd ed., enlarged, Moscow, Gospolitizdat, 1962, pp. 426, 429–31, 435–51, 462–7).

The urge towards a collective economy came from below and was felt by both the poor and the middle peasants. The vast extent of industrial development and the labour achievements of the workers made a strong impression on the broad masses of the peasantry. They saw how the Soviet power, the workers, surmounted difficulties to build plants for the production of tractors and new agricultural machinery, ever greater numbers of which came to the villages. The Soviet government helped the peasantry by organizing stations for renting machinery, tractor units and machine-and-tractor stations. Numerous peasant delegations visited factories and construction sites, attended workers' meetings and became infected with their enthusiasm. Upon their return to the villages, the advanced representatives of the peasantry became initiators of the organization of *kolkhozes* (collective farms). The turn of the peasant masses towards the *kolkhozes* was also influenced by the stimulating experience of the first *kolkhozes* and *sovkhozes*. The peasants became convinced in practice of the advantages of large-scale economies and collective work over individual farms. The *kolkhozes* and *sovkhozes* were the centres of advanced agrotechnical practices. They helped the surrounding peasant population with machines, pedigree cattle and high-quality seeds. By the beginning of 1930 in a number of districts in the country the *kolkhoz* movement had led to all-round collectivization. Entire villages joined the *kolkhozes*. The poor peasants were followed by the middle peasants. However, the achievements of *kolkhoz* construction in that period were accompanied by grave errors. In view of the attachment of the peasants to their individual, private economies; in view of the considerable number of *kulaks* (about 5 per cent of the peasant households) who resisted collectivization and the socialist reconstruction of the countryside; and in the absence of any historical experience of such reconstruction, the transition of the peasantry to a collective economy was the most difficult and complicated problem of socialist construction. V. I. Lenin understood all the difficulties connected with collectivization and in his time called for great discretion in approaching this objective. He warned that allowance must be made for the attachment of the peasant to his farm and, hence, that he was not to be forced, that too much haste was harmful. The practice of collectivization in the first two months of 1930 proved that these well-warranted warnings had not been heeded, that the Leninist principle of voluntarism in *kolkhoz* construction had been violated. Stalin called for the speeding up of collectivization. His under-estimation of the peasant's attachment to his small private holding, his refusal to listen to the rational proposals of the party workers in the countryside was the greatest miscalculation and the source of many errors at the inception of the mass *kolkhoz* movement. However, by the spring of 1930 the Party realized what the situation had come to in the villages, and took the path of liquidating the errors committed. The main attention was directed to the organizational-economic building up of the new *kolkhozes*. The errors of *kolkhoz* construction had not shaken faith in the correctness of Lenin's co-operative plan, in collectivization as the only way of saving the toiling peasants from enslavement by the *kulaks*, from poverty and ignorance, the only way to a free and happy life.

12. In the opinion of Soviet scholars, one should not identify the personal policy of Stalin during the period of his cult with the policy of the Communist party and the Soviet government. In the resolution 'On Overcoming the Personality Cult and its Consequences' (1956) the Central Committee of the CPSU wrote: 'Fulfilling Lenin's behests, the Communist Party undertook the socialist industrialization of the country, the collectivization of agriculture, and the accomplishment of a cultural revolution. . . . J. V. Stalin, who for a long period occupied the position of General Secretary of the Central Committee of the Party, together with other leading figures actively fought for the realization of Lenin's behests. . . . However, incorrectly all our great victories became associated with his name . . . successes in the construction of socialism, the strengthening of the USSR, were ascribed to Stalin as a consequence of the cult of the personality.' 'The Twentieth Party Congress and the entire policy of the Central Committee after the death of Stalin show convincingly there was a well-knit Leninist nucleus of leaders, who correctly understood the needs of the moment both in domestic and in foreign affairs. It is impossible to say that there was no resistance to the negative phenomena associated with the personality cult, which were acting as a brake upon the forward march of socialism. Moreover, there were certain periods—for example, during the war years— when Stalin's one-man rule was confined within narrow limits, and when the harmful effects of illegal and arbitrary acts were felt much less severely. It is well known that precisely during the period of the war members of the Central Committee, and also leading Soviet army commanders, took into their own hands certain spheres of activity at the front and in the rear, took independent decisions, and together with local Party and Soviet organizations, by their political, economic and military work assured the victory of the Soviet people in the war. . . . Immediately after the death of Stalin the Leninist nucleus of the Central Committee embarked upon a resolute struggle against the cult of personality and its grave consequences. . . . It would be a serious mistake to conclude from the existence in the past of the cult of personality that changes of some sort took place in the social structure of the USSR, or to seek the source of the cult in the nature of the Soviet social system. This would be absolutely wrong, since it would not correspond with reality, would go against the facts.

Despite all the harm which the cult of Stalin as a personality did to the Party and people, it could not alter and did not alter the nature of our social system. No cult of a personality could alter the nature of a socialist state based on public ownership of the means of production, the alliance of workers and peasants, and the friendship of people. . . .' (*KPSS v rezolyutsiyakh i resheniyakh syezdov, konferentsiy i plenumov TsK* [The CPSU in the resolutions and decisions of its congresses, conferences, and Central Committee plenums], 7th ed., Pt. IV, Moscow, Gospolitizdat, 1960, pp. 227–31).

Indeed, even at that time, despite Stalin's distortion of many Leninist principles of Party and Soviet leadership, the CPSU and the Soviet state were carrying out a policy that accorded with the interests of the Soviet people. As a result of this correct activity the USSR was able to emerge victorious in the second world war, and also to restore its economy rapidly after the war.

'Despite the personality cult, and in conflict with it, the popular masses, led by the Communist Party, the product of our system, showed tremendous initiative, performed their great historic task, and overcame all difficulties that faced them in the building of socialism. . . . The very fact that the Party itself boldly and frankly raised the question of liquidating the cult of the personality, of the impermissible errors which Stalin committed, is convincing proof that the Party stands firmly on guard over Leninism, the cause of socialism and communism, that it observes socialist legality and the interests of peoples, and that it safeguards the rights of Soviet citizens' (*ibid.*, p. 233). Cf. Note 17 to Chapter XXIII.

13. Professor A. A. Zvorikine observes that the authors of this chapter do not have a clear

idea of the specific features of the Soviet economy; they picture the development of this economy as the result of measures taken to reward those who work well and to punish those who work badly. The very attitude to work has changed in the USSR. The early years of the Soviet power already saw the rise of socialist emulation, which became a powerful stimulus in the development of the socialist economy. It began in the years of the Civil War when the workers of the Moscow–Kazan Railway organized the first communist subbotnik* on May 1, 1919, and became widespread in the years of the first five-year plan (the shock-workers and Stakhanovite movements). Socialist emulation continued to develop in the years of the war and during the period of rehabilitation of the national economy in the postwar years. Today it has become a powerful movement for communist labour, in which millions of working people participate. A testimony to the changed attitude towards work is the urge of the workers themselves to find ways of improving technology—as expressed in the rise of industrial invention and innovation. In 1961, 2,594,000 persons offered 4,152,000 inventions and rationalization proposals, and of this number 2,676,000 were recommended for application in production. One can cite examples, unthinkable in capitalist society, of Soviet workers making material sacrifices for the sake of improving production records. Valentina Gaganova, a worker of the Vyshnevolotsky cotton goods factory, volunteered to lead a lagging brigade in order to teach its members advanced techniques although for her, personally, this meant a material loss. Gaganova's act met with the approval of public opinion in the country, and many others followed suit. It would be a vulgarization to regard such acts as a response to reward which is an external stimulus. Their roots reach much more deeply, for they are connected with the growth of the people's consciousness, with the development of new socialist ethics. The selfless labour of the Soviet people is based on the deep inner conviction, on the realization that they are working for themselves, inasmuch as the means of production have passed from private hands into the hands of the working people themselves. The abolition of private ownership of the means of production and the establishment of social ownership were the decisive factors in changing the attitude towards work in the USSR. At the same time great importance is attached to material and moral incentives. People who achieve high labour productivity, give excellent quality of production, reduce the cost of production are accorded respect and honours in the USSR. The finest of them become national heroes; the newspapers write about them, there are radio broadcasts about them, their portraits are prominently displayed in the towns and villages of the Soviet Union. The Soviet system of wages which is based on the principle of socialism—from each according to his abilities, to each according to his work—is so organized that people are materially interested in quantity and quality of their output. Socialism does not deny material incentives, to which it adds moral incentives. In addition to the system of incentives there are also measures of reprisal which are applied to idlers and those who violate labour discipline and take the form of reprimands and public censure. In the case of a malicious breach of discipline the offender may be discharged. However, discharge is resorted to only in exceptional cases and then only with the sanction of the trade union organization. The authors of the chapter confuse the punishments meted out to law-breakers with measures for organizing production. Restrictions on the right of workers to leave their employment were introduced in the years of the second world war when there was already the threat of an attack upon the USSR and it was necessary to mobilize all forces to resist the enemy. When the rehabilitation of the national economy was completed after the war, these restrictions were lifted. They were always regarded as an extreme measure called for by extraordinary circumstance, and were not considered the norm for Soviet society. As for the assigning of specialists to jobs upon graduation from educational institutions, this cannot be regarded as a form of compulsory labour. Soviet youth who receive free education and material aid during their course of study consider it their honourable duty upon graduation to work for two or three years in those enterprises and organizations, and in those parts of the country, where there is a need of specialists. In general, recruitment of the labour force for work in any part of the country is carried out exclusively on a voluntary basis. During the Soviet years millions of young people volunteered to work on the new construction projects of the Urals, Siberia, the Far East and on the virgin lands. The methods of organizing the

*Subbotnik—labour freely given to the state on off days or overtime.

socialist economy, far from impeding economic progress, prompted it. The facts reported in the Soviet press about the hoarding of surprus reserves on some enterprises and about other anti-social acts are not characteristic, and by no means a result of the socialist form of organization of production.

Reference:

V. I. Lenin, *Kak organizovat sorevnovaniye* (How to Organize Competition) *Collected works* (4th Russ. ed.) (Moscow, Gospolitizdat, 1949), Vol. 26, pp. 367–76.

V. I. Lenin, *Oscheredniye zadachi sovetskoi vlasti.* (The Immediate Tasks of the Soviet Government) *loc. cit.* (Moscow, 1950), Vol. 27, pp. 230–3).

V. I. Lenin, *Velikii pochin* (A Great Beginning) *loc. cit.* (Moscow, 1950, Vol. 29, pp. 377–400.

(The works of V. I. Lenin are available in all the main languages.)

V. I. Gershberg, *Dvizheniye kollektivov i udarnikov kommunisticheskogo truda* (Movement of Communist Labour, Collectives and Shock Workers) (Moscow Gospolitizdat, 1961).

U istokov kommunisticheskogo truda (At the Sources of Communist Labour) (Moscow, Sotsekgiz, 1959).

I. I. Changli, *Sotsialisticheskoye sorevnovaniye i noviye formy kommunisticheskogo truda* (Socialist Competition and New Forms of Communist Labour) (Moscow, Sotsekgiz, 1959).

14. Academician E. S. Varga writes: 'Even prior to the end of the war serious disagreements arose between the Soviet Union and its allies, particularly Great Britain, in regard to the social order and system of government in the countries that had been liberated from the Hitlerite yoke. The allies wanted to ensure in advance the maintenance of the capitalist system, and to hand over power in Poland and Czechoslovakia to the leaders who had emigrated to London and had proclaimed themselves to be the governments of these countries. The Soviet Union considered that the peoples of these countries themselves should settle the question whether they wished to establish a regime headed by their former leaders or introduce a new regime led by those who had fought against fascism within their own country. The question whether the countries of central and south-eastern Europe should preserve a capitalist system or form a new socialist system, became one of the most important issues in the development, after the war, of the "Cold War".'

By liberating the countries of central and south-eastern Europe from the Hitlerite occupation forces, the Soviet Union paved the way for the activity of the forces that had organized the resistance movement against fascism and its internal allies. There developed a prolonged struggle between the capitalist and anti-capitalist forces which, after three or four years, ended with the victory of the latter and the transition to socialism in all countries of central and south-east Europe, with the exception of Greece where British forces intervened. On the former territory of Germany two states came into existence: The Federal Republic of Germany and the German Democratic Republic.

15. The treatment of Eastern Europe in the text for the period following World War II has been criticized by scholars who think that the 'satellite' relationship between these states and the Soviet Union has not been shown adequately. Among those expressing this view are Professors Oscar Halecki and Robert Strausz-Hupé (United States).

16. *The Author-Editors point out that they have made no attempt to characterize by any single term the complex economic, political and military relationships between the Soviet Union and the states of Eastern Europe.*

17. Academician S. G. Strumilin notes that the stability of the economy of the socialist states is not based on methods of coercion, as the authors maintain, but on the planning of the economy on a national scale. One of the chief advantages of the socialist system over the capitalist system is the possibility of carrying on the entire economy according to a single plan. The planned character of our economy implies conscious observance and consistent implementation of the principle of proportional development of all branches of the economy.

S. G. Strumilin, '*Planirovaiye: nashe reshayushcheye preimushchestvo*' (Planning: Our Decisive Advantage'), in *Molodoy Kommunist* (The Young Communist), 1957, No. 3, p. 12.

CHAPTER XXII

SOCIAL INSTITUTIONS

THE changes of the twentieth century left no institution untouched and scarcely a relationship unmodified. This included the basic unit of all societies, the family, as well as the various systems of social stratification which gave to the individual his status outside the family group. As these traditional institutions changed their character and as new situations altered the individual's place in society, many relationships came to be determined through voluntary associations based on common economic situation, on common political views, or on age, sex or common interest. In the mobile and constantly changing societies of the twentieth century, however, no substitute was found for the relatively stable relationships which gave security of status and role to most members of most societies in the past. The modern individual thus faced a uniquely difficult task of making his own place amid the complexities of modern life.

I. THE FAMILY*

During the twentieth century the family underwent major changes in its composition, function and structure in virtually every part of the world, whatever had been the family's traditional form and role in the culture of each area.

At the opening of the century family forms varied widely. In the West the traditional rural family, closely identified with the land and maintaining its continuity in relation to it, retained its characteristics both among peasant proprietors and landed gentry. This family was generally patriarchal and authoritarian; typically it included three generations and a more or less extended group of relatives; marriages were where possible designed to improve the position of the family as a landholder. Where primogeniture prevailed, as in Britain, one branch of the family remained intact and related to the land while younger sons, and daughters who failed to marry into a land-inheriting family, made their way to towns and cities or emigrated. Where, as in France, the system of inheritance led to the division of lands among family members, subdivisions into uneconomic units sent those who could not make a living on their small plots to seek employment in the towns or, as frequently in Italy, to seek new opportunities overseas.

In urban communities of the West, the two-generation family of parents and children had become the norm. This nuclear family was generally strongly

---

* For the application of social science to family life and child rearing, see Chapter XVII, The Home.

patriarchal, the authority of husband and father being supported by both Anglo-Saxon and Napoleonic law, though in practice the strength of paternal authority varied from dominance, as in most German and Italian families, to more limited authority, as in many urban families of the United States. Where the heritage from days of slavery had left its mark on family structure, as in the Caribbean and among many Negroes in the United States, both rural and urban families often tended to be matriarchal in actual form, for slavery had negated family life, generally accorded children the status of their mother and allowed the father neither authority nor responsibility.

Outside the western culture areas some form of the joint family owning its property in common, or of the extended family of mutually supporting but not co-owning members, was usually though not universally the base of the social structure. In China the joint family was further extended by concubinage and by family societies beyond the joint household. The Indian joint family was predominantly patriarchal, though some communities also had a matrilineal system of joint family, and it retained as common property the wealth of members who had taken up city pursuits as well as those living within the rural family group. The Muslim family, strongly patriarchal, followed generally the extended family form; its female members were secluded in the home or veiled from the eyes of other men and their first responsibility was to bear sons to carry on the family line; unless the particular marriage contract specified otherwise, they could be divorced by their husbands at will and additional wives could be brought into the household. In tribal Africa and among tribal peoples elsewhere, usually polygamous families were integrated with tribal institutions to provide the social structure of these areas.

During the first half of the twentieth century each of these family forms was modified by the social changes of these years.

1. *The urban family in the West*[1]

Under the impact of industrialization and urbanization the two-generation, nuclear family tended to replace the more extended families of predominantly rural areas. This urban family in turn was affected by changing economic conditions, the changing status of women, changed attitudes toward children, the democratization and individualization of social relations and, perhaps most fundamentally, by a growing sense that man could in some measure control his destiny and need not bow wholly to fate. As a result the urban family was reduced in size, modified in function, individualized and democratized in structure and became increasingly unstable as a social group.

(*a*) *Change in family size.* The trend in western urban society, and in rural societies where urban influences and values spread, was toward a decrease in the family size. Under the urban conditions of the twentieth century children became economic liabilities rather than economic assets as child labour laws and compulsory education postponed their economic contribution and lengthened their period of dependency. The cost of rearing and educating children mounted as years of schooling increased and the standards of what was essential to the full development of the child rose. Congested urban housing presented a further deterrent to large households.

At the same time the concept grew that children are a responsibility to be assumed positively, not merely accepted as fate, and that parents should be able to ensure them a good upbringing. Families of two or three children became the urban norm, and parents planned their families accordingly.

The idea that the size of the family was a matter for conscious planning and control had grown during the last quarter of the nineteenth century and it spread widely during the twentieth century. The movement for birth control was motivated originally by several distinct considerations: concern of the neo-Malthusians over the possibility of over-population, the desire of reformers to help workers to limit their families to the number of children they were able to support, and the belief of those seeking to defend the welfare and rights of women that they should have some choice and not be subjected to continuous or undesired child-bearing.

The first bureau set up to offer advice on how to prevent unwanted pregnancy was established in Amsterdam in the 1880s by the first Dutch woman physician, Dr Aletta Jacobs, as part of her effort to promote maternal health. But it required a vigorous struggle to bring the issue of birth control into the open and to make knowledge of contraceptive methods generally available. Laws relating to the distribution of obscene or pornographic literature were applied to the dissemination of contraceptive information; Mrs Annie Besant was brought to trial in England in 1877 on such a charge. Her trial gave impetus to the spread of contraceptive information, however, and stimulated the formation of Malthusian leagues in many European countries. The first international neo-Malthusian conference was held in Paris in 1900, followed by others during the next twenty-five years. Famous trials over this controversial subject took place in Belgium, France, Australia and India.

In the early years of the twentieth century the efforts of Dr Marie Stopes in Britain and Nurse Margaret Sanger in the United States emphasized the health aspect of the problem and drew the support of many doctors, as well as of women leaders such as Mrs Ottesen Jensen in Sweden. Their efforts were reflected in the formation of the Birth Control League in the United States in 1914 and the establishment of birth-control clinics in London and New York in the early 1920s. Mrs Sanger travelled abroad in 1922, arousing interest in Japan, China and India. The matter began to be actively discussed in Central and South America. The movement grew in spite of the opposition of many groups, especially the Catholic Church which firmly resisted the relaxation of laws and the extension of clinical facilities; it was not checked by repressive measures enacted in Italy and France in the 1920s in the effort to stimulate an increase in the birth rate.

In the second quarter of the century the movement changed its emphasis from the negative one of preventing unwanted pregnancy to the positive one of family planning. The shift was made realistic by the reduction in infant and child mortality and the consequent expectation that those born would generally survive. The Birth Control League was replaced by Planned Parenthood, whose objective was to help families to have the number of healthy children which they desired and thought they could care for. Clinics offered help in overcoming sterility as well as in using effective methods of contraception to space children and limit their number. By the middle of the century conscious determination of family size had become a widespread practice in the industrially developed countries.

The decline in family size was most marked in the larger cities and among the more educated and higher occupational elements in the population. Differences in family size between urban and rural areas and between upper and lower classes thus tended to be in inverse ratio to the ability of the family to provide for its members. In all western countries, average family size in most of the larger urban areas had dropped by the second world war below the level at which the city population was maintaining itself through natural increase, and urban growth depended on migration to the city from rural areas where families continued to be large. This trend was less marked in Latin America where the pattern of larger families persisted. But in Europe in the inter-war years a number of countries adopted measures, such as family allowances, special subsidized housing for large families and other public benefits, in order to reduce the burden of child rearing. The objective was to encourage larger families among those who took their parental responsibilities seriously, practised family planning, and were more likely to have fewer children than the less responsible elements in the population.

In the years following the second world war trends in family size were somewhat modified. On the one hand the small-family pattern spread to more elements in the population as knowledge of contraception became more general and as workers and farmers aspired to a manner of living and to opportunities for their children similar to those of the families who had practised family planning in the past. On the other hand the tendency toward extremely small families on the part of the more educated, urbanized elements was modified under the psychological and economic conditions of these years and the three- or four-child family became the norm among some groups which a generation before had tended toward a norm of two or three. This trend was apparent for example in France, which had gone furthest in the direction of very small families. As a result the differentials between social groups—urban–rural, class differences, and ethnic differences where these had prevailed—were diminished, though in the decade after the war they did not wholly disappear.

(b) *Modification of family functions.* The developments of the twentieth century stripped the urban family in the West of many of its traditional functions. It retained few of its economic features as a unit of production when it became part of an urban economy. Urban employment was predominantly on an individual not a family basis. To an increasing degree large-scale enterprise took the place of craft production, where father and son had often worked together at the same bench. Although much retail trade continued to be carried on by family businesses—grocery stores, tobacconists or dress shops—the trend toward chain stores, department stores and supermarkets reduced even this form of family enterprise. Some productive activity did remain in the home, and tended to increase with the development of home appliances as, for example, home laundering after the advent of the washing machine. But this did not counterbalance the much more general shift of former home activities, such as the making of clothing, bread and prepared foods, to factory production.

The small family continued, however, as an economic unit for purposes of consumption and mutual support. The extent to which the earnings of individual members working for wages outside the home were pooled to sustain the family group varied considerably with the culture of the country and the practice of the individual family, but the responsibility for mutual support between parents and children, brothers and sisters, grandparents and grandchildren not only was strong but generally had the sanction of law. Even as a unit of consumption, however, the family lost some of its scope with the growth of public eating places which partly replaced family meals, and with forms of recreation, entertainment and social activity enjoyed by individual family members with age-mates or people with common interests rather than with the family group.

The role of the family as educator was also diminished in proportion as the training which the child received became more and more remote from the content of family life and the range of parental experience, and as the task of education was assumed by the state through the extension of publicly supported schools or by the Church. Where the son had been expected to follow in his father's footsteps and the daughter in her mother's, instruction in agriculture, crafts and household duties could be imparted by parents in the home. But in the urban societies of the twentieth century the child needed to acquire a rapidly expanding body of scientific, technical and literary knowledge, of which the school rather than the family was the repository.

In many situations, in fact, the school functioned as an agency of the community vis-à-vis the parents as well as the child, both determining what the child should learn and influencing parental behaviour. Among immigrant families whose children were moulded by the schools to the culture of the country of adoption, or among rural–urban migrants whose children learned city ways, or in countries which were engaged in bringing about rapid social change, children not only learned at school many things that their parents had never known but often acquired attitudes and values at variance with those of the home.

The mobile urban family also lost much of its function as a means of giving status to its members. At the highest social levels and within some limited groups, the individual's place continued to be defined by his family connections. He was primarily *who* he was rather than *what* he was. But for the majority of people, especially in the bigger urban centres, the family largely ceased to give status to its members. The urban individual, in his many kaleidoscopic relationships at school, at work, in a neighbourhood, in the pursuit of interests or recreation or in casual daily contacts, was known by what he did much more than by who he was. Personal attributes—occupation, education, wealth, talents, personality—became the principal determinants of status; while family connections still might contribute to advancement, opportunity or marriage, they tended to play a supplementary rather than a primary role.

But while the family's traditional economic, educational and status-giving functions were diminished, its central role in the formation of personality and as a source of affection and security was enhanced. The small urban family had to equip its children to meet the strains, pressures and anonymity of modern life and to cope with constant and threatening change. Psychologists called attention to the importance of the child's earliest experience to his whole mental and emotional development and to the inner security essential for his effective functioning as a mature individual.

A major problem for the twentieth-century urban family was therefore how to perform this key function. Anxious parents, impressed with the ill effects which according to Freud and his followers might result from too rigorous or unsympathetic an early training, sought guidance in the multitude of best-selling books on child rearing and articles which filled the popular magazines. Much of the rising tide of juvenile delinquency in urban areas and some mental illness were attributed to failures originating in the family.

The very conditions which brought emphasis upon the family's emotional role made the performance of this role progressively more difficult. The ambitions which families with middle-class standards sought to realize for their children often set up strains in view of the family's inability to supply directly the means for satisfying such ambitions, since these depended upon social factors and the individual's own achievement. Working-class parents in their turn were sometimes too unsure of their economic future, their present status, and the values appropriate to the society of which they found themselves a part, to transmit firm values and exercise confident authority over their children. In successive generations, as these children became parents in their turn, their own insecure childhood could make them even less well equipped emotionally than their parents had been to provide their children with a stable home. As they took on the more apparent middle-class values, these were often grafted on to a very uncertain base. The twentieth-century urban family thus became an uneasy unit, far more self-conscious about its role than its predecessors had been.

In these circumstances conscious efforts were made to strengthen the family in its continuing role. Studies, symposia, institutes and conferences on family life abounded. Schools concluded that preparation for family life could not be left wholly to the home, and introduced classes in sex education, human relations and child care. Instruction in home economics was expanded from the practical household tasks of food preparation and clothing to include 'family life education'.

(c) *Individualization and democratization of family structure.* Many of the same forces which modified the family's size and its functions altered its internal structure and relationships. The individualizing influences of the money economy, urban milieu and social values of the West were reflected in emphasis on the personal as against the interfamilial aspect of marriage, on romantic love and on the priority of individual interests over those of the family group. The changing status of women affected the balance within the family and the roles of its members. The general trend toward democratization in social relations had repercussions in the home, altering the relative positions of parents and children. These trends combined to loosen traditional family bonds, to undermine the authoritarian position of the family head and to substitute for a sternly hierarchical structure a pattern of more equal relationships.

The foundation of the twentieth-century urban family was generally marriage based on romantic love, although marriages for money or to further the interests of the family continued to be arranged. In such a family system courtship took on central importance, since young people had to find their own mates rather than to depend upon their parents to do so for them. When the need to provide opportunities for courtship was reinforced by the popularization of Freudian psychology, it led to the relaxation of many of the traditional restraints and taboos concerning the relations among young people, to changed patterns of sexual behaviour and to the development among adolescents of a virtual sub-culture of their own. Once the family was formed, romantic love continued to be relied upon as the principal cement to hold it together, and dissolution of the marriage bonds when this cement failed became increasingly acceptable except in the Roman Catholic Church.

Freedom of association between boys and girls replaced the separation during adolescence and strict chaperonage which had been the norm followed more or less rigorously in different countries in the past. The clearest evidence of this trend was the spread of coeducation, whose principal objective besides that of economy was to encourage boys and girls to know each other and to share common interests in order that they might have a basis for judging character and for establishing relationships not limited to those based on sexual attraction alone.

Free association among adolescents produced new patterns of behaviour to which teenagers were under pressure from their peers to conform, and often conflicts arose between parents and children over the limits which the adults attempted to place on the social activities of the young. These tendencies were particularly marked in the United States, but by the time of the second world war they were to be seen in many other urban communities in the West.

A freer attitude toward sex was part of the new pattern. The line between the good girl whose virginity was her most carefully guarded possession and the bad girl who made a profession of sex became less sharp. With the aid of flourishing cosmetics industries and designers of clothing and bathing suits, respectable girls adopted ways to make themselves alluring which had been reserved for the professionals or semi-professionals in the past, and glamour became one of the major industries of the twentieth century. The cinema played its part in accentuating this trend, not only by making sexiness the principal stock-in-trade of the movie stars but by developing the stereotypes of the 'good-bad' and the 'bad-good' girls who largely replaced the pure heroine and unpure vamp as stock characters.

Patterns in adolescent behaviour changed with the times. The post-war generation of the 1920s earned the name of 'flaming youth' or the rebellious generation. In the years which followed, the freedoms which had been shocking in the 1920s became commonplace. The generation of young people which grew up during the depression of the 1930s and the war years of the '40s took their freedoms for granted and were more concerned with achieving a measure of security and stability than with shocking their elders.

After the second world war two quite opposite tendencies were apparent, one toward early marriage and the establishment of a stable home, the other toward capricious anti-social behaviour. The first of these patterns, characteristic of the majority, reflected the eagerness of young people to find some security in marriage in a world full of insecurities; though such marriages often took place while both partners were still pursuing their education, they were not generally entered into experimentally in the manner advocated by the *avant-garde* of the 1920s, but with the intent to establish a home and start to rear a family.

The patterns of wanton violence in which a conspicuous minority engaged, sometimes marking themselves off by a distinctive style of dress, baffled parents and authorities on the European continent, in Britain and in the United States, for the boys and girls who broke windows, tore up flowers in parks, killed animals in the zoo, raided farms, assaulted passers-by and showed general disrespect for life and property did not fit the stereotype of the juvenile delinquent as the victim of poverty, broken home or other form of deprivation. These children and young people belonged to all social levels and some came from homes where they lacked no opportunity for education or material well-being, as well as from the opposite type. The widespread appearance of the phenomenon of vandalism led educators and responsible citizens to ask what features of modern life were producing such conduct. Did it reflect a breakdown of traditional family authority without the successful substitution of a basis for responsible behaviour? Was it the uncertainties of the adult world or the unusually wide gulf between the generations in a period of rapid social change? Had a misinterpretation of the principle of individualized education led to abandonment of standards and discipline? Or did the very affluence of the society itself give parents and children alike a sense of ease and leave them without the need to struggle and without challenging goals?

The family based on romantic marriage was not expected wholly to supersede the interests and ambitions of the individual members but to contribute to them or to permit their independent development. Most especially it was expected to give the children the best start in life that it could. The main line of responsibility ran from the family to the child; the child was not expected to subordinate his personal goals to those of the family group.

In the urban milieu, influences and interests outside the family were many and tended to pull it apart. The urban community, paying little attention to family identity and unity, offered a variety of other bases for association. Where space was at a premium and apartment dwelling the usual form of housing, family members tended to seek companionship and interest outside their often crowded dwelling. Children and young people were exposed to school, club, street, movies, television, comic strips and other outside influences whose standards, shared by the child's age-mates, competed with and often took precedence over those of the home. Such influences tended to lessen the family's coherence as a social group.

One of the indications of these individualizing and loosening influences was the increase in the proportion of marriages that ended in divorce. In recognition of marriage as a personal union which might be dissolved when its affectional base disappeared, laws with respect to divorce were liberalized in most countries during the period under review, and divorce became more socially acceptable. Among those who took their standards from the behaviour of movie stars, it even became fashionable, though in the decade after the second world war the number of divorces dropped sharply from the immediate post-war peak.

The increase in divorce was generally regarded as evidence that the family had become a more unstable institution than it had been in the past. It was not wholly clear, however, that the divorce trend reflected in fact a great increase in broken homes, for desertion and separation had long been common, and continued to constitute the 'poor man's divorce' and a means of terminating unsatisfactory relationships where divorce was not provided for by law or was forbidden by religion. Some of the apparent increase in family instability may have reflected only a larger proportion of legally recorded break-ups and the conspicuousness of divorce among people in the public eye.

Meantime, the Catholic Church remained firm in its position that no divorce was permissible, some countries provided no legal grounds for divorce, the British royal family backed by the Church of England refused to countenance it in its ranks, and divorce laws in many places required legal subterfuge or considerable indignity on the part of those who sought to free themselves from their marriage bonds. On the other hand there was a broad trend toward the principle accepted by the Scandinavian countries which regarded divorce as an honourable and dignified way to terminate a relationship, once the basis in mutual respect had been lost.

Within the great majority of families, which remained intact, relationships among the members became less rigidly defined. As women acquired the possibility of economic independence through job opportunities outside the home, and as they received political recognition through the extension of voting rights and the right to hold public office, their dependent and subordinate position in the home was inevitably modified. In most areas under Anglo-Saxon and Napoleonic legal systems, family law was revised to remove many, sometimes all, of the traditional disabilities of married women—their obligation to provide their husbands with their services or their earnings, their inability to handle their own property where they could not enter into contracts or sue and be sued, their ineligibility to be made legal guardians of their children. At mid-century some of these traditional legal limitations survived in some countries, but the trend was toward their abolition.

A practical factor contributing to the changing relationships within the family was the disappearance of a cheap servant class. This was most pronounced in the United States but spread with the social revolutions of the period. In the small nuclear family without servants' help and without the extra female relatives generally present in extended families, the full burden of caring for the children and performing the household tasks rested on the mother. In spite of the household appliances and factory-produced food and clothing which lightened her load, these responsibilities were heavy and exacting. Under the force of circumstances fathers and husbands were called on to share many tasks of the home and the lines between the roles of husband and wife in the household became less distinct.

The growing emphasis on democratic social and political values helped to undermine the exercise of strict paternal authority. A new concept of family relationships envisaged the family as a more or less democratic group in which there was mutual understanding of family problems, the child was expected to assume responsibility, decisions were shared and the father's word was no longer the supreme law.

The most extreme breakdown of traditional authority came where the roles of parents and children were reversed under conditions of rapid social and cultural change. Children of immigrants often broke sharply with the traditions of their parents and, on the basis of their superior knowledge of the adopted language and culture, told their parents how to behave in the new milieu. Revolutionary societies counted on the indoctrination of the young and the development of their energies and leadership to effectuate change.

All these tendencies to loosen family bonds and democratize the family structure were carried to great lengths in the measures taken by the Soviet Union in the years immediately following the October revolution. In its initial effort to destroy what it considered the exploitative features of the bourgeois-capitalist and patriarchal families, it equalized the duties and rights of men and women, established institutions to assume or share child-rearing functions, abolished virtually all forms of inheritance, permitted unrestricted divorce and legalized abortion. Children, educated by the schools to the communist way of life, often came into conflict with their conservative parents and were encouraged to take the initiative in guiding the family along new lines.[2]

As non-authoritarian family patterns developed and spread, they were challenged by critics who reasserted traditional values. Easterners in contact with the West were often struck unfavourably by the individualism within the family group and the diminished role of the family head; the relative merits of eastern and western family forms became a frequent theme of Asian writers. Within western societies, some doctors, psychiatrists, writers and parents expressed concern lest the modern western family become dominated by the selfish demands of the young. They insisted that the democratizing trend had gone too far when cartoon strips in the United States presented fathers as slightly ridiculous and rather helpless figures, easily manipulated by daughters, wives and ingenious young children. These critics insisted that children needed the support of authority and that too much freedom could be as damaging as too little in equipping them to make choices and assume responsibilities in adult life.

Toward the middle of the century some of the trends toward family instability appeared to be in process of modification in favour of a larger, more cohesive and more stable family group. The increased size of urban families, the trend toward early marriages and the eagerness of young people at mid-century to establish stable homes has already been noted. For some whose loose family structure had been historically associated with low social status, as among Negroes in the United States, achievement of a stable family and home was the mark of social advancement.

Suburban living set the pattern for a growing proportion of urban families. In one respect the influence was divisive, for the breadwinner who commuted to his job had interests in the central city while his wife and children lived most of their lives in the suburban neighbourhood. But in contrast to the city where there was little except television to hold family members in the home, the suburban home itself became for many families a focus of effort and a common venture. Whether it was a matter of gardening, cutting the lawn, making household repairs, engaging in household decoration or pursuing a hobby at home, suburbanism tended to focus activities of the family around the business of living. Separated from the attractions and distractions of the metropolitan centres, suburban families tended to find more of their resources within the family group and their participation in suburban community life was often as a family or in relation to family interests. For those who married young and lived in small family units, this could be limiting in outlook and scope.

In the Soviet Union, too, the family was strengthened. By the 1930s the Soviet family, based on full equality of man and wife and on a community of their interests, had come to be regarded as a firm unit within the system of social relations, and the state took a number of measures to ensure greater stability. Divorce and abortion were made difficult, family duties and respect for parents were emphasized and the family was supported as an integrating force in the society. Motherhood was honoured with a medal for mothers who had brought up five or six children and the orders of Glorious Motherhood and of Mother Heroine for those who had reared eight or nine and ten or more children respectively.

2. *The joint family in the East*

The joint or extended family which for centuries had been the central social institution of eastern societies, notably in China and India, and in many other parts of the world, was altered and in many cases broken up as a result of developments of the twentieth century. In its traditional form the joint family provided a kind of social security for its members, for no one was wholly dependent on his own resources, and any misfortune befalling a member of the family group was shared by the total body. The joint family encompassed the individual's principal personal relationships and defined his status. Only a relatively few members in the course of their lives experienced the role of family head; most—younger brothers and sisters, and younger generations— lived throughout their lives under the direction of father, grandfather, grand- mother, uncle, older brother or husband. Nor did the individual experience control over something that was distinctively his own property or a room of his own in the family home. He was, as it were, a transient member of an on-going institution.

Many factors brought a modification in the traditional joint family, some operating gradually and partially, some suddenly and drastically. Commerce and industry brought income and property to individuals, not always to a family group. In general, the legal instrumentalities of the western colonial powers tended to individualize. British, French and Dutch administrations recognized individual ownership in land, and individual contractual relation- ships and obligations, and placed demands such as taxation or labour service upon individuals. Employment was on an individual basis, whether as a plan- tation worker or a factory hand or a civil service employee. These economic and legal factors did not, however, automatically destroy the joint family, for individual earnings could be pooled and individually owned land could be claimed as joint or family property.

A second factor tending to break up the joint family was the changing posi- tion of women. In the joint family women generally had no rights of inheri- tance or independence of action. But as the idea of the emancipation of women spread around the world it brought restlessness within the joint family struc- ture. The movement for individuality and equal rights for women paved the way for their equality before the law with rights of inheritance as well as opportunity for education and the right to vote.

The joint family structure was also weakened by rapid social change which tended to undermine the authority of the elders. Where westernization was challenging ancient ways, and young people were acquiring new standards and bodies of knowledge at variance with the knowledge and the values of which their elders were the repository, it was not easy to maintain filial loyalty and respect in the traditional degree.

The joint family in some cases survived the process of urbanization; in both China and India extended urban families living together in compounds had long existed in ancient urban centres. But the movement of individual members to the city tended to erode the joint family, even when it remained as an institution in its village and on its land. Urban housing, with its small dwellings and crowded conditions, made it difficult to accommodate an extended family group.

Although these factors tended to undermine the joint family, it was not until the revolutionary changes of the years after the second world war that the institution was dealt a direct blow in some of the areas of its principal strength. Under the constitution and laws of the Indian republic, the breaking up of joint families was accelerated by taxation, inheritance laws and laws according rights to women. Although joint families had been able to partition their joint property by agreement in the past, the new system of taxation and inheritance placed pressure on families to convert themselves into small single-family units. Partition of joint families did not, however, necessarily mean the adoption of the western family form, for most marriages continued to be arranged and the western pattern of romantic courtship and marriage remained unacceptable to most Indian groups.

In China the traditional joint family and the institutions which contributed to its functioning, already under attack during the Republic, became major targets of the communist régime. In place of arranged marriages, virtual selling of daughters in many cases, concubinage and other features of the joint family structure, the communist régime stressed marriage as a matter of personal choice and responsibility. Confucian ethics, with their stress on filial respect and the family as the focus of social and personal relationships, were rejected as obstacles to the attitudes and activities which the communist régime sought to build up. Collective ownership of land and enterprises replaced family units.

In the Islamic countries the Muslim family was a focal point in the conflicts relating to social reform. Except in the most conservative areas, there was some trend toward monogamy, emergence of women from purdah and increased independence on the part of children. This was especially true of urban areas, and in countries such as Egypt where there had been greatest interaction with the West; but even in such countries as Saudi Arabia, Yemen or Afghanistan there was some tendency toward a weakening of the traditional family system in the cities by the middle of the century. Up to the 1950s, however, Turkey was the only Muslim country which had directly adopted the western family form; and even here the change in law was by no means universally followed in practice.

The experience of Turkey well demonstrated the kinds of problems encountered in the attempt to transplant the family institutions of one society into another. Although Ataturk replaced Muslim family law by the Swiss code in 1925, only a fraction of peasant marriages during the following decades conformed to legal requirements, and the Turkish state found it necessary to pass legislation in 1933, 1945, and 1950 legitimizing children of unregistered unions.

Practical difficulties in applying the Swiss procedure in Turkish villages were partly responsible for the persistence of traditional forms—the need to produce birth certificates where none existed, or the requirement of a medical examination where no doctor was available. But in addition, peasants were reluctant to enter a form of marriage which appeared to them not to fulfil the requirements of their situation. The new form precluded the established practice of marrying any additional unattached female who came to live in a household, as an agricultural worker or because a widowed relative was without a place to live, and the Swiss system of inheritance, which excluded parents from inheriting if the deceased had descendants, seemed to the peasants to leave old people unprotected in a country where social security had not yet replaced family responsibility for the aged. Divorce was made difficult, though equal for men and women, and it required a distasteful inquiry into the personal life of the couple.

Yet such objections as these were overcome and the new form was adopted when direct benefits were involved; members of the armed forces, for example, hastened to bring their marriages into conformity with the law in order that their families might receive allowances.

3. *The tribal family in Africa*

The disruption of the African tribal family as a result of European contact and urban industrial development brought perhaps the most drastic change to which any family system was subjected during the twentieth century. The family and kinship systems, which in most parts of tribal Africa provided the essential structure of relations among individuals and the integration of the society, were radically undermined where European influences were felt.

While the traditional structure of the African tribal family varied among different tribal groups, each specific form was strongly sanctioned by custom, and kin groups largely defined the social roles of the members of the tribe. In one of the usual forms, encountered with variants in many areas, the family was polygamous, each wife with her children forming a unit. The family group might live in an enclosure where wives and other members of the extended family might have their separate huts, assigned in accordance with their age or their relationship to the head of the household and to each other; groups of enclosures linked by kinship formed larger social units.

In most tribal communities the family or the larger kinship group was a self-contained economic unit for purposes of production and for consumption in which all shared; when times were good all benefited and when they were bad all were affected; division of labour was based on the functions traditionally assigned to persons of the appropriate age, sex or position in the family. It was also generally a unit for purposes of child rearing. The authority of all elders in the family group extended to all children, so that the immediate parents did not have full and unsupported responsibility for their young.

The marriage upon which the family relationships rested, arranged within whatever limits might prevail in the tribe, was in the nature of a union of families or households rather than of individuals, and was generally entered into on the basis of some reciprocal arrangement, sometimes a gift of cattle by the husband to the bride's family. Women often remained in the status of minors, first in relation to their fathers and then to their husbands, but in some tribes older women enjoyed freedoms and responsibilities not accorded them as young wives.

Whatever its forms the family largely determined the status of the individual; but each had his defined relationships, from the head to the first and later wives, the older and younger children, male and female, relatives on the father's or the mother's side. With each status went a corresponding role, and clearly defined conduct attached to it. Children had their established roles during childhood and their passage to adulthood was marked by initiation rites in which they learned the duties and responsibilities which went with their new status.

Ultimate responsibility for the actions of individual members of the family was generally borne by the head of the household who must answer for their misdeeds, protect them when in trouble, represent them in tribal courts or councils, and intercede on their behalf with the ancestral or other spirits; he enjoyed full authority commensurate with his responsibilities. The family contributed to the structure of government through a system of chieftaincies, councils or other forms of authority based upon lineage and kinship. It often also played a religious role, for the responsibilities of the family head and other appropriate family members frequently included performance of religious rituals and were no less spiritual than material.

In the course of the twentieth century, under the impact of European domination, the tribal family structure was largely negated in the cities and was weakened in many parts of the country. Even in rural areas it felt the effect of missionary teaching; since the great bulk of the education carried on during the twentieth century in all parts of tribal Africa was by missionaries, this influence was considerable. Christian missionaries attacked the polygamous family; for their church members they insisted upon monogamy and upon dependence upon the rites of the church rather than the marriage bargain as the marriage sanction. Muslim influence was less disruptive, for polygamy was not contrary to the precepts of the Quran and religious teachers did not seek to put a stop to it.

Colonial administrations generally left customary family institutions intact, except as they were indirectly affected by measures designed to deal with commerce or administration. But occasionally the latter had the actual result of undermining the family form which held the tribal society together, as in the classic case of the effort of the British authorities in Nigeria to reduce excessive litigation among the Tiv people. In the process, they disqualified the form of marriage which had not only provided family stability and continuity but had been essential to the rites to make fertile the land and protect the society against evil, and they in effect legalized only the form which had been used by the Tiv for impermanent unions and for ones involving the purchase of slaves.

The principal disrupting influences, however, were industrialization and urbanization. Men who went away to work in the mines left their family group impaired—in its self-sufficiency, its occupational structure and its structure of authority. Even when their absence was temporary and they returned home after a period or intermittently for parts of each year, the pattern of family life was broken. The major breakdown came when women accompanied their men to the mining towns or the cities and established urban family units in the African 'locations' of Johannesburg, in Broken Hill, Kampala or Nairobi, in Dakar or Brazzaville, in Lagos, Accra or Leopoldville.

From one end of Africa to the other, the ever growing number of urban African families represented a break with virtually every element in their traditional structure, even though they often retained close ties with their relatives in the country. Their economic self-sufficiency based on the contribution of all and shared consumption by all was gone; each individual wage-earner was expected by his employer and by the urban authorities to be economically responsible for his immediate family of wife and children, though the members of his extended family might still expect him to share whatever he had as he would have done in the tribal community. If he found himself in difficulty from unemployment, illness or other misfortune, no head of an extended group was at hand to mobilize the resources of all for the protection of the unfortunate member. The loss of this family function was only very partially made up by the formation of voluntary associations for mutual aid. Numerous savings associations, burial societies, co-operative organizations and occupational groups, sometimes cutting across tribal lines, offered a measure of economic protection and also some common sense of belonging, as when members of a burial society might wear the same colour cloth to commemorate a deceased member.

The structure of authority also was undermined. No compact body of elders reinforced the parents' authority over their children; yet by training and experience parents were not equipped to carry the responsibility single-handed. This lack was doubly serious, for expectations with respect to behaviour were no longer agreed upon and understood. Neither a man's own status and role nor that of his wife, his children, his relatives or his neighbours, was any longer clearly defined and universally recognized. From a society in which the structure of the family ensured that no one should experience uncertainty as to who he was or what was expected of him, the urban African found himself in a society in which these certainties had been swept away.

The urban African family was thus forced to reconstitute itself almost from the ground up and with no source of guidance, especially in the many cases where religious and political authority had also been vested in the family and exercised through the structure of the family group. In fact the very circumstances which made the reconstruction necessary intensified its difficulty, for at the same time that the African was pulled into the new society he was to a greater or less degree denied full participation and status in it.

The situation was clearest in the Union of South Africa where the largest number of urbanized Africans were to be found and where their exclusion from participation in the life of the community was most systematic. Here the urban African encountered the congestion and squalor of the 'locations', the indignities of police passes, exclusion from types of employment carrying prestige and bringing higher incomes, denial of political participation and constant exposure to the contradiction between the principles of European society taught in school or Church and the application of European authority to Africans in their daily life. This environment offered little on which the detribalized African might construct an alternative social system to replace the family-tribal structure whose basis had been destroyed.

The situation was somewhat less harsh and negative elsewhere, but the essential problem remained unresolved. In the Belgian Congo, where a colonial policy of training Africans for responsible participation in economic life distinguished the area from other parts of colonial Africa, the price was detribalization and the destruction of the tribal family. In its extreme form this took the shape of boarding schools where children, removed from their families at an early age, were brought up wholly outside of the structure of tribal life. As the African territories moved toward self-government and independence, the growth of an urban society and the extension of its influence into the hinterland brought similar kinds of breakdown in traditional authority, problems of status and role and uncertainty as to the basis for a new family form throughout the rapidly changing African continent.

II.   SOCIAL STRATIFICATION[3]

The twentieth century saw a change in the social stratification of virtually all societies, a change which in general made less sharp the lines of division, expanded the middle group, however that group was defined, introduced new bases for social groupings and provided new means of social mobility.

1. *At the opening of the century*

At the opening of the century most of the world's societies were fairly rigidly stratified along class lines, although nineteenth-century industrialization had upset many of the old relationships and the settlement of new lands had created societies which had never had the hierarchical structure of the traditionally feudal societies from which their settlers were drawn.

In the countries of Europe, with the exception of a few places such as Norway where the feudal system never enjoyed a firm hold, and some of the older cities with long-established merchant traditions, remains of the feudal structure provided a continuing framework of relationships. This was particularly the case in Russia and eastern Europe. Paralleling and partially interlinked with the remnants of feudalism was the class structure of the capitalist economy, an upper or middle class of employers and independent entrepreneurs and a proletariat of industrial workers. Where the landed upper class remained substantial it held a social position above that of the families whose wealth, though often greater, came from the less honoured occupations associated with trade and industry. A professional class, drawn principally from the landed and business classes, generally occupied the lower levels of these upper groups, while the intelligentsia of scholars, writers and artists, also derived from the same social groups, moved in related circles, though with greater inter-class freedom than was enjoyed by others. The beginnings of a white-collar class of clerical workers and minor bureaucrats occupied a position below the business and professional level and above that of urban workers and rural peasants.

In the new lands overseas, especially in North America and Australasia, the absence of a feudal tradition and the geographical and social mobility attendant on the filling up of a new continent produced a much less sharply defined class structure. Wealth rather than an inherited social position tended to define class, no landed aristocracy outranked the captains of industry, and people of nearly all economic and occupational levels regarded themselves as middle class, or aspired to such a status if not for themselves then at least for their children.

In areas which had been peopled by a succession of immigrants from different countries, stratification tended to follow ethnic lines at least in the first generation, with immigrants of an earlier period occupying a more secure and favoured position while later immigrants filled the lower socio-economic ranks. As members of each group rose in the occupational scale, acquired wealth which put them on a par with earlier migrants and moved out of the neighbourhood settled by their compatriots, ethnic lines tended to be replaced by those based on economic or occupational position. Where there was a heritage from days of slavery, divisions were perpetuated on the basis of colour or race. In extreme situations, as in the southern states of the United States, stratification along racial lines was supported by laws requiring racial segregation.

The structure of the Latin American countries, based on large-scale land-holdings or other exploitative industries such as mines, was closer to the feudal pattern of Europe than to the societies composed of family homesteads and middle-class entrepreneurs in North America, Australia and New Zealand. A small Europe-oriented upper class and a mass of Indian, *mestizo* and Negro peons characterized these countries, their proportions varying from such predominantly Indian areas as Bolivia and Guatemala to almost wholly European populations in Argentina and Uruguay, with the Negro element prominent along the Caribbean littoral and the north-east coast of Brazil. Inter-class distances were very wide, nowhere was there a large and prominent middle class, and a sharp line was drawn culturally between those whose lives were led within an indigenous cultural milieu as 'Indians' and those who were culturally European, the *blancos* or *ladinos*. The colour line, though present, was not sharply drawn or supported by law but was associated with class differences—the darker skinned being concentrated for historical reasons in low occupational and income groups—and with the presence of indigenous tribal organization.

South Africa, in the aftermath of the Boer war, presented a complex ethnic pattern. Two mutually hostile groups of Europeans, the predominantly rural Afrikaners chiefly of Dutch extraction, and the predominantly urban British, were working out relationships between themselves and the non-Europeans. The latter included the Coloured of mixed racial ancestry who followed a Europeanized way of life, the East Indians, most of whom had been brought in as labourers in the late nineteenth century and who carried on trade and business, and the African population which continued to live in tribal villages but was being drawn more and more into work in the mines, as farm labourers and as servants in the growing towns.

All these western societies at the opening of the century, both in Europe and overseas, were in varying degrees mobile, fluid and changing under the impact of expanding commerce and industry and large-scale migration.

In other parts of the world most societies at the opening of the century still maintained their ancient systems of stratification, subject to modification almost exclusively at the points where they came into direct contact with colonial powers or through trade and missionary activity. In colonial areas an upper class of Europeans, distinguished by both position and skin colour, was superimposed on the class system of the locality. In some areas, especially in south-east Asia, middle-stratum functions of trade or administration were carried on by a Eurasian element or by distinct ethnic communities, frequently Chinese. In all the largely illiterate societies, the *literati* formed a special class, most notably in China with its history of scholar-administrators and India with its Brahmin caste, but also in such forms as Muslim *ulemas* and some Buddhist monks. Religious and ethnic communities often functioned as discrete entities within the overall social structure.

In most parts of the Middle East a small wealthy landholding upper class was separated by an unbridgeable gulf from the poor peasants who worked their lands and from the nomadic peoples, generally living in tribal groups, who made the deserts their home.

Indian society was one of the most complexly stratified in the world by reason of its elaborate caste system, which provided in some instances a basis for hereditary occupations, and by the division of the society into religious groups with separate institutions and personal law. Elsewhere in south Asia the stratification was less complex. Relatively equalitarian village societies formed the base; a small *élite* made up the top—the royal family with its many ramifications in Thailand and Cambodia, petty aristocracies in the Malay States.

In China wealth and landholding in the country and merchant wealth in the cities provided the basis for an upper class while peasant proprietors or tenants on infinitesimally small holdings and a mass of urban and rural coolie labourers made up the bulk of the vast population. Under the traditional system of civil service examinations which prevailed until the beginning of the twentieth century, however, opportunity to enter the ranks of the bureaucracy was open in principle to any who could meet the test of scholarship, and a road to advancement was thus available for the few talented peasant boys who might manage to secure instruction in classical Chinese learning. In Korea similar examinations were open to the sons of bureaucrats and landed gentry. In Japan the remnants of a feudal structure not only continued to set the pattern for rural life but were to a considerable extent transferred into the growing industrial system, where relations between employers and workers followed a semi-feudal pattern.

Social stratification in tropical Africa followed complex tribal patterns which had begun to be cut across by European-imposed political divisions and uprooted by movement to cities and towns. British colonial policy tended to support the existing tribal structure by delegating administrative authority to certain of the tribal chiefs. In French, Belgian and Portuguese areas the tendency was to draw the few 'assimilated' Africans into the superimposed European structure. In the Union of South Africa the African population was being converted into a permanent substratum of labour.

2. Changing patterns of social stratification

During the twentieth century in all parts of the world the growth and spread of industrialism expanded the middle class which commercial capitalism had created or brought a new middle class into being. The technology of industrial production and organization brought this tendency, whatever the political and cultural orientation or the stage of industrial development, and however much the character of the middle group might change.

(a) *In industrial societies.* In the early period of European and American industrial development much commercial and industrial activity had been carried on by small entrepreneurs who constituted the backbone of the original middle class. As the economic structure became more complex, a new middle class emerged composed of the administrators of large-scale enterprises and the host of technicians upon whom modern industry and trade depended. Managers, engineers, accountants, advertising men, lawyers, salesmen, bank managers swelled the upper ranks of the middle class; clerical workers, who filled the lower middle-class ranks, increased more rapidly than production workers, for machines were constantly replacing men in the plants while clerical operations became more and more elaborate as economic units grew in size and complexity.

Production workers, in turn, began to move into the technical middle class as mechanization took over routine tasks, and the industrial proletariat was gradually replaced by a growing class of technicians—mechanics who could keep the machinery in working order and various levels of engineers. Finally, even the less skilled took on some middle-class characteristics as higher wages, made possible by increased productivity, enabled them to share the consumption patterns of the middle class. What some people referred to as the 'nouveau riche proletariat' provided the market for mass-produced goods and were able to afford some of the houses, cars, clothes, travel, entertainment and education for their children which had been the prerogatives of the professional, commercial and managerial groups that made up the old middle class.

The new middle class drew recruits from still other sources—from the expanding bureaucracy which carried out the ever increasing functions of government and industry and from the wide range of professional or semi-professional services which highly productive societies could afford. Though marked cleavages remained among these elements, and terms such as 'blue-collar', 'white-collar' or 'black-coated' worker, or 'man in the grey flannel suit', were used to distinguish these categories, the major effect of the spread of industrial technology was to expand the groups whose functions required a measure of education, skill and responsibility and whose income permitted common patterns of consumption above the level of subsistence.

As the middle class grew from all these sources, the lines of stratification which had characterized earlier industrial societies became less marked. Measured in terms of income, the tendency toward a reduction in class differentials was clear, though income alone did not fully reflect the factors of prestige and power that also affected the status of individuals and groups. In addition the extension of public services and educational benefits greatly reduced the gap in real income even where differences in money income were marked.

The transformation came earliest and most completely in the fluid societies of North America and Australasia, but it was remaking the class structure of European countries also. In London in 1930 a survey committee reviewing the changes in 'life and labour' during the forty years since the first London survey in 1890 noted that class differences were no longer clearly visible to the naked eye in distinctions of dress between residents of the fashionable West

End and the slums. By the decade after the second world war the services of the welfare state combined with a high level of employment, heavily graduated taxes on inherited wealth, and scholarships for promising students were making Britain into a middle-class society. Similar trends were swelling the middle-class ranks of other northern and western European countries.

Yet although the general effect of industrial development was to enlarge the middle class and to blur traditional lines, some conflicting tendencies had the effect of heightening stratification rather than of undermining it. The long and costly training required for advancement in an age of specialization could handicap the child whose family was unable to support him through a prolonged period of training or, because of its own social and cultural level, did not see the necessity. Studies in the United States showed that many children from lower-class homes dropped out of school when they reached the legal age because they did not see their own future in terms of the fruits of further training; Dutch universities at mid-century were still drawing only a tiny minority of their students from the homes of labourers. The increase in the size of the industrial enterprise and the concentration of industries in the hands of powerful corporations or the state made it increasingly difficult for new entrepreneurs to enter the market in many industrial lines, and enhanced the advantage enjoyed by those whose wealth and contacts gave them a head-start. Where a single large industrial concern replaced many small units, the number of places at the top became much fewer and the power of those at the top was immensely increased.

In the USSR the October revolution effectively destroyed the upper classes —landowners, capitalists, kulaks—by means of expropriation and, for some who resisted, exile or execution. The Soviet state created a new intelligentsia of technical and professional workers by training scientific personnel and cultural workers drawn from the ranks of workers and peasants and by re-orienting members of the old intelligentsia who threw in their lot with the revolution. Educational policies at first aimed to give priority to the children of workers and peasants, who came to form the bulk of the new technical class; later, restrictions imposed on the non-working classes were withdrawn. Membership in the Communist party was considered an indication of active, conscious, purposeful participation in the building of communism and carried with it prestige and influence.

After an initial period of equalization, policies of differential pay and incentive rewards provided stimuli for working people to raise their technical, educational and cultural levels. The range in income, including supplements such as housing and extended holidays, between upper officials, scientists or artists and the less skilled of the industrial workers and peasants was similar to the range of salaries and wages in other industrial countries, though artists and scientists generally stood higher in the scale. Such differences, however, did not provide a basis for hereditary class differences since inheritance, though not abolished, was strictly limited and educational opportunities were open to all. Inequalities in accumulated wealth thus tended to be reduced. It was the policy of the state, moreover, in line with Marxist–Leninist theory, that the distinction between manual and intellectual work should disappear. Toward this end, educational programmes were modified to provide direct work experience, and progressive mechanization and automation was expected to break down the line between the ordinary factory worker and the technician.

In both capitalist and communist countries bureaucracies which operated large structures, whether industrial or military or governmental, produced their own hierarchies. The importance of this development was noted by some observers in both societies in spite of their respective theories to the contrary. James Burnham (*The Managerial Revolution*, 1940) in the United States described the growing power and organization of industrial bureaucracies as the creation of a 'managerial class'; Milovan Djilas in Yugoslavia (*The New Class*, 1957), applying what he considered a Marxian analysis to the conduct of the communist upper bureaucracy and the logic of their behaviour, thought that he saw the characteristics of a new class.

Stratification along ethnic lines persisted among mixed populations of diverse origins, although the trends which were blurring class distinctions tended to diminish ethnic differences as well. Such differences were most tenacious where reinforced by religion or by colour. Job discrimination and other practices which prevented upward social mobility had the effect of converting ethnic difference into class distinction, or perpetuating class difference by resort to colour or religious prejudice. A variety of group institutions—fraternal societies, churches, clubs, restaurants, grocery stores, newspapers, sometimes radio programmes in the language of the group—tended to sustain ethnic distinctions.

Changes with respect to ethnic stratification were brought about in part by general economic and social tendencies and in part by public policies which varied markedly from one country to another. The decline of white supremacy around the world, both in fact and in theory, put those who practised racial discrimination on the defensive. In some countries ethnic separateness was formalized in law; in others it was expressly discouraged. Canada, where the French population had retained its identity after the area was transferred from France to Britain in the eighteenth century, had pursued a policy which encouraged immigrant groups to settle in national units. In the twentieth century this policy of group settlement was replaced by one of assimilation, but some institutions, notably the school system, helped to keep alive the divisions which had grown out of the earlier policies. Brazil followed a somewhat similar course, first accepting group settlement which produced ethnic colonies of Germans and others, then, in the second quarter of the twentieth century, reversing the policy. In Australia the large numbers of new Australians who immigrated from Europe in the decade after the second world war were systematically integrated into the economic life of the country in a manner designed to prevent their forming ethnic islands or becoming a lower class.

The United States had never pursued the Canadian policy of group settlement but had expected what was commonly referred to as the 'melting pot' of American life, aided by an English-language public school system, to produce generic Americans out of polyglot foreigners. It was with some shock that Americans discovered at the height of the mass immigration before the first world war that the touch of American soil had not immediately transformed Italian and Polish peasants into 100 per cent Americans, in the image of the dominant Anglo-Saxon, Protestant middle class. In actual fact each successive wave of immigrants entered the society at the bottom of the socio-economic ladder, filled the poorest paying and least skilled jobs, lived in the poorest housing among neighbours who spoke the same language, and were looked down upon by those who were already well-established and who had separated themselves from the newcomers by superior jobs and place of residence. When restrictive immigration laws cut off the flow from Europe after the first world war, the familiar process of ethnic stratification was repeated again as low-paid jobs drew to the slums of industrial centres, and the low social status of newcomers, American 'hill-billies' from isolated mountain hollows or worn-out lands, Mexicans from over the border, Negroes from the rural south and Puerto Ricans from their crowded island.

Where colour differences set the group apart, social stratification on the basis of ethnic differences persisted most strongly. In the United States the principle of the melting pot was not expected to apply to Negroes, for there was presumed to be a colour line between 'white' and 'Negro'. Throughout the first half of the twentieth century the colour line continued to act as a bar to opportunity, but in the course of these years, and at an accelerating pace, barriers were lowered, the gap in levels of income, occupation and education was narrowed and segregation as a legal principle was outlawed by the courts. By mid-century grandchildren of slaves along with children of immigrants had entered the ranks of the expanding and levelling middle class.

In other areas where the colour line was less sharply drawn, notably in the countries of Latin America and in the Caribbean, the same tendency existed toward lowered barriers and increased social mobility. As it affected the indigenous Indian population of these regions, the trend was toward the incorporation without discrimination of those who became part of the national life; the line based on ethnic identity was converted into one based on the cultural isolation of tribal groups. Migration of West Indians to Britain in the 1950s introduced the colour factor for the first time there, and large numbers of Algerian workers in France placed a strain on the tolerance of colour differences which had been traditional in that country. The migration of Eurasians to Holland at the time of Indonesian independence presented a problem of assimilation. But only in the Union of South Africa did the colour line become sharper and the policy of *apartheid* gain in strength while it was weakening in other parts of the world.

(*b*) *In non-industrial societies*. In the stratified hierarchical societies of the East and of Africa, a major instrument of change was the body of western-educated individuals who were in a position to challenge the traditional *élite* of the old society.

The nature of the westernized element and its position differed markedly from country to country. In China the western-oriented constituted a group apart, drawn largely from the merchant classes of the port cities who dealt with foreign traders, and from students at mission schools who commanded the western languages necessary to permit them to study abroad and were in line for scholarships. In their efforts to remake Chinese society they came in conflict with those who represented tradition and power, and they were out of touch with the masses of the people. When the communist régime came to power it could readily reject the western-oriented element as 'foreign' and could discredit them by reasserting traditional Chinese cultural values while themselves remaking Chinese society with technology and institutions derived from the West.

In Japan, on the other hand, westernization was not confined to a distinct group which separated itself from the rest of the population but permeated the society to a greater or less degree. Rather than creating a new social stratum, it produced a conflict within the minds and behaviour of a large proportion of the population, leaving the structure of the society essentially unchanged. In Korea the limited influence of missionaries remained the principal source of westernization until after the second world war, when all segments of the population began to share in a rapid process of modernization. In Thailand westernization came through the pursuit of western education by the royal family and court-centred aristocracy, and thus did not create a new social class but modified the conduct and attitudes of the existing *élite*. In the Arab areas, where the class gulf between peasants and landowners was extreme, virtually all educated elements were drawn from the upper class.

Colonial governments depended for the extension and operation of their rule upon a local element trained for certain tasks. The policy of the Dutch in Indonesia was to develop the Indo-European element as the principal adjuncts to the Dutch administrators while providing little western education for Indonesians; this produced a westernized class which was ethnically distinct. When the Indonesians secured their independence they directed their indignation against this privileged class with such force as to drive a large proportion of them from the country; only a tiny group of western-trained Indonesians was available for the development of the Indonesian state. The British in Burma used Indians for most technical and civil service posts not filled by British, while the Burmans who attended English schools became almost completely identified with European culture and interests. Leadership in independent Burma came from men who had remained closer to the people. In India the development of a westernized element through an extensive system of English education designed to provide for the civil services was accompanied by a series of strong movements for the reform of the society from within and by the movement of Indian nationalism. As a consequence the western-educated elements were not separated from those who remained part of the traditional structure, but acted as a leaven in the total body politic.

The most conscious and determined efforts to change the class structure in Asian countries came in Japan and India and in the revolutionary society of communist China. Elsewhere measures to improve the lot of the peasants, the beginnings of industry, the expansion of the bureaucracy and of the educated professional groups pointed the direction of change, but by mid-century these influences had hardly made a dent on the basic social structure.

Japan introduced a series of reform measures following the second world war in its conscious effort to remake its society on a democratic basis. These affected land tenure, access to education, the status of labour and the position of young people and of women. In their initial impact, these reforms modified outward aspects of the society. But it remained a question how deeply they affected the highly structured pattern of relationships which were entrenched in and reinforced by modes of speech and address and by countless details of prescribed daily conduct.

In India the hereditary caste system had been under attack by reforming movements of the nineteenth century. The most westernized had attacked the system directly, while the Hindu reformers had insisted that the fourfold division of Vedic society did not imply that distinctions should be passed on by heredity but rather that they should reflect personal character and natural capacity. In the 1920s, under the leadership of Mahatma Gandhi, the movement against caste distinction and untouchability gained momentum and became part of the nationalist movement. In Gandhi's own *ashram*, untouchables—whom he renamed *harijans*, meaning 'beloved of God'—lived on a basis of equality with others; he encouraged inter-caste marriage and through constant preaching hammered away at the caste structure. *Harijans* themselves organized to demand the removal of disabilities.

By the time of independence a strong public sentiment against untouchability had been built up and the practice had broken down at a number of points. The Indian constitution abolished it outright and made the enforcement of any disability arising from it a penal offence. Barriers to inter-caste and inter-faith marriage were also removed by the Hindu Marriage Validating Act of 1949 and subsequent acts in 1954 and 1955. These measures took away all legal sanction from the maintenance of caste on an hereditary basis.

Many aspects of the caste system survived in practice when it had been abolished by law, however, and untouchability could not be destroyed overnight. In some respects castes gained a new *raison d'être* from the introduction

of democratic suffrage, for candidates seeking support for political office naturally turned to their own group, and this meant their own caste. But political
parties cut across caste lines, and the longer effect of suffrage was to give the
advantage to the groups which were more numerous rather than to those
which had been more influential and thus to establish a new basis for relations
among social groups.

The most potent factors in breaking down the rigidity of traditional caste
stratification were the growth of modern industry, the development of new
professions which cut across the traditional occupational lines that coincided
with caste, and the mobility, juxtaposition and public activity which characterized life in urban communities and in industry. Taxation, land reform, the
break-up of the joint family, the presence of millions of refugees all made it
impossible to maintain a traditional status and contributed to the development
of new social forms.

Stratification on the basis of ethnic and religious distinctions was even
more ingrained in Asia than in the West, for until the idea of the national,
secular state made its way into Asia the concept of common citizenship was
foreign to the traditions of Asian society. Religious and ethnic groups were
expected to retain their identity and distinctive institutions, including their
law and the practices enjoined by their culture. In the multi-cultural societies
of Asia, therefore, national citizenship was slow to erase, or even to lessen, the
divisions between ethnic or religious communities.

There was scarcely a country of Asia, with the exception of Japan, Korea
and China, where this problem did not present itself sharply. It was perhaps
most dramatic in Malaya, where under British rule the Malays enjoyed certain rights not shared by citizens of Chinese or Indian extraction, though these
numbered more than half of the population of the Malay state at the time of
independence. But it was present in the separate status of the Chinese populations of Indonesia and Thailand, and in the Tamil language issue in Ceylon.
A crucial question confronting India and Pakistan was whether India
could succeed in incorporating its Muslim minority as citizens of a secular
state, and what status would ultimately be enjoyed by the Hindus who
constituted 10 per cent of the population of the avowedly Islamic state of
Pakistan.

Ethnic stratification was complicated where these divisions coincided with
economic class lines, as they often did. This situation existed in Turkey,
where the liquidation of the Armenian population and the expulsion of the
Greeks largely deprived Turkish society of its merchant and artisan classes.
The Chinese in Indonesia, and to a considerable extent in Thailand and
Malaya, were similarly an economic as well as an ethnic group.

Ethnic distinctions thus remained of vital importance to the structure of
society in Asia and the Middle East up to the middle of the twentieth century.
Events tended both to intensify and to mitigate these distinctions. The rise of
nationalism accented ethnic identity, as did the fierce communal strife atten-

dant upon the break-up of the Ottoman empire and the partition of the Indian sub-continent. In the years after the second world war the existence of the Chinese People's Republic made the Chinese in the non-communist countries politically suspect as well as the object of economic envy, and the creation of the state of Israel brought an exodus of Jews from their ghettos in eastern lands.

But there was a tendency for ethnic lines to lose their importance wherever the process of urbanization was accompanied by the loss of distinction in dress, by entrance into unaccustomed occupations and by the substitution of new identities for those associated with an ethnic past. Everywhere there was a tendency to produce what the sociologists termed the 'marginal man', who enjoyed a dual cultural orientation or was in the process of losing an old cultural orientation and seeking to acquire a new one. Though ethnic minorities clung fiercely to their separate loyalties, the new nationalism, with its universal education and indoctrination into the language and culture of the nation-group, tended to make Indians, Iraquis, Indonesians, Malays, Pakistanis and Lebanese out of the multi-cultural units which composed these new and proudly self-conscious nation states.

III. VOLUNTARY ORGANIZATIONS

1. *Functions of voluntary organizations in modern society*

As the family shrank in size and in the range of social functions which it performed, and as class stratification and ethnic groupings lost much of their sharpness and ability to define the status and role of the individual, voluntary organizations came to play an ever increasing part in giving shape to modern society and in defining the identity and status of its members.

Voluntary organizations were of many types and were based on many kinds of common interest. The largest and most pervasive were political parties, of growing importance to the operation of the modern democratic state.* Among the most ubiquitous associations were those formed to promote or protect the economic interests of their members—labour unions, organizations of businessmen into trade associations, employers' associations and chambers of commerce, farmers' organizations, professional associations, associations of consumers or taxpayers. As organizations of this type grew in influence, they sometimes tended to become monopolistic bodies, largely controlling the practice of certain professions, opportunities for certain types of employment or access to certain markets and sources of supply, and thus to lose some of their voluntary character.

Some associations offered their members the opportunity to engage in a variety of social activities with age-mates, especially among youth, or in women's organizations on the basis of sex; some were dedicated to civic or

* See Chapter XXIII, Political Institutions.

benevolent activities; others permitted their members to pursue a common hobby or cultural interest.

These many and varied organizations were spontaneous reactions to the need to find means of participating in complex urban life, for they provided the groupings through which social contacts were maintained, interests pursued and influence exerted. The individual who could no longer define himself wholly in terms of his family had to define himself in terms of his occupation and of the groups with which he was identified—his church, his political party, his trade union, his club, association or fraternal order, or the civic or benevolent society to which he belonged. When he met another person, it was often in terms of an association with one organization or another that he might form his expectations of the new acquaintance, beyond the identification provided by his job.

The voluntary organization, moreover, was an increasingly essential instrument for the operations of liberal democracy. Modern democracies could not depend on the direct forms of communication that characterized the village, the Greek city state or the New England town meeting. Some channels were essential for the thought of the populace to take shape and to be expressed. Voluntary organizations offered more intimate and personal sources than the mass media for formation of opinion and attitudes and provided people with a means of group expression through which they could participate actively in the democratic process.

In the socialist societies also voluntary organizations played a special role. In line with the conception that all people should participate in the long run in the administration of public affairs, organizations such as trade unions, professional associations and similar bodies exercised public functions; they were entrusted with appropriate powers and responsibilities, and settled many questions on their own. Moreover, they embraced virtually the entire population; trade union membership, for example, included practically all factory and office workers, while youth organizations covered the bulk of the young people.

2. Economic interest organizations

(a) Business organizations. Associations of businessmen to promote their interests took the form of trade associations for separate industries, employers' associations with which to confront labour, and chambers of commerce to promote the business interests of a particular locality. All these organizations had their prototypes in mediaeval craft and merchant guilds, as did also the labour unions, but their existence in relation to modern industry dated from the second half of the nineteenth century, and in the period during and after the first world war their number increased and their functions were extended.

Trade associations originated in efforts by producers to modify unrestrained competition and to strengthen their position against manufacturers of alternative products. They engaged in research, promoted the publication of trade data, and sought to influence public policy in respect to such matters as tariffs and freight rates in favour of their products. In competition between industries, they engaged in institutional advertising, promoting the products or services of a whole industry rather than those of a single company.

The first world war gave a strong impetus to the growth of trade associations when industries were called upon to make a concerted effort to meet the demands of the governments for war products. In the years after the war they extended their activities to the development of standards for products, such as uniform sizes for screws and bolts or safety standards for electrical equipment. They were made the instruments of experiments in economic organization, in Mussolini's corporate state where they were entrusted with governing powers over industry and in the short-lived American effort to bring the economy out of the depths of the depression of the 1930s by means of codes drawn up by trade associations to cover wages, prices and business practices in each industry.

Trade associations performed social and educational as well as economic functions, for they enabled businessmen to identify themselves with producers in a common field and to maintain social contacts within the group. Their publications, in addition to informing of matters strictly related to their business, contributed to the formation of opinion and the spread of general information.

Employers' associations were sometimes formed explicitly to cope with labour relations; elsewhere trade associations included this role. In their initial form most employers' associations were aggressively anti-union, and engaged in activities designed to prevent the formation of unions, to oppose their demands and to develop a climate of opinion unfavourable to their existence or operation. As unions gained in strength employers' associations generally dropped their extreme belligerency and became instruments for negotiating agreements with labour or, as in several European countries and in Australia and New Zealand, for representing the employers' interest in government machinery for the adjustment of wages or of labour disputes. Some anti-labour employers' associations survived in the United States after they had lost their belligerency in most other countries, and were found in the 1930s to be engaged in violence, intimidation, the maintenance of private police and the conduct of high-powered public relations campaigns to discredit organized labour. It required the enactment of national legislation and skill in its administration to detect and check the many devices by which such associations sought to nullify the workers' legally assured rights to bargain collectively through unions of their own choosing. Whatever their position, employers' associations did much to form the attitudes of their members and thus contributed to the climate of opinion within which labour relations were conducted during these years.

Chambers of commerce overlapped trade and employers' associations in membership but constituted a distinct class of voluntary organization composed of the members of a local business community—not only the merchants as their name, commerce, implied, but manufacturers, bankers and other business interests as well. Their chief *raison d'être* was to promote conditions favourable to the economic interests of the locality—to maintain a tax policy or a labour market favourable to the needs of local business, to stimulate the industries or trades which flourished in the area or which they hoped to attract there, to sustain the purchasing power of their customers. Chambers of commerce frequently acted as the spokesmen for their communities. In the sprawling and anonymous cities it was often the chamber of commerce which defined the city to itself, and which articulated the interests of 'the community' and the manner in which they should be pursued. In so doing they tended to identify the interests of the community with those of the business group and to contribute to the dominance of the business element.

These business organizations, whether based on trade or locality, were bound together in national federations which constituted the voice of business on a national scale. The national associations of manufacturers and national chambers of commerce exercised informal leadership in some countries and rigorous control of their member units in others. Their presence in every country on a truly voluntary basis was assumed when the International Labour Organization was formed in 1919, and they remained one of the bases for the tripartite representation of each country by labour, employers and government in the structure of that organization.

Business associations were not only linked on a national basis but internationally, both according to trades, and through the International Chamber of Commerce formed in 1919, which served as a channel of informal interchange between business groups in different countries.

(b) *Professional bodies.* Professional organizations became increasingly important as the number of specialized professions grew. Many of these organizations were bodies of long standing, such as the national associations of doctors and lawyers in most countries. Subdivisions of specialists within these broad professional categories, such as psychiatrists, formed separate associations as the speciality became distinct. New professions, such as social work, set up their associations as they acquired professional standing.

The general function of professional associations was to establish, promote and often to police the profession. They prescribed criteria for membership in terms of training, established codes of professional ethics and withdrew the privilege of membership, and with it the right to practise the profession, from those who violated the ethical principles laid down by the body, and they undertook to keep their members abreast of the developing body of knowledge in their fields. The part played by the professional association in licensing for practice and in inspecting and qualifying training institutions varied from country to country. In some these functions were performed by public agencies, in others by professional associations and in still others by the professional organization acting on behalf of the state. Professional associations also provided a channel for their members to voice their views on matters of public concern. In the field of health, for example, the organized medical profession had great impact on the development of health services, both in raising standards of service and in supporting or opposing specific health measures.

(c) *Labour unions.* Labour unions, organized to provide workers with bargaining power *vis-à-vis* the employer, offered industrial workers a means by which to identify themselves with a struggle, and a body in which they could assume responsibility and learn to function in a social group. As unions became more firmly established and more a matter of routine which workers joined automatically in order to hold their jobs, and as they assumed responsibilities before labour courts or in the administration of agreements or of social security benefits, they lost some of their old meaning for the individual worker. Instead of being an association which the worker regarded as his own, the union sometimes became merely a large organization with which he must deal and to which, like the state, he must pay his quota. Yet the labour union remained the largest voluntary organization, apart from the church and the political party, with which the people of industrial countries were identified.*

(d) *Farm organizations.* Farmers and peasants formed voluntary organizations less generally and less durably than did workers and businessmen. Voluntary organization among farmers was sporadic and partial, with some notable exceptions such as Denmark where from the third quarter of the nineteenth century economic, political, and cultural organizations of farmers were a major element in the structure of the state. In countries of advanced agriculture farm organizations were mainly geared to the improvement of their economic operation. In still-feudal peasant societies they were a part of political movements for social reform.†

(e) *Other economic interest associations.* Other kinds of common economic interests afforded a basis for association. Associations of local taxpayers or ratepayers or owners of homes and real estate frequently represented the interests of existing residents or investors in local land or business in efforts to prevent changes in the character of their neighbourhoods or to avoid the burden of supporting new public services. In France in the 1950s, these small investors were roused into a political movement known as *Poujadisme* by their resistance to taxation. The need for buyers of complex industrial products to have an independent check on the claims of manufacturers led to the formation in the United States in the 1930s of membership organizations to test products offered on the market and to report the result of such tests in order that consumers might know what they were buying. So valuable did this service become that by the mid-1950s one such organization counted well over 100,000 members.

---

* See Chapter XXX, pp. 1110–1132, Labour
† See Chapter XXX, pp. 1132–42, Peasants and Farmers

(*f*) *Co-operatives*. Individuals banded together into co-operative societies to protect their interests as consumers. The co-operative movement, which had originated in England in the mid-nineteenth century among poor workers who saw a chance to stretch their pennies by returning to themselves the middle-man's profits, grew slowly in most countries. In Britain co-operative societies developed virtually as arms of the labour movement; in Belgium they promoted and became part of the socialist movement; they were active in the Scandinavian countries.

Co-operative organizations of consumers generally played a relatively small role in the total economy. Although in many places there were credit unions, co-operative stores, housing co-operatives or group-purchased medical care, consumer co-operatives rarely included a large proportion of the public or accounted for a substantial part of their purchases.

Even where co-operatives were few and small, however, they tended to have importance for their members beyond their economic effect, for the principles established by the original co-operative at Rochdale prescribed a course of education and discussion before members should launch any co-operative endeavour and required that a portion of the group's annual income should always be devoted to social and educational objectives. In a few places, notably among the fishermen and poor farmers of the province of Nova Scotia in Canada, the co-operative movement became the means of reinvigorating a depressed economy, as it had raised the depressed rural economy of Denmark in the latter part of the nineteenth century. It was one of the forms of organization for rural communities in Israel, alongside of the communal *kibbutz* and the settlement with individual landownership. By mid-century a number of countries with newly developing economies, notably India and to a lesser extent Indonesia, had taken steps to facilitate the formation of co-operatives in the hope that their citizens might choose this means to advance their well-being. In the communist countries the co-operative was sometimes used as an intermediate step on the way to collectivization or state operation.

3. *Mutual benefit organizations*

Mutual aid in time of distress continued to provide a basis for voluntary organization, although the extension of social security and the benefits of the welfare state reduced the need for such associations as a means of protection.

The fraternal orders which spread from Britain to the overseas British dominions and to the United States during the second half of the nineteenth century were outgrowths of the Friendly Societies formed by working men in British industrial centres for mutual aid in case of illness or death. They had both protective and social features—as insurance societies, often badly managed at first but in time operated on a sound actuarial basis, and as lodges patterned on the Freemasons, with secret rituals to which their members were initiated. When health insurance and other social insurance measures were adopted, the fraternal orders were either registered as agents through which a part of the public programme was administered, as under the British health insurance scheme of 1911 or, as in Australia, their activities were limited to those benefits which the state system did not provide.

Their principal importance in the twentieth century, however, was in their social role. 'Lodge night', when members went through secret rituals, addressed each other by elaborate titles and shared a sense of fraternity, offered an escape from the monotony of industrial tasks and the anonymity or urban life. When a lodge member moved to a new community he could count on finding 'brothers' there. In the second quarter of the twentieth century the importance of fraternal orders declined somewhat, as cinema and television offered some of the escape entertainment which the lodge had furnished and public social insurance made mutual insurance less necessary. Yet fraternal orders continued to provide means by which otherwise anonymous individuals could establish social links and a claim to social kinship with others.

Wherever recent immigrants congregated, they too formed mutual aid societies, to stand by each other in sickness and death and as a means by which people in a strange land could enjoy together the customs of the homeland they had left behind. With the decline in mass immigration from Europe after the first world war, immigrant societies declined in importance, for association based on the country of their parents' origin had little appeal to the second generation, especially where societies had been formed on a village or provincial basis as were, for example, most of the Italian immigrant associations. Several of these societies changed their purpose from mutual aid to relief for their former compatriots during and after the second world war, and some immigrant associations that had been on the wane revived on this basis. In the urban communities of Africa a wide variety of mutual aid societies were the principal social units which began to give shape to the life of Africans uprooted from their tribal homes.

Voluntary associations along ethnic lines went beyond mutual aid to promote the interests and improve the status of disadvantaged groups. The National Association for the Advancement of Colored People acted as a spearhead in the efforts to improve the status of Negroes in American society; the All-India Depressed Classes Association acted as spokesman for the untouchables of India.

The most extensive ethnic group organizations were those maintained by Jews. In the centuries of their life as enclaves within other societies, the Jewish people had developed an almost complete set of social institutions through which their separate life was conducted. Where they no longer led a ghetto existence, they continued to sustain ethnic organizations for a wide variety of functions—for the relief of Jews abroad and the support of Zionism, for the provision of welfare services to the Jewish community, for defence against discrimination and for civic participation with other elements in the population.

Other factors of common experience provided the basis for associations devoted to furthering the interests of their members. In a period which saw two world wars involving large segments of the population, organizations of war veterans sought the extension of benefits and privileges, and renewed from time to time some of the camaraderie of the past.

4. *Organizations for social activities*

Voluntary organizations were by no means limited to associations to promote the direct interest of their members. They offered a means of association for a multitude of purposes—social, recreational, civic, benevolent or the pursuit of a common educational or cultural interest. Voluntary associations based on age and sex proliferated in most countries during this period.

(*a*) *Youth.* The conditions of urban industrial society made organization important for youth. Longer schooling and child labour laws combined to raise the age at which young people started to work, to sharpen the distinction between the adult world and the world of the child and to prolong the period of adolescence. In the urban milieu, with its highly individualized relationships and multitude of cross-currents, the small family unit could not provide the basis for status and social relationships which the young person required and had generally found in an extended family group within a stable rural community. For urban adolescents and older children, clubs, gangs or societies composed of contemporaries met their need for something to which they could belong and from which they could derive status, a sense of identity and an opportunity for social life. Youth organizations, whether street corner gangs, boy scout troops, church clubs or political youth movements all served this basic function for their members.

In the many parts of the world where revolutionary political and social changes were taking place, youth organizations performed an additional role. Either spontaneously or under the direction of political leaders, they served as spearheads for movements to bring about change and as instruments for reorienting the values and relationships of their society and for consolidating new structures of power.

The multiplicity of youth organizations which proliferated in number and expanded in membership during the twentieth century had their roots in several quite distinct developments of the nineteenth century: the politically oriented youth movements, represented by Mazzini's 'Young Europe' and corresponding liberal revolutionary movements in Germany, Poland and elsewhere; the spontaneous organization of youth in revolt against adult authority; the efforts of political, religious, labour and other organizations to rally the youth in their ranks; and the efforts of civic, religious and welfare leaders to meet the social needs of working-class youth in the growing industrial communities.

The political youth movements were chiefly composed of university students and other young intellectuals, except for the socialist youth movements which drew from the working class. These young people were in conscious revolt against established institutions and they pitted their idealism and vision of a new political and social order against the attitudes and leadership of the older generation.

In the years before the first world war youth movements of this type in many countries acted as the spearheads for a variety of political movements, staging demonstrations and engaging in both propaganda and direct action in support of their political causes. In the countries where social and political tensions were at a minimum and existing institutions permitted orderly and continuous change, such as Britain, Denmark, Canada or the United States, such politically oriented youth movements were absent or of little significance. But wherever revolutionary tensions were present and the social and political structure was under fire, from the countries of Latin America to those of Asia, spontaneous movements by students and their associates played a part in the struggle to bring radical change. The Young Turks who undertook to remake the Ottoman empire and the Chinese student movement which provided much of the support for Sun Yat-sen and for the revolutionary cultural-political movement known as the New Tide were but two of the more conspicuous examples. Indian students in the 1930s and 1940s were an active element in the struggle for independence, and in the 1950s students took part in the over-throw of the dictator in Cuba, and in many demonstrations elsewhere.

Alongside of the primarily political movements, and also independent of the educational, recreational and character-building organizations founded and governed by adults, autonomous self-governing youth organizations arose in a number of European countries, notably among the Germans, Czechs, Scandinavians and Dutch. These groups went hiking and camping and engaged in sports; sometimes they took part in movements, such as temperance, or acted as the advance guard of the socialist movements.

The most considerable of these groups was the German youth movement, or *Wandervögel*, which originated shortly before 1900. It was in revolt against all forms of traditional authority, in the home and in the rigid, half-militarized, half-paternalistic system of German education. The movement reflected the desire for a new way of life, for greater liberty, sincerity and beauty as opposed to the materialism and conventionalism of the time. It revived romantic German traditions, folk songs and dances and folklore, and formed groups drawn together by the warmth of emotional life and trusting in the leadership of older comrades. Although it fought against all established authority, it had no clear or definite political or social aims as an alternative to the existing order, and it longed for a new authority, a real *Führer*, in place of the established authority of the father in the home and the bureaucratic leadership in the state. Its 'wandering' represented the old, traditional German unrest and the new unrest of dissatisfied youth, involved in a deep conflict that was changing the relations between parents and children, and it constituted a sentimental expression of the striving for freedom within the political and social structure of pre-war Germany.

In the years after the first world war, both the politically oriented youth organizations and the autonomous romantic youth movements were taken over by dictatorial régimes and converted into instruments to consolidate the power of the leader and to remake the society along lines dictated from above. The Italian fascists' *Ballila* and the Nazis' *Hitler Jugend* were not spontaneous expressions of youth directed against the established adult leadership but, rather, tightly organized and disciplined arms of adult organizations. Instead of being composed largely of students and intellectuals, they were drawn predominantly from those social groups which had not exercised social or political power. Although they rejected the authority of their elders more completely than the spontaneous youth movements had done, they acted at the behest of a new ruling adult leadership.

Following the October revolution, the Young Communist League in the USSR became the Communist party's assistant in all fields of social activity, including industry, culture, the upbringing of children and youth, public education, sports. Its members took the lead in many campaigns, such as the opening up of new farmlands, Komsomol construction projects, campaigns for industrial economy, for safeguarding public order. It undertook to train its members as well-educated self-disciplined individuals capable of displaying creative initiative in every undertaking. It guided the work of the Young Pioneers whose purpose was to help the school and the parents in the bringing up of children of school age with a view to their becoming active full-fledged members of the community.

Where youth organizations were enlisted either as followers or as partners in the remaking of societies, they not only offered to their members an active social role and a group to which to belong but they developed in them an intense sense of dedication and identification with the interests of the people and the state. Elsewhere, youth organizations which played an active part in bringing about political revolution and social change often lacked a clearly defined role after these objectives were obtained, as was the case among Indian students whose continued outbursts of passive resistance in the years after independence were regarded as 'student indiscipline' by some of the same people who had urged such conduct during the fight against the British *raj*.

Far different in origin and purpose, but serving some similar functions for their members, were the multitude of youth organizations which reflected the efforts of adult society to meet the needs of urban youth. From beginnings in the Sunday School movement to take factory children off the streets in Birmingham and Manchester and to give them instruction, churches provided organized activities for young people as part of their regular function, and as a means of attraction or to hold them within the church. Through countless clubs, guilds and societies attached to churches of every denomination in most urban areas, young people found opportunities for social contacts and group activity and a channel through which they could render a service to their community, express neighbourly concern for their fellows or establish contacts with other young people across class, ethnic or geographical lines.

Voluntary organizations with religious orientation supplemented those directly affiliated to churches. The Young Men's Christian Association, and its counterpart, the Young Women's Christian Association, established in London in 1844 and 1855, became world-wide in scope with total memberships in the 1950s of over 4,000,000 men and half a million women. These organizations did not confine their membership to Christians, or to any specific denominations, yet their Protestant origin and continuing leadership gave them larger memberships in predominantly Protestant than in Catholic or non-Christian areas. Catholic youth organizations in many countries claimed large memberships composed of parish youth groups and organizations of students in Catholic and non-Catholic colleges and universities. Similar organizations were formed among Jewish youth.

The groups which participated in church-sponsored or religiously oriented organizations differed in age between countries and among individual churches or local communities. The programmes of some churches were primarily for younger children; in some countries the Young Women's Christian Association was composed almost wholly of young adult working women. In combination, however, they included a wide range of children, adolescents and older youth.

Though the churches were first in the field, non-religious organizations initiated by welfare workers and civic leaders became numerous and large. Boys' clubs began to be organized by welfare workers in the 1860s, especially in the United States. The Settlement House movement spread rapidly in the last decade of the nineteenth and early years of the twentieth century from its beginning in London to many cities in Britain, the USA and northern Europe, devoting much effort to the formation of clubs for the boys and girls of the crowded city slums.

Several organizations whose separate units followed a standardized pattern of activity were formed early in the twentieth century and numbered their members in the millions fifty years later. Boy Scouts and Girl Guides founded in England in 1908 and 1910, were organized throughout Europe, the USA and the British Commonwealth countries before the first world war, and in Latin America, Asia and Africa during the next two or three decades. By 1955 the Boy Scouts, with national organizations in nearly every country outside the communist areas, estimated their world membership as 6,500,000 the Girl Scouts or Guides numbered over 4,000,000 members in 35 countries. Boys' club federations, following the pattern established in 1906 in the United States, were formed in other countries and linked in an international organization. Junior Red Cross societies after the first world war followed similar programmes in many countries and were internationally affiliated. Innumerable sport and athletic clubs engaged in team competitions and tournaments.

All these organizations tended to bridge the gap between generations rather than to accentuate it. In one way or another they had an educational character-building objective. They afforded opportunities for the development of personality, social responsibility and leadership while providing recreation and activities designed to develop skills. Through such activity as camping, they enabled predominantly urban young people to acquire some experience in dealing with nature. By giving their members a chance to manage their own affairs responsibly, they offered a training ground for democratic citizenship. Through their national and international affiliations they established communication between young people of different background and nationality, promoted identification across social and national lines and provided their outstanding members with opportunities to take part in national and international conferences or assemblies.

Membership in formal youth organizations was drawn primarily from the middle and professional classes and from the more stable ranks of the industrial population. It was the widespread, if not universal, experience of the Boy Scouts and Girl Guides, the Young Men's Christian Associations and the Young Women's Christian Associations, the Boys' clubs, athletic leagues and clubs at settlement houses, churches and community centres that they attracted chiefly boys and girls with active interests and ambitions from families which could afford to buy a uniform or which encouraged church attendance or were concerned for the education of their children. Although the welfare-oriented youth organizations had been originally established to counteract the disorganizing influences of the city upon the children and young people whose families had the least to offer, few of the socially unstable elements found their way into any of these organizations. For such young people wholly autonomous neighbourhood gangs, sometimes anti-social and often in violent conflict with other groups who might threaten to invade their territory, provided a basis for identification, loyalty and the assertion of their personalities.

Although street corner gangs, Scouts, boys' and girls' organizations, and clubs sponsored by welfare and religious agencies were chiefly to be found in urban areas, organization of rural youth also became well established in a number of places. In contrast to the private origin and support of most urban youth organizations, governments frequently sponsored clubs for rural youth as part of their programme for raising the level of agricultural technology and rural life. Many countries followed the pattern developed by the Extension Service of the United States Department of Agriculture which inaugurated its 4-H club programme in 1914. With technical guidance these clubs for boys and girls built their programmes around agricultural and home-making projects which stimulated their members to learn and use the best agricultural and home-making techniques and to develop their capacities for leadership.

Whatever their character, purpose, or auspices, youth organizations in the twentieth century reflected the changing social conditions which brought them into being and determined their form: reduction of traditional parental authority, increase in social freedom, greater association between the sexes. They operated, too, to develop norms of conduct to which they exacted conformity from age-mates and, ultimately, acquiescence from their elders.

(b) *Aged.* The organization of older people was far less widespread and purposeful than that of youth, but in the second quarter of the twentieth century, and with growing momentum after the second world war, the movement for old people's associations grew. In the United States the tendency to organize on the basis of old age received a major impetus during the depression of the 1930s when a quasi-political movement led to the formation of Townsend clubs, named after their founder, to agitate for old age pensions and incidentally to enjoy social activity. With the provision of old age insurance and assistance in 1935, much of the political effort was dissipated, but the social impetus continued, and took the form of the establishment of 'golden age' or 'silver age' clubs in many communities. Elsewhere retired persons organized to seek improved pensions or to form social groups.

Clubs for senior citizens, however, could be regarded only as a beginning toward finding a means by which older people could retain a functional place in a society where life expectancy was greatly extended but in which the small family of parents and young children constituted the active family group, in which many lines of employment gave preference to the young and in which emphasis on youthfulness tended to make older people feel on the shelf. In some places in the USSR groups of retired persons met this situation by undertaking projects on behalf of the children of the community.

(c) *Women.* Women's organizations were ubiquitous and grew in number and scope. Feminist organizations to promote the cause of women's rights lost much of their importance as rights were achieved, but the role of women in civic affairs expanded. Women organized for mutual support and assistance, as for example university women who joined together to provide a means for continued self-education, to raise fellowships for women scholars, to strengthen standards of women's education, to promote the employment of qualified women and to facilitate interchange and intercommunication among women of common interests in other countries. An international federation formed in 1919 linked university women's associations of fifty countries by the 1950s. Business and professional women organized for comparable purposes.

Some women formed civic organizations, for specific purposes such as the women's temperance societies which were numerous in the nineteenth century and continued in some countries in the twentieth, or for more general purposes. A common religious affiliation provided the basis for some organizations, such as the associations of Catholic, Jewish or Protestant church women. The basis of some organizations was ill-defined and their purpose vague, as in many women's clubs or women's guilds which might have any number of interests, from gardening to adult education, and which were often linked into national federations. Some were formed primarily for welfare purposes, to sustain a particular charity such as the care of unmarried mothers or the provision of workshops for the handicapped.

Apart from the women's auxiliaries of some labour unions or corresponding farm groups and women's divisions of political parties, women's organizations drew most of their members from the middle classes. They represented the efforts of women with some leisure to use their leisure constructively and at the same time to enjoy the society of others. In addition they provided a means, in the highly mobile urban society of the twentieth century, by which women could establish social contacts in new communities to which the vicissitudes of their husbands' jobs or their own might take them.*

5. Civic associations

Voluntary civic bodies of various sorts were indispensable to the structure of the local community in many parts of the world. Much of the business of local government was done on a voluntary basis, or at least by persons whose professional job lay outside local government and who received only expenses or minor fees for the services which they rendered to their community. Local magistrates and local councils in Britain, for example, consisted of volunteer citizens; in the United States the entire school system was governed by local volunteer school boards, generally elected by the locality. While the increasing complexity of local administration brought the professionalization of many municipal services, it also multiplied the areas in which citizens were called upon to give voluntary service as members of boards and committees to oversee, advise or supplement the work of public officials. This form of civic activity drew most heavily on members of the middle and upper classes, but with the growing importance of labour organizations, civic committees and boards included more and more representatives of workers' groups.

In addition to voluntary bodies which carried direct responsibility for local government or services, organizations of prominent citizens set the civic tone of their communities. Some of these, such as the Rotary clubs composed of one representative of each of the major professions and business activities in a community, the Kiwanis clubs, and the Lions clubs, were international in scope, as were their women's counterparts, Zonta, Soroptimists. Rotary International was formed in 1910, five years after formation of the first club.

These clubs met regularly for sociability and to discuss community affairs, welcomed to their meetings members from other communities who happened to be in town, offered hospitality to distinguished visitors, and provided a sort of community leadership. Sometimes called 'service clubs', they stressed the responsibility of their members toward the civic advance of their communities, though they were sometimes accused of being merely a front for the business interests, unsympathetic to labour, and inclined to be conservative in the matter of civic improvements which might involve the raising of taxes. They generally sponsored some welfare projects, varying with the state of the community's social development. In towns with poorly developed welfare services, they might undertake an elementary piece of philanthropy or they might

* See Chapter XXX, pp. 1142–63, Women.

inaugurate efforts to develop a needed service. In large metropolitan areas with a multitude of power groups, the influence of these service clubs was less than in smaller cities and towns where they comprised a larger proportion of the professional and business element. They were however one more example of the voluntary organizations which gave shape and leadership to otherwise amorphous societies.

In many newly developing countries after the second world war, voluntary civic activity received a great impetus from the community development programmes. In Jamaica an extensive programme was built very largely on the basis of voluntary planning committees; in India the government used its influence to stimulate the formation of voluntary organizations as an indispensable means of developing a democratic structure; in the Philippines, Pakistan, India and elsewhere the main task of the village workers who staffed the community development programmes was to stimulate the organization of citizens for voluntary civic activity. Ceylon's rural development programme was based wholly on the formation of voluntary village societies.

6. *Benevolent organizations*

Benevolent organizations to support an endless range of welfare services, and to promote such causes as the protection of children, the prevention of cruelty to animals, better care and treatment of prisoners and their rehabilitation upon release, were among the most numerous of voluntary organizations. Many of the voluntary agencies had their origin in the late nineteenth and early twentieth century, when the social conscience was aroused against the ills of industrial society and the services of the welfare state had not yet been developed. Frequently they had a religious base; in some instances they were maintained by religious orders which provided nursing services, worked as teachers or provided a refuge for unmarried mothers or juvenile delinquents. Virtually every country had its Red Cross or Red Crescent organization ready to mobilize voluntary effort in case of disaster or emergency.

Innumerable associations were formed in the field of health to promote public health, combat tuberculosis, cancer or heart disease, prevent blindness, promote care for crippled children or the hard of hearing, aid the victims of infantile paralysis or cerebral palsy, or stimulate research on one or another unconquered disease. Such associations were generally formed at the initiative of professional personnel working on the problem and persons who had been victims or were relatives of victims. They provided means by which the leadership of professionals and the participation of interested members of the public could combine in seeking a common social goal. They enabled lay people in a highly complex and specialized society to direct their efforts toward objectives which they sensed in general terms but with which they personally had no technical competence to deal.

In spite of the extension of public welfare services, voluntary welfare agencies continued to function where they had been established in the past. Often they changed their role in order to supplement rather than duplicate the services of public agencies, or were used by public agencies to carry out publicly supported programmes. Voluntary welfare efforts were important, too, in countries which were newly developing their social services. Although such countries established welfare services as a public responsibility, they also sought to arouse in their people a spirit of self-help. States where the masses of the people had been neglected for centuries confronted the danger that those who had long been passive under the whip of adversity would wait passively for the new benefits which they now expected to receive. Wherever developing countries envisaged their role in terms of a modern welfare state, they included among their central objectives the promotion of voluntary mutual effort on the part of their citizens.

7. Cultural and interest groups

Finally, voluntary organization provided a basis for the pursuit of any number of cultural interests. Literary, musical and art societies, and private organizations to support the arts, to engage in amateur dramatics, to form community orchestras or to provide art classes and hang each others' paintings were to be found in many cities. Garden clubs, stamp collectors' clubs, organizations of radio amateurs, movie enthusiasts, anglers, or others joined to pursue common hobbies. Amateurs of sports of all sorts were organized into teams and leagues, to maintain playing fields, conduct tournaments and uphold the standards and rules of the games. With the tremendous increase in the amount of leisure enjoyed by men and women and young people in the twentieth century, the growth of organizations to pursue cultural interests was without limit.*

IV. THE INDIVIDUAL IN THE TWENTIETH CENTURY

The twentieth-century individual, in virtually all parts of the world, thus found his identity, his status and his role in society less and less simply and clearly defined by the agencies which had traditionally given him identity and status—his family, his social class, his parent's occupation, his ethnic identity. All these factors continued to operate in the social life of the period, but the mounting complexity of social relationships and the great increase in geographical and social mobility reduced their relative importance. The individual derived his identity, his status and his role from many different components in his life—his nationality, his occupation, his membership in a trade union or a political party, his religious affiliation, his place of provenance, his educational achievement, his ethnic background. In the many circumstances in which he found himself, one or another of these identifications might, for the purpose in hand, be the major determining factor in his status and relationships.

* See Chapter XXVII, Use of Leisure.

In the fluid anonymous life of the modern city he constantly had to establish his identity anew, to the strangers with whom he dealt, and often even to himself. He was less and less likely to wear his identification in the form of distinctive dress, although at a United Nations gathering it was not difficult to recognize the members of the 'sari bloc' or the 'sarong bloc', though class distinctions were clearly apparent on the streets of Cairo where men of the lower classes continued to wear the long galabieh, and though there were even some villages in Holland where Catholic and Protestant farmers still wore their caps in a distinguishing fashion. He was less and less likely to spend his life in contact with people who could place him by his father's name.

Even when he had found terms in which to establish who he was and to discover the identity of others, he often was still without a reliable guide as to the conduct appropriate to his status and role, nor could he count on others to interpret their relationship to him in the same light as he did and to expect the conduct which he might expect of himself. The difficulties arising from this situation were particularly great where changes in social status were rapid and threatened the position of superior groups. Changing relations between classes in Britain, between Negro and white in the United States, between Indian and *ladino* in central America, between Asian and European, between employers and workers—everywhere the uncertainties of such new relationships were reflected in hypersensitiveness, aggressiveness or other expressions of insecurity among members of the rising group, and in self-consciousness, prejudice or other reflections of uncertainty or resistance among those unable to readjust their conception of their own superior role.

The mobility and the social change of the twentieth century thus placed millions of individuals under kinds of strains that past societies had rarely imposed on large numbers of their members. Where the strains were too great, the individual might find an external object on which to project his inability to cope with the confusions of his age, or he might turn his uncertainty in upon himself. It was no accident that the twentieth century saw, along with a great and general acceptance of the essential unity of mankind and respect for cultural differences, a vicious tendency to seek a scapegoat and to persecute fanatically—witness the sadistic fury of the Nazi effort to exterminate the Jews, the unexpected violence of communalism in Turkey and India, the outburst of suspicion against 'subversives' in the United States or the British 'teddy boy' attacks on inoffensive Jamaican immigrants. Nor was it an accident that psychiatrists found that the point of breakdown in many of their mentally ill patients was in the sense of self.

Only a minority of people felt certain and secure—the minority of convinced religious men and the minority who identified themselves wholly with a new ideal. The former, whatever their religion, held securely to old patterns; the latter, certain of a new vision—the coming of a communist society or the development of one of the new nations—felt themselves securely embedded in a new pattern. But for the great majority of mankind, the individual in the twentieth century faced unprecedented demands on his ability to organize his personal social world and to relate himself flexibly and securely to it.

NOTES TO CHAPTER XXII

1. It is the view of the commentators from the Italian National Commission that the treatment of the family overemphasizes comparatively unimportant aspects, and that it proceeds from a relativistic premise which causes the authors to 'forget the distinction between that which is truly changing and that which is constant'. The position of the Catholic Church with regard to matrimony and the family was restated by Pope Pius XI in the Encyclical *Casti Connubi* (1930). Excerpts from this letter follow:

 '5. . . . let it be repeated as an immutable and inviolable fundamental doctrine that matrimony was not instituted or restored by man but by God; not by man were the laws made to strengthen and confirm and elevate it but by God, the author of nature, and by Christ our Lord by whom nature was redeemed, and hence these laws cannot be subject to any human decrees or to any contrary pact even of the spouses themselves. . . .

 6. Yet, although matrimony is of its very nature of divine institution, the human will, too, enters into it and performs a most noble part. For each individual marriage, inasmuch as it is a conjugal union of a particular man and woman, arises only from the free consent of each of the spouses; and this free act of the will, by which each party hands over and accepts those rights proper to the state of marriage, is so necessary to constitute true marriage that it cannot be supplied by any human power. . . .

 11. Thus among the blessings of marriage, the child holds the first place. . . .'

Further readings in this field are:

British National Conference on Social Work, Bedford College for Women, 1953, *The Family; Report.* (London: National Council of Social Service, 1953).

Famille d'aujourd'hui, situation et avenir. Compte rendu in extenso. (Lyon: Chronique sociale de France, 1958.)

Robert D. Hess, *Family Worlds: A Psychological Approach to Family Life* (Chicago, 1959).

John L. Kane, *Marriage and the Family: A Catholic Approach* (New York, 1952).

Clifford Kirkpatrick, *The Family, as Process and Institution* (New York, 1955).

Talcott Parsons, *Family, Socialization and Interaction Process* (Glencoe, Ill., 1955; London, 1956).

John Ryan and Alan Keenan, *Marriage, a Medical and Sacramental Study* (New York, 1955).

F. J. Sheed, *Marriage and the Family* (New York, 1957).

Carle C. Zimmerman and Lucius F. Cervantes, *Marriage and the Family* (New York, 1956).

2. Candidate of Juridical Sciences A. Bovin asserts that in the Soviet family children were never encouraged to 'defy' their parents. In the early period of Soviet power there occurred in individual families conflicts which were due to the divergence between the new ethical idea of children brought up by school and society in the spirit of Communist morality, and the backward views and outlook of members of the older generation. These conflicts sometimes became a subject of discussion among wide segments of public opinion. (See G. M. Sverdlov, *Sovetskoye semeynoye pravo* (Soviet Family Law), Moscow, 1958; pp. 13–16.)

3. In the eyes of Soviet scholars this section does not indicate the essential facts about mankind's social structure, since the authors take as the basis of social divisions all manner of derivative differences (way of life, type of employment, incomes, ideas, consciousness, education, etc.) and give a very nebulous and confused picture of 'social stratification'.

 The basis of the social structure is the diverse status of men *vis-à-vis* the means of production. In modern capitalist society there exists, in the status of men *vis-à-vis* the means of production, an opposition that has developed to the pitch of contradiction. This has led to the division of that society into two fundamentally antagonistic classes, the bourgeoisie and the proletariat.

By 'bourgeoisie' is meant the class of capitalists, the owners of the means of social production, employers of hired labour. Closely connected with the bourgeoisie is the class of large landowners. The main source of income of such landowners is the land rent which they receive from agricultural capitalists farming their lands. The bourgeois class and the class of large landed proprietors together form one pole of modern capitalist society.

The other principal class of capitalist society is the proletariat, or working class. The 'proletariat' is the class of modern hired workers, who have been deprived of means of production of their own, who sell their labour power to capitalists and are the direct producers of surplus value, capital, for these capitalists.

Thus one pole of capitalist society consists of the bourgeoisie and large landed proprietors and the other of the proletariat, including both industrial and agricultural workers. However, the capitalist social structure does not manifest itself in a pure form, in the form of these two poles alone. Capitalism is characterized by a network of social relationships and transitional stages between one class and another. The social groups situated between the two poles of the social structure, taken together, form the middle social strata of society. The middle strata do not form a single homogeneous whole economically, socially and politically, as the social classes do. Their representatives occupy different places in the system of material relationships, and consequently stand in a different relation to the means of production; they occupy different places in regard to one another in the process of production and in the sphere of distribution.

(See V. Semonov, *Problema klassov i klassovoy borby v sovremennoy burzhuaznoy sotsiologii* (The Problem of Classes and the Class Struggle in Modern Bourgeois Sociology), Moscow, 1959, pp. 76–7, 82–3.)

CHAPTER XXIII

POLITICAL INSTITUTIONS

CHANGES in political institutions in the twentieth century were intimately bound up with the changing role and expanding scope of the state under conditions of modern industrial society. They reflected, too, changes in the state's form, most notably the development of new political institutions in the states which adopted communism. The focus of the present chapter is on changes in the state as an institution and on the instruments through which the political machinery operated. It deals primarily with the changing political institutions of the liberal democratic states and the new institutions of the communist states.[1]

A number of states operated under a variety of authoritarian forms during these years, but with the exception of Fascist Italy and Nazi Germany their political institutions did not represent a new development. They are to be described primarily in negative terms—the rejection or discarding of democratic institutions. In positive terms they may be said to represent government based upon and supported by military force.[2, 3]

The Fascist and Nazi states went beyond mere reliance on force, to proclaim alternative conceptions of the shape which the institutions of the state should take. Mussolini, in addition to permeating the state with military, para-military and quasi-military forms, conceived of the organization of the state on a corporate basis, with bodies formed along functional lines exercising authority over their members. Toward this end he gave to associations of companies in a particular industry administrative responsibility with respect to the affairs of the industry. The Nazi régime was built on the leadership principle and the mystical unity of the state. Its institutions were designed to weld the entire society into a single unit, responsive through all its organs to the leader's will and his vision of the purpose and nature of the state. During the period of Hitler's ascendancy that purpose was the remilitarization of the state and its whole-hearted dedication to military objectives.

Both of these states went down to defeat and destruction in the second world war after a brief period during which their institutions remained in a formative, provisional or emergency state. Some features of these systems penetrated into other states and many forms of authoritarianism, old and new, continued to assert themselves in the years after the second world war. But the institutions of Fascism and Nazism as such were abortive, and during the period under review they did not become consolidated into a lasting alternative structure of political life.

Many of the new states which came into existence after the second world war—in numbers which virtually doubled the world's independent political units—lacked the tradition and experience of liberal democracy yet did not directly follow the communist pattern. In their efforts to find institutions appropriate to countries of high illiteracy and varied cultural traditions, which needed to achieve rapid economic development under conditions of the modern age, they introduced a mixture of political forms. By the end of the 1950s it was not yet clear what direction these developments would ultimately take and whether new political systems would eventually evolve.

I. FORMS OF THE STATE

1. Monarchy

At the opening of the century monarchs ruled throughout the greater part of the world. The republics of North and South America, Switzerland and France were almost alone in having a non-monarchical form of government.

By the middle of the century a mere handful of monarchs remained. Most of the powerful hereditary rulers were gone—the Hapsburgs, the Romanovs, the Hohenzollerns, the Manchus, the Ottoman sultans, the ruling houses of Spain, Portugal and Italy. Monarchy survived as a form in Europe only where the effective power had long since passed out of the monarch's hands and he functioned mainly as the symbolic head of a parliamentary state, as in Britain, the Low Countries and Scandinavia. It survived in the few small states of Asia and Africa which had never come under direct colonial rule—Ethiopia, Thailand, Afghanistan and Iran—and in Japan, though the nearly divine emperor had become little more than a respected symbolic figure. A few of the new states of Asia and Africa—Libya, Morocco, Jordan, Iraq and Saudi Arabia—adopted monarchical forms at the time of their establishment, but most chose a republican form and set themselves up under some adaptation of a liberal democratic constitution.

By the middle of the century autocratic monarchy may thus be said to have become an anachronistic form of government. Over most of the world, people in their political aspects were citizens, not subjects, and the totality of the people were seen as constituting the state.

The first world war marked the turning point in the history of monarchy as a state system. Though even before the war Portugal had expelled its king and become a republic, and revolution in China had put an end to an imperial tradition of over 2,000 years, it was the disappearance of the four great empires which represented the tradition of autocracy—the Russian, Austro-Hungarian, German and Ottoman—that marked the downfall of the monarchical ideal.

In the following years other monarchies fell and those that survived underwent change. The loss of the British monarch's major colonies was signalized by the abolition of the title of emperor. The last major claimant to monarchy by divine right, the Japanese emperor, gave up the claim under pressure from the victorious Allies. At least in theory, the remaining kings or emperors reigned as a result of national will or with the consent of the people, except perhaps in Ethiopia, Yemen and Saudi Arabia.

Even where monarchy survived only in a symbolic role and the royal house was warmly regarded by the people, the hierarchical social system which the institution of monarchy perpetuated was out of tune with the equalitarian tendencies of the times. Criticisms levelled at the monarchy in Britain and efforts of the Dutch and Scandinavian royal families to behave in a democratic manner were indications that people recognized an incongruity between monarchy as an institution and the social trends of the mid-twentieth century.

2. Liberal democracy

In the great majority of states where monarchical authority was unseated its place was taken by some form of what may be termed liberal democracy.[4, 5] This term is here used to denote states where political authority rested in the people acting through elected representatives, and where an elected executive was responsible to the expression of popular will. The term is used in preference to 'parliamentary democracy' which connotes the system of executive responsibility to the parliamentary majority, or 'republic' which excludes the parliamentary democracies with nominal royal heads, or 'representative government'. The term liberal democracy is not used in the nineteenth-century sense of *laissez-faire* liberalism, but rather to distinguish a broad group of states with a parliamentary or representative political tradition from the communist states which designated themselves as 'people's democracies'.[6, 7]

Most generally the form followed by the liberal democracies was the parliamentary pattern with executive power vested in a cabinet responsible to parliament and drawn from the majority party or combination of parties. In some instances the structure approximated the United States pattern of an independently elected executive separated from the legislative authority. But whether parliamentary or presidential, old or new, all democratic states changed much of their inner form during the twentieth century. To meet the needs brought by urban industrial society, the state enlarged its scope of activity to provide a more adequate framework for economic life, to control economic power and to provide common services.

In the first place it became a legislating state to a degree previously unknown. The great expansion of state activity and extension of state services involved a new view of legislation and its role in society. It was no longer merely to protect the state, to assure its revenue and to define and safeguard the rights of the citizen. The traditional concept of law as mainly codifying and interpreting customs and usages which had already become part of social practice was supplemented by a more active concept. Law came to be looked upon and used as an instrument to promote the well-being of the people and to carry out the purposes of the state.[8]

With this new concept the volume of legislation increased immensely. It was estimated that the British Parliament enacted more legislation in the first half of the twentieth century than in all its long previous history, and other legislative bodies showed a similar trend.

In the second place the doctrine of popular sovereignty upon which the democratic states rested became all-inclusive as the franchise was extended to classes formerly excluded and, with few exceptions, to women. From the years following the first world war, and stimulated by the total participation called for in the war, the doctrine that the total people was vested with effective sovereignty became the basis for the functioning of the democratic states.[9]

With this final expansion of democracy came its claim to the totality of powers. No sphere of human activity was recognized, in principle, as lying outside the scope of the democratic state. The distinction between what ought to be directed by public wisdom and what ought to be left to the discretion of the individual or to spiritual authority all but disappeared. Except as limits were explicitly set forth by bills of rights in democratic constitutions and recognized in practice, the state claimed the right to control every aspect of human life, according to the dictates of the popular will.[10]

This gradual but fundamental change in the nature of democratic institutions was one of the outstanding features of the political life of the twentieth century.

3. Authoritarian state forms

In a number of states democratic institutions proved unstable or unable to cope with the crises of the time and they were replaced by some form of authoritarian rule which discarded the institutions based on the principle of popular sovereignty but retained and intensified the principle of the totality of state powers. In some instances monarchical authority gave way directly to a dictatorial régime; the Kemalist revolution in Turkey, for example, set up from the beginning an authoritarian régime into which some democratic features were later introduced. Elsewhere dictatorial régimes took over democratically organized states, notably in eastern and southern Europe in the years between the two world wars, in new states of Asia and Africa in the 1950s and sporadically in Central and South America. Thus, though there was a continuing trend toward liberal democracy, and the victory of the democracies in both world wars gave prestige to the system and impetus to its spread, the tendency toward a revival of autocracy was as real a feature of the development of twentieth-century political institutions as was the predominance of liberal democratic institutions and the rise of communist state forms.

The structure of authoritarian government everywhere showed three principal characteristics: a head of state or leader with exceptional powers, with a party or a special group to support him; a legislative body elected generally by a system which proscribed parties or groups opposed to the régime or considered dangerous to the philosophy of those in power; and a bureaucratic administration which maintained no pretence of being subject to popular control.

The authoritarian states differed markedly in the extent to which they interpreted the totality of state power as implying the moulding of every institution within the state in conformity with and as a part of the state structure; in the extent to which they required uniformity of outlook and negated all civil rights; and in the degree to which the state became an end in itself. The extreme position on these points was taken by Hitler's totalitarian National Socialist state, while some dictatorships went so far in the other direction as to declare their ultimate purpose to be the development of effective democracy. But the same features were present to some degree in all the states under authoritarian rule.

4. *Communism*

The democratic and authoritarian states were not new forms of political organization, though they took on new content in the twentieth century. The new development in state form was the structure of the communist states.

All the communist states, whether federal in structure like the Soviet Union or with centralized constitutions, had certain distinctive characteristics in common. From the lowest unit—a Russian village soviet or its Chinese counterpart—to the highest, every organ of the state was elected on a pyramid basis, with power centralized at the top. Each elected body exercised its authority subject to the supervision and control of the immediately higher one, with final authority in all matters vested in the supreme organ.[11]

Equally distinguishing a feature of the communist states was the role played by the Communist party. As the repository of the interests of the people, the Party held the ultimate authority although it exercised power indirectly. It acted as the formulator of policy and watched over its execution at all levels and in all spheres of activity.

5. *Colonial systems*

In the case of European nations exercising imperial authority over colonial people—the British, French, Belgian, Dutch and Portuguese—the state had a dual aspect, the first relating to the mother country and the second to the colonies and other dependent areas. The colonial empire headed by a liberal democratic state was a type of state organization which combined two contradictory principles, self-government and freedom at home, autocracy and denial of freedom outside. It was characteristic of all imperial states in the twentieth century that the basic conceptions of government were different in the metropolitan and colonial areas.

Not only was the organization of government different but so also were the administration of justice, policies in relation to education, the rights of the individual *vis-à-vis* the state. Two different standards were applied even in the administration of law. The overriding consideration in colonial government was the prestige and authority of the ruling power. In most colonial territories a gradual change, often more of form than of substance, became visible from the period after the first world war, but the dual nature of colonial rule persisted until colonies became independent states.

The actual structure of colonial government differed among the colonial powers and in different parts of the same colonial empire. The British empire presented the greatest variety of patterns. In the areas settled by European immigration the democratic institutions of the mother country had been transplanted and self-government was the rule, although it was not until 1931 that Canada, Australia, New Zealand and the Union of South Africa formally ceased to be dominions of the British empire and became associated states of the British commonwealth. The Indian empire, which comprised Burma and Aden as well as what became the independent states of India and Pakistan, occupied the special position of an empire within an empire. Operating under a special secretary of state responsible to the British Parliament, the British government in India maintained its own foreign office and entered into treaty relations with states on its border and in the Arabian peninsula; its prestige and authority entitled it to consultation in the shaping of imperial policies affecting Asian states. It maintained a large military establishment out of its own revenues and a civil service whose higher posts were generally filled from Britain.

The remainder of the British empire was administered as a series of crown colonies under the Colonial Office, the manner of governing each area varying with the historic tradition and the social and economic conditions of the area and the principal objectives of imperial rule. Especially in parts of Africa outside the regions of white settlement the system used was that of indirect rule, according to which the local ruler or tribal chief continued to exercise authority, but on behalf of the colonial power.

In addition to the areas which were actual parts of the British empire, Britain exercised effective authority over certain 'protectorates', such as Egypt from 1914 to 1923, or the Sudan; in these the local government remained intact and control of policy was achieved by means of a system of advisers on foreign relations, financial and military matters. In addition, Britain enjoyed spheres of influence through treaty concessions in parts of the Middle East and China.

The French colonial structure was also adapted to differences in local conditions and in the relations of the area with the mother country. In French Indo-China the states of Cambodia, Annam and Laos remained under subordinate monarchies, the French government utilizing the machinery of indigenous administration for the exercise of its authority; Tonkin and Cochin

China were directly administered as colonies. In North Africa Tunisia and Morocco were both administered as protectorates through their local rulers, with the French population settled in the area entitled to special political rights; Morocco, however, enjoyed an international position, while Tunisia did not. Algeria by contrast had the status of three departments of metropolitan France with representation in the French Parliament; until the late 1950s the electorate was composed principally of French settlers. French possessions in tropical Africa until the mid-1950s were under direct administration from France; under the principle of 'assimilation', those who acquired French culture also took on the status of French citizens, with representation in the French Parliament at Paris.

The Dutch, Belgian and Portuguese colonial structures were even more authoritarian than those of Britain and France. The Portuguese system was distinctive in that after 1933 the areas outside the metropolitan country were not organized as dependencies but as provinces of the metropolitan state. Within these areas, however, only a tiny element of Portuguese and 'assimilated' natives enjoyed the status of citizens. The masses of the population in Portuguese Africa constituted a subject people without citizenship rights. Portuguese rule differed, too, from that of the other imperial powers in that the metropolitan government itself did not rest on the application of democratic principles at home, and the disparity between internal and external political structures was therefore not so great.

With the rising tide of anti-colonialism during the twentieth century and the struggle for national self-determination on the part of colonial peoples, colonial powers found it expedient to grant concessions to their dependent territories and the latter tended to take on some of the features of their metropolitan states. In India the British had already begun to introduce British criminal and commercial law in the middle of the nineteenth century as part of their administrative system and to incorporate Indians into the lower ranks of the civil service; in the 1880s they began to introduce a small measure of local self-government. Through successive reforms in 1909, 1919 and 1935 undertaken in response to Indian pressure, the British government extended institutions of government which followed the pattern of the British domestic system, though with limited scope, at the provincial and then at the national level. When it became clear during and after the second world war that colonialism was doomed, Britain accelerated the process of preparing other parts of the empire for self-government and independence, extending in each case the institutional forms developed at home.

France, too, offered its domestic institutions as a legacy to its colonial peoples. Until the close of the second world war the prospect of ultimate independence or self-government had not been part of the French colonial system; rather, the ultimate stated objective, at least for the African territories, was incorporation into the French Union, and as late as 1944 the idea of autonomy, self-government and any possibility of development outside the

French empire was excluded. But it was France's practice to extend its institutions as completely as possible to those who became 'assimilated'. When after the second world war France undertook a vigorous programme of road building and education in its African colonies, it duplicated in Africa the institutions of France. And in 1957 when France finally conceded a measure of self-government under the *loi cadre*, the African ministers who put the system into effect were men who had gained their political experience as members of the French Parliament.

In a similar way the limited Dutch concessions to the demands for political participation in Indonesia, beginning in 1916, were based on Dutch parliamentary forms. The Belgian government, which did not begin to offer self-government in the Congo until the 1950s, started by introducing the institution of the Belgian commune as a basis for local self-government.

By the middle of the twentieth century, however, the efforts to keep colonial structures intact were in the nature of rearguard actions. Britain divested itself systematically of one territory after another—Ghana, Malaya, with the British West Indies and others scheduled to follow—while at the same time holding tenaciously as long as possible to territories which it continued to regard as holdable and as vital to its national interest, such as Cyprus, East Africa, Gibraltar, and protectorates on the Arabian coast, only to relinquish in turn such of these as could no longer be held. France was forced to abandon her vision of Africa as a land of black Frenchmen as the tide of nationalism rose in her territories. The Dutch empire was virtually gone, although Holland continued to claim West New Guinea (Irian Barat) and retained some small territories in the West Indies. In its effort to keep out disturbing influences, Portugal practically closed its African territories to the outside world. By the late 1950s colonialism as a state system was virtually dead; the question which remained was only whether any relation other than that among separate and sovereign nations would be retained among former members of the onetime colonial empires.

6. *Associated States*

While colonialism declined as a basis for aggregating political units into a common structure, there emerged several patterns of associated states, more closely linked than by mere alliances yet not integrated into either a single state or an imperial structure. The most noteworthy of these associated structures was the British commonwealth.

The Commonwealth evolved as a special form of state organization by successive stages. At the beginning of the century, only such overseas territories of the British empire as had a population predominantly of British stock—Canada, Australia and New Zealand—enjoyed the right of self-government, but even they did not enjoy sovereign status, for the British Parliament still claimed the right to legislate for them and they had no diplomatic relations with other countries. The first major change came in 1910 when the

Union of South Africa Act added the first self-governing dominion which did not claim a common inheritance with the British. The political arrangement incorporating the Boer people opened the door to multiracialism, though still in terms of a population of European origin, for the Boer republics excluded non-Europeans from political participation.

The second major change came as the aftermath of the first world war, in which the United Kingdom had depended heavily on the dominions and India for carrying on the war and these in turn claimed the right to share in the determination of foreign policy. After a decade of negotiation and discussion, the principle of equal independent sovereignty was finally agreed to in 1926 and enacted in the Statute of Westminster in 1931, and the self-governing dominions became, with Britain, the British Commonwealth of Nations.

A further constitutional change became necessary after the second world war when India became a republic and agreed at the same time to remain within the Commonwealth. By the inclusion of India, Ceylon and Pakistan, the Commonwealth had already ceased to be exclusively of European origin. With the acceptance of republican India as a member, what had previously been considered the uniting bond, allegiance to a common sovereign, also vanished. In the middle of the twentieth century the Commonwealth thus presented a picture of an international, multiracial, political association. In its evolution it had provided a means of relinquishing control while retaining association. It remained to be seen whether it would continue as a durable political form or would serve only as a bridge between empire and complete separation.

There were other efforts to transform former possessions into associated states. France until the late 1950s hoped to create some form of French community which would provide a basis for continued association with those parts of her former empire which might wish to retain some kind of tie with France. The effort of the Dutch to work out a basis of association with Indonesia failed, however, and the tentative relationship established at the time of independence was abrogated by the Indonesians six years later. The former United States possession of Puerto Rico, rejecting both independence and incorporation as a state of the American union, chose to constitute itself, by compact, the Associated Commonwealth of Puerto Rico, remaining within the customs union of the United States and retaining American citizenship for its people but conducting its own internal affairs.

In the years after the second world war patterns of association were being developed among states which had no former colonial relationship. India maintained a special relationship with the small state of Nepal on its northern border, assuming responsibility for its military defence. The states of eastern Europe which joined the communist camp, Poland, Czechoslovakia, Hungary, Bulgaria, Rumania, Albania and Eastern Germany, were linked to the USSR through aspects of their economic structure, partial integration of their military forces, and the operation of their Communist or People's Democratic party. Western Europe created supranational instrumentalities—legislative, administrative and judicial—to operate its Coal and Iron Community, its Common Market and Euratom, modifying the functions of related national agencies. The North Atlantic Treaty Organization not only involved an integration of parts of the armed forces of the member states but the creation of common institutions.

The international organizations were themselves a form of association, although they were based on the principle of the equal sovereignty of all member states. The Arab League attempted to provide some kind of institutional base for association among the Arab states in the Middle East. The Organization of American States established machinery which was used successfully to intervene when armed conflict threatened among its members. On a world scale the United Nations provided judicial machinery, although the submission of disputes to the Permanent Court of International Justice was voluntary, and it was the means of uniting military forces, albeit only on an *ad hoc* basis during the first dozen years of its existence.

In spite of the strength of national sentiment and the multiplication of national states, these many forms of association, and the constant enlargement in the scope of the activities of international agencies, were all evidences of the strong tendency in the middle of the twentieth century for the wholly independent national state, as well as the wholly dependent colonial empire to be modified by forms of association which better fitted the complex, interdependent patterns of world society and the needs and aspirations of the world's peoples.

II. INSTITUTIONS OF THE LIBERAL DEMOCRATIC STATES

1. *The electoral system and political parties*

The electoral system was at the heart of the structure of liberal democracy, for it was the basic machinery by means of which popular sovereignty was exercised.[12]

Political parties provided the mechanism for selecting candidates and mobilizing support at the polls. They varied significantly in different countries, but all had certain common features. They were voluntary organizations, generally national in scope, composed of people who agreed at least to some degree on desirable public policies. Their purpose was to capture the legislative and executive organs of the state by the method of popular election in order to get their policies accepted and to give effect to them. The work of party organization was carried on to a very large extent on a non-paid voluntary basis, though a nucleus of paid workers was generally necessary.

The enlargement of the electorate increased immensely the importance of party organizations in political life, for it made it practically impossible for individuals to get elected without the support of a party organization. The variety of the issues arising from the enlarged functions of the state greatly complicated the problem of creating and maintaining an informed electorate which could use its franchise responsibly. In addition the methods of influencing popular opinion through new techniques—the cinema, radio, television and other mass media—became too complicated and costly for individuals to undertake. Candidates continued to appear at public meetings, to answer questions and to shake hands with the voters, but the influencing of public opinion on a mass scale became a specialized technique. Mobilization of political support was planned and carried out at high cost on a nation-wide scale, in a manner which required nationally organized and well-financed parties. Party organizations thus came to occupy a pre-eminent place in the functioning of liberal democracies.

Parties were integral parts of parliamentary structures. The role of the opposition as well as the responsibilities of the majority were recognized and the offices of both majority and minority leaders were commonly financed by funds provided for the operation of the legislative establishment. Relations among parliamentary parties were such, moreover, that in spite of opposition the minority gave sufficient support to the policies voted by the majority to provide essential continuity, it functioned as a 'loyal opposition' until it in turn succeeded in becoming the majority. Much of the process of policy formation took place within the parties, which maintained research bureaux and publications and established liaison with press and citizen groups. Through these means the political parties developed information and thinking on major issues and cast the results into legislative form.

Although political parties were thus indispensable to the exercise of popular sovereignty under the conditions of modern national states, they functioned quite differently from country to country.[13] In Britain, the United States and the commonwealth states of British origin, parties were few and stable, and each party tended to embrace a wide range of views and interests. The democratic institutions of these countries operated on an essentially two-party system, with the parties sufficiently balanced to permit the minority party to become the majority by gaining a small additional share of the votes. Major parties might split or a third party might gain sufficient support to displace one of the major parties, as the British Labour party displaced the Liberal party, first as the opposition and then as the government. The essential feature of these parties, however, was their comprehensive character and their ability to endure by adjusting to changes in circumstances and in public opinion.

Since in this type of party system each major party sought to attract to itself a majority of the voters, it necessarily included in its platform policies which had wide public support. Although the major parties retained sufficient difference in emphasis to appeal to different groups of voters and to offer alternatives to the independents who did not vote purely on the basis of party allegiance, the tendency was for party platforms to approximate each other; popular issues introduced by one party were taken up by the other and programmes introduced when one party was in power were carried on by its successor. Retention by the British Conservative party when it came to power in 1951 of many of the social policies with which the Labour party had undertaken to create a welfare state was a case in point. Under this type of party system issues were rarely deeply divisive, party organization did not reflect fundamental cleavages in the society and political institutions were characterized by a high degree of stability.

The situation was quite different where parties corresponded to deep cleavages in the society or where the issues which they were organized to promote involved fundamental questions of the nature of the state and the form of government. In Austria, for example, socialist and Catholic parties tried to pull the state in opposite directions for twenty years, until what was left of democratic government collapsed in the Nazi take-over; after the war these parties worked as a coalition for more than a decade and thus maintained stability, but they sustained a working relationship only by filling all types of public jobs proportionately from each party. A somewhat similar pattern was followed in Holland and Belgium after the second world war. In Colombia a system of 'parity' and an agreement to alternate the presidency was adopted jointly by the two major parties in 1958 in an effort to bring to an end a decade of political conflict and disorder verging on civil war. Where the Communist party had a large following, as in Italy and France, party issues involved the basic form of the state. In republican Spain after 1931 the cleavage was so deep as to prevent the state from functioning and it led to civil war.

Still another role was played by parties in those countries where a multitude of small parties reflected a range of opinion from left to right. France offered an outstanding example of this type of party structure. In contrast to the British and American parties whose main objective was to secure the support of as wide a segment of the population as possible in order to get elected to office, each French party expressed a particular shade of opinion. No French government had behind it the organized strength of a majority party, but always had to depend upon the collaboration of several units, each ready to pull out whenever policy veered away from its particular position. Much of the instability of the French parliamentary system during the twentieth century was a product of a party system which fragmented voters rather than consolidating them into practical and responsible majorities. The Fifth Republic came into existence in 1958 as a reaction against this system.

But whatever the particular system, the presence of competing parties which organized voters and contended for their support on the basis of issues freely discussed was and remained the prime essential of the liberal democratic state.

2. *Other expressions of political opinion*

Although political parties were the principal agencies for developing and reflecting public opinion on political issues, they were by no means the only institutions which contributed to the exercise of popular sovereignty. The multitude of voluntary organizations which brought people together around common interests—occupational, civic, religious, educational, avocational, benevolent—provided common ground for the discussion of public issues and the shaping of a common outlook among their members.

Some of these had direct links with or formed integral parts of political parties, as did the trade unions in several European countries. Some went to great lengths to influence the opinion not only of their own members but of the general public on issues which they regarded of particular importance to themselves, as did the American Medical Association on the issue of compulsory health insurance in the United States. Some were formed for the express purpose of promoting certain measures, such as minimum wages or child labour laws or disarmament. Some merely discussed public issues among themselves; others adopted positions as a group and made their positions known.

Amid the complexities and conflicts of interest in industrial societies, these voluntary associations played an indispensable role in giving shape and voice to opinion. With few exceptions political representation was by geographic areas; yet interests cut across geographical lines and political districts were apt to be far from homogeneous. Voluntary organizations provided one means by which such interests could find political expression. In the intervals between election campaigns, moreover, they afforded a channel for registering voters' views.

A more sensitive instrument for registering public sentiment between elections was the public opinion poll which was used extensively in the second quarter of the century. Taken on the basis of carefully developed sampling techniques, these polls gave legislators an insight into the public mind, and showed party leaders some of the trends in voting which they might expect, although polls did not generally bring out differences in intensity between views which were lightly held and those which reflected strong convictions.

3. *Legislative structure*

The development of the legislating state with its expanded functions, brought an alteration in the institutions through which the legislative bodies themselves functioned. While procedures traditional to each such body generally persisted in respect to voting and debate, the major work of legislatures moved more and more from the floor of the house to the committee room. This was especially the case where there was a separation of legislative and executive functions, as in the United States, or a multi-party system as in

France. In two-party systems with cabinet responsibility, as in Britain, there was less tendency to use parliamentary committees in the ordinary course of preparing legislation and more reliance on study and drafting by the party in power, but some legislative committees functioned here also.

Committees were in no sense new features of the parliamentary structure, for legislative bodies had always delegated responsibility for special inquiries to committees or used them to review aspects of proposed legislation in advance of general debate. It was simply the enlargement of these functions which gave legislative committees their new importance.

The enormous volume of proposed legislation could not be adequately studied, absorbed and evaluated by each and every legislator. In the United States Congress, for example, as many of 15,000 bills might be introduced in a two-year session. The subject matter of legislation, moreover, became increasingly complex and technical, so that only an expert could recognize issues of policy embedded in seemingly minor differences in phraseology. The committee system enabled a few members of the legislature to become thoroughly familiar with each particular area of legislation and thus permitted the body as a whole to act more responsibly on the basis of committee study and recommendation. In addition, committees familiar with legislation in a specific field could provide a measure of oversight in respect to its execution, and thus could help to give reality to the overall responsibility of the legislative body to the electorate for the conduct of the state.

In these circumstances the operating units which carried the main burden of legislative work became increasingly the legislative committees. Where their procedures for reviewing proposed legislation included the taking of testimony from citizens or citizen groups with special knowledge or interest in the subject, as was the case in the Congress of the United States, they provided a direct channel for the expression of public opinion. As they developed professional staffs they came to provide the legislators with an independent basis for expert judgment on technical matters with which legislation had to deal.

4. Bureaucracy

The major institutional development in the democratic states, however, was not in the electoral and legislative machinery but in the executive arm with the growth of bureaucratic administration. Though the roots of modern bureaucracy lay in the nineteenth century when the system of civil service came to be organized in the democratic countries of Europe and America, its emergence as a major factor was a characteristic of the twentieth century. A few figures will indicate the magnitude of the change. In 1855 in the United Kingdom the number of so-called civil servants, including postmen, office keepers and messengers, was less than 18,000; a hundred years later the same categories numbered over 700,000. In 1900 the federal government of the United States employed some 200,000 persons; at mid-century the number exceeded 2,000,000.

The change in the character of the state was responsible for the growth of bureaucracies. From a political state concerned with legislation on broad policies and the maintenance of peace and order, it became an administering state concerned with the detailed effectuation of policy on an ever increasing range of subjects. This required a vast army of trained personnel at all levels, capable of seeing to the execution of government decisions in every corner of the country, and it called into being an immense machinery which no state in the past had ever had the means to create or control. The extended activity of the state involved two major types of function, regulatory and operating. In order to contain the mounting power of great industries, to carry out protective legislation, to control traffic or indiscriminate building or many other aspects of modern life, the state intervened with regulations and set up administrative bodies to make them effective. These bodies performed not only administrative but quasi-legislative functions of rule-making within the framework established by the legislature, and also the quasi-judicial functions of determining whether or not violations had occurred.[14]

Government agencies also carried on direct operations in many fields— in the physical construction of dams, roads and countless types of public works, in a widening range of government enterprises in such lines as transport and communication, mining, shipbuilding, the generation and distribution of electric power, in maintaining hospitals, clinics and many welfare institutions, and in enormously expanded military establishments with their concomitant activities in scientific research and weapons production.

The enlarged bureaucracies for these purposes required not only high competence in administration but a multitude of specialized skills related to the new and specialized activities and services. The civil service systems inaugurated in the nineteenth century had sought to place administrative posts outside the arena of partisan politics and favouritism and to fill them on the basis of competence. The most famous of these civil services, the British, made a broad liberal education, intelligence and integrity the qualifications for most posts, on the assumption that the nature of public administration was such that a person with these qualifications would be equipped to execute established policy faithfully, to handle all types of situations that might arise, and to develop on the job whatever special knowledge might be required.

But the highly specialized and technical fields into which the state penetrated required more than general education, intelligence and integrity. They required engineers and physicists, economists, physicians, statisticians and a host of other specialists. As the new bureaucracies came to be filled with technical specialists engaged in new kinds of tasks, new problems of organization and functioning arose. Public administration itself took on the character of a special field of knowledge in which principles were developed to guide the relationship between those concerned with the technical aspects of a particular activity and those responsible for maintaining the organizational structure and making administrative decisions.

New organizational forms were also devised for carrying out specific activities. In part the expansion of the bureaucracies took the form of enlargement of the regular administrative departments and the creation of new departments as required. But where government engaged in economic activity or entered various other spheres of operation, the normal government department, however well administered, did not seem an adequate structure. The result was the creation of special autonomous corporations or other semi-autonomous units for these special purposes.

The most widely used form was the autonomous corporation established by statute, with extensive but defined authority, functioning more or less as a subordinate arm of the state with a bureaucracy of its own. Under the broad lines of policy laid down by the legislature it functioned without interference. The Tennessee Valley Authority in the United States and the British Overseas Airlines Corporation were examples of this kind of enterprise. In addition semi-autonomous government bodies, not given formal autonomy by statute but in fact practically independent of other branches of government, had charge of specific functions, as in the case of the Coal Board and the Electricity Board in Britain and numerous similar bodies elsewhere. This pattern was widely followed for the operation of nationalized industries. A third type was the independent corporation, set up like a private corporation under company law but with the majority of shares, sometimes the entire stock, owned by the government.

Whatever the form, two features stood out in regard to all these institutions. In the first place a delegation of authority from the state was the basis of these new bodies. They constituted in effect a division and decentralization of the state's functions along functional lines. Secondly, these organizations themselves developed large-scale bureaucracies, thereby reproducing the same tendencies noted in the direct administrative arms of the state.

The changes in the structure of governmental administrative institutions followed the lines along which industry itself developed, that of mammoth corporations. The change-over from comparatively small industrial units to large corporations has already been noted. In its economic and industrial activity the state followed similar principles and reproduced a similar organizational form, giving to the modern state in many areas the appearance of a collection of big corporations, with the traditional political authorities co-ordinating their work, maintaining law and order and managing international relations.

At the same time the autonomous or semi-autonomous bodies were one of the means by which the democratic states sought to preserve a measure of the variety and freedom of action which was fundamental to their principles as states and societies. Large and bureaucratic though these units might be, they were far smaller than the immense administrative organization of the total state. These bodies, entrusted with a measure of independent authority and initiative, were devices by which the liberal democratic states in spite of the enormous extension of their activities avoided a monolithic structure and the regimentation of their people.

The bureaucracies, whether departmental or semi-autonomous, acted in theory under the ultimate authority and control of the political organs of the state, which were the repository of the sovereign will. In states with a parliamentary form this control was exercised directly through the responsibility to the parliament of the cabinet which headed the administrative structure. Where the presidential system prevailed and the executive branch of the government, headed by a president elected by and responsible to the people, was independent of the legislature, the latter still exercised substantial control through the terms of legislation, the legislative intent expressed in debate, the power of investigation and especially through the appropriation of the funds on which the administrative agencies depended.

Nevertheless, the growing independence of the bureaucracy was a major feature of the twentieth century. In the course of these years, it became in practical effect no longer the servant of the state, passively carrying out policies determined elsewhere, but an active element sharing in the making of state policy and the exercise of state authority.

The reasons for this development were not far to seek. At best no legislative body could give attention to the immense amount of detail involved in the administration of a welfare state, yet the actual impact of state policy upon the citizen was embodied in decisions on just such matters of detail. Such attention was even more impossible where services or activities were highly technical; here the technicians who manned a service tended to become its proprietors. Wherever there was some measure of economic planning, even many major policy decisions were of so technical a nature that they had to be made by the planning agency rather than by the political body. The factor of defence added a further barrier to political control. As modern warfare came to involve all aspects of life—most industries, the pursuit of science, many forms of training—large sections of national activity had to be entrusted to a specialized bureaucracy. Even apart from work specifically involving military secrets, the shadow of defence fell over a wide range of activity, and the political state, whatever the theory, could exercise only limited control.[15]

5. *Administrative law*

A major aspect of this development was the growth of a large body of administrative law, formulated and interpreted not by judges but by administrative departments. More and more of the parliamentary legislation in all liberal democratic countries left the rule-making powers—such rules having virtually the force of laws—to administrative agencies, the rules themselves to be interpreted and administered not by courts but by civil servants. Whether in respect to income tax or building regulations or currency control or labour standards and labour relations, the receipt of social insurance benefits, economic assistance or public services, citizens found themselves confronted by decisions taken by anonymous officials who established their own procedures, made their own interpretations of fact and merit, and handed down decisions that had much of the force of judge-made law without going through the 'due process of law' which was generally established in these countries as a citizen's right.

The possibility that this development of administrative law might lead to abuse of bureaucratic power and seriously impair civil rights was well recognized. Yet the impossibility of legislating all the rules and of entrusting their enforcement to the slow procedures of already overburdened courts was equally clear. In these circumstances efforts were made to set bounds to administrative decisions, to prevent arbitrary action by developing standards and procedures, and in some cases to create special courts or to provide for review of administrative decisions by the regular courts.

A dramatic example of the effort to keep the scope of administrative decision within bounds was furnished by the action of the Supreme Court of the United States in 1935 when it declared the legislation for economic recovery enacted at the depth of the depression to be unconstitutional and therefore void because Congress had delegated what were in effect legislative powers to administrative agencies without sufficient expression of policy and without adequately circumscribing the administrative authority. In Britain, in respect to city planning, principles regarding the remuneration of property owners whose property was affected by the action of administrative bodies were laid down by a leading jurist in 1942* and were made the basis for legislation and a guide for the action of administrative agencies. Special courts were created in a number of countries to deal with such matters as labour disputes or tax appeals.

Two general principles entered into the development of administrative procedures, the principle of eligibility and the right of appeal. Wherever entitlement to any sort of service or benefit was involved, uniform publicly announced standards of eligibility were the first safeguard against arbitrariness and favouritism. Some machinery for appeal from an administrative decision was generally provided, either to a special board within the agency itself, or under some conditions to the regular courts.

In these ways liberal democratic countries sought to prevent the vast range of administrative activity from turning into a new despotism. But not a few thoughtful persons expressed a genuine fear that the spreading tentacles of the welfare state would destroy the individualism and initiative which had given European civilization much of its dynamic quality. The full significance of what some people liked to describe as a system of 'parliamentary bureaucracy' and the full impact of the growth of administrative law on the citizens of democratic states was still not yet realized at the middle of the century.

* *Final Report of Expert Committee on Compensation and Betterment* (1942).

6. *Judiciary*

Meantime the judiciary continued to play its traditional role of regulating relations among individuals on the basis of civil, commercial and family law, of safeguarding society and the state through the application of the criminal code, of guarding individual rights *vis-à-vis* the state through such institutions as *habeas corpus* and other elements of 'due process of law', and in some countries acting as guardian of the constitution against the whim of the majority.

In performing this continuing role under the conditions of the modern state, courts of law were constantly confronted with new situations not covered by specific precedent and by the need to take into account factors outside the frame of reference formerly regarded as the domain of law. The new relationships created by the large corporation could not be encompassed within the traditional concepts and principles relating to property and legal personality. Employer-employee relationships could not be fitted into the strait-jacket of a commercial contract for the purchase and sale of labour. Courts found themselves forced to include in their considerations the economic reality as well as the legal form, the social implications of the issues before them, and even the meaning of such concepts as 'equal protection of the law' in psychological terms.

In spite of the great extension of administrative law, the independent judiciary remained a bulwark of the liberal democratic state. At times it functioned as a conservative force, slow to encompass and give legitimacy to new social trends. But it was no accident that wherever democracy was supplanted by totalitarianism, the judicial system was one of the first institutions to be altered. Nor was it an accident that a judicial system, inherited from a colonial power or voluntarily adopted from the West, was one of the corner stones on which the new states which adopted democratic constitutions sought to build a structure to fulfil their democratic hopes.

7. *Problems encountered by new states in adopting democratic forms*

The new states of Asia and Africa with few exceptions adopted some form of parliamentary democracy upon their establishment as independent states. With local variations, they modelled their constitutions on those of the older democracies and they established electoral procedures, parliamentary institutions and administrative structures designed to put these principles into effect. In so doing they encountered formidable problems of government, intensified by their basic problems of economic and social development. One after another they found that the system which they had adopted was not working effectively; several, with the conspicuous exception of India, suspended or abrogated features of their original constitutions, generally under the leadership of the military, in an effort to evolve new forms suited to their experience and needs.

In these countries neither a republican form of government nor democratic institutions based on elected representatives had a genuine local tradition behind them. In most cases, both the experience and the psychological background for putting such institutions into operation were lacking; the full implications of the parliamentary system, with cabinets, legislative bodies and all the other paraphernalia, were imperfectly understood not only among the masses of the people but often by the leaders themselves.

The central problem which they faced was the problem of obedience. The authority of the monarch or his deputy had been well understood; it had been in fact virtually axiomatic. The monarch had been hedged about with 'majesty'; in the formula with which the emperors of China had ended their orders, the populace was expected to 'tremble and obey'. But authority in a democracy, the will of the people, or more particularly the will of the majority as expressed through parliament, was not clearly understood and accepted; obedience to the majority was far from axiomatic. Occasional or chronic rebellion, seizure of power by non-constitutional means, dismissal of parliamentary bodies or cabinets by governor or president to override majority action in one after another of the new states during the first decade of their existence, were evidence that the principle of democratic obedience had yet to become a working basis for many of the new states.

The problem presented itself in acute form in the issue of the supremacy of civil authority over the armed forces. The supremacy of civil over military authority in a democracy depends on a widespread and ingrained democratic spirit among the people. Even in many old and well-established democratic states, the military had at one time or another in their history challenged civil authority; where democratic institutions had functioned imperfectly it had offered a chronic threat. In the new states whose people were long used to accepting authority based on effective power, the threat was very much present and the danger to the survival of democratic institutions was great.

The operations of a democratic state depend upon a series of institutions which were alien to the experience and habit of thought of the new states. Chief among these was the institution of the 'loyal opposition', a party or parties whose opposition to the policies of those in power was freely expressed, who could seek to win a majority to their view and who if successful were in a position to accept power and assume responsibility for government. In many of the new states where opposition had traditionally been synonymous with sedition, it was not easy for those in power to accept organized opposition or for those out of power to seek it in a responsible manner.

Democratic institutions, moreover, require the association of people with government at all levels; a parliamentary system which tries to operate only at the centre, with no experience of democratic functioning at the local level, can have little reality for those going through the motions of casting a ballot. In this respect the countries which had formed part of the Indian empire had an advantage over other new states, for some measure of local government had been introduced in the 1880s, and people had thus become familiar with democratic assumptions and procedures and had learned to operate them locally before being called on to make them work on a larger scale. But elsewhere this sort of experience was generally lacking. Even in Pakistan the initial effort to establish nation-wide democratic institutions was short-lived and these were replaced after a coup by an administrative structure under military leadership. With the declared purpose of developing the basis for a functioning democracy, the new leadership partially re-established local democratic elections as a training ground where Pakistanis could acquire the experience which in time would permit the restoration of democratic institutions at the national level.

Lacking, also, was a process for the generation of ideas and the formation of public opinion. Parliamentary institutions are designed to carry out ideas generated throughout the society, not to be the fountain-head of thought. In the established democracies the vast and varied programmes of national welfare and public policy were shaped by the voluntary intellectual activity of dynamic groups in which intellectuals provided an arsenal of ideas and public discussion hammered out views and issues.

But institutions of higher education were absent or very young in most of the new states, and in the period of colonial rule such intellectual centres as existed could not engage freely in political study and debate. Parties had been built up prior to liberation in order to carry on the struggle for independence. The problem was whether these parties could transform themselves into continuing organizations for participation in democratic government and whether a widespread interest in public affairs could be sustained among a large enough group in the population to keep the democratic machinery functioning.

The most fundamental problem of all arose from the fact that democracy is not simply a set of political institutions but a total complex, a way of life. In each of the older democracies distinctive political forms were related to other aspects of national life; the differences among such countries as Switzerland, France, the Netherlands, Britain and the United States amply indicated the extent to which specific democratic institutions were integral elements in a total structure of society. It was of the essence of democracy, furthermore, that its conceptions and institutions should constantly change as the society changed—that freedom and equality should acquire different concrete meanings in the twentieth century from what they had had a hundred years before.

The problem in the new states was that democracy might remain merely a borrowed ideology—a sort of textbook democracy. The specific forms of democratic institutions which most of these states adopted were patterned on those of their respective metropolitan powers and bore little or no relationship to the social structures on which they were imposed. To the extent that countries accepted political forms without interpreting democratic values in terms of their own life, they faced the danger that their democratic institutions would remain imitative and artificial and would be but a façade behind which a dictatorship or an oligarchy or disorder and instability would rule. There were signs in some of the new states during these years that this danger might be real.

The bureaucracies which the new states inherited from the period of colonial rule, and on which in the first instance they were forced to rely, varied in number and quality, but in all cases they had to be greatly expanded and revamped to provide the necessary machinery of administration. In the colonial civil services, including the most highly developed of them, the Indian civil service, superior posts had been filled almost entirely by personnel from the metropolitan country; in the little-developed services, as in the French colonies or the Sudan, few people from the locality had occupied even the lower posts. The scope of colonial administration, moreover, was extremely limited, involving generally little more than the collection of revenue, the maintenance of law and order and the promotion of favourable conditions for trade. The immense range of functions and services which had to be performed in the newly independent states lay almost wholly outside the sphere of the civil services of the colonial period.

The new states thus faced a threefold task if they were to sustain their state structures and bring about the economic and social changes essential to their development: they must find or develop persons with sufficient competence, training and integrity to fill superior posts, they must enlarge their total civil service enormously and rapidly, and they must develop a body of technicians with a wide range of specialized technical and managerial skills to carry through the specialized operations of a modern state.

In the countries where the educated class was extremely small at the time of independence it was necessary to rely heavily on the temporary device of recruiting administrative personnel from abroad, as was done for example, in the Sudan. Elsewhere, notably in India and to a lesser extent Pakistan, there was a sufficiently large number of educated persons who could be recruited for the public service to permit a very great expansion of the total number and an effective system of promotion to fill the higher posts. But even in the latter countries the problem of finding and training sufficient technical and managerial personnel was formidable. India, which more than doubled the number of its engineers in the ten years after independence, calculated that it would need to achieve a fourfold increase in the next five years to staff the enterprises and services called for in its development plans. Most other countries were much more deficient in needed skills. The stability and progress of the new states thus depended greatly on the rapidity with which they could build up a competent, trained and honest administration which would provide their governments with the necessary stability and with the instruments to implement national policies.

At the same time the scope of activities in which the new states had to engage was far greater than that required in the older democracies, for in the absence or insufficiency of many of the private enterprises and voluntary services which existed elsewhere they had no choice but to do through government many things which were at least partly done by non-governmental agencies in other countries.

The economically backward countries were caught in a vicious circle: the productive capacity of the community was not sufficiently developed to enable the public to look after its own welfare; and without welfare services to improve the standards of life productive capacity could not be expected to increase. So the state had simultaneously to see that the welfare services were undertaken on a nation-wide scale and that industrial and other production increased. This involved the state in every form of activity, from family planning and nutrition to the creation of modern industries and an active role in production. It required not only the provision of better health, education and housing but changes in social structure, in attitudes, in the distribution of land and other wealth.

In the newly independent countries the state had thus to be all-inclusive in its activity, dealing with marriage laws while it encouraged the latest scientific research, promoting preventive medicine along with the modernization of transport, attempting to provide for universal education and to plan for the development of rural life, concerned with large-scale industrialization and with the encouragement of art and literature. The creation of new life in the rural areas, for example, involved not merely the organization of a new machinery of government capable of operating on an extensive scale, but the creation of non-official leadership in the areas concerned; training institutions for village-level workers became as necessary as institutions for the training of technicians. The success of schemes for large-scale industrialization depended not only on the latest technicial knowledge but on the development of a managerial element with trained executive ability. Management of money and credit at national and inter-national levels, the ability to fight inflationary tendencies that were unavoidable where large-scale expenditure was necessary—these too required special training and ability. The skills and capacities needed for these purposes, moreover, were of the highest order, for on every side the problems to be met were of infinite complexity and difficulty.

A special feature of the political institutions of the new states was the part played by law. By the middle of the twentieth century at least some legal principles and institutions based on European law, either on the Napoleonic Code or on the Anglo-Saxon common law, had been incorporated into the legal systems of all countries except the extremely conservative Muslim states such as Yemen and Saudi Arabia, and the communist countries. By one means or another western law was superimposed on the customary or religiously based law of non-western areas or it was combined with it or it replaced it.

The introduction of western law into non-western areas was most complete in respect to commercial and maritime law, which by the nature of trade and commerce tended toward universality. Penal codes tended, by a process of borrowing, to approximate either the Napoleonic or the Anglo-Saxon systems of criminal justice with their related procedures. The area of personal and family law, which involved the heart of the social structure, was least or last to be affected. Law with respect to land, both in the matter of inheritance and transfer, often presented a special area of uncertainty and of conflict between old and new legal principles.

Western law reached non-western areas in various ways. From the sixteenth century on, European commercial law had gained a foothold wherever trading companies had established bases, and other aspects of European law had spread from these footholds by treaty, example and the exercise of colonial authority. Under the system of 'capitulations' Europeans within the Ottoman empire were judged by European law in extraterritorial courts. Similar privileges were secured by Europeans in other Muslim countries, including Persia, Egypt, Morocco and later Iraq, and in China, Japan, Siam and Ethiopia. This extraterritorial jurisdiction extended generally not only to disputes among Europeans but to those between a foreigner and a national, and even to some nationals in the employ of Europeans.

Although extraterritoriality was bitterly resented and its abolition became a focus of national effort, it made European legal principles and practices familiar to numbers of people in these areas. By the time that the system was abolished, first by Japan in 1899 and virtually everywhere else in the 1920s and 1930s, the legal systems of the countries involved had come to approximate those of Europe.

The adoption of western systems of law by non-colonial countries was part of their conscious efforts at westernization or modernization. Japan was the first Asian country to promulgate a new code of laws based on western conceptions. It adopted a penal code modelled on the French in 1882 and a civil and commercial code modelled on the German and English in 1899. Siam subsequently took over a considerable portion of the German code.

The most dramatic and complete substitution of a European system came in Turkey following the Ataturk revolution of 1923. A considerable amount of European law had already been adopted in a piecemeal and unsystematic fashion in the course of the nineteenth century, including codes of criminal, commercial and maritime law and procedures for criminal, commercial and civil courts. In a drastic move to secularize the state, westernize the country and bring social reforms, as well as to bring order into the Turkish legal system, Ataturk promulgated new penal, civil, commercial and maritime codes and codes of civil and criminal procedures based on Italian, Swiss and German legal codes. The Swiss civil code was adopted for the hitherto untouched area of private and family law, and religious courts and Muslim law were wholly replaced.

Quite a different process was followed in Persia, where the effort was to combine western and Muslim law and to adapt them to each other rather than to effect a complete substitution. The first steps, in 1912 and 1914, were to set up a judicial administration along European lines and a system of commercial courts, but the religious courts continued to function. In 1926 a penal code based on the French was adopted. Two years later a civil code was introduced which was based upon the Muslim *sharia* but with adaptations from the French code. Codes of procedure based on the French were adopted for civil, criminal and commercial cases. The modified Muslim law was to be administered by the civil court as a uniform system throughout the country, not according to the individual interpretation of the local *mujtahids* or Muslim judges, and all marriages and divorces were to be registered in the civil courts.

In the areas under colonial rule the legal institutions of the metropolitan power became part of the system of colonial administration, although in Indonesia they were applied only to Europeans and other non-Indonesians. The results of this introduction of western law were most notable in the countries which composed the Indian empire, where for a hundred years the principles of British commercial law, criminal justice and civil and criminal procedure were built into the political structure. The nature of Anglo-Saxon common law had a bearing on the results of this process. In contrast to the civil law embodied in the legal systems of the European continent, it was not a code of legal rules but a set of procedures for determining fact and for settling disputes according to either custom and precedent or on the basis of legislation. As such it introduced basic concepts such as equality before the law, and basic procedures such as *habeas corpus* and rules of evidence, but it modified customary relationships only where legislation was involved. The family law of Hindus and Muslims remained almost wholly unaffected.

The states under former British rule thus acquired a set of legal principles and procedures and the idea of legislation as a means of establishing new relationships which by the time of their independence they had already learned to use. It is noteworthy that the Indian constitution of 1949 in its articles on the judiciary specifically enumerated the various writs such as *habeas corpus, quo warranto, mandamus* and *certiorari* which were parts of British legal procedure, and that the Islamic constitution of Pakistan in 1956, while stating that no law should be repugnant to the injunctions of Islam, also specified that its high courts should have the power to issue these same writs for the enforcement of the fundamental rights guaranteed by the constitution or for other purposes. These and other new states, moreover, saw their power of legislation as an instrument for changing customary law, and used it to bring further reforms to their society.

The legal concepts and procedures adopted from the West were essentially those of nineteenth-century Europe. The ancient codes of customary laws and the legal institutions which had religious sanction were modified by the impact of the liberal ideas of the nineteenth-century European jurists. Whether they were adopted deliberately in an effort at westernization or absorbed during the period of colonial rule, they were major instruments of social reform and the principles and relationships which they established and the procedures which they created were fundamental to the operation of these states as liberal democracies or related forms.

III. INSTITUTIONS OF THE COMMUNIST STATES

1. *The Communist party*

The most distinguishing feature of the communist state, for which the Soviet Union may be taken as the prototype during this period, was the role played by the Communist party. The Communist party regarded itself as the embodiment of the will of workers and peasants and, as such, as the true vehicle for the expression of the popular will. The formal machinery of the state provided a complex of organs for carrying out the sovereign will expressed in and through the Party. In this sense the Party was superior to the state; the Party congress was the supreme body and the Party leaders who composed the Central Committee functioned as permanent executives. Identifying itself thus with the people, the Party claimed complete and all-embracing authority—in laying down domestic and foreign policies, determining the correctness of theories, planning and directing political strategy, leading, guiding and overseeing every organ of the state.

The Party consisted of the most active elements among the people. It was a dedicated vanguard trained in the doctrines of communism and subjected to a period of probation. Recruitment to the Party was not merely by enlisting those who accepted its general programme. A candidate must prove himself in the various work groups of the state—factory, collective farm, union of intellectual workers or other body—demonstrating his theoretical and his practical capacity and his loyalty and orthodoxy in order to become a full member of the Party. The Party numbered perhaps 1 to 4 per cent of the population, an estimated 8,000,000 in the Soviet Union and 10,000,000 in China in the mid-1950s.

The functions performed by the Communist party differed in essential respects from those performed by political parties in liberal democratic states. Since the Communist party itself acted as the repository of the popular will, the general electoral machinery was not a device for registering a choice among rival candidates and between alternative views on public issues. The function of public elections in the communist state was merely to re-confirm public confidence in the Party and its decisions as the embodiment of the people's will. Voters were therefore simply asked to vote 'yes' or 'no' on the slate of candidates offered by the Party.

Although the Party comprised only a small part of the population, it was the means by which a very large number of people were constantly and responsibly active in the formation and execution of public policy. Every Party cell, local committee or higher Party unit was expected to engage in continuous discussion and to exercise constant vigilance. Every unit was part of the transmission belt for policies determined at the top, part of the reporting system for registering the implementation of policy and keeping upper echelons informed, and part of the mechanism to permit issues to be raised and debated at successively lower levels and opinion to be transmitted to the higher organs engaged in the process of policy formation. Subject to control by the higher unit, which might remove an officer of a lower unit for failure to carry forward the responsibilities of his office, choice of leadership within each group was by election, and higher organs of the Party were composed of delegates selected by the lower units.

The Party not only provided most of the cadres for government work but also the membership of the political bodies within the state. It thus provided the key personnel for all the organs of the state. In addition it functioned at all levels as a guardian, not merely to prevent irregularities and to secure efficient action from the very bottom upwards, but to ensure a uniformity of approach, to see to it that policy was uniformly understood throughout the state and that changes in policy were followed uniformly. It was in fact the Party that gave the monolithic character to the communist state. In these circumstances, the organs of the state were in some respects less important than those of the Party for the weight carried by members in the government depended less on the office they held than on their position in the Party.[16]

2. Organs of the state

The central function of the state in a communist society was the development of communist ethics and a superstructure which applied the principles of the society. Since in Marxist-Leninist theory society derives its character from the processes of production and the means of production must be in public hands, the conduct of economic affairs was a central activity of the state and its major organs were therefore the organs of economic life. In this respect the communist state was sharply distinguished from the liberal democratic state, whose central function was to provide a framework of orderly society within which economic and other activities could be carried on independently and which took on direct economic responsibilities only as this action appeared necessary for the general welfare.

The communist state was an enterprise state. Its goals were conceived in economic and social terms and in terms of its world position. Its prime function was to carry on direct operations. From top to bottom—from the overall state to the smallest factory, farm, clinic, school or army unit—the communist state was a great enterprise. As an enterprise it was all-inclusive and highly organized in every aspect of life. Its administrative organization inevitably dwarfed that of any less inclusive state in size, extent and complexity and its structure was designed to further the success of the enterprise —to build a socialist, and ultimately a communist, society.

The first principle of organization was that of 'democratic centralism'. As conceived by Lenin, the institutions of the state were to operate according to a two-way process. Central direction and control were to be combined with widespread public participation through functional organizations and lower state organs from which opinions would rise and reach the centre. After Lenin's death a struggle among his principal followers resulted in the accession of Josef Stalin to the Party leadership, and for the next three decades the machinery of the Party and the state was operated by Stalin as a stern dictator whose excesses were later deplored by his successors. Under the conditions of these years—revolution, industrialization, collectivization, war and reconstruction—the features of central control and domination of all agencies and all aspects of life from the centre were accentuated.

During Stalin's régime, the method used to handle opposition or potential opposition was the 'purge', or removal from office. In serious cases persons thought to be dangerous to the state were arrested, induced to make a public confession of their guilt, and sent to labour camps or executed as the gravity of their offence and the importance of their position seemed to require. This method served the double purpose of removing opposition and of making very clear the line of Party policy.[17] In the major purges of the mid-1930s large numbers of persons who had favoured some of the alternative policies among which the Party had had to choose in the years since the revolution were eliminated and the unity of both policy and organization under Stalin's policies and leadership was assured. Stalin in fact sought to make these features of domination and repression permanent. While the 1936 constitution established in principle many features of socialist democracy—greatly extending the powers of the Supreme Soviet, calling for a more democratic electoral system, providing for the democratization of the judiciary—most of the newly established political forms remained inoperative in the face of mounting fear of fascist aggression and the conditions produced by the second world war.

After Stalin's death in 1953, and in the changed circumstances of the time and the stage of industrial and social development of the USSR, his successors sought to reduce extreme centralization and discontinue harsh measures of control. Transfer to lesser posts served in most cases to remove opposition and to consolidate the policies of the dominant element in the Central Committee of the Party, while public acknowledgement of error or guilt continued to serve as a device for keeping Party policy before the public and making its meaning clear in uniform terms. Steps were taken to decentralize a measure of authority to the several Soviet republics and to place greater responsibility on functional organizations such as trade unions, writers' congresses or youth groups in the conduct of their affairs, thus seeking to bring the state more in line with the balance between central direction and widespread participation which Lenin had conceived.

The general administrative structure of the Soviet state followed functional lines in relation to the economy. The principal ministries were entrusted with one or another economic area—heavy industry, electricity, textiles. The basic unit of organization was the productive unit—factory, collective farm, hospital. Intermediate organizations included enterprises and sometimes groups of enterprises formed into trusts, which might be highly centralized or partially decentralized. Geographical organization was supplementary to functional organization. Geographical organs such as town or district bodies had direct responsibility for those activities which did not depend principally on their link with other areas, such as local handicrafts and for the provision of some local amenities and cultural activities. Their indirect responsibility was to further the success of enterprises within their area.

The responsibility of the lower organs was based on the delegation of authority from the centre. The USSR was organized as a federal union with separate governments in each of the republics. Within this federal structure, however, the responsibilities carried by ministries of the republics were determined by the central authority. The federal structure had been established in the USSR in part because of the multi-national character of the country, and the structure included a series of organs based on nationality, centred in a Congress of Nationalities; but this structure, too, was supplementary to the functional structure.

After 1957 the decision to decentralize some of the activities which had been controlled from the centre placed new responsibilities on the institutions of the several republics. A considerable number of factories previously in the charge of central government agencies were transferred to republic and regional organizations. The central agencies relinquished the function of drawing up codes of law, which they transferred to the competence of the republics. National ministries of justice and internal affairs were dissolved, greater powers were assigned to the lower courts and the militia was subordinated to district and regional soviets.

The central organ of the state was the state planning agency. The activities of the state, at all levels and in all fields, revolved around the formulation and the execution of the Plan. The state as an enterprise, and all its component parts, were directed and carried forward through the setting of production goals—whether of tons of steel to be produced or numbers of children to be taught or hospitals to be built or hectares to be planted; performance of each organ or each official was judged by fulfilment of goals. Planning thus became the major administrative instrument for organizing and carrying out the purposes of the state.

Various devices were developed to stimulate the initiative and responsibility of individuals and to avoid the dangers associated with bureaucracy while at the same time maintaining supervision and control. In the USSR each enterprise operated as a separate unit, engaging in contractual relationships with other enterprises from which it secured its materials or to which it supplied its products, and it was accountable financially as well as physically for exceeding or at least being sure to meet goals set by the Plan. Within each enterprise the accountant, quality-control officer, chief of maintenance and trade union leader each carried independent responsibility and was accountable to superiors in the higher organ for the aspect of the enterprise with which he was involved. The Party group in each enterprise was responsible directly to the Party organization for vigilance in the fulfilment of the Plan. In addition, the central authorities maintained a system of inspectors to check on enterprises where there was reason to suspect irregularity or inefficiency, and the organs of state security were also available to intervene if sabotage or other serious offence was suspected.

Because the communist state required the involvement of all the people toward a common, active goal in line with uniformly understood and applied policy, the instruments of propaganda were essential instruments of the Party and the state. The difference between the communist and the liberal state in their concepts of popular sovereignty led to quite different concepts relating to the formation of public opinion. The parliamentary state assumed the existence outside government of independent centres where ideas on political issues would be generated and whence they would find their way to the governing body, to be reflected in public policy. In communist theory and practice the Party itself, as the embodiment of the sovereign people, was the organ for the formation of opinion, the guardian of theory, the leader and shaper of thought. It was therefore its function to stimulate widespread popular discussion within the framework of issues and policies determined at the centre, to control the instruments for the formation of opinion and attitude and to use them fully and systematically both in order to create and maintain public opinion in line with the policies of the Party, and to provide the Party with knowledge of public reactions which it might consider in formulating policy. The press, the radio, the artistic and literary professions, were therefore regarded and treated as arms of the state.

A special feature of the communist state was its use of law as an instrument of both administration and education.[18] In their initial periods communist states discarded the structure of law which had formerly existed. The USSR replaced the legal system in existence under the tsars and the Chinese communist state scrapped the code of law which the former republic had developed with the help of legal advisers from the West. In theory it was initially expected that correction of economic conditions would correct the conditions which in capitalist society led to crime, and would make law in the sense used in capitalist countries unnecessary. Treatment of deviant behaviour was to be through education rather than punishment and offenders were subjected to an intensive process known as 're-education', often administered by the culprit's own social group.

In the course of time complete reliance on re-education was found insufficient and penalties related to the gravity of the offence were introduced. These were however more in the nature of administrative tools than the application of legal principles. Offences were primarily those which impeded the operation of the state as an enterprise—negligence in the pursuit of production goals, waste or damage to state property. Punishment for failure to co-operate fully and effectively in the national effort was the obverse of the premiums, honours or other recognitions with which fulfilment and over-fulfilment were rewarded.

The judicial system thus did not operate in the manner conceived in liberal democracies, as an independent branch of government with rules and principles of its own. Court procedures were not hedged about by the rules of evidence, writs for bringing persons to speedy trial, or other paraphernalia which gave the court systems of the liberal democratic states their basic character. Although a system of legal warrantees was developed in time which gave persons brought to trial a defined status, the legal and judicial institutions continued to be considered as political and educational organs rather than instruments of justice in the traditional sense used in the liberal states.

The communist states functioned during these years under conditions of revolutionary change. Their Party and state structures were the instruments of that change—of the liquidation of former proprietors as a class, of the industrialization of non-industrial or partially industrialized societies, of the immense expansion in economic activity called for by such a change, of extreme efforts exacting heavy sacrifices, and of consolidating national communist states in a world, the greater part of which was hostile to their aims and efforts. The particular form taken by the institutions of the communist states during this period must therefore be seen not only as the application of communist theory but as practical means of implementing revolutionary social change.

While the principal development of communist institutions took place in the Soviet Union, and it is primarily in these terms that the political institutions of communist states have been discussed, some variations in structure were appearing in the other states which adopted the communist political form in the years after the second world war.

The most divergent institutions were developed in Yugoslavia, which though a communist state remained outside the international communist movement after 1948. Here the key principle was decentralization, through workers' councils responsible for the conduct of each enterprise, and local councils with a large measure of responsibility for each locality. In contrast to the Soviet Union where centrally organized production planning provided the directives for the efforts of each unit, planning in Yugoslavia during these years was used only to furnish a framework and climate for local effort, to formulate economic objectives, not to provide the instrumentalities for carrying them out. Indirect methods such as favourable or unfavourable rates on loans were used to stimulate or discourage the capital expenditures called for by the plans.

The institutions of communist China, on the other hand, moved in the opposite direction. In the course of its first ten years the Chinese People's

Republic introduced successively more and more instruments of central direction and control, including the organization of communes to replace peasant family units, villages and collective farms, and control over the movement of people from one place to another. These institutions permitted the state to mobilize millions of workers for major tasks and to carry forward a programme of staggering proportions to remake the economic life and the society of this ancient land.[19]

NOTES TO CHAPTER XXIII

1. Several critics regret the absence of material which is ordinarily associated with the traditional political treatment in a work of this kind. Professor Lynn M. Case writes about Chapter XXIII, 'Political Institutions': 'There should be a little more of the *why* to go with the *what*. . . . There is no explanation for the rise of fascism, nazism, or other totalitarian states. All the political institutions seem to occur in a vacuum.'

2. Candidate of Juridical Sciences A. Bovin points out that at the present time governments 'based upon and supported by military force' do not only exist in countries with fascist regimes. Militarization of the state apparatus is nowadays a characteristic feature of some 'liberal democracies' as well. This has been commented on by many Western public figures and scholars—sociologists, philosophers, and political scientists (see *A Symposium: Disarmament and the American Economy*, ed. H. Aptheker, New York, 1960). The prominent American journalist F. Cook, in his popular book, *The Warfare State: Juggernaut* (New York, 1961), gives a number of examples to illustrate the fact that militarism has penetrated into all branches of the American economy and that the American militarists have captured key positions in the country's state apparatus. Similar processes can be observed in the Federal Republic of Germany, Great Britain and France.

    See:

    (1) Fred Cook, *The Warfare State: Juggernaut* (New York, 1961).

    (2) John P. Davis, *Corporations: A Study on the Origin and Development of Great Business Combinations and of Their Relation to the Authority of the State* (New York, 1961).

    (3) E. Khesin, 'Militarizm i voyenniye kontserny Anglii' ('Militarism and British Arms Firms'), in: *Mezhdunarodnaya zhizn* (International Affairs) (1962), No. 1.

    (4) N. Tsygichko, 'Zapadnogermansky militarizm i yego doktrina' ('West German Militarism and Its Doctrine') in: *Mirovaya ekonomika i mezhdunarodnoye otnosheniye* (World Economics and International Relations) (1961), No. 9.

    (5) E. Fajon 'Nastuplenie monopolií na prava frantsuzskikh trudyashchikhsya' ('The Onslaught of the Monopolies on the Rights of French Workers') in *Mezhdunarodnaya zhizn*, No. 9, 1961; Y. Ostrovityanov, A. Sterbalova: 'Yest li vykhod iz tupika voennoy ekonomiki?' ('Is there a way out of the blind alley of war economy?') in *World Marxist Review* (Prague, 1961), No. 4.

3. *The Author-Editors have treated as a category governments 'based upon and supported by military force' having in mind those governments brought to power by military action and/or maintained in power by this means, in defiance of or in the absence of other established procedures for giving a government legitimacy. The use of this category does not preclude recognition of the influence of the military in time of peace as well as in time of war within states of various forms with legitimately established governments. See Chapters XI and XXIV for a discussion of this influence.*

4. Candidate of Juridical Sciences A. Bovin thinks that it is incorrect to say that the main tendency in the evolution of political institutions during the twentieth century has been in the direction of liberal democracy. At the present time this form of political organization is on the decline; out of the liberal democracies that existed in the Europe of 1918 only fifteen still remain today. And even in these countries various forms of restrictions of the democratic liberties proclaimed in the eighteenth and nineteenth centuries are

being introduced. (See D. E. Brown, *The Growth of Democratic Government*, Washington, 1959, p. 3.)

The democratic countries that have arisen in the former colonial and dependent territories cannot be regarded simply as copies of Western models. They are something radically new. The peoples of the former colonies and dependencies are at different stages in their struggle for complete emancipation, for national independence, the liquidation of the consequences of domination by foreign capital, and development along the road of social progress.

All these tasks can be successfully accomplished by establishing and developing states of national democracy. A national democracy is a state which consistently defends its political and economic independence, fights against imperialism and its military blocs and military bases on its territory. A national democracy is a state in which the peoples enjoy broad democratic rights and liberties, are able to carry through agrarian reform, and realize other demands for democratic and social reforms. (B. Ponomarev 'O gosudartsve natsionalnoy demokratii' ('On the National-Democratic State'), in *Kommunist* (Communist), No. 8, 1961, pp. 36, 41.)

5. *For a discussion of newly independent states, the Author-Editors refer the reader to pages 806–813.*

6. Candidate of Juridical Sciences A. Bovin points out that the definition given here of the term 'liberal democracy' does not indicate the qualitative difference between this form of democracy and other forms.

The People's Democracies, which the authors oppose to 'liberal democracy', also have representative political institutions and traditions. It is precisely these representative organs of state power, both national and local, that constitute the basis of the entire state apparatus of the People's Democracies. In the European People's Democracies such organs include People's and National Assemblies, State Assembly, Seym, People's Chamber, and People's Skupshchina (Parliament); and at the local level People's Councils or National (or People's) Committees. The People's (or National) Assemblies and People's (or National) Councils (Committees), as the most democratic organizations of the working people, with the strongest mass basis, are formed as a result of democratic elections held by the working people themselves and are fully sovereign organs of the state power of the working people in the cities and the countryside.

So far as democratic traditions are concerned, they exist and are rooted in the People's Democracies in the specific historical development of these states. It is well known that the People's Councils (Committees) were set up already during the war in clandestine conditions, as organs for carrying on the struggle for popular emancipation from the invaders and their allies within the country, as embryonic organs of the people's democratic power. Those who took part in setting up such organs included the democratic parties, public organizations, and also certain political groups that advanced the platform of uniting all the democratic forces in the struggle for freedom and independence. The working masses saw in the People's Councils the prospect not only of national liberation but also of the realization of their democratic aspirations, since the power of the People's (National) Councils (Committees) is the power of the people themselves, i.e. of the workers, peasants and all working people. [See (i) *Gosudarstvennoye pravo zarubezhnykh sotsialisticheskikh stran* (The State Law of Foreign Socialist Countries), Moscow: Academy of Sciences of the USSR, Institute of Law, 1957, pp. 83–5; (ii) *Konstitutsii zarubezhnykh sotsialisticheskikh gosudarstv* (The Constitutions of Foreign Socialist States) Moscow, 1956.]

The differences between 'liberal democracy' and People's Democracy is much more fundamental. The heart of the matter is that 'liberal democracy' is bourgeois democracy, i.e. one of the varieties of political organization of society that is based on private property, the competitive struggle, and exploitation. In contrast to 'liberal democracy', the People's Democracy is the political form corresponding to a society of a different type: a socialist society based on public ownership of the means of production, a planned economy, and freedom from exploitation (see *Gosudarstvennoye pravo zarubezhnykh sotsialisticheskikh stran*, Moscow 1957, pp. 7–14).

This point of view is shared by the Hungarian scholar Vilmos Peschka. He writes as follows:

(a) Section II on the 'Institutions of the Liberal Democratic States' occupies—disproportionately and at the expense of Article 3, dealing with the institutions of the socialist states—by far the greater part of the chapter.

(b) Never, in discussing the institutions of the socialist states, is the term 'democratic state' used in connection with the socialist states.

(c) The chapter is built upon the categories and concepts of liberal democracy, and it examines, primarily, the traits of liberal democracy. It should be noted that what the author advances is an apologia of the institutions of liberal democracy. For should the author evaluate even the data and circumstances adduced in the respective part of the chapter, the conclusion would inevitably be reached that the so-called liberal democratic states are no longer liberal democratic in the original sense of the term.

It is the traits and institutions of liberal democracy that the authors are looking for in the authoritarian and socialist states; and inasmuch as they fail to discover them in the state they scrutinize, that state is declared to be, not a democratic, but either an authoritarian or a socialist state. This method of analysis is incorrect, so far as the socialist states are concerned, as it distorts the facts and leads to false conclusions. Socialist democracy cannot be explained in the terms of liberal democracy: socialist democracy is democracy of a new type, that is built on institutions and embodies organizational principles which, in respect of their mass basis as well as the wide scope and fullness of democracy, are far superior to the real democratic principle of the liberal state—democracy that does not accord with what is set forth in this chapter.

7. *The Author-Editors explain that they have not treated People's Democracies (or, in the case of China, People's Republic) as a separate category from 'communist states'. As is pointed out in the note by V. A. Tumanov (Note 6 to Chapter III), 'the basic features of the Soviet and People's Democratic forms of government are the same'. The authors have used the term 'liberal democracy' in Chapters III, XXIII and XXVIII rather than simply 'democracy', or any other term, to identify those states which fall within the democratic tradition of Western Europe and America or follow this model.*

The text presents the institutions of the liberal democratic and communist states as separate wholes. The Author-Editors note that these systems could also be analysed in terms of their corresponding institutions for performing the common functions of governance in modern, complex industrial societies.

Any governmental system must provide institutions: (1) to relate the governing body to the governed, (2) to establish policy, (3) to maintain a measure of continuity of policy and procedure and also to accept and guide change, (4) to execute the functions of the state, and (5) to resolve conflicts among citizens and between the individual and the state. The institutions for performing these functions and their manner of operation tend to be similar by reason of the similarity of function, and to differ by reason of the differing state orientations, in this case between a system of government designed to enable a pluralistic society to change itself through the free interplay of its component parts and one whose role is to lead the society to the goal of communism.

8. Candidate of Juridical Sciences A. Bovin underlines that the reflection in the modern bourgeois legislation of measures directed to the defence of workers' interests is the result of the struggle of workers' organizations and progressive forces, and does not arise from the nature of the bourgeois law itself. On the contrary, in the system of bourgeois legislation there are plenty of legal regulations that have been adopted against the people's will. Such is anti-labour legislation (e.g. the Taft-Hartley Act), anti-democratic legislation (of the type of the McCarran-Wood Act), and militaristic legislation, which has assumed grandiose proportions in Western Europe and the USA since World War II.

(1) *Sovremennoye trudovoye zakonodatelstvo imperialisticheskikh gosudarstv na sluzhbe monopolii* (Contemporary Labour Legislation in the Imperialist States in the Service of the Monopolies) (Moscow, Institute of Law of the USSR Academy of Sciences, 1962).

(2) M. V. Baglay, *Zakonodatelstvo S Sh A v borbye s zabastovochnym dvizheniem* (The US Government in Its Struggle with the Strike Movement) (Moscow, 1960).

(3) S. A. Ivanov, *Mezhdunarodnaya organizatsiya truda i profsoyuznie prava v kapitalisticheskikh stranakh* (International Labour Organization and Trade-Union Rights in the Capitalist Countries) (Moscow, USSR Academy of Sciences, 1959).

(4) S. L. Zivs, *Krizis burzhuaznoy zakonnosti v sovremennykh imperialisticheskikh gosudarstvakh* (The Crisis of Bourgeois Legality in the Modern Imperialist States) (Moscow, USSR Academy of Sciences, 1958).

(5) S. L. Zivs, *Razvitie formy prava v sovremennykh imperialisticheskikh gosudarstvakh* (Development of Legal Forms in Modern Imperialist States) (Moscow, USSR Academy of Sciences, 1960).

9. Candidate of Juridical Sciences A. Bovin points out that the doctrine of popular sovereignty is not 'all-inclusive' by the middle of the twentieth century, as asserted by the authors in the text. Not all 'liberal democracies' recognize the people as the sole source of authority in the state. Of twenty-three European bourgeois countries, complete popular sovereignty is proclaimed only in eleven (Austria, Andorra, Great Britain, Ireland, Iceland, Italy, Luxembourg, Norway, the Federal Republic of Germany, Finland, and France). In the remaining countries it is enunciated only in part, i.e., legislative authority is shared by the people and a hereditary monarch who is not elected. This is the case in Belgium, Greece, Liechtenstein, the Netherlands, and Sweden. The map of Europe also features states where the principle of popular sovereignty is not recognized at all. These are: Spain, Portugal, Monaco, and the Vatican City. In the Swiss Confederation the principle of popular sovereignty is still the privilege of the stronger sex alone in most cantons.

In addition, even in those bourgeois states where the principle of popular sovereignty is proclaimed in full, in practice it is very often merely a fiction. In modern states of liberal democracy the electoral law incorporates a whole system of limitations (qualifications) which, to a significant extent, curtail the proclaimed general, equal, and secret suffrage. Thus, in the USA in various States there are more than sixty kinds of electoral qualifications, including those of literacy, residence, 'good behaviour', payment of electoral tax, and so on. The result of all these limitations is very often a distortion of the will of the electors, i.e. defiance of the principle of popular sovereignty. See: *Konstitutsii burzhuaznykh gosudarsv Evropy* (The Constitutions of European Bourgeois States) (Moscow, 1957); L. Dadiani, 'Kak prokhodyat vybory v kapitalisticheskikh stranakh' (How Elections are Run in Capitalist Countries), in *Kommunist* (Communist) (1962), No. 4, pp. 111–12.

10. Candidate of Juridical Sciences A. Bovin stresses that in the socialist countries, where the sovereignty of the state coincides with that of the people, there is taking place not a consolidation of the power of the state over society, but a strengthening of the influence of public organizations and the role they play in social life, the encouragement of citizens to take an active part in administering the state, and an extension of the rights of local self-government. Participation of the working people in the state administration is an immutable principle of socialist state organization, which bears witness to the profoundly democratic character of the Soviet system. The administration of the country's affairs is not the exclusive privilege of the group of citizens who specialize in the techniques of administration (Soviet state employees), but is genuinely the affair of the people as a whole. An active and direct part in the state administration is also played by Soviet citizens who occupy no official positions in any of the existing state organs or institutions. Consequently it is the overwhelming majority of the population, without any direct association with the state apparatus (i.e. not working in it) which takes part in administration.

The number of persons involved in the administrative apparatus in socialist countries is clearly decreasing. (See *Sovetskoye gosudarstvo i obschhestvennost v usloviyakh razvernutogo stroitelstva kommunizma: sbornik statey* (The Soviet State and the Soviet Public in the Conditions of the Extended Building of Communism: A Collection of Articles), Moscow, 1962.)

11. Candidate of Juridical Sciences A. Bovin points out that in the socialist countries the system of subordination of the lower organs of authority and administration to higher organs presupposes, firstly, full realization of the principle of popular sovereignty in all representative organs, and secondly, broad autonomy for local institutions within the limits of their competence.

The highest organ of authority in socialist countries is a representative body, elected by the whole population on the basis of universal and equal suffrage, by a secret vote, for a period of 4–5 years. All citizens, men and women, who have attained a certain age (generally 18) have the right to vote, and there are no restrictions with regard to race, nationality, social class, etc. A specific feature of the electoral system in the socialist countries is the right to recall deputies. It is exercised by electors in case a deputy should fail to justify their confidence. Although this right is not exercised very often, its mere existence has a tremendous significance. It ensures constant control by the masses over the actions of their chosen representatives, enhances their feeling of responsibility to their electors, and the energy with which they perform their duties.

Local organs of authority are elected by the population of the area concerned on the basis of universal, equal and direct suffrage, by secret ballot. In accordance with the idea of popular sovereignty these local bodies' powers derive directly from the people, and not from higher organs of authority. Their powers are sufficiently extensive to enable them to guide all aspects of the life of the area concerned. (See: (1) *Constitution of the Union of Soviet Socialist Republics* (Moscow 1961); (2) *Vysshiye organy vlasti stran narodnoy demokratii* (The Higher Organs of Authority in the People's Democracies) (Moscow, 1960)).

12. Candidate of Juridical Sciences A. Bovin thinks that it is only with grave reservations that the electoral system in the liberal democracies can be called 'machinery by means of which popular sovereignty was exercised'. A large number of Western political scientists and public figures have noted that the electoral systems presently in force in bourgeois countries are organically incapable of expressing the will of the majority, as the principle of popular sovereignty requires. Thus, the well-known American jurists, C. B. Gosnell, L. W. Lancaster and R. S. Ranklin, hold that, in view of the inadequacy of the American electoral system, 'popular sovereignty' has been reduced to a sort of 'moral right of veto' (see C. B. Gosnell, L. W. Lancaster, R. S. Rankin, *Fundamentals of American National Government*, New York, 1955). The British political scientists E. Lakeman and J. Lambert, in their work *Voting in Democracies* (London, 1956) take the view that the British electoral system leads to a situation in which the House of Commons does not reflect the feelings of the nation. Leading French political figures also consider that, on account of the electoral procedure now in force in their country, the French Parliament after the 1958 elections 'does not reflect the views of the people' (V. Rochet, Polozhenie vo Frantsii i politika frantsuzskoy kompartii', in *Kommunist* (Communist), 1962, No. 3, p. 85). In general the electoral systems in modern Western democracies are far from perfect. They may be classified into two basic types: proportional and majority systems. Majority electoral systems (such as exist in the USA, Great Britain, France and elsewhere) afford very wide scope for various manipulations with the electors' votes. The proportional system is more democratic, but it is not very widespread and also suffers from major shortcomings. A critique of the electoral systems currently in force in Western countries is given in the following works:

(1) E. Lakeman and J. Lambert, *Voting in Democracies: a Study of Majority and Proportional Electoral Systems*, London, 1956.

(2) R. J. Ross, *Parliamentary Representation*, London, 1944.

(3) I. D. Levin, *Sovremennaya burzhuaznaya nauka gosudarstvennogo prava* (Contemporary Bourgeois Science of Public Law), Moscow, USSR Academy of Sciences, 1960.

(4) L. M. Belson, *Sovremennoye burzhuaznoye gosudarstvo i narodnoye predstavitelstvo* (Contemporary Bourgeois Government and Popular Representation), Moscow, 1960.

13. Candidate of Juridical Sciences A. Bovin points out that the political parties represented in the parliaments of the Western countries are no better able than the electoral systems to express the principle of popular sovereignty. In the largest liberal democratic countries the parties in power, which have a preponderance of seats in Parliament, are as a rule parties of a minority of the population that is most powerful economically. Thus the British Conservative Party, the party of the wealthy strata of the population, for which only 38 per cent of the total number of votes was cast on October 8, 1959, nevertheless remained the party in power and obtained more than 57 per cent of the seats in the House of Commons.

On the other hand, the French Communist Party, which is a democratic mass party, obtained about 4 million votes, i.e. 300,000 more than the Union for the New Republic

(UNR), the party of the bourgeoisie. Yet in the National Assembly there were only 70 Communist deputies and 220 deputies of the UNR. (See V. Rochet 'Polozhenie Frantsii i politika Frantsuzskoy kompartii' ('The Position in France and the Policy of the French Communist Party'), in *Kommunist* (Communist) (1962), No. 3, p. 85.)

14. Candidate of Juridical Sciences A. Bovin points out that the assumption of legislative functions by executive organs is not a positive aspect of the development of political institutions in the twentieth century. The mass of legislative acts issued by officials which regulate in detail the life of society is in the first place evidence of the decline of parliamentary control over the actions of the executive power and in general indicates the decay of the system of liberal democracy itself.

Parliamentary control over governments was one of the bourgeois-democratic institutions which the progressive forces of bourgeois society always sought to establish and perfect. But at the present time the bourgeoisie is attempting by every means in its power to limit the capacity for the popular masses to express their political will through the electoral system, and is taking important steps to restrict the powers of parliamentary bodies. Hence the tendency to strengthen executive governmental-administrative power *vis-à-vis* representative institutions, and the enormous increase in the amount of so-called delegated legislation issued by various governmental departments and committees. Delegated legislation is uncontrolled legislative governmental activity which bears witness to the colossal authority concentrated in the hands of senior officials. Very frequently this uncontrolled activity by the executive is directed against the interests of the democratic strata of the population. Many western scholars have expressed alarm at the growth of 'delegated legislation' at the expense of constitutional rights, and have pointed out that such a state of affairs constitutes a serious 'threat to freedom'. (See C. B. Gosnell, L. W. Lancaster, R. S. Rankin, *Fundamentals of American National Government*, N.Y., 1955, p. 247.)

See the following works on this question:

(1) I. D. Levin, *Sovremennaya burzhuaznaya nauka gosudarstvennogo prava* (The Contemporary Bourgeois Science of Public Law) (Moscow, 1960), pp. 334–6.

(2) B. S. Krylov, 'Kritika sobremennykh burzhuaznykh teoriy parlamentarizma' (A Critique of Modern Bourgeois Theories of Parliamentarism), in *Sovetskoe gosudarstvo i pravo* (Soviet State and Law) (1962), No. 1, pp. 111–15.

(3) S. L. Zivs, 'Osnovnye tendentsii v razvitii sovremennogo imperialisticheskogo gosudarstva' (Basic Tendencies in the Development of the Modern Imperialist State), in *Sovetskoe gosudarstvo i pravo* (Soviet State and Law) (1961), No. 10, pp. 177–8.

(4) S. L. Zivs, *Krisis burzhuaznoy zakonnosti v sovremennykh imperialisticheskikh gosudarstvakh* (The Crisis of Bourgeois Law and Order in the Modern Imperialist States), Moscow, 1958.

15. Candidate of Juridical Sciences A. Bovin points out that correctly noting the tremendous size of the bureaucratic apparatus in modern democracies, the extent of its functions, and its independence of parliamentary control, the authors incorrectly present such a state of affairs as necessary for the effective management of the complex affairs of the 'welfare state'. Actually the process of bureaucratization of the economic, political and entire social life of modern capitalist states is in the direct interests of monopoly capitalism. The basic trend of this growth of bureaucracy is set by the private corporations. The bourgeois parties, reactionary organizations and the state copy the forms and methods of bureaucratic control elaborated by the monopolies.

The bureaucratic inflation of the bourgeois state machine is manifested in the first place in the creation of departments and organizations serving to enhance the economic and financial power of the private corporations at the workers' expense. Secondly, the development of the bureaucratic state apparatus is closely connected with the policy of militarization. The reality of life in modern capitalist countries is characterized by a sharp increase in the role of the military element which interferes in all spheres of activity: in economics, politics, in science and education, in the propaganda system. The military bureaucracy, as is known, is distinguished by the frank crudity of its methods of command, its lack of even an appearance of democracy. In general bureaucratization is a manifestation of the characteristically imperialist tendency to renounce the forms of bourgeois democracy. See:

(1) M. Lerner, *America as a Civilization* (New York, 1957).

(2) C. W. Mills, *White Collar* (New York, 1956).

(3) S. L. Zivs, 'Osnovnye tendentsii v razvitii sovremennogo imperialisticheskogo gosudarstva' ('Basic Tendencies in the Development of the Modern Imperialist State') in: *Sovetskoye gosudarstvo i pravo* (Soviet State and Law) (1961), No. 10.

(4) Yu. A. Zamoshkin, 'Byurokratizatsiya burzhuaznogo obshchestva i sud by lichnosti' ('The Bureaucratization of Bourgeois Society and the Fate of the Individual'), in *Voprosy filosofii* (Problems of Philosophy), No. 4 (1961).

16. Candidate of Juridical Sciences A. Bovin asserts that the Communist party was never 'superior to the state' and is not at the present time 'the supreme authority in the state'. It cannot take the place of state organs. (See *Constitution of the Union of Soviet Socialist Republics*, Moscow, 1961, Art. 30; *Statute of the Communist Party of the Soviet Union*, Moscow, 1961.) In the socialist countries parties are voluntary associations of like-minded individuals who have united to ensure the triumph of communist, socialist and democratic ideals. They determine their policies by taking into account the opinion of the non-Party masses, and put this policy forward for examination by state organizations elected by the entire people. The Communist party of the Soviet Union acts as leader in the whole system of democratic organizations. This role is not imposed upon society. Society itself, or to be more precise its overwhelming majority—workers, peasants and intelligentsia, in a word the toiling masses—put the Communist Party forward as their leader. This is to be explained by the fact that the Party has shown itself the most consistent and active defender of the nation's interests. Everywhere and at all times it fought so that the people should come to power. After conquest of power by the working people, when the Communist Party has become the ruling party, it sets about implementing a programme for the rapid development of productive forces in order to bring about on this basis a radical improvement in the wellbeing of the people, their culture, and their lives generally.

The Communist party seeks to exercise a decisive influence on the activity of all other organizations, including organs of authority and administration. This task is eased by the fact that communists are members of all or almost all organizations. It is through them, in the first place, that the Party realizes its programme. The Communist Party is constantly enlarging its membership by attracting the most conscious elements of the population. The Party consists of approximately 6 per cent of the population, i.e. over 9 million persons in the USSR. It is a genuinely popular party.

The fact that the country is led by such a goal-oriented and disciplined force as the Communist party gives the whole of society a monolithic quality, so that it successfully withstands attempts at intervention from without and solves immense problems in the spirit of Communist ideals. This of course does not mean that the Party takes upon itself the functions of other organizations. On the contrary, the Party is interested in encouraging the broadest possible initiative by each link in the political system, seeing in this a guarantee of the successful solution of the tasks facing the people as a whole. (F. M. Burlatsky, 'Rastsvet sotsialisticheskoy demokratii' (The Development of Socialist Democracy), in: *Vestnik istorii mirovoy kultury* (Review of the History of World Culture), No. 5, 1961, pp. 5–61.)

17. Candidate of Juridical Sciences A. Bovin points out that the anti-Party, anti-Leninist methods of leadership practised in certain cases by J. Stalin should not be presented as methods which served to make the practice of the Party 'very clear'. These were methods that discredited the Party's policy, which did no small amount of harm to the clear line of the Party, and which were condemned with all severity by the twenty-second congress of the CPSU in October 1961.

However, the cult of the personality could not alter either the social-economic essence of the socialist system or the democratic nature of its political system. Precisely on account of the socialist character of its social and political system, which was alien to the cult of 'a chosen personality', on account of the fact that the working masses remained the decisive force under all circumstances in the construction of socialism and communism, under the leadership of the Communist party, linked by the closest bonds to the people, it proved possible to limit very materially the damage done by the personality cult, and then to overcome it and its consequences. ('Sovety i stroitelstvo kommunizma' ("The

Soviets and the Building of Communism'), leading article in *Kommunist* (Communist), No. 2 (1962); pp. 4–5.)

See also Note 12 to Chapter XXI.

18. Candidate of Juridical Sciences A. Bovin points out that the Soviet judicial system was never 'an instrument of administration' but an organ of justice.

The administration of justice in the USSR is an independent function of the state, separate from the general administration. The lower links in the judicial system are elected by the population, the medium-level and higher ones are organs of authority. The courts are independent and subject only to the law. Legislative activity is carried on in such a way as to leave a certain scope to the courts, which include as well as permanent judges, who have no other duties to fulfil, people's assessors—workers in some branches of production or culture, pensioners, etc.

The principle of controversy, the right of defence, recognition of the presumption of innocence, the widest right of appeal up to the Supreme Court, and active participation by the public both on the side of the defence and of the prosecution—these and other principles ensure discovery of the truth in the course of a trial.

Moreover, Soviet jurisprudence proceeds from the principle that the activity of the court has an educational as well as a penal function. Wide use is made of various kinds of penalties that do not involve deprivation of freedom, such as suspended sentences, public censure, etc. Increasing importance is coming to be attached to the practice of handing over minor offenders for trial by their collectives at their place of work. This measure is as a rule more effective than punishment under the penal code. (See *Constitution (Fundamental Law) of the USSR*, Ch. IX: The Courts and Procurator's Office); F. M. Burlatsky, 'Rastsvet sotsialisticheskoy demokratii' ('The Development of Socialist Democracy'), in: *Vestnik istorii mirovoy kultury* (Review of the History of World Culture) No. 5, 1961; p. 9. For a detailed examination of the section 'Institutions of the Communist States', see Volume VI, Tome II, of the *History of Mankind: Cultural and Scientific*.

Bulgarian scholars consider that the chapter 'Political Institutions' suffers from a major defect: the tendency to consider forms of government, legislative activity, etc. by themselves, in isolation from the class struggle in society, the development of productive forces and social economic phenomena—the factors and causes that give rise to them and eliminate them.'

19. Professor E. N. Anderson notes that the Author-Editors fail to make clear one of the outstanding characteristics of the first half of the twentieth century, that of the widespread use of brutality, torture and other forms of violence. Brutality has been present in all human societies and in all historical periods, and it would be strange not to encounter it in an age described as that of 'cultural crisis.' The special features of violence in the present period have been its mass character, the variety of its forms and uses, and its spread among peoples of the highest level of education and technology, as well as among backward areas, among all classes and among groups of strong religious faith along with those devoid of religious affiliation. Brutality has been adopted as official governmental policy, it has been legally disclaimed but officially tolerated or condoned, and it has been invoked in defiance of authority. In many countries violence has become so much a part of the mores that it is difficult to set criteria by which to distinguish between the amount and kinds of violence that are normal to most societies and are subject to the controls of criminal law, and the amount and kinds that stretch far beyond the norms of organized society.

Although it may be impossible to categorize the major forms of violence of this half century, the attempt to do so may clarify the significance of the phenomenon. There is illegal or non-legal violence that reflects racial, national or religious hatred at local, voluntary, informal levels. A second kind concerns opposition by force of arms to a new organization of society. Another category includes the type of individual and of movement analysed by Albert Camus in *The Rebel*. Hatred of existing society and its organization and lust for power in order to remake society led to arson, assault, murder, and the endless harassments of private and public personages flowing from total contempt of opposition. Still another type consists of the legal and official organization of violence. Psychological torture, brain-washing and similar pressures belong in this category.

Systems of law and a judicial organization are frequently introduced to give all these forms of violence the appearance of legality. Thus secret police pervade society, secret arrest and trial and, if the regime regards it is advisable, secret punishment receive the sanction of law, and governmental control of food rationing and officially implemented starvation become essential instruments for dealing with potential opponents. Into this category of official action must be entered the endeavour to wipe out an entire people, the best known example of which is the treatment of the Jewish minority by the National Socialists in Germany. Threat of a reappearance of this type of violence led the United Nations to identify and condemn it as the crime of genocide. National Socialists added a further example of state-directed cruelty in putting to death the mentally deranged or mentally retarded, the physically misformed, the incurable and socially unproductive and of sanctioning experiments for so-called scientific purposes upon enemies of the regime. Still another category of violence closely related to the preceding is that of the forced flight of millions of people from their homes, the brutality connected with exchange of populations and the expulsion of refugees.

The list of categories could no doubt be extended and refined. Sufficient data have been given, however, to support the judgment that this century has been, and continues to be, a period of ruthless animosities and of varied means of committing physical and mental violence upon individuals and upon masses. It is possible that the extent of brutality is unique in world history.

The literature on this subject is extensive, especially for Europe.

CHAPTER XXIV

MILITARY INSTITUTIONS

MILITARY institutions came to occupy an increasingly important place in the societies of the twentieth century as the character of warfare changed and affected more and more deeply the life of every modern state.

In all periods military institutions have reflected the overall structure of society and in turn have affected it. This was doubly true of the establishments which came to reflect the structure of modern industrial society and to accentuate many of its features. Twentieth-century methods of warfare brought a reintegration of civilian and military institutions which the trends of the nineteenth century had tended to separate. The process of industrial mobilization involved the redirection of civilian institutions to military purposes and the reorientation of the military to make them able to utilize the machinery of industrial production.

The importance of military institutions has always been enhanced by periods of warfare. The occurrence within a period of twenty-five years of two wars of world-wide scope, as well as an almost continuous series of lesser military operations, kept military leadership and organization more or less constantly to the fore. As warfare became more and more total, it required the conscious planning, co-ordination and control of the multitude of separate but mutually interdependent elements of which industrial societies are composed. It was thus the most potent force making for comprehensive large-scale organization. In the centrally administered states it merely intensified the peacetime organization. In other states it required the creation of new instrumentalities which did not wholly disappear after hostilities were ended.

The military institutions of the twentieth century were also instruments of social change. Although they were usually conservative, with strong traditions and dedication to the maintenance of the *status quo*, the nature of modern warfare made them powerful innovators. In some circumstances, moreover, military institutions became the conscious spearheads of social change. The Soviet Red army after 1917 and the People's Liberation army of China were direct instruments of revolution and reconstruction. The military provided much of the leadership for revolution and modernization in such countries of the Middle East as Turkey, Iran and Egypt. In some of the industrially underdeveloped countries, such as Thailand after the second world war, the armed forces were one of the agencies through which modern technology reached into a country. The armies of India and the United States contributed to the integration of disparate social groups.

I. TRADITIONAL MILITARY INSTITUTIONS

In the early years of the century the military establishments of most countries had many common characteristics, although the detail of their form and their role in national life varied considerably from place to place. The German army, from the time of its victory over the French in 1870 to the opening of the first world war, provided a model, or at least an inspiration, to the professional military groups in most other countries, very notably in Turkey and Japan.

All the countries of continental Europe, and also Japan, had conscript armies composed of a permanent officer group, a nucleus of army regulars, chiefly non-commissioned officers, and a large reserve of manpower which had experienced military training, usually for two years. At any given time the forces in being consisted of the permanent elements plus the young men, generally 18–20 years of age, who were doing their compulsory military service. Elsewhere, notably in Britain and the United States, volunteer armies were the rule. Navies depended on volunteer recruitment, although in some countries a certain number of conscripts could choose navy duty.

A sharp gulf separated officers from men. Officers were generally drawn from the upper strata of society and an officer's career was looked upon as a high calling. In some volunteer regiments with special reputations and traditions, most frequently cavalry or guards units, enlisted personnel also enjoyed a special prestige, though they were still separated from the officer class by an unbridgeable gulf.

In many countries a special social group, usually the large landowners, provided the core of the officer personnel—a heritage from feudal society in which the two functions of landowning and fighting were combined. Among the Prussian Junkers, British landed gentry, estate-owners of Russia, the Austro-Hungarian empire or Latin America, at least some member of the family—a second son perhaps—was expected to enter a military career. For many, especially the Prussian aristocracy, these careers were practically hereditary. Professional classes also furnished many officers in these countries and the majority of officers in countries without an aristocratic tradition, such as Switzerland.

Since military leadership tended to be drawn from the upper strata of society and from the agricultural rather than the urban–industrial segment, military institutions were apt to reflect the outlook of these elements. This outlook was not only conservative, *élite* and generally opposed to policies based on commerical interests but, with some outstanding exceptions, it tended to be indifferent to scientific knowledge. German officers objected to having the least competent of their sons excluded from military schools, while their British counterparts insisted that it was a boy's performance on the playing field rather than in the classroom which revealed his fitness for a military career. Navies were on the whole more scientifically oriented than armies because by the opening of the twentieth century they were already more mechanized, although those responsible for the vessel's operation did not enjoy officer status.

The officer group was everywhere organized in a strict hierarchical structure within which position defined not only responsibility but status. Sea and land forces were separately organized with their respective hierarchies, neither subordinate to the other, and with separate training institutions, traditions, administration, and relation to the structure of government. Advancement to higher officer ranks was open to all within the group, and the desire to provide opportunities for promotion often led members of the military bureaucracies to recommend policies which would make this possible. Speed of advancement depended upon the rate of expansion of the service. Friction sometimes existed between the younger men in the lower ranks and the older men at the top, and systems of early retirement were introduced in some services to keep the leadership fresh and the lower ranks filled with new men capable of rising.

While an open system of promotion existed within the officer group there was, prior to the first world war, virtually no access to this group from below. An enlisted man could be elevated to a non-commissioned position—army corporal or sergeant or naval petty officer—but there was rarely any possibility for him to qualify for entrance into the officer corps.

The rigid separation characteristic of military structures and reinforced by difference in social origin contributed to the authoritarian nature of military establishments. In essentially authoritarian societies military institutions were in keeping with the general social pattern. The Prussian and Japanese armies, for example, might be described as exaggerated versions of the pervasively authoritarian and persistently feudal structure of those societies. The German army had in fact helped to stave off the growth of liberalism in that country during the nineteenth century.

The Japanese army combined a strong feudal tradition and complete loyalty to the emperor with features of military structure and organization learned from Germany. Japanese military leaders occupied at all times a strong position from which they sought with fluctuating success to dominate national policy.

In Great Britain the military structure reflected the continuing class divisions but its authoritarianism was not in keeping with the trend toward democratic political forms. The fact that the British armed forces were, in the early years of the century, mainly stationed overseas and were chiefly engaged in maintaining the British empire, however, minimized the possible conflict between authoritarian and democratic attitudes, for the latter did not extend to the relations of the British with their colonial subjects, and it was these among whom the armed forces chiefly lived. In countries such as the United States, the Scandinavian countries or Holland the authoritarian military institutions were at odds with the democratic ethos of the society and were the object of general suspicion on the part of civilians.

In the Latin American countries military organizations were in effect a part of the structure of government. In spite of the fact that most of these republics lived under constitutions which called for free elections, only a few, such as Uruguay, had followed constitutional procedures consistently. Many governments were in fact maintained and changed by the intervention of the army.

The major colonial powers organized and trained some of their colonial peoples and formed native regiments, chiefly for use within the colonial territory. The principal colonial military bodies were the Indian army and the French African legions. The Dutch also trained Indonesian troops, as well as 'colonials' from the home country who signed for service in the Netherlands' Indies. Spain recruited Moroccans and the British enlisted a number of Africans.

The British maintained two distinct military bodies in India, both with British officers, one composed of units of the British army stationed there, the other made up of regiments recruited and trained in India. The Indian army was the arm of the British empire in non-European areas, and was used in Burma, the Persian Gulf and Africa, as well as on the frontiers of India and to maintain British authority in the sub-continent.

French colonial troops were recruited as part of the main French army, to fill manpower deficiencies in the French forces. After the defeat in 1870 of the more highly trained but smaller French army by the more numerous German forces, France sought to keep up with its rival in number of men under arms. The small French population and low birth rate, however, set limits on the capacity to keep up the race, even though in the years before the first world war the French were calling up 83 per cent of those bound to serve while the German army called up only 53 per cent. The French army therefore drew on its colonial and overseas areas. On the eve of the first world war nearly a tenth of France's effective troops were African, largely Senegalese. The officers of these troops were all French and remained so with only a few exceptions up to the second world war.

Military establishments were self-governing and aspired to as much independence of action as they could achieve. In the liberal democracies they were subject to civilian control of funds and determination of policy, but even in these countries such controls were rarely effectively extended into either internal structure or the making of military decisions.

The overall body responsible for military policy and strategy was the general staff. This institution was developed in the German army, taken over *in toto* by the Japanese, and adopted in various modified forms by the armies of other countries, especially Russia. In Germany those who became members of the general staff were selected from among the officer corps solely on the basis of competence and were subjected to intensive training for three years in the War Academy. The small proportion of the entrants to the Academy who completed this exacting training then served a two-year apprenticeship under existing general staff officers. The training covered all aspects—operations, intelligence, transport, supply—together with historical and theoretical studies of techniques of warfare, with the objective of equipping the staff officers to understand and think imaginatively, in strictly military, non-political terms, about overall strategy and military planning.

The German general staff, thus trained and distinguished by a special uniform, was a small select group, numbering 276 at the outbreak of the first world war. Relationships among the members were based on a strong *esprit de corps* and were personal rather than bureaucratic. The concept of the German general staff was of a group rather than of a line of command.

A general staff officer was placed in each headquarters from the divisional level up to the supreme command and functioned as the close adviser of the commanding officer, sharing his decisions and issuing orders in his absence. Communication between general staff officers was direct, without passing through the commanding officers. The whole general staff was expected to have a common knowledge, understanding and view of the complete military strategy and thus to provide unity of purpose and direction to the military effort. It planned and functioned as a virtually autonomous power within the state.

Among the various general staffs developed in other countries, none followed their German model in making the group small, *élite*, permanent and bound together by essentially personal ties, though the pattern was most closely approximated in Japan, both in the closeness of the group and its identification of public policy with military objectives. Elsewhere the general staff was large—the French general staff at the opening of the first world war was more than three times the size of the German for an equivalent number of troops and it was bureaucratic in its interrelationships. Sometimes, as in the United States where the whole idea of a special *élite* group found little favour, it was composed of a changing membership. In Britain the idea of competence in all fields was replaced by a division between operations and intelligence on the one hand and transport and supply on the other. But within every military structure there was a body which had the function of providing the intellectual co-ordination and leadership of military planning and endeavours, and which spoke for the military *vis-à-vis* the civilian authorities and population.[1]

The military establishments in the early years of the century were primarily concerned with men and only secondarily with equipment. Since few military leaders were drawn from the urban–industrial parts of the population, their mentality tended everywhere to be pre-industrial. Their values and relationships were strongly personal. The habit of economic calculation, the tendency to substitute machine for human power, the patterns of industrial organization were all foreign to their experience. They were not in a position to project in their imaginations the importance of industry or its possible relation to military operations or objectives. Almost completely lacking in knowledge or experience of scientific or industrial methods, the military left the initiative in weapon production to private industry.

II. THE ARMAMENT INDUSTRY

By the opening of the twentieth century the production of munitions was a highly organized, independent activity. While the military establishments themselves clung to an essentially feudal-agrarian outlook, the weapon makers were transforming the nature of warfare and ultimately the nature and role of the military itself.

A group of great private munitions firms, each the result of a series of mergers and expansions, dominated the fields. The Nobel Dynamite Trust Company Ltd., which constituted an amalgamation of the dynamite and smokeless powder interests of the Swedish magnate, Alfred Nobel, was at the centre of the international trade in explosives. The Vickers-Armstrong merger in England in the 1890s had made this giant concern the largest armaments company in the world, producing ordinance, armour plate and naval vessels for a world market. It had branches in Spain, Italy, Russia and Japan and an affiliate in Germany. The German Krupp works had absorbed in the 1890s smaller firms with specialized productions and had added naval vessels to its former line of armour plate and guns. Together with its enterprising competitor, Erhardt, it largely monopolized the German market and had extensive markets abroad. Schneider-Creusot in France, one of the oldest of the munitions enterprises, was the leading designer of field guns. The Austrian Skoda works in Bohemia, manufacturing mainly artillery pieces, armour and vehicles, used some of the Krupp patents. The Putiloff concern in Russia operated with the collaboration of British, French and Austrian firms.

In the United States armament production was never a distinct branch of industry, although there were specialized producers such as the Dupont Chemical Company. Output for military purposes was an outgrowth of already existing industrial production and was scattered among many firms. There were no armament kings and no great American combine which entered the world armament market. In Japan the development of heavy industry itself was to an important extent aimed at military production, and from the start it had a large measure of government backing and participation. The smaller powers generally purchased their weapons from the major producers, though some had facilities for making certain munitions or constructing naval vessels.

The great munitions makers were not wholly divorced from civilian production. Most of them had grown out of enterprises making civilian goods, such as iron and steel and various kinds of tools. On the eve of the first world war 60 per cent of Vickers' production was for non-military orders. Krupp remained a major producer of steel for German industry, and of industrial products, especially railway equipment.

Yet the thrust of these companies was to expand the market for munitions wherever it could be stimulated, and in the interest of profits to use every device known to the commercial or political world to help create the appetite for more and better arms. They were the developers and promoters of new designs. Collectively they were often referred to as the 'merchants of death', and the dramatic cloaked figure of Basil Zaharoff, chairman of Vickers-Armstrong, moving in sinister fashion from chancery to chancery became the symbol of the malign role of the munitions makers.[2]

III. TRANSFORMATION OF MILITARY INSTITUTIONS BY TOTAL WAR

Both the nature of military establishments and their place in the total society changed with the coming of total war. The first world war made obsolete nearly everything which linked military establishments to the feudal past. Cavalry went out in the face of mechanization, except in Russia where extreme cold and deep mud made the use of motorized vehicles at certain times impracticable. The special guard regiments which were the pride and ornament of several armies proved of little value. The exclusive officer class gave way, though only partially, to men of different backgrounds as armies were expanded during the war. Mechanized warfare called for technical knowledge and skills and required the organization of many more auxiliary services and for calculations based as much or more on war material as on personnel.

The new character of warfare also changed the relationship among the several military services. Armies and navies had been under separate commands. The rise of air power introduced a third service. In every country air forces had to struggle for status against the efforts of the older services to treat aviation merely as an adjunct to their operation, not as a separate arm. Nowhere were the three services integrated or even fully co-ordinated. The traditions of self-government, loyalty to the particular service, secrecy, the difficulty faced by anyone who tried to think in comprehensive terms about the overwhelming complexities of modern warfare and the orientation given by each military person's training and experience all combined to keep the three services independent of each other, and often in competition. Technical developments however continually thrust the air force into a more and more central position.

The new military establishments took on many of the features of great industrial enterprises. Modern business methods, office organization, systems of record keeping, the use of duplicating, sorting and communications equipment and all the paraphernalia for carrying on large industrial operations gave military institutions many of the characteristics of their civilian counterparts.

In order to deal with industrial mobilization, special branches or units were set up. The usual pattern was for the general staffs to continue to deal with military operations while distinct bodies were created to deal with industrial and supply aspects, such as the Ministry of Supply in Great Britain, the Army Industrial College in the United States, the Economy and Armaments Office in the German Supreme Command. These bodies were responsible for assessing the industrial potentials of their respective countries, developing procedures for dealing with civilian firms and setting up economic mobilization schemes.

Where central economic planning was developed in the years after the first world war, as in the Soviet Union, military planning became an integral part. In Soviet Russia, under the successive five-year plans, requirements of the Red army were handled through the same machinery for allocating resources and setting priorities as were those of other commissariats such as those for electric power, agriculture or transport. The five-year plan was in essence a plan for rapidly increasing the industrial potential of the Soviet Union; when war objectives replaced those of peacetime it could be quickly converted into a 'war economy plan', as was done in August 1941. The German four-year plan of 1936, while originally designed primarily to meet raw material deficiencies, became the framework for economic mobilization for the second world war.

In countries such as France, Britain and the United States, where general economic activity remained unco-ordinated, the plans for industrial mobilization formulated by military authorities took the form of outlines which were used, especially in Britain, to guide the industrial aspect of rearmament in the 1930s and which were intended to furnish an administrative blue-print for the direction of resources in time of war. In Japan a series of industry-wide control associations provided the machinery through which in the decade after 1931 an eighteenfold increase in military expenditure shaped the Japanese economy for war.

The munitions industries also underwent a transformation. Prior to the first world war the armaments trusts had been extra-national private ventures producing and selling instruments of war on the open market. That each of the munitions trusts was the principal supplier of the armed forces of its own nation was no more than was the case with the output of most industrial concerns whose first buyers were in the home market.

When the first world war made it apparent that a few munitions firms could not meet the needs of a mass army and governments began to draw on all their industrial resources, the munitions firm lost its central role and became only one among many producers of military supplies. In particular the initiative in military design began to pass from the industries engaged in making products to armies and navies looking for new weapons.

Furthermore the new total war—the war of peoples and of total involvement—made the independence and private character of the munitions makers no longer consistent with the character of warfare and the nature of the national interest. When a nation was embarked on a great collective effort which required all its united energies and when the nation's military capacities came to be defined in terms of productive capacity rather than military manpower, the national munitions maker became a national military asset, not an independent entrepreneur. The sale of armaments to another country, in which the old munitions-makers had freely engaged, became a political move not a business transaction. Although the great munitions works continued to flourish and expand they lost both their key position as armament producers and their independence of action outside the country. In place of the symbol of Basil Zaharoff seeking to boost his sales by pitting one country against another in competitive bidding for the arms which Vickers-Armstrong had to offer, the new symbol was the long procession of industrialists negotiating with their own governments for an endless variety of military orders that might represent anywhere from 5 to 90 per cent of their peacetime and 100 per cent of their wartime production.

The concept of the total economy of each state as one overall national war production machine was expressed most completely in the autarchy sought by Nazi Germany and to some degree by other powers. Recalling the effects of blockade during the first world war, Hitler attempted to make the German economy independent of trade with other countries and set scientists to the task of developing substitutes for the materials which had been imported from abroad. Japan's programme of expansion sought to build a self-contained economic area in which the resources of Korea, Manchuria, the Chinese mainland and south-east Asia, especially those essential to military production, would be integrated and the densely populated islands of Japan with their limited resources would no longer depend on the hazards of international trade. Under the actual conditions of the second world war, however, the British economy which had not attempted to become self-sufficient was more completely mobilized and integrated into the war effort than was that of Germany.

Changes in military organization reflected changes in the surrounding society as well as changes in methods of warfare. The structure of the Soviet army and the relationships between officers and men reflected the structure of Soviet society and the role played in it by the Communist party. Since the Party directed all aspects of state activity, the political commissar representing the Party was an essential part of the military organization. His position varied with organizational changes in the army and navy and with the need to enhance Party influence at definite periods.

The sources from which the Soviet military leadership was drawn were also the reverse of tsarist days, except for those tsarist officers who threw in their lot with the new régime. New officers came primarily from among the sons of workers and peasants, who rose through an intensive educational system designed to single out the ablest for advancement; in time many were the sons of Red army officers themselves. Academic brilliance in scientific and technical subjects, together with Party reliability, were the keys which opened a military career. Within the military structure, too, the old gulf between officers and men was replaced by more easy social relations and an open path to advancement for those in the ranks who qualified for training as officers. In the course of time, when general Soviet policy shifted from broad egalitarianism to higher pay for those who performed greater service to the state, the officer corps became a highly paid group, and rank, titles and insignia again came to the fore. The Red army was a microcosm of Soviet life.

The Chinese People's Liberation army became a unique body. Militarily it was organized both for guerrilla fighting and for organized warfare. As an instrument of social revolution it reformed the peasant villages in the areas under its control, making the peasantry almost part of the army itself.

In the fascist states military organization was the pattern and ideal for the organization of society. As expressed by Alfred Rosenberg, the philosopher of National Socialism, the permanent style of life which Germans were finding under National Socialism was 'the style of the marching column, regardless of where and for what purpose this marching column is to be used'.* The conversion of all institutions into military institutions was carried furthest in Nazi Germany and in Japan after 1931, but it was central to the principles and structure of fascist Italy and falangist Spain, and coloured the military dictatorships of eastern Europe.

The pervasive military organization of civilian life was in part an expression of the concept that war is the essential purpose of the state. In the words of Benito Mussolini in his article on 'The State' in the *Enciclopedia Italiana*, 'only war brings human energies to their highest tension and ennobles those peoples which dare to undertake it'. Beyond this, however, the military style constituted a way of life in itself.

In Nazi Germany the totalitarian principle was everywhere clothed in military forms. All organizations which rested on a democratic base were replaced by quasi-military bodies. The labour unions became the Labour Front, each factory a military unit in which the management occupied the relationship to the workers of officers to enlisted men. Youth was enlisted in Hitler Youth organizations, women in the Women's Front, and each profession had its official organization in which military structure prevailed. Military terminology pervaded the language of all human activity.

Amid the quasi-military institutions of this militarized society the armed forces themselves took central place, both as models to others and in the authority which they represented. They combined the characteristics, personnel and attitudes of the traditional military class with new features reflecting the new mechanized warfare and the social changes which accompanied the Nazi régime. Although the officer corps continued to come from the old groups—in 1936 five of the six top officers and nearly a quarter of those from the rank of colonel up were members of the nobility—some new talent was being drawn in; the colonels and major-generals in that year included five Ph.Ds, all with non-noble names. The regular army was supplemented, and its position challenged, by Hitler's personal forces, the storm troopers and especially the Waffen S.S., composed of young men from all classes whose brown and black uniforms gave them status and authority.

* *Gestaltung der Idee* (1937), pp. 303 ff.

IV. MILITARY–CIVILIAN INSTITUTIONS OF
THE SECOND WORLD WAR

The second world war completed the transformation of the military establishments into central institutions of industrial societies, sharing and often leading in technical and scientific development. The much more complete economic mobilization and mechanized operation of that conflict led to the incorporation of civilians with special knowledge and skills, such as production engineers, administrators, scientists and technicians of all sorts, into the armed services with ranks which reflected their civilian experience, not their progression through the military hierarchy. The global logistics problems of supply were met by the formation of elaborate organizations overshadowing even the largest of the industrial corporations. Except in communist states where central administrative bodies functioned continuously, wartime administrations had to be created by the expansion of existing agencies, as in Germany, France, Italy and Japan, or by setting up new agencies as in Britain and the United States.

To design and describe millions of war items, establish standards, secure production and arrange for delivery at the right time and place required enormous staffs, elaborate systems of accounting and reporting and a knowledge and understanding of industrial processes which greatly exceeded that necessary for normal peacetime functioning. The complexity of these processes made largely inapplicable the traditional concept of a general staff which could comprehend and direct all phases of the war effort. General staffs everywhere tended to have their scope limited to field operations while manpower mobilization and industrial expansion were placed under the direction of such bodies as the British Ministry of Supply with a staff expanded from 5,000 to 68,496 or the American War Production Board with 300,000 employees.

Mass production and delivery introduced a serious problem of rigidity since most industrial products require one to two years from initial design to actual mass output, yet improvements in weapons came so rapidly that a new model would often be planned before the old one had started to come off the assembly line. In the United States, in order to avoid further delays in production, 'modification centres' were established to remake completed products. Once supplies had been shipped, they flowed toward their destination in the order and with the timing established at the point of departure, and only by maintaining extensive records and establishing diversion depots along the line could they be re-routed when needed elsewhere.

The balancing of competing demands for manpower and the expansion and utilization of the labour force involved a continuous complex process of recruitment, replacement, training and retraining. As much as two-thirds of the total labour force might be directly engaged in military service, war production and civil defence; the estimates for Great Britain were 22 per cent in military service, 33 per cent in war production and perhaps 10 per cent in civil defence, leaving to the remainder the task of producing civilian supplies. The labour force was expanded by using women, youth below military age, and in Germany some 10,000,000 forced labourers from occupied areas or war captives.

The traditional system whereby the able young men went to the fighting front while others remained at home conflicted with the need for specialized skills in war production, as the French discovered when they seriously disrupted their industrial mobilization process by calling up their military manpower on this basis in 1939. Some system of exemption from military service for those in critical jobs had to be worked out.

As skilled civilians were drawn into military activity, persons of less skill had to be up-graded with the aid of special training, while those of still lower skills or new recruits to the labour force had to be trained to fill the places of the latter. In the United States at the peak of the war effort, 22 per cent of the total labour force was involved at a single time in one or another of the training programmes developed to meet this situation and a fifth or more of the entire population migrated in the process of adjusting manpower to wartime needs. In countries subjected to bombardment or invasion the problems of manpower adjustment, with attendant problems of housing, transport and community facilities, were even greater.

The manpower requirements of total war forced a radical expansion of the concept of national service. In the French National Organization Act adopted in 1938 after fourteen years of discussion and experimentation, the principle of 'universal military service' was replaced by the concept of the 'duty of national defence' which embraced all citizens, whatever wartime duties and peacetime preparation they might be called upon to undertake. The British Emergency Powers Act of 1940 expressed the same principle in stipulating that all persons might be called upon to place 'themselves, their services and their property' at the disposal of His Majesty. A similar principle was applied even more thoroughly in the Soviet Union. It was applied less systematically in Germany, Italy and Japan.[3]

Economic stabilization in the face of intense inflationary pressures required the substitution of administrative judgment for the market forces through which most peacetime economic relationships in the non-communist countries were determined. Large administrative organizations reaching into every single community had to be built up to administer systems of price and wage control, rationing and the allocation of materials. To maintain the active support of the population and to undermine enemy morale, extensive propaganda and morale agencies sought to strengthen the civilian front at home and to carry psychological warfare to the opposite civilian camp.

The problems of co-ordinating all these aspects of warfare, both within the military structure and between military and civilian segments, became more intense as warfare absorbed national energies more completely. While every country set up some machinery for these purposes, the traditional autonomy of each military service generally proved too strong to be submerged. The British wartime administration was one of the few which managed to develop a picture of combined military and civilian requirements and total resources to meet them, and to make and carry through the decisions necessary for the most balanced use of manpower and materials. In the USSR the peacetime administrative direction of the total economy embraced all military and civilian requirements and their interrelations and was thus in an advantageous position to co-ordinate national military efforts.

V. MILITARY INSTITUTIONS OF THE NUCLEAR AGE

As warfare after the second world war became an intense contest for scientific advance, the military establishments added to themselves great scientific bodies engaged not only in applied but in basic research. Especially in nuclear physics, where research required enormously large and expensive equipment, military funds were used to provide facilities. The work of laboratories operated directly by the military establishments, such as the Naval Research Laboratory in the United States, was supplemented by a large volume of research carried on under contract for the armed forces in universities and other institutions.

While the fields selected for study were initially inspired by military problems, such as the need to know the basic structure of metals or more about the ionosphere upon which radar depends, they led to research at the most basic scientific level. The nature of warfare had become such that the most fundamental scientific discoveries were directly applicable to military purposes, and in the anxious era after the second world war science, in its turn, was dependent for much of its further advance on large funds which the military were in the best position to command and supply. The possible threat of this relationship to the future creativity of science had become a matter of grave concern to many scientists.

In the field of military production the role of the military establishments continued to expand until they became inextricably interwoven with the civilian economy. In a close working partnership between industry and the armed services, the military defined the problem to be met and often proposed the designs. Producers, especially the larger ones and those specializing in particular products, worked out improved models, competing among themselves in the effort to meet the military's requirements and to secure orders for manufacture, and vying to attract the best engineering minds.

In general, orders for military supplies tended to go to the larger firms in spite of much discussion of the value of scattered and flexible resources not so vulnerable to a concentrated attack. The large firms could best meet the demand for large volume and uniform specifications. With hundreds of thousands of items to be procured, it was easier for the military to deal with a large contractor than with many small ones, and if the productive resources of the latter were needed they could be tapped by letting the main contractor make a sub-contract with the smaller firms. The result was to strengthen the larger concerns, and it was with these that the military establishments became most closely interrelated.

The extremely rapid technical and scientific developments that made each new device obsolete almost before it could be produced presented the problem of whether the military should accumulate stockpiles of weapons or should concentrate their effort on assuring that industrial capacity was ready on a stand-by basis to be converted to war production if needed. Prior to the first world war most military leaders had assumed that modern wars must be short and decisive and that any war which might break out would be fought principally with weapons already in being at the opening of hostilities, though British strategists, relying on sea-power, had thought in longer terms. In the long-drawn-out conflict of the first world war the outcome depended on the ability of the belligerents to keep a huge stream of newly produced materials flowing to the front. Thereafter, military preparation took the form not simply of armaments but of plans for the mobilization of industrial and scientific resources. With the coming of nuclear weapons, supersonic flight and guided missiles, the question again presented itself whether to think in terms of a short, decisive conflict or a prolonged struggle and whether therefore to rely on weapons in being or on the capacity to produce additional ones.

At mid-century the question was unresolved and most nations were following both courses. Their factories were kept partly busy filling existing military orders, while their equipment used to make civilian goods was geared for immediate conversion to war production if this should be required. The inter-penetration of the military and civilian economies was so close at every level, from the placing of current orders for supplies to capital equipment and finally to the financing of fundamental scientific research, that it was no longer possible to draw the line between one and the other.

Military service, which was required of most or all of the young men in most countries, provided a common experience to all segments of the population, acted as at least a temporary melting pot for the diverse groups of each nation's young citizens, and exposed them all to the attitudes which prevailed in military circles. In all modern armies this training included some degree of political indoctrination and defence against psychological warfare. The youth in training, plus the permanent military establishments, constituted a large drain on productive resources. In the countries which were most reluctant to accept conscription as a peacetime institution, notably Great Britain and the United States, the question was persistently raised as to the value of mass reserves compared to a highly trained specialized force equipped to handle specialized modern weapons.

The military for their part participated actively in many civilian roles. They filled political, diplomatic and administrative posts and high officers frequently headed business enterprises when they retired from active service. The military services offered a field for the development of a number of essentially civilian activities such as engineering, medicine and psychiatry. As military services became more and more technical the training which they supplied prepared young men for a number of civilian occupations such as electronics or aviation technician, civilian aircraft pilot and countless other trades. In some countries specific civilian training was included in the military service, as in El Salvador, Central America, where recruits from rural areas received training in modern agricultural methods during their military service as part of the national programme for agricultural development. In India one-fifth of the places in the military academies were reserved for civilians not in training for an army career.

In some cases the army served as a positive instrument for change in civilian life. The armed forces of the United States, which had used Negroes prior to the second world war mainly in services of supply, gradually admitted them to full participation during the war, first in separate regiments officered increasingly by Negroes, then in technical services not limited to Negro units, and finally in mixed units in all ranks without distinction. In the years during and after the war, when racial segregation was being slowly abandoned in American life, the armed forces served as a spearhead and model. The Indian army served the new Indian state as one of the important instruments for binding the nation together and furthering the policy of breaking down caste lines. The Indian government encouraged enlistment from all parts of the country and all groups in the population and created new all-India regiments where men of all backgrounds and castes would share a common experience.

Military institutions also cast their long shadows into civilian life by way of the special position enjoyed by war veterans. In every country some form of benefit was received by those who had seen active service in time of war, at the least by those disabled by their war service and sometimes by all who had served.

The outlook of youth was also affected, not only through the expectation of a period of military service but also through the presence of cadet corps or military-type youth organizations that oriented children and young people to types of military behaviour and attitudes. Military institutions thus came to play a pervasive role even in those societies with the strongest civilian, democratic and even anti-military tradition.

In countries where the military had traditionally played an important role within the state, they continued to exercise their customary influence. Armies in some of the Latin American countries continued to use their power to support or unseat governments of various types, always maintaining their own position of influence. It was the army which enabled Juan Perón to overthrow Argentina's constitutional system and rise to power in 1942 and which in turn threw him out and promised to restore free institutions in 1955. It was the army in Bolivia that brought in the first Latin American government outside Mexico which seriously undertook major land reform. It was the army in

Venezuela which heard that country's first elected president, Ramón Gallogos, declare in his inaugural address in 1948, 'the army shall be the servant, not the master of the people', and in less than a year drove him out of office and into exile because he had given the military insufficient place. Dictatorships in Spain and Portugal continued to rest on a firm military base.

In some of the countries of the Middle East and Asia the army was the instrument of political change. It was the army in Egypt which ended the monarchy and established a revolutionary government in 1952, the military group in Thailand which executed a political coup in 1951, and military leadership which took over in Pakistan and Iraq in 1958.

In the liberal democracies the tradition of civilian control remained strong. The parliaments of Britain and the Commonwealth countries and the Congress of the United States retained control of military budgets and of basic policies with respect to the military establishments. The chiefs of staff were subordinate to a civilian ministry or council. Nevertheless, the huge size of the military budgets, the inability of legislators to understand the intricacies of modern warfare, and the insistence of the military that they could not reveal budgetary details without revealing military secrets made it ever more difficult for civilian legislators to exercise effective control. Many thousands of millions of dollars, amounting to 30–40 per cent of the budgets of the various major powers, and to some 10–14 per cent of the gross national income of the NATO countries, were turned over to the military with fewer limitations on how they should be spent and less thorough systems of accounting for their use than generally prevailed for civilian outlays. In the communist countries civilian and military institutions were part of a common all-embracing national structure in which the Communist party maintained effective leadership.

Military organization was also developed at the international level. It had taken rudimentary form with some integration of the allied forces towards the close of the first world war and had reached extensive proportions among allied forces in the European theatre during the second world war, though not in the Pacific or on the eastern European front. After the second world war permanent structures were erected under the NATO alliance and the Warsaw pact. In North America a joint United States–Canada defence organization practically merged the forces of the two countries in respect to early-warning systems and air patrols. For the British commonwealth the Imperial War College provided a machinery for exchange of information among the military leadership of commonwealth countries. International military organization under conditions of modern warfare involved not only the incorporation of military units into a common command but the more difficult integration of supplies, with attendant problems of standardization of design and the dovetailing of delivery schedules.

The NATO organization was the most elaborate permanent international military structure which was developed in the decade after the second world war. It included a high command, with a general staff or military committee composed of officers from each country under a rotating chairmanship, and a series of commands for specific areas, each held by a land or naval officer of a particular country commanding the combined forces of several countries. It maintained a staff college, the NATO Defence College, to develop a body of officers trained in methods of international military co-operation and it set up agencies for the standardization and co-ordination of procedures, communications systems, aviation training and supplies. In its initial stages the organization made substantial headway in standardizing administration, communications, weapons design and training, but the multitude of supplies that rested on the whole fabric of civilian production could not be standardized short of an overall co-ordination of the total economies of the member states.

Integration of the military establishments of Russia and the east European communist countries under the Warsaw pact was achieved by means of Red army specialists placed in staff positions within the several armies to provide an integrating structure under a central high command.

The idea of a permanent international force which would help to keep the peace was conceived by the founders of the League of Nations as a possible outcome of the formation of that body. But no such force took shape under the League, or during the first decade of the United Nations' existence. The forces brought together loosely under the United Nations flag in the 1950 Korean conflict were organized on a purely *ad hoc* basis. The police force created to keep the antagonists apart after the Suez Canal intervention in 1956, though hardly sufficient to be regarded as a military force, pointed to the possibility that a permanent force might in time become a reality, perhaps drawing, as did this body, on the forces of the small nations instead of on the great powers as the founders of the League of Nations and United Nations had envisaged. But there was little thought in the middle years of the century of any world military organization which could stand against the national forces of the major powers.

NOTES TO CHAPTER XXIV

1. Professor N. Talensky points out that the description of the German and Japanese General Staffs, given in the text, is incomplete. From the moment it came into being the German General Staff was an organizer of aggressive wars; it played a decisive role in the conduct of military operations and exerted great influence on the foreign and domestic policy of Germany. Like the German General Staff, the Japanese General Staff was a focus for the most aggressively disposed elements in the army and the navy, obsessed by an unquenchable thirst for conquest. It is here that the wild schemes for the creation of an empire of Greater Japan were hatched, and here that the actual strategic plans for the acts of aggression committed by Japan in the first half of the twentieth century were worked out.

2. In the opinion of Professor Talensky, it should be added that the heads of the armaments firms and monopolies mentioned, as well as of many others, are amongst the men who

bear the immediate guilt for the unleashing of the first and second World Wars. He considers it useful to mention that in its day the world press commented extensively on the out-and-out betrayal of their countries' interests of which the heads of these firms were systematically guilty by supplying, through a third party, to an enemy in wartime arms and ammunition which were later used against their own armies.

3. Professor N. Talensky underlines that the text clearly underestimates the degree of militarization of the population in Germany, Italy and Japan prior to, and during, the second world war.

CHAPTER XXV

RELIGION

I. GENERAL TRENDS IN MAJOR WORLD RELIGIONS

IN the twentieth century every great religion reasserted its vigour and renewed its inner core in the face of the strongly secular tendencies of modern life, the challenge of science and rationality to non-rationalistic systems of belief, and the growth and multiplication of non-religious institutions. In some cases such reassertion expressed resistance to new knowledge and new social forms and a retreat from the modern world; in others it involved the discarding of what to modern eyes appeared to be anachronistic trappings, the stressing of social content and an effort to help modern man to re-examine and renew his values in the face of the new potentialities and threats which science had brought. For many of the peoples of Asia and some of Africa, revitalizing of the traditional religion was associated with the new self-image and nationalistic expression. In areas dominated by communism traditional religion was rejected or decried and communism itself constituted a comprehensive system of thought and belief.[1]

At the opening of the twentieth century the world's major religions and their principal subdivisions were distributed over the globe much as they had been at the end of the seventeenth century after the expansion of Europe overseas, the retreat of Moors and Turks from Europe, the halting of Muslim expansion in India and the termination of the religious wars in Europe. Some slight changes had occurred in the intervening centuries: Christianity had been carried by missionaries into Buddhist and Hindu areas of east and south Asia where it acquired numerically small but sometimes influential groups of converts. Arab traders had left a widening trail of Muslim converts along the trade routes of the east coast of Africa and the slave routes of the south Sahara, and Christian missionaries were beginning to penetrate that continent. The Eastern Orthodox Church had accompanied Russian expansion into Siberia. Mass immigration of European Catholics and Jews to the United States had begun to modify the strongly Protestant character of that country.

In the course of the twentieth century relatively little change occurred in the distribution of the world's religions, whether by proselytizing, persecution or migration, with some important exceptions. A large proportion of the Christians were eliminated from the Turkish areas of the Near East by the massacre and deportation of Armenian people during and after the first world war and the exchange of Greek and Turkish populations of Asia Minor and Macedonia in the early 1920s. The Jewish population was largely eliminated from its main centre in central and eastern Europe and became concentrated in the United States and Israel, through migration in the early part of the century, systematic extermination by the Nazis in Germany and in the areas of eastern and western Europe which came under Nazi control during the second world war and migration to Palestine before and especially after the war. The Muslim and Hindu populations of India were partially separated from each other by the establishment of Pakistan and the emigration during partition of some six to eight million Hindus and a roughly corresponding number of Muslims. The separation was by no means complete, however, for nearly forty million Muslims remained in India and some eight million Hindus in Pakistan, constituting approximately a tenth of the population of the respective countries. The emigration of Indians to such areas as Mauritius, Fiji, Malaya, South and East Africa and the West Indies spread Hinduism outside the area to which it had historically been confined. Continued immigration from Catholic regions of Europe, French Canada, Mexico and the Caribbean made the United States an important Catholic area.

Christianity, the only religion to engage in extensive, organized missionary activity, made little headway in Asia in the face of mounting nationalism and the revival of Asian religions, but both Christianity and Islam continued to recruit new followers in Africa. The religions of tribal peoples in Africa, Asia, the Pacific and the Americas were, generally, progressively undermined wherever tribal isolation broke down, although some of the pressures against tribal religions were relaxed as anthropological studies revealed a higher philosophic basis than specific religious practices had led outsiders to suppose.

While the geographical distribution of religious groups remained relatively stable, their political status changed in several areas. The Roman Catholic Church was restored to temporal power by the Lateran treaty of 1929 with the government of Italy under Mussolini, which re-established the Vatican City as a political territory. This treaty recognized the right of the Pope, who had considered himself a 'prisoner' in the Vatican since the Papal States were incorporated into the kingdom of Italy in 1870, to rule as a sovereign and to exchange diplomatic representatives with the nations of the world. The Eastern Orthodox Church, by contrast, was displaced by the October revolution from its position of partner with the rulers of the autocratic Russian empire and became a restricted institution in an anti-religious state. It retained a strong position however in Greece, and remained an important segment of the Christian community.

With the dissolution of the Ottoman empire and the creation of a secular Turkish state, Islam was disestablished in the principal area where Muslims had been free from foreign rule at the opening of the century, and the caliphate was abolished in 1924. But in most of the areas of north Africa, the Middle East, south and south-east Asia where Muslims had lived under non-Muslim rule at the opening of the century or after the fall of Ottoman power, Muslims became politically dominant. In central Asia they came under communist rule which disparaged all religion. Hindus in India and Buddhists in Ceylon, Burma and the states of Indo-China, who had also been under Christian colonial rulers at the beginning of the century, became masters in their own houses. The withdrawal of colonial rule, and in China and Turkey the abrogation of treaties of extraterritoriality, removed from Christian missionaries the special protection which the extensions of European political power had brought. Jews, who had occupied the position of a precariously tolerated or persecuted minority in most of the lands of their dispersion for nearly 2,000 years, acquired the state of Israel as a national home in 1948.

The status of Catholic and Protestant churches in various Christian countries changed somewhat during these years. In the main the established churches continued to enjoy state support and official recognition, with freedom of religion enjoyed by other Christian sects and non-Christians. The Catholic Church was, however, disestablished in France and Mexico and both Catholic and Protestant churches were repressed by the Nazi régimes in central and eastern Europe and their position was restricted when eastern Europe came under communist control. In the few countries where the principle of the separation of church and state prevailed at the opening of the century—the Netherlands, the United States, Canada except French Catholic Quebec, Australia, New Zealand—the influence of religious bodies on matters of public concern, particularly that of the Roman Catholic Church, increased somewhat during the period.

Outside the anti-religious communist-controlled areas, the position of the several religions was thus stronger at mid-century than at the beginning, and most peoples were living under régimes where their own religion predominated.

In all the great religions during the first half of the twentieth century some forces undermined while others strengthened the hold of the religion on its followers, the position of religious institutions and the part played by religious leadership. As these forces interacted, the net effect was to enhance the influence of all the major religions except the Eastern Orthodox Church.

In the years before the first world war factors which tended to lessen the influence of religion generally predominated. The rising tide of secularism and materialism threatened to swamp religious attitudes, especially in the western culture areas and among westernized elements in other parts of the world. Rationalism challenged faith and science threatened to destroy the bases of revealed religion. Many of the intellectual currents of the nineteenth century had led to agnosticism, and not infrequently to conflict with religious authority. To the author of the classic *History of the Warfare of Science with Theology in Christendom*, Andrew D. White, writing in 1896, it appeared that every forward step in the quest for knowledge had been fought in the name of religion.

The scientific spirit penetrated increasingly into the sphere of religion itself, as it had been doing since the eighteenth century, leading to critical study and historical investigation of the religious texts of Christians, Jews, Hindus and Buddhists. Through a mass of historical and archaeological studies, the Old Testament gradually took shape as an historical record of the Hebrew people, fitted into the rough chronology which excavations in Mesopotamia, Egypt and Asia Minor revealed. The evidence with respect to the life of Jesus was scrutinized in the effort to determine its historical validity. Literary and anthropological studies examined the poetic and prophetic books and traced the myth and symbolism which they contained. Sanskrit scholars applied similar methods to the sacred literature of Hinduism. The discovery and interpretation of Mahayana texts and the translation and critical editions of Hinayana texts gave a new interpretation to Buddhism. The virtual absence of similar critical and historical study of the Quran distinguished Islam from other major religions.

Although many people ultimately found that the scholarly criticism of the scriptures, and the re-evaluation of religious beliefs which such study required, strengthened their understanding and provided a new basis for accepting their historic faith, the immediate effect was undoubtedly to lessen the influence of those religions to which it was applied.

The apparent conflict between religion and scientific rationalism had its principal impact on the religious attitudes of educated elements in the populations. Masses of common people, meantime, especially the urban proletariat, were turning away from religion or becoming indifferent to it because they were convinced that it did not help them in their struggle for a more decent existence, and often obstructed their efforts. At a time when social ferment and democratization were spreading over the world, the complacency of the *élites* of various societies who stood nominally in the forefront of religious as well as social life marked religious institutions as bulwarks of the *status quo*. This was equally true of the Brahmans of India, the scholar-officials of China, the Catholic *élites* of Latin America and Europe, the Russian Orthodox hierarchy closely associated with the court, the upper and upper-middle class Protestant churches in Britain, America, and the Low Countries, the Muslim landlords backed by the *ulema*. All these elements often appeared to stand for selfish interests and indifference to the welfare of the masses of the people.

In some countries the reaction of workers was vigorous anti-clericalism, as in France and Spain, or in Mexico where the revolution which started in 1910 overthrew simultaneously the Church, the political régime and the landed aristocracy. More generally it took the form of indifference to religion among the urban working classes.

The pattern of working-class alienation appears to have been already well established in Europe by the end of the nineteenth century, according to the scattered evidence from industrial parishes. In England Benjamin Disraeli is reputed to have replied to the Archbishop of Canterbury in 1860, when the latter complained that the Church had lost the towns: 'Your Grace is mistaken, the Church never had the towns.' In the mobile, impersonal city, paced by rapid social change, the Church could not re-establish the central social position which it occupied in stable and simple rural societies; the idiom of the Church, its images and symbols, were remote from industrial experience and most of the clergy remained aloof from the social and industrial struggle; a doctrine which accepted earthly suffering did not meet the temper of those who sought to change their lot by means of their own organized efforts. Wherever Marxian socialism gained strength, Marx's dictum that 'religion is the opiate of the people' intensified the workers' indifference to or rejection of religion. As the urban industrial population grew, religion ceased to be supported by the social milieu and came to figure mainly in the lives of those who were moved by personal devotion rather than by the place of religious institutions in the life of the whole community.

The sense of religious certainty was also being undermined by growing culture contacts around the world. To the extent that each religion rested upon an ethnocentric belief in the rightness of a particular doctrine embedded in a particular culture, awareness of different peoples through intercommunication and from anthropological studies tended to arouse a wider appreciation of the possibility that truth might take many forms and to weaken the sure sense that the religion and culture of a particular group was the only right one. This tendency was still in its infancy in the early part of the century, for belief in the superiority of western culture as well as of the Christian religion still motivated missionary efforts, and the revivals of Asian religions which accompanied mounting nationalist resistance to missionary activities asserted rival claims. But although these attitudes had not by mid-century wholly given way to mutual respect, the developing sense of cultural relativism tended to make the views of others more comprehensible to the followers of each religion.

Against these trends which reduced the influence of religion in many parts of the world, some contrary developments must be noted, not strong enough at first to offset the weakening tendencies but mounting in force until they produced a broad revival of religion in the mid-twentieth century. Against the faith in science and the growing materialism was an increasing bewilderment in the face of the power and complexity which science had brought. As science penetrated beyond the easy certainties that had appeared to be within reach, some scientists themselves stressed the uncertainty of scientific knowledge and the mystery which continued to lie beyond the bounds of scientific discovery. Scholarly criticism was turned by some people into a basis for an intellectually tenable faith.

Movements to stress the social content of the faith and its implications for the reform of social ills in some Christian, Hindu and Muslim circles countered the charge that religion was preoccupied with ritual and other-worldly matters while men suffered here and now. For some people, too, the evidence of anthropology and the knowledge of alien religions emphasized the function of religion in all societies and thus reinforced its place at home. More emphasis in missionary efforts on the provision of educational and health services brought continued support from some who could no longer encourage proselytizing.

Especially, religion tended to gain strength and vitality wherever it was associated with the sense of nationalism. Catholic Poles and Irish, for whom religion was a rallying point for the maintenance of cultural integrity and national aspirations against the alien rule of Anglican British, Eastern Orthodox Russians or Lutheran Prussians, were more intensely Catholic than for example the people of Italy, where the dominant religion was taken for granted, and they carried this difference in loyalty with them even when they migrated to the United States and elsewhere. Indian nationalism both stimulated and was fed by the revival, reinterpretation and reassertion of the Hindu religious tradition. Zionism was from its beginning often associated with intense adherence to the Jewish faith, but the persecutions of Jews in the 1930s led many to seek or to support a Jewish homeland for primarily humanitarian and political reasons. Resistance to British rule in Burma and Ceylon took the form of efforts to re-establish Buddhist education which had been largely destroyed. Japanese nationalism was embodied in the Shinto cult. Islam found its most dynamic expression in the efforts to free Muslim peoples from alien domination.

After the first world war religion suffered a number of heavy blows in some parts of the world but elsewhere the forces of revival gathered strength. The most severe blow was dealt by the Bolshevik revolution which dethroned religion over a wide area. Communist Russia not only disestablished the Orthodox Church but engaged in active anti-religious propaganda. Turkey, once the greatest and most extensive Islamic empire, not only abolished the caliphate but discarded Muslim law in favour of legal codes of the West and substituted western customs for those associated with Islam. The New Tide Movement in China developed a strongly anti-religious programme. The Nazi régime deprived religious bodies of their independence in order to bring all independent institutions in line with the party and state.

The forces which had brought religious indifference or alienation in the early years of the century continued to operate. Secularist tendencies remained strong and spread to non-western areas with the extension of scientific knowledge, education and western cultural influences. Although the certainties of the mechanistic science of the nineteenth century gave way to scientific relativity and uncertainty, science penetrated into more and more of the areas which religion claimed, as biologists and chemists pressed closer and closer toward understanding the nature of life, astronomers gained new insights into the probable origins and future of the universe, and psychologists, penetrating the realms of emotion and the subconscious, explored the area of religious experience. The ever expanding industrial city provided a religiously unfavourable social milieu for more and more of the earth's people. In the communist-dominated areas scientific knowledge about the universe and society was disseminated as one means of fighting against religious beliefs, and the institutions of religion were regarded as a cloak for bourgeois exploitation which had no place in the new society.

Yet at the same time powerful tendencies were strengthening religious sentiment. The crisis of European civilization arising from the first world war undermined faith in science and progress and threw many people back on traditional sources of value and support. The Roman Catholic Church, which since 1864 (encyclical *Quanta cura* and *Syllabus of Errors*) had set its face resolutely against doctrinal concessions to the learning or spirit of the time, reasserted the basic elements of mediaeval church doctrine and the superior values of the age of religious civilization. The encyclical *Quadragesimo anno* in 1931 renewed the social teachings of *Rerum novarum* (1891) and again made the concept of social justice the key to social reform. The restoration of the Pope to temporal status, the encouragement of Catholic education and the growing wealth of the Catholic population of the United States brought new strength to the Church and renewed its prestige. Young Catholic worker movements sought to keep working-class youth within the Church. Catholic Action mobilized lay groups to promote religious observance among their neighbours and to support the work of the Church. A movement for conversion among a section of the intelligentsia, including prominent European writers who called for a return to mediaeval values, helped to usher in a Catholic renaissance in Europe and Latin America.

The great spiritual leadership of Mahatma Gandhi became a world-wide force in support of religion. By demonstrating the power of non-violence, by his successful attack on the caste system and other social ills and by his acknowledgement of spiritual kinship with other faiths, he had an impact far beyond the borders of India and outside the Hindu religion from which he drew his major inspiration. As the movements for national liberation among Muslim, Buddhist and Hindu people grew in intensity and approached fruition, the religious aspect of each movement became more prominent, most notably among the followers of Islam. The impact of the Nazi persecutions forced Jews all over the world to study their traditions anew and generally strengthened adherence to the faith even among some who had drifted far from religious observance.

By the years after the second world war the forces supporting religious institutions and religious leadership appeared to be ascendant in the parts of the world outside communist control. In the troubled and dynamic years after the war religion, linked with triumphant and emerging nationalism, played a role in the achievement of cultural and political self-realization, it offered a haven and source of stability amid strain and change and, against the spread of anti-religious communism, it took part in the world contest for the command of men's minds.

The Hindu revival contributed to the vitality and spirit of the new India even though the state was established on a secular basis. Buddhist philosophy gave orientation to the new Burma and Ceylon. Pakistan undertook to create a viable modern state in Islamic terms, the Egyptian constitution of 1956 declared Islam to be the religion of the state, and two out of the four largest political parties in the new Indonesia were Muslim parties. In some parts of Africa reassertions of native religion accompanied African nationalism. Christian Democratic parties provided much of the leadership for the reconstruction of Europe after the second world war.

In these years, religion offered to many people a sort of sanctuary against the evils of a time with which much of mankind felt hardly able to cope. Fifty years before, when societies had appeared more stable and progress more sure, such a refuge had seemed less necessary. But in a world torn by two world wars within a generation, wracked by a decade of economic collapse, filled with people uprooted from their base by voluntary or forced migration, over-shadowed by the fear of atomic and hydrogen bombs, degraded by methods of police states and shaken by social disorganization which followed in the wake of social change, religion seemed to many people to provide an anchor and an escape from present ills. Amid the anonymity, confusions and conflicts of modern life it offered a sense of identity and basis for group solidarity. Especially in Europe and America where indifference to religion had been most widespread, the revival of religion appeared to reflect a desire to rediscover some inner core of integrity which seemed lost, and to recapture values and concepts which once reigned supreme in western culture.

In this resurgence of religion, both religious liberalism and religious orthodoxy played a part. The effort to reconcile science and religion continued to be carried on by a small segment of those concerned with religion, and the task seemed less difficult than it had seemed fifty years before. Non-dogmatic attitudes became increasingly widespread among conscientious churchgoers. But the principal vitality came from the dogmatic churches, such as the Roman Catholic which rejected Modernism in matters of dogma and from those Protestant sects and religious leaders which offered an apocalyptic vision, a non-rational appeal to emotion, or a path to personal fulfilment outside the realm of rational thought and secular concern.

Among the followers of eastern faiths religion did not offer the same sort of haven in these years that it did in the West, for there had not been the same degree of secularization. But in Hindu, Buddhist and Muslim areas it provided a stabilizing force, and many leaders supported religious institutions as a means of holding their societies together under the stresses of moderni-zation, industrialization and the processes of rapid social change. In these areas, too, conservative religious elements appeared to be strong during these years.

Religious organizations played a growing part in the years after the second world war in the world contest for power. The most highly organized and potent of the world's religious bodies, the Roman Catholic Church, placed itself in the forefront of the opposition to communism, seeking to rally not only its own adherents but non-Catholic Christians and even non-Christians to resist the spread of a materialistic doctrine. Wherever its following was large it enhanced its influence in the total body politic. In Latin America, where the Church had shown little vitality in the early years of the century, it manifested renewed vigour and made a new bid for influence which had slipped away from it. In Europe it reversed the anticlerical trend in such countries as France and Spain and it brought back to the fore in Holland, Belgium and France the issue of public support for religiously operated schools, making gains in each country in respect to the education of the young. It sought to take full advantage of the growing size and wealth of the Catholic population of the United States and the position of that country in the world.

Protestant churches took a more restricted part in the power struggles of these years. They too presented themselves as part of the defence against atheistic communism and they achieved a new degree of unity through the formation of the World Council of Churches in 1948; but they remained deeply split along sectarian lines and further divided among various modernist and fundamentalist factions, and their basic individualism limited the scope of concerted action. They usually lent their support to the cause of internationalism against extreme nationalistic and isolationist forces, and generally, but not universally, defended the liberal principles of freedom of thought, conscience and expression against the encroachments of the modern state.

Next to the Catholic Church the major religious body to become involved in world issues was Islam. With no centralized structure like that of the Roman Catholic Church, its force rested on the acceptance by its followers of the authority of the Quran, the respect accorded to the learned scholars, the *ulema,* who interpreted it, the basic concept of the unity of Islam and the principle of *jihad,* the holy war or struggle, which might be invoked in case of danger to give common direction to the efforts of Islamic peoples. Strategically situated between Europe and Asia and extending into both, astride the greatest known deposits of oil in a world become dependent on motor power, occupying the southern border of much of the communist world, and with strong and growing influence in the awakening continent of Africa, Islam had become by the mid-twentieth century a greater factor in the world than at any time since the expansion of Europe began.

Yet while the major religions increased their active role in other parts of the world, the communist system, in which 'worship, though legal, is unworthy of Soviet youth', consolidated its power, was extended into eastern Europe and China, and offered its appeal elsewhere. The intensity of the early antireligious propaganda in the USSR was somewhat relaxed in later years, but religious institutions were not allowed the privilege of imparting religious instruction outside the home, and religion was excluded from every aspect of the highly organized public life of the Soviet Union. In this officially nonreligious milieu, Eastern Orthodox, Roman Catholic, Protestant, Jewish and

Muslim leaders, as well as devout parents, strove to keep religious feeling and knowledge of the faiths alive in the new generations. The people's democracies of eastern Europe, especially Poland, showed more readiness to allow the Church a larger role.

Time alone would reveal how on the one hand the communist system would succeed in its effort, unique in the history of mankind, to relegate all religion to the place of outworn superstition and to satisfy the spiritual as well as the material needs of people through building a socialist society; and how on the other hand the world's major religions would fare in the face of the continuing changes in man's way of life brought by the inexorable impact of science and technology.

While the broad picture presented above holds for the world as a whole and for the general similarities and dissimilarities in the trends of the world's major religions, a more detailed examination of each faith will show more fully the development of its religious institutions and their response to the conditions and currents of the age.

II. CHRISTIANITY

Christianity felt the full brunt of urbanization and industrialization, and of the other factors which undermined the hold of religion and the place of religious institutions during the twentieth century. At the same time its fundamental spirit was in line with the social drives of the age, for the emphasis on the worth, dignity and individuality of each human personality was the spiritual essence of democracy, and the Christian conscience, guided by the precept to 'love thy neighbour as thyself', found secular expression in the welfare state.

Christianity suffered most directly from the apparent conflict of science with revealed religion and the application of critical scholarship to sacred texts; from the secularization of thought and the mechanization of life; from the failure of the Church to speak the idiom of industrial society and, in spite of its social doctrines, from what often appeared to be an indifference to the misery of industrial workers; from the positive denunciations of Marxian socialism and the degrading of religion in the Soviet Union. As the missionary faith of dominant European nations it suffered from the growth of Asian and African nationalism which often identified Christianity with colonialism. Yet in the course of these years the Christian churches met and survived many of these challenges, and except for the Eastern Orthodox Church they appeared to be stronger at the middle of the century than at the beginning.

The widespread alienation of the European urban proletariat was the most serious quantitative loss to the Christian churches outside the Soviet Union. Careful historical and sociological studies of a number of European cities showed a clear and consistent pattern.* Church attendance was much lower in

* Rev. Joseph N. Moody, 'The European Workers and Organized Religion', paper presented to the American Historical Association (December 1956), citing *Essai de la sociologie religieuse*, Secrétaire du centre d'études des complexes sociaux (Grenoble, 1954), F. Isambert, *Cahiers internationaux de sociologie*, Vol. XIV (1953), and a large number of other studies.

working-class than in middle-class parishes, it declined with socio-economic status and it was very low among manual workers. The class contrast was even more marked among devout practitioners than among mere conformers; a Paris study in 1955 found ten times as many 'devout' in a middle-class as compared with a working-class parish and five times as many 'conformists'. For urban communities as a whole, those practising their religion were in the minority, ranging from 10 to 35 per cent of the adult population attending church on any one Sunday in most of the European cities studied, and the proportion tended to be lower the larger the size of the community. The situation in two French cities and a predominantly working-class parish in Paris illustrated these general trends:

PERCENTAGE OF POPULATION ATTENDING CHURCH, *c.* 1950*

	Small industrial city (St. Etienne)	Large industrial city (Nancy)	Paris working-class parish (St. Hippolyte)
Management and engineers	50-60	43	13
Liberal professions	40		10
Employees	30	22-35	4·5
Artisans and skilled workers	20	9	4·5
Manual workers and miners	5-10	6	2·5

The phenomenon of working-class indifference was not new in the twentieth century, for it had been well established during the initial period of industrialization; but there was every evidence that it increased during the period as cities grew in number and size, and the new urban-born industrial populations failed to recreate the rural social structure in which the Church had occupied a central place. In the Netherlands, where data on religious affiliation were reported by the decennial census, 17 per cent of the population claimed to be without religious identity in 1949 as compared with 2 per cent fifty years before. For many European workers who retained a strong sense of class difference, the Church tended to be identified with the bourgeois class of employers from whom they felt separated by a wide gulf; among socialist and communist workers it was commonly regarded as an instrument of the opposing class.

Alienation of the workers from the Church was greatest in France where anticlericalism was traditional and nineteenth-century Catholic leaders had

* Moody, *The European Worker and Organized Religion, op. cit.* The occupational categories used in the separate studies were not identical and permit only rough comparisons.

been generally unsympathetic toward efforts of French workers to improve their conditions. Elsewhere the gulf between workers and organized religion was less. Catholic trade union federations drew a substantial proportion of the organized workers in Belgium and Holland; in Germany, where Catholic leaders in the nineteenth century had set a more sympathetic tone, a third of the members of the pre-Hitler labour movement were in the Catholic unions. In Britain evangelical Methodism, the moral leadership of Christian socialists and the occasional prominent Anglican who raised his voice in the workers' cause gave the British labour movement a broadly Christian orientation, though it did not make the organized church an important factor in the lives of most working people.

In the European industrial area as a whole, the anticlerical element constituted a militant minority, amounting to perhaps a fifth of the industrial population where it was most active; a nucleus of personally devout workers, amounting to perhaps as much as a fifth in the centres where the Church was strongest, continued to practise their religion actively; a broad pattern of indifference characterized the great majority.

In the United States, on the other hand, religious indifference did not appear to be as general or to follow class lines as clearly as it did in Europe. Although American religious observance was not subjected to the same careful study as in Europe, the evidence pointed to essentially different patterns which may have contributed to the strength of religion there in the middle of the century.

Basic to the American situation was the separation of Church and state, guaranteed by the constitution and reflecting originally both the country's traditional Protestantism and the attitude toward religion of the eighteenth-century Enlightenment. Every religious sect was free to flourish or languish, without the need to fight an established church that claimed universality or enjoyed official support. The variety of religious institutions thus could reflect the variety of the population and meet its diverse needs. In view of this religious fluidity and the lack of identification of the Church with the employing class, American workers had no reason to develop the anticlerical attitude which reflected the workers' situation in Europe.

Historically, immigrant populations brought to America their respective religious affiliations. As successive waves of population entered an area, the church of the earlier settlers became the church of the more prosperous and established *élite*, while that of the newer and poorer arrivals reflected their lower position in the social structure. In the twentieth century the majority of new immigrants came from Catholic areas, and made the Roman Catholic Church the church of the urban masses. For some of these uprooted people migration meant a loss of religious affiliation, as it did in the cities of Europe. But for many, especially those such as the Irish, Poles and French Canadians for whom religion had been a cherished mark of identity, the Church offered a link with the culture which they had left, a rallying point and a defence against the alien environment. In contrast to the European Catholic Church, which was generally identified in the minds of workers with their capitalist opponents, the Catholic Church in America was not infrequently seen as the church of the workers, for large numbers of its parishioners were workers while the employers were more apt to be members of well-established Protestant churches.

New religious denominations in America had repeatedly arisen or spread by appealing to the masses of the people when older ones had become associated with more conservative or socially select groups. By the opening of the twentieth century the largest Protestant religious units were the major evangelical bodies, Baptists and Methodists, which had enrolled the poorer rural populations and the Negro slaves in the eighteenth and early nineteenth centuries; other denominations with substantial memberships had developed on the westward moving frontier of settlement.

In the twentieth century new churches which appealed to the uprooted urban masses grew up and spread. Some were offshoots of older bodies, others the creation of a charismatic leader such as 'Father Divine'. Calling themselves by such dramatic names as Jehovah's Witnesses, Pentecostals or simply The Church of God, carrying on their activity in empty buildings or wherever they could find shelter, generally scorned by the clergy of well-established denominations, making a strongly emotional appeal against the materialism and rationalism of the age, they offered their followers a haven and sense of personal identity. Although they constituted a small minority of all church membership, their significance lay in the fact that they reflected the disorientation and met the needs of a segment of the urban population which the traditional churches could not hold. They were the urban twentieth-century counterpart of the evangelical and frontier churches which had arisen to serve the masses in earlier periods of America's history.

In the fluid and mobile society of the United States religious observance had never been a universal practice, or in many communities even the practice of the majority, but its vitality had been periodically renewed by the institution of the 'revival', an emotional appeal to entire communities which caught up large groups of people and stimulated public declarations of faith and dedication to a renewed quest for salvation. The emotional revival, originally conducted in the open air or a tent in rural areas, was aimed at urban audiences and used the facilities of mass communication. The most successful of mid-twentieth century revivalists, Billy Graham, refined the techniques which had been well developed by his predecessor Billy Sunday, the leading dramatic evangelist of the early 1900s. Carefully organizing the co-operation of the Protestant clergy to whom the names of all who responded to his appeal were given for follow-up, utilizing all the techniques of mass appeal through press, radio, television and other media, expending over a million dollars on his campaign in a single major city, he called nightly on the packed crowds who filled the largest auditorium available to come forward and 'declare for Jesus'.

He carried his message and his technique to cities in Christian and non-Christian countries around the world.

Thus while religion was losing much of its popular support among the industrial populations of Europe, these various factors gave it a continuing mass base in the United States.

The principal response of the churches to the loss of following among the urban industrial masses was to stress the social content of the Christian gospel and to enlarge the churches' social role. The papal encyclicals on labour, *Rerum novarum* (1891) and *Quadragesimo anno* (1931), and similar calls to promote social justice from Protestant leaders, sought to use the influence of the churches to restrain the selfishness of employers and to arouse a moral urge to improve the lot of industrial workers. Christian teachings calling for dedication to the Kingdom of God on earth and responsibility for and service to one's neighbour received new emphasis. Seminaries for the training of the clergy introduced social studies into their curricula, first in the seminaries of the more liberal Protestant denominations and then in others, both Protestant and Catholic.

Concern with social conditions was not new, for a strong social conscience had permeated, especially, certain Protestant groups and had provided much impetus for nineteenth-century social reforms, including the abolition of slavery, improvement of factory conditions, humane treatment of the insane and the spread of general education. Under conditions of the twentieth century the social emphasis helped churches to hold their own among the multitude of urban institutions and to compete with schools, fraternal bodies, improvement and charitable societies, labour unions, political parties and a wide range of other organizations, all of which claimed the interest and allegiance of urban individuals.

Churches developed welfare programmes which offered a channel of service to some of their members and social aid to others and lent religious support to social action. Home missions sustained centres to provide health and recreation services, vocational training and adult education, day nurseries, libraries and other facilities in poor and congested neighbourhoods and many city churches developed a wide range of social activities for their members. The function of the Christian pastor, unique among the clergy of major religions in that the priest's role was not only to perform the rituals and serve the deity but to minister to the needs of the flock, was expanded to include more aspects of the life of the congregation. Jesuit educational institutions sponsored programmes of labour education for workers and training in industrial relations for workers and employers. Youth organizations such as the YMCA and YWCA spread in many countries. All these activities strengthened the institutional position of the churches; in Europe they helped to reduce the antagonism between socialist and Christian elements and to pave the way for close co-operation between Christian and socialist trade unions.

The social gospel did not come to dominate either Catholic or Protestant churches in their entirety. One Catholic priest might construct a community centre attached to his church on the ground that 'my people should be able to find whatever they need in the church' while his counterpart in the next parish might scornfully declare: 'If the Word of God through the ages has not brought people to Him, my taking the boy scouts for a picnic will not do so.' The Catholic Church, moreover, showed that there were definite limits beyond which it would not go. In 1954 it suppressed the *prêtres ouvriers* in France who for ten years had lived and worked as industrial workers in order to minister to their fellow workers more directly and to help them to voice their needs.

Protestant ministers, also, were very far from unanimous in their concern for social issues. Some were conservative or indifferent; others in their zeal overstepped the bounds deemed appropriate by their superiors or the laity of their congregations. Many in Europe followed the influential Swiss theologian Karl Barth (1886–   ), who turned back to the traditional Protestant theocentric and christocentric preoccupations of Luther and Calvin after an initial period of religious socialism. Yet in spite of Barth's insistence on an intensely personal form of religion—the obligation of man to engage in a constant dialogue with God—his followers were drawn into the social and political arena, for he became a principal spiritual and intellectual leader of the Confessing Church which protested against the unchristian and inhuman spirit of National Socialism.

On none of the major social issues of the twentieth century, however, did the Christian churches provide consistent leadership for social change, though some churches in some places made substantial contributions to such causes as international co-operation and racial equality. As the concept of the welfare state came to be widely accepted, the social conscience became broadly secularized.

While the indifference of the working classes meant the loss of numbers of active followers, it was the apparent conflict with science, rationality, secularism and materialism which undermined the church's intellectual leadership and its influence on the thought of the western world.

In the early years of the century the mechanistic world-view drawn from the physical sciences presented an unsympathetic face to the claims of religion, while those who subscribed to a form of Christianity which rested on revelation and a literal interpretation of the scriptures could not accept scientific attitudes and methods if these touched the realm which religion claimed for itself. Efforts to 'reconcile' science and religion took the form of a retreat by religion and a tendency to discard much of the traditional content which scientific evidence seemed to deny. The alternative appeared to be a head-on clash. As late as 1925 a school teacher in a small isolated American community dominated by fundamentalist religious thought was brought to trial in a court of law for teaching the theory of evolution, in one of the *causes célèbres* of the century.

But later developments of both science and religion changed the frame of reference for their reconciliation, co-existence or conflict. Twentieth-century science became easier for religion to live with as it abandoned its earlier certainty and arrogance and accepted uncertainty as a basic principle. Yet it also became harder for religion to escape as its fields of exploration widened and it penetrated to phenomena which could not be directly observed but only inferred. Religion on its side moved away from the literal-minded position which brought it most strongly into conflict with scientific rationalism, and it found a variety of ways to accommodate new scientific knowledge without abandoning basic tenets of faith.

A number of individual scientists disavowed the presumed conflict between science and religion. Such physicists, biologists and astronomers as J. A. Thomson (*Science and Religion*, 1925), James Jeans (*The Mysterious Universe*, 1930), J. B. S. Haldane (*The Sciences and Philosophy*, 1929), A. S. Eddington (*The Nature of the Physical World*, 1928) and Robert A. Millikan (*A Scientist Confesses his Faith*, 1923) expressed their sense of the inadequacy of science alone to reveal the ultimate mysteries of the universe and of man.* Some drew a boundary between science and religion; others agreed in essence with Alfred N. Whitehead that 'there were wider truths and finer perspectives within which a reconciliation of a deeper religion and a more subtle science will be found'.† The Jesuit naturalist, Père Teilhard de Chardin (1881–1955), expressed the view that 'religion and science are the two conjugated faces or phases of one and the same act of complete knowledge—the only one which can embrace the past and future of evolution so as to contemplate, measure and fulfil them'.‡ Although during his lifetime he was forbidden to teach in France and to write on philosophical subjects, his *Phenomenon of Man*, published immediately after his death, aroused widespread interest among scientists, religious leaders and the general public.

Some of the churches met the rationalist critique half way, with a reinterpretation of dogma which left room for historical, symbolic or rational explanations of the meaning of the scriptures, articles of faith, rituals and the nature of religious experience.

The Roman Catholic Church set its face squarely against efforts to seek a basis for dogma outside the tradition of the Church. It wholly rejected the Modernist movement which arose within the Church among both clergy and laymen at the end of the nineteenth century and which sought to adapt the teaching of the Church to the conclusions of modern scientific and critical research. By the decree *Lamentabili* and the encyclical *Pascendi dominici gregis*, Pope Pius X in 1907 condemned Modernism as substituting purely subjective criteria in matters of faith and morals for the authority of the

* For similar expressions of some continental European scientists, cf. B. Bavinck, *Das Weltbild der heutigen Naturwissenschaften und seine Beziehungen zu Philosophie und Religion* (1933, 2nd ed. revised by K. Otte, Iserlohn, 1952).

† A. N. Whitehead, *Science in the Modern World* (New York, 1925), p. 265.

‡ Pierre Teilhard de Chardin, *The Phenomenon of Man* (London, 1959), p. 285.

Church, and in 1910 required all priests to swear an anti-Modernism oath. The position remained unchanged, and set the limits within which inquiry was permissible. The encyclical *Humani generis* in 1950 reaffirmed the absolute truth of Catholic dogma and condemned other opinions as false.

In the matter of liturgy, however, the Catholic Church looked with favour upon scholarly study into the origins of existing practices and accepted the possibility of revision in the light of new historical evidence. Work in this field, for which the Benedictines in Minnesota, USA, provided a world centre, focused on worship, and the results of historical research were regarded as possible bases for additional rites which would be conducive to religious experience under conditions of modern life.

The Protestant churches, on the other hand, lacking the same authoritarian structure and source of infallibility in matters of faith, did not sweep aside movements to bring their dogma in line with modern thought. While some sects countered these tendencies by reasserting fundamentalist dogma, most of the larger denominations were characterized by a range of views among their membership and their clergy. The modernist view was energetically sustained by some of the seminaries which trained clergy for the liberal churches of various denominations. Most denominations however also contained a fundamentalist element. By mid-century the general public acceptance of the scholarly critique of religious texts was manifested by the enormous interest expressed in the discovery of the Dead Sea scrolls and the light which might be cast by these documents on the Christian gospel. Books on the scrolls were published in pocket editions for mass reading and even appeared on best seller lists in the United States in the late 1950's.

From the Modernist controversy at the opening of the century the Catholic Church emerged more integrated than before. The Protestant denominations, however, continued to include both modernist and fundamentalist elements, though the distinction between the two approaches tended to become less clear and the conflict of views less sharp as the years passed.

Meanwhile, the deep sense of uncertainty with which western man faced his changing world nourished a growing trend toward irrationality. A succession of European schools of philosophy moved further and further away from a strictly rationalistic base. Conspicuous literary figures who found the modern world a waste land turned to religion, seeing the Church as the repository of essential tradition and experience without which life would lose its meaning, as did T. S. Eliot, or, like Jacques Maritain, reasserting the values of mediaeval Christianity as superior to those of the day. The most ambitious and widely read mid-twentieth century historian, Arnold Toynbee, made religion the key to the success of civilizations through the ages. The stress laid by Sigmund Freud on the irrational component in human behaviour was widely interpreted by his followers as providing a scientific justification for irrational attitudes and beliefs, although Freud himself had sought to apply scientific methods to the study of irrationality.

The anti-rational trend with its many manifestations changed the intellectual climate of twentieth-century western society outside the communist areas. Many who had sought to reconcile science and religion gave up the effort and returned to a neo-orthodoxy, omitting science or even rejecting it, and fundamentalist sects or segments of Protestant churches were among those which made the greatest gains in membership. While the change in intellectual climate did not restore religious observance where it had ceased to be general, it sustained those who continued in their religious faith, aroused fresh interest in many who had become indifferent and, by making the practice of religion respectable again, cut the ground from under those who had found it popular to scoff. Fear of communism added a further stimulus.

The renewed interest in religion did not, however, redound wholly to the benefit of the established churches, for much of it was highly subjective. It led to the popularity of writers and preachers who used the devices of modern advertising to offer religion as if it were packaged merchandise, to explorations into Vedanta and forms of eastern mysticism, to a wide variety of cults which seemed to offer religious satisfactions which the organized churches failed to provide, and to such widespread movements as Moral Rearmament which used religious revival to counteract secular tendencies toward social change.

While the swing to neo-orthodoxy at mid-century appeared to be strong, some scientists, laymen and men of religion, fearful lest a society dominated by science but unable to come to terms with it in the realm of values would lose its bearings, continued to press for a meeting-ground upon which an integrated scientific–religious culture could be built. Some found support for the view that the revelations of science confirmed and might further enrich the fundamental insights of religion. Others saw two kinds of reality, accessible through the two distinct processes by which man can know—the scientific method of observation, conceptualization and verification and the religious process of direct experiential perception and intuition. Still others saw the meaning of religion in the role which it plays in human life and not in the truth or falseness of any theological construct.

Christianity, moreover, by virtue of its emphasis on the worth of the individual, contained a strong component of humanism in spite of its God-centred creed. The humanistic view, which had shown itself in the period of the Renaissance and in the eighteenth-century Enlightenment, gave spiritual meaning to man's own striving and made human integrity in its fullest sense an essentially religious goal. In the mid-twentieth century a small number of people, largely unorganized but often individually influential, gave expression to a deeply humanistic faith. Inheritors of both the scientific and the religious traditions of the Christian world, they faced the scientific age without despair, accepted religious insight without retreating to non-rational beliefs, and drew from the spiritual heritage of Christendom compassion, hope, dedication and faith toward mankind. In making a place for such views as these, liberal

Christianity showed its ability to accommodate currents of scientific thought and to offer meaning to scientific minds.

By the opening of the twentieth century the Christian missionary movement, which had accompanied the extension of western dominance in the nineteenth century was meeting resistance from the aroused Asian nationalism and self-awareness which these same western contacts had stimulated. A revived Hinduism not only countered the claims of Christianity in India, but attracted the interest of many people in the West. Japan integrated the Shinto cult with patriotism and education, and presented a national front to missionary endeavours. Repeated violence against missionaries in China, culminating in the Boxer rebellion of 1900, revealed a deep hatred of the 'foreign devils' and of the 'secondary devils', their Chinese converts.

Christian missionary efforts continued, however, although the prospect of bringing large numbers within the Christian fold appeared more remote as the tide of western imperialism receded from Asia and Africa. The mission field drew many devoted workers whose major efforts often came to be directed toward combating disease and illiteracy and whose activities made substantial contributions to health and education. The most noted of these, Dr Albert Schweitzer, enlisted world-wide support for the hospital which he established in Africa, and many people who had little interest in missionary efforts were moved by his insistence on 'reverence for life'.

In both Asia and Africa missionaries were encouraged by the colonial powers, which depended upon them to provide social services—except in Korea and other Japanese colonial areas where the Christian missions were a rallying point for some of the anticolonial sentiment. In the Portuguese dominions the Church was entrusted with full responsibility for education and for imparting Christianity and Portuguese culture simultaneously. In the British and Dutch areas missions provided many of the educational and health services; only in the British dominions in Asia were substantial provisions made for these services by secular agencies prior to the second world war.

From the point of view of the Christian churches, however, the greatest mission field was not any of the colonial areas but China, where the size of the population, the absence of a vigorous entrenched religion, the weakness of central government and the obvious need for health and other social services made this a most attractive area to missionaries of every denomination and every country. Support for Christian missions throughout the world, moreover, was never confined to the colonial powers and came to be provided increasingly from the United States.

By the 1930s the assurance with which Christian missions carried their western culture and faith to what they regarded as the 'backward heathen' had been shaken. A thoughtful review of missionary activity by a distinguished and respected group of Protestant laymen, published in 1932 under the title *Rethinking Foreign Missions, a Layman's Inquiry after One Hundred Years*

(New York, 1932) offered the conclusion that Christian missions might have something to learn from those whom they sought to serve and that mutual interchange rather than one-way indoctrination might well become their goal. Yet conscientious church-goers, who continued to support Christian missions with annual budgets running to many millions of dollars at mid-century, assumed that their voluntary contributions were helping to spread the true faith; members of forty-four Protestant denominations in the United States contributed 59,000,000 dollars to foreign missions in 1954. They were among the last to recognize how deep and widespread was the resentment which their attitude of superiority had aroused.

The history of Christian missionary effort in China revealed in accentuated form the characteristics and problems of such efforts throughout the world. Under treaties imposed on China in 1853 after the wars to open the country to western trade, missionaries had enjoyed freedom to travel and preach and the right of extraterritoriality for themselves and protection for their Chinese converts, who thus became a privileged group under the protection of European powers. During the anti-foreign Boxer rebellion of 1900, Christian churches and schools were destroyed and Chinese Christians massacred. But the hope of converting large numbers continued and missions were re-established with the aid of indemnities imposed for Boxer damages.

The Roman Catholic Church regarded China as so important a field for the extension of its great influence that the Pope personally consecrated the first two Chinese to be made bishops, in 1925. At that time more than a million and a half Chinese were attending some 30,000 Catholic schools, including 1,000 in five institutions for higher education, and Catholic missions maintained approximately 700 hospitals, 2,000 dispensaries, 1,500 orphanages and 80 leper asylums. By the time that the communist government took over the country, Catholic schools were attended by some 5,000,000 pupils, health services were reaching an estimated 30,000,000 people, and the native Chinese clergy numbered 4,000 priests and 12,000 members of Catholic religious orders.

Protestant missions, especially from Britain and the United States, were correspondingly numerous and varied in scope, but they ceased to expand after the first quarter of the century when the movement for nationalism and cultural revival gained force. Many of the western-trained young Chinese who led the revival had been nominally Christian, but they now showed themselves to be anti-religious, anti-foreign and anti-Christian. A distinguished Chinese historian, looking back at mid-century on the role of Christian missionaries in his country, summed up the reaction of this group. He had attended missionary school in his village as a child, been a youth at the time of the Boxer uprising, studied abroad, been rector of a leading Chinese university, and had followed the Nationalist government to Formosa. 'We liked the missionaries because they fixed our water pumps and cured our malaria', he said; 'but they told us that their God was a jealous God, and we did not want any *jealous* gods in China.'* When the communists came to power, Christian missions were among the first institutions to be liquidated.

Nowhere did the extensive missionary activity of the nineteenth and twentieth centuries bring a substantial proportion of the population into the Christian fold. The best estimates of the numbers of Christians in various non-Christian countries, including members of the Church of South India which dated from the early Christian era, ranged from less than 1 per cent of the population in China to something over 4 per cent in Indonesia and parts of tropical Africa and 6 per cent in Indo-China.

The small proportion of Christian converts did not of course wholly reflect the total impact of Christian missions during these years, for missions numbered among their converts many who became national and international leaders, such as Sun Yat-sen at one time, Chiang Kai-shek, Toyohiko Kagawa. Leaders who did not embrace Christianity were to some extent influenced by Christian thought, as were Rabindranath Tagore and Mahatma Gandhi, and its impact produced reform movements among other faiths, such as the Bramo Samaj in India. Mission schools trained many of the men and women who provided the leadership for the modernization of their countries.

The largest proportionate results were secured in parts of Africa, notably in East Africa where an estimated 6 per cent of the population was counted as Christian at mid-century; but here Christian missions often met severe and successful competition from the missionary activities of Islam, as they had at an earlier period in south-east Asia where Islam had offered a means of protest against western supremacy. It was easier for many Africans to believe that the Islamic doctrine of racial equality was genuine and to accept the religion of Arab traders and slavers than to understand what European missionaries could mean by Christian brotherhood when European administrators were enforcing differential wages, Native reserves and police passes for Africans. And although Islam required its converts to change some of their tribal ways, it did not challenge many traditional practices, such as polygamy, which Christians did not accept. Yet Christian missions offered education and medical care which many Africans strongly desired, and they continued to play an important role in African development when their influence had been greatly reduced elsewhere.

For the Roman Catholic Church missionary activity was part of the Church's never-ceasing effort to extend its dominion and to realize its concept of the Church Universal. At mid-century, having weathered the storm of secularism in its old centres, it was prepared to withstand the current of anti-colonialism by developing local clergy and indigenous leadership for its young churches in other lands.

Protestant missions were more vulnerable when the assurance of western superiority was undermined and they encountered self-conscious opposition from those whom they hoped to convert. Since Protestantism rested on the

* Interview with Chiang Monlin, February 1955.

assumption that each individual must, in the last analysis, find his own way to God, it was a small step to concede to the non-Christian that he too might have found a path. In the new situation of the mid-twentieth century many older missions lost much of their proselytizing character and concentrated on providing technical services of health, education or agricultural improvement, in co-operation with the local community. The most generous support for new missions came from some highly evangelical groups such as Adventists, Mennonites, Jehovah's Witnesses, Pentecostals, who regarded their fellow-Christians as needing to heed their call to repentance quite as much as non-Christians and who were among the most ardent critics of much of western civilization rather than its proponents.

Most generally, however, the Protestants, like the Catholics, shifted from the role of alien intruders to that of supporters of the local Christian churches which a hundred years of missionary activity had produced. Missionary activity thus was converted into a means of co-operation between old and new churches. Although these new Christian churches in non-western lands constituted small minorities in relation to the total population, some of them formed substantial units. As they took their places in the structure of their societies and in the councils of Christendom, Christianity became less characteristically the religion of the West and more a part of multi-religious societies around the world.

The Christian churches sought to strengthen their position through organization. In this the Catholic Church achieved considerable success. Under a series of strong Popes who commanded wide respect outside as well as within the fold, the Papacy provided the Church with vigorous leadership. The celebration of jubilee years in 1925, 1933 and 1950 brought multitudes of the faithful to Rome and enhanced the sense of the Church as a world community. Codification of the Canon Law reaffirmed the integrity of the Church's system of jurisprudence.

In spite of severe setbacks the Catholic Church consolidated its position in most countries. It lost its official position in France by the separation of church and state in 1905 and the expulsion of the religious orders, but after the first world war a *modus vivendi* favourable to the continuance and extension of Church influence was established, the conversion of several famous French authors added to its prestige, and the canonization of Jeanne d'Arc cemented the bond between the Church and France. The temporary loss of influence in Spain in the 1930s under the anticlerical Spanish republic was followed by the complete entrenchment of the Church in the régime of General Franco. The position of the Church in Poland was strengthened when that country regained its independence after the first world war, for it had been associated with the national identity and aspirations of the Polish people against their Russian Orthodox and German Protestant rulers. It lost ground there, however, when the communists came to power after the second world war, though it established a working relationship with the communist régime. After the re-establishment of temporal power the Vatican City served as a diplomatic centre.

The Catholic Church came to terms with each reactionary government in the period of its ascendancy—with Mussolini, Hitler, Franco, Perón— accepting governments of the right as bulwarks against threats from the anti-religious left. When totalitarian excesses appeared to leave no room for the independent authority of the Church, it stood up to these same dictators and offered Catholic leadership to the democratic governments which followed the dictators' downfall. In spite of severe criticism from Catholics in democratic countries against the Church's policy of temporizing with fascist and Nazi dictators, the proportion of Catholics and their influence grew in such democratic countries as Holland, Britain and Belgium during these years.

In Latin America the Mexican revolution dealt the Catholic Church a hard blow, but after its initial repression it was allowed to revive under severe limitations and without the restoration of its wealth and status. In other Latin countries religious indifference was widespread, but countries differed markedly; in Venezuela great areas were almost wholly without religious services while in neighbouring Colombia the Church played a vigorous part in national life. By mid-century there were many signs of a Catholic revival in most of the Latin American areas. The traditional distance between priests and people was beginning to be bridged as individual priests launched social programmes in their parishes and seminary training began to include instruction in social issues and in methods of working with people on their social problems. Catholic Action developed a vigorous lay apostolate for the faith in several countries.

The greatest source of the Catholic Church's renewed strength, however, came from its growth in the United States, where it became the largest and most powerful single religious denomination, including in its membership about a fifth of the total American population and a majority in many of the large cities. The traditional separation of church and state in predominantly Protestant United States gave full opportunity for the Catholic Church to develop its activities and institutions. Its growing wealth as the nation prospered and its followers rose in the socio-economic scale enabled it to take advantage of the opportunity. Under a system which permitted the establishment of private schools, the Church set up parochial schools wherever a parish was able to support a school from parents' fees and donations, and by missionary funds in poorer parishes. By the middle of the century the question of public financial aid for parochial schools had become a live issue, in spite of the firmly established American principle of support for public schools alone, and the use of public funds had been allowed for auxiliary services such as school buses, health services and school lunches, and for scholarships and text books for students attending non-public schools.

Profiting by the American tendency to form organizations of all sorts, the Church reinforced its ecclesiastical organizations and religious sodalities with a multitude of other bodies—organizations of Catholic men, women, youth, boy scouts, Newman clubs for students in non-Catholic institutions. A host of welfare agencies reaching out to influence many facets of American life co-ordinated their efforts through the National Catholic Welfare Conference.

From America's position and resources, the Church drew the means of extending its influence in the rest of the world. By the Legion of Decency, a quasi-official Catholic agency set up to evaluate films for the benefit of the Catholic segment of the audience, it made its point of view felt in the film capital of the world and ensured that its concepts and its representations would always appear through that medium in what it considered an accurate form. Whatever resistance Protestant Americans might have offered to the rising influence of the Catholic Church was undermined after the second world war by the fear of communism, for by claiming the role of champion of the free world against communist atheism and tyranny, the Church placed itself beyond attack from its ancient critics. The influence of the Church of Rome in the mid-twentieth century reached more widely, though it penetrated less deeply, than it had done even in the Middle Ages when Christendom extended over only a small segment of the globe.

Neither the Eastern Orthodox nor the Protestant Christian churches could claim the same organizational and political success. For the Eastern Orthodox Church, the virtual destruction of its most influential patriarchate following the strongly anticlerical October revolution constituted the worst defeat for Christianity since the rise of Islam. The complete secularization of the state, the anti-religious teaching in the schools, the failure for some time to appoint a new patriarch after the death of the Patriarch Tichon in 1928, and the requirement that religious groups must apply to the State Council for Religious Affairs for all church building, printing or other needs, reduced the Russian church to virtual impotence. Although freedom of religious worship, as well as of anti-religious propaganda, was guaranteed by the Soviet constitution of 1936, the Church had no standing and religion was officially considered to be a product of the system of exploitation which the socialist society of the Soviet Union had abolished. The Eastern Orthodox Church had no weapon against secularism except its continuing belief that man is by nature religious, and the hope that the Russian people would one day seek to renew their faith.

The organized response of the Protestant churches took two opposite forms: the proliferation of new religious groups in response to the unmet needs of disoriented and uprooted urban people, and the oecumenical movement which sought to unite the Protestant churches and to find their common ground. The first of these developments, most noteworthy in the United States where the multiplication of sects was traditional, had no great effect on the institutional position of the churches. The second, which centred originally in Europe, was a direct attempt to increase the influence of organized Christianity.

The oecumenical movement grew out of efforts to strengthen foreign missions which drew several of the Protestant churches together, and out of the broad tendencies toward internationalism which led the national churches of individual denominations to establish closer ties with their fellow religionists in other lands. It may be said to date from the international missionary conference held at Edinburgh in 1910 which established the International Missionary Council as a permanent body. Meetings in Switzerland and Holland in 1914 and 1919 led to the first world conference of churches in Stockholm in 1925, attended by Protestant church representatives from seventeen countries. A second oecumenical organization, 'On Faith and Order', was formed in Lausanne in 1927. In 1938 the two groups joined to draft a constitution for a single world council, but it was not until after the second world war, in 1948, that the constitution was ratified at Amsterdam and the World Council of Churches established.

This loose body, styling itself a 'fellowship of churches which accept Jesus Christ as God and Saviour', brought together more than 130 of the major church organizations of Christendom, including the Eastern Orthodox, but not the Church of Rome which never relaxed its claim to be the only true Church. The World Council of Churches offered a means by which the non-Roman Catholic Christian churches could reinforce each other in their moral influence, in their stand against secularism and the anti-religion of communism and in the conduct of foreign missions. As a union of churches whose most common feature was the fundamental individualism of Protestantism, however, it could do little to unify doctrine or create common organization.

At mid-century supporters of Christianity were claiming that never in history had it or any other religion 'been as widely extended geographically, as deeply rooted among as many peoples, and as much a force in the life of all mankind'.* They could point to the fact that its principal revival and a growing proportion of its support came from one of the most technologically advanced countries of the mid-twentieth century, the United States. There, a larger proportion of the population was reported to be church members than at any previous time, expenditures for church buildings, benevolences and foreign missions were at an all-time high, church attendance was on the increase and appeared to be as high in large cities as in village and rural areas. The majority of those questioned in a national survey in 1954, reported by the National Council of the Churches of Christ in its *Yearbook*, attributed the growing interest in religion to fear, uncertainty, reaction following the war and renewal of faith. The very conditions which had seemed most to threaten the hold of religion appeared to be providing a fertile soil for its renewed vigour.

* Kenneth S. Latourette, *Challenge and Conformity: Studies in the Interaction of Christianity and the World of Today* (New York, 1955), p. 10.

III. JUDAISM

Judaism in the twentieth century was profoundly affected by the events which befell the Jewish people, as well as by the currents of thought and knowledge which impinged on all religions during these years. At the opening of the century the Jewish population was centred in eastern Europe, where Jews were largely isolated from the surrounding culture and lived a life which was intensely permeated by the spirit of Judaism and organized to permit its daily practice. Most of the centres of Jewish learning and the spiritual leadership of Judaism, as well as the numerical preponderance of the Jewish people, were to be found there.

Under the Nazi programme of systematic extermination, east European Jewry was virtually destroyed. Of an estimated six and a half million Jews in countries which came under Nazi domination, less than a million remained at the close of the war, while another million survived as refugees. In the centre of the east European Jewish community, Poland, where 3,300,000 had been living in 1939, a mere 80,000 were left. By mid-century principal centres of Judaism had been transferred to the United States and the new state of Israel.

This shift in centre had a twofold impact on religious developments: in America Judaism had to provide for the religious life of Jews who were fully participating members of a modern, predominantly Christian, society. In Israel it had to resolve the relationship between Judaism as a religion and Israel as a Jewish state, and meet the religious needs of people who brought a wide variety of experience and expectation to their new national home.

In the Jewish communities of eastern Europe up to the time of their destruction, Judaism furnished the structure and content of the way of life. The tradition of Jewish learning in which all shared provided the basis for respect and authority in the community; the learned scholar was listened to, whatever his economic position or other basis for rank; the child who showed diligence and prowess in the Hebrew studies which were the core of his education earned parental and community approval and even deference; community resources were used to provide stipends for poor students so that they could devote their time to study, and the men of the community spent their time in study and discussion of the Torah and the Talmud, in a room which every synagogue provided for this purpose.

The lives of the people were filled with an elaborate body of ceremonial observance in synagogue and home. These included prayers and blessings daily and on many personal occasions; weekly observance of the Sabbath, from sundown on Friday to sundown on Saturday, with ceremonies in the home and the synagogue and with rigid abstention from every kind of work including household tasks such as lighting fires or cooking; observance at home and in the synagogue of frequent holidays throughout the year, some extending over a number of days; and observance of dietary laws which prescribed the kind of food which might be eaten, the manner and supervision of slaughter, permissible combinations of foods, and separate sets of dishes. The isolation of Jewish life from that of the surrounding milieu was forced on the Jews of ghetto and Pale, and was reinforced by the Jewish community's indifference to the often uneducated population of the area, by language differences between Yiddish-speaking Jews and their neighbours, by rigid restrictions against marriage outside the group and by generations of self-contained Jewish life.

In the west European communities this pattern of intensely Jewish life had been modified before the opening of the twentieth century, for Jews had there achieved toleration, emancipation from externally imposed restraints and, finally, in the liberal movements of the nineteenth century, full status as citizens. In western Europe Jews attended secular schools and universities, shared the currents of contemporary thought and not infrequently inter-married with non-Jews. Especially in Germany, secularization spread and movements for religious reform appeared. These tendencies toward integra-tion into the total society, secularization and religious reform became even stronger in the United States, as the Jewish community in that country grew from under 10,000 at the opening of the nineteenth century to over a million at its close.

By the opening of the twentieth century the pattern of the American Jewish religious community had been established as the result of the efforts of Jewish leaders to arrive at a basis for the religious life of American Jewry. Leaders of one group, Reform, who sought to adapt Jewish practice to the condi-tions of American life, and of another, Conservative, who insisted that traditional or historic Judaism was the only basis for continued vitality, had given up the effort to find a common ground by 1885, and had formed two wings with separate theological seminaries, rabbinical organizations and federations of congregations. A third division, calling itself Orthodox, had come into existence in the 1890s, distinguished from the Conservative group primarily by the fact that its congregations were composed of new immigrants from eastern Europe. The third wing, organized into the Union of Orthodox Jewish Congregations, established in 1898 a Yeshiva, in the manner of east European communities, for the study of the Torah for its own sake. The seminaries of the Reform and Conservative groups undertook to train rabbis in the manner of American specialized institutions of higher learning; they included secular studies or arranged for their students to receive such studies elsewhere, while the Yeshiva originally was unconcerned with secular knowledge.

The three divisions were not separated from each other on matters of basic doctrine, but primarily on matters of practice. The Reform movement, in its platform and prayer book, departed from traditional Judaism in abandoning the dietary laws, simplifying many of the ceremonies, substituting English for Hebrew, seating women and men together in the synagogue, and relaxing the observance of the Sabbath, particularly where people had to work on Saturday to earn their livelihood; it even went to the point of shifting Sabbath worship from Saturday to Sunday. It rejected Zionism and looked upon America as the promised land where the life of Israel should be built. The Conservative and Orthodox wings firmly retained the traditional practices, though the practical conditions of American life made strict adherence to daily ritual, dietary laws and Sabbath observance extremely difficult, if not very nearly impossible.

In the early years of the twentieth century no religious body felt the impact of secularism more strongly than the Jews in western Europe and America. Immigration and interaction with the surrounding culture detached large numbers of the younger generation from their religious roots; for many of the young people growing up in the United States, Americanization meant secularization. In addition, substantial numbers in western and eastern Europe joined socialist parties and adopted a Marxian anti-religious attitude. At the same time the Orthodox element in the Jewish community was greatly reinforced by the flood of emigration from eastern Europe which brought many east European Jews to west Europe and a million and a half to the United States, where the Jewish population nearly trebled between 1900 and the outbreak of the first world war.

After the war Judaism in the United States became increasingly American in leadership and composition although it continued to draw scholars from the main centres of Jewish learning in Poland. With the cutting down of immigration, first during the war and then by restrictive legislation, the Jewish community ceased to be reinforced annually by large new groups of east Europeans with their intellectual and spiritual leaders. Immigrant neighbourhoods, where the synagogues were the centres of life, shops were closed on the Sabbath and kosher food was sold, began to dissolve as their residents moved to less poor and congested areas and no new immigrants took their place. Like the children of other immigrant groups, American-bred Jewish children tended to reject their parents' foreign ways. Orthodox as well as Reform and Conservative congregations took on an increasingly American outlook and, by force of circumstance, many American practices.

The Americanization of the Orthodox wing was strikingly evident in the field of education. In 1928 the Yeshiva abandoned its effort to reproduce the traditional centre for informal rabbinical studies characteristic of the east European Jewish communities and became Yeshiva University, offering a formal course for the training of American rabbis which included general as well as rabbinical subjects. At the elementary school level a movement was started in 1938 to establish parochial schools similar to those maintained by the Catholic Church, where children would receive a general education along with instruction in religion, Hebrew and Jewish history.

On the other hand the Reform movement returned to some aspects of the traditional pattern which it had discarded as inconsistent with modern life. Concluding that the core of belief and ethics alone was insufficient to hold its people against the inroads of secularism unless it was supported by some of the traditional forms, it reintroduced a number of practices which it had dropped, revised the prayer book to restore prayers which had been omitted, and encouraged the many traditional ceremonies in the home which had been very largely abandoned by most Reform families. A new statement in 1937 to replace the original platform of 1885 represented a partial victory for those who maintained that only by the intensification of Jewish practice would the vitality of Judaism be maintained.

The Reform wing also abandoned its firm opposition to Zionism, though it did not as a body espouse the Zionist cause. When some of the outstanding Reform rabbis embraced Zionism, the issue split the Reform group. In the face of United States immigration restriction and Nazi persecution the negative position lost more and more adherents, until a declaration in 1935 that Reform Judaism was neutral on the subject officially recognized the disagreement within the Reform ranks. As the Jews of America watched the destruction of east and central European Jewry, more and more of the Reform element joined in the demand for immigration to Palestine and the establishment of a Jewish homeland but, in contrast to the Orthodox Zionist organization, they supported a political haven rather than a religious centre for the world's Jews.

The major growth in American Judaism came in the Conservative congregations. Adhering to basic traditional practices, the Conservative wing discouraged deviations but did not condemn those congregations which introduced them; accepting the idea of change and development as characteristic of any vital religion, it refused to try to reduce to an official statement the complexity and fluidity which it regarded as the essence of a living faith; ready to reach out into the community and to find a common meeting ground between the ways of American society and the ways of Judaism, it developed synagogue centres with activity programmes similar to those of American churches and quite different from the east European synagogues where men gathered to study and dispute.

The three branches of American Judaism never regarded themselves as separate sects, but rather as different directions of development of a common faith and common religious body. In the second quarter of the twentieth century each sought to put its stamp on the total body and to take each new congregation under the wing of its organization. From 1926 on, the three groups worked together through the Synagogue Council, their representatives joining in such efforts as collaboration with non-Jews in inter-faith bodies, sponsorship of Jewish chaplains to serve the American armed services, preparation of exhibits of Jewish history and tradition, and relief for Jewish communities in Europe and in Palestine. The differences which persisted tended to become more and more organizational rather than religious and to reflect social differences arising from national origins and time of immigration. As leadership of all groups passed into the hands of the American-born generations, these distinctions too became irrelevant.

The unity of the Jewish community was strengthened by the large number of agencies for immigrant aid, Jewish education, welfare, recreation and relief which were set up outside the synagogues and cut across the divisional lines. These many organizations, applying traditional Jewish principles of charity and mutual aid, made the Jewish community one of the best organized and best served segments of American society, as an integral part of the American social structure, not isolated from it. The trend at mid-century was to try to give the programmes of these organizations 'Jewish content' rather than to allow them to become indistinguishable from secular organizations performing the same functions. But Jewish leaders were by no means agreed as to what this content should be.

It had been the distinction of the Jews through the ages that they had accepted only the authority of conscience. Firm in the sense that they had committed themselves to follow the path of righteousness by the repeatedly renewed covenant of their ancestors with God, they stood for the ultimate freedom and moral responsibility of the human spirit against all external authority. Their religious practices kept vividly alive the history of the Hebrew people, in which their responsibility toward God was manifested. Judaism was expressed in no declaration of faith but rather in the acceptance of its discipline; it constituted a way of life, comprehensive and complete.

The problems confronting twentieth-century Judaism in America arose from the difficulty of following the traditional discipline while living in a milieu whose rhythms were geared to the demands of industrial society and to non-Jewish patterns of life. Little conflict arose in the realm of thought, for the Jewish tradition of unrestricted inquiry and intense, logical analysis was fully consistent with a scientific mentality, although scientific and other secular fields of learning competed for interest and attention with traditional rabbinical studies. And the essential spirit of moral responsibility and human dignity was in line with the strivings of the time.

The broad revival of religious interest which swept the United States in the years after the second world war was shared by the Jewish community. For some Jews this was a form of self-identification. Shaken by the evidence from Germany that assimilation might offer them no surety in time of crisis and that they might be thrown back on the resources of their group, they felt that they could ill afford to be cut off from their cultural tradition and many sought to renew their allegiance to their historic faith.

In the other major centre of Judaism, the state of Israel, the mere fact that for the first time in nearly 2,000 years the Jewish people had an opportunity to build a Jewish society did not resolve all questions as to the place of religion and the forms of religious practice. And in Israel, as in the United States, Judaism faced the problem of how far traditional practices were in line with the conditions of life inherent in a modern industrial society.

The Zionist movement, which created the state of Israel and shaped its ideology, was itself the product of diverse and antagonistic points of view. As the movement gathered momentum after the opening of the twentieth century, it attracted men of widely varying religious ideologies ranging from the strictly Orthodox to the violently atheistic, so that no one attitude toward religion could ever be considered the official standard of Zionism.

For some, resettlement in the ancient Jewish homeland meant political autonomy, for others a cultural—though not necessarily a religious—revival, and for still others a re-gathering of all Jews into one state and the abolition of Diaspora Jewry. Some desired the establishment of a country in which Orthodox law could reign supreme, while yet others hoped that this resettlement would break the so-called rigidity of traditional Judaism and cause a newly creative and vitalized religion to spring forth.

The one religious position common to all branches of Zionism was that the Jews are not merely a religious body but are a people, a nation. In this sense Zionism was a reaction not only against the ravages of anti-Semitism, but also against the view of the Jewish enlightenment, *Haskalah,* which had 'denationalized the religion'.

By attempting to solve the problem of the Jewish people through its national regeneration, Zionists saw themselves as modern prophets of the ancient Messianic conception of Judaism. Rejecting the doctrine which asked that the Jewish people wait for supernatural intervention and bear its burden of exile with patience, Zionism called for immediate action through the agency of the Jewish people itself. Since, in the opinion of many, traditional Judaism was responsible for the passivity of the Jews in the face of persecution, the Zionist movement also included a revolt against this traditional Judaism as well as against the past history of the Jewish people. The exilic ghetto and all things associated with it were objects of Zionist hatred and contempt. Religion, being so closely connected with such life, could not escape this contumely and became for some the symbol of that which most hindered Jewish efforts to be free.

While many Zionist pioneers were convinced that a break with the past was necessary to ensure the survival of the Jewish people, they still retained a strong nostalgia for the customs and folk patterns of European Jewish religious life. The extent to which observances such as holy days were secularized and nationalized varied sharply, but only among the actively Orthodox did they completely retain their traditional religious aspect. With few exceptions, the pioneers longed to continue the chain of tradition from generation to generation, but for many the Land was substituted for the Law. They looked to the country, and to social ideals such as the dignity of labour for their binding principles, and not to the traditional religion which, they felt, had kept the people alive in Exile but had outlived its usefulness.

Those who brought the state of Israel into existence thus ranged in ideology from the deeply religious, through the central group of General Zionists who were sympathetic to religion, to the left wing who rejected ritual observance and dogma but retained a kind of dedication to the Land.

In the state of Israel during the first ten years of its existence, many traditions of religion, such as the festivals, were observed in public celebrations as official holidays, while dietary laws and certain Sabbath regulations were also matters of municipal observance, and the Sabbath was the official civic day of rest. As for individual observance, each person had the choice of following his own path. For some this meant the acceptance of a few regulations and observances, for others virtually none. In general, governmental, social and economic conditions were favourable for the practice of Judaism and the schools provided children with a knowledge of the Bible, Jewish history, literature and traditions—a necessity for Jewish religious life.

Traditionally religious Israelis raised their children to follow firmly their religious beliefs, with the aid of excellent religious schools which were part of the state school system. The ranks of religious families were swelled by the huge influx of religious Jews from Arab lands, but the folk customs of these newcomers, unfamiliar with western civilization, made it difficult for them to hold their children. The transition to secular Israeli life involved a clash of eastern and western cultures, and stimulated young people to revolt against parental values, including religion.

Communal settlements determined their community observances according to their ideological position. Some of the *kibbutzim* were strongly anti-religious, others strongly religious. By virtue of its membership and position, the religious *kibbutz* became one of the most positively active religious groups in the country. Fully Israeli in the national sense, educated and modern, the young people in these religiously oriented pioneer farming communities succeeded in demonstrating the compatibility of religious life with the demands of modern existence and in integrating the ideals of the state with the ideals of their religion.

Over the years calls for a renewal of religion began to come from both religious and non-religious elements. Among the Orthodox some advocated reconsideration, within strictly traditional methods, of certain Jewish laws which make life in a modern industrial society difficult if not impossible, or suggested that a Sanhedrin be reintroduced to deal with all questions of Jewish law. Among the non-religious, appeals for a return to religious values appeared with some frequency in speeches and publications. Much of the active antagonism toward formal religion on the part of the original settlers disappeared among the native-born generation whose lack of institutionalized religious upbringing generated indifference in place of their parents' attitude of rebellion.

The majority of the population occupied an indefinite position, non-religious but not atheistic, between the Orthodox and the few extreme leftists to whom religion appeared a stumbling block in the path of social progress. They discarded the binding character of the complete traditional system of Jewish law and theology, but not the concept of God as interpreted by Orthodox Judaism. The non-Orthodox population accepted the results of scientific scrutiny of the Bible as well as of religion in general. The findings of Biblical criticism were taught in the secular schools, and the foundation of Orthodox life, a supernaturally revealed tradition, thus ceased to be assumed by the average Israeli. In the absence of any other satisfactory basis for formal religion, Judaism remained a general belief and observance of certain customs which were aesthetically or nationalistically appealing.

Furthermore, the oft-repeated contention of the Orthodox that only the person who observes each detail of the traditional regulations can be termed religious contributed to the feeling that no midway position in belief and observance was possible. The few attempts at Reform or Conservative synagogues, the product of German or English-speaking elements, were not indigenous and had little attraction for the native Israeli.

The rabbinate in this period, moreover, offered little spiritual leadership in reinterpreting Judaism which could attract the new generation. Its major function appeared to be its official duty under the government to administer certain areas of personal law such as marriage and divorce, which in the Middle East had traditionally been under the jurisdiction of the religious leadership in each community. This stirred up some antagonism amongst the anti-religious who were compelled to acquiesce to rabbinic regulation and disturbed some liberals who felt that such matters should be under lay not religious authority and who felt that the principle of a secular state was being subverted. Moreover the involvement of religion with party politics under-mined some of its prestige. As a participant in the political arena it became merely one more ideology alongside others.

Nor did the synagogue in Israel assume a function similar to that of the American synagogue-centre. Social needs were filled by other agencies, while Jewish education was the province of the government schools. There was no need to express one's Jewishness by congregational affiliation, as living in a Jewish country provided for such a tie in everyday life.

The knowledge of the Jewish heritage possessed by every Israeli, however, kept alive the interest in Judaism, though the basic impetus behind such learning was interest in the history of the Jewish nation. The country was filled with sites of religious interest, the national classical literature was religious, and the language was infused with the terms of religion which even the ardent secularist must use to express himself. Non-religious Israelis who were committed to a continuation of Jewish tradition and peoplehood thus had basic knowledge of Judaism, and they were familiar with religious forms, many of which they accepted in a secular version. Some among them hoped for a dynamic leadership that could combine traditional Judaism with modern scientific and philosophic concepts, and find a religious way which would offer religious guidance without rigidity or control, and which would spring from the needs of the nation and its people.

In both its major centres the central issue confronting Judaism at mid-century was how far, and in what forms, the religious component was essential to the continuing vitality of the Jewish tradition which had given the Jewish people their power of survival in the past and which served them still in the lands of their adoption and in the development of their national home.

IV. ISLAM

Islam in the twentieth century was inextricably involved in the political and social developments of the time. As a religion which encompasses the law and way of life of its followers, it was inevitably a factor in the movements to liberate Muslim peoples from non-Muslim rule and in the spread of social changes into the Muslim world. On the other hand it was less affected by currents of scientific thought and historical criticism than were other major faiths. And though some areas were strongly affected by the secularizing influences of the times, the main tendency through most of the Muslim world appeared to be an intensification of religious loyalty.

The major expressions of Islam in the twentieth century, and its major problems, came in the political sphere. The Islamic revival was part and parcel of the political and social ferment among Muslim peoples. In providing a spiritual source of cultural as well as political nationalism Islam gave to the struggle against western dominance some of the quality of a religious conflict. As a guide to political conduct its uncompromising insistence on equality among the faithful was in line with modern democratic trends, but some of its other commands and practices appeared to challenge or diverge from the tendencies of the time. Its principle of universality within the ranks of Islam was at variance with the trend toward national states but in line with tendencies toward internationalism, though its sharp distinction between believers and non-believers was a potential bar to both national and international unity.

Even what appeared as a major blow to the status of Islam, the dissolution of the Ottoman empire, and the abolition of the caliphate in 1924, indirectly enhanced Islam as a political force for it released Arab nationalism in lands which had been under the control of the sultanate. In these areas, and in the lands from Indonesia to Morocco where Muslims had lived under non-Muslim colonial rule, movements for political liberation brought new nations into being. A number of independent Muslim states thus gained the opportunity to govern themselves in the light of the principles of Islam, while the abolition of the caliphate had little effect on the structure of Islamic authority since real religious power rested in the *ulema*, the learned religious leaders throughout the Muslim communities.

Islamic nationalism as a religio–political movement had been stimulated in the second half of the nineteenth century by Jamal ad-Din al-Afghani (1839–97) who, from one end of the Muslim world to another, preached a Pan-Islamic revival linked with local nationalism as a first step. As the movement, under local leaders, grew in vigour during the twentieth century, Islam provided a dynamic force for movements of liberation, anti-imperialism and resistance to western domination from Morocco to Java. The Islamic republic of Pakistan was the most distinctive product of the movement, but in a sense Arab nationalism was an even more direct political expression of a movement with deep religious roots. The Arab area was the centre of the Muslim world and Arabic was the language of the Quran. Although Arabs constituted only a fifth of the strength of Islam and were greatly outnumbered by two other groups, the Muslims of India and Pakistan and those of Malaya and Indonesia, it was in the Arab lands that the faith had had its historic centre and period of greatness. It was here that the holy city of Mecca was located and the language of the faith was spoken and printed.

Yet though Islam found expression in national self-rule during these years, the sense of the Islamic world community and the firm line drawn between believers and non-believers were at variance with the trend toward political nationalism and the exaltation of the geographically based political state. And the traditional Islamic law, the *shariah*, shaped in an earlier and far different society, appeared in conflict with many social trends in the modern world.

In its thought and theology Islam remained virtually untouched by modern developments. The authority of the Quran as a revealed Book remained unchallenged, as it had throughout the history of the faith. The *ulema* retained the prestige which enabled them to continue to perform their role as the interpreters of the sources of the Islamic faith.

Various sects and religious orders, with their leaders and following, functioned within their particular area or group, some growing and others declining. The puritanical reform movements such as the Wahhabi, which called for a return to the purity and unity of early Islam and rejected both the theological elaborations of the mediaeval schoolmen and the mystical experience of the Sufi religious orders, remained influential, especially in the Arabian peninsula, and the idea of a direct return to the Quran and the Sunnah continued to offer the main direction of thought for both progressive and reactionary reformers.

The two sects whose growth and impact was greatest during the twentieth century were the Ahmadiya and the Ismaelis, followers of the Aga Khan. The orthodoxy of the Ahmadiya, who acknowledged a later religious leader and accepted his interpretation of Islamic doctrine in terms of modern life, was questioned by most other Muslims, but the sect was strongly organized to carry on missionary activity in the name of Islam, as well as to proselytize among fellow Muslims. The Ismaelis grew from a minor group to a widespread sect, emphasizing social and economic development, abolishing purdah, and ensuring education, hospitals and other social services to their members by means of trusts sustained by the collection of tithes. Both the missionary Ahmadiya and the Ismaelis had their main influence outside of the principal Muslim areas; their greatest growth was in Africa and they accounted for much of the spread of Islam in that area. None of the sects or religious orders, however, exerted a major influence over the main currents of Islamic thought.

The impact of western contact and education brought efforts in the late nineteenth and early twentieth centuries to integrate western and Islamic thought and led to the development of what might be termed Islamic modernism in Egypt, India and Turkey. In Egypt Mohammed Abduh (1849–1905), convinced that no conflict would be found between western science and Islamic thought if each were pursued to its fullest meaning, undertook to restate the doctrines of the Quran in contemporary terms. In India Sir Sayyid Ahmad Khan (1817–98), acting on the hypothesis that the essential quality of Islam is its conformity to nature and the laws of science, founded a modern Muslim university in order to strengthen the faith and confidence of Indian Muslims by bringing them abreast of modern thought. The Indian jurist Sayyid Amir Ali, in his influential book *The Spirit of Islam* (1891), invoked the authority of the Quran to support contemporary social ethics in such matters as slavery, polygamy and divorce by repudiation, and he stressed Islam's role as a progressive civilizing force. He found sanction in the Quran for the vigorous pursuit of secular learning, and claimed that modern scientific thought was natively Islamic since its foundations came to Europe by way of Arab scholars in the Middle Ages.

These and other modernists and reformers, with their acceptance of modern scientific knowledge and their concern for social reform, had an important social impact on Muslim society which they sought to revitalize and they enabled young men with western education to remain within the faith and take pride in Islam. Their main impact was on the social aspects of Muslim life for they encouraged the idea of social change and helped to provide the urge for movements for women's rights, education and labour organization which grew in most Islamic areas during the twentieth century. But they had no effect on the structure of religious authority or the content of the faith and they made no attempt to bring modern scholarship into the realm of doctrine.

Religious authority continued to reside in the *ulema*, who clung strictly to the traditional mediaeval presentations of Islam. Dedicated to traditional learning, the *ulema* of the great mosques of al-Azhar in Cairo and az-Zaytunah in Tunis, and their counterparts elsewhere, remained outside the currents of secular study and thought. Few others concerned themselves with religious questions or had any influence even on *élite* groups. The kind of scholarly historical criticism and archaeological study to which the Hebrew and Christian scriptural texts were subjected did not reach into Islamic theological and religious studies. The modern universities established in Muslim lands contained no theological schools or departments of religion comparable to those of the West. Modernism nowhere took shape as a definite school of Islamic thought. Such modernist ideas as were advanced, limited in extent and partial in content, were no match for the orthodox conservatism of the *ulema*.

In the first quarter of the twentieth century Islamic nationalism and modernism appeared to go along together. Mohammed Iqbal in India (1873–1938) drew on the ideas of Nietzsche and Bergson in elaborating his conception of Islam, as well as on the early liberal intellectual tradition of Islam itself; it was he who projected the concept of the Islamic state of Pakistan. In Turkey Ziya Gökalp (1875–1924) applied the positivist thought of Comte and the sociological doctrines of Durkheim to the analysis of Muslim religious institutions and concluded that these were symbols of the collective will and cultural values of Turkish society; he became the proponent and spiritual godfather of Turkish nationalism. Mohammed Abduh's follower, Shaikh Rashid Rida (1865–1935) of Syria, edited a journal, *al-Manar*, which carried both reformist and Pan-Islamic ideas through the Muslim world. Most Muslim leaders, whose energies were devoted to the struggle against western political and economic domination, assumed that the useful aspects of western scientific thought could be readily absorbed by a liberated Muslim society.

But in the second quarter of the twentieth century a strong fundamentalist revival took form in many areas. The secularization of the Turkish state, with its substitution of western legal code for the law of Islam and the mandatory discarding of fez and veil, seemed to show that reform, modernism or any acceptance of western ideas could only lead to secularism. The reformist journal *al-Manar* became ardently fundamentalist, rejecting all westernism and regarding every deviation from the most strict observance of religious prescriptions as a threat to the integrity of Islam. The *ulema*, never having accepted either the efforts of reformists to discard tradition and return to the purity of the Quran or the modernists' assumption that western knowledge was compatible with Islamic doctrines and mentality, insisted on the rigour of their authority and secured the dismissal of university professors and public officials who ventured to introduce new lines of discussion, such as the Egyptian writer Taha Hussein. Muslim activist movements with mass appeal, of which the Muslim Brotherhood in Egypt, Syria and Iran and the Ahrars in Pakistan were the most noted, were prepared to go to any lengths to free Muslim people from foreign ideas as well as foreign domination and to bring about a return to the most literal application of Muslim orthodoxy.

A number of factors contributed to the vitality of religious conservatism. To a degree, the reformers themselves were responsible. They generally shared an attitude of anti-intellectualism, considering theological controversy an impediment to the social reform and spiritual awakening to which they gave priority, and their very insistence that all essential thought could be found within Islam reinforced the sense of orthodoxy. As modern transport made it possible for more and more people to make the pilgrimage to Mecca, increased numbers of *hajis* returned home to exert their prestige and swell the conservative ranks in every part of the Muslim world. For all factions the battle for the liberation of the Muslim community called for intensity of faith rather than concern as to its content. The very strength of the emotional commitment to political goals consolidated the psychological rigidity of conservatism. A questioning mind or less-than-full acceptance could be readily interpreted as a sign of defection from the active struggle to which the tightly organized fundamentalist groups contributed a fierce vitality.

Although the Muslim extremists were opposed by the moderate elements which generally furnished the dominant political leadership and though their organizations were repeatedly suppressed or their leaders imprisoned, their hold remained strong, for they asserted in positive terms the religion to which the state was committed and they insisted that the development of self-rule was an act of religious fulfilment. The fundamentalists could thus put all others on the defensive. In the difficult years after the second world war during which the Muslim states struggled to establish themselves and to tackle their immense problems of poverty and need, inevitable frustrations invited the search for a scapegoat. Extremists could use the 'western' taint to damn their opponents and the fundamentalist appeal could command a practical mono-poly of the emotional drive which had brought liberation and continued to seek expression. Liberal tendencies continued, but the extremists tended to force the issue into a choice between fundamentalism and secularism.

While religious revivalism was following a fundamentalist direction, the practical march of events and pressures of the time were bringing many adjustments which appeared to the fundamentalists to be contrary to the prescriptions of the faith. Pressures for the social reform of Muslim society, both from within and from without, brought successive modifications of Islamic law and custom. Apart from personal law relating to such matters as marriage, divorce and inheritance, British criminal and civil law replaced Muslim law in the Muslim-administered native states of India as well as in the rest of the sub-continent; Egypt adopted the Napoleonic code in 1884. By the middle of the twentieth century the Muslim *shariah* was the law of the state only in Afghanistan, Saudi Arabia and Yemen. Except for these extremely conservative states there had either been some modification of the personal law or proposals looking to its modification were under serious study, although Turkey remained the only Muslim country to replace Muslim personal as well as civil and criminal law with law derived from the West.

As most Muslim areas in the twentieth century became testing grounds for the integration of Islamic principles into the governance of a modern state, two areas, Turkey and India, offered tests of Islam's ability to function in a secularized society, either as the faith of the majority or where its adherents were in the minority.

In Turkey in the 1920s Kemal Ataturk, who carried out his social reforms with the support of a westernized urban *élite*, not only secularized the state and discarded Muslim law but deliberately sought to sever the Turks' connection with the Arabic roots of Islam by discarding the Arabic script in favour of the Latin and by prescribing that the prayers should be said in

Turkish. Thirty years later a political party favourable to the restoration of some religious influence came to power, and took the first step of reintroducing the teaching of religion into the elementary schools. Perhaps more significant was the establishment of a faculty of divinity within the secularly oriented University of Ankara. It remained to be seen what, if any, contribution to the future of Islam would come from this first attempt to bring together Islamic and modern studies at the highest level.

In India 40,000,000 Muslims remained after partition, enjoying full citizenship in a secular state composed predominantly of Hindus. Historically, Indian Muslims had resisted integration into Hindu society under the pre-national, pre-modern conditions where caste determined status and relationships, citizenship in the western sense was unknown, and family and religion formed the basis of communities. The constitution of the Indian state abolished caste, secularized the law and guaranteed freedom of religious practice and democratic rights and responsibilities to all citizens. Those leading Muslims who remained in India in the belief that a satisfactory life for Muslims could be developed on this basis became active participants in government and other fields. They were committed to demonstrating that Islam could exist and flourish as a personal faith within a multi-religious democratic society without being reinforced by the legal or political structure prescribed in the Quran.

For the substantial Muslim populations in central Asia, the impact of communist rule minimized the role of Islam. Muslims were directly subjected to anti-religious pressures, particularly intense during the period of the first Soviet five-year plan, 1928–32, when there was widespread destruction of mosques, deportation of religious leaders, suppression of religious literature and the Arabic alphabet, and settlement of non-Muslims in Muslim areas. Since Islam was associated with minority status and often, especially in the case of nomads, with a way of life which was being radically modified, the processes of modernization and integration into Soviet society tended strongly to orient people away from Islam. Similar forces were at work among the Muslims of Chinese Sinkiang.

Throughout Islam the conditions of the second quarter of the twentieth century presented conscientious Muslims with what some acknowledged to be a 'soul-scorching' problem of how to integrate, or choose between, the demands of the faith and the pressures of the modern world. The problem was present in Pakistan for those who staked their lives and futures on the creation of a separate Muslim state; in the Arab lands for those whose guiding force was Arab nationalism; in India for those who were committed to achieving a satisfactory pattern of Muslim life as citizens of a secular democratic state; and in Indonesia for those engaged in bringing 'unity in diversity' to their far-flung, culturally varied archipelago. The issue in Islam was whether and how the new vitality which it had shown in the preceding decades could give expression to an absolute, revealed, religio–political faith, within the pressures, the mentality and the necessities generated by the world conditions of the mid-twentieth century.

V. HINDUISM

Hinduism provided much of the spiritual dynamic for India's revival in the twentieth century. Reinterpreted and revitalized, it renewed its ancient core and became converted from a doctrine of renunciation to one of activism and from a sanction for rigid custom to a force for social reform. In so doing it reasserted its hold on the Indian people.

During the nineteenth century Hinduism, under the impact of Christian thought and European authority, was generally on the defensive and its more significant movements were sectarian, influenced directly by missionary teaching or resulting from resistance to such influence. They were primarily movements of reform, accepting in the main the western criticism of Hindu thought and attempting to work out adjustments which were considered necessary to make Hinduism modern. Of these, the most important was the Brahmo Samaj, founded by Ram Mohan Roy (d. 1831), which based itself on ancient Hindu teachings but was markedly influenced by liberal Christian thought.

But during the second half of the nineteenth century a new spirit began to manifest itself within the fold of orthodox Hinduism, as new voices were heard emphasizing the necessity to preserve the spiritual heritage of Hinduism. Two quite distinct movements emerged. The first was a militant, revivalist form of Hinduism known as Arya Samaj, founded by Swami Dayananda Saraswati (1824–83) and based on faith in the revealed nature of the *Vedas*. The Arya Samaj opposed the orthodox Hindu organization of caste and untouchability, it emphasized social service and it carried on a militant campaign for reconversion to Hinduism of those who had turned to other religions. Adopting the methods of Islam and Christianity to combat them, it insisted that the Vedas were comparable to the Quran and the Bible as a sacred text, it introduced rigid organization unfamiliar to Hinduism in order to serve the function performed by the church among Christians and, in line with Muslim and Christian practice, it sought individual conversion, in contrast to the tradition of Hinduism which provided for conversion only to incorporate whole groups as separate castes. Thus the Arya Samaj was combative, it entered into competitive activities with Islamic Christian missions and it built up a large and extensive educational system in the Punjab meant to withstand the influence of the mission colleges.

The central figure of the second movement, Sri Ramakrishna (1836–86), mystic *yogi* and a saint in the traditional style of Hinduism, made a deep impression on the Bengali society of his day, especially among the younger generation. He not only arrested the movement among the intelligentsia for a general break-away from Hinduism, but revived their faith and provided them with a dynamic view of life.

The most notable among his disciples, Vivekananda (1863–1902), became the apostle of a new Hinduism, fired by revivalist zeal. A prolonged visit to America and a tour of England influenced his patriotism and his desire to rejuvenate Hindu society and to give to Hinduism a social purpose. His fervent declaration that he did not 'believe in a religion that does not wipe out the widows' tears or bring a piece of bread to the orphan's mouth' expressed the changed temper. His own mission he described as 'to find the common bases of Hinduism and to awaken the national consciousness to them'. That common basis he found in the Vedanta which he interpreted in popular phraseology and preached untiringly all over India. In addition he trained up a body of missionaries, men of education, pure life and religious zeal, to carry this message to the villages. Innumerable other *sanyasis* and learned men, belonging to no particular sect, were preaching the same message in many different places.

The Theosophical Society, under its American founder and organizer Colonel H. S. Olcott, and later Mrs Annie Besant, also was active in the promulgation of Hindu religious ideals among the educated classes in the first two decades of the twentieth century. Through Mrs Besant's translation of the *Gita* (1895) and the society's educational work, it did much to strengthen the faith of the Hindus in their own religion.

It was the reinstatement of the *Bhagavad Gita* as the supreme scripture of Hinduism that enabled the leaders of thought to cast the new spirit in terms of Hindu orthodoxy. Since at least the third century AD the *Bhagavad Gita* had been one of the authoritative texts of the Hindu doctrine, a scripture to which every political writer or apologist turned for arguments in support of his thesis. In the last decade of the nineteenth century and first quarter of the twentieth it was the subject of commentaries by nearly all the major political and religious leaders and it became the most influential single book providing inspiration for a social, ethical and spiritual regeneration of the Hindus.

The political activist B. G. Tilak (1856–1920) was the first to insist that the message of the *Gita* was not renunciatory and other-wordly, as others had taught, but was essentially a scripture preaching a dynamic social ethic, a doctrine of social activism, where action for human good without personal attachment was the first imperative. In his *Secret of the Gita* (1915) he based his interpretation on the *Gita's* description of the ideal man as one who, with a mind which has attained equability, performs his duties in this world without desiring selfish ends and solely for the benefit of the world, and considers such action as dedication to God.

The *Gita's* teaching on sacrifice, he pointed out, emphasizes the *Brahma yajna*, or dedication of all action to the welfare of the world, in contrast to the ritualistic sacrifice, or *yajna*, of the Vedas. This conception that it is the duty of the individual actively to uphold a world order was directly opposed to the renunciatory creed which had dominated much of Hindu thought for hundreds of years.

Tilak maintained that the social order which the *Gita* contemplates is a structure based on *swadharma* or the duty of an individual to act according to the law of his own nature and to hold fast to his own righteous way. This interpretation rejected the meaning that doctrinal teachers had given the word *swadharma* in terms of caste society—that man must be content with the station in which he is born. The *Gita*'s view of society as an hierarchical organization based on functions and qualities, he insisted, has nothing in common with the caste system where division is based on birth. In declaring that the fourfold division was divinely ordained and represents a permanent feature of social organization, the *Gita*, in Tilak's interpretation, denies birth as the basis of the social orders and emphasizes quality and action as the grounds for differentiating the several functions. In this view all persons, including the lowest, are entitled to equal development so long as they cultivate the equable mind, work unceasingly with the sole object of general good and dedicate their works to God. The *Gita* thus was seen as essentially a scripture of democracy.

Even more significant was the interpretation of the *Gita* as offering a doctrine of the rejuvenation of society. Krishna declares: 'Whenever and wherever *dharma* declines and unrighteousness prospers, I shall be born in successive ages for the purpose of destroying evil-doers and re-establishing the supremacy of the moral law.' In the new interpretation the *Gita* foresees the inevitable decay of all institutions and the necessity of revolutionary changes to restore the harmony of life.

To a static society held down by custom and tradition and suffocated by the accretions of ages, the teaching that change is divinely ordained when society has decayed came as a life-giving revelation. No stronger weapon could have been put in the hands of those who desired to reshape Indian society and give it purpose and vitality. The new doctrine of the *yoga* of action not only gave religious fervour and vigour to political action but transformed Hinduism itself from a static organization to a dynamic force. A partial attempt to break the renunciatory tradition had already come from Vivekananda whose lectures on the *Karma Yoga* showed that renunciation need not be identified with a withdrawal from the world and its activities. The monastic order of the Ramakrishna Mission, too, had been an attempt to reconcile the doctrine of the welfare of the world with worldly renunciation, for the monks of that order did not retire into the forests or secluded *asramas* but pursued a career of service in all fields of social activity. But it was Tilak who furnished a more positive statement of the gospel of action by his emphasis on Krishna's call: 'Therefore arise, and fight the battle of *dharma*.' He viewed all the doctrinal teaching of the *Gita* as having the sole purpose of energizing the righteous man into action.

It was easy for Tilak to arouse the young men of India by appealing to the *Gita*. In *The Secret of the Gita* he expounded the doctrine of energism with a wealth of scholarship and an unimpeachable orthodoxy, and with no direct allusion to politics. But the political meaning was clear, for Tilak was the recognized leader of the extremists of Indian nationalism who considered it their duty 'to rise up and fight' the foreigners on Indian soil. To Tilak India was the field of righteousness, and only through the message of the *Gita* could India save herself.

If activism was what Tilak emphasized, it was the doctrine of selfless service that Gandhi taught by his commentary on the *Gita*. He was in fact the embodiment of the *Gita* ideal of the man of equable mind, the *sthitiprajna*, who, unmoved by anger or by fear, had his feet planted firmly in the world and directed all his action to the benefit of the world. His commentary on the *Gita* was therefore a statement of his personal credo.

Gandhi's special contribution to the integral teachings of the *Gita* was the emphasis which he placed on the means. To him it was not sufficient that the ideal should be the welfare of all, the means must be ethically right. His doctrine of *ahimsa*, or non-violence, expressed the concept that the force of action should not be such as to injure the true nature of another's law of life.

The most comprehensive interpretation of the *Gita*, in the sense of being the most integrated in its spiritual values, was that of Sri Aurobindo (1872–1950). Raised in the classical tradition of the West, Aurobindo first appeared as the inspirer of the terrorist movement in Indian politics, but he underwent a spiritual transformation during his incarceration in jail and for nearly forty years, from 1911 to his death in 1950, he was one of India's great spiritual teachers. In view of his training and background, his commentary had wide social significance. He emphasized the ethical nature of the *Gita's* teachings, tore down mercilessly the obscurantist interpretation that polemical writers had given to its social message and helped the Indian public to understand its teachings in terms of life's problems.

The *Gita* thus became the scripture of the new age, the main foundation on which its ethic, its social doctrines and even its political action depended. Its message was carried daily to the common man in a thousand popular versions, as the number of books on the subject published every year in every Indian language amply testified. It was the inspiration and guide of modern Hindus.

Other factors and personalities contributed directly to a universalization of Hindu thought and to a general awakening of social conscience. Rabindranath Tagore (1861–1941) revived the tradition of devotionalism and offered a poet's interpretation of the universalized doctrines of Hinduism. Dr Ananda Coomaraswamy (1877–1947) interpreted its symbolism; Sir John Woodroffe (1865–1936), a British judge of the Calcutta High Court, redeemed the *tantra* forms of worship of the mother goddess from the extravagances to which many of their practices had fallen; Sister Nivedita, an English convert to Hinduism, was responsible for emphasizing the social value of many Hindu institutions.

The contribution of the West to the Hindu reformation was considerable. The *Gita* itself became popular with the educated classes mainly through

English translations. Mahatma Gandhi's first introduction to the teachings of the *Gita*, for example, was through Sir Edwin Arnold's poetic translation entitled *The Song Celestial* (1885). For over a generation Mrs Annie Besant's prose translation of the *Gita* text under the title *The Lord's Song* was the companion of every Hindu student. Though Tilak's commentary was written in Marathi and Gandhi's in Gujerati, it was through their English versions that they came to have all-India influence. The main literature of modern Hinduism was in English. It would be no exaggeration to say that it was the universality of the English language in India that made an all-India movement for the reformation of Hinduism possible.

So long as the great Hindu scriptures were available only to those who knew Sanskrit, their knowledge was confined to a small group of people, mostly Brahmins. Translations of the *Vedas* and the *Upanishads* were not available in India's popular languages; nor were the great commentaries on which the philosophic structure of Hinduism was based. *The Sacred Books of the East* (1875 ff.), published in English in the last quarter of the nineteenth century under the scholarly editorship of Professor Max Müller, made these texts available to the modern western-educated Indians. The interpretation and popularization of Hindu philosophy was also through the medium of English. Vivekananda's discourses and speeches, Aurobindo's *Essays on Gita* and his *Life Divine* (1916–19), Dr Radhakrishnan's *Indian Philosophy* (1927) and most other classics of modern Hindu religious literature were written in English. The political unification of India and the existence of a language which, though foreign, had become a vehicle of national expression reaching every part of India were essential prerequisites of the Hindu revival.

One result of all the movements emphasizing the general philosophical and ethical background of Hinduism was the decline of sectarianism. From the time of the first Muslim invasion to the middle of the nineteenth century, reform movements in Hinduism had generally led to the foundation of new sects. The process of unification which followed the revival of Hinduism was so marked that even the most differentiated among the new sects, the Brahmo Samaj, was practically absorbed into general Hinduism.

A further phenomenon connected with the revived Hinduism of the twentieth century was the large number of genuine saints and holy personalities who, by the spiritual greatness they achieved and the great moral influence they exercised, stemmed the tide of unbelief and provided inspiration for the new generation. The great figures of Sri Ramakrishna, considered by many to be an incarnation and worshipped as such, Sri Aurobindo and Sri Ramana Maharshi were in a sense canonized by universal consent. There were numerous others in the same tradition. In practically every part of India many such holy men and women, by their mere lives, without teaching any doctrine or preaching any philosophy, bore witness to their faith; they were sought out by people of all ranks from within and outside of India and exerted great influence on large masses of men. Revived Hinduism found its support in the lives of these dedicated men and women who, having renounced the world, still lived among the people, practising unattached action for the welfare of the world.

Thus, armed with a scripture of undisputed authority interpreted in terms of modern social needs and based on a philosophical doctrine which provided an answer to the challenge of other religions, Hinduism in the twentieth century could be applied to the problems of social adjustment.

Popular Hinduism continued in the old way, sectarian, devotional and holding fast to a variety of traditional practices, but it also underwent major changes in respect to the social customs which had had religious sanction. Social disabilities based on caste declined, many temples were thrown open to untouchables and, in the most orthodox province of Madras, Hindu religious endowments were placed under the control of public bodies. Popular Hinduism displayed a more vigorous life than it had in recent times, but it lost much of its conservative character and temper while keeping many of its forms.

Although the social institutions of Hinduism, which in a large measure had become identified with religion itself, were deeply ingrained in law and custom, they did not claim divine sanction nor were they sustained by an organized ecclesiastical authority. They could therefore be changed by legislative action. When the legislating state came into existence in India after the first world war, central and provincial governments passed fundamental legislation affecting Hindu practices. The Civil Marriage Act of the Central Legislative Assembly in 1923, making possible marriages between men and women of different castes, struck at the very root of the orthodox Brahminical conception of caste. The Age of Consent Act of 1929, raising the marriageable age of girls to fourteen, made illegal the custom of child marriage which had been traditional for over two thousand years and was considered compulsory at least for Brahmins. Independent India made the modernization of Indian society one of its primary objectives and formulated as an essential part of its constitution a comprehensive system of fundamental rights enforceable by law, which provided for the absolute abolition of untouchability and gave women equal status with men. The Hindu social legislation which followed was the consummation of a hundred years of effort to reorganize Hindu society on a modern basis.

Essential to the ability of modern independent India to achieve its objective of transforming Hindu society was the removal of religious sanction from outworn social institutions and the reform of religious beliefs so as to provide a sanction for change and a common background to the community. This was the achievement of the Hindu reformation which, acting through many channels and deriving its inspiration from many sources, national and foreign, brought a religious revival which provided the Hindu people with a sense of unity and urge for social welfare. The modern Indian state found the ground ready and prepared, for the victory of social reform had already been won in the public mind even before the legislators gave it statutory recognition.

VI. BUDDHISM

At the opening of the twentieth century the religion of the Buddha was nearly everywhere in a low state of prestige and effectiveness. This was especially the case among the Buddhists of China, Korea, Vietnam and Japan. The disestablishment of Buddhism had been one of the first acts of the Meiji restoration in Japan in 1868. In China, though the Manchu emperors gave their patronage to a form of Lamaism, Buddhism as a religion had little standing; the intellectuals devoted themselves to Confucian studies, while the function of the Buddhist clergy was limited chiefly to the performance of ancestor rites, primarily for the peasants.

In some of the areas of south-east Asia which followed the Hinayana or Theravada Buddhist tradition, as distinct from the other major tradition, the Mahayana, followed in China, Korea, Japan and Vietnam, the position was a little better. In Cambodia, Laos and Siam, where the monarchy continued to uphold the faith, the tradition of religious life remained fairly vigorous and unbroken. But when Burma ceased to be independent Buddhism lost its special position in that country; without central direction or discipline, the Sangha, or church, ceased to be a vigorous force, especially as the official patronage of the British government went to Christianity, and Christian missions became active. In Ceylon, the heart of Theravada, centuries of foreign occupation and the conversion of a considerable section of the higher classes to Christianity left Buddhism depressed. Only in the isolation of Tibet could Buddhism be said to have been in a flourishing state.

By the middle of the century the situation had greatly changed. The celebration of the 2,500th anniversary of the death of the Buddha in 1956 found his religion vigorous and mounting in strength. The revival came principally in the Theravada area, where it was associated with nationalist movements. It was stimulated by the researches of western scholars, which made the classic religious texts of Buddhism available to the educated youth, and which led to the development of critical Buddhist scholarship not only in the Theravada area but also in Japan.

In Thailand the religion had never fallen to so low an estate as elsewhere, and the rulers had historically supported and aided the Buddhist church. In 1888 the Siamese monarch Rama V assumed the title of Defender of the Buddhist faith. Among the many steps which he took to carry out his mission were the publication of a new edition of the *Tripitaka* in 1893, reorganization of the Buddhist religious order and the establishment of a Buddhist school.

As the official religion of Thailand, the Buddhist church continued to be organized nationally under a Sangharaja or Supreme Patriarch appointed by the king, and the state, through its Ministry of Religious Affairs, promoted the interests of religion. The Buddhist temple remained the principal institution of the villages, a repository of wealth and often the only source of education and medical treatment; in towns, where public education came to replace or supplement the education supplied by the monks, the temples acted as hostels for students from a distance. All Buddhist young men in Thailand were expected to spend some period of their life as a monk, if only a few months. In the years of change and uncertainty after the second world war, a Buddhist youth organization sought to help young people to find their path among traditional and western ways.

In Ceylon the decay of Buddhism had gone deep during the more than 400 years of foreign occupation. Many people under the Portuguese and the higher classes during the Dutch and British periods, had accepted the forms of Christianity and at the beginning of the twentieth century the Buddhist religion was followed mainly by the lower classes. Many who had not become Christians had become indifferent to a religion which had no prestige in the country and was not favoured by the government. Buddhist temples had fallen into decay and the system of Buddhist education had been destroyed.

The recovery of Buddhism was part and parcel of the revival of the Ceylonese national spirit. It centred around the revival of Buddhist education, and the founding of the Ananda College in 1886 by Colonel Henry S. Olcott may be taken as the first step toward the re-establishment of Buddhism as the national religion. Under the leadership of Sir Baron Jayatilaka, who was also active in the formation of the Ceylon National Congress, the college became the centre of a Buddhist revival, and a generation of young people grew up after the first world war in the conviction that a genuine Sinhalese tradition was inseparable from Buddhism.

Since Buddhism has always welcomed converts, reconversion was at all times a normal process, and many of the younger leaders who started life as Christians reverted to the Buddhist faith. Those who aspired to work for the nation soon recognized that without going back to the religion of the Buddha it was not possible to gain popular hearing or influence. The men who were to become chief political leaders and high officials of independent Ceylon were among those who returned to their ancestral faith and became ardent advocates of Buddhism. The Buddhist religious orders themselves were spearheads of nationalism. After independence, political parties looked to them for organized support, and they remained a major factor in developing the policies and guiding the destinies of the new state.

In Burma Buddhism was no less a part of the national movement and a factor in the new national state. Its influence there was more continuous than in Ceylon, for it was only with the imposition of British rule in the second half of the nineteenth century that the Buddhist hierarchy was abolished and the religion lost its official position. Even then, the monasteries continued to provide a system of elementary education all over Burma and to act as the upholders of Burmese culture. Though the discipline among the monks became lax when the central organization was destroyed, the religion never lost its position among the common people.

When the national movement began to take shape, it was the Buddhist priests—the *pongys*—who carried its message to the villages. Gradually the nationalist movement became associated with a Buddhist revival and a public affirmation of Buddhist conformity became necessary for those who aspired to local or national leadership. Immediately after independence the prime minister, U Nu, himself a lay monk who periodically retired to the monastery, restored the Buddhist hierarchy, re-established stricter discipline among the Buddhist priesthood and drew upon the inner strength of Buddhism for the reorganization of national life on which the new state was engaged.

The elaborate arrangements made in Rangoon for a World Council of Buddhism in 1956 were an indication of how much Buddhism was identified with Burmese national development. The conciliar tradition in Buddhism was ancient, dating from the period immediately following the Buddha's death, but it had been in abeyance for many centuries. Its revival under the auspices of a modern state was a major event in the religious history of Asia. The object of this council, attended by representatives of all Buddhist countries, was not as on previous occasions to settle points of dogma but rather to discuss the discipline of the monastic order and to take steps to reinvigorate the religious life of Buddhist countries.

Marked interest in Buddhism was also revived in India, its original home. Here again it was nationalist sentiment that led to a new appreciation of the Buddhist tradition and its increasing acceptance as one of the major aspects of Indian life. The study of Indian history revealed Buddhism as an important historical trend in Indian life and thought; a large number of Buddhist texts in Sanskrit, originally written in India, were rediscovered and recovered from China and Tibet, and it became apparent that Indian influence in east Asia was to a large extent based on the spread of Buddhism in those areas.

In recognition of the place of Buddhism in Indian life, the Indian government encouraged the establishment of institutions of Buddhist studies at various centres of importance, and arranged for the repatriation of Buddhist relics from Britain. The 2,500th anniversary of the death of the Buddha was celebrated as a great national Indian festival. It was not difficult to accord this recognition, for Hinduism had at no time considered Buddhism as something separate, like Islam or Christianity, and the Buddha himself had always been recognized as a Hindu divinity. Though conversions to Buddhism were not very numerous, apart from some mass conversions of former untouchables, Buddhism ceased to be looked upon in India as an heretical sect. It came to be seen as a great and valuable tradition in Indian life which should be reintegrated with the national culture of modern India.

Buddhism experienced a much less vigorous revival in the countries which followed the Mahayana tradition than it did in the Theravada areas.

Throughout the twentieth century Chinese Buddhism was under constant attack. Both its popular form as practised by the peasantry, and its philosophical interpenetration with Confucianism and Taoism, came under fire from a succession of movements. From the beginning of the century a movement to expand education called for the appropriation of temple property and its use for the support of schools. In 1917 the Chinese renaissance movement, the New Tide, opposed Buddhism in all its forms. Strongly secular and scientific in its emphasis, it denounced popular Buddhism as superstitious and regarded Buddhist philosophy, together with Confucianism, as unscientific and a backward social influence. In the 1920s the Nationalist party struck at popular Buddhism by ordering the systematic destruction of images in the temples, with the declared purpose of purifying and reforming the religion. In self-defence the Buddhist monks initiated some educational activity and introduced some educational reforms. But although the movements for the confiscation of temple property and the destruction of images were carried out only sporadically and often in the face of opposition from the local peasantry, the Buddhist religion was placed on the defensive throughout these years.

With the coming to power of the communists, Buddhism in China found itself in a relatively favourable position, though the fundamentally secular character of communism left little place for any form of religion in the long run. The major targets of the Chinese People's Republic were the Christian missionaries, who were expelled, and the system of Confucian ethics, which was denounced. Buddhism, however, presented no comparable threat to the objectives of the régime and could be accepted as a link with China's past, and a way of rejecting the foreign bourgeois influence of recent years. Many temples were restored with public funds as historic monuments, and scholarly research into the early history of Chinese Buddhism was promoted. It may be said in fact that here too it was the link with nationalism which gave Buddhism such renewed standing as it enjoyed at the middle of the century.

Buddhism in Japan never fell to so low an estate as in China, although after the Meiji restoration Shinto became the state cult, and people were no longer required to be members of a Buddhist temple under a priest who also played the role of inspector. A number of Buddhist universities were maintained by the various sects into which Japanese Buddhism was divided and these served as centres for Buddhist study and preserved traditional dogma and practice.

At the turn of the century, the impact of western Buddhist scholarship reached Japan through the work of Japanese scholars who studied in Europe and returned to preside over Buddhist studies at the national and Buddhist universities. The emphasis of these scholars was on the original Buddhist texts and on a return to purity of the religion which had been obscured by later elaboration and by the development of sects. This movement, however, was mainly among the Buddhist laymen and youth; it did not meet with favour among the priests in the Buddhist universities. These retained their sectarian interests and clung to their traditional dogmatic methods, expelling those among the younger priests who adopted the methods of critical scholarship.

Although Shinto served as the state cult, the organized Buddhist church lent itself to the support of the emperor system and to the programme of the militarists in the decades leading to the second world war; during the war it became a part of the official propaganda organization. After the war Buddhist leaders sought to make the religion independent of politics, and during the period of defeat and confusion numbers of people turned back to their original Buddhist faith.

The six Buddhist universities continued to carry on traditional Buddhist teaching; Buddhist studies were also conducted in a number of other institutions, and national organizations were formed to promote research on Buddhist subjects. The formation of federations of young Buddhist groups and of Buddhist women's organizations attested to a widespread interest. Japanese Buddhism asserted its continuing vitality before the world by acting as host to the second Buddhist World Conference in Tokyo in 1952.

Thus it may be seen that there was a strengthening of Buddhist tradition and a revival of religious life in the countries of south and south-east Asia where the religion became identified with national regeneration. The religion showed continued vitality and capacity to survive under the much less favourable circumstances of China and Japan, and in its homeland, India, it came back not as a religious revival but as an element in India's varied culture. Like other major religions the religion of the Buddha thus revealed new vigour in the middle years of the twentieth century.

NOTES TO CHAPTER XXV

1. The treatment of religion is commented upon from directly opposing positions, that is for failure (1) to recognize the inner spirituality of religion and to give it a central place in the cultural development of mankind; (2) to regard religion as a mere self-defence of capitalist society. Three Italian scholars, Mario Bendisciolo, Silvio Golzio, Vincenzo Cappelletti, ask 'why the religious component of the history of humanity should be treated under the practical heading of social transformations, whereas religious thought should be considered along with philosophy and science, as providing the intellectual and spiritual horizon of twentieth-century history'. They regard as 'intransigent scientism' the manner in which 'the authors have traced the outlines of science and religion'.

Another scholar, Professor Dhanis, finds that:

'An exposition of a very complex reality is presented in this chapter with solicitous attention to objectivity and on the basis of reliable information. However, the great religions are considered from a point of view rather exterior to the subject. Without taking a position in favour of one doctrine or another, it would have been possible to indicate what each of the great religions wishes to offer mankind—in particular, to men of our own days—to describe the moral and spiritual ideals which they propose, and the inner vitality they possess. Instead of this, religion is considered primarily from the point of view of its relationship with cultural and social progress. This is an important aspect, but not the primary one.

'More could have been said about the results which the Christian ideal of justice and charity has achieved in our times. The firmness with which the Catholic religion has maintained its supernatural message against rationalist denials, is rightly noted; but the progress and the vitality of the philosophical, theological and biblical sciences in modern Catholicism are not sufficiently taken into account.'

Communist commentators take an opposite view. Mr Imre Revesz writes:
'The opening sentence strikes the key-note of the whole chapter: it is said that in the
twentieth century each of the major world religions has regenerated in its "inner core . . ."
However, there is no hint—or almost none—as to the actual spring of this great religious
revival. It is in fact a desperate act of self-defence on the part of capitalist society (riddled
as it is with feudal survivals, or, in some places, blended with them altogether) in the
face of the triumphant march of socialism and its final goal—communism. The great
religions are still, to this day, the mainstays of capitalism (and, broadly speaking, of social
antagonism), which they reflect ideologically. If, today, every now and then, they appear
more sympathetic towards social and cultural progress than they were, say, a hundred or
a hundred and fifty years ago, that sympathy is as yet far too feeble to counterbalance
tendencies inherent in *each* established religion. It is too weak to break religious and
ecclesiastical *autotelism* (which can have no place in future society) in general, or, in
particular, the drive of the major religions and churches for political power, and their
material, economic, independence (in which the trait of exploitation—open or concealed
—is always recognizable).'

Three commentators from the USSR (I. K. Grigulevich, E. A. Belaiev and G. F.
Ilyin) explain the communist attitude as follows:
'Communists fight against religious prejudices by disseminating genuinely scientific
knowledge about the universe and society among the population and by building a new
socialist society, in which the exploitation of one individual by another has been eradicated, and in which the spiritual and material needs of people are being satisfied to a
greater and greater extent.'

Additional readings for Roman Catholicism may be suggested:

J. Y. Calvez, *Église et société économique* (Paris, 1961–63), 2 vols.
Joseph Folliet, *World Catholicism Today* (Westminster, Md., 1961).
Joseph Nestor Moody (ed.), *Church and Society: Catholic Social and Political Thought and
Movements, 1789–1950* (New York, 1953).
Papal Encyclicals, like that of Pius XII, *On the Sacred Liturgy* (1947).

For religion under communism may be suggested:

Cyril E. Black, *The Transformation of Russian Society* (Cambridge, Mass., 1960).
Robert Pierce Casey, *Religion in Russia* (New York, 1946).
John S. Curtiss, *The Russian Church and the Soviet State, 1917–1950* (Boston, 1953).
Constantin de Grunwald, *La vie religieuse en URSS* (Paris, 1961).
Boleslaw Szczesniak, *The Russian Revolution and Religion: A Collection of Documents
concerning the Suppression of Religion by the Communists, 1917–1925* (Notre Dame,
Indiana, 1959).

For studies of world religions consult:

Marcus Bach, *Major Religions of the World* (New York, 1959).
C. J. Bleeker, *Anthropologie religieuse; l'homme et sa destinée à la lumière de l'histoire des
religions* (Études publiées sous la direction de C. J. Bleeker, avec l'aide de l'Unesco et
sous les auspices du Conseil International de la Philosophie et des Sciences Humaines
(Leiden, 1955).
Johnson E. Fairchild, *Basic Beliefs; the Religious Philosophies of Mankind* (New York, 1959).
V. T. A. Ferm, *Living Schools of Religion* (Ames, Iowa, 1956).
Sir Julian Huxley (ed.), *The Humanist Frame* (New York, 1961).
Benson Young Landis, *World Religions: A Brief Guide to the Principal Beliefs and Teachings
of the Religions of the World and to the Statistics of Organized Religion* (New York,
1957).
Guy S. Métraux and François Crouzet, eds., *Religions and the Promise of the Twentieth
Century* (New York: New American Library [Mentor Books], 1965).
Paul Ramsey, *War and the Christian Conscience* (Durham, North Carolina, 1961).
Kenneth Thompson, *Christian Ethics and the Dilemma of Foreign Policy* (Durham, N.C.,
1959).
H. F. Vos, *Religions in a Changing World* (Chicago, 1959).
Charles C. West, *Communism and the Theologian* (Phila., Penn., 1959).

CHAPTER XXVI

EDUCATION

I. INTRODUCTION

EVERY current of the times, whether intellectual, social or political, had its impact on education. It is in the nature of education that this should be the case, for the educational system of every society embodies and transmits the values, attitudes and norms of the society, hands on a body of tradition and knowledge and seeks to equip the new generation for what it may meet in the future. As an instrument both of conservation and of change, education is thus inevitably affected by changes in social structure, by new bodies of knowledge, by changing technology and by changing social and intellectual attitudes.

The outstanding influence on education in the twentieth century was change itself. In a world where changes of all sorts came at a staggering rate, education was forced to serve more as an instrument to facilitate and cope with change and could not function mainly as an institution for conserving and perpetuating old ways. This was most clearly apparent in the societies which were undergoing conscious revolution, where education was used as a deliberate means of carrying through revolutionary objectives, as in the USSR, Turkey and the new states of former colonial peoples. But science and technology were remaking all societies during this period, while shifts in world power and changing social patterns cast all manner of people in new roles. Rapid change was the basic factor in educational development in virtually every country in the world.

The central component of the changes which directly affected education was science and its application, both as the spread of the scientific attitude affected the objectives and methods of education, and as science constantly augmented the body of knowledge which it was the task of educational institutions to transmit. Pedagogy itself became a field of scientific study; the fruits of scientific research in biology, psychology, sociology and anthropology provided new bases for many educational procedures; the range of devices available to the educator was immensely increased by new techniques of communication. Modern education had to develop individuals with inquiring minds and with a scientific outlook toward life in terms of which to respond to the new experiences and new knowledge which they were bound to meet. And it had to transmit ever growing bodies of knowledge in the natural sciences and in wide areas of social, anthropological, archaeological and historical inquiry, not only as theoretical knowledge but in relation to a vast and complex range of applications.

In broad terms it may be said that education in the twentieth century was extended and redesigned to meet the requirements of industrial society.

As industrialism spread, no areas remained free from its imperatives and no people could persist without its tools. The twentieth-century individual required a kind of training which would enable him to grow with the times, to shift his job, to recast his thought, to modify habits relating to food, health, child-rearing, to understand and cope with new social situations, to establish new relationships, to absorb the impact of mass communication. Less and less of what he had to have could be provided by parental instruction and practical apprenticeship.

Every country, from the most highly industrialized to those just embarking on industrialization, needed a public equipped with knowledge, skills and the capacity to handle new information and ideas; all needed an expanding supply of technicians, experts and professionals at all levels and in all fields of human endeavour. Neither mass literacy nor the traditional training of the liberally educated *élite*, nor any combination of these, could meet the demand for engineers, mechanics, nurses, aircraft pilots, managers and thousands of other occupations which rested upon specialized knowledge and skill; nor could they keep a country abreast of the scientific developments of the age. The educational systems of all countries were subjected to tremendous pressure for a great variety of training for more and more people.

The needs of industrial societies for trained personnel were paralleled and reinforced by the needs of democratic states for educated citizens. As democracy in the traditionally democratic states came to embrace all the people and as democratic principles spread to other parts of the world, education inevitably followed in the wake. The educational requirements of workers and peasants, women, racial minorities and others once regarded as of the 'lower orders' changed with changing aspirations and status, from those which would have been sufficient if these people had 'kept their place' to those due to them as equal citizens of a democratic society. National self-assertion redefined the educational needs of 'backward peoples'. In the twentieth century education came to be regarded as the birthright of all the people—as much education as they could absorb and as society could manage to provide.

The main responsibility for the ever expanding volume and range of education designed to reach more people for longer periods, and in greater variety, rested on the state, by reason of the state's expanding functions and its expanded power. Among the first responsibilities of the welfare state was the provision of education for its citizens. In addition education was one of the most direct ways by which the state, with its enlarged powers and intensified national objectives, could achieve its aims. This relationship was clearest in the countries experiencing revolution or seeking rapid economic development. But education bore a close relation to the aims and purposes of the state in other countries as well, both those with highly centralized educational systems such as France, and those with local administration of education such as the United States.

The impact of these factors brought common trends in educational practices throughout the world, however different the cultural background, level of economic development, political system or class structure might be. Education spread to the masses of the people, including women. There was a universal tendency to lengthen the term of schooling for each child, until secondary and even some form of higher education also became, in many places, accessible to broad segments of society. The costs of education mounted steadily as years in school were increased, the pay of teachers was raised, and costly buildings, laboratories, libraries and other equipment came to be required. There was a world-wide trend to professionalize the task of the educator, to equip the teacher with special training in educational methods in addition to a knowledge of his subject, and to study the educative process systematically with a view to providing the educator with scientifically based knowledge as part of his professional equipment.

In line with the demands of industrial society, the purposes of the state and new insights into the processes of learning, there was a trend to bring the content and methods of education closer to life experience and to give a more practical cast to school activity. Education tended to be concerned with the total development of the child, to enlarge its scope to take in every facet of his growth, and to view the educative process less in terms of the information to be imparted than of the individual as a person and his ability to function in the society of which he was a part.

Everywhere there was a tendency for education to extend beyond the child in the classroom, both to encompass extra-curricular activities during his school years, and to continue the educational process in later life; further education of youth and adults became part of the educational programme of nearly every country, whether in the form of fundamental education, workers' education, adult education, university extension, correspondence courses or training and retraining on the job.

The democratization of education narrowed the traditional gulf between the possessors of knowledge and the ignorant masses and opened the door to large-scale vertical social mobility. In so doing it both aroused and sustained the aspirations of people toward individual and social change. Mass education also provided a mass audience for literature and the arts and for the mass media, thereby affecting the level and quality of literary and artistic expression. While it offered the means of developing an informed citizenry, it also provided a channel for the indoctrination of people by centralized states.

Education during these years tended to produce a multitude of people equipped with much, but often fragmentary, knowledge drawn from beyond their direct experience. As a result societies came to be composed of a great mass of semi-informed people instead of a small *élite* highly endowed with learning and a basic population equipped by practice and example to deal primarily with the concrete content of their daily lives.

These world-wide trends were not without counteracting tendencies which left unresolved many issues of educational theory and practice. In fact there was scarcely a country in the world at mid-century where education was not a central public issue and where questions of objectives, methods and costs were not the object of intense discussion, study and often controversy as nations and communities sought ways to equip their rising generations to live in the modern world.

Though the trend was to recognize and use the educational system as a means of adjusting to or furthering change, more or less strong elements in many countries resisted the trend and sought to emphasize the conservative function of education as the preserver of traditional values and knowledge. In view of the rapidity of technological and social change during this half-century, it is perhaps as remarkable that educational systems in Europe, the Americas and Asia changed so little in structure, content and method as that they changed so much.

There were counter-trends, too, to the tendency to incorporate scientific materials and a scientific attitude and to expect the educational system to meet the needs of industrial society. In particular the tendency to introduce vocational material into general education was strongly resisted by those who insisted that this subordinated the spiritual, moral and intellectual development of the child to material objectives. Such resistance was especially strong in those societies which placed a relatively low value on action as compared with philosophical thought; educators in the Latin American countries liked to contrast their societies with North America on this score and to attribute to this difference in value systems the lesser tendency to include practical content or methods in their schools.

Nor was the trend toward the democratization of education equally strong everywhere, or unopposed. Where feudal or quasi-feudal relationships and attitudes survived, as they continued to do in Spain and in parts of Latin America and the Middle East, mass education was at best a matter of indifference on the part of the controlling element in society; at worst it was flatly opposed. The persistence of very high rates of illiteracy in many of the Latin American countries up to the middle of the twentieth century is to be explained, at least in part, on this score. In conservative Muslim countries the negative attitude toward mass education was particularly strong with regard to women. The virtual prohibition of the education of women outside the home which continued in Saudi Arabia into the 1950s was an extreme example of this counter-trend. Colonial powers, too, through most of the period were indifferent or opposed to education for the mass of their subjects, though a movement for general education in some of the remaining colonial areas developed after the second world war, building on earlier voluntary efforts which had originated in the metropolitan countries.

The trend toward state responsibility for education also did not go un-opposed. The most effective and organized opposition came from religious bodies which claimed the right and responsibility for educating the young. Of these the Roman Catholic Church was most vigorous,[1] but there were some challenges to secular education from other Christian denominations and from Buddhist and Muslim sources. Less formal opposition, primarily to the mono-poly of education by the state, came from groups and educators who rejected the idea that the interests of society were paramount over those of the indivi-dual and who feared the use to which the omnipotent state might put the educational system were it completely in its hands.

The common educational trends brought common problems throughout the world which remained unsolved during these years. The most practical of these were the cost of education and the difficulty of finding and training teachers fast enough to keep pace with the growing demand. Where expansion was relatively slow and where resources were many and the backlog of edu-cated persons available for teaching was large, these problems were least severe. But in the years after the second world war pressures from mounting birth rates and from the expansion of mass education at the secondary level brought crises in many educational systems. Even in the richest and most economically developed countries, alternative demands upon the public treasury and alternative fields of employment made the problem of school financing and recruitment of teachers very real. At the opposite extreme, these problems were critical and acute in the new states which were pressed by the circumstances of their establishment and the nature of the times to develop with great rapidity both a literate population and a sufficient body of educated and trained people to advance their society.

The expansion of education and the tendency to make it universal at higher and higher levels brought a major pedagogical problem of how to combine quality with quantity—how to preserve a high quality of intensive education for the professionals and scholars, who once were the only candidates for education above the primary level, while extending educational opportunities to large numbers of students whose academic interests were less strong, in-tellectual capacity was often more limited and educational needs were different. There was widespread complaint that standards had been lowered, though few doubted that the best students were as good as the limited group which had once constituted the entire student body.

Educators struggled everywhere with the problem of how best to combine the two processes of mass and intensive education, from the point of view both of pedagogical effectiveness and of the disposition of available educational resources. Like the practical difficulties of educational costs and recruitment of teachers, this problem was especially acute in the countries which had to use limited resources to cope simultaneously with mass illiteracy and the need to train highly qualified personnel. In these countries it was further complicated by the additional problem of language, for the vernacular which served as the vehicle for mass education could not give access to advanced bodies of know-ledge, and higher levels of education had to be carried on in a foreign tongue.

Beyond the pedagogical problem of how to balance mass education with the training of an educated *élite* was the intellectual problem arising from the presence of the half-educated. Intellectuals could no longer monopolize the realms of thought and expression, for they found themselves confronted by those whom they could not continue to ignore but who yet did not belong to their old world. Whether this was a source of lament or congratulation depen-ded upon the outlook. The Spanish writer, Ortego y Gasset, representing the aristocratic intellectual tradition which was nowhere stronger than in his native Spain, deplored what he called the *Revolt of the Masses* (1932) as a degrading, levelling-down influence which substituted for independent rational thought the tendency to follow emotional impulses and to accept uncritically the ideas of others. But from another point of view it was a levelling-up, and it provided a new mass base whose potentialities were yet to be fully revealed.

The common trends and problems in education took distinct forms in different educational systems, and these systems in turn varied in importance during the twentieth century according to their influence and the numbers of people affected by them. The British and French systems were extensively followed outside Britain and France. The general British pattern prevailed throughout the British commonwealth and its dependencies; the London Matriculation examination, for example, was widely used as a university en-trance or school finishing examination. French education not only was applied to French residents and 'assimilated' natives in the areas of French domina-tion, but was a model for much of the education developed in the Middle East. The German system was influential throughout eastern Europe, and during the early years of the century German institutions, especially in technical and scientific fields, attracted students from abroad and provided a pattern for the technical institutions of several countries. The educational system of the United States embodied and emphasized many of the trends which were gen-eral during the first half of the twentieth century, and the influence of some of its leading educators and pedagogical institutions was felt in many parts of the world.

By the middle of the century the educational system of the Soviet Union was attracting widespread attention, for the USSR offered the outstanding example of a country which had made a well-supported educational pro-gramme one of the pillars of its national development; it had rapidly overcome mass illiteracy and had trained very large numbers of persons at all technical and scientific levels.[2] For the countries still facing the dual problems of mass illiteracy and the need of rapid economic development, the educational methods employed by the Soviet Union held special interest. General interest also attached to the developing systems of both India and the Chinese People's Republic, for together these countries comprised roughly a third of mankind, and the distinctive manners in which they were meeting the problems of modernizing their vast populations could not fail to be of concern to the rest of the world.

It would not be possible in the pages which follow to delineate the separate developments in these and the many other distinctive national systems. The educational experience of particular countries will therefore be considered only as illustrative of broad developments common to many places.

II. EDUCATION AT THE OPENING OF THE TWENTIETH CENTURY

The main framework for twentieth-century education was already in existence at the opening of the century and it must therefore be reviewed in order that the changes during these years may be understood.

I. *Extent*

At the opening of the century the idea of universal, free and compulsory elementary education was generally accepted as an objective in western countries, and literacy had been achieved for the majority of the people of northern and western Europe, North America, New Zealand and Australia. It had been adopted as an objective which was well on the way toward fulfilment in Japan, and to a lesser degree in eastern and southern Europe. But even where the principle was most fully accepted many practical obstacles stood in the way of its implementation.

Universal education sprang from the need of industrial society for a literate population and the conviction in the countries committed to democratic principles and representative government that an informed citizenry was essential to the effective functioning of that system. In countries where Protestantism predominated, the need to be able to read the Bible or religious texts had stimulated the establishment of common schools before the demands of industry added a secular motivation. Universal education was generally added to an older system designed for an educated *élite* who made up the liberal professions, the priesthood, the scholars, administrators and men of cultivated tastes.[3]

Among western countries national systems of education, well-developed by the opening of the century, provided the educational structure for their respective populations and had begun to influence other parts of the world through colonial administrations, missionary efforts or cultural impact. The systems of Great Britain, France and Germany followed similar but distinct lines while that of the United States differed in basic structure; educational institutions maintained in many lands by the teaching orders of the Roman Catholic Church adapted their special point of view and method to a variety of local conditions.

In the British and continental European systems, mass education and education for the *élite* were separately organized and followed separate lines. An elementary system, generally state supported, led to a terminus usually at the end of six years; in some countries, notably in Germany, Holland and Russia, students completing the primary school could receive additional technical or commercial education in special schools. A system of secondary schools, overlapping the primary system and generally charging fees, led to the university.

The two systems were based upon and perpetuated class differences, for while elementary education was available to all who lived within reach of a school and was generally free and compulsory, secondary education was available chiefly to those who could pay. Determination of whether or not the child would enter the secondary system was usually made at the age of 10 or 11 years or even earlier. University education was enjoyed chiefly by those prepared in fee-charging schools, sometimes privately supported, especially in the case of those attending the older British universities. Some exceptional students, however, were able to secure higher education in all these systems and some of those who later became leaders of social change had taken advantage of such opportunities.

In contrast to the European, the American system was a single continuous structure of free education from primary to secondary and university years. Without either the intellectual class or the aristocracy of Europe, with a strong Protestant tradition and a frontier society, the United States relied heavily on this open system of public education to realize its goals of republican government, national progress and individual opportunity, and to serve as a melting pot for the children of its immigrants from many lands. How far the individual was able to go through the system depended in part on his financial ability to stay out of the labour market and to receive family support during the years of his secondary and higher education; but ambitious students were expected to work their way through school and college, earning money from any job, however menial, which they might be able to secure.

Private fee-supported schools and universities existed alongside the publicly supported institutions, enjoyed prestige and were patronized by those who preferred what they had to offer and possessed either financial means or the exceptional qualities which commanded scholarship aid. For children in rural areas, schooling was often less available or extensive than for urban children, and in the southern states Negro children attended separate and generally inferior schools. Yet the principle of general education, democratically available to all, had been adopted as a guide to educational development in the United States.

The Latin American countries, on the other hand, followed the traditional European system of education for an intellectual *élite*. Only a few, notably Argentina and Chile, had begun to add the concept of mass education.

Education of adults as well as of children was already a recognized part of the educational systems of western countries at the opening of the century. Mechanics' institutes had grown up in many countries in response to the impact of industrialization in the middle of the nineteenth century, and although these had lost some of their vogue, workers' education movements, closely related to the growing trade unions, were beginning to take shape. All manner of informal educational programmes reflected the widespread desire of people to pursue educational interests during their adult years, through correspondence schools, university extension classes, such forms of popular education as summer camp meetings, lecture circuits and reading circles, and a growing number of public libraries which catered to the general reader rather than to the scholar. In the United States, where great numbers of immigrants presented the double problem of illiteracy and ignorance of the local language and culture, night schools had been organized in major cities.

By the opening of the century the educational principles, practices and, frequently, the personnel from western Europe and North America were penetrating to other parts of the world. In Japan universal elementary education along western lines, first modelled on French and then on German patterns adapted to Japanese objectives and cultural norms, was 'designed to give children the rudiments of moral education and of education especially adapted to make of them good members of the community, together with such general knowledge and skill as are necessary for practical life'.* A limited system of middle schools and of higher schools for boys led to the university.

In the largely non-literate areas of the Middle East, Asia and Africa, well-established missionary schools and some institutions provided by colonial administrations were offering a western type of education for a growing westernized *élite*. Colonial powers in the main furnished such education as they required for the administration of their dependencies. British educational activity was most extensive in India, where the government maintained some primary and secondary schools and subsidized others under missionary or private auspices. These schools went somewhat beyond their principal task of training for the civil service, for various technical government operations such as railways and irrigation systems and for the lower ranks in industrial establishments in India and nearby Burma. In Indo-China and north Africa French culture was being imparted to a segment of the population largely through Catholic mission schools. The Dutch administration of Indonesia, almost completely in the hands of Europeans, rested on a limited educational system designed primarily for European residents, the Chinese and Indo-European middle classes, and some members of the local aristocracy.

Missionary education, chiefly from Britain, France and the United States, was extensive in China and among the subject peoples of the Ottoman empire. In Korea it was modifying the position of women and introducing new knowledge and social ideas. French cultural influence was felt in the higher educational circles of Iran as well as in Syria, while the educated *élite* of Egypt and Turkey drew on French, British and German sources. Among the non-literate peoples of Africa, missionary education, far more limited than that which had become well established in Asia, was beginning to modify the outlook of some members of some African tribes and to provide a bridge to the outside world.

* Imperial Ordinance No. 215, relating to elementary schools, 1890.

Missionary and colonial education at the beginning of the century did not, however, represent mass education as did elementary education in Europe and America.

Nor were there widespread indigenous systems of education in these countries. Some traditional elementary education was provided by Buddhist monks and Hindu religious and charitable establishments. Quranic schools in Muslim countries offered a very limited form of education for boys, often confined to oral memorizing and reciting of the Quran text with such explanatory comments as the mullah might offer. For the rest, the rigorous training of the limited numbers of scholars, monks or priests in the traditional religious and classical learning of Confucian, Buddhist, Hindu or Muslim scholarship and devotion constituted the prevailing form of education, apart from the training provided to apprentices in the shop and children in the home. Each of these systems produced a small key group of literati. The Chinese system of classical scholarship was the most noted, providing as it did for access to civil and military posts through examinations on classical subjects open to any man who could acquire such knowledge. At the turn of the century this examination system was abolished, the University of Peking was established (1898) along western lines, and students were returning from study in Japan and the United States imbued with western educational concepts.[4]

2. Auspices and financing

The principle of state responsibility for the provision of at least basic education had been generally accepted in western countries during the nineteenth century. A large proportion of schools, however, remained under religious auspices. In Europe the state's educational obligations were largely fulfilled through confessional schools, as in the Scandinavian countries with an established church where state schools were confessional or in Germany where the majority of state school inspectors were members of the clergy. Britain and the Netherlands maintained an integrated system of state schools and religious schools which received state aid. In the Austro-Hungarian empire the state supported schools of different denominations, as well as schools for segments of the population using different languages.

Only France among European countries maintained a wholly state-supported and publicly controlled system after the secularization laws of 1882; the suppression of the religious orders in 1905 substantially reduced the number of schools in the voluntary system of Catholic education which functioned independently. In the United States the constitutional principle of the separation of church and state was the basis for a wholly state-supported and state-controlled system of public education, but privately supported schools were permitted and large numbers of denominational schools existed without public support. In colonial areas, with the partial exception of India and Indonesia, education was provided chiefly through religiously administered schools, with or without state support.

In line with the claim of the Roman Catholic Church that education of its communicants is the responsibility of the Church and that it is the duty of Catholic parents to send their children to church schools, Catholic schools were to be found in all countries where there was a substantial Catholic population. In the Iberian peninsula and Latin America, where the population was predominantly Catholic and the state had assumed little independent responsibility for education, Catholic schools provided the principal or sole educational system; elsewhere they flourished, with or without state support, in proportion to the size of the Catholic population and the vigour of the prevailing interest in education. Catholic schools, maintained by Jesuits and other teaching orders, were designed to provide an education infused with religious doctrine and a religious outlook, but they followed local educational patterns in respect to the secular content of instruction. Although several Protestant denominations also maintained educational institutions, especially at advanced levels—witness the multitude of denominational colleges in the United States—they rarely sought to enrol all their followers except where they constituted, in fact, the state system.

3. *Teachers*

In order to supply teachers for the large number of schools required for universal elementary education, teacher training had been systematically organized in western countries. Each of the northern and western European systems provided for two distinct groups of teachers, drawn from and fed back into the elementary and secondary school systems respectively. In the United States, too, in spite of the absence of the two-system structure for pupils, elementary school teachers were trained in normal schools patterned on those for European elementary teaching, while secondary school teachers, as in Europe, were usually drawn from the universities.

4. *Content and method of education*

The objectives and consequently the content of education in the several western systems at the opening of the century were far from uniform, but they followed certain common lines. In all the European systems primary education was designed to provide the basic tools of literacy and ability to compute which had become essential for an increasingly urban society, and to impart in addition such attitudes and skills as each country's educational organizers deemed essential. In the main the secondary and higher educational systems passed on a traditional body of classical learning, though there was a strong and growing movement for acceptance of science and modern languages on a par with classical studies. Universities prepared chiefly for the liberal professions and the responsibilities of government.

Within this general pattern emphasis and structure varied. In Great Britain the elementary schools provided the basic tools for living in an industrial society while secondary and higher education were designed to train persons to a level of high competence, largely through humanistic studies, thus equipping them to enter the flexible and responsible civil service and to pursue the arts and professions. French education, highly centralized and formalized, provided uniform, rigorous minimum training in and knowledge of French language and culture, with competitive access to higher levels of classical academic study and specialized advanced instruction, limited by posts open or expected to be open to those completing various degrees. The German and Russian systems offered vocational and technical training to those not entering secondary and higher schools, and thorough training for research in a chosen field to the intellectual *élite*. The open school system of the United States still furnished a predominantly classical education beyond the elementary years, but it had begun to accept the elective principle and to offer a variety of content in line with the wide range of students' interests and society's needs.

Prevailing methods of elementary education relied heavily on learning by rote and made little effort to adjust to the individual capacity or needs of the children, although a body of education theory, notably the work of Pestalozzi, Froebel and Herbart, had been developed during the nineteenth century to support such an approach.

Universities everywhere served as centres of traditional learning and of preparation for liberal professions, but technical institutions offering courses of university grade in agriculture and engineering had been established in Europe and North America.

III. EXTENSION OF EDUCATION AS A MASS PROCESS

During the twentieth century mass education was extended everywhere, at secondary and higher levels in countries of advanced industrial development, at elementary levels in the rest of the world, and everywhere for adults who needed to keep pace with constant change. In every part of the world more and more people received more and more education, systems for providing formal education grew in size and complexity, and education absorbed an increasing proportion of the wealth, energy, time and personnel of the community.

The pattern in each country depended on various factors: the cultural traditions of the country, its changing social system, the degree of industrialization, the economic resources available for educational expansion, the extent to which the society was dedicated to the principle of equal opportunity, and the determination with which the country was consciously pursuing economic development and sought to use education as a tool in this process. The extension of education thus reflected both the needs of the individual and the needs of society.

Much of the history of educational development in the twentieth century involved the interrelation between the systems designed for mass education and those for training an educated *élite*. The ever mounting demands of industrial society called for a constant increase in knowledge and competence on the part of the masses of the people. The problem of how to meet these quantitative, practical needs while still developing intellectuals of high quality was present in one form or another in virtually every country, at every stage of educational development and in respect to every aspect of education.

1. *In countries of high literacy*

(*a*) *Democratization of secondary education.* For countries which had already achieved a base of universal elementary education by the opening of the century, extension of mass education meant expansion at the secondary level until education beyond the elementary stage was envisaged or achieved for the whole population. In these countries a combination of the increased productivity of industrialized labour and a decline in the ratio of children to adults in the population made child labour unnecessary and provided the resources to support children during adolescence and to finance their schooling. As it became less possible for the uneducated to function effectively, parents demanded more education for their children to enable them to make their way in the world.

In the United States the single, continuous school system, based on the principle of equal opportunity for all and the development of the individual to his fullest capacity, could be readily expanded at the secondary level. High school enrolment grew by leaps and bounds, until it embraced the great majority of the adolescent population. In one state after another, the compulsory school age was raised to 16 until by 1950 all the forty-eight states required attendance to that age and ten had higher requirements. By the opening of the second world war secondary education in the United States had become mass education. In 1952, 82 per cent of the children between the ages of 14 and 17 were attending school.

European countries took various steps to increase the number of students receiving education at the secondary level and they modified their separate systems for mass and *élite* education in the process.

In the first quarter of the century and especially after the first world war there were strong movements in each of the European countries to make a longer period of general education available to all, to provide additional technical education at the secondary level, and to make it possible for children to advance from one level to another and to higher education without having the door closed and the child's future finally determined at 10 or 11 years of age. It was only after the second world war, however, that elementary and secondary systems were more closely integrated and that efforts were made to provide a range of educational opportunities which would fully utilize the capacities of all the children and would make it possible for them to advance through the system without regard to their economic and social status. At mid-century the trend in this direction was very marked; by 1950 some 50 to

80 per cent of the children between 14 and 17 were attending school in all the west European countries except Spain, Portugal and Italy.

In the Scandinavian countries middle school education was made widely available; Denmark in 1937 adopted the principle of 'secondary education for all' for its urban schools and made the middle school an automatic continuation of the elementary system. Great Britain enacted legislation in 1918 raising the school-leaving age as soon as facilities could be made ready, establishing continuation schools, and providing increased grants to finance secondary education. As a result secondary education for both boys and girls expanded sharply, as did university education, but it was not until after the second world war that the new school leaving age of 15 years was made compulsory. Under the British Education Act of 1944 which provided for three types of secondary education—academic, technical and general—the child usually chose his course at the age of 11, but there were opportunities for transfer from one course to another on the basis of interest and quality of performance.

In France there was a strong though unsuccessful agitation after the first world war for the establishment of *l'école unique*, a common, single school system in place of the separate free elementary schools and fee-charging secondary schools. Passage from the elementary to the secondary system was facilitated when the curricula of the overlapping last years of the primary and the first years of the secondary schools were made more similar. School fees were finally abolished in 1933, though the two systems remained under separate administrations. The German Weimar republic established a single *Grundschule* for all children—though with separate, state-aided Protestant, Catholic and Marxist units—and provided financial aid to promising students so that their choice of further education would not depend on financial status.

None of these measures, and similar steps taken by other European countries, fully democratized European education, nor did they wholly discard the basic two-part structure or make secondary education as completely mass education as in the United States. But they did reflect a common trend in this direction.

The Japanese system, in which attendance up to the sixth year was made compulsory in 1907, followed the European pattern of mass elementary education, with access to higher education only for boys who could attend the limited number of higher preparatory schools. After the second world war the Japanese system was recast and followed the American model of continuous progression from bottom to top according to the capacities and interests of the individual, with a resultant great increase in secondary school and university enrolment.

With the momentum of Soviet development, the USSR expanded all aspects of its educational programme at a dramatic rate. Inheriting a European-type two-track system in which mass education reached only a fraction of the population, it created a single, basic general school system, made four years compulsory in 1930, seven years for urban children in 1947, and eight years of general polytechnic training for all in 1958. It insisted that only where all education is publicly supported can a system be considered democratic.

The number of pupils in general schools more than trebled in the dozen years between the launching of the first five-year plan and the outbreak of the second world war. In addition institutions offering technical training and those for higher education were enormously increased and every sort of facility was offered to adults to increase their training or to make up past deficiencies—through trade unions, factories, night schools, correspondence courses, special schools to enable those who had failed to receive regular schooling to enter institutions of higher education. The Soviet government estimated at mid-century that one out of every four persons in the entire population was going to school at least by correspondence.[5]

(b) *Extension of higher education*. After the second world war higher education also began to take on the character of mass education, most conspicuously in the United States. The provision of educational benefits to war veterans, including subsistence while studying for as many years as the veteran had been in military service—usually four—brought higher education to many thousands who would have terminated their education at an earlier stage.

None of the European systems went as far as the American in opening education at the top to large numbers, but university enrolments increased by as much as 50 per cent or even 100 per cent over pre-war levels and specialized higher-level institutions continued to be established. Access to higher education, moreover, ceased to be limited primarily by ability to pay or to attend fee-charging preparatory schools and became increasingly dependent on ability to compete successfully for stipends awarded to the abler students.

University-level education in Japan, which had been expanded markedly after 1918, was still further enlarged in the reorganization after the second world war. Educational expansion in the Soviet Union included a great multiplication of institutions of higher education, and a similar situation existed in the people's democracies of eastern Europe.[6]

(c) *Adult and informal education*. Mass education was also extended to adults. In a world where new knowledge was continually opening up and new occupations were becoming available, people did not outgrow either the need or the desire to go on learning when they left school or university. Schools offered night classes and universities conducted extra-mural, extension and correspondence courses to meet the demand. Mounting numbers of people continued their general education from the point where their formal schooling left off, or studied to prepare for a new or better paid occupation, or to bring themselves up to date in their own field. Many large employers, whether in industry or government, offered in-service training to enable their employees to advance. In some countries special programmes of vocational rehabilitation offered retraining to persons whose skills were made obsolete by technological change or who were prevented by accident or disease from continuing in their original occupation.

Workers' education in a number of countries helped workers to function more effectively as trade unionists and citizens. In co-operation with schools and universities, trade unions developed educational programmes for their members which included economic and social subjects, labour history and trade union methods. Some special schools for workers were set up, either independently or in connection with educational institutions. Workers' education associations, notably in Britain, Sweden and the United States, developed educational methods and materials, sponsored courses, and provided leadership for the workers' education movements. As labour gained political power and community influence, the content of workers' education programmes was expanded to equip their students for greater responsibility. The folk high school, developed in Denmark in the nineteenth century as part of the movement for national regeneration, spread to neighbouring countries, offering the village young men and women intellectual and cultural stimulus, social experience and economic perspective.

Programmes of social and civic education reached many other adult groups, through community forums conducted by educational institutions or organizations, and through countless study groups organized by voluntary associations such as the British Women's Institutes, Canadian film groups, or reading circles organized by libraries.

Any discussion of the extension of education would take a very narrow view if only formal education were included. An enormous amount of education was carried on, consciously and incidentally, through the many organs of mass communication to which the twentieth-century citizen was exposed. In most countries radio was regarded and consciously used as an educational tool; where it was operated commercially, as in the United States, Canada and Latin America, its programmes designed for entertainment were embellished by many educational features. The same was true of the cinema and television. The daily press and the weekly or monthly magazines offered information and instruction on a very wide range of subjects. News, entertainment, political propaganda, even advertising, played an important part in the education of twentieth-century man.*

2. In countries of high illiteracy

(a) Extension of basic education. Outside the United States, Europe, the British commonwealth, the USSR and Japan, mass education spread slowly before the second world war and with great rapidity and intensity thereafter. In the 1920s and 1930s Mexico and Turkey followed their revolutions with determined efforts to bring schools to their largely rural populations, and Egypt started to put its primary education on a mass basis.

Mexico centred its programme on the development of realistic rural education; it also modified its urban schools to make them more practical and less verbal, and established a variety of technical and vocational schools at all

* See Chapters XI, Communications, and XXVII, Use of Leisure.

levels. Rural cultural missions, composed of specialists in public health, agriculture, construction, trades, industries, rural mechanics, music and recreation, focused on the improvement of rural life and foreshadowed the many similar rural programmes developed in other countries two decades later. Serving first as travelling institutes for cultural awakening and the training of practical rural teachers, the missions later became devices for community education. Through these and other educational efforts, Mexico succeeded in bringing its illiteracy rate down to 23 per cent by mid-century, although half the children were still without schools.

Other Latin American countries expanded their primary education—Argentina and Chile building on the base already laid at the opening of the century, Brazil making an effort to provide for the development of its wide territory, and small countries such as Uruguay, Costa Rica, Cuba and Panama gradually reaching a large proportion of their children.

But many obstacles stood in the way of the spread of mass education in a number of the Latin American countries. Political instability hampered the creation and continuous support of educational systems. The upper-class *élite* of landowners, merchants and intelligentsia supported private education for their own children and felt little necessity to assure schooling for all. In countries with large indigenous Indian populations the isolation of these groups and their language differences were additional deterrents. Where education was traditionally the responsibility of the Church, the impetus for state-supported education was often weak. A very strong literary tradition discouraged the development of practical types of training. Extreme poverty presented an ever-present problem.

By mid-century only a little over a half the children of primary school age in the Latin American republics were in school. Five countries—Haiti, Nicaragua, Honduras, Bolivia, Guatemala—reported two-thirds or more of their children out of school, and nine countries still estimated their illiteracy rate at over 50 per cent. Similar factors impeded the spread of mass education in the Iberian peninsula and, prior to the second world war, in southern Italy and some parts of eastern Europe.

In the colonial areas most of the administering powers followed a policy of substantial but limited expansion of educational opportunities, especially in later years as the demand for education mounted with growing self-consciousness. In the territories under British administration the usual pattern was elementary vernacular schools and English-language secondary schools, the latter leading to matriculation examinations for British or local universities. Especially in Africa, schools continued to be conducted largely by missionaries, with financial aid from the colonial government. French colonial education was patterned directly on that of France and produced a small colonial *élite* grounded in French language and culture. Belgium, after a period of almost complete neglect, introduced a programme of technical education in the Belgian Congo, conducted in the French language and designed to equip

Africans to participate at increasingly high levels of skill and responsibility in the industrial development of the area.

The Dutch in Indonesia, while still offering secondary and advanced education to relatively few non-Europeans, embarked on a popular education movement which involved translation into the vernacular of numbers of books and encouragement of literacy education; in addition, nationalist leaders and intellectuals inaugurated 'garden' schools to reach the Javanese people who were virtually without educational services and taught there with little or no pay. In the Philippines under American administration the 'community school' became the centre of social development. The system introduced by the Japanese in Korea was similar to that in Japan but on a more limited scale, and compulsory education was not put into practice. Education of Africans in Portuguese areas was very limited before 1940. Thereafter it was wholly entrusted to the Church, with state aid, while both state-operated and state-aided or supervised schools served the European and 'assimilated' local populations.

In most of these areas, education of an *élite* preceded mass education. The Belgian Congo offered a conspicuous exception, for basic education and practical training were extensively provided there before virtually any opportunity was offered to Congolese to acquire higher education. More typically, Britain followed the colonial policy of training a leadership group, leaving to a later stage the broadening of education among the masses of the people. This policy was clearly expressed at the close of the second world war when the British government, faced with rapidly mounting pressures for self-rule, established or enlarged eight universities in its colonial areas 'to produce men and women who have the standards of public service and capacity for leadership which the progress of self-government demands, and to assist in satisfying the need for persons with the professional qualifications required for the economic and social development of the Colonies'.*

In a number of countries there were special efforts to spread literacy among the adult as well as the child population. The experiments with methods for doing this which attracted widest attention had in common the idea that the spread of literacy cannot depend on the work of formal teachers alone, but must enlist the co-operation of any and every person who can read and write. In China Jimmy Yen inaugurated a literacy programme in the 1920s which used school children to teach groups of adults in after-school hours, and which stimulated group enthusiasm by singing and other activities. A former missionary in the Philippines, Frank Laubach, raised hopes that a short cut to literacy might be found, but his rapid method and programme of 'one teach one' proved superficial and ineffective, and his followers often left discouragement in their wake. The widespread efforts to conquer adult illiteracy made it fully apparent that the task was a complex and difficult one and that success was

---

* *Report of the Commission on Higher Education in the Colonies* (H.M.S.O., June 1945, reprinted 1954), p. 104.

closely linked with continuing use of the new skill; merely teaching people to read did not make them effectively literate.

The decade following the second world war was as revolutionary for education in areas of high illiteracy as the late nineteenth century had been for establishing the principle of universal elementary education in Europe, North America and Japan. For the vast populations of the newly liberated countries of Asia and the Middle East, for Africa and the aspiring peoples of Latin America, education became a magic formula for social reconstruction and for national self-realization.

Pressures for the spread of mass education were intense. Adult franchise, the need for new skills at all levels to achieve economic advance, and the world-wide idea that education was a basic right which every modern state must guarantee to its people, made universal education an inescapable imperative upon the new states. But it presented problems of staggering proportions. With their enormous backlog of illiteracy, with the majority of their children without access to school, and with the population growing by leaps and bounds each year, they had to expand educational facilities rapidly merely to prevent the situation from deteriorating.

The dimensions of the task could be seen in India where, in the decade after independence, the enrolment of primary school pupils virtually doubled, while admissions to technical schools increased fivefold and to engineering training threefold. This meant some fifteen million more primary pupils and an additional fifteen thousand technical students and six or seven thousand engineering candidates for whom teachers, buildings, books and equipment must be provided. But even an average expenditure per child of less than 1 per cent of the amount spent in the United States severely taxed the country's resources.

(b) *Balance between mass education and education of élite.* Even more than in the older democracies, moreover, the new states faced the problem of how much of their educational energy to devote to mass education and how much to the training of an educated *élite*, and how to balance educational efforts so that they would contribute in a sustained way to the total advance of the country. These countries urgently required a well-educated class to man the services and conduct the affairs of the state, and to provide the leadership for the economic and social development which would ultimately bring jobs, incomes and increased well-being for the masses of the people. In addition they had to train technical personnel and to develop men and women who could contribute to scientific advance, for without the capacity for scientific development they could only fall further and further behind as the scientifically advanced countries leapt further ahead.

But the problem of finding and developing professors who could assure high quality to the institutions of higher learning was even more difficult than to find and develop the resources for mass education. Local resources could be supplemented to some extent by personnel from abroad, but one of the chief sources of such personnel in the past, missionary education, became less acceptable. Most countries took steps to facilitate foreign study by promising students, and to make use of opportunities offered by national and international agencies. But these measures could only mitigate, not resolve, the problem of developing the scientific, technical and administrative leadership which they required. Traditional prejudices in favour of legal, literary or philosophical studies in preference to technical fields and ambitions for the career of an official rather than that of a technician further complicated the task of attracting and training personnel of high quality.

Egypt well illustrated the struggle to increase both *élite* and mass education when resources were limited and the need great. Egypt's western-oriented education derived from the institutions established by Mehemet Ali after 1836 to train engineers, doctors and other experts who would put the country on a footing with western powers, and from the fee-charging secondary and primary schools, conducted in French or English, set up to prepare students for these colleges. The education available to the masses consisted of instruction in the Quran and the Arabic language provided free by the mosques. When Egyptians took control of their own domestic affairs in 1923, they looked on education as the road to social reform and devoted increasing percentages of their national budget to improving both mass education and the training of specialists.

Successive Egyptian governments put their emphasis on different phases of the programme: one endeavoured to make available to all children six years of primary education on a level similar to that which had previously been open only to those who could pay the fees of the western-type preparatory schools; another accented the development of leaders and expanded secondary and higher education; still another focused on the creation of technical schools to reduce the pressure on secondary schools with an academic curriculum and to provide minor technicians. Primary school fees were abolished in 1944 and free school lunches and textbooks were also prescribed in the 1949 constitution. In 1951 the Egyptian parliament made primary education compulsory between the ages of 6 and 12.

In order to speed up the spread of schools and reduce costs, educational authorities appealed to notables in the provinces for donations of land and buildings. The number of children receiving primary education in government schools increased four and a half fold from 1925 to 1950 (222,761 to 1,030,486). By the 1950s the government was attempting to expand mass education above the primary level by establishing three-year higher primary schools offering practical studies—rural skills in the villages, industrial and commercial training in the towns—and technical schools at the secondary level for training assistant engineers and other technicians. From 1944 on it sponsored literacy campaigns to bring basic education to adults; landowners, factories, social centres, co-operatives, trade unions and benevolent societies organized classes designed to teach reading and writing, religion, and Egyptian national aims.

At the same time Egypt expanded and strengthened higher education for the training of specialists. In 1925, 8,059 boys and 41 girls were attending government secondary schools; by 1950 there were 80,957 boys and 12,810 girls. The number increased so fast that after 1949 entrance requirements were stiffened and scholarships were provided for able students who could not pay, in the effort to secure the best talent. At the university level the same expansion was in progress. The first university along modern lines, the University of Cairo, was established in 1925; by 1952 there were three modern-type universities with a fourth in the making, serving a total of 33,000 students, double the number enrolled in 1945.

Each country met the problem of balancing mass and *élite* education in its own way. While India was striving to meet its primary school needs, its university enrolments swelled to enormous proportions. It is perhaps an indication of the effort to move forward on both fronts that the ratio between students enrolled in institutions of higher education and those in primary schools in India and Egypt in 1950 was comparable to the ratio in European countries. In spite of their own great needs, both of these countries supplied teachers and technical personnel to other countries of Asia and Africa where the educated element was even less sufficient.

(c) *Fundamental education and community development.* One of the most distinctive developments of the years after the second world war was the approach to mass education of adults which was at first called 'fundamental education'. In contrast to the literacy movements of previous decades, which stressed learning to read for its own sake with little attention to the use which could be made of the new skill, fundamental education regarded literacy as a means rather than an end and concerned itself with vital learning directly related to daily life. The Mexican rural cultural missions furnished one of the models for the development of fundamental education programmes, but many other methods were used to put into effect the basic purpose of enabling people to learn to live better and the basic principle that in spite of a lack of formal education people can learn from materials which have real meaning for them and from experiences in which they are directly engaged.

Greatly stimulated by Unesco, which directed much of its energy toward developing this field, fundamental education brought to the masses of people outside the industrial areas basic modern principles of good health, good nutrition, good agriculture, family living, techniques of work and civic responsibility. Co-operative, self-help and community development activities provided learning experiences through community projects for construction, sanitation, soil conservation or child care. From one side of the world to the other, mass education in the form of fundamental education and community development reached non-literate rural people, modifying the outlook, spirit, health and competence of millions in Asia, Africa and Latin America and helping to canalize newly aroused vitality. Yet in large areas of the world illiteracy remained at mid-century a still unconquered problem.[7]

IV. ADMINISTRATION OF EDUCATIONAL SYSTEMS

1. *Auspices*

Support of mass education and consequently the control over education came more and more into the hands of the state. The trend reflected the expanding concept of the role and responsibility of the state, as well as the very practical consideration that only the state was in a position to finance the expanded educational programme which modern industrial society required. Where the state undertook the positive role of moulding its citizens, especially in countries involved in revolutionary change, education offered a major instrument to achieve defined objectives. In nearly all countries the extension of education by the state was seen as the fulfilment by the government of a responsibility which it owed to its citizens.

Countries differed considerably in the extent to which state-supported schools were administered directly by public agencies—either a central or a local authority—or were conducted by non-governmental agencies with support and a measure of supervision from the state. France maintained a highly centralized system in which every state school followed the schedule, syllabus and other details laid down in the state plan. The pattern in most democratic countries, however, tended to be one of administration either by a local public authority or by non-governmental bodies.

British local educational authorities had primary responsibility for administering the schools, within a general framework of school structure and advisory standards of teacher pay set by the central government. General education in the United States was the responsibility of local school districts acting through elected school boards, with the states setting standards and furnishing financial and technical aid and the central government providing only advisory services or assistance to special categories of students such as war veterans or to special programmes such as vocational and agricultural training. In the Netherlands the policy of leaving confessional or other groups free to conduct their own schools produced a system under which nearly two-thirds of the educational funds spent by the state for general education went to support schools which were privately administered and subject only to government inspection in respect to buildings, equipment, training of teachers and curriculum, and to government-administered examinations for government-conferred diplomas. Where privately supported schools maintained a separate existence without financial aid from the government, as in the United States, the mounting costs of education tended to make their position precarious.

The extension of state control in virtually every educational system did not go unchallenged. Religious bodies continued to regard education as their function and to assert the priority of their responsibilities *vis-à-vis* the state; the Catholic Church fought in every country which contained a Catholic population for the maximum authority over education which it was able to achieve.

In the first quarter of the twentieth century the general tendency toward secularization and the extension of state power and responsibility seemed to mark a trend away from religiously controlled education but, except in communist countries, the Church gained in influence over education in the second quarter of the century. After the second world war it made a determined bid for the restoration of public aid to religious schools, and succeeded in making the matter a live political issue in France and Belgium and in gaining concessions in the form of state funds for school health or school bus services even in the United States where the principle of separation of church and state was most strongly entrenched. In multi-religious societies such as Canada, the United States or the Netherlands the presence of religiously dominated education, with or without state support, tended to divide the society and to counteract the effect of the public schools as a 'melting pot' for the children of different backgrounds.

Religious control of education was an issue not only in the areas where the Catholic Church, and to a much lesser extent some of the Protestant denominations, asserted prerogatives, but in Muslim and Buddhist countries in relation to the schools maintained by the mosques and by the Buddhist monks. Since neither mosques nor Buddhist monasteries were in a position to provide the mass education required, however, and since they had traditionally taught only boys, they tended to become peripheral to a general system of state education.

2. *Financing*

Education became constantly more costly and harder to finance. As standards rose it was no longer sufficient to provide a poorly paid teacher in a bare room with only a blackboard, slates and a handful of books in order to have a school. The cost per child rose with the longer period of schooling, more individualized instruction and more elaborate equipment required by newer content and methods. For the total educational system, costs mounted through the increase in the number educated, the need for better prepared and therefore better paid teachers, rising standards of adequacy for buildings and equipment to keep pace with general technological change and standards of life, and the addition of services such as school health and feeding not formerly included within the scope of education. Where schools were consolidated into larger units in order to permit a wider range of educational offerings and more extensive equipment, costs of transport to and from school were also added.

In a few places elementary education continued to be financed by the parents of those who could pay and offered as charity to the poor. Religious schools were maintained by the various religious orders dedicated to teaching, with contributions from parents and other members of the parish or from donors to missionary efforts. But as school attendance was made compulsory, state financing of elementary education became general, for all except those who chose to avail themselves of private educational resources in preference to public. Where the financing of education depended on local resources, however, the poorer communities, even with greater than average effort, could offer to their children less adequate educational opportunities than those enjoyed in richer localities.

Before the first world war secondary and higher education in most countries was generally supported by fees and private endowments, supplemented by scholarships to permit able students to continue their education beyond the limits set by their family's means. In the United States, however, the publicly supported secondary schools and universities were providing education without charge to a growing proportion of the population.

After the first world war the problem of how to finance education became acute. The spread of secondary education required a more than proportionate increase in the investment of tax funds or private resources, for the need to provide more laboratory and library equipment and to pay higher salaries to teachers usually made secondary education more costly per pupil than primary. Where secondary as well as primary education came to be publicly financed, education became one of the largest items in the budgets of educationally advanced countries. Central governments were called upon to supplement the resources of poorer communities in order that children in those places should not be disadvantaged by the inability of the locality to afford the kind of education to which all parts of the country aspired. The issue of public support for religiously administered schools was intensified as the costs of providing education increased.

In virtually all countries after the second world war population increase placed additional strains on educational resources, both in the countries of relatively low birth rates where a sharp upturn in births brought unexpected millions to the school doors and in those whose rapidly increasing child population reflected increased rates of survival. Education had to compete with other items in the budget for national and local funds—with expenditures for physical or economic development, for the protection of health and safety, for social services and for military establishments.

3. *Supply and training of teachers*

The rapid increase in the volume of education outran the supply of teachers, both in countries which already had mass education at the opening of the century and those which were trying to achieve universal elementary education at mid-century. In addition the alternative opportunities for employment in expanding industry and government made it difficult in many places to hold teachers in the profession or to attract able people who could secure higher salaries in other lines of work. As a practical matter, throughout most of the world primary teachers were paid on about the level of unskilled workers, secondary teachers that of skilled workers, and university teachers no more than junior executives. In many countries it was particularly difficult to secure qualified teachers for rural areas because of low pay and lack of amenities in rural communities.

At the same time that additional teachers were needed and alternative employment opportunities were making recruitment difficult, the qualifications for teachers increased, making it harder to train an adequate supply. In teacher training institutions the trend was toward raising the professional level and expanding the content of training, because teachers required greater competence in order to cope with the wide range of new materials introduced into the school curriculum and to apply new knowledge of child behaviour and the learning process in skilful teaching.

Where the supply of teachers had to be expanded more rapidly than was possible through regular methods of teacher training, countries resorted to a variety of improvisations in order to meet immediate needs while preparing a more solid basis in teacher training for the future.

The Turkish programme for rural teachers offered an example of such improvisation. With schools in only about a tenth of its villages at the time of the Ataturk revolution, Turkey needed some 40,000 new teachers but was adding only about 400 a year through its regular normal schools. Since the success of its social revolution obviously depended upon bringing educational opportunities to the 75 per cent of the population which lived in villages, the Turkish government in 1936 evolved a scheme for using *eğitmen* to spread schools rapidly to rural areas.

Eğitmen were drawn from among peasants, usually with a primary education, who had distinguished themselves during their military service and had risen to the rank of sergeant. They were given an intensive eight-month course, taught by former village teachers and instructors from the School of Agriculture, to consolidate their knowledge of reading, writing and arithmetic and to give them some idea of history, geography, the sciences and teaching methods, together with theoretical and practical lessons in agriculture and building. Each *eğitman* was sent to a village of less than 400 population to teach a three-year primary school and also to help adult villagers with agricultural and building problems. He was supplied with a house, a strip of land, grain, machines, a loom and medicines and directed to teach by example as well as in classes and village meetings. By the use of *eğitmen* as a temporary expedient, the number of children in primary schools was doubled in ten years.

As a second step the Turks established rural institutes, set up like villages, for the general and practical training of rural teachers. In a five-year course, village young people with primary schooling were trained not only to teach in the classroom but to build their school, take care of its garden and its arable land as examples to the villagers, make the school's workshop of use to people of the village, direct the general education of the children and instruct them in health education, and to participate in various agricultural, artistic and technical projects designed to raise the economic and cultural level of the community. By 1952, 21 village institutes were training about 2,000 teachers a year to replace the *eğitmen* and extend the basic primary course to five years, and 55 per cent of rural children were attending primary school. After 1943 the institutes and the university offered an advanced three-year course to train inspectors whose duty it was to help rural teachers to keep in touch with new educational developments.

Since the greatest deficiencies in education were in rural areas, many countries concentrated especially on this aspect of teacher recruitment and training. Some followed the principle used in Turkey of recruiting rural young people who, it was hoped, would be willing to continue to work outside the cities. Egypt launched a programme of centres for rural services, including education, with adequate housing and other amenities and a large enough group of professional workers in various fields to provide some of the qualities of living found in the towns. The Organization of American States made an inter-American rural normal school, located in Venezuela, its major form of technical assistance in the field of education in the 1950s.

Institutions and methods for the training of teachers paralleled the development of the systems in which they were to operate. The tendencies toward democratization of education were reflected in steps to raise elementary school teaching to the level of a profession and in some efforts to break the closed circle of normal school training which prepared the products of elementary schools to teach in the elementary systems, while secondary schools were manned by university graduates. In some countries, such teacher training institutions were raised to higher levels, while some colleges and universities introduced courses to equip their students as teachers for the elementary schools.

At the beginning of the century the principal content of teacher training related to what to teach rather than how to teach. The development of educational theory and methodology brought a new emphasis on training teachers to understand the child and to design learning situations which would be in line with what was known of the process of learning. The specialized training institutions for primary teachers undertook to equip them with pedagogical methods, and to supplement the knowledge of subject matter which they had derived from their general schooling.

Teachers in secondary schools and technical institutions had been expected to be able to perform adequately if they had a command of their subject matter and in many places, notably in Latin America, this assumption continued. As pedagogical theories and techniques were elaborated, however, these were no longer thought important for elementary school teaching only, and special pedagogical training began to be given to secondary and technical teachers also. Where the shortage of teachers persisted, however—and it was widespread in the years of high general employment and expanding secondary and higher education after the second world war—the specialized training of teachers was hampered and teachers were often employed on the basis of emergency training or preparation below the standard which had been set.

The status enjoyed by the teacher had an important bearing on the successful performance of his duties and on the recruitment of people to the profession. Somewhat contradictory tendencies were to be noted in most countries in the first half of the twentieth century. On the one hand there was a trend toward giving greater professional status to the occupation of teacher, through higher qualifications and specialized training and through raising the level of teacher pay. On the other hand, as societies became more mobile and open, the teacher no longer enjoyed the prestige which had been his in a stratified society with few professions. Rising living costs which tended to mount faster than teachers' pay made it increasingly difficult for teachers to maintain the style of living which their position demanded, while industrial wages and salaries in other fields rose more rapidly and offered attractive alternatives in employment. In the United States, for example, the rapidly rising level of average manufacturing wages crossed the line of slowly rising teacher salaries in 1941 and the disparity continued to increase in the following years. In some fields, such as science and mathematics, the higher prestige of alternative occupations, along with higher salaries, accentuated the crisis in teacher recruitment.

The need for good teachers was the most pervasive of all problems in the school systems throughout the world.

V. CHANGING CONTENT AND METHOD OF EDUCATION

Along with increased schooling for more and more people went changes in the content and method of instruction. These changes involved: modernizing the curriculum to incorporate new bodies of knowledge or to direct education toward aspects of the modern world rather than the classical tradition of the area—Greek and Latin in the West, Arabic, Sanskrit or Chinese in their respective cultures; providing technical competence required by modern society; meeting the range of interest and capacities represented in a cross-section of the population; applying the results of pedagogical study and of psychological knowledge and theory as to individual growth and development; and carrying out the purposes of the state.

1. *Modernization of curriculum*

In the early years of the century European classical secondary education began to be supplemented by modern subjects, that is, by more study of modern languages and science and some social studies. The highly centralized French system, in which courses for each grade were prescribed, began to provide a course for 'modern' municipal secondary schools (*collèges*). In time the number of such modern schools grew, and modern content was introduced into the so-called 'classical' schools until by mid-century 40 per cent of the secondary schools were classed as 'modern'; the distinction had lost importance, however, for both classical and modern curricula were generally offered in both classical and modern schools.

Holland established modern high schools alongside the classical gymnasia, as did Germany also. After 1917, when the Dutch high school diploma was made a basis for taking university examinations, gymnasium and high school programmes overlapped. The classical gymnasium diploma was required for admission to the faculties of theology, literature and philosophy and the non-classical and non-scientific high school diploma gave access only to the faculties of economics or social science. But both the gymnasium and the high school offered a modern diploma admitting to the faculties of medicine, mathematics and physics, as well as law, economics and political and social sciences.

In other European countries traditional classical subjects were similarly supplemented or replaced by modern languages and literature, science and social studies. The trend was even more marked in the United States, where classical studies were crowded further and further aside both at the secondary and at the university level. By the 1940s few American universities still required a classical language for admission or for receiving a degree.

Outside the western culture area, modernization of education meant westernization as distinguished from such classical systems as the Chinese, Hindu or Muslim. The content of westernized education, however, generally followed the traditional academic lines of education in the metropolitan area. Schools in French-dominated territories received the same syllabuses from the ministry of education as those in France. Elsewhere schools designed to make it possible for students to attend metropolitan universities had to offer the classical subjects required for admission. The educational systems of independent non-western countries gradually developed curricula which combined the mathematics, science, modern languages and history characterstic of modern western schools with some traditional local elements, adapted to the current interests and needs of their people.

2. Introduction of technical and vocational content

The incorporation of technical, vocational and other practical content brought a more radical departure from tradition than did modernization. Germany led the way in the nineteenth century with the establishment of special technical schools at post-primary and higher levels. Some countries such as Holland developed a great range of special technical schools at elementary and secondary levels for many different fields: wood and metal trades, fishing and navigation, agriculture, commerce, fine and industrial arts, home economics, midwifery. Others such as the United States included a wider and wider range of technical and vocational material in the programme of the general school. Britain's educational reorganization after 1944 attempted to place technical secondary education on a par with general secondary education and academic grammar school training.

The rapidity of technological change complicated the problem of technical education. Although the number of occupations and professions requiring specialized training multiplied, techniques and skills learned in school were likely to become obsolete by the time that the child was ready to use them, or might cease to be useful in the course of his working life. While the schools were under strong pressure to teach techniques, educators agreed that what the modern urban child needed was a basic understanding of scientific principles, adaptability and the capacity to learn new ways and to respond to change. The introduction of an increasing number of technical subjects into general education was thus balanced by the tendency to make technical training more basic and less a matter of specific skills.

The inclusion of vocational content raised a question as to the purpose of education which divided the opinion of educators; was it the task of general education to provide the community with trained personnel and to equip children to earn a living when they became adult, or was its function to pass on the cultural heritage and to develop the individual's personality, capacity for growth, and social adjustment? Especially in the United States where the line between general and vocational education was less clearly drawn than in Europe, grave concern was expressed lest the educational system produce only competent technicians, not individually developed and socially aware personalities. In the USSR, on the other hand, practical training and experience in productive activity was regarded as essential to the aims of Soviet education, 'to develop versatile, active and conscious builders of a communist society.'*

3. *Adaptation of content to changes in student body*

As secondary education reached a wider segment of the population, its content had to be enlarged to correspond to the varied capacities, interests and objectives of the pupils. The concept of secondary education for all imposed on the schools a far more complex task than that confronted by schools which served a limited group selected on the basis of social status or intellectual level. Since all adolescents could not be expected to have intense intellectual interests, mass secondary education was virtually forced to include a broad range of subject matter. The presence of a majority of essentially non-intellectual pupils in the school population, moreover, tended to tip the scales in favour of the more practical subjects.

Some school systems met this situation by adjusting the whole programme to a cross-section of the school population, allowing room for flexibility and choice within it, as was usually the case in the United States. Others tried to provide separate programmes for distinct groups, divided according to capacity and interest. The British, after 1944, tried to select the intellectually inclined children on the basis of tests, school performance and interest and route them into grammar schools or grammar school courses in combined schools, preparatory for the university. Children who showed a mechanical bent or technical interest were routed into technical schools or courses. The majority of children were provided for in secondary modern schools in which the

---

* M. Deineko, *Forty Years of Public Education in the USSR* (Foreign Language Publishing House, Moscow, 1957), p. 8.

attempt was made to combine academic and practical subjects and to adapt programmes and methods to the variety of needs, interests and capacities of the students. In Holland, the problem of student diversity was met through the system of specialized technical institutions.

Within the various systems educational and vocational counselling was provided to help the individual choose from among the offerings in the light of his interests and talents and the likely opportunities for employment. Aptitude and personality tests were developed to help to give a basis for such counsel and to supplement the evidence from the child's performance in the classroom. Schools recognized, too, a responsibility to equip all students with social knowledge, regardless of their special field of training. The social content of all courses tended to be expanded to include psychology, human relations, social institutions, modern history and some knowledge of economics and government.

The extension of education to women raised the question of whether the content should be the same for them as for men. At the elementary level the tendency was to place boys and girls together in the same school with a common body of studies, although some separate schools for boys and girls continued, especially in Muslim and Roman Catholic areas. Even at the elementary level, however, schools which introduced practical activities and physical education had to resolve the question of whether girls should be taught to sew and cook while boys learned to handle tools and whether their physical training should be the same. At the secondary level the problem was sharpened by the inclusion of vocational subjects and material relating to daily life, such as home economics and child care. In school systems where variety and flexibility of courses was provided to meet the needs of a range of students, as in the high schools in the United States, such flexibility made it possible to offer subjects of special interest to boys or girls without excluding either from courses where the other sex predominated.

Universities followed the path of the secondary schools, expanding their fields of study in response to the increase in the number of students receiving university education, to the development of new areas of knowledge, and to the multiplication of professional fields requiring higher education. The traditional European university consisted of faculties of theology, law, medicine, philosophy and letters, and the natural sciences. British universities offered degrees in classics, law, modern history and literature, medicine and the sciences. American universities contained four-year liberal arts colleges with departments corresponding to each field of knowledge, plus graduate schools offering advanced degrees in these fields and professional schools for medicine, law, engineering and other professions. As subject matter was enlarged, European universities added new departments or whole faculties, such as psychology, sociology, economics, political and social science or engineering. British universities offered degree examinations in additional fields, and American universities established new departments both in academic areas and in applied fields such as home economics, business administration or public health. In addition separate technical universities or institutes specializing in the newer fields were set up in many countries.

The character of the university student body also changed and, like that of the secondary school, began to reflect the total society. Students who came from educationally limited homes often did not bring to their university study the richness of cultural background which had been the common property of former student bodies. Partly for this reason there was a tendency to broaden the liberal content in the education of engineers, lawyers, doctors or scientists, who would be called on to use their professional knowledge and influence in a social and cultural context which they needed to understand. As the number of women enrolled increased, they showed some tendency to concentrate in certain courses, but they were not excluded from less usual areas such as engineering, and a few women entered these fields even in places such as the Muslim or Latin American countries where the participation of women in many aspects of public life and employment was recent and limited.

At both secondary and university levels the diversification of content to suit a cross-section of the population and the need to reach average students as well as those of exceptional ability presented the problem of how to prevent the presence of large numbers of heterogeneous students from so diluting the quality of instruction as to keep the able few from developing their highest capacities.

Efforts to resolve the problem took various forms: special schools or classes, 'A-streams' for gifted children, acceleration of the best students through the system, the individualizing of instruction within a common classroom or school in such a way as to enrich the programme of the able student without setting him apart. Each of these approaches had its supporters and detractors. Some educators thought it desirable to separate intellectually superior children from the mediocrity and the distraction of their fellows and group them for mutual stimulation, while others insisted that segregation bred snobbery. Some wanted to encourage the bright child to go forward at his intellectual pace, but others objected that acceleration pushed the child beyond his social maturity. Some maintained that flexible, individualized teaching could bring out the child's full intellectual potentialities without sacrificing his democratic social development.

The immense variety of subject matter offered to students, moreover, presented what might be termed the problem of 'half-knowing'. Mass education exposed large numbers of people to a wide range of knowledge, but it could provide them with only a very partial and limited command of it. The proliferation of specialized fields virtually precluded the kind of integrated and comprehensive grasp to which intellectuals of the past had aspired. One of the most challenging problems brought by mass education was how to live with and interrelate fragmentary parts of the world's vast, increasingly complex body of knowledge.

4. *Development and application of pedagogical principles*

Changes in both content and method were dictated by developments in pedagogical principles and by the results of scientific study in fields related to learning.

Twentieth-century pedagogy followed the broad line of development marked out by the pedagogical pioneers of the nineteenth century—attention to the child as a learner. In the phrase familiar to all readers of text-books or treatises on pedagogy, the verb 'to teach' governs two accusatives: the subject matter, and the person taught. Following the lead of such influential writers and experimenters of the late eighteenth and the nineteenth century as Johann Heinrich Pestalozzi, Friedrich Froebel and Johann Friedrich Herbart, twentieth-century educators focused their attention on the second of these, the person taught. They brought to bear increasingly refined techniques of observation and tools of theoretical analysis in their efforts to understand the child's growth and development and the elements which enter into the learning process.

Some of the significant developments in educational method in these years grew out of work with handicapped children, for the attempt to meet the special needs of these groups led to an appreciation of the needs of normal children. This was true of the work of Maria Montessori who began her teaching with sub-normal children in Rome in 1898. She insisted that the child must be free to learn for himself, and she designed teaching materials from which the child could learn, with a minimum of interference, if he followed the activity which interested him. The principles of her system were widely adopted in many countries of Europe, especially for children of kindergarten age. The Belgian educator, Ovide Decroly (1871–1932) also developed his educational principles from his work with mentally defective children. He, too, built his educational method around the child's own interest, and sought to design learning opportunities and to identify centres of interest which could be pursued actively and practically in an informal atmosphere, and which were suited to the needs of the child at successive ages and to the differing needs of individuals.

The most pervasive principle of twentieth-century education, which affected methods within many different systems, was that education is not something apart from life but is, rather, life itself. Closely related to this principle, though resting on an independent psychological base, was the idea that learning is a total process, not merely something that goes on in the mind, and that learning by doing, or to satisfy an aroused curiosity, has more dimensions and a more enduring meaning for the learner than merely learning about something which he may use later in life.

The leading exponent of this view, probably the most widely influential educational thinker of the period, was the American pragmatic philosopher and educator, John Dewey. Dewey insisted that education is life, not merely a preparation for life, and that as long as growth continues education continues. The school in a democratic society—and he predicated his thinking on the principles of such a society—must itself be a democratic community where children may gain social experience. The modern child will continuously face new situations and problems throughout his life, and must therefore develop a problem-solving way of thinking. Believing deeply in human potentialities and the possibilities of human development, Dewey maintained that education must preserve and enhance the child's creativity, for as he grows he must select and reorganize his cultural heritage, recasting it to suit his needs in an ever-changing world.

The educational principles enunciated by Dewey were most congenial in countries such as his own United States which had a tradition of democracy and of continuous social change and which accorded high value to action as compared to thought or contemplation. But they made some inroads in most parts of the world, even where, as in Latin America, intellectualism was traditionally regarded as superior to practical sense, or in imperial Japan where society was highly structured and authoritarian.

Similar pedagogical theories which stressed the creativity, freedom and activity of the child, and which came to be known as 'progressive' or 'new' education, were developed by educators in other countries in the first quarter of the century, and these reinforced tendencies set in motion by Dewey and his followers. The Swiss educator Adolphe Ferrière sought to put the movement for 'activity' schools on an international basis by establishing the International Bureau of New Schools at Geneva in 1899. Bertrand Russell in England, with his concept of *Education and the Good Life* (1926), stressed the development of qualities of courage, vitality and sensitiveness, as well as intelligence, through a school in which the child could actively practise self-expression, engage in co-operative activities and take part in free discussion.

Such German educators as Berthold Otto (1859–1933) and Ludwig Gurlitt (1855–1931) rejected the formalism, coercion and standardization traditional in German education and sought to provide activity to stimulate the child's curiosity, as well as to introduce self-government into the school. The Viennese art teacher Franz Čižek demonstrated in his work with gifted children how the child's natural powers could be released through creative expression. His success reinforced the tendency to substitute the child's free expression for the teaching of formal techniques. Stanislas Shatsky (1878–1934) in the USSR converted the idea of activity for its own sake into the concept of socially useful labour and he stressed the relationship of the total and integral development of the child to the requirements of the society of which he is a part. Even within the centralized and formal system of French education, some experimentation was carried on under the stimulus of the New Education Society, organized in 1921 by Roger Cousinet to promote progressive education in France.

The wide spread of these pedagogical principles was reflected in the establishment of 'child-centred' experimental schools. Educational experimentation was of course not new, and the well-rounded personality had been familiar as an educational objective from the time of the Renaissance. The distinguishing feature of the experimental schools of this period, however, was the application to an unselected school population of the concept of the total development of the child, not merely of his intellect, the individualizing of each pupil, and the effort to develop his creative ability and emotional maturity through activity programmes carried out with a minimum of formal discipline.

The methods of progressive education and the principles ascribed to John Dewey, Maria Montessori and others, like any system, were subject to abuse in the hands of those who understood them only imperfectly or lacked the necessary skill to put them into practice. Some critics in fact insisted that these methods required exceptional qualities of sensitivity and creativity on the part of the teacher which the majority of teachers could not be expected to possess, and as such they were impracticable for application on any large scale. These critics insisted, too, that it was too much to expect of most children that they would be motivated by inner drives and interest, without such external stimuli as formal grades, competitive achievement, rewards for excellence and blame for failure. The inexpert application of these principles in fact frequently brought the whole idea of progressive education under attack on the score that it discarded discipline, it looked for creativity in the child without giving him anything to be creative about, produced people who could only work if they were interested and gave students fragmentary rather than systematic bodies of knowledge.

There were counter-movements to 'get back to fundamentals' in the course of these years, but the leaven of the ideas and principles of school reform worked at least to modify educational methods, where they did not revolutionize them. Health and physical education, work and manual activity, music and the arts to stimulate and release the child's creativity, and social experience and study to develop his social maturity all became widely accepted as appropriate and essential features of the modern school. Initially this reorienting of education was principally applied to very young children, but in time it was extended to older children and adolescents and entered into the planning and thinking of entire school systems in many countries.

Closely akin to progressive education, but distinct in its origin, emphasis and certain aspects of its method, was the system of 'basic education' developed in India by Rabindranath Tagore and Mahatma Gandhi. Their educational principles were formulated in response to the conditions of their country where extreme poverty was pervasive and where manual work was held in low esteem by the educated classes or was associated with low status in the caste hierarchy. Both Tagore and Gandhi broke through the barrier between education and labour; they sought to dignify manual labour and to make it a basis for the training of hand and mind and for the regeneration of Indian society. Toward this end they gave central place to the learning of a craft.

In Gandhi's formulation, a handcraft, taught in such a way as to stimulate and enrich the mind as well as to discipline the hand, offers a means of teaching many subjects—mathematics, geography, general science, language—and at the same time it enables the student to engage in useful, productive work. To him, activity itself was not enough; it should be useful activity. The craft must be learned and performed efficiently, to create habits of efficiency and to develop self-reliance and self-respect. He thought, moreover, that by engaging in useful work, students could make their school at least partially self-supporting—an attractive idea in a poor community desperately pressed for the resources to provide general education for all its children.

The specific crafts which Gandhi introduced were spinning and gardening, selected because they were related to the basic human needs of clothing and food and because they required a minimum of costly equipment and supplies. In addition, spinning directly symbolized Gandhi's campaign to free India from dependence on British manufacture. His principles were applicable, however, through any craft which met the criteria of social usefulness. Although it was clear to Indian educators that Gandhi's emphasis on crafts was as much political as pedagogical, that the scope of what could be imparted through craft training was limited and that the effort to make the school pay its way threatened to turn it into a child labour centre, some of the activity principles developed by Gandhi were incorporated into the basic educational system of India.

Soviet education, in its initial phase following the October revolution, drew ideas from progressive education and sought to adapt them to socialist objectives. After the early years of experimentation, however, it was guided by distinct pedagogical principles of its own, within the framework of Marxist-Leninist ideology. A number of teachers and public figures contributed to the development of Soviet pedagogy, among them N. K. Krupskaya, M. I. Kalinin and F. E. Dzerzhinsky. One of the chief formulators was A. S. Makarenko (1888–1939) who tested his ideas in the colonies of homeless children which he directed from 1920 to 1934. He considered the most important pedagogical principle to be 'how to combine with the most exacting demands upon the pupil the utmost respect for his personality'.* He rejected the theory of 'free' education as leading to laxity, lack of initiative and the inability to meet difficulties, and he discarded the use of intelligence tests and other procedures which assumed or implied that the child's personality was predetermined by heredity or a fixed environment.

According to his biographer, 'His entire pedagogical system is imbued with Bolshevik confidence in man's vast potentialities, with great optimism, and faith in the creative powers of people organized in a collective'. He

---

* A. S. Makarenko, *Road to Life* (Moscow, 1951), p. x.

thought that man must have something joyful ahead of him to live for, which meant, in pedagogical terms, that 'in the first place, the joy itself has to be organized, brought to life and converted into a possibility. Next, primitive sources of satisfaction must be steadily converted into more complex and humanly significant joys'.* He considered the collective to have great educative power and elaborated in detail the manner of using it educationally. He set great store by the effect on the student of engaging in socially useful work, and developed in his own institutions a combination of schooling with productive labour, designed to develop the total child through mental, character, physical and aesthetic education and polytechnical instruction.

The principles formulated by Makarenko were incorporated into the Soviet educational system in the years following the inauguration of the first five-year plan. They were reflected in the exacting demands placed upon students, the system of rewards, the group stimulus to individual achievement, and the combination of schooling with socially useful labour, the effort to maintain a buoyant atmosphere, and the integration of physical, aesthetic and vocational training with other aspects of general education.[8]

Standing firmly against all these modern secular trends represented by progressive education, Gandhian principles, Soviet pedagogy and other forms of experimentation was the system of Catholic education, which remained unshaken in its principles though it might adjust its methods in detail.

Catholic pedagogy rested squarely on Catholic doctrine: on the concept of the dual nature of man, both natural and supernatural, the fall of Adam which deprived man of his supernatural life, man's redemption through Christ, the mission of the Church and of Christian education to enable man to realize his supernatural destiny. The unchanging objective of Catholic education, as stated in the papal encyclical on *Christian Education of Youth* (1929), was 'to co-operate with divine grace in forming the true and perfect Christian . . . the supernatural man who thinks, judges, and acts constantly and consistently in accordance with right reason illumined by the supernatural light of the example and teaching of Christ. . . . It must never be forgotten that the subject of Christian education is man whole and entire, soul united to body in unity of nature, with all his faculties, natural and supernatural . . . . Since education consists essentially in preparing man for what he must be and for what he must do here below, in order to attain the sublime end for which he was created, it is clear that there can be no true education which is not wholly directed to man's last end. . . .'

The enduring principles of Catholic education did not imply specific methods, and there was considerable range in those employed. Though teaching orders like the Jesuits continued to apply their well-developed teaching techniques, some Catholic schools adopted devices, such as the project method, associated with other types of education. The distinguishing feature of Catholic education was that it kept spiritual values always to the fore. It

* Y. Medinsky, Introduction to *Road to Life, op. cit.* pp. xvi, xvii.

insisted that no education could exclude the religious factor, and that secular schools could give only an incomplete and distorted form of education from which the most important aspect, the religious, was missing. It was this insistence on 'man whole and entire' and on man's supernatural end which made the Church hold tenaciously to the proposition that the education of its children could be in no other hands.

5. *Application of new psychological insights*

The development of educational methods was affected during these years by developments in the field of psychology, especially as these related to the processes of learning and to the nature of human growth and development.*

Before the turn of the century, mounting interest in the psychology of the child had led to the founding of child study associations in Great Britain, Germany and France and the introduction of courses in child psychology into some university departments. In the years before the first world war efforts to devise means of differentiating children according to their innate capacity, notably the so-called intelligence tests developed by Alfred Binet in France and carried forward by E. L. Thorndike in the United States, laid the foundation for a scientifically oriented approach to individual differences. Psychologists were first appointed to the staffs of school authorities in London in 1913 and Los Angeles, in the United States, in 1912. Their initial function was to differentiate the children of subnormal intelligence who were unable to profit from the regular school programme. In time their role expanded with the elaboration of testing techniques to detect differences in aptitude, personality characteristics and emotional balance and development.

Better diagnosis of the child's needs and capacities provided a basis for directing his education more effectively. Most of the tests, however, were developed in western culture areas and for urban children. Although they were variously adapted and efforts were made to design tests which would be as independent of cultural factors as possible, they remained inadequate for determining the 'intelligence', aptitudes, potentialities and emotional adjustment of rural and of non-western children.

The issue of how far education itself, or other experience, could modify what were assumed to be innate capacities also remained unresolved. Substantial evidence, however, accumulated in the fields of nutrition, infant care, public health and mental illness, indicated that the child's ability to respond to education might be severely reduced by deficiencies in his nutritional status, by emotional deprivation in infancy or by poor physical or mental health, and that improvement in these respects might, conversely, increase his educability; 'nature' to some extent appeared to depend on 'nurture'. •

The growth of experimental psychology, with its emphasis on stimulus and response, perception, association and conditioning, revealed some of the

* See Chapter XVI, The Scientific Approach to Human Behaviour and Human Relations, and Chapter XVII, The Home.

components of the learning process. *Gestalt* psychology stressed the point that new facts or ideas are not grasped in a vacuum but as part of a total concept in the mind of the individual into which each new observation is incorporated. These findings called into question the old pattern of rote learning without reference to a structure of ideas and the assumption that something learned in one context would necessarily be remembered or even recognized in another context.

Through developments in the field of psychiatry, educators also became aware of the emotional element in learning and of the consequent need to be concerned with the child's readiness to absorb material, his motivation for learning and the emotional factors which might block his ability to understand. As it became apparent that the individual must be positively involved in the learning process and not merely a passive vessel into which knowledge is poured, a psychological basis was provided for learning by doing as an educational method and for relating learning opportunities to the child's aroused interest. Greater emphasis was placed on adjustment in early childhood, with a resultant growth of the nursery-school movement. For the mounting proportion of young people who went through the emotionally difficult period of adolescence at school rather than at work, schools sought to design programmes which would help them grow to maturity.

Understanding of social factors, particularly of the role of culture in shaping personality, provided an additional basis for interpreting the child's behaviour and gearing education to his needs. The school had to recognize and deal with the child's social maladjustment as well as with his mental retardation or physical malnutrition. It had to distinguish when a child was deviating individually from his group norms and when his behaviour was that of a conformist to norms which might be at variance with those of school, home or other elements in the community. The modern school recognized that so-called 'behaviour problems' might be reflections of social conflict in the community, or the child's effort to deal with situations beyond his scope, or symptoms of personality disorders. Child guidance services, at first primarily associated with juvenile courts, were gradually extended into the schools and teachers were trained to recognize early symptoms of emotional maladjustment and to refer the child for specialized help. The child who was failing in his school work was studied to determine the reasons for his failure; he was not simply punished, kept back or otherwise disciplined in the effort to force him to learn, but was treated with whatever resources the school and community could provide.

Rapid social change often produced a disparity between the knowledge and values of the school and the home, and the school was forced to seek methods to enable the child to handle such disparities as he might encounter. This was a major undertaking in countries where the school population consisted of the children of immigrants from many lands, in those with a complex of shifting class and value systems, in the rapidly developing countries where schools

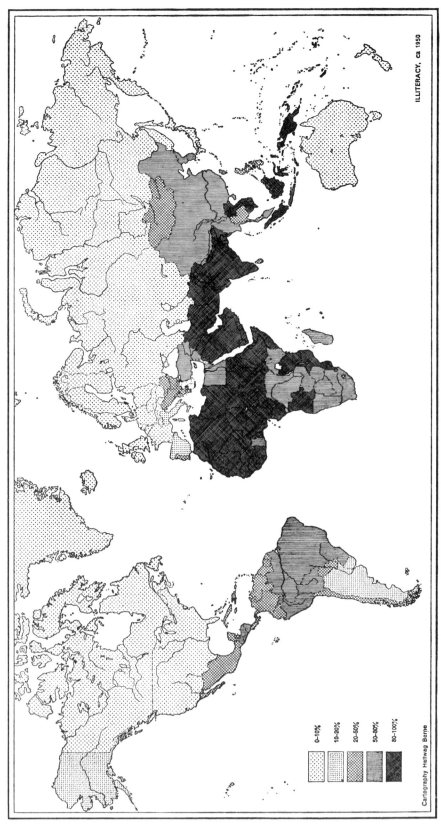

ILLITERACY, ca 1950

Illiteracy c. 1950

0-10%
10-20%
20-50%
50-80%
80-100%

Cartography Hallwag Berne

were instruments of radical social change, and in the urban settings where a constant stream of rural–urban migrants were experiencing a transformation of their lives. Schools organized programmes of parent education and encouraged parent-teacher associations or parents' councils in the effort to bring school and home closer together in their education of the child. The Unesco study, *Education and Mental Health* (Paris, 1955), concluded that the school's methods must sustain the child's relation to the home while helping the home to move in the direction in which the child is developing, and at the same time they must enable the child to cope with difference and conflict in the complex society of which he is a part.

New insights into the processes of learning were applied to the teaching of special skills, notably reading and the fundamental operations of mathematics, although there was sharp and continuing disagreement over method. Experiments with the use of audio and visual materials were designed to permit greater effectiveness of educational effort.

Needs of special types of pupils were also recognized. Special methods were devised and classes established for retarded children in larger schools or for groups of schools, and for children with defective sight, hearing and severe health handicaps. The European educators who reviewed the need for such special provisions in 1952 concluded that, on the basis of the most conservative estimates, 'it seems likely that no less than one child in five or six needs some kind of special educational or psychological help if he is to stand a fair chance of satisfactory and happy growth and if he is not to act as a brake upon other children in the normal class'*. They found that children with some types of special needs were recognized in most countries but that provisions for them were rarely adequate and that children with other kinds of problems were often overlooked.

6. *Use of new technology*

Educational methods were also affected by technical developments. The gramophone, motion picture, tape recorder, radio and television served as educational equipment, along with blackboards, pencils, desks and books. The new media offered great possibilities for enlarging the student's experiences beyond that which the teacher or the library could make vivid, and they could bring the best music into the classroom. Recording devices let the student of foreign language hear his own pronunciation. Closed circuit television enabled a particularly effective teacher, or a special demonstration, to reach many classrooms simultaneously. While none of the mass communication media could take the place of direct contact between teacher and pupil, they greatly extended the teacher's resources and scope.

Schools were slow to take advantage of these media, which did not fit immediately into the classroom pattern of instruction; but their use became progressively more widespread. In part, schools adopted mass communication

* *Education and Mental Health, op. cit.*, p. 249.

techniques for economy; in part they did so in self-defence, recognizing that the child was bombarded in his out-of-school hours with the sound of radio and the visual images brought by the cinema and television, and that they must compete for the child's attention and sense of reality. In countries where the mass media and the educational system were under a common control, the media afforded a powerful reinforcement to the impact of the school.

7. *Educational content and the aims of the state*

The content of education was strongly affected by political developments and by the purposes of the state. The first world war enhanced its nationalistic tone in nearly all countries, heightening the emphasis which had been present since the state assumed responsibility for universal education. As new countries emerged, or where revolutionary forces established a new order, education was redirected to support the new régime and build a loyal and dedicated citizenry. Countries which felt threatened by national rivals without or revolutionary forces within used their schools to strengthen national sentiment as a bulwark against such threats.

Where liberal democratic principles were reflected in educational policy, one of the major aims of education was to develop each individual for his own sake, according to his capacity and regardless of his social origin. This concept of education was fully expressed in the educational philosophy of John Dewey, who based his thinking on the American Declaration of Independence and the political assumptions of Thomas Jefferson. It implied that education must address itself to the needs and ambitions of all the people and that facilities must be expanded and adapted to assure equality of opportunity.

The course of education in the United States during the twentieth century reflected this basic orientation—in the constant expansion at higher and higher levels, the enormous proliferation of subject matter offered in schools and colleges, the child-centred school for the development of the whole child, and the emphasis on the school's contribution to the child's social adjustment. The many extra-curricular activities carried on in connection with schools and by out-of-school youth organizations had the same objectives. Such organizations as Boy and Girl Scouts, YMCA and YWCA, 4-H clubs for rural children and countless recreational, church or sport groups, all undertook to build character and to develop individual responsibility and the capacity for effective participation in community life.

European education also moved in a similar direction, with marked differences among countries in their educational organization and emphasis. In each country, school reforms were introduced which tended more or less strongly in the direction of the democratic, child-centred school which sought to stimulate the child's creative activity, concerned itself with his total development, included physical education and programmes of school health and school feeding, and which made special provision for children with mental, physical or emotional handicaps. To meet the demands for trained personnel at all levels, countries expanded the technical or vocational content of their education in one way or another, either through specialized schools or through diversification of subject matter in general schools. But at the same time that European systems went far toward accepting the principle of education for all in accordance with capacity and interest, they sought to maintain the values of limited-access, high-grade education for those who were to fill positions of high authority and responsibility and those who required high professional competence.[9, 10]

The content of education reflected state policy most clearly where states were engaged in swiftly remaking their societies. Each revolutionary government used education in its own way. To reorient the Turkish people, Musta-apha Kemal Ataturk used drastic educational measures. By substituting the Latin for the Arabic script in the preparation of all teaching material, he made traditional literature and thought largely inaccessible to the ordinary student and directed his mind toward the future. In Italy Mussolini first concentrated on using out-of-school youth organizations and after-work activities for adults to remould the Italian people to the fascist state. When, as a second step, he sought to bring both religious schools and secular instruction under full state control, the Church stood firm in reasserting the primacy of Church and family in the education of youth. Hitler's educational measures were inspired by his need to destroy centres of independent thought. Since the Nazi régime rejected both rationalism and religious instruction and wished to use mass education to inspire devotion to the Leader and to train men for military life and women for the home, it recast the schools to this end and entrusted the task of indoctrination to the politically faithful.[11]

The Soviet Union made the most far-reaching, ambitious and thorough use of education for the remaking of a people and a state. Its educational task was to develop the kind of people who could create a socialist society, to imbue the rising generation, as well as the adult population, with communist ideology, morality, loyalty to the Party and dedication to the Soviet state, to transform a largely illiterate, predominantly peasant people into competent producers in industry and mechanized agriculture, to replace the class of bourgeois intellectuals with a new body of intellectuals drawn from the ranks of workers and peasants, and to train the technical personnel needed to achieve rapid industrialization and to administer the state and the economy.

In the decade following the October revolution the elementary schools were converted into a system of 'unified labour schools' with a curriculum focused on 'socially useful labour'. In these schools, organized as collectives of pupils, teachers and other school workers, 'socialist competition' between brigades of children took the place of the traditional examination and grading of individual students. The authority of the teacher was minimized, since the growing school system had to be staffed with many old teachers who lacked understanding of or sympathy with communist ideology and new recruits who lacked training and experience. Party control and the teaching of communist principles through the school was achieved in part through the activity of the communist youth organizations—the Young Pioneers and League of Young Communists.

The education of adults was pressed simultaneously. Every centre—trade union, factory, agricultural tractor station—was used as a channel for education, to teach literacy, raise the occupational competence of the men and women at the work benches and in the fields, and develop a capable body of industrial and agricultural workers. In the effort to build a new class of intellectuals drawn from workers and peasants, the Soviet leaders opened the doors of all institutions of higher education to all men and women over 16 years of age without tuition fees or educational requirements for entrance. Since those who lacked preparation could not follow university courses, special preparatory schools known as *rabfac* were established to enable students of worker or peasant origin, and especially members of communist youth organizations, to make up their educational deficiencies quickly and to acquire training at higher levels.

By the time that the first five-year plan was launched in 1928 with its tremendous need for all sorts of technicians, engineers, scientists and administrators, a new intellectual class drawn largely from worker and peasant backgrounds had been created, and a new body of teachers, devoted to communist principles, had been trained. Thereafter the Soviet educational system could concentrate on the fullest development of the Soviet citizen and the training of personnel at every level to participate in the great national effort of building a highly productive communist society.

Emphasis was placed on the mastery of knowledge. School discipline and the authority of the teacher were restored, together with rigorous examinations and grading of individual pupils. Standard textbooks, continually revised to incorporate new knowledge and state policies as they developed, provided the subject matter to be covered. The teacher was required to teach his subject systematically and clearly, using various methods, and to check systematically on the retention of material taught.

Competitive examinations admitted to the various institutions of higher education; stipends to provide a subsistence allowance permitted those who qualified to continue their training. After 1940, when tuition fees were reintroduced into the higher schools, the stipends were granted to the ablest students. An elaborate system of awards and honours to those who did well stimulated student effort and academic achievement. Every medium—press, radio, public occasion—was used to give prestige to the educated person and to inspire the Soviet citizen with zeal to achieve as much education as he could get.

The curriculum of the general school placed great emphasis on mathematics and the physical sciences from the earliest grades. Revisions of the curriculum gave more place to physics and chemistry, increased the amount of time in the laboratory and made additional provision for manual labour and practical work. Nearly half of the school time in the ten-year general schools, which became standard in the larger cities in the early 1950s, was devoted to scientific and practical subjects. The rest was spent on Russian language and literature, history, geography, a foreign language and physical education. After the revisions of 1958 which sought to co-ordinate education more closely with productive work, the time devoted to direct vocational training and productive work was further expanded, amounting to nearly half the school time by the eleventh grade. The Marxist-Leninist ideology provided a framework for the study of all subjects. The curriculum was uniform through the USSR, except in the non-Russian speaking republics where Russian was taught as a second language.

Schools of all types formed part of a unified system, and state guidance ensured not only unity of curriculum but succession in the work of schools and other educational institutions and the proper distribution of educational resources. A variety of schools at different levels provided specialized content related to the fields for which they prepared. The *tecknikum* was designed to produce middle-trained technicians for industry and also for medicine, education, music and the arts; its graduates were assured employment upon completion of the course and had to work for three years in the field for which they had been trained before applying for admission to the university, except for the top-ranking students who could go directly to a higher institution in their fields. Youth between 14 and 17 drafted into the labour reserve, after this practice was instituted in 1940, received six months to two years of industrial training in special labour reserve schools, after which they worked in state enterprises for a period of four years.

Specialized higher education was provided through universities, in technical, medical, legal and other institutes, and in pedagogical institutions for teacher training. Students entered by competitive examination, except for the top graduates of the ten-year schools and the *tecknikums*. The number of places open to students in each field was determined by the requirements of the economy, and the tendency was for courses to become increasingly thorough and specialized. Graduates worked for at least three years in the posts to which their ministries assigned them.

Advanced degrees beyond the university, the first requiring three years of further study plus examinations and defence of a thesis and the second requiring an original and significant contribution to science, drew the ablest scientists on to still further efforts. Military and naval academies, with specialized preparatory boarding schools leading to them and special schools for the training of Party personnel provided specialized training in these areas. Middle technical schools were reported as turning out specialists at the rate of 312,000 a year and higher specialist institutions 224,000 during the period of the fifth five-year plan, 1951–55.

The Soviet educational system, supplemented by press, radio, a network of public libraries and other cultural institutions, was thus designed to give the entire population a scientific outlook, basic understanding of the processes of production and dedication to the principles of the communist society, to create socially oriented citizens and to produce the well-trained personnel required for the rapid economic, social, political and military development of the Soviet Union.

The reorganization of the Japanese educational system after 1945 offered a dramatic example of the redirection and reshaping of education to serve a changed objective of the state. In the years prior to the second world war the highly centralized Japanese system was dominated by the military leadership —military officers were attached to all secondary and higher schools after 1925—and was focused on the duties of the individual to the state which he must serve. During the war most of the secondary and higher educational institutions were closed to release their students for productive or military service and many were physically destroyed.

After the war, acting on the principle that defeat had proved the old ways wrong, Japan set out to build an educational programme which would sustain a democratic rather than an autocratic state and society. The curriculum in all schools put more emphasis on social studies, applied mathematics, science, health, sports and recreation, in an attempt to build sound minds in sound bodies and good citizens of a democracy. Schools provided school lunches and health examinations. A system of general secondary schools similar to those in the United States, open to both boys and girls, replaced the limited number of higher preparatory schools, open only to boys, which had formerly provided virtually the only access to the universities.

In the large number of colleges and universities which offered higher education in science and liberal arts and gave professional and teacher training, students received a broadly cultural education in the humanities, social sciences and natural sciences, in addition to their specialized fields. Both vocational training and social education for adults were also expanded, through extension courses from universities, libraries or museums and in citizens' public halls which were constructed in towns and villages with some aid from the central government. In these halls general cultural courses were offered, library services were provided and recreational and organizational activity was carried on.

Through these measures, and the informal channels of radio and press, Japan sought to make its educational institutions contribute to the development of a general culture 'rich in individuality' and to offer equal opportunity to all according to their ability. A decade after the inauguration of this educational reform, the number of secondary school and university-level students had increased substantially and several thousand women were taking advantage of their new opportunities for higher education. Some educators felt that the change was resulting in less adequate command of certain subject matter than had resulted from the old system and feared that the added numbers would drag down the quality of education at the higher levels. Others, however, noted a greater 'elasticity of mind' and other attributes more in line with the new objectives of post-war Japanese society.

In its tremendous drive for modernization and socialist construction, the Chinese People's Republic used education as a vital instrument to help the country to 'leap ahead'. Even before the communist régime came to power, while the Eighth Army was building up its base in the north-west provinces, the movement placed great stress on education. With few resources and under war conditions the communists undertook not only to teach communist principles, but to develop literacy among soldiers and peasants and to conduct schools and colleges even of university level. Once in power, the communist régime launched a vigorous campaign to overcome the mass illiteracy of the peasants, spread schools as fast as possible throughout the country, and to strengthen the technical and scientific institutions in order to prepare the technical personnel essential to the tasks of economic and social development.

In less than a decade one province after another was able to report that its literacy campaigns had reached nearly the whole of its non-literate population, that whole families from grandparents to young people were enrolled in literacy classes, and that people were painting newly learned characters on walls, trees, tools and furniture to help them to learn and remember. In order to make literacy education feasible on a mass basis, as well as to facilitate intercommunication through the country, measures were taken to establish the use of simplified characters and to make the pronunciation used in the region of Peking standard throughout the country.

To supplement the schools furnished by the state, co-operative farms as well as factories were stimulated to set up their own schools, constructing the buildings and furniture with their own labour and recruiting teachers from every source—government functionaries or technicians sent out to work on the farms, demobilized soldiers and young members of the co-operatives who were school graduates. As the number of schools increased most co-operatives came to have some members who had been to school and could teach others. The more advanced co-operatives went on to set up middle schools and then secondary schools. Meantime, the number of institutions for higher education were multiplied many times over in every major centre, and their enrolments shot into the millions. At every level up to the highest scientific institutes, the expansion of education followed the line laid down by the Communist party for all endeavours—'more, faster, better and more economically'.

The immense expansion of education was at the heart of the technical and cultural revolution which was training new working-class intellectuals and which aimed to eliminate the difference between physical and mental labour. Education was closely integrated with production, and the tie became progressively closer. Factories established schools in which their workers spent part of their working day, receiving partial pay for the hours spent learning new skills; schools organized and operated factories where their pupils learned by doing and at the same time contributed productive labour. Some classes on

co-operative farms were conducted in work breaks. Students in technical institutes worked on designs for machinery or buildings for local factories,
reservoirs, agricultural equipment, the control of a locally serious diseases or
other real and practical problems directly related to production. Scientific
institutes developed projects designed to bring China to the level of international scientific standards, or above, in as many fields and as quickly as
possible.

For the new states which emerged from colonial status the content and
method of education presented a major challenge. The education inherited
from colonial administrations was not well designed to meet the needs of a
modern state. It was mainly literary, it was imbued with material and points
of view more related to the culture of the colonial power than to that of the
area, and higher education was carried on in a foreign language which tended
to cut off the educated element from the masses of the people who did not
command this medium. It provided neither incentive to practical work—the
educated *élite* were above soiling their hands in toil—nor training for the
technicians and scientists required by any modern society, most especially
one aspiring to rapid industrialization.

In India Gandhi had broken through the barrier between education and
labour with his educational programme based on the dignity of work. But even
the momentum provided by his immense prestige did not make it easy to overcome the prejudice against practical activity. Moreover, his emphasis on
handicraft, if literally applied, could impede technical education for the urban
child rather than promote it. In other countries, where no Gandhi had shown
the way and given work his blessing, the task of developing a positive attitude
toward work and technical skills was even more formidable.

Education in the new states had not only to develop a positive attitude
toward work, but to create a new social ideal and a new kind of self-esteem.
Under colonial rule schools had tended to place the local culture in low esteem,
to exalt outside values, to discourage zeal for reform, and to do little to enhance and much to undermine the self-confidence of the people. The educational system of the new states had the problem of developing such a sense
of social purpose as would predispose young people to serve the community
and of building sufficient self-confidence to enable people to use their capacities effectively without either withdrawal or aggressiveness. The problem
was well illustrated in Korea where the Korean language had been banned
from the schools during the Japanese occupation and the country's history
and arts disregarded. The immediate task of Korean educators was to recover
their cultural heritage while at the same time working to readjust the traditional culture to the new democratic ideal.

It was a difficult task to adapt the content and method of education to the
new situation. Old teachers, with a literary background, rigid methods and
traditional attitudes, often could not command the pupils' interest or respect,
and new teachers of the calibre required for the creative task of cultural

reorientation were not attracted to a profession where prestige could no longer compensate for meagre pay. Students who inherited traditions of protest from the days when they took part in the struggle for liberation were restless and critical. A number of countries had to deal with what Indian educators termed 'student indiscipline', as many young people, impatient to reach new goals, found their studies irrelevant and their teachers unimpressive, and expressed their unrest in indifference to study, disorder or passive resistance. In the many countries of Asia, the Middle East and Latin America which were seeking to bring rapid social change by democratic means, it was not easy to use the educational system for the purpose of reorientation and change without resorting to methods inappropriate to their goals and the structure of their societies.

The new states faced an acute problem in the matter of language. Mass education in Europe and America had developed in countries with fairly uniform, well-developed languages. When it was extended to Asia, Africa and the Pacific, to many of the peoples of the Soviet Union and to the Indians of Central and South America, it reached peoples whose spoken tongue was sometimes unwritten, sometimes at variance with the literary language and sometimes written but with a very meagre literature.

Universal education had to be carried on in the local language. Pedagogues agreed that the child's initial instruction should be in the language of his home, and local and national pride was also involved. Multi-language countries had the additional problem of the need for a unifying means of communication, to be taught to the newly educated. At the same time modern subjects were accessible only in the major European languages. In time a local langugage might through use become a language for scientific work, as French and English had supplanted Latin, and as German and Russian had later replaced French for scientific work in German- and Russian-speaking areas. Japan went far toward demonstrating that an Asian language could be transformed into a vehicle for modern scientific study and thought, but the process was slow and the need for highly trained scientists and technicians was immediate. The new states had little choice but to carry on at one and the same time the process of developing mass education in the vernacular, the elaboration of a national language as fast as possible, and the continuing use of a European language as a vehicle for the immediate training of the highly educated personnel essential to the development of the state.

India undertook to strengthen its mass education system in local languages, and it redrew its state boundaries with the practical objective of bringing people who spoke a common tongue within the same administrative and educational area. At the same time it sought to make Hindi the official language of the Indian union, introducing it in the third grade in school and aiming to make it ultimately the language of official communication. English was taught as an additional language at the secondary school level to at least as large a proportion of the population as had learned it under the limited educational system of the past. Some of the universities wished to keep English as their language of instruction in order to retain the advantage of a language which gave access to the world's knowledge without the enormous task of translation and publication involved in developing a comparable body of material in Hindi or in the many local languages.

Indonesia and Burma, with similar yet different problems, turned to other solutions. Indonesia, inheriting schools taught in Dutch and a largely illiterate population speaking a variety of local languages, created a national Indonesian language on the basis of Malay and made it the language of general instruction at all levels in some areas and from the third grade in others. At the same time it substituted English for Dutch as the European language which would be used to provide access to advanced bodies of knowledge and a means of communication with other parts of the world. Burma, inheriting vernacular education which, according to an Education Policy Enquiry Committee in 1946, 'practically ended in a blind alley', plus an English and Anglo-vernacular system which 'led only to the bottleneck of the University', planned to retain English as a language of general use and for secondary and higher education, with early primary instruction in Burmese. It sought to expand the limited literature existing in Burmese, to record traditional oral material, encourage literary expression and translate some world classics, but not to try to make major bodies of knowledge available in Burmese.

In China the educational reformers after 1919 sought to resolve the problem of disparity between the formal literary medium and the many spoken dialects by adopting a written vernacular which permitted colloquial expression. The communist régime took the further steps of standardizing the pronunciation of the 'common speech' and developing simplified script. Israel made Hebrew a spoken language through which to integrate its immigrant population with many backgrounds and tongues.

The language problem was perhaps most acute in the education of Africans who spoke a multitude of unwritten tribal languages. Since strong forces were at work breaking down tribal bonds, the value of reducing many of these languages to writing and building a literature from scratch seemed questionable. The trend appeared to be toward the increased use of a few African languages in certain areas, such as Swahili in Tanganyika, and the use of English and French in West Africa, with Arabic competing for place in the Sudan.

Two factors facilitated the carrying out of educational objectives in states of high illiteracy, the availability of the media of mass communication and the educational aspect of community development programmes. Educational programmes in many countries were carried by radio to the village store or some other place where local people could gather to listen and discuss. In one such programme in Colombia, South America, parish priests organized groups to follow courses in agriculture and other practical subjects. The priests and their assistants acted as discussion leaders and monitors for those attending this radio 'school', and the central office furnished those enrolled with seed, fertilizer or other material called for in the course.

Such illustrations could be multiplied from many areas. In all such programmes, however, it was recognized that information received via the mass media was no substitute for active learning by the person himself. The training centres for fundamental education sponsored by Unesco in Mexico for the Latin American republics and in Egypt for the Arab states, and other centres elsewhere, emphasized the principle of using the person's own experience as the basis for his learning.

Community development programmes offered ample opportunities for learning. Designed to arouse village people to a sense of their own potentialities and to stimulate their co-operative efforts to raise the level of village life, these programmes were basically educational in their approach. In fact the relation between 'community development' and 'fundamental education' was so close that they were sometimes regarded as merely different names for the same basic process.

The community education programme in Puerto Rico offered an example of an educational programme which used both mass media and community development techniques to achieve the fundamental education-community development objective of raising the level of life within the rural community. In this programme 'group organizers', equipped with jeep, loudspeaker system, motion-picture equipment, posters and mass-produced pamphlets, worked in villages and hamlets. First they read and discussed a pamphlet with a group of citizens and arranged for its distribution in the village. Then they returned with a motion picture on the same theme, which always carried a suggestion for community self-help, and with a loudspeaker through which both organizer and citizens could comment on the film or on matters of common interest. When the people of the village, stimulated by these educational activities, expressed an interest in undertaking some community project, the organizer helped them to mobilize their own resources, to tap the technical and other sources available in the area and to develop the capacity to work toward common objectives.

VI. INTERNATIONAL CONCERN WITH EDUCATION

Although education in each country was closely related to national institutions and objectives, its common features and its overall importance made it a matter of international concern and co-operation. A series of international congresses dating from the eve of the first world war brought together individuals interested in the interchange of educational experiences and views. Education became the subject of intergovernmental concern in the 1920s with the establishment of the League of Nations Commission for Intellectual Co-operation and the transformation of the International Bureau of Education, established at Geneva in 1925, into an intergovernmental institution in

1929. At the first intergovernmental conference on public education held in Geneva in 1933, governments reported on their educational systems and received recommendations from the international gathering.

The main lines of international activity in the field of education were in the exchange of information and in the conduct of comparative studies of school administration and organization and of educational content and methods. *The International Yearbook of Education*, published by the International Bureau of Education from 1933 on, made available to each country the trends in experience and thought in other countries of the world.

Unesco, established in 1945, expanded the exchange of information and international documentation and organized international conferences around specific educational problems. Together with the United Nations and the other United Nations specialized agencies, it fostered the exchange of students and teachers. In response to requests from member governments it offered technical assistance in administration, teacher training and the preparation of educational materials. With the co-operation of other United Nations agencies and the Organization of American States it maintained fundamental education training centres for the Latin American countries and the Arab states.

Thus at every level, from the smallest village to the world community, education became a major preoccupation of twentieth-century societies throughout the world.

NOTES TO CHAPTER XXVI

1. Father François Russo, SJ, supplements the Author-Editors' statement about education with the following remarks:

The Roman Catholic Church maintains that responsibility for education rests in the first place with the family and in the second place with the Church, though the State has the right, and indeed the duty, to concern itself with education on the national scale and to set up non-denominational schools. It is the duty of the State to make it possible for the children attending such non-denominational schools to be given religious instruction if their families so request.

The Roman Catholic Church asks parents to send their children to a Catholic school whenever the educational system of their country allows of this. The Church considers that a child cannot receive a satisfactory, all-round education except in a Christian educational environment, since religious teaching, though of fundamental importance, is only one among a number of elements contributing to the Christian upbringing of children.

It is sometimes suggested that in accepting Catholic schools, one is setting up an obstacle to national unity. This view seems very short-sighted.

Far from jeopardizing national unity, a Catholic school does much to foster it—by its broadminded teaching, and by the devotion to the commonweal which is a direct result of Christian education. There is, moreover, ample opportunity for different categories of children to meet together, even if they are attending separate schools. The Roman Catholic Church, while remaining firmly attached to the principles set forth above, recognizes that present-day problems of instruction and education are such that they call for much more State intervention, both in organization and in finance, than was needed in the past, and that Catholic education can no longer be planned independently of the general national educational system. But while the Catholic schools are thus prepared to accept a considerable measure of integration in the national educational system, they declare that it is possible to allow them to retain their spiritual independence.

For other statements of the Catholic position consult:

John D. Redden and F. A. Ryan, *A Catholic Philosophy of Education* (Milwaukee, 1956).

Kevin J. O'Brien, *The Proximate Aim of Education* (Washington, D.C., 1958).

And for other views consult:

M. F. Ashley Montagu, *Education and Human Relations* (New York, 1958).

Aubrey E. Haan, *Education for the Open Society* (London, 1962).

Max Lerner, *Education and a Radical Humanism* (Columbus, Ohio, 1962).

Frederick Meyer, *Philosophy of Education for our Time* (New York, 1958).

National Educational Association, American Education Research Association, *Philosophical and Social Framework of Education* (Washington, D.C., 1958, 1961).

David Riesman, *Constraint and Variety in American Education* (New York, 1958).

Ephraim V. Sayers and Ward E. Madden, *Education and the Democratic Faith: An Introduction to the Philosophy of Education* (New York, 1959).

2. I. Ekholm underlines that the establishment of a single democratic school system in the USSR has made it possible to realize the principle of universal and equal education in an exceptionally short space of time. Many other countries are now following in the path of the Soviet Union which in its work in the field of education incarnates the aspirations of the peoples of the world.

3. I. Elkholm reminds that from the very outset, laws making education compulsory were difficult to put into effect and in fact did not become a reality in some countries, mainly owing to the depressed material situation of the masses and because states which made universal education a statutory requirement did not always provide the necessary backing for legislation in the form of financial appropriations for the expansion of the network of schools, for their equipment and maintenance, for the training of teachers and so on.

4. I. Ekholm writes: The vigorous national liberation movement at the beginning of the twentieth century in colonies and in countries which were not independent led to some democratization of life which was expressed in a certain expansion of the school network and in the training of indigenous administrative, technical and military staff.

5. Professor E. N. Anderson thinks it important to stress the relation between education and national leadership. Writers on the history of education note that the nature of secondary and higher education basically conditions the character and achievements of a society by determining the kind of training that the leaders receive. They tend to regard primary education, although essential in itself, as a reservoir from which the ablest pupils are chosen for advanced training as members of the future policy and decision-making groups. The question must be posed as to whether the Author-Editors have brought out sufficiently the impact of developments in secondary and higher schools in Europe on the achievements of their countries, especially in the economic and social areas of life.

The main problem which Europeans faced in education in the first half of the twentieth century lay in the field of secondary and higher training. Countries entered the period with a record of achievement in developing primary education, whereas the secondary schools in many states had received modest adjustment to meet the needs of the great increase in population and of the emergence and expansion of industrial and technological economy. The character and limitations of secondary training set limits to the achievements of the universities, for the nature of the preparation of the entering students conditioned the kind of education which the latter could instil. The class basis of secondary and higher education in most countries—peasants and workers being largely excluded—was maintained, among other ways, by continuing to offer a curriculum aimed at transmitting a knowledge of the humanities and at preparing young males for the bureaucratic career or for the professions. In most countries, facilities for training engineers, scientists and business men were neglected; Germany and the small states of north-western Europe offered the main or only exceptions, and Germany suffered from denigration of secondary and higher education during the regime of the National Socialists.

When the new states were created after World War I, they followed the educational example in this respect not of pre-Nazi Germany but of France and Italy. The result was that after the positions in the bureaucracies of these new states were filled, there quickly appeared a very high rate of unemployment in the learned professions, with a consequent drift of these persons into radical rightist or radical leftist movements. New professions or occupations which industrialism had made essential lacked social appeal in countries that had not yet achieved substantial industrialization; these countries found themselves expending a disproportionate amount of their incomes supporting a bureaucracy which did not take the initiative in establishing an educational system to prepare personnel at a high level to create an economy capable of sustaining the new state and its apparatus of government. Nor was this condition restricted to Eastern Europe. Spain and Portugal were in a similar situation, and Italy, France and Great Britain, at the mid-century, were still debating the issue. Their educational systems were still not of the kind to train personnel —engineers, scientists, business administrators and other business leaders—in sufficient numbers to man expanding industry. The nature of the demands was acutely revealed by the experience of war, when scientific and technological ability and leadership in production and distribution were desperately sought.

In the years since World War II, European countries have attempted to speed, on a scale varying from country to country, adjustment of secondary and higher education to the needs for trained personnel in non-traditional areas of endeavour, and to break with the old restrictive relationship between social class and the system of education. They have begun to seek out and to train ability irrespective of social origin. However, resistance within the educational system to innovation remains strong. Whether secondary and higher schools will expand and adjust to meet demands or whether centres for training personnel will be set up outside the established institutions is a question which France, for example, has not yet answered, and certain other countries are even further away from facing the issue.

Bibliography for this subject is understandably extensive in today's world. Useful for any especially interested reader are the reports issued by UNESCO in its *World Survey of Education*, for example, the report *Secondary Education* (London, 1961). Important reports have been issued in Great Britain. Examples may be cited in the Newsom Report by the Central Advisory Council for Education, *Half Our Future* (Her Majesty's Stationery Office, 1963), and in the Robbins Report, *Higher Education* (HMSO, 1963). One should also consult Stephen R. Graubard (Ed.), *A New Europe?* (Boston, 1964), for its several articles on education in Europe today. Consult also:

Margaret A. Clapp, *The Modern University* (Cornell University Press, 1950).

W. R. Fraser, *Education and Society in Modern France* (London, 1963).

George F. Kneller, *Higher Learning in Britain* (Berkeley, 1955).

W. M. Kotschnig, *The University in a Changing World* (London, Oxford, 1932).

W. M. Kotschnig, *Unemployment in the Learned Professions* (Oxford, 1937).

Donald W. Miles, *Recent Reforms in French Secondary Education—with Implications for French and American Education* (New York, 1953).

OECD, *Forecasting Manpower Needs for the Age of Science* (Paris, 1960).

Jean Thomas and Joseph Majault, *Educational Problems Common to European Countries*. Report to the Third Conference of Ministers of Education (Rome, 1962).

6. I. Ekholm adds that in the Chinese People's Republic a reform of higher education has also been carried through. The teaching of the reactionary scholastic disciplines has been abolished and the study of Marxist theory and of the history of the Chinese revolution introduced. Great attention is given to the furthering of technical education.

7. I. Ekholm adds: The problem of school education in rural areas which was the subject of special discussion at the Twenty-first International Conference on Public Education is of particular urgency. As the UNESCO material showed, there are still 250,000,000 children in rural areas of the world who have no possibility of attending a school. In many countries there is a noticeable insufficiency of school buildings and teachers. Often the children of poor peasants leave school without completing the primary education course and start working on the family holding. The problem of rural schools is complicated in some countries by the survival of vestiges of feudalism, by a lack of religious and national unity in the population, by serious economic difficulties and by the existence alongside state schools of private schools—missionary, Muslim, Jewish, etc.—most of which

belong to religious bodies or are under their influence. The extremely low rate of remuneration of teachers' work is a substantial obstacle in the way of the development of rural
education. The problem of the rural school is being successfully solved in countries which
have started on the road to socialist development, and there it is an organic link in a single
state system of education. See N. K. Goncharov, *Narodnoe prosveshchenie v SSSR*
(Public Education in the USSR), Report submitted to the International Seminar in
Tashkent (April 1961), Moscow, 1961. (Parallel texts in French, English, and Spanish.)

8. I. Ekholm writes that in 1958 when the USSR entered the phase of detailed construction
of communism, and life confronted the schools with new tasks, a large-scale programme of
educational reconstruction was elaborated which, after nation-wide discussion, received
its confirmation by the Supreme Soviet of the USSR in the form of a law. The main point
in this programme, the realization of which has been successfully begun, is the consistent
application of the principle of instruction coupled with productive labour and of productive labour coupled with instruction. One of the principal means for putting this principle
into effect is the system of polytechnical education.

9. I. Ekholm points out that the period under review was characterized by new forms of
organization of children which to a considerable extent affected their education. With the
strengthening of the mass revolutionary movement under the influence of the October
Socialist Revolution democratic organizations of the children of workers began to be set
up. First came the communist groups in Germany which set up the 'Spartacus' children's
organization. Soon after the October Revolution similar bodies began to come into
existence in Soviet Russia. In May 1922 the All-Russian Conference of the Russian
Young Communist League took a decision to set up an organization of Young Pioneers.
In the twenties and thirties children's democratic organizations were founded in many
countries including the USA, United Kingdom, Belgium, Switzerland, Austria and
Sweden. After the second World War this movement embraced more than thirty
countries in Europe, Asia and Latin America. It is in fact an effective means for inculcating
into children and young people the best human virtues.

10. See further material on youth groups in Chapter XXII, pp. 776–81.

11. I. Ekholm points out that even the representatives of pre-Nazi pedagogy, whilst verbally
asseverating their concern for personality and pretending to safeguard its interests,
emphasized the formative significance of religion and race, lauded nationalism and
championed the education of youth in a spirit of militarism and chauvinism. It was
precisely these highly reactionary ideas which were developed when the Nazis came to
power. The concept of the racial superiority of Germans and their rights to world domination, the cult of the Führer and blind obedience—all misanthropic ideas—became the
basis for the education of children and young people. Courses in racial studies were given
in the schools and an intensified military training of youth was carried out.

CHAPTER XXVII

USE OF LEISURE*

I. THE NEW LEISURE

No aspect of modern industrial society was more distinctive than the new leisure enjoyed by the masses of the people. The ways in which this leisure was spent and the institutions which grew up in relation to it led to the development of mass culture which became more and more pervasive with each decade, placing its stamp on the habits and outlook of industrial societies and spreading with the extension of modern technology and industrialization to many parts of the world.

For the first time in history the masses of the people in the industrial countries were free during a substantial part of each day and each week from the activities necessary for survival—the daily labour in the field or at the bench and the endless routines of household life. Leisure, which had been the privilege of the rich who could command the labour of others, became the common lot of the ordinary citizen.

The very concept of 'leisure' which emerged during these years embodied a new idea and a new attitude toward living. In pre-industrial societies such leisure as the masses of the people had enjoyed took the form of many religious holidays—literally holy days—of family celebrations connected with weddings and other family events and of festivals celebrating the rhythm of agricultural work, especially planting and harvest festivals common to agricultural societies.

The early factory system reduced the free time of workers, for the continuous hours of work in the factory up to fourteen hours a day, six or seven days a week, week in and week out, offered none of the flexibility of agricultural labour or the seasonal periods when work was slack, and the time allowed for the celebration of religious holidays was strictly specified and usually cut down to the minimum. But by drawing a sharp line between time at work and 'free' time, industry laid the basis for a division of life into 'work' and 'leisure', and for an attitude toward leisure or leisure time as something which was desirable in itself, something which men could acquire and 'use'. It established the concept of the annual holiday—a period wholly free from work—and the idea that people could be entitled to such an interval as part of the pattern of living.

Basically, the new leisure was the product of modern technology. Machine production so increased the productivity of the worker as to enable him to

* Dr Dorothy Jackson collaborated in the preparation of this chapter.

earn enough for a livelihood in a reduced working day and work week, and even to earn sufficient in this shorter time to have money to spend on the enjoyment of his non-working hours.

It was not without a struggle, however, that industrial workers gained an increasing measure of leisure for themselves. At first, trade unions had demanded shorter hours on the grounds of health and the need of time for home duties, but by the early twentieth century, when the ten-hour day had become general, the demand for shorter hours was couched in terms of the desire for leisure. Workers associated it with upper-class privilege and in the age of democracy they intended to have it, along with other tokens of equality. They demanded, and step by step achieved, successive shortenings of the working time, then annual holidays with pay and overtime pay for work on Sundays and public holidays. Employers meantime came to recognize that a quota of leisure contributed to workers' efficiency.

By the 1950s the general concept of shorter working hours and holidays with pay, outside agriculture, had been accepted in all western industrialized countries, barring economic pressures such as wars which brought long overtime hours, or slumps which brought unemployment and enforced free time. The forty-hour week was general in the United States and Canada for industrial and white-collar workers, while forty-two to forty-eight hours were usual in most other areas, with a tendency toward further reduction. By 1960 the average for factory and office workers in the USSR was under forty; in Japan, however, it was still more than fifty hours per week.

For many housewives, too, the new technology meant new leisure. House-hold appliances and the industrial production of baked, canned and frozen foods released women from many hours of washing, cleaning and cooking; the old saying 'woman's work is never done' was no longer so true. For middle-class women whose leisure had formerly been made possible by ser-vants, the new devices helped to redress the balance when their former servants went to work in factories where they could earn enough money to afford some of the new leisure for themselves; for women who had never had the help of servants, the new machines and new products brought some leisure for the first time.

Young people also enjoyed more leisure time, both because the additional earnings of their parents enabled an increasing proportion of them to remain out of the labour market and in school through adolescence, and because labour-saving devices lightened some of their household chores. Many had spending money of their own instead of having to help support their families. This development, in conjunction with the new freedom of association widely allowed to adolescent boys and girls, provided the basis for what came to be virtually a mass sub-culture among the urbanized teenagers of the industrial countries.

Once leisure became available to the masses of the people, the question arose how it would be used. The answer lay in part in modern technology itself, for the means of mass communication and transport gave access to new forms of entertainment and enjoyment. In part it depended on the facilities provided by public or commercial agencies and the choices which people made as to how to use their time and energy.

In the advanced industrial countries an ever larger amount of economic activity was devoted to the production and distribution, the repair and the advertising of products and services which provided for men's leisure-time pursuits rather than for the necessities of food, clothing and shelter. Where productive activity was guided primarily by consumer expenditures, the interaction between consumer demand and the effort of producers to market their wares resulted in a pattern of leisure-time activity which reflected the public tastes and the influence of commercial interests.

The public was eager for entertainment of all sorts, for information along many lines and for the opportunity to engage in a multitude of sports and hobbies. Mass entertainment industries took advantage of the new instruments of communication and developed them for the mass market in the form of mass magazines, the production and distribution of motion pictures and, in countries where radio and television were commercially controlled, entertainment over the air. The vast industrial complex involving pleasure vehicles and their use grew larger and more ubiquitous with every year, while the manufacture of equipment for sports and hobbies flourished and expanded.

The entertainment industries with their ready-made audiences offered a powerful medium for advertising all manner of products and came to depend for much of their support on companies willing to pay for access to this potential market. Advertisers, in turn, adopted entertainment patterns to catch and hold attention and they even sought to make the entertainment itself into a vehicle for selling their wares. Producers and advertisers thus helped to form tastes as well as catering to them, and the patterns which developed resulted from the constant interplay between producer and public.

Nowhere however was provision for the use of leisure left entirely to the operation of the market and the initiative of commercially motivated enterprise. Everywhere some responsibility for the citizens' leisure was assumed by the state and by co-operative, religious or philanthropic agencies. The public provision of parks, playgrounds, museums, zoos and libraries was already a well-established feature of urban communities before either the shortened work-day or the attitudes associated with the welfare state made further provisions for leisure seem necessary and appropriate.

When the eight-hour day began to make substantial amounts of non-working time available, many employers, leaders and welfare workers in industrial countries expressed the fear that working people would not know what to do with their spare time and would use it in drinking and idling. Historically, the major development of industrialism and capitalism had come in those societies which regarded work, savings, accumulation and prudent investment as moral virtues and feared that free time would be spent in frivolity or idleness which would corrupt the population and undermine its moral stamina. When leisure began to become a mass reality, communities where these attitudes prevailed saw a need for people to be taught to use leisure fruitfully and to be provided with the means of doing so. At the same time a widely expressed concern lest the monotony of factory work should destroy the industrial worker's humanity led to efforts to promote activities which would provide a substitute for the old satisfactions of craftsmanship.

The outcome, in the 1920s, was a great extension of organized recreation in the form of sports facilities, handicraft classes, opportunities for amateur dramatics, music, dancing and discussions. Some of these recreational activities were sponsored by governments, others by private organizations. In Britain for example they were often maintained by such organizations as the Women's Institutes, the Workers' Education Association, the British Drama League or by welfare agencies such as settlement houses.

Most countries, either on a national or community basis, experimented in ways of bringing books, arts, music and theatre to a wider public by expanding their library systems and museums, and by establishing orchestras and a variety of art and theatre projects. School programmes were enlarged to include a wide range of sport and other extra-curricular activities designed to develop interests and skills that might lead to the creative use of leisure. Organized recreation was included in the social planning of the depression years and in efforts to maintain morale during wartime. Depression, war and acceptance of the role of the welfare state brought increased provisions by governments in those countries where much recreation was privately sponsored, and stimulated the further enlargement of public parks, playing fields, gardens, zoos, swimming pools, golf courses and the like.

Industrial enterprises and labour unions also concerned themselves with the workers' use of leisure time. Many large corporations provided athletic facilities for their employees and backed company teams, choirs, orchestras and art exhibits. Labour unions secured the co-operation of educational agencies in union education programmes and encouraged their members to make good use of their time in further study or by engaging in sports and hobbies.

With time at their disposal and a variety of commercial and public resources at hand, people chose to spend their time in ways which reflected a range of attitudes toward leisure itself, as well as a multitude of tastes and interests. Persons who wanted to use their time for self-improvement, and those for whom the line between vocational and avocational interests was not sharply drawn, tended to spend their leisure time in ways which increased their skills and supplemented their working life. Others used their leisure chiefly to enhance their enjoyment of life. They were positive in their approach to pleasure, and they did what seemed enjoyable without regard for its effect on their position or the improvement of their personalities.

Some used their leisure time simply for relaxation or to escape from the drabness or strain of their surroundings, to forget what was worrying them and to live another life at least in their mind's eye for a moment; the cinema, radio and television fulfilled this purpose successfully and so gained immensely in popularity. Others, by contrast, devoted many of their leisure hours to the service of their communities, filling posts of responsibility in civic organizations, volunteering their time for such activities as boy scout leadership or as hospital aides, or engaging in activities which promoted a cause, through their trade union, political party, church or other body.

The need for sociability and the immense range of interests which could be pursued under modern urban conditions produced an endless variety of clubs, teams or informal groups formed in communities or at places of work or in connection with a school, church or recreational institution. The list of no less than twenty-one special interest clubs formed in the 1950s by employees of the United Nations at its headquarters in New York was representative of the kinds of association that might be open to people. Such clubs provided a means for people with like interests to get together and enjoy themselves without reference to where they lived, who they were or what position they held, and they served as the nuclei around which many people built their social activities. Common interest took the place of status in providing a basis for a sense of belonging to those exposed to the impersonality and anonymity of urban life.

These ways of using leisure time fell into two broad categories, passive and active: those which entertained people as spectators or listeners and those which involved active participation. The line between the two types was not always sharp, for in the 'passive' forms of entertainment there were degrees of passivity, from the keen interest and informed attention of the music or sports enthusiast who listened to each note and recognized the fine points of each play, to the inactivity of the person who kept the radio going for little more than the noise and who went to a ball game just to follow the crowd. But in all types of passive entertainment the individual depended on the performance of someone other than himself.

By the middle years of the century the factors which affected the use of leisure were producing a common mass culture. Its development had gone farthest and could be seen most conspicuously in the United States, where conditions were especially favourable. But all the essential features were present elsewhere—shortening of working hours, rising incomes, the blurring of old class lines, the development of entertainment industries. *Per capita* movie attendance was higher in Britain in the 1950s than in the United States; Paris set aside an area in the Bois de Boulogne where motoring French campers could pitch their tents; the Scandinavian countries developed special low-cost holiday facilities not only for workers taking their paid holidays but for holidaying housewives as well; Japanese periodical and book output was among the largest in the world. Mass culture was taking on common qualities in all the industrialized regions.

In the socialist economies the trends which characterized the countries where producers were free to cater to and influence public desires were subjected to controls in the interest of the socially advantageous use of resources and the development of what were considered to be socially desirable activities. In these countries the government, either directly or through the participation of public bodies such as trade unions, supplied the kinds of facilities for the use of leisure which were generally provided by public agencies in other countries.[1] They made no provision for types of activity not deemed of social value, or which represented a claim on resources which could not be met in the light of other national needs. The development of unacceptable tastes was directly discouraged and the means for satisfying them from abroad were curbed by censorship and the regulation of imports.

In these societies, planning with respect to the use of leisure was viewed as an integral part of national planning. The USSR included at all stages in its development the provision of local facilities for the use of leisure, it converted the homes and estates of the rich into sanatoriums and holiday rest homes for workers, and it encouraged activities positively designed to promote the physical development and raise the cultural level of the people.

Parks of 'culture and rest' in cities and towns served the combined purposes of providing places where families could relax outside their crowded homes, of furnishing play-space for a variety of activities and of offering a wide range of exhibits and informal educational displays. Athletic stadiums, sports grounds, playing fields and gymnasiums provided facilities for sports and other physical activities. Clubhouses or other meeting rooms in factories and collective farms became the scenes of a wide range of cultural activities carried on by informal groups, with the stimulus and often assistance of the local Party unit. Wall newspapers, magazines, study circles, discussion and writing groups were encouraged and musical, dramatic and sports groups were formed.

At all levels Soviet workers were encouraged to use their leisure time in study in order to improve their skills or train for a higher job, and many types of educational facilities were provided to make this possible. Cinema, radio and television were regarded as educational instruments and were used directly through documentary films or educational broadcasts, and indirectly through dramatic presentations.

The USSR and the people's democracies, which pursued an essentially similar policy with respect to provisions for the use of leisure, thus sought to guide the development of the mass culture and to produce values, tastes, habits and personalities consistent with their image of the society which they were building.

In the course of these years both the new leisure and mass culture spread to the newly industrializing areas. To a certain extent leisure and mass culture spread independently. Where industry developed it brought leisure. The norms which had been reached in the industrial countries over a period of a hundred years were taken over bodily along with factory organization and machine processes. Standards established by the conventions of the International Labour Office, including the eight-hour day, were adopted in principle and were more or less fully applied. Although for the bulk of the population which remained in agriculture and related activities leisure continued to be a matter of religious and family festivals, for those who came within the sphere of industrialization it became part of their new way of life.

At the same time, and to an even greater degree, mass communication brought elements of mass culture to all people, both those with leisure and those without. Films in the major Indian languages, for example, became a favourite form of entertainment in that country, not only in the cities where cinemas were chiefly located but in many rural areas, where several hundred touring cinemas exhibited in tents. Radio entertainment, too, was not limited to industrialized elements in the population of underdeveloped countries but reached all manner of people in towns and villages.

Popular music was widely spread by radio and cinema. Indian films popularized what came to be known as 'film music', light music with some of the flavour of traditional Indian music but without its rigour. Similar popularizations based on Arab musical modes were sung and played over the air in Arab countries. Turkish popular music might be heard almost anywhere in the country—in a coffee shop, outside a store or in a public square.

The principal active use of mass leisure in newly industrializing countries was in sports. Whereas such sports as polo or horse-racing had long been the hobbies of the rich, the growth of popular sports was a twentieth-century phenomenon. The particular sport varied, and some areas were more active than others. Wherever British influence extended, sports were especially encouraged; Indian, African and West Indian football, cricket and hockey teams took part in contests within the Commonwealth. In Latin American countries, soccer or baseball was played on any vacant lot. Successful teams and individuals brought prestige to their community and their nation.

The pattern of mass leisure remained more pronounced in the industrialized countries, it was carried much farther there, and the way of life was more deeply affected by it. But the essential trends in the use of leisure and in the development of mass culture which were well developed in the industrial countries were becoming world-wide by the middle of the twentieth century.

In the account which follows, the several ways in which large numbers of people used the new leisure are discussed both in terms of the development in the activity and of the ways in which related facilities were provided, commercially or by public agencies, in the capitalist areas and as part of planned national development in the socialist societies.

The use of leisure and the shape of the mass culture were intimately related with other aspects of technological and social development and with the development of literature and the arts. The following pages must, therefore, be read in conjunction with the chapters on Communications* and Transport†

* Chapter XI.   † Chapter X.

which present the technologies which revolutionized much of leisure-time activity, and the chapter on Education* which traces the spread of mass literacy on which the vast development of popular literature rested. It should also be read in connection with the chapters on Literature and the Arts,† for no sharp and clear line can be drawn between popular expression, enjoyment of leisure or entertainment on the one hand and literary expression and the arts on the other.

II. LEISURE-TIME ACTIVITIES

1. *Reading*

For many people reading was a favourite form of relaxation, both as an end in itself and as an aid to the pursuit of other interests. This had long been true of the educated classes, but now the higher general level of education for the masses of people combined with increased leisure to provide a great new potential reading public. Publishers responded with mass-circulation newspapers and magazines and a great variety of paper-bound books, in addition to their customary publications. As a result, by mid-century about 90 per cent of the populations of the leading industrial countries read newspapers every day, the circulation figures for magazines went on climbing year by year, and paper-bound books were beginning to be available in neighbourhoods and shops where books had not previously been in demand. Libraries spread in urban communities and many rural areas.

With the widening of the reading public the character of the material offered changed, and new types of newspapers, magazines and books appeared alongside older types modified to meet new demands. The new types ranged from tabloid newspapers to digest and picture magazines, and to paper-backed editions of classics, self-education texts, and an infinite variety of detective, science fiction and adventure novels. Both old types and new included many accounts of travel in remote areas, much biographical or auto-biographical material and a wide range of reports on developments in the sciences and arts.

(a) *Mass-circulation newspapers and magazines.* Newspapers, from their beginnings in the seventeenth century, had been chronicles of events for the use of merchants and politicians, and means of political propaganda; in the twentieth century they came to be also vehicles of entertainment. Nineteenth-century readers had demanded financial and political coverage, local news and reviews of cultural and sporting events. Twentieth-century readers wanted all these, reports on scientific discoveries, more complete sports coverage, reports on the weather, and a variety of columns devoted to leisure-time activities. Papers began to add to their news-coverage advice on gardening, photography and other hobbies, sample bridge hands and notes on how to play them, crossword puzzles, travel news, radio, motion picture and television reviews,

* Chapter XXVI. † Chapters XXXI, XXXII.

recipes and suggestions for meals and parties, and fashion sections. Many introduced cartoons and cartoon strips or 'comics'.

The new mass-circulation magazines, like the newspapers, sought to be both vehicles of entertainment and purveyors of information and interpretation of developments in science, technology and a wide variety of other fields. They appealed to all strata of society, all age groups and to people with all kinds of interests and tastes. Magazines of this type were particularly strong in the United States. After the second world war publications in this style began to circulate widely in other countries.

Presenting information and entertainment at various levels of sophistication, these magazines took for granted a common stereotype with which their readers could identify themselves. They assumed a progressively higher standard of living with more and more labour-saving devices and the latest or best in clothes, houses, cars, cosmetics, vitamins and wonder drugs. The image which they conveyed featured romantic love, family life, children brought up according to the latest principles of child psychology, ample leisure and an air of perpetual youth.

Though these magazines were filled with information, they were not primarily designed to stimulate thought or question values. They catered to unfocused curiosity about current events, nature, remote parts of the earth, the workings of machinery and of the mind, medicine, religion, sports, outer space, and the daily lives of film stars, sports heroes and other celebrities. Some offered vicarious violence in standardized forms or escape into fantasies of glamour, sex, crime and adventure.

Much space in the mass magazines was devoted to advertising, upon which they depended for a large part of their revenue. In the hands of highly paid craftsmen skilled in making forms designed to produce immediate attention, interest and action, advertising was a source of information and a constant generator of new desires. Some of the finest photography and use of the graphic arts were to be found in the advertising pages, along with paintings reproduced to suggest the prestige of a product, striking colours, superlatives in language and other attention-drawing devices with emotional impact. Advertising thus often became in itself a form of entertainment.

Within the general pattern the quality of presentation varied, and the points of particular attention were chosen by editor and publisher according to specific audiences and their presumed interests.

A number of general magazines, such as *John Bull* in England and *Saturday Evening Post* in the United States, printed well-written stories, informative articles on many timely subjects and cartoons making fun of everyday problems of living; they appealed to moderately well-read audiences which ran into millions. At first these magazines appeared in varying degrees of taste, but gradually they became more uniformly well-printed and colourful.

The most popular of the general magazines, *Reader's Digest*, had the biggest circulation in the world. From its beginning in 1922 it grew to a circulation of nearly 12,000,000 in the United States in 1956 and 3,000,000 in twenty-eight foreign editions. Every month it printed abridgements of articles chosen from many other magazines of the preceding month, a condensation of a best-selling novel, and stories of individuals who had overcome some difficulty with heartening dignity. It told the story of progress in a thousand fields with sustained and earthy optimism. In such a field as bringing up children, it explained problems in terms of the most advanced psychological research; but in its analysis of business enterprise it reiterated many of the values of early capitalist society. It was followed by other digest magazines in many specialized fields, for even the new leisure contained too little time for anybody to read the informative articles in all the periodicals and many people came to depend on getting information or literature in capsule form.

The powerful American publishing empire of Time, Inc., which included *Time* (1923), *Fortune* (1930), *Life* (1936), *Architectural Forum* (acquired 1935), *House and Home* (1952) and *Sports Illustrated* (1954), set standards of popular knowledge at the sophisticated level and defined the meaning of success. *Fortune* was the first magazine to dramatize the giant corporations—their world-wide scale, their use of science, the men who ran them—and to present twentieth-century industry as 'a world of art comparable to skyscrapers'.

News weeklies, such as *Time* and its imitators, which covered the main events that an up-to-date citizen wanted to know about, included a broader range of subject matter than the older journals of opinion and assumed less basic knowledge on the part of their readers. They thus appealed to newly educated mass audiences and their circulation figures kept rising.

Pictorial journals used all the resources of modern photography to meet the needs of widening audiences for news which could be quickly grasped, and they satisfied the craving for swift, dramatic impact. Magazine publishers had used pictures for illustrations for many years—the *Illustrated London News* and *l'Illustration* dated from 1842 and 1843. But with the immense improvement in cameras and films, permitting action shots, close-ups and candid pictures of people at crucial moments, the photographs themselves became the core and the illustrated magazine gave way to the pictorial journal. The many magazines of this type, such as *Life* which took its format from the French *Vu*, told their stories in pictures and used text only to give continuity and explanations when needed. They commented on events by means of the pictorial essay, an arrangement of photographs in a pattern which highlighted points that the editor specially wanted to bring out.

Women's magazines kept increasing in circulation throughout the period, and by the 1950s ranked with the pictorial journals among the most popular types of periodicals. The general women's magazines had a little of everything that might be of interest to women: articles on education, labour-saving devices, politics or community affairs; beauty hints, special sections on fashion, homemaking, architecture and interior decorating; short stories, poetry, a film review and a condensed novel. Standards of these magazines varied widely, more noticeably in Britain and other European countries than in the United States because publishers in those countries aimed at providing magazines for different social levels. As a group, they grew in popularity and influence. When the largest of these magazines, the United States *Ladies Home Journal*, put out a retrospective volume in 1956 commemorating its 75th year, many non-readers were astonished to find that with great consistency it had published stories, articles and poems of writers who came to be considered the best of their time. These writers had found the *Journal* a good place in which to appear because of the price it had been able to pay to its contributors and because its circulation placed it third among popular magazines in the United States.

Other popular magazines were those having to do with the entertainment world, including periodicals such as the best-selling British *Radio Times*, which gave the radio and television programmes for the coming week and news and comment about them, and the widely read magazines in many countries given over to gossip about screen, radio and television personalities.

Many low-level mass magazines, sold by the millions of kiosks, tobacconists, drug stores and other news-stands, played up the crudest aspects of sex and violence in extreme forms. Confession magazines, westerns, lurid crime and horror stories depended on sensationalism to attract and sell. Some of the crudest and most violent adopted the cartoon or comic strip form widely used for simplified presentation of stories and information. When this occurred, parents and teachers became aroused and agitated for the banning of horror comics. The agitation came up against the principle of freedom of the press, but it served to focus attention on the results of mass literacy in providing a market for crude sensationalism. It caused much thought about how to get people beyond a juvenile mentality and how to deal with commercial incitement to cruelty without resort to authoritarian controls over expression.

The mass-circulation magazines existed side by side with an infinite variety of periodicals produced for special interest groups. A few literary reviews, political journals and society magazines, inherited from the nineteenth century, managed to hold their own. So did professional and technical journals and semi-educational publications like the geographic magazines and the popular, interpretative scientific monthlies. These were joined by a host of new periodicals. All kinds of occupational groups and even corporations began to put out their own weekly, monthly or quarterly reviews, and the great publishing houses produced new magazines aimed at reaching age groups, social groups or interests not previously thought large enough or rich enough to warrant separate publications. For example, high-fidelity enthusiasts, gourmets and teenagers acquired their own handsome glossy reviews, some with circulations of more than a million. Science fiction and detective story magazines had their devotees in many parts of the world and in all levels of society. A large proportion of these special publications, learned journals and popular-appeal magazines alike, were purveyors of information for people pursuing hobbies or for those who used them to keep up with new information in their professional field of interest.

Among the special-interest magazines were the journals of opinion and the literary reviews which raised questions about values within the mass culture and about industrial and political forces. Weekly journals such as the *Spectator*, the *New Statesman* and *The Economist* in Britain presented the news with a definite and well-understood set of political assumptions—right, left or centre—and with analysis designed, as *The Economist* put it, 'to appeal to thinking people everywhere'. In addition to the old-style literary review, a new type, represented by the *Saturday Review of Literature* in the United States, tried to encourage a widening audience of newly educated people to some critical discrimination in their approach to books and theatre and to the new forms of film, radio, television and records. These magazines had increasing difficulty in surviving because their specific appeal and questioning attitudes meant limited circulation and they did not therefore draw large advertising revenues, while rising publication costs were too large to be met only by increasing rates of subscription.

Indeed powerful economic forces were tending to concentrate the publishing of mass magazines in the hands of a few large houses. The vast range of materials from which selection was to be made, the possibilities of swiftly printing editions running into several millions, and the increasing use of colour made immense capital investment necessary; world-wide networks of correspondents and photographers and teams of research workers collected materials; distribution became a major operation in itself. All these factors made it difficult for the isolated publication to survive and led to the formation of 'families' of magazines which could command, in combination, sufficient resources to serve the mass market.

Mass-circulation magazines in the socialist countries, where magazine publication was a public enterprise, differed from those in countries which enjoyed a free commercial press in the absence of advertising and sensational appeal, but they resembled them closely in other respects. The tone and content of the magazines, designed as they were to raise the cultural level of the people, were unaffected by the presence of tastes and interests among the readers to which commercial publishers elsewhere found it profitable to respond. In so far as they dealt with products and their use, it was as these were brought on to the market in a planned manner and their most appropriate use indicated. In place of the latest appeals of advertisers, the readers of mass magazines in the Soviet Union and people's democracies found the latest forms of official propaganda, and in place of sensationalism, material condemning amoral behaviour and crude, primitive interests.

Like mass magazines elsewhere, however, these publications were purveyors of information to people with a wide range of general curiosity and special interests, and their style followed a similar course, with pictorial journalism, the use of colour, fine printing and skilful layout. General magazines assumed that their readers wanted to know about many things. Specialized magazines of all sorts abounded—for women, young people, farmers, metal workers and every type of professional and technician. Journals covering social and political life and literary reviews were also popular.

(b) *Popular books.* The continuous flow of books from the world's presses was ample evidence that periodicals were not supplanting them as reading matter. Unesco's survey of book production in 1952 found seven countries producing over 10,000 titles annually—namely USSR, United Kingdom, India, Japan, German Federal Republic, United States and France, in that order—and sixteen others publishing more than 3,000 titles.

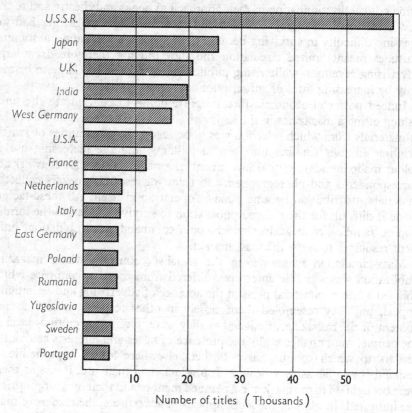

Number of titles (Thousands)

CHART XXIV. Books Published, 1957. Number of titles by countries with the largest book production (countries differ in what they include as 'books'; e.g. pamphlets, government reports, etc.).

Source: *U.N. Statistical Yearbook,* 1960.

The movement for establishing public libraries which had developed in the nineteenth century was greatly extended, and libraries became not only custodians of books but promoters of their use. In many countries city libraries opened neighbourhood branches, put on exhibits, offered lectures, organized discussion groups, provided special reading rooms for children,

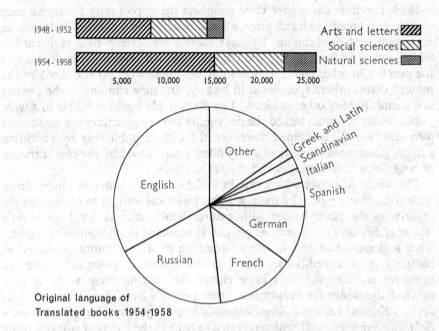

CHART XXV. Books Translated. Annual average world output by subject matter 1948–52, 1954–58; and by original language, 1954–58.
Source: *U.N. Statistical Yearbook*, 1960.

and employed reference librarians to help people find their way to the information which they sought. From the 1920s on, central libraries in cities and in some rural areas sent out travelling bookmobiles which penetrated into regions which had previously been quite cut off from supplies of books, making weekly or bi-weekly visits and enabling readers to request books they especially wanted.

Library coverage was much more complete in some countries than in others, but everywhere library services made more and more books available to more and more people. Sweden was one of the countries whose *per capita* facilities were among the greatest. The Ministry of Culture in the USSR maintained a network of public libraries which extended down to the district level and operated neighbourhood lending centres and itinerant lending libraries and supplied books to libraries established by club-houses, cultural centres, collective farms and other groups. The United States system of public libraries, comprehensive in some cities and regions and less extensive in others, was supplemented by many thousands of school and university libraries and by the specialized libraries of public agencies and organizations, which members of the public could arrange to use. The British public library system was supplemented by a system of ubiquitous low-cost rental libraries.

Book purchase clubs gave their members the opportunity to receive each month, at a greatly reduced price, a book selected by a panel of judges from among current publications. By 1951 there were seventy-four such nation-wide book clubs for adults in the United States and eleven for children, and the number in other countries was growing. Some were general 'book of the month' clubs, others specialized in history, art, new editions of the classics and a multitude of other subjects. The clubs made books available to a wide public, many of whom lacked the discrimination or opportunity to make their own selection. They helped to reduce the cost of publishing by providing a large, guaranteed market, and they filled a gap caused by the concentration of bookshops in larger cities and central locations.

The kinds of books which caught and held public interest ranged from romantic novels, especially those with an historical setting, to semi-scientific reports on the latest battles with nature. Books such as Sir John Hunt's *Ascent of Everest* (1953) enabled people, vicariously, to pit themselves against snow and mountain and to learn something of the techniques involved in planning great expeditions. Travel books and anthropological studies of primitive societies achieved huge circulations during these years as they satisfied the desire for insight into other people's lives. Books on wild life, such as Konrad Lorenz's *King Solomon's Ring* (1952) or Henry Williamson's *Salar the Salmon* (1948), which revealed to readers the habits of animals, birds and fish, appealed to young and old. Biographies and autobiographies of all sorts became best sellers among readers who wanted to know how important people reacted to the problems they faced and among those who enjoyed the role of amateur historian and liked to compare various accounts of the same happenings. Also popular were books which aroused nostalgia for childhood or a remembered way of life and those which offered reassuring answers to common personal problems.

Whatever the subject, whether historical, geographical, biographical, psychological or scientific and whether fiction or reporting, readers demanded authenticity of detail and a sense that their reading was adding to their information and to their insight into reality, past or present.

Books became easier to acquire with the appearance of cheap paper-backed editions on magazine and newspaper counters and in all kinds of retail outlets. The attempt to provide inexpensive books was not new; from the middle of the nineteenth century German Tauchnitz editions had made English and German authors available in cheap printings. But the great expansion came when publishers discovered that by printing books as they did magazines, on high-speed rotary presses, and selling them in quantity they could make a profitable business. Following the lead of the British Penguin series, publishers reprinted standard works and published new ones in inexpensive pocket editions. Since the paper-backed book trade depended on wide circulation, books began to appear not only in bookstalls and on tobacco counters, but in department stores and even grocery shops.

The paper-backs covered a multitude of subjects. The earliest ones were either well-known books, reprinted on the assumption that people would buy paper-backed editions because they were cheap, or else 'penny dreadfuls'. Later, publishers began to offer a mixture of detective, adventure, and science fiction, reprints of famous novels and plays, guides to birds, minerals, stamps, psychoanalysis, and treatises on subjects varying from political theory to the great religions and from archaeology to music—in fact, any and all subjects which appeared likely to have public appeal. The immense range of interest to which the ever-changing array of new titles was addressed bore witness to the fact that, though expressions of mass culture were often garish, fragmentary and crude, they also reflected a new awareness of the world beyond the tiny circle of any one person's circumscribed life and a lively effort to encompass at least some part of its meaning.

In the communist countries where every effort was made to develop a nation of readers out of the newly literate workers and peasants, millions of cheap books were published and distributed and libraries were established in factories, farms, schools and other centres. Editions of Russian classics, the works of Soviet writers, and foreign works from Europe, America and Asia were put out in editions of more than 100,000 copies; they appeared in Russian and in the various languages of the Soviet republics. At the Brussels World's Fair in 1958, the State Publishing House of Fiction and Poetry of the USSR received the Grand Prix for the wide range of the books which it published.

2. *The cinema**

Of all the kinds of entertainment available in the twentieth century probably the one that most people had in common was the cinema. From the 1920s on, more and more people went to the pictures, some occasionally, and some often. Figures for 1952 showed the British to be going on an average of 25 times a year, New Zealanders 18 times, Australians 16, and Americans 15; but whatever the nationality—French, German, Japanese, Indian, Mexican or any other—people all over the world shared a taste for the movies. They shared too the personalities and the stories which went to make up this world of illusion created by the twentieth century's 'story-teller of the people'.

The development of the cinema reflected the constant interaction between the producer, testing out his medium and his market, and the public, res-

* For discussion of the cinema as a form of art, see Chapter XXXI, Literature and the Arts, pp. 1265–71.

ponding to the spectacles which it was offered and having its outlook shaped by them. In no other form of leisure-time activity was the role of the producer so important and the nature and quality of the entertainment so dependent on the circumstances and exigencies of production. The making of films was a complex and costly affair and their distribution required elaborate organization and equipment. The motion picture as a medium lent itself to use at all levels of entertainment and art, but the economics of film production required a mass audience. Film producers strove constantly to find formulae which would ensure a mass appeal, and they repeated each successful pattern until a drop in box office receipts showed that it would no longer attract the public.

As a form of entertainment the cinema was dominated throughout the period by Hollywood except in the communist-controlled areas, where these films did not penetrate. Up to the second world war Hollywood provided 70–80 per cent of the films shown in the non-communist countries and even in the 1950s it continued to supply as many as two-thirds of the films exhibited in these areas. A review of the cinema as a form of entertainment during these years, therefore, must give major place to the phenomenon of Hollywood and its impact in the shaping of mass culture, although producers in other countries made greater contributions to the development of the film as an art form and although in the years after the second world war growing national film industries, especially in Asia, were supplying audiences at home and were entering world markets.

The American motion picture industry was built up by men who shared the background and tastes of the masses to whom they appealed. The initial entrepreneurs included a number of former fur workers and salesmen who operated bright, cheap little penny arcades where people from crowded city neighbourhoods could find a variety of machines that provided amusement, including peep-hole motion pictures for a penny a look. The most successful of the arcade owners made enough money to open small theatres which showed short films for a small admission fee, or vaudeville houses which included moving pictures among their acts. When these entrepreneurs became the major Hollywood producers, they continued to think in terms of the recent immigrants and other city workers who had crowded the penny arcades, and they learned only gradually that the public would respond to more sustained, sophisticated and artistic entertainment.

In Europe, by contrast, films were initially an extension of the theatre, and after the first experimental stages the theatre producers who developed them thought in terms of theatre audiences and the film as a form of art.

Until the first world war the centre of the film world was in Europe, but after 1915 it shifted to the United States because the industry there had audience and financial backing unequalled elsewhere. By that time the American 'penny arcade' men had acquired chains of theatres around the country and had organized large producing companies. Representatives of some of the biggest and richest corporations in the United States sat on their boards of directors. In short, the films had become part of big business.

After a period of intense competition the major American motion picture companies emerged as combinations of producing, distributing and exhibiting units. In the early years producers made films and rented them on the open

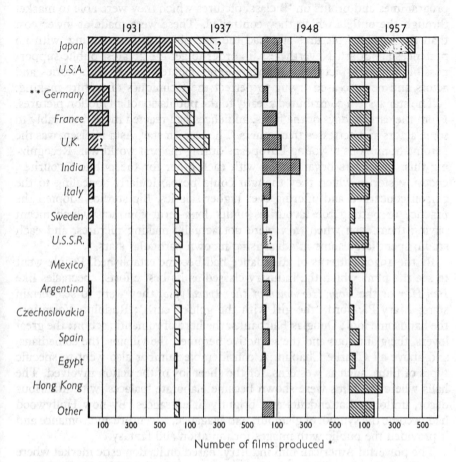

CHART XXVI. World Production of Motion Pictures.
Source: *U.N. Statistical Yearbook*, 1951, 1960.

market to exhibitors but, as the industry grew, some of the richer producers began to collect theatres in order to ensure places to show their films. Owners of big theatre chains in their turn collected producing studios in the effort to have some control over charges and to ensure films for their theatres. The resulting combinations had large resources at their command and, by the nature of their struggle for survival, were intent on pleasing a mass public.

For years both producers and exhibitors underestimated what the public would take. They developed the custom of making a few first-rate pictures aimed at attaining the highest standards while relying for the bulk of their programmes and profits on 'B class' pictures which they were able to market through the outlets which they controlled. These were made at lower cost than the 'A class' pictures and had the sole object of entertaining, with no pretences about art. Nevertheless, in order to get the greatest public support possible for such pictures, producers experimented widely with stories and actors and never ceased trying to perfect the techniques of picture making.

The star system contributed greatly to the popularity of all motion pictures. From the earliest days of the films, audiences had reacted more favourably to some actors and actresses than others. The Danish star, Asta Nielsen, was the heroine of millions of young Europeans during the first world war. Recognizing this, producers began to vie with each other for the public favourites, choosing stories which they thought could be particularly appealing to the person concerned and offering ever higher salaries. Big studios adopted the practice of putting the favourites under long-term contracts which meant paying them even when they were not actually making pictures, and each studio spent large sums in advertising its own particular stars.

By the 1920s patterns of attendance had become established. People went to see the films which the industry classed as its best efforts, spectacles like *Ben Hur* or the *Four Horsemen of the Apocalypse*; they went to see certain stars: Mary Pickford, 'the girl with the golden curls'; Rudolph Valentino, the handsome idol; Douglas Fairbanks, the hero of romantic action; the great lovers, the glamorous and the seductive heroines, the villains, the comedians, and above all Charlie Chaplin. A considerable number also went to specific types of films, such as westerns, for the sheer joy of the action involved. The halls where the films were shown became elaborate 'palaces' with luxurious décor, uniformed attendants and brightly lit entrances. By now Hollywood had become the symbol of glamour, extravagance, adventure and romance and it provided the public with images for imitation and fantasy.

The powerful American film industry, based on its domestic market where two-fifths of the world's motion picture houses were located, expanded its operations abroad. By 1925 American films were being shown in seventy countries, with their subtitles translated into thirty-seven languages. Eighty per cent of all the feature films shown in Britain were American and 60 per cent of those shown in Germany, which ranked next in total film production. Yet despite the predominance of Hollywood, the European industries continued to make film history, and pictures by the great producers in Germany, Russia, France, Denmark and elsewhere won world renown.

In these circumstances European producers appealed to their governments for aid on the ground that the cinema was a national interest as much as any other form of art or communication. The British Parliament passed an Act in 1927 requiring that a percentage of all films shown must be of British origin and putting limitations on imported films. Other countries made similar attempts to foster their own film industries by means of differential taxation, import regulation, or requiring their exhibitors to show a proportion of the home product.

In 1926 came sound. Although the technical means to achieve it had existed from the early years of the century, it was not introduced until rapidly declining American attendance figures made Hollywood aware that the public wanted something new. The first films with a synchronized musical score and with dialogue were immediate successes and the industry recognized that it must make whatever adjustments a changeover to sound might require. Pictures began to depend on dialogue as well as action and spectacle for their appeal; witty social commentaries and pleasant films about everyday life proved unexpectedly popular. Fine actors with especially effective voices, such as Greta Garbo, rose in favour.

Once sound had been accepted and mastered, the cinema developed the world patterns which existed until after the second world war. The United States, France and Britain dominated the world's screens during these years. The American industry produced many excellent feature pictures, a high percentage of the world's newsreels and animated cartoons, but it also went on producing great quantities of second- and third-rate love and adventure stories. Its mastery of technique made these pictures acceptable to audiences around the world when nothing else was available, but some of Hollywood's leaders warned that it must improve the general calibre of its pictures if it wanted to keep public favour.

The French achieved international pre-eminence in the realm of artistic films. The best of the French films always aimed at select audiences, though the industry also made ordinary films for commercial distribution. Russian films of the 1920s and 1930s were noted for their realism, their close-up studies of human types and the dramatic intensity with which they conveyed their message. The British developed a school of documentary film-making which won critical acclaim and proved most useful during the second world war as an instrument of propaganda and reporting. They also had a sizeable world audience for the best of their feature films, especially those which combined humour and suspense, or such a dramatic masterpiece as *Henry V*.

After the second world war, the world film situation changed, as new and expanding local film industries reduced Hollywood's pre-eminence and television provided a competing source of entertainment. American films underwent a gradual transformation which led to the production of a smaller number of pictures annually, but these generally of a higher standard. During the war years people had gone to see virtually anything; but when television came the public stayed home. In an effort to regain favour Hollywood exploited colour and the wide screen to the limit of their possibilities; it made more pictures on location, thus achieving authentic background and local colour; it produced fewer cheap Class B pictures; it did more social reporting, and it began to try to cope with the reality of human emotions, as distinguished from its earlier largely external approach. Yet though it cut down the number of films, it continued to be the largest producer until after 1955 when Japan and India surpassed the United States in the number of pictures produced.

Britain and France continued to make and export high-quality films, and other nations also began to gain recognition. Italian films attracted attention, both those with bitter realism and those which gave a more suave and humorous treatment of society. Swedish films had a high reputation generally and a few, like the nature film about an otter, *The Great Adventure*, were considered among the most beautiful films made. More Mexican films also began to appear abroad. Canadian documentaries, produced by the National Film Board and translated into five languages, went all over the world. The USSR used films extensively both for instruction and entertainment, and developed regional film industries with the languages and materials of the Soviet republics. In the 1950s vivid Russian films, such as *The Cranes are Flying*, reappeared on the world market, as did some from West Germany. Asian film industries followed the general lines of those in America and Europe, developing their own patterns of glamour, romance, and extravagance, their favourite stars, their musical entertainment, their spectacles and their dramas of daily life. The pace was closer to the long, diffuse forms of entertainment to which Asian audiences were accustomed than to the fast pace and dramatic tension of American and European films.

The most highly developed of the Asian film industries, the Japanese, dated from the early days of the cinema, but it was only after the reorganization which followed the second world war that Japanese films entered the world market. Then their few outstanding art films won prizes in international contests and received world-wide acclaim for their exquisite photography and sensitive portrayals. Most Japanese films continued to offer their people romances out of the past, gay scenes of modern life, sensitive views of nature and highly popular romantic dramas involving the conflict between personal love and family duty.

Indian films relied heavily on music, dance and costume effects for their appeal. They also included romance, the portrayal of high society, and historical drama and biography. An Indian film enquiry board in 1951 complained that the films pandered to a low level of taste and principle and failed to serve as an instrument to promote attitudes in line with the social and cultural development of the country. The Indian government itself produced newsreels and short documentary or educational films which exhibitors were required to show along with each commercial film. After 1955 a few Indian films containing realistic portrayals of daily life received international recognition and were widely shown abroad. The main export of Indian films was to places where there were Indian audiences in Africa, south-east Asia and the Middle East.

In the years after the second world war other substantial film industries producing for the Asian market developed in Singapore, Hong Kong, Manila and Formosa. Those of Singapore, Hong Kong and Formosa made chiefly musical pictures and comedies; the Filipino industry followed the Japanese and Indian in presenting costume dramas based on early history and legends. For films about modern life, family problems were the key themes, especially harsh in-laws, a perennial subject in Asian literature. The Chinese People's Republic used the cinema extensively to carry communist principles throughout the country, frequently using a modified form of the traditional Chinese opera.

Although Hollywood and European pictures continued to be shown in Tokyo, Bangkok and Bombay in the 1950s, Asian films were providing the principal motion picture fare for the audiences in Asian countries. They were creating their own images for fantasy and imitation and were helping to define the mass culture which was taking shape in these lands.

As film producers and film audiences throughout the world interacted upon each other, some forces tended to debase and others to elevate the quality of the product and therewith its influence on the cultural life of the people. Over the years these pressures tended to raise the level of the mass entertainment which the films offered.

The world's literary classics, both great novels and great plays, became the common property of all viewers, as they never would have been in written form, and their presentation on the screen stimulated viewers to become readers. As audiences developed more discrimination and were less ready to flock to anything which might be offered, film critics writing for newspapers and popular magazines became more influential. From 1929 on, the Motion Picture Academy of America presented annual awards, known as Oscars, based on a combination of the critics' and the people's choice, which carried prestige and were a way of attracting audiences to the films named. The popularity of some films of outstanding excellence was further evidence of the level to which popular taste had risen by the 1950s. The picture which broke all records by the length of its run in a major New York theatre was the British film, *The Red Shoes*, a distinguished work of art combining all the special expressiveness of films—shifting scenes, colour, dance, music—in a drama of a ballet dancer's conflict between her profession and her love, which played continuously to capacity audiences for two years.

The result of the wide diffusion of films, both nationally and internationally, was to introduce new ideas and new approaches to life to many people otherwise insulated from such variety of experience. It brought a sense of the cultural diversity of the world, however distorted the view which was often conveyed. In the words of the British committee which investigated the films in the 1920s, the cinema was 'undoubtedly a most important factor in the education of all classes of the community, in the spread of national culture and in presenting national ideas and customs to the world. Its potentialities moreover in shaping the ideas of the very large number to whom it appeals are almost unlimited.'* No other medium had quite the world spread, nor reached as many different kinds of people, as the cinema.

3. *Radio*

Radio and, later, television were the instruments which brought entertainment and mass culture into the home. They made both the world of reality and the world of make-believe a part of the daily lives of men, women and children, intimately, continuously, insistently and without effort on the part of the listener. From early dawn until far into the night, the housewife in her kitchen, the father home from work and the child home from school had but to turn a knob to bring music or news, drama, sports or information to where they were. These sounds would travel with the motorist along the highway or go with the holiday-maker to sea; they filled the air in eating places, stores, public squares, factories, buses. They were the constant accompaniment of everyday life in the second quarter of the twentieth century.

Broadcasting of entertainment and news did not begin until the 1920s, though wireless had been used as an instrument of communication from the opening of the century. It was inaugurated in 1920 when a radio station in Pittsburgh, USA, broadcast the result of the American presidential election before the newspapers had had time to print the news. The public was immediately interested, and it only remained to build on this interest with further experiments. Stations in the United States and Britain began to transmit regular programmes and soon stations elsewhere followed suit.

The earliest programmes were made up of news, music and novelties— the magnified heartbeats of a butterfly or voices from a submarine—but shortly sports reporting and other popular programmes appeared. At first stations broadcast for only a few hours at a time, but before long they had programmes extending from early morning exercises through news and music, sketches and jokes to keep housewives entertained while they did their chores, to afternoon programmes for children, and sports and variety programmes for the evening hours. People began to look to the radio for the latest news—some even suggested that the new medium would supplant newspapers altogether—and for the latest melodies from new musical shows before the sheet music or the records were on sale in local shops—and for a continuous flow of free entertainment such as never had been known before.

The sale of radio sets went up by leaps and bounds as people became increasingly interested in what they could hear over the air-waves. In the United States, where the radio very soon began to seem indispensable, the number of

---

* Quoted in *The British Film Industry*, a report by P.E.P. (Political and Economic Planning, London, 1952), p. 13.

homes with radio sets rose from 60,000 in 1922 to 3,500,000 by 1925, and 9,000,000 by 1929; the number of broadcasting stations increased during the same years from 30 to 57 to 618. In other countries the rate of expansion was less rapid, but everywhere the new communications medium, with its almost unlimited potentialities, grew in popularity. The United States had half of the world's total, but the number of sets ran to many millions in the USSR, the United Kingdom, other European and Commonwealth countries and Japan, and to many thousands in virtually every country in the world. However remote the region and whether the reception was in homes, gathering places or the open air, radio was providing entertainment and ideas for people in all lands.

In the course of the 1920s and 1930s, three general patterns of organization and financing evolved which affected the manner in which the radio would be used and the programmes heard over it: the private enterprise system with active competition among stations and a minimum of government control, characteristic of the United States, the Latin American countries, Japan and, in part, of Canada and Australia; the public corporation system exemplified by the British Broadcasting Corporation; and the system of direct government ownership and control of broadcasting operations characteristic of the communist countries, of most new Asian and African states and, in combination with one of the other systems, also used in European and British commonwealth areas.

In the United States, with its multitude of radio stations, broadcasting was financed by advertisers who paid for the privilege of announcing their wares to listeners attracted by an entertainment programme, while listeners paid nothing directly for the entertainment they received, beyond the original cost of their receiving sets. Under this system radio was regarded as a source of entertainment and only very incidentally as a means of education. Most programmes were light; if they were informative, they were varied and dramatic. They were short, or were broken up into a variety of music, dialogue and comment, with frequent interruptions for advertising. Advertising itself became a form of entertainment in order to hold the attention of the listener. Since the federal law required that a certain amount of time be devoted to public service programmes as a condition of receiving a licence to use the air-waves, there were always a certain number of programmes devoted to serious music, discussions of public issues or presentations of information on such subjects as farming or child care, as well as to the latest news and weather.

Even more than the mass magazines, the radio was under pressure to interest the largest possible audience, for the programme to which people listened was the one which advertisers were willing to support. The types of programmes which made up this all-appeal mass entertainment contained variety shows combining comedy skits and the latest popular songs, quiz programmes, sporting events, serialized stories of ordinary people and their emotional crises, mystery dramas, westerns, interviews with public figures and quantities of music, some live and much recorded. Advertising itself, moreover, became part of radio entertainment as advertisers couched more and more of their appeals in entertainment forms.

The main programmes throughout the United States were those provided through four major networks supported by national advertising, although large numbers of local stations operated in most cities of any size, supported by local advertisers and presenting local performers or local interviews, along with recorded music. The large sums paid by advertisers to the networks made it possible to hire the best dramatic, musical and newscasting talent for these programmes, but the listening public could enjoy them only at the cost of constant exposure to a stream of advertising and a tendency toward sameness at the level of maximum popularity. As a result, various educational institutions began experimenting with stations of their own which attempted to programme on the basis of different interests or tastes. So also did local 'good music' stations established in a number of major cities in the 1940s with programmes made up chiefly of classical and serious modern music.

In other countries where radio broadcasting was supported by advertising, a similar pattern and type of mass-appeal programme resulted, with some variation in the extent to which time was set aside for educational broadcasts and in the way in which such time was used.

Where broadcasting was carried on by a public or semi-public agency, it was not necessary to aim all programmes at the widest possible audience, and programmes were designed for distinct bodies of listeners. Even in these systems, however, some of the same pressures toward popular types of programmes were at work.

The British Broadcasting Corporation, operated as a publicly authorized monopoly subject to parliamentary review, made a definite attempt to interest audiences at three different educational levels: the Light Programme, primarily for entertainment, offered variety shows, popular music, popular drama and human interest stories; the Home Service, also designed to attract a wide audience, gave programmes dealing with the arts, science and world affairs at levels which did not demand specialized knowledge, symphony concerts, dramatizations of famous novels, talks, discussions and children's programmes; while the Third Programme was deliberately experimental without regard for popular taste. Started in 1946 with the hope that it would in the long run raise the level of all British programmes, the Third Programme attracted an unexpectedly wide range of listeners. Offering new music, experimental plays, lectures presenting new knowledge and thought-provoking analyses of current events, it proved so successful that Italy, Spain, Greece, Germany and France all devised similar programmes, and educational stations in the United States, British commonwealth and Latin American countries made use of its transcriptions for some of their broadcasts. Even so, the BBC in the late 1950s reduced Third Programme time and offered instead the more popular and practical Network Three programmes designed for listeners interested in specific hobbies or in learning languages.

The state radios of the communist states were used primarily for educational purposes as well as to give people throughout the country a common outlook and interpretation of events. The USSR developed its broadcasting services under the auspices of the ministry of education, which provided national programmes and supervised the programmes of regional and local stations. It built redistribution facilities to give overall coverage to rural areas and provided millions of wired receivers and loudspeakers in public places to ensure that as many people as possible could listen to broadcasts. Radio Moscow regularly broadcast three simultaneous programmes for listeners throughout the USSR, a programme of general interest, a programme for specialized groups such as agricultural and industrial workers, and a programme of formal educational broadcasts. In the decade after the second world war the Moscow radio, together with more than a hundred local committees of radio information located in the capitals of the Union republics and other administrative centres, provided programmes of these types throughout the Soviet Union in some seventy languages. All these programmes informed the working people about the latest in science and technology and popularized the finest works of Russian and world literature, music, fine arts. The popular 'universities of culture' and 'universities of artistic training' programmes devoted to science and engineering, agricultural science and other subjects offered opportunities both for use of leisure and for raising the people's educational and cultural standards. Great importance was also attached to children's programmes.

In other countries with state or public corporation systems, radio was used educationally. The Indian government designed its publicly operated radio programmes for a variety of purposes, including promoting the use of Hindi as a national language and familiarizing the public with traditional Indian music. About 75 per cent of all Australian schools subscribed to that country's school broadcasts in the 1950s. Norway experimented with short-wave educational programmes beamed to its merchant fleet plying the seven seas. But even government-operated radio systems were under some pressure to adapt their programmes to popular tastes in order to hold the attention of the listeners.

Whatever the character of its programmes, radio tended to provide its listeners with a common set of images and body of experience. The styles of speech and patterns of entertainment of New York or Hollywood, London, Paris, or Moscow were heard uniformly throughout the areas to which the broadcasts were beamed, whether in rural areas or cities, in the homes of the rich or the poor, of educated or uneducated. Naturally, there was a certain amount of listener choice, and some receiving sets stood silent much of the time while others operated constantly. But the choice was limited and the radio was ever present in the home, the car, the workshop, constantly speak-

ing the words and playing the music heard in other homes and shops across
the land. The radio came to people; they did not have to go out to seek it,
as they did the cinema, or the books and magazines which they borrowed
or bought or the sports events which they attended. Thus the radio was one
of the most potent instruments giving a common content to mass cultures
throughout the world.

4. *Television*

Television, introduced after the second world war, threatened both the
cinema and the radio. People no longer had to go to the cinema for visual
entertainment; it was theirs for the turning of a button in their homes. And
with the added dimension of the picture, television produced a richer fare
than the radio could offer with sound alone. The immediate effect was to cut
down attendance at the cinema and cause many of the most popular radio
programmes to shift over to the new medium. After a time, however, it
became apparent that the small television screen placed limitations on the
range of visual presentation, while the radio could continue as an accompaniment to other activity without demanding the full attention and fixed
position which television required.

Since 1930, broadcasters in the United States, United Kingdom, USSR,
France and Germany had experimented with ways of exploiting the addition of sight to sound broadcasting, but regular television programming
did not begin till the late 1940s. Once it was introduced, television spread like
wildfire. All over the world people were ready to adopt it and incorporate it
into their way of life, for they had become thoroughly accustomed to the
ever-present radio in the home and to turning to the cinema for entertainment,
while the industrial structure present in these industries was readily adaptable
to the new device.

By 1955 television was operating on a regular basis in 34 countries, was
being developed in 12 others and was in the planning stages in another 19.
The United States took a strong initial lead with an estimated 80 per cent of
the world's sets in 1955, but everywhere the number of receivers skyrocketed.
The number of sets did not fully reveal the extent of television's influence,
moreover, for many sets were located in taverns, waiting rooms, clubs and
other public places.

The organizational pattern of the television industry in most countries
tended to follow that of radio, with some modifications. In the United States
most television programmes, like radio, were supported by advertising. The
British Broadcasting Corporation introduced a television programme, but
in 1955 in answer to public pressure an independent television system was
added, financed by commercial advertising. In most European countries
television broadcasting was operated under state control. In Latin American
countries it was commercially sponsored. In the USSR and the people's
democracies it was widely extended as part of the state system.

Television programming resembled that worked out for radio except that it had a smaller proportion of music, more drama and used moving picture films as a major resource. In Russia all motion picture features were automatically shown on television, but elsewhere films only became available as studios released their old cinema libraries. Mostly these were films made a number of years before, but some proved a tremendous hit on television and revived the names and fame of many former favourites.

Variety, quiz and human interest shows were consistently popular everywhere, as were sports events which could often be witnessed in the home more clearly than in the arena as the camera brought a close-up of each play. Drama ranged from fine performances of well-known plays to the general run of serialized romances, westerns and mystery dramas. Documentaries reconstructed past events, pictured phases of contemporary life or recorded the processes of nature. Leading figures were brought to the screen for interviews or to take part in discussions of public issues.

A distinctive feature of television was that it enabled the public to witness directly many public events—a political convention, the coronation of a Pope, a meeting of the United Nations. Millions of people felt intimately acquainted with public figures, for they had watched their expressions and mannerisms during a debate or when they were not the centre of the stage as well as when they were addressing the public through the television medium. Public figures, in their turn, consciously strove to cultivate their 'television personality' and to arrange their television appearances according to the techniques required for dramatic success.

At the start television carried over directly the forms of radio and cinema, but all programmes were not equally appropriate to the new medium. After an initial period of imitation and experiment, certain types of programmes began to emerge as particularly well adapted to television presentation in a small space with a small image and in the intimacy of the home—plays, panel discussions such as the 'Brains Trust' programme presented weekly by the BBC, informational programmes which involved exploration or demonstration, quiz programmes where the audience could identify with the person questioned.

A major problem of television broadcasting was how to get enough talent to occupy all the time at the broadcaster's disposal. The costs of a production for one short showing on television were tremendous. Even where stations broadcast only five or six hours a night, it proved difficult to get enough first-class material. More and more American programmes were filmed rather than presented live, and their production was carried on in Hollywood studios closely associated with those of the film industry.

International programme co-operation helped to meet this situation. From 1954 on, Europe had an exchange relay network known as Eurovision which grouped eight countries—Belgium, Denmark, France, the German Federal Republic, the Netherlands, Italy, Switzerland and the United

Kingdom. Its first telecast showed the 1954 world football championship matches from Switzerland. Programmes of this type continued to be especially popular but in the course of time, besides sports and entertainment, Eurovision provided intimate glimpses of life as it was lived by ordinary people in each of these countries, thus helping viewers to gain understanding of people in other lands. From 1953 on, the United States provided filmed television programmes for Latin America and later began to make them available to Japanese and European stations.

Although the sheer volume of television programmes tended to limit their average quality, there were signs that audiences which had become accustomed to seeing or hearing first-rate talent at the cinema and over the air would not readily be satisfied with second-rate performances on television, once the novelty had worn off. Some of the same factors that were tending to raise the level of mass entertainment in the cinema and radio were thus at work in this new medium as well.

5. Theatre groups

Amateur dramatics remained a popular form of leisure-time activity, in spite of the ubiquity of films and television. The quality and seriousness of amateur performances ranged from the near-professional levels attained by some community and university theatre groups to simple skits for the self-entertainment of clubs or school plays which combined education and entertainment. In the 1920s and 1930s there was a strong movement to establish 'little theatres' with community support, sometimes to provide an outlet for local dramatic talent, sometimes to show plays which did not find a place on the professional stage. As cities expanded their public recreation services they included dramatics among the activities offered.

Outside the main urban centres repertory theatres provided a principal source of dramatic entertainment. Such theatres, which often served as proving grounds for both dramatists and actors, were sometimes closer to the amateur community theatre and at others to the professional stage. They received support from private organizations and public bodies interested in the arts.

In the USSR and the people's democracies workers and peasants were encouraged to enjoy and appreciate music, theatre and ballet, both as spectators and through amateur participation. Professional theatres, ballets and orchestras were maintained in cities and towns of all sizes—some 500 repertory theatres in the USSR in the 1950s—while amateur musical groups or people's art theatres rehearsed and performed in factories, collective farms and educational institutions. These professional and amateur groups drew on the rich background of Russian music, ballet and theatre and also on the traditional folk expression of the different regions. Where there was no theatre tradition the art was developed, as in the Uzbek republic which had no indigenous theatre but by the 1950s was maintaining twenty-six theatrical companies which presented performances of all types. Regional and national arts festivals stimulated these developments.

6. *Popular music and dancing*

Especially for young people, listening to popular music and dancing were favourite ways to spend leisure time. It was in fact chiefly the adolescents who gave successive styles of music and forms of dancing their popularity, supplying the market for popular records and sheet music, and much of the audience for popular music over the air. The current styles in these forms of expression were often of no interest or even distasteful to most adults but were central features of the adolescents' sub-culture.

Popular music in the twentieth century had three principal origins, musical shows, jazz bands and hit songs which caught the public's fancy when sung by a radio entertainer or night club singer. With the aid of radio and television, new songs or tunes could become the favourites of millions overnight. New hits were heard over and over again on radio programmes, sales of records and sheet music soared and then, generally, as quickly dropped. The songs could be simple and even crude and the rendering poor by any musical standards, but if the singer was the current idol of the adolescent listeners or if the song successfully expressed a current mood, the song became for the moment a part of the mass culture.

Musical shows proved extremely popular with audiences which could see them and supplied a large proportion of the popular music which was played constantly over the air and on gramophones in the home. The European type, referred to as the Viennese operetta in recognition of the master of light music, Johann Strauss (1825–99), was gay, tuneful and romantic. These operettas had their heyday in the years before the first world war, and tunes from some of the favourites of that period by the Strausses, the Hungarian Franz Lehar (1870–1948), and others retained their popularity or were revived repeatedly in the following decades.

After the first world war the type of musical show which had the greatest vogue and provided much of the popular music was the American musical comedy which took shape as a distinct entertainment form on Broadway. It had its origin in the tradition of the vaudeville stage and the accident of a fire in 1866 in a New York theatre where a French ballet troupe was to perform. When the manager of the troupe put his ballet on to the vaudeville stage in order to avoid a financial loss and interspersed a miscellany of song and dance, he inaugurated a type of entertainment which depended on a combination of catchy songs and the attraction of 'girls, girls, girls'.

In the course of time the thread on which these features were strung became firmer and musical comedies included more semblance of plot, characterization and dramatic structure. Shows depended less on the attraction of scantily clad, shapely chorus girls and more on costume and stage effects, humour and gay or elaborate dance routines. Well-constructed musical scores and clever lyrics, both romantic and satiric, became the basis for a show's popularity. Some shows came to be based on full-scale plays, like the hit of the 1955 Broadway season, *My Fair Lady*, based on George Bernard Shaw's play *Pygmalion*.

The best of the musical comedies were consistently the leading theatrical attractions on Broadway, and some of them ran to packed houses for years while their songs were heard over every radio and records of the hits or the entire score reached tremendous sales. In time the most popular shows were filmed and they played to millions of people who already knew and relished many of the tunes. By the 1950s this popular form of entertainment appeared to be moving toward a distinct art form. It remained a show that was assembled out of disparate parts, rather than an integral whole that was composed; it was still essentially theatrical entertainment made up of music and dance and spectacle, strung on a story. But some critics saw the best of the musical comedies as commentaries on life which derived a unity of form from the common attitude expressed by the décor, the music, the dance, the lyrics, the performers, the direction. And the particular outlook which the musical comedy expressed theatrically, extravagantly and exuberantly, was a sense of the ridiculousness of cherished institutions combined with a warm affection for the very institutions which the show held up to satire.

While musical comedies provided most of the popular songs, jazz bands furnished the popular dance music. As a musical form, jazz traced its origin to West African rhythms combined with melodic and harmonic forms and musical structure derived from European marches, hymns, work songs and popular ballads. Sociologically it was the music through which New Orleans Negroes released their pent-up energy, anger, nostalgia, sadness, sense of irony and exuberance. When it invaded the night clubs and dance floors of the rest of the United States at the time of the first world war, it brought shock to most adults who were attuned to the suave romanticism of the popular music of the time, and a welcome release to the young.

The essence of jazz was improvisation, so it could never be wholly dissociated from the men who made it. Famous bands had their followers whom they drew to the cafés and dance halls where they played regularly and to dances elsewhere for which they provided the music. Their several styles became familiar through recordings played over the air or on the gramophone, and jazz enthusiasts relished the virtuosity of their favourite performers.

In the course of the years new bands developed new styles, and a succession of distinct types commanded popular favour. The original jazz style of the years before 1914 was heavily accented and lively, exciting to dance to. From the mid-1920s the jerky New Orleans rhythms gave way to smoother and more sophisticated tempos known as 'swing'. By the years after the second world war jazz had ceased to be primarily music to dance to; it had become music to hear and composers were beginning to give serious study to the jazz idiom and to write jazz compositions. The adolescents of the 1950s no longer found jazz exciting to dance to, for it had become, for them, intellectual and sophisticated, the subject of critics' attention and of formal festivals which drew large and serious adult crowds.

Both as dance music and music to listen to, the various forms of jazz spread around the world and groups of young people in many lands danced to it, listened to it, discussed it and imitated it.

A succession of popular forms of dancing caught up each successive generation of young people. Lively dances to jazz rhythms such as the Charleston were popular in the 1920s, the slow fox trot in the 1930s. South American rumbas and tangos won wide favour, followed by variations of them like the samba. 'Jive' was the dance form of young addicts of fast jazz; consisting of elaborate improvisations of a simple basic step, it represented each individual's attempt to express his own reaction to the savage beat of the music. By the mid-1950s, 'rock and roll' was being danced with energetic abandon to a thumping, formless mixture of western cowboy songs, South American dance music and popularized jazz.

Where folk music remained alive, as it did in much of eastern Europe and among many of the peoples of the Soviet Union, traditional melodies and rhythms formed the basis for popular songs and dances. It was part of the policy of these countries to encourage the appreciation and use of folk culture, as in Hungary where the composer, Zoltan Kodaly (1882–   ), worked unceasingly to introduce folk music into the schools and to stimulate the development of choral groups which became well-known throughout the region.

7. Sports

Sports provided the people of the twentieth century with much of their entertainment, many of their heroes, a means of personal development or relaxation and, for some, an avenue of advancement. The vast majority of people played only as amateurs, but in the role of spectators they provided the opportunity for professional athletes to achieve a status akin to that of the great popular entertainers.

Large numbers of people in all the western countries liked to spend their Saturday or Sunday afternoons at football or baseball games or at the races. Others liked to go in their free evenings to prize fights or to hockey games, basketball games, ice skating contests or wrestling matches. More than sixty million Americans turned out each spring and summer for a succession of major and minor league baseball games, and fifteen million for high school, college and professional football games. Their British, French, Italian and South American counterparts went in proportionate numbers to football games or the races. The enormous interest in sports was reflected in the space devoted to sports reporting in the press.

Television brought the best of the spectator sports events into the home, and at first had the effect of reducing attendance. A 1950 survey in the United

States, however, showed that people who had owned their television sets for more than a year or two not only watched games on television, but also attended sports events more than non-television owners. Regardless of the impact of television, spectator sports went on drawing huge crowds for whom the excitement of a race or a competitive game was intensified by actual attendance at the arena, and the opportunity to join actively in the betting.

Personal participation in sports grew markedly with the greater amount of leisure time. People had always hunted and fished, bowled and played games. More and more people joined in these and other activities, stimulated by a growing enthusiasm for physical fitness and aided by the provision of playing fields, tennis courts, golf links, pools and skating rinks by municipalities, schools, private clubs or commercial enterprises. Schools and clubs encouraged team sports because of their value in teaching co-operative effort as well as for the fun they gave participants and spectators.

Sports held an important place in the planned use of leisure in the socialist societies. With the goal of positive health and harmonious physical development, active participation in all manner of sports was encouraged for both men and women. Teams from thousands of factories, farms, schools and towns competed in many fields, and successful athletes were honoured as local and national heroes. Every effort was made to send champion performers to international contests.

Each country had sports it particularly loved: the British played cricket, Americans baseball; Germans hiked, Norwegians and Swiss skied, Italians cycled. But varied activities were popular everywhere. Water sports attracted a large and growing body of people. Swimming became increasingly popular and public pools came to be accepted as a part of normal recreational facilities. But swimming was only the beginning. Especially after the second world war, numbers of people took to water-skiing or donned flippers and oxygen cylinders and went exploring in the underwater world which had previously been known only to professional divers. Some speared fish, others observed the habits of marine life or photographed the weird and beautiful world they had so recently discovered.

Millions bought boats. Boating had long been a widespread holiday pastime in Scandinavian countries, Britain and Australia, but in other countries it had been looked on mainly as a rich man's sport. In 1957, however, a New York paper noted that America's outstanding shift in recreational habits had been from highways to waterways, as yachting, the sport of millionaires and princes, had come down to more democratic size and become 'pleasure boating'.

But if millions headed for rivers, lakes and seaside to spend their leisure hours in or on the water, other millions were land lovers who preferred to walk rather than swim, climb rather than dive, and to investigate the habits of animals instead of fish. Some walkers were amateur geologists or botanists. Others bought field glasses, rose early and went out to watch and listen to the birds. The most vigorous pitted their strength against mountains, and blazed trails and built hostels to accommodate themselves and others in all the great mountain chains of the western countries.

Young and old became outdoor campers. City children in mounting numbers learned to live in the open in summer camps conducted by youth organizations and welfare agencies or as private enterprises. Families packed camping equipment into their cars and pitched their tents on the camp sites supplied with water, sanitary facilities and fireplaces in public parks or private camping grounds, or in farmers' fields. The number of persons camping for a week-end or longer holiday on the camp sites provided by national and state park services in the United States rose by leaps and bounds from the 1930s on, reaching a million or more before the interruption of wartime petrol rationing and at least doubling every five years in the decade following the war.

Winter sports, especially skiing, gained ever larger numbers of devoted adherents, and newspapers began to carry detailed reports on the condition of the snow in various ski resorts as a guide to city dwellers who were planning week-ends or holidays. For those who preferred skating, many cities had rinks where the ice was carefully swept and controlled and people could indulge their fancy for either speed or figure skating without dependence on outside weather. In the cities, bowling alleys and roller-skating rinks, squash courts, swimming pools and gymnasiums provided winter exercise and a release from tension to men and women who were confined in offices or factories for the greater part of their working days.

National and international competitions were held in all lines of sport, amateur and professional, both among teams and individuals. The most famous of the international contests, the Olympic Games, were revived in the 1890s by a Frenchman, Baron Pierre de Coubertin, who was interested in fostering the amateur spirit in sports in order to preserve those characteristics of nobility and chivalry which distinguished sports in the past. The first successful games took place in London in 1908 and thereafter they were held every four years, except in wartime, in major centres around the world. Athletic organizations in the competing nations spent the years between the games in competitive elimination matches to choose the best teams and individuals to represent their nations at the next Olympics. The intensity of this preparation and the support given to it by organized bodies, facilitated, especially in the communist countries, by the state, aroused serious discussion of the line between amateur and professional in sports and questions as to whether the amateur spirit was in fact being fostered and preserved.

8. Travel

With the aid of automobile and aeroplane, travel became a well-nigh universal way to spend week-ends, annual and public holidays. If the weather was propitious, the first question in more and more families was 'where shall we go?' A little trip in the family car might mean visiting some place of special interest, exploring unfamiliar territory or a picnic at a favourite spot, but the result was the same everywhere; roads full of traffic.

Foreign travel came to be possible and attractive for increasing numbers of people. Some travelled to the Olympics or other major sporting events, others to musical events like the Edinburgh or Salzburg festivals, or to special art exhibitions or to international trade fairs. Some travelled for scenery and some for historical monuments. Gourmets went to France to eat, mountain climbers to Switzerland to conquer the Alps. All manner of coach tours offered people opportunities for inexpensive holiday trips. Whatever people did for their main relaxation during the working months of the year was likely to influence their choice of place and event when they planned their travels.

As more and more people travelled and came to know the countries closest to them and had made the traditional 'grand tour' of European centres, their desire to get further afield grew. If money permitted they began travelling to parts of the world where tourism had not been common, and thus began to learn about cultures and regions quite foreign to their own. In this way travel, like so many of the other leisure-time pursuits which people enjoyed, acted also as a form of education.

In the USSR travel took the form mainly of trips to museums, historic sites, festivals or major cities, and of holidays to the many rest homes and holiday resorts available to workers in the Crimea, Caucasus and other parts of the country. Trips of special interest were enjoyed as rewards for superior productivity on the job or for outstanding performance in sports or the arts.

9. *Hobbies*

For many—perhaps most—people, one or more of an endless variety of hobbies constituted an area of interest which supplemented, and sometimes competed with, their major occupation. Occasionally a hobby even led to a change of profession, as in the case of the amateur pet-fancier who became the head of one of the world's largest zoos; more often a hobby provided the basis for an occupation after retirement. Since hobbies required the individual to be active and to become expert to at least some degree, they served an educational as well as a recreational role and were the means of developing people's tastes, knowledge and capacities.

(a) *Gardening.* Gardening ranked as the number one hobby of all groups in Britain, the United States and most of western Europe, except for city dwellers who had no outdoor space, and even some of these indulged their taste through window boxes or plots in community gardens. The Dutch bulb growers were able to make a fortune out of supplying improved varieties of bulbs to other nations and the business of improving and adapting seeds, plants and fertilizers for the use of amateur gardeners proved lucrative in many countries.

Some gardeners gave their greatest attention to the design of their gardens, others to growing perfect roses or dahlias or even vegetables, others to special herb or rock gardens or to collecting wild flowers. All these special interests provided a basis for community, regional and national flower shows, for books and magazines about how to attain desired results and news of what other people with similar interests were doing, and for garden clubs, which existed in most towns or suburban communities to provide social activities and an opportunity to exchange specimens and information on gardening techniques.

(b) *Arts and crafts.* All manner of arts and crafts were immensely popular. Art classes and study groups in drawing, water colour, oil painting, modelling and in crafts such as weaving, woodworking, enamelling or pottery flourished. Sometimes the classes were neighbourhood or shop groups, working for pleasure under a semi-professional teacher; sometimes they were organized units of adult education courses offered by an educational or welfare agency. Amateur artist societies in communist countries received special state encouragement. Everywhere members of classes or groups exhibited their work in neighbourhood displays held in social halls, public squares, schools, shops, museums, libraries and public buildings, and entered those judged to be the best in city-wide and national exhibits, in addition to using them to decorate their homes. All this activity not only gave people a chance to express themselves creatively, but it also helped to raise the general level of taste, for people learned basic principles of art as they experimented with design, colour and technique.

The home itself, especially under suburban living conditions, often provided an opportunity to apply old craft techniques such as carpentry and metal working, which were revived for pleasure when they were no longer necessities of existence. Many householders enjoyed decorating their houses or repairing the structure, equipment or furnishings. In the 1950s 'do-it-yourself' became a craze in many areas where the high cost of labour added a practical consideration to the delights of developing manual or artistic skills and acquiring new knowledge.

(c) *Photography.* Photography was one of the most distinctive of twentieth-century hobbies. Camera addicts bought finer and finer cameras and experimented with faster and faster film as it came on the market, and with colour film. Amateurs and professionals joined camera clubs and held exhibitions in which the prizes went to those who had produced the most effective studies, judged in terms of art as well as technique. To get the best results possible, serious photographers read up on chemistry and the theory of light and processed their own films. They studied photographic magazines, camera annuals, and books representing the best work of the world's most famous photographers, and then experimented with their own studies of people and places, animals and flowers. By the 1950s millions of people were recording home events and travel scenes in amateur motion pictures.

(d) *Music.* Music, always a favourite hobby in some circles and among those with musical talent, became widely popular as radio and gramophone made all types available in the home and as tape recorders enabled amateurs to experiment with sound.

At the beginning of the century, when people suggested an evening of music they usually meant gathering around a piano to sing popular songs or, if they were serious musicians, playing in a string or wind ensemble or singing in a choir. In the following years people with musical talent still played musical instruments and joined choirs and quartets, or school, community or shop orchestras for the pleasure of making music themselves as well as enjoying that of others. In many cases radio and television acted as stimulants, for when individuals or groups were good enough they might find opportunity to be heard on local programmes.

The gramophone won great new audiences for both classical and popular music. Still only a scientific toy at the beginning of the century, it came into its own when musicians began to use it to document their work and commercial companies started to offer presses of Artur Rubinstein playing Chopin or Enrico Caruso singing Italian opera. At first only a few people collected these records, but as radio broadened the musical taste of its audience more and more people began to collect records—and as the market expanded the selection grew more varied. After the invention of high fidelity systems, long-playing records and unbreakable light plastic discs, the popularity of record collecting grew still greater and people began to buy their discs not only in terms of the particular music or the artist but of the technical quality of the recording. Record collectors became expert in their chosen field, broadening their knowledge through radio programmes and reading, and deepening it by listening to their own records.

The tape recorder permitted people to make records themselves. Some people used it merely to record outstanding radio performances or to record their own musical efforts, but others used it as a means of experimenting with sounds and combination of sounds: car horns, church bells, train whistles, the crashing of surf, the howling of the wind. The most elaborate experiments came from France in what the French called *musique concrète*. By slowing sounds and quickening them and by combinations of all kinds, experimenters achieved in music something similar to surrealist experiments in art.

(e) *Mechanical hobbies*. The many gadgets of the machine age provided a series of hobbies to those who grew up surrounded by them. Automobile engines held great fascination, especially for young people, who delighted in taking old machines to pieces, recombining parts, rigging them so as to provide extra power, and converting a broken-down old car into a high-speed vehicle.

Radio, from its start, became a favourite hobby of hundreds of thousands of men and boys who experimented with sending out messages and receiving signals from the most distant points which their homebuilt equipment could reach, establishing contacts and participating in human dramas far away. Judging from the number of 'radio hams' who secured licences and the increase in their average age in later years, this was a hobby which did not depend for its appeal on the novelty of the invention or the youth of the experimenters. Other electronic equipment also lent itself to experimentation, particularly high fidelity sound systems which were among the most popular of the gadget hobbies in the 1950s.

Thus the use of the new leisure in all these ways modified the manner of life and affected the outlook of the people. In a sense it might be said that the twentieth century, with all its devices permitting people to have and use leisure, was making it possible for the masses of people in industrial countries to do what leisure classes had always done—enjoy themselves and develop their personalities through self-education of whatever kind pleased them most. But the forms of the mass leisure went beyond the kind of personal development and individual enjoyment associated with the use of leisure by a privileged few. No less than other major features of twentieth-century life—new occupational patterns, urban living, mobility, the prolongation of life by medical science—the new mass leisure and its many uses were re-making the cultural life of a growing proportion of mankind.

NOTE TO CHAPTER XXVII

1. Soviet commentators call attention to the following point: An important part is played in the planning of leisure in the USSR by state and public institutions, by trade union and youth organizations and by sport, artistic and other voluntary bodies which are autonomous in their activity and not subordinated to state control.

The radio, television, cinema, professional theatres and orchestras, museums, gardens and parks, part of the clubs and libraries, and most publishing houses are under the direction of state institutions. Sanatoria, holiday homes, tourist excursion bases and many clubs and libraries are run by the trade unions. The programmes of the People's Universities of Culture and the public lecture halls as well as amateur art activities, athletics and some museums and publishing houses come under the control of public bodies.

PART THREE

THE SELF-IMAGE AND ASPIRATIONS OF THE PEOPLES OF THE WORLD

INTRODUCTION

A MONG the factors which helped to shape the cultural development of mankind in the twentieth century were the aspirations of nations and groups, which gave direction to their efforts to bring the actuality of their lives into line with their ideals. In the atmosphere of constant change, the sense of new possibilities moved men both to dream and to act. Drives toward self-realization in one form or another were part of the dynamics of these years.

The three chapters which follow examine some of the principal self-images in terms of which nation-states and other groups with a sense of common identity visualized themselves and voiced their common aspirations. These chapters are not concerned with the economic forces or power factors affecting the course of historical events or the institutional changes taking place,* but rather with the outlooks of groups of people and the manner in which these helped to focus the conscious efforts of individuals and groups. The validity of these self-images and aspirations is not examined according to any independent criteria; except for some indication of their relation to broad currents such as nationalism, each of these views is examined in its own terms, on the assumption that an understanding of the cultural developments of any period requires an appreciation of how people appeared in their own eyes.

In this era of nationalism, collective aspirations were shaped and expressed in national terms. The internal policies of states and their external relations embodied the views which the people of each nation-state held of their collective destiny. These national formulations were both political and cultural. In a world which entered the twentieth century dominated culturally as well as politically by Europe, drives for cultural expression and recognition were no less real than those for the achievement of political aims. The assertion of cultural independence and uniqueness was a motive force for colonial peoples seeking political independence and others whose political independence was assured but whose cultural expression was undeveloped or overshadowed. Drives for cultural reorientation within countries were associated with changes in the position of ethnic or social groups. In a number of regions, multi-cultural societies faced the problem of how to achieve a cultural *modus vivendi* in the conflict between intensified nationalism and drives for cultural autonomy.

Any attempt to present the self-images of nations and the aspirations which guided their public policies encounters the difficulty that each nation was unique, the aspirations of nations were not static, and no single attitude permeated all sections, classes, occupations, ethnic elements and personal outlooks even in the most centrally administered or totalitarian states. In this

* See Chapters I–V and XXI–XXIII.

and the following chapter it will be possible to touch on only the major features of the aspirations of nations and peoples which contributed to the cultural development of mankind during these years.

In each case the national self-image which had been noted has been that of the dominant element which provided articulate leadership. To avoid an endless catalogue of more than eighty nations, countries have been grouped together on the basis of certain common features. It must be remembered, however, that the basis chosen is only one of the groupings which could have been made, that the outlook of the dominant element in one state was often shared by non-dominant elements elsewhere, and that the divisions and conflicts of view within nations were no less significant than the differences among nation-states.

Within each society, moreover, individuals belonging to disadvantaged categories sought the opportunity to participate as full members of the societies of which they were a part. Most notably, workers whose labour had been treated as a commodity sought bargaining power and status as human beings, peasants yearned for their own land, women strove for a more equal status with men, and racial minorities or castes subject to discrimination struggled for full citizenship. Such groups resorted to organization and launched a variety of efforts to gain for themselves the same measure of freedom and respect as was accorded to those who enjoyed a favoured position in their societies.

Whether as nations or as culture groups or as individuals seeking first-class citizenship, people in the twentieth century made conscious efforts to bring about the social changes which would enable them to achieve their aspirations and to realize the self-images in terms of which they projected their hopes.[1,2]

CHAPTER XXVIII

THE SELF-IMAGE AND ASPIRATIONS
OF NATIONS

To a degree rare in previous ages, the nation-state of the twentieth century, with its demand for supreme, collective loyalty, provided the terms in which its members defined their outlook and desires.

The process of formulating national aims, as well as the nature of the formulation, varied from centralized authoritarian states to those with a looser structure which provided more channels for reflecting the popular view. But everywhere there was in some degree a reciprocal interaction between the people and the state, even where a small element imposed its will on the majority and sustained it by dictatorial means.

The most common ingredient in the national aspirations of peoples was the drive for equality of national status. As the great empires broke up after the first world war and colonial peoples became nations in their own right after the second world war, states large and small saw themselves as autonomous units legally on a par with others. The more than eighty nations which composed the United Nations in the late 1950s shared a sense of their identity as nations, the assumption that their voice, however weak, would be heard and that their integrity, however precarious, should be respected. Although the great powers dominated the United Nations as they had the League of Nations and the world before the first world war they moved among a growing number of others who enjoyed, at least technically, the status of equally responsible members of the family of nations.[3]

At the heart of the idea of equality of national status were two concepts, self-determination and self-realization. The first of these was an essentially political idea, derived from the doctrines of liberalism and democracy and the view of man as a rational being capable of determining his own fate and entitled to do so. In the form inherited by the twentieth century, it had not been applied outside the political arena. It was, moreover, at least partly a negative concept, implying primarily freedom from outside interference and asserting national independence and sovereignty.

The self-realization of peoples was a broader concept which involved not only independence from alien rule or domination but the positive cultural orientation of a people and their development in accord with their systems of values. It could mean very different things according to each nation's image of itself. For the liberal democratic states, historically committed to self-determination in its more limited, political sense, it meant a widening of the concept to encompass economic and social as well as political aspects of life;

for those who saw world history in Marxian terms, it meant the identification of a people with the historical process of dialectical materialism and a unified all-out effort to build a socialist society; in the hands of romantic nationalists, such as Mussolini, it became an effort to recreate the greatness of a distant past; to those such as Hitler or the Afrikaans leaders of South Africa, who saw their race endowed with a mission, it could mean a drive for dominance over 'lesser' peoples within and without the state; for those committed to a religion which made religious and political life coterminous it might mean, as in Pakistan, the effort to define a state in religious terms or, as in Israel, to create a homeland for members of a religious faith; for non-European countries in the days of European expansion, such as Japan or Afghanistan, it might mean such adoption of European ways or such insulation from European impact as would provide the strength to resist; for the peoples of Africa, emerging from tribalism and European domination, it could mean a groping for terms on which to enter the modern world. But whatever the form, the drive for self-realization could be summed up in the simple answer of Prime Minister Nehru to the question of what he regarded as major trends in the twentieth century: 'I think that people want to be themselves.'*

I. LIBERAL DEMOCRACY:
THE SELF-IMAGE OF WESTERN EUROPE

The countries of western Europe saw themselves as the bearers of the great liberal tradition which had come down from the Greeks by way of the Renaissance and they assumed that they were in the vanguard in the evolution of human society. The liberal tradition had provided the cultural milieu within which science and technology had taken root and a dynamic industrial civilization had grown and flourished. Western Europeans and those who represented the extension of western European culture in other lands assumed that the values of their society and the institutions of liberal democracy were favourable to this development and that these values could fruitfully be adopted and applied throughout the world.

The liberal tradition of western Europe was essentially the product of a series of historical events: the fourteenth-century defeat of the French knighthood by the Flemish burghers and the death of the Duke of Burgundy at the hands of the Swiss in the fifteenth century; the Dutch wars of independence in the sixteenth century, which were at the same time a social and economic revolution; the English social, economic and political revolutions of the seventeenth century and the French and American revolutions of the eighteenth century. The main intellectual roots were in the Renaissance, the scientific revolution of the seventeenth century and the eighteenth-century Enlightenment. In economic terms it rested on the destruction of feudalism

---

* Interview, January 12, 1956.

and the rise of commerce and industry together with the middle classes which were the products and instruments of these developments.

European liberalism was rooted in the idea of human nature which had been part of European thought from the time of the Renaissance, and especially from the period of the Enlightenment—that man is rational, responsible and capable of exercising control over his own affairs. In this view the fullest development of the individual is the aim of society; it is also the means of achieving that aim and the measure of success. The initiative and enterprise of the individual and the process of free inquiry bring benefit to all. The individual is endowed with essential and inherent rights which must be protected and respected. These rights were historically defined in terms of freedom—freedom to enjoy life, liberty and property except as restrained by due process of law, freedom of association, freedom of thought, speech and religion. The history of mankind was seen in terms of the progressive emancipation of the human spirit from ignorance, superstition, and authority and from submergence of the individual in the group.

It was a Europe conceived on these lines, theoretically convinced of the equality of man while in practice maintaining the right and duty to rule and guide the 'less advanced' parts of the world, that had partitioned Africa and established dominion over most of Asia. This lofty ideal of a world in progress led by Europe was a reflection of the self-consciousness of European civilization. From the time of the Roman empire and the spread of Christianity, Europe had seen itself as guarding the heritage of Rome, Greece, Egypt and the Near East and as confessing the only true religion. This self-image of Europe as the bearer of world culture, a view which was even shared, perhaps subconsciously, by many who opposed colonialism, reconciled in the European mind the principles of liberalism and the practice of imperialism.

The classic statements of rights and freedoms which expressed basic liberal principles had been contained in the British Bill of Rights, the American Declaration of Independence and the Bill of Rights of the American Constitution, and the French Declaration of the Rights of Man and of the Citizen. Restated by President Woodrow Wilson as the war aims of the Allies in the first world war, the principles were essentially unchanged, and enjoyed high prestige at victory; they were embodied in the political institutions of the successor states in eastern Europe and in the German Weimar republic.

When a President of the United States again formulated the aims of the liberal democracies aligned in war, the formulation had changed. The 'four essential human freedoms' enumerated by President Franklin Roosevelt included a new freedom, 'freedom from want'. This was the formulation, with its implication of economic measures on behalf of all the people, that was adopted by the new states which emerged after the second world war, when victory had again raised the prestige of liberal democracy. And these were the terms in which the United Nations Charter declared its purpose 'to promote social progress and better standards of life in larger freedom' and the UN

Universal Declaration of Human Rights defined the rights of 'all human beings'.

The newer formulation of liberal democracy was often far from clear, for it was not easy to reconcile the essentials of individualism with the realities of economic organization and the administration of welfare services. But however imprecise their concepts and uncertain their practices, the liberal democracies retained their faith in human capacity and in the rational potentialities of man, in spite of evidence of his irrationality, and they sought to strengthen these capacities in order to enable him to function more fully, more rationally and more humanely.[4, 5]

Although western Europe shared in many ways a common civilization, it was sharply divided by the boundaries between national states each of which maintained its own form of European culture. In the course of the twentieth century the conflicting interests of European national states, reaching all over the world, were sufficiently intense to lead to two disastrous world wars. Each European nation saw itself as unique, and projected its self-image not only in terms of its special emphasis within the liberal tradition but in terms of identification with its historic past. The elements of which liberal principles were compounded—British legal and parliamentary institutions, French rationalism and egalitarianism, and bourgeois economics often reinforced by Protestant ethics—carried different weight in different places. In some countries two or even more competing self-images persisted through the years and found expression during this period in alternations of policy or the domination of one self-image over the other.

For the British the main focus of democratic liberalism was on the parliamentary processes, the common law and non-interference in ordinary daily life. In spite of an aristocratic social structure and authoritarian colonial role, liberal principles were very deeply engrained in the British outlook; according to their own self-image they were the bearers of these principles to other parts of the world where their influence extended. With this view they carried the legal and political institutions of liberal democracy to areas under their rule, and when it became clear that they could no longer hold these areas in subjection they tried to help them to become liberal democratic states. At home British society moved toward its democratic ideal at an accelerated pace, taking on the shape of a welfare state, and it found no difficulty in assimilating many of the principles of democratic socialism to its basic liberal institutions and point of view.

In France, by contrast, the main components of liberalism were the rationalism of the Enlightenment and the belief in human equality regardless of race or position, rather than any set of political institutions. Successive changes in constitutional forms and weakness and confusion within the parliamentary system did not negate the basically liberal orientation of French society. At the same time, France saw herself as the heir of Charlemagne, Louis XIV and Napoleon. Her sense of power was expressed in terms of *la gloire*, the glory of a great nation, rather than in dominion, although she assumed, far more completely than did Britain, that she would place the stamp of her own culture on her subject peoples. The self-image of France was always more intellectual and cultural than it was political, and she viewed her 'civilizing mission' in terms of the rationalism and humanism of the French view of life.

Even more clearly than did the French, the Germans saw themselves in two distinct and opposing terms, both of which were the fruit of a conscious effort to create a self-image. The Germans saw themselves on the one hand as *das Volk von Dichter und Denker*—the people of poets and thinkers—and on the other hand as *das Herrenvolk*—the master race. Both these self-images originated in the eighteenth century and were in a measure a reaction to a sense of frustration. The German middle class, excluded from a political role in the feudal structure dominated by the princes of some hundred petty states and by the Prussian monarchy, turned to literature and philosophy and produced the Germany of Lessing, Goethe, Schiller and Heine, of Kant and Hegel and the other great 'poets and thinkers' of the era. Meanwhile the self-image of the *Herrenvolk* grew from the frustration of the princes, and especially of the Prussian Hohenzollerns, whose desire to play a prominent part in European politics was not realized until the late nineteenth and early twentieth century, and was then lost again in the self-evoked catastrophe of 1918, to be revived for the short period of the Third Reich and lost again in its collapse.

In the smaller countries of western Europe where liberal democracy was rooted and strong, liberalism rested on a firm historic base of owning farmers and capitalist enterprise and it developed a strong welfare component in these years. Each of these countries, too, saw itself both as the bearer of a common European culture and in terms of its unique history and the quality of its life.

After the second world war a series of motives led to the idea of a united Europe, not only in the traditional sense of a common European culture but as an economic-defensive unity in the face of the new strength of the United States and the Soviet Union. In the initial phases the steps taken involved only part of the western European area, they revealed the persistent strength of national interests, and even the most comprehensive proposals stopped at the line which set off from western Europe those sections of central and eastern Europe which had become part of the communist system.

Outside western Europe the liberal tradition formed a more or less important part of the national self-image in four areas: the overseas communities created by western European migration—the United States and Canada, Australia and New Zealand; the republics of South and Central America which won their independence from Spain and Portugal in the first quarter of the nineteenth century; the states of eastern Europe that took shape after the first world war; and the new states that came into being with the break-up of the colonial empires after the second world war.

The most complete assumption that liberal democracy defined the character of national life was in the countries of North America and Australasia. In these new societies, created by people who had sought new homes in their quest for one or another form of freedom or opportunity, there were no remnants of an earlier feudal society, of monarchical or other authority, of religious orthodoxy or of a rigid social system which could offer an alternative to the conception of the liberal society and state. So completely and exclusively were liberal principles embedded in these societies, in fact, that they became a kind of orthodoxy in themselves. Other possible social and political values lacked reality, or appeared more as aberrations than as serious alternatives. Canada relied on these principles to sustain a working union between her French-speaking and English-speaking peoples, to hold together small population groups separated by great, empty distances, and to regulate her relations with a neighbour ten times her size across 3,900 miles of unguarded frontier. Australia and New Zealand were the first countries to extend the franchise to women. Though such expressions as the first world war slogan 'make the world safe for democracy' or the term 'free world' applied to non-communist countries might sound hollow to others, for the people of the United States they carried a sense of reality. Pragmatic modifications of institutions and practices might be adopted and assimilated, but the essential image remained.

In the course of the years some of the old meanings for the terms of liberalism and democracy became less and less clear, especially for the growing urban populations in these countries. In the United States uncertainty expressed itself after both world wars in hysterical waves of suspicion which were levelled ostensibly against those who rejected liberal principles, but which actually expressed authoritarian attitudes and sometimes even attacked those who stood for liberal ideals. The issue was confused by the fact that in other countries both fascists and communists had shown themselves prepared to take advantage of liberal democratic freedoms and rights, only to destroy those rights and freedoms once they had gained power.[6] In the divided world of mid-century, moreover, even the subordination of the military to civil authority began to seem less important than national security. But however uncertain the evolving forms, however indistinct the image and however strong the self-criticism, the peoples of these countries saw themselves in no other terms than those of the basic liberalism which had always provided the outward formulation and the inner drive of their societies.

The states of South and Central America had inherited their institutions and attitudes from Spain and Portugal, where the principles of the English Bill of Rights, the commercial revolution and the Enlightenment had never been an integral part of the culture. At the time of their independence each of the formerly Spanish areas had formally adopted the principles of liberal democracy, modelling their constitutions on that of the United States; Portugal's former dominion, Brazil, eventually followed suit. For all these countries liberal democracy remained a stated ideal. Some such as Uruguay made it a dominant component of their self-image; Mexico used it as a pragmatic guide for realizing, over the years, the fruits of a political and social revolution; others came back to democratic principles repeatedly after periods when the authoritarian, paternalistic, *élitiste* values which were deeply rooted in their Iberian traditions had been in the ascendant; some, at mid-century, had not yet found the means to make liberal democracy a substantial reality in their societies.

For the states of eastern Europe established after the first world war liberal principles were one of the components in their self-images. The tradition of Jan Hus was alive for the Czechs, of Kosciusko for the Poles, of Kossuth for the Hungarians. But other traditions associated with the continuing feudal societies were stronger elements in the nationalism which emerged, and in the years of crisis these were evoked by the leadership of each of the new states except Czechoslovakia. Under Thomas Masaryk and Eduard Beneš, that country, the most industrially developed in the region, identified itself with the liberal democratic tradition of western Europe until it, like its neighbours, was subjugated by the Nazis. When all of these states emerged again after the second world war, their leadership soon passed into the hands of the communists, and it was in terms of revolutionary socialism rather than of liberal democracy that they overthrew the institutions associated with feudalism, clericalism and the types of social structure and authority which had been dominant in much of the area.

In the new states which came into existence after the second world war, the concept of a secular nation-state, with equality of citizenship and civil rights, was an essentially new idea. For most of the new states liberal democratic principles were not an integral part of the new nationalism, even though they were expressed in the first constitutions of each of the states. Asian traditions tended to identify peoples in terms of the religious community to which they belonged or to rely on authoritarian rule; communism offered an obvious alternative to liberalism, especially after the communist régime took over in China and launched a vigorous programme of development. In these circumstances India looked upon itself, and was looked to by others, as the major test of whether liberal democracy could be realized as a national ideal in Asia and Africa. For only in India was liberal democracy an essential part of the self-image, at least of the leadership and the educated elements, and not merely a newly adopted state form scarcely related to their conception of themselves.[7]

II. MARXIST–LENINIST COMMUNISM[8]

The USSR and the states which acquired communist governments in the years after the second world war regarded themselves as the results and the instruments of the dialectical historical process, described by Karl Marx and Friedrich Engels and elaborated to cover new circumstances by Lenin, which inevitably and irreversibly was leading mankind towards socialism and ultimately communism. They saw themselves as the inheritors of the great cultural traditions of the past and the creators of a new day in human history in which man, having conquered nature, would be freed from the 'empire of necessity' where nature had held him in her grip. In this view all history prior to the achievement of communism is the 'pre-history' of human emancipation.

According to the concept of the historical process set forth by Marx, the determining factor in the development of human society is the process of production. The forces inherent in industrial production must ultimately work themselves out into the classless society, for capitalism breeds within itself the means of its destruction and its inner contradictions lead eventually to revolutionary change. The instrument of revolution and the builder of the classless society, once the exploiting classes have been suppressed, is the proletariat.

Marx had assumed that the revolution would come in countries which had reached an advanced stage of capitalism and that the socialist society would follow the capitalist as a later stage in historical development. He had expected the leadership in the world revolution to come from advanced industrial countries—Germany, Britain. He had seen the common bond among the workers of the world as closer and more binding than unity of the workers with the exploiting classes within the same nation.

In the light of conditions at the opening of the twentieth century, however, when the major capitalist countries were enjoying both rising productivity and profits from colonial areas, and workers in these countries were organizing to share to some extent the returns from these sources rather than to overthrow their régimes, Lenin extended the Marxian analysis to envisage the possibility that revolution would come in industrially backward areas. In Lenin's view capitalism in its advanced stages maintained itself at home and brought relative prosperity to its own workers by exploiting the weaker economies abroad, either within colonial empires or in other less-developed areas. In so doing it set in motion two forces, the antagonism of the colonial and industrially weaker peoples against their exploiters, and the conflict among the capitalist-imperialists for markets and sources of raw materials. These conflicts, Lenin believed, would lead inevitably to wars which would weaken the capitalist economies and bring about their ultimate downfall.

Lenin also designed an instrument which could bring about revolution in the absence or immaturity of a revolutionary proletariat. This was the centralized Party, the vanguard of the working class, which would formulate the will of the proletariat and would activate it. It would also activate the peasants. Whereas Marx, thinking in terms of the revolution in an advanced stage of industrial development, had focused on the industrial proletariat, Lenin included peasants in his concept of the revolutionary potential of countries where peasants made up the vast majority of the population.

The successful October revolution validated Lenin's formula for the revolutionary leadership by a select, centralized Party, and showed the possibility of enlisting the support of the peasants for the revolutionary action of the urban proletariat under the Party leadership. It confirmed the fact that revolution could start in a relatively backward country, although Lenin and his associates hoped and expected that revolution would follow in the advanced countries, and that these would provide the USSR during the period of its economic weakness both with a shield against capitalist powers and the advanced technology for industrial development.

When the abortive German revolution of 1918 failed, it became apparent that for the time being revolution was not going to spread to the industrial countries and that the USSR would stand alone in a capitalist world. Although the leaders of the USSR believed that the contradictions of monopoly capitalism would eventually lead to self-destructive conflict among the capitalist economies, they faced the immediate situation of the USSR as the sole embodiment of the historical process of revolutionary change toward a classless society, forced to pursue a strategy of 'socialism in one country'.

In this situation the state assumed a much more positive role than had been envisaged in the original Marxian view. Marx had regarded the state as the instrument of class oppression in bourgeois society and had expected it to 'wither away' once class oppression had been terminated and a socialist society achieved. This concept remained as part of the ultimate picture of the final stage of society, following the ultimate world revolution. But so long as the USSR stood alone or communist societies existed in a divided world, the state was a necessary agency for administering the society and conducting the strategy of internal development and external policy.

Throughout the first forty years of its existence, this was the basic self-image in terms of which the leaders of the USSR shaped policy and guided the outlook and motivation of the people. Tactical changes in internal and external policies and the cruel exigencies of war did not alter the fundamentals. In this self-image the Soviet Union and all its people were building a socialist society in competition with the capitalist world. So long as this society was weaker than that of capitalism, it believed that it was threatened by what it presumed to be the need of capitalism to try to prevent the successful development of a socialist society. The USSR therefore must give priority to heavy industry and scientific advance as the basis for achieving a level of productivity equal to or surpassing that of the most advanced capitalist economies.

In the drive to realize this self-image all available resources were focused on the common objectives. Stalin saw the state as the main instrument to organize the society, to maintain unity, to exact necessary sacrifices and to resolve or suppress conflicts, and he built up its machinery for administration, police, propaganda, censorship and economic operation.

The full apparatus of education and training was dedicated to producing a people who were scientifically and technically equipped to operate a technically advanced and highly productive economy and who were oriented to the task of building a socialist society. Man was viewed as a rational being full of capabilities which were realized in relation to society. The resources of the arts and of mass communication were enlisted to project the reality in terms of the socialist ideal, on the assumption that if people thought in terms of the goal, they would act, under the leadership of the Communist party, in ways which would help to bring it about.

The Marxist–Leninist philosophy was a philosophy of action, designed to change the world, not merely to interpret it. Although it regarded the direction of the historical process as inevitable, it called for conscious action by the revolutionary class or group. Men who were aware of the historical process could align themselves with it and accelerate it. It was thus appropriate that socialist society should be continually pictured as it should be, or with emphasis on its constructive features, in order that present contradictions or imperfections might not confuse the sense of direction and impede action. Similarly capitalist society was to be seen in terms of the contradictions leading to its downfall in order that these might be enhanced. This manner of viewing the present in terms of the desired future was termed 'socialist realism'.

So the Communist party taught the Russian people to look upon the successful building of socialist society as an essential stage in the historical process of the world revolution inaugurated in October 1917. In order to carry out numerous socialist reforms it was first necessary to establish certain economic and cultural prerequisites by attaining an adequate level of industry and agriculture. With the main instruments and means of production in the hands of the proletarian state, enabling it to interfere actively in the country's economic life, much more favourable opportunities could be provided for the speedy setting up of these prerequisites than would be possible under the capitalist system. The historical experience of the Soviet Union was seen as demonstrating that the proletarian state could guide the activities of the working people and the working intelligentsia in the task of prompt, effective and expedient creation of an advanced industrial society.

After forty years of communist rule the Soviet people saw themselves as beginning the task of building the foundations for a communist society. The tremendous economic and political achievements of the Soviet Union in such a brief span of time ensured the complete and conclusive triumph of socialism in that country in the sense that the USSR felt itself fully guaranteed against the possibility of forcible restoration of capitalism. The new task was to create conditions of life, both material and cultural, which would encourage the desire of working people in all countries to remake life on the basis of new, communist principles. The Soviet Union invited capitalist countries to compete in attaining a higher standard of living for working people and in setting up the most favourable conditions for all-round harmonious development of all their forces and abilities, confident that it would win in this competition for it believed its economic system to be by far the more progressive of the two.

The USSR thus saw world events from 1917 on as confirming the Marxist–Leninist view of history. Success of the October revolution demonstrated that the period of transition from capitalism to socialism had acutally set in and must be effected through revolution and not evolution. The victory of revolution in backward Russia confirmed Lenin's prediction of revolution in countries with weaker economies. They saw the strength and growth of capitalist economies during the period as a temporary stabilization which merely made the contradictions of capitalism less apparent, while the world wars and the breaking away of colonial peoples were seen as demonstrations of Lenin's concept of the declining course of capitalist imperialism. The success of revolutions in eastern Europe and China after the second world war seemed to indicate that it was only a matter of time before the working people of more and more countries, led by the Communist party, would bring about change in their countries and become part of the world revolution.

In short, despite all of history's zig-zags the Soviet people saw the main process outlined by Marx—the process of transition from capitalism to socialism on a world-wide scale—as making steady progress and as constituting the dominant trend of the modern age. Whatever variety in form the transition might take, the essentials were identical and followed the theory elaborated by Marx, Engels and Lenin. The people of the Soviet Union were sure that the future belonged to the system whose foundations were being laid in the USSR and the people's democracies.

As the USSR ceased to be the only communist state and as it approached its goal of high productivity and displayed prowess in scientific fields, it saw itself moving to a new position as the leader of the expanded and expanding communist segment of the world. And it saw itself, in line with Lenin's prediction that the rising of the peoples of the East would be decisive in the world struggle for communism, as stimulating the underdeveloped peoples of the world to choose the communist path and align themselves with the course of history.

The communist countries outside of the USSR followed essentially the same Marxist–Leninist self-image. Yugoslavia rejected the Leninist principle of democratic centralism and saw the proletariat as carrying out its revolutionary role through workers' councils and other decentralized organs. Mao Tse-tung gave the peasants an even more important role in bringing communism to China than Lenin had envisioned in his concept of the peasants as supporting the efforts of the industrial workers. But wherever Marxism–Leninism furnished the basis of the national self-image, the people believed that in building a socialist society they were carrying out the irreversible and irrevocable laws of historical development.

III. ANTI-LIBERAL AUTHORITARIANISM

In the states where an authoritarian tradition was strong and liberal democracy never effectively replaced the remains of feudalism, anti-liberal authoritarianism reasserted itself and, in its extreme form, became intensified into totalitarianism.

During the years when liberal democracy had become integrated into the thought and action of northern and western Europe, North America and Australasia, the monarchies of Germany, Austria-Hungary and Russia continued to provide an alternative pattern which retained much of its force. Even after the fall of the monarchies themselves, the system which they had represented and the attitudes on which their system had rested furnished the basis for a resumption of authoritarianism when liberal democracy appeared inadequate to meet crises of inflation, depression and defeat. In Spain, Italy and Greece authoritarianism associated with economic and social inertia persisted behind a parliamentary façade. The concept of man as active, responsible and guiding himself rather than being guided by others, which was basic to liberal democracy, had never been widely accepted in traditionally authoritarian societies, especially where prevailing attitudes were conditioned by the Catholic Church's time-honoured view of man's weakness and its hierarchy of authority for his guidance.

In the pattern of the monarchies inherited by the twentieth century, an authoritarian ruler administered a power state through a bureaucracy, drawn from the ruling class, with the aid of the military, officered by members of the same class. In the late nineteenth century some parliamentary machinery had been added as an appendage to, rather than as the law-making body over, the ruler, bureaucracy and army. The growth of nationalism had furnished an emotional and ideological force which strengthened the authority of the state.

With the spread of liberal and socialist ideas, the traditional authoritarian rule had yielded to new forms, but in such a way as to preserve the essential authority. The rulers of central, eastern and southern Europe had used the power state to support the social and political structure of the old régime; but the spirit of nationalism called for the inclusion of the total population, not merely the ruling class, in the benefits of the state. Bismarck had shown the way by a combination of nationalism and social legislation which expanded the beneficiaries of the state and the basis of its power, without seriously undermining the dominance of the ruling class, or the authority of the monarch and the position of bureaucracy and army. In the process there was no weakening but rather an enhancing of the power of the state *vis-à-vis* the individual.

When the old structure of authority broke down in these societies, there was no effective transfer to popular sovereignty. Before the leaders of the successor states which followed the dissolution of the Hapsburg and Hohenzollern monarchies had more than begun to develop a democratic structure for the exercise of power, new pressures forced them to surrender authority to dictators who claimed to act for the benefit of the people. Throughout southern, central and eastern Europe parliamentary institutions appeared inadequate to deal with urgent problems requiring vigorous state action, and authoritarian habits were readily invoked by a charismatic leader—a Mussolini, Pilsudski, Horthy, Metaxas, de Rivera, or Hitler.

Authoritarianism as a positive principle of state organization received a twentieth-century formulation with Mussolini's accession to power in Italy in 1922. The symbol chosen by Mussolini, the *fasces* borne by Roman lictors as symbol of authority and of the binding together of all elements in the state, gave the name fascism not only to Italy's authoritarian régime but to similar patterns throughout the world.

The essence of the fascist state was unlimited authority. In the words of Mussolini: 'Our programme is simple: we wish to govern Italy. They ask us for programmes, but there are already too many. It is not programmes that are wanting for the salvation of Italy but men and will power.'

Fascism rejected completely and uncompromisingly the principles of liberalism and democracy as foolish and ineffective. For the conception of equality it substituted a permanent, beneficial, hierarchical order of society; for the rights and liberties of the individual, it substituted the rights of the state, a mystical entity to which the individual was subordinate; for the concept that the leaders should be the elected representatives of the people, responsible to them, it substituted the opposite concept that the people were responsible to their superiors who in turn were appointed by those above. As conceived by Mussolini, military discipline and obedience must permeate civilian life, for he exalted war as the highest function of the state and military activity as the highest duty and fundamental virtue of man. The objectives of the state were couched in terms of national greatness. In the case of Italy, Mussolini evoked a vision of the rebirth of the Roman empire.

The imperatives of fascist society were the imperatives of action; parliamentary and other institutions of liberalism were condemned as merely contributing to irresolution of the will. Only a leader was capable of making the swift and bold decisions called for by the 'inexorable dynamics' of the factual situation. Only unqualified obedience could translate the leader's decisions into effective action.

As a doctrine of authority, fascism implied that there could be no alternative foci of power and no alternative bases from which the leader's authority might be questioned or challenged. Since the leader knew intuitively what was best for the nation, he was beyond criticism even though national welfare was theoretically the overriding consideration. The doctrine implied the single party, the alignment of all instruments of education and propaganda—schools, press, radio—the suppression of independent associations, whether trade unions or other groups, and the bringing of every type of organization under the ultimate direction of the state. It rested on a view of human nature which denied the concept of man as a rational being capable of guiding his own destiny and asserted the view of man as weak and irresponsible, needing the guidance and direction of those with superior resolution, knowledge, courage and wisdom.

The revival of authoritarianism and the direct rejection of liberalism in principle and in practice spread during the 1920s and 1930s throughout eastern and southern Europe, and had its echoes in the strengthening of authoritarian tendencies in other parts of the world, notably in parts of Latin America and in Japan. The dictatorships which assumed power in one after another of the successor states of the Austro-Hungarian empire, in Greece and in Spain varied in the degree to which they were committed to the full implications of fascism as Mussolini had formulated them, but all had in common a conception of the power state, headed by undisputed authority which subordinated or suppressed individual rights, political parties and parliamentary institutions as inconsistent with the safety of the state, and all linked authoritarianism to nationalism.

In general, the dictatorships retained and strengthened the ruling classes of landowners and industrialists, and received the active support of these groups who hoped thereby to retain their position and power. They varied in the extent to which they involved militarization, but they were generally brought to power and headed by military men, or men who assumed a military pose, and their immediate followers adopted military trappings and symbols—black, brown or green shirts, and some form of the fascist salute. Each drew on the attitudes and symbols which were part of the national tradition and all invoked some vision of historic greatness projected into the future to define the national aspirations for which the people were called upon to make sacrifices.

The authoritarian states differed, too, in the relation between religious and secular authority. In Spain and in Austria clerical forces joined the secular, reinforcing each other. Where they did so the principle of corporatism—of syndical bodies with a measure of law-giving and executive authority over their members in the manner of mediaeval guilds—received support from the papal encyclical *Quadragesimo anno* in 1931. Mussolini at first received clerical support, along with that of the king and other conservative elements, but when he attempted to bring all education under his control, the Church challenged his power.

In each of the countries which adopted authoritarian systems during these years, the Church initially associated itself with the régime, or came to terms with it. But it was a potential source of dissension and of challenge to the tendency toward totalitarianism, for clerical authority derived from an alternative, supernatural source, not from the mystique of the state or the leader's will. Where the state carried through the integration of all institutions into a monolithic structure under the leader, as in Nazi Germany, the Church became an opponent of the régime.

The fascist states thus gave a new and intensified form to traditional views of human nature, of hierarchical society, of authority and of the place of military activity and military virtues. They drew upon religious as well as secular patterns of subordination. And they offered the appeal of a charismatic leader who embodied the national image and a vision of national greatness to lift the spirits of people who were confused or dismayed by the events of the inter-war years and had no commitment to the liberal principles which had seemed axiomatic to those who had tried to make them the basis for national life.

Authoritarianism in its fascist form met defeat in the second world war as monarchism had gone down in the first world war. Liberal democratic institutions were restored in Italy, Austria and Germany. The states of eastern Europe came under communist régimes. Authoritarianism survived only in the Iberian peninsula and for a time in several of the Latin American republics. But though the image of the authoritarian state lost its hold, the problem remained of how much authority is required to make a modern state effective and how people accustomed to authority may develop the degree of independence and responsibility which modern conditions demand. There remained the possibility of the resurgence of authoritarianism wherever the tradition of authority was strong or liberal democracy might fail to meet the problems of the modern age.

IV. RACIAL SUPERIORITY

1. *Nazi Germany*

While the fascist elaboration of the authoritarian state originated in Italy, it was Hitler's Germany which carried the idea to its farthest extent and which not only provided the strongest element in the fascist axis but imposed its image on other countries with authoritarian régimes.

The distinguishing feature of Nazi Germany, which at first set it apart from the merely authoritarian countries, was its racial dogma. In the hands of Adolf Hitler, authoritarianism, fascism and the leadership principle became racialism; the drive for a greater Germany was a drive to subject to the *Herrenvolk* not only the Jews, but the 'lesser' peoples of the European continent, especially the Slavs.

Like Mussolini, Hitler found a fertile soil for the development of his National Socialist movement in the disorder and disillusionment following the first world war. In defeated and occupied Germany, racked by runaway inflation, the effort of the Weimar republic to implant liberal democracy in place of the defeated Hohenzollern monarchy was fraught with immense difficulties. Many attitudes inherited from the nineteenth and early twentieth centuries provided a background for the acceptance of fascist principles and of racialist ideas.

Authoritarian habits were deeply ingrained in German society, and hierarchical status was recognized in modes of address and in patterns of education and occupation. The German romantic tradition, which had found expression during the nineteenth century in political theory and philosophy, literature and the arts, fostered the idea of a ruling *élite* and exalted the heroic leader. In this tradition German culture was endowed with special qualities of emotion and dynamic originality, in contrast to the 'artificial' intellectualism of western Europe; in its extreme forms it was anti-rational and anti-intellectual.

Nowhere in the world, except perhaps in Japan, was the military tradition stronger or were military virtues more highly regarded than in Prussia; leading political writers had repeatedly held that might is right. Nowhere did romantic nationalism have a stronger hold. The German state which achieved unification in 1871 was conceived as more than a political structure; it embodied the mystic unity of the *Volk*. As such, its mission was to carry German culture, and not a few voices had been raised calling for a pan-German unification of people of German stock, wherever they might be; still more had called for *Lebensraum*—living space—for the vigorous, expanding German people.

The doctrine of Nordic superiority had received support from many quarters during the nineteenth and early twentieth centuries, and not alone in Germany. Richard Wagner had glorified the ancient god-like heroes, conceived as the true type of German and the true embodiment of the German soul. Racial theorists, such as Count de Gobineau, a Frenchman, and Wagner's English son-in-law, H. S. Chamberlain, had ardent followers, and similar views aroused popular interest even in the United States where they influenced the immigration laws of the 1920s. Many people believed that the German *Herrenvolk* was destined to rule.

The concept of Nordic superiority and of racial purity had been linked with anti-semitism. To Wagner, to the Prussian polemicist Eugen Karl Dühring and to many others, the Jews had seemed to personify the antithesis of the qualities which were prized as 'German'. The conservative, aristocratic, romantic and nationalist elements had identified the Jew with Marxian socialism—Marx was himself a Jew—with cosmopolitanism, with urbanism and capitalism as against love of the land, and with rationalism as against 'blood and soil'.

The components of National Socialism were thus available from German tradition and experience when at first defeat, then inflation and finally economic depression offered the opportunity to someone who would integrate them into a movement through which a proud and defiant people could canalize its frustration and hate and could reach out for self-respect.

To this situation Hitler brought a ruthless intensity which galvanized the German people into action. The focus was his passionate anti-semitism. Although Jews had appeared to have been integrated in German society, and the restricted ghettos and recurrent pogroms which continued in eastern Europe had long since ceased to be part of the pattern of Jewish life in Germany, the undercurrent of anti-semitism proved extremely strong when Hitler identified all the evils which he attacked with the Jews. He had seen anti-semitism at work in Vienna during his struggling days before the first world war, where leaders of extremist parties had combined violent and scurrilous attacks on the Jews with both anti-capitalist and pan-German appeals. In his book *Mein Kampf* (1924) he recorded his view that 'it is part of a great leader's genius to make even widely separated adversaries appear as if they belonged to but one category', and the category in terms of which he focused all his own hate and that of his followers was the Jew.

In so doing he aroused the German people to share his passionate conviction that the Jews were in fact the embodiment of evil—whether as Jewish capitalists, or Jewish internationalists, or Jewish trade unionists, or Jewish intellectuals—and he led the nation first to degrade and then to exterminate all with Jewish blood. In time his view that the Jews were a sub-human category fit only for the gas chamber was not only imposed on the areas overrun by the Nazis before and during the second world war, bringing death to the vast majority of European Jews. It spread to fascist movements which had had no racial content originally, to turn Italian fascist policy against the small, assimilated Jewish population of Italy and to make anti-semitism one of the hallmarks of fascism the world around.

Hitler voiced especially the outlook and frustrations of the lower middle class from which he came, a class which felt itself despised by those above and threatened by those below. Before the first world war the upper *bourgeoisie* and the landholding aristocracy had shared the leadership of political, economic, military and social life and had filled the upper ranks of the civil service. The lower ranks of the bureaucracy and the petty tradesmen and artisans had found their position deteriorating as the industrial proletariat became organized and articulate and pressed for workers' rights. The post-war inflation struck them with especially devastating force. National Socialism was aimed against both the upper *bourgeoisie* and the 'Jewish' Marxist trade unions. Its anti-intellectualism rejected the intellectual classes and appealed to the romanticism so strong in German minds.[9]

In glorifying the military ideal in a disarmed Germany Hitler gave an outlet to one of the deepest frustrations. He offered this source of self-satisfaction and self-respect, moreover, to the little people who had not been privileged to enjoy it under the Prussian military system in which the officer cadres were recruited almost entirely from the upper classes of landed gentry and professional men. His brown-shirted storm troopers and *élite* black-shirts could enjoy the sense of identity with the military caste and the power of military force, while at the same time depending for their status wholly on Hitler who hence became indispensable to them as leader and symbol.

Since Hitler appeared to represent each of a number of different aspirations, he received support from many quarters. The regular army—*Reichswehr*—supported him for his military emphasis and intent to rearm the German Reich. Industrialists supported him as a bulwark against trade union organization and Marxist thought. Conservative and reactionary elements supported his attack on the liberal principles and parliamentary procedures of the Weimar republic. Many who felt threatened by the presence of Bolshevik Russia to the east, and who remembered the 1918 effort of the German communists to seize power as it fell from the Kaiser's hands, saw him as a defence against communism. And even those who opposed his methods and many of his ideas welcomed his reassertion of German nationalism, his repudiation of the treaty of Versailles, his vision of a Greater Germany, his renewal of the demand for *Lebensraum*. Each group thought that he spoke for them and none believed that he would have the desire and ultimately the power to subordinate their own interests—the regular army, industry and the established social classes—to his system and his will.

Hitler's appeal and his ability to surround himself with men who carried out the various aspects of his programme came in part from the very fact that he discarded all the rules of established society and gave free rein to his imagination and that of his associates. In one field after another his lieutenants with unrestrained zeal laid out the lines of the new order which, he said, was to last for a thousand years.

Alfred Rosenberg projected the outward extension of the Reich in geopolitical terms to take in the plains of Russia and the Middle East and to make the overseas Germans, loyal to their 'blood' rather than the state of which they were citizens, instruments of a global strategy of domination. For Joseph Goebbels propaganda was an equally open field. Hitler was in no sense the inventor of propaganda, for it had been well developed by all the belligerent countries during the war and it was skilfully and consciously used for advertising in capitalist countries and in the USSR as one of the techniques for building a socialist society. But his bold exposition of the technique of the 'big lie' gave his propaganda minister full scope to destroy the capacity for critical response and to use all the force of the mass media to produce desired action. Heinrich Himmler was free to develop the secret police—the Gestapo —and to direct them in unimagined brutalities, unrestrained by legal procedures or citizens' rights. Julius Streicher could go to all lengths to discredit and eliminate the Jews. Doctors could experiment on human beings in concentration camps as they would on rats in the laboratory. Economists had the challenging task of operating an autarchic economy. Lawyers could have a free hand in working out criteria and procedures which would give effect to the established concept of National Socialist justice—'Right is whatever profits the German nation; wrong is whatever harms it'. Educators were called upon to design a new education which would train the emotions and develop the character and attitudes that would make people dedicated followers in the Nazi state.

For the leader and his associates, National Socialism thus offered a challenge to the imagination and the opportunity for action. For the German people it offered a sense of mission. The basis was a precarious one, for in a society where everything stemmed from the leader there was the ever-present danger of intrigue and of the capricious exercise of power. Many fled from the terror or chose exile and the chance to live as free, critical-minded human beings rather than to become part of a system which extolled 'thinking with the blood'. Others remained submerged and unhappy with the course of events. But for those who shared in some measure the sense of adventure which National Socialism offered, its dangers seemed a small price to pay for release from the humiliation of defeat and the bewilderment and hunger of depression.

With failure in the second world war National Socialism as such came to an end, its leader dead and its doctrines discredited. The German nation, divided by the occupying powers at the close of the war, set two courses, as a liberal democracy in the west and a communist state in the east, both segments making vigorous but not wholly successful efforts to purge themselves of Nazi ideas and personnel.[10]

Yet though Nazism was destroyed, it had showed some of the forces latent in society which could be set loose and which another leader might exploit in another time or place if the situation should become ripe. Such a situation did exist, though in a very different form, in the Union of South Africa.

2. *South Africa*[11]

In the years after the second world war the Union of South Africa stood against the world current which was bringing equality of status to formerly subject and depressed peoples. Rejecting the principles proclaimed in the Universal Declaration of Human Rights, it took a firm position in support of the idea of a permanent master race and took drastic steps to translate its position into the institutional structure of its society. Its attitude and policy were expressed by the Afrikaner Nationalist party, which came to power in 1948, as *apartheid*.

The situation in South Africa was unique: a nation of some twelve and a half million people in the mid-twentieth century of whom two and a half million were Europeans.* The Europeans were divided in the ratio of three to two between Afrikaans-speaking descendants of the Dutch who originally settled the southern coast in the seventeenth century, and English or English-speaking Europeans who came first as traders, then as masters, after the Cape of Good Hope became part of the British empire during the Napoleonic wars, and then as miners and industrialists after 1870 to exploit the fabulous riches of diamond mines and gold.[12]

Eight and a half million of the non-Europeans were native Africans of the Bantu tribes who had migrated south into the area north of the coastal range at the same time that the Afrikaners were reaching it in their trek up from the south. They had first fought among themselves and then with European

---

* The following discussion relates to the self-image and aspirations of the dominant European minority, not the African majority. For the latter, see *Infra*, pp. 1033–44, 'Emerging Nationalism: Africa'.

settlers for the empty land, and had finally in the nineteenth century settled among the Europeans and in tribal areas known as 'native reserves', whence they emerged in increasing numbers as farm labourers and then for the heavy and menial occupations in the mines and cities.[13] A million 'Coloureds', located principally in the Cape Province, were of mixed blood; most traced their ancestry to early settlers and either Malay slaves or the Bushmen and Hottentots who occupied the area at the time of original European settlement; few were the product of mixture in recent times. Some half million Indians, mostly in Natal, were the descendants of indentured workers brought in between 1860 and 1911 to work sugar plantations in that province and of merchants who followed in their wake.

In the Union of South Africa in the twentieth century, a small divided European element thus confronted a large population of native Africans and other non-Europeans. A wide cultural gap separated Europeans and Africans, they were in constant conflict over possession of land, and the Europeans had established an economic and social pattern based upon the exploitation of cheap labour and a master–servant relationship between the races.

The principle of *apartheid* by which the Afrikaner Nationalists sought to meet the immense problems of such a society had two aspects: the permanent superiority of the European within a European society which the African was to enter only to contribute his labour; the physical, social and cultural isolation of African from European, and the cultural development of African society on the basis of their own traditions and skills, not those of European society. At the time when it was enunciated, however, an estimated two million Africans had already become permanent urban dwellers and many more had been exposed to European industrial practices and manner of life. The number which had acquired western education was exceedingly small; less than half of the African children entered school, and of these only 5 per cent completed the primary grades; only a handful reached the university entrance level. But several generations of missionary efforts, and increasing public provision for the education of Africans since the establishment of the South African Union in 1910, had created a detribalized population which had come to share European values and to aspire to the way of life which Europeans enjoyed.[14]

The most striking feature of *apartheid* was the intensity with which the policy was pursued. That intensity was a product of the Afrikaner mentality, rooted in the history of the Afrikaner people. It was a reflection of a self-image which had been formed in the seventeenth century and had retained its force into modern times, to such an extent that those who held it were prepared to breast the major tides of world developments in the fierce determination to make it survive.

The Afrikaners of South Africa had lived in isolation from the time of settlement, and had preserved in their isolation the seventeenth-century Calvinist outlook which they had brought with them. This was a stern doctrine which placed on those whom God had 'elected' responsibility to live according to their understanding of His precepts and to make these prevail among the non-elect. It carried the spirit of hard righteousness which had ruled in Calvin's Geneva. The North American colonies had shared a similar heritage but there it had been tempered by the admixture of settlers of gentler faiths, by life in a less hostile environment which had enabled many to stray from the fold, and by continuous reinforcements from Europe which had brought a flow of developing ideas, until the eighteenth-century Enlightenment had found in North America a receptive home.

But in South Africa each successive experience had hardened the religious and cultural attitudes of seventeenth-century Calvinism. Armed with sturdy resolve and the sense that they were God's elect, working out His will, the Afrikaners had struggled to bring under cultivation the coastal plain, the more difficult hinterland and then the dry and empty veld. They had trekked north *en masse* in the early nineteenth century to preserve their doctrines in purity and to escape the domination of the British into whose hands the fortunes of European wars had brought the Cape of Good Hope; beyond the mountain barrier they had formed their own republics of Orange Free State and Transvaal. In their expansion they had encountered the Bantu peoples migrating south, and it had seemed still part of God's work to battle with them for the unclaimed wastes, to withstand their raids, and to set them to work tending cattle and tilling fields.

They were still following their God-fearing way of life when the Kimberley diamond strike of 1870 and the discovery of gold in the Transvaal in 1884 exploded the industrial revolution in their midst. This opened the floodgates to European immigrants—*uitlanders*—introduced the heterogeneity and disorder of urban life into the rural society which the Afrikaners had built, and brought British economic imperialism in its most ruthless form. Economic penetration and resort to military force finally culminated in the Boer war of 1899–1902 between the British and the Boer republics of Transvaal and Orange Free State.

From the opening of the twentieth century the Afrikaner mentality, which had never lost its seventeenth-century Calvinist ethos, was deepened and embittered by the sense of aloneness and the resentment of defeat. Although the Boer leadership accepted the Act of Union in 1910, including the idea of partnership with fellow South Africans of British extraction and the prospect of working out their destiny within the British empire, the feeling of apartness was intensified. Two years after Union, one of the leaders, General Hertzog, formed the National party on the ground that true partnership would only be possible when Afrikaners were on a par economically and culturally with the British. He looked towards a future merging of two separate streams, British and Afrikaner, rather than the immediate integration of a single South African people as the party led by General Jan Smuts proposed. Hertzog led a successful movement to resist the policy of anglicization and to substitute

Afrikaans for Dutch as the second official language. The Afrikaner nationalists, later led by Dr D. F. Malan, never relinquished the hope of regaining the independence which had been lost and of an Afrikaner state in southern Africa.

The Afrikaner nationalists saw themselves as occupying a special place in the world. In their eyes British South Africans were members of a world-wide English-speaking community, with a cultural home, Britain, and brothers in Australia, New Zealand, Canada and the United States; if they should lose their identity, their culture would still survive. But Afrikaners were a people apart. They were no longer Dutch: not in language, for their own speech had become distinct; not in affiliation, for this link had been broken more than a hundred years before; nor yet in sense of identity, for few immigrant reinforcements had come from Holland in the 300 years since original settlement. They were only themselves, one and a half million of God's elect, precariously located at the tip of a vast continent filled with blacks, faced with an economically aggressive, culturally strong and politically reinforced British element which, though outnumbered three to two, had the self-confidence of imperialists, entrepreneurs and victors.

The nationalists were determined that Afrikaners should survive as a people. Their secret society, the Afrikaner Broederbond, formed in 1918, had as its declared objective: the abolition of inferiority of Afrikaners and their language; strict segregation of all non-Europeans; an end to exploitation of South Africa and its people by 'aliens'; and the Afrikanerization of public life and education in the Christian National sense. According to its general secretary: 'The Afrikaner Broederbond is born from a deep conviction that the Afrikaner nation was planted in this country by God's hand and is destined to remain as a nation with its own character and its own mission.'*

In the troubled decades after Union, the leadership of Jan Smuts, Jan Hofmeyr and others managed to keep tensions within bounds. In spite of intense and unreconciled opposition, South Africa joined Britain in both world wars. In the depression of the 1930s, the major parties joined, subordinating differences of policy with respect to group separateness to the urgent need of coping with economic developments, though when the second world war broke out the parties again fell apart. Gradually the economic division between the rural, farming Afrikaners and the urban, industrial British and *uitlanders* became blurred as Afrikaners learned industrial skills and took urban jobs. A common educational system, though separately conducted in the two languages, offered common content and maintained a common standard.

But the Afrikaner current of nationalism and separateness ran on, compounded of cultural separation from the British and racial separation from the Africans, and it contained for many years the still living dream of political

* Quoted in G. H. Galpin, ed., *The South African Way of Life* (New York, 1953), p. 138.

independence. Political hopes for a restoration of the Boer republics dwindled as Johannesburg in the Transvaal became a bustling modern centre, not only for the gold to which it owed its birth but for the growing industrial complex of South Africa's expanding economy. But on the cultural issue Afrikaners made constant gains as Afrikaans became the language of instruction in schools for Afrikaner children and an Afrikaans literature began to appear. And on South Africa's number one problem, relations between European and African, their unswerving position of separation seemed to more and more people to provide an appealing answer to a gnawing problem which no one else saw a way to solve.

The constitutions of the Boer republics had reserved the franchise and all other political rights to the Europeans and had stated unequivocally that the native population was to have no part, now or in the future, in either church or state. Boundaries had been drawn between native reserves and European areas, excluding each from acquiring land within the other's domain. African workers in the European areas were treated as temporary sojourners for the purpose of work, without the status or any of the rights of citizenship. The ban was extended to Indians who were forbidden to enter the Orange Free State or to acquire land in the Transvaal. In their unyielding separateness from Africans and Asians, Afrikaners were intent on retaining their racial integrity. Stern Puritan *mores* helped to maintain the separateness of racial stocks.

In the Cape Colony on the other hand, where the population at the time of Union consisted of roughly a fifth European, a fifth Coloured, and three-fifths Native, a more inclusive pattern prevailed. All who could meet residence, property and educational qualifications, regardless of race, were enrolled on the voting lists, though only Europeans were eligible for election to public office. Under the terms of the Union, each province kept the franchise which it had at the time, and the rights enjoyed by Coloured and Native in Cape Province were entrenched by the provision in the Act of Union that they could only be modified by a two-thirds vote of the combined membership of both houses of the legislature.

English-speaking South Africans no less than Afrikaners, however, took for granted their superiority over the native Africans. As a body, they went along with the assumption of a privileged European society, resting on an African labour base. Trade unions composed of white workers insisted on apprenticeship regulations and other measures to exclude all except European workers from skilled occupations and thus to protect their wage levels, based on scarcity of labour in an expanding economy, from African competition. In Natal the discriminatory conditions imposed on Indian labourers were so severe that they led Mahatma Gandhi to develop the techniques for protest which he used successfully after his return to India in 1914. But British South Africans, with an easy-going feeling of racial superiority toward Africans and cultural superiority toward Afrikaners who could boast no Shakespeare, or

Newton or Adam Smith, lacked the intensity and the sense of 'election' which enabled the Afrikaners to make *apartheid* an article of faith.

There were some members of both British and Afrikaner groups who could not accept the assumption of permanent superiority over the majority of South Africa's population. In the Afrikaner ranks such individuals were few; among the British the number was substantial. Members of the Anglican clergy tried to apply the concept of Christian brotherhood; the Dutch Reformed Churches of the Afrikaners clung to the doctrine of the 'elect' and equated it with the distinction between themselves and Africans, though some individual ministers dissented. Missionaries, welfare workers and teachers tried to prepare individual Africans for participation at higher levels in South African society and co-operated with the small group who received training in their efforts to secure broader rights.

In the course of the years the Afrikaner attitude came to prevail more and more over the less restrictive policies of the Cape. The effort of General Hertzog in 1926 to get the Natives removed from the rolls in the Cape Province failed for lack of the required two-thirds vote, but it succeeded ten years later, with the support of the moderate leader, General Smuts. At that time the parties of the two leaders were brought together into a United Party by Hertzog accepting Smuts's position on the integration of British and Afrikaner as South Africans, and Smuts accepting Hertzog's position on permanent exclusion rather than gradual incorporation of the non-European populations. The British gradually lost influence within the political institutions which they had devised and, when the Afrikaner Nationalist party came to power in 1948, they found themselves taking second place in a state dominated by Afrikaner extremists.

The triumph of Afrikaner nationalism and the policy of *apartheid* bore down upon the Coloured and Indian, as well as on the native African. The Coloureds, mainly located in the Cape Province, were culturally a part of the European society; no tribal ties or alien ways set them apart. In language, religion and cultural values—in all except colour—they were indistinguishable from the Europeans among whom they lived. As the principle of *apartheid* took hold, the Coloureds found themselves shoved into becoming a separate community. Finally, they were put off the voting rolls after successive efforts to do so were held unconstitutional by the Supreme Court.

The Indians were regarded as alien and unassimilable. Although all but a handful were South African born, often of South African parents and even grandparents, the declared *apartheid* policy was to seek their 'repatriation'. But it was they who furnished the basis for bringing the whole question of South Africa's racial policy before the United Nations, for the Delhi government championed their cause and repeatedly insisted that the issue was an international one and not merely a matter of domestic policy as the Union of South Africa maintained.

The South Africa of the 1950s was thus the expression of Afrikaner nationalism. What once had been a drive for separation of the Boer republics from the Cape had become the domination of the whole nation, and its orientation to the Afrikaner mentality. The principle of *apartheid* was not alone a device for the permanent subjugation of the African majority to the European element. It was the means by which the Afrikaners set themselves apart, defined themselves as a people and sought to guard their identity and their survival.[15]

World events both played into the hands of the nationalist extremists and undermined their base. The waning prestige of the British empire and the emergence of new powers from colonial rule made British dominance in South Africa seem less inevitable. Nazi Germany contributed the terminology and the institutions to assert racial superiority and apply totalitarian methods. The Nationalists admired them openly, adopted some of their terminology, opposed South Africa's participation in the war and voiced their sympathy with the Nazi cause. The intensification of nationalism all over the world reinforced the nationalistic sentiment and its extreme expression. The earlier, moderate leaders, Smuts and Hertzog, had condemned the Afrikaner Broederbond; Smuts had excluded its members from the civil service. Many of the leaders of the Nationalist party at the time when it came to power were known to be members of the Broederbond.

But while rising nationalism around the world stimulated the expression of Afrikaner nationalism, it also threatened it, for the native Africans were not immune to its appeal. The independence of the Sudan in 1955 and of Ghana in 1957 converted the vague aspiration among various African peoples into concrete demands and timetables for independence. African nationalism within the Union of South Africa, however, did not take the form of separatism or of revival of tribal cultures, for moves in these directions were regarded with suspicion as measures designed to deny to Africans the advantages of modern civilization. Rather, the Africans of South Africa demanded a place in the society and the right to learn the skills which would enable them to enter the modern age. World opinion, as incorporated in the Universal Declaration of Human Rights, supported such aspirations. International communism was ready to capitalize on these aspirations if they continued to be frustrated.

Most directly affecting the course of *apartheid* was the march of industrialism, inexorably complicating its application and negating its premises. When industry first came to South Africa the Afrikaners had shunned it, although the main mining strikes were in their territory—the Transvaal. British and other European capital had opened up the mines; European immigrant labour had exploited them, aided by native Africans on heavy unskilled jobs. At first the Africans came as transient workers, returning to their tribal areas when they had earned enough to pay their taxes in cash. They had lived in labour camps and carried passes which permitted them to come and go. In time more and more of the African workers became part of a permanent labour force. But they still lived in labour camps, called locations, which were bad enough as temporary makeshift accommodation for transient workers, but were appalling slums for permanent workers and their families. And they still carried passes permitting them to go about their business on sufferance.

After the first world war the sons of Afrikaner farmers began to learn city trades and to enter industry. The process was accelerated by the rapid expansion of industry and the mounting labour shortage during the second world war and in the following years. South African industry ceased to be financed from abroad; local capital, including some from Afrikaner sources, sustained the expansion. Nor could it depend on foreign labour—more and more native Africans were drawn into industry to fill the labour requirements. But, as in other parts of the world, industrial labour increasingly required skills as machines took over routine tasks. Yet limitations on jobs and training for non-Europeans barred the way.

In many ways industrial expansion and *apartheid* were in direct conflict. *Apartheid* called for separation, for drawing boundaries between Europeans and Africans as in the days when tribal reserves were set apart from areas of European farms; but industry demanded more and more workers, to work on the spot, not in isolation. *Apartheid* called for restricting the African's level of skill; but industry called for a wider and higher range of competence. *Apartheid* called for encouraging the development of tribal African cultures; but the inevitable exposure to modern industry, to the daily characteristics of urban life, and to the penetration of ideas which no barrier could exclude ensured that the process of transforming tribal people into modern citizens would go on. In the vivid and realistic words of a former South African historian: 'Every inhabitant of the Gold Coast who casts a free ballot, every native of the Congo who drives a locomotive, every native of Uganda, or Tanganyika who independently raises and sells cotton or coffee in the world market, every native worker in a Northern Rhodesia copper mine who strikes against his company, becomes unconsciously and remotely a critic of South Africa's racial policies, establishing contradictions and alternatives which all the world may observe and which no frontier patrol can prevent from entering into the minds of South Africa's own native population.'*

Perhaps the most crucial question was whether seventeenth-century Calvinism would continue to give to city-bred and industrially trained generations the intensity and moral sureness required for a people determined to maintain continuing dominance over the restless and rising masses by whom they were overwhelmingly outnumbered, in the face of the world-wide revolution in race relations of the twentieth century and of the newly independent nations of the African continent.

---

* C. W. de Kiewiet, *The Anatomy of South African Misery* (London, 1956), p. 8.

V. STATES OF RELIGIOUS ORIGIN OR OUTLOOK[16]

While the major drives of the twentieth century were toward some secular form of national consciousness, two states came into existence whose basic unity and definition were religious—Israel and Pakistan. The former had been the constant dream of a scattered people which had never lost the sense of identity with its 'homeland'. The latter was the product of Asian communalism, and came into being in the crisis of liberation. Both Judaism and Islam offered a basis for many aspects of secular life, for they provided systems of law and prescribed the values and relationships of daily life. Both Israel and Pakistan aspired to develop modern, democratic, economically effective national states and considered their religious origin and identification wholly consistent with this objective.

Certain other countries retained a traditional religious orientation into the middle of the twentieth century, notably those such as Saudi Arabia, Yemen and Afghanistan which had remained largely isolated and relatively free from the impact of the West. Elsewhere national movements against western dominance were identified with religious reassertion, especially among Muslim peoples and in such Buddhist areas as Burma and Ceylon.

1. *Israel*

For nearly two thousand years the Jewish people, dispersed through many lands, included in every synagogue service a prayer for the welfare of Palestine, the Holy Land, and for the return of God's presence to Jerusalem. Through centuries of persecution, when one place after another that seemed to offer a haven turned into a place of torment, expulsion and death, the dream of a return to the Jewish homeland remained always as a ray of hope. Throughout Jewish history a few dedicated people, from all over the lands of Exile, made their way to Palestine.

In the last two decades of the nineteenth century and the years before the first world war, when a great flood of Jews were pouring out of pogrom-ridden eastern Europe, the trickle to Palestine grew, and Zionist organizations of Europe and America lent support to those who made their way there. When the Balfour Declaration of 1917 stated that the British government viewed with favour the establishment of a Jewish national home, and the door of free immigration into the United States was closed in 1921, Palestine became a principal place to which immigrants from eastern Europe turned their course. In the 1930s it offered a refuge from destruction at the hands of the Nazis. In 1947 the land of Palestine was partitioned by recommendation of the United Nations and on May 14, 1948, Israel emerged as an independent state.

The background of the 'return to Israel' thus lay in the continuous history of the Jewish people; its conversion into the reality of an integrated Jewish state was the product of world conditions in the twentieth century and of the efforts of the Jewish people in these years.

At the opening of the twentieth century two-thirds of the Jewish population of the world lived in east and south-eastern Europe, especially in the region which had been Poland; the remainder lived in western and central Europe where they had been gradually readmitted, mainly after the Peace of Westphalia in 1648, in the Muslim lands of North Africa and west Asia where they had settled when expelled from Spain and Portugal after 1492, and in the United States where their numbers were increasing rapidly from the great tide of immigrants that had been pouring in from east Europe since the 1880s.

The Jews of western Europe, outside the Iberian peninsula, had generally come to enjoy full civil and political rights as one country after another during the nineteenth century had removed the religious qualifications which prevented their political participation, opened the doors of schools and universities and removed restrictions on entering the professions. Their recently achieved security had been shaken after 1880, however, by an ominous growth of anti-semitism, especially in Germany and Austria, directed against Jews as a 'race', not against their religion as in previous periods.

Conditions in eastern Europe were much less favourable. Restrictions on landholding, limitation of areas of settlement, extreme poverty, pressure of population and frequent pogroms had set in motion a westward migration that brought poor immigrants into the well-established Jewish communities of west Europe and the flood of immigration to the United States. The rate of Jewish migration rose from an average of 5,400 a year between 1840 and 1880 to 38,200 a year from 1880 to 1900 and 114,500 annually from 1901 to 1914. The United States and Canada admitted immigrants freely and accorded them full civil and political rights.

Since the middle of the nineteenth century, Jews of western Europe and America had been organized to assist their fellow Jews of the east and to intervene wherever the freedom and status of the Jews appeared to be threatened. Organizations such as the Alliance Israélite Universelle established in France in 1860 and similar bodies in England, the United States and Germany, were set up to give educational and philanthropic aid abroad. Support for Jewish settlement in Palestine was one of the forms of such help, and leading individuals in Europe and America responded to appeals from groups in the east European ghettoes who managed to organize for settlement.

It was at the turn of the century, however, that Zionism became an active movement. Though the Conservative Jewish congregations in America supported the return to Israel in principle and immigrants brought with them their 'Lovers of Zion' and 'Seekers of Zion' movements, it took the publication in 1896 of Theodor Herzl's *Der Judenstaat* to precipitate Zionism as an active Jewish world movement.

During the first decades of the twentieth century many events continued to build up a sense of Jewish nationalism and contributed to the growth of Zionism. The Dreyfus affair in France, which involved the espionage trial of the first Jewish army officer to be appointed to the French general staff, his conviction and imprisonment, retrial, pardon and final vindication, revealed violent anti-semitic sentiments as it divided France and focused the attention of the world for a decade. In Germany and Austria vigorously anti-semitic political groups continued to secure seats in central and local legislative bodies and violently anti-semitic newspapers circulated among the populace.

The growing nationalism of the peoples among whom many of the Jews lived threatened the status of minority groups. Minorities which had lived comfortably within the Ottoman empire found their position precarious as Turkey became a nationalist state; the intense nationalism of the new states of east Europe after the first world war boded ill for their Jewish minorities. In the effort to protect the Jewish communities within the new states, representatives of European and American Jewish organizations appeared before the Peace Conference at Versailles to secure the adoption of minorities treaties designed to guarantee the rights of such minority groups. At the same time the Balfour Declaration of 1917 converted the dream of the Jewish state into a positive hope.

When the United States closed its door to free immigration by its restrictive laws of 1921 and 1924, the flood of Jewish emigration was sharply checked. By the late 1920s Jews were coming to the United States at only one-fifth the rate at which they came when emigration was renewed after the war. Although numbers going to South American countries rose, total Jewish emigration in these years was cut by 60 per cent, from 426,930 in 1921–25 to 172,908 in 1926–30. The 'Jewish homeland' began to look like more than a centre for Jewish religion and culture and to take on the character of a haven. When the Nazi terror struck and exterminated an estimated 6,000,000 of Europe's 8,000,000 Jews, it was Palestine which received the greatest number of those who escaped.

In spite of the growing strength of the Zionist movement in Europe and America, support from the Jewish communities was far from unanimous, and those who lent the movement support differed fundamentally in the kind of 'homeland' which they envisioned. Jews of west Europe and America were divided along complex ideological and social lines. Some of the intensely religious and orthodox supported Zionism ardently, and the Orthodox wing maintained a special arm of the Zionist movement dedicated to Israel as a religious centre where the precepts of Orthodox Judaism could be carried out to the full. The branch of Judaism in the United States which called itself Reform, however, took a firmly anti-Zionist stand in 1869 from which it did not retreat until 1935. Many of the more secularized and indifferent had little emotional attachment to the Holy Land of Israel and were likely to be anti-Zionist. Yet there were outstanding political Zionists among the non-religious who saw the Jewish homeland in national rather than religious terms.

Differences among Jews on the question of assimilation also affected their attitude toward Zionism. Assimilationists sought the integration of Jewish people into the general culture of the country of their residence, retaining their distinctive religious faith and engaging in group activities within the framework of a multi-religious democratic society, but taking their places as individual citizens, associating with others on the basis of occupation or interest, residence or responsibility in the total community. Against this view stood those who maintained that the Jewish heritage was too precious to be discarded, that only intensive Jewish life could provide the milieu for it to flourish, and that Jews should maintain a separate identity as a community. The assimilationists were on the whole opposed to Zionism. But the rise of Hitler, the imposition of the Nuremburg laws and similar laws in fascist Italy, excluding from the privileges of citizenship what had appeared to be the most completely assimilated of Jewish populations, and finally the campaign of extermination, cut the ground from under the assimilationists and made many converts to Zionism.

A third line of cleavage within Jewish communities was between the strongly socialist workers' groups and economically conservative elements. Marxian socialism drew strong adherents from among the Jews of both Germany and Russia, and both groups brought their interests and attitudes to the United States. Religious Zionism had little appeal to these indifferent or anti-religious elements, but among the workers' groups were many who looked to a Jewish homeland as a place in which to build a socialist state.

These different concepts of the Land of Israel within the Jewish communities were reflected in the schools for Palestine settlers supported by the respective wings of the world Zionist organizations. The schools supported by the general Zionist organization were essentially secular; they provided a place for the Bible and Rabbinical literature in the curriculum but they offered no formal religious teaching. The schools supported by the Orthodox Mizrachi wing were religiously oriented and devoted much time to Rabbinical literature and the Bible. The Labour and left-wing Zionists maintained non-religious schools with a vocational emphasis which included virtually no Rabbinical literature in the curriculum.

All who supported Israel agreed on one feature, its role as a centre of learning, so vital to the life of Jewish society. The Hebrew University of Jerusalem, for which ground was broken in 1918 and which admitted its first regular students in 1924, became a centre not only for Jewish studies but for general fields of knowledge. The Hebrew Institute of Technology founded in 1912 at Haifa became the leading school of engineering in the Middle East.

While the factors which underlay the creation of the state of Israel and determined its character and policy lay deep in Jewish history and experience, its shape was forged by those who committed their own lives and direct efforts to the venture. From the closing years of the nineteenth century the groups of settlers who made their way to Palestine set to work at the hard task of rebuilding an agricultural economy in the unfriendly desert. In 1885 there were some 23,000 Jews in Palestine, living mostly in four cities; by 1947 there were 643,000, living in 330 Jewish communities and settlements of which 302 were agricultural. Constituting some 27 per cent of the Palestine population, they produced some 50 per cent of the citrus fruit of the area, 89 per cent of the fodder, considerable amounts of greens and a small proportion of the grains, and were responsible for approximately 85 per cent of the country's industry and trade.

Settlers came from many different places—Hungary, Russia, Poland, Lithuania, Rumania, Bulgaria—aided by money from their own communities and from other countries—Germany, France, Britain, the United States, Turkey. Distinguished leaders from many countries—lawyers, professors, members of parliament, ambassadors—intervened with the Turkish government on behalf of the Jewish settlers. Every sort of Jewish group contributed financial support—charitable and mutual aid organizations, youth groups, fraternities, clandestine and revolutionary bodies.

The Jewish settlement of Palestine was thus the product of the collaboration and the expression of a very broad cross-section of world Jewry and it drew its character from the whole Jewish people rather than from any one of the many facets of Jewish life and thought. Each new wave of immigrants, composed of people who felt that they were going 'home' to the land which they already knew intimately, reinforced those who had gone before. In spite of the tremendous diversity of background and viewpoint, the tensions inherent in the relations among groups and the gap between the dream and the reality, the people who hammered out a nation were integrated through struggle and dedication to a common historic ideal.

The varied settlements were unified by a common language, Hebrew, which was developed from a language of scripture and prayer into a living language of daily use, the language of the school, the culture, the science, the learning and the public life of the people. The earlier settlements were separated from each other by language and cultural differences and retained their respective ties with the places from which they had come. The spoken Hebrew was unique to Palestine, but it was the common heritage of all. It won final acceptance in 1912 when the pupils and teachers of the newly founded Hebrew Institute of Technology, backed by the Palestine community, succeeded in making Hebrew the language of instruction over the opposition of many of the Institute's founders who wished the teaching to be in German.

When Israel became an independent state it opened its doors to Jews from all countries, however difficult it might be to assimilate them rapidly. By the Law of Return, every Jew was given the right to settle in Israel. The number of immigrants during the first four years, 688,000, exceeded the total population of the country at the time of independence. In the next five years some 150,000 additional settlers arrived. Although some continued to come from eastern Europe as they could escape from those countries where their position remained insecure, more than half of the total, including the bulk of the later immigrants, were from the Arab lands of Africa and west Asia where Jews had lived for centuries in enclaves within the Muslim communities, largely isolated both from the surrounding culture and from the Jews of Europe and America. The assimilation of these populations into a common culture offered a further problem of integration to the young Jewish state.

In its initial form Israel took the shape of a modern democratic nation-state of which any Jew could become a citizen by immigration and in which the existing Muslim and Christian citizens enjoyed rights identical with those of Jews, both individually and as communities. Except in matters of personal law such as marriage and divorce, its institutions were secular; for personal law it retained the separate ecclesiastical courts for Jews, Muslims and Christians which it inherited from the Ottoman empire and the British mandate. The practice of the Jewish religion was facilitated, for example, by making the Jewish Sabbath the weekly day of rest and observing the Jewish dietary laws in the armed forces, but both Jewish and non-Jewish religious establishments received support from public funds. It was by its existence as a homeland for the Jewish people rather than by its Jewish institutions and practices that Israel fulfilled its purpose as a Jewish state.

The Jewish settlement in Palestine and the establishment of a Jewish state took place in the face of strong opposition. Up to the first world war the Turkish administration tried to forbid entry into Israel, claiming readiness to admit Jews to any other part of the Turkish dominions but resisting what they recognized as the Jewish settlers' sense of coming 'home'. In spite of the Balfour Declaration, the British government of the Palestine mandate pursued an uncertain policy of admission and restriction in the face of conflicting pressures from Arab and Jewish populations. The surrounding Arab countries would not accept the establishment of Israel, and the state came into existence only after war with her neighbours.[17]

To the neighbouring Arab states Israel, with its modern economy and western outlook, was a beachhead of the West, a trespasser on Arab soil, a temporary phenomenon which must be destroyed. Whether in the violent language with which President Gamel Abdul Nasser of Egypt encouraged border raiders, or in the scholarly tones with which a professor at the American University of Beirut concluded that the only possible future for Israel was the fate which befell the Latin Kingdom of Jerusalem, or in the song of the girl scouts in an Egyptian village, 'Go away bad Israel, you shall not have our dear Palestine', the intention was the same. The state of Israel must not live.

For the Jews of the world, whatever their previous attitude toward Zionism had been, Israel was a heartening reality. More, it was a fulfilment of the age-old dream from which even the non-religious were not far removed and which the religious repeated constantly in their prayers.

For the people of Israel, their mission was to survive, not alone for self-preservation or patriotism to the country which they had made, but because they believed themselves to be the instruments of an historic destiny, the keepers of the Covenant, the means of realizing the prayer, repeated through the years in every synagogue, that God's presence might return again to the Land of Israel.

2. Pakistan

Although Pakistan came into existence only seventeen years after the first proposal for a Muslim state in the Indian sub-continent, its roots went deep into history. From their advent into the sub-continent the Muslim population had been unique among the succession of invaders in resisting the process of absorption into Hindu society. Equalitarian, monotheistic and proselytizing, Muslims would not be fitted into the caste-structured, polytheistic and tolerant Hindu culture. In spite of much intermingling and interaction of Muslims and Hindus through the centuries, the two societies never merged. Under the Mogul emperors, especially after the rule of the sternly puritanical Alamgir who attempted to restore the purity of Islam in the late seventeenth century, the gulf between the two communities widened.

From the beginning of British influence and rule in India, the position of the Muslims fell and that of the Hindus rose. Regarding the Muslims as the main obstacle to the expansion of their authority, the British at the beginning of their rule adopted the policy so often used by conquerors of favouring the non-dominant element, and deliberately encouraged the Hindus. Furthermore, the commercial character of the British intrusion made the Indian class of merchant-bankers, the *banyas*, allies and beneficiaries of the process while the Muslims, who in Bengal were engaged principally in agriculture, administration and minor crafts, suffered economically. In a generation the Muslim population was reduced from the dominant element to an impotent minority.

When the British in 1833 introduced a system of western education in the English language in order to train for the ranks of the civil service, Hindus took advantage of the opportunity while Muslims held aloof. By the time of the uprising of 1857, Hindus were already becoming integrated into the British administration, and although both Hindus and Muslims participated in the rising, the stern punitive measures of the British were directed primarily against the Muslims.

The Hindu revival which grew in strength through the nineteenth century intensified the Muslims' sense of exclusion and depression. European historical and cultural studies of the Hindu-Sanskrit religious literature and the pre-Muslim history of India fed the revival and made the reawakening of India essentially a rebirth of Hinduism. As the Hindus became dominant, Muslims found their social position intolerable; with the loss of Muslim political authority and in the face of Hindu caste exclusiveness, they felt that they were being looked upon as an alien element in society.[18]

Against this background, the Muslim revival which led to the creation of an Islamic state followed the only course which seemed open, to rebuild the Muslim community as a distinct entity within the modern framework established by British rule. Convinced that the policy of aloofness from western education would have to be reversed if the Indian Muslim community was to rise from its depressed state, Sir Sayyid Ahmad Khan founded in 1875 the college which became the Aligarh Muslim University and launched the training of a new leadership for the new Muslim community of India. By the time that Britain was ready to extend self-government at the local level to the Indian population through the Morley–Minto reforms of 1909, the members of the organized Muslim community were convinced that they could only hope to function politically in the face of the Hindu majority if they established themselves as a separate electorate. In securing recognition of the principle of communal voting—Hindus for Hindus and Muslims for Muslims—the Muslims expressed and the British accepted the concept that the people of India constituted in effect two nations. From separate electorates to a separate Muslim state was a short and logical step.

As the Indian nationalist movement against the British gained momentum, however, many Muslims made common cause with the Hindus in the movement for national liberation. The Indian National Congress, though predominantly Hindu, numbered prominent Muslims among its members, including for a period Maulana Muhammed Ali and Muhammed Ali Jinnah, who later became the leader of the Muslim League and the moving spirit in bringing about partition. Mahatma Gandhi appealed to Indians of all faiths to join the movement of passive resistance. But the very terms of Gandhi's appeal revealed the deep Hindu roots from which his thought and expression came, and even those Muslims who joined the movement did not feel that his voice was theirs. The opposition of the Indian National Congress to the principle of a multiple society made up of separate electorates and its insistence on a society in which the basic unit was the individual appeared to the Muslims to mean simply that majority votes would always be against them.

As it became apparent that British power would soon be withdrawn and as the ferment of Muslim nationalism spread throughout the Islamic world, the concept of an Islamic state took shape. First formally proposed by the Muslim poet and influential religious philosopher, Mohammed Iqbal, at the session of the All India Muslim League in 1930, then given a name to suggest the area envisaged for such a state by three students at Cambridge University, England, it was finally made the fighting goal of the Muslim League under the vigorous leadership of Jinnah.

In its original conception the Muslim state was to be composed of the north-western provinces indicated by the name 'Pakistan', Punjab, Afgania, Kashmir, Sind, Beluchistan. Its relation to other parts of the Indian subcontinent was not fully envisioned, for it was by no means clear whether British power would devolve upon a unitary Indian state or some looser federation. But as the movements for independence and partition rose to a climax and tension between Muslim and Hindu mounted, the demand grew for the inclusion of the densely Muslim area of East Bengal as well as the north-western area. When partition came, and the furious violence revealed

how intense were the latent antagonisms among people who had been neighbours for centuries, millions of people streamed across the borders to participate, by choice or by fear, in the creation of the new state. Yet of approximately 100,000,000 Muslims in undivided India, only about two-thirds
became part of the Islamic state, while the other third remained as citizens of
the secular state of India.

The leaders who brought Pakistan into being and directed the shaping of
the new nation were the product of western education and the Aligarh
movement, not of religious fanaticism. They had absorbed many of the
political, economic and social concepts of the West and were convinced that
these were consistent with the basic principles of Islam.

In the ten years after independence they undertook to provide the structure
for a democratic, modern, economically sound Islamic nation. The enormous
practical difficulties which confronted the country almost overshadowed the
effort to define a modern Islamic state. The government of Pakistan had to be
built virtually *de novo*. The relatively small numbers of Muslims in the old
civil service left Pakistan far less well supplied than India with experienced
administrators at all levels. The problem of absorbing nearly 8,000,000
refugees into a total population of 80,000,000 placed a tremendous burden
on the community, and the difficulty of uniting two areas separated by more
than a thousand miles was enhanced by differences in language, economic
conditions and local loyalties. The disruption of normal economic relationships by partition increased the already difficult problems of economic
development while international tensions required the formation and support
of a military establishment. To these and other practical problems was added
intense disagreement as to how far a Muslim state should be 'Islamic' and what
that would mean. It took nine years of deliberation to frame the first constitution, which attempted to embody the principles on which Pakistan had
been founded.

In the constitutional struggle, the Islamic extremists accused what they
called the 'westernized ruling group' of being ignorant of the Law (*sharia*)
and of the true principles of Islam, of being able to see 'only through the
coloured glasses of western thought', and of wishing to establish not an
Islamic but a 'national democratic' state. They called for an ideological rather
than a national state, in which authority would be derived from God, not
from the people, and for the creation of a thoroughly Islamic society, the
complete replacement of prevailing law by the Muslim legal code, and the
enforcement of every prescription of the Quran and Sunnah. 'Indeed, if
secular and Godless instead of Islamic Constitution was to be introduced and
if the British Criminal Procedure Code had to be enforced instead of the
Islamic Shari'ah what was the sense in all this struggle for a separate Muslim
homeland ?'*

* Syed Abul 'Aka Maudoodi, *Islamic Law and Constitution*, ed. by Khurshid Ahmad
(Karachi, 1955), p. 17.

The extremists rejected the principles of the parliamentary system with a cabinet responsible to the majority party. They wished to exclude women from active politics and public office and to establish two classes of citizenship, Muslim and non-Muslim, placing the non-Muslims in the traditional status of *zimmis* under the guarantee of protection by the state.

The constitution as adopted in 1956 established the principle that sovereignty resides in God alone, with governmental powers to be exercised within the limits set by the Quran and the Sunnah. But it provided only that the state should endeavour to facilitate the practice of Islam by Muslims, not that it should require or enforce such practice; it reserved for Muslims no position except that of president; it made no legal distinction between Muslim and non-Muslim citizens, except that only Muslims would be taxed to support Muslim institutions, and precluded discrimination in access to the public services, including defence; it left open the question of whether voting should be as common citizens for a single electoral roll or separately, by religious or other communities; it provided for a parliamentary system of the British type, and reserved a number of seats for women to assure their participation.

The constitution declared that 'the principles of democracy, freedom, equality, tolerance and social justice as enumerated by Islam, should be fully observed', and it guaranteed to all citizens a list of fundamental rights which corresponded closely to those enumerated in other democratic constitutions. The Islamic provisions specified that 'no law shall be enacted which is repugnant to the Holy Quran and Sunnah' and called for setting up an organization for Islamic research 'to assist in the reconstruction of Muslim society on a truly Islamic basis' and for a commission to make recommendations on how to bring existing and future legislation into conformity with the Quran and Sunnah. The 'Islamic' provisions could not affect the personal laws of non-Muslims or their status as citizens, or any of the fundamental rights and other provisions of the constitution.

The Islamic state of Pakistan thus took shape in terms which sought to integrate the spirit and practice of Islam with the requirements of the modern age and the institutions of parliamentary democracy. Only two years after its adoption, however, the constitution was set aside in favour of military rule. It seemed to General Ayub Khan and to the president who handed over power to him that the urgent tasks of organization and development required firmer and more positive leadership than the parliamentary system was providing. But he declared his intention of laying a basis for effective democracy by developing it first at the local level, and his reforms were dictated by the practical needs of a modern state for strong and efficient administration rather than by the demands of the Muslim extremists or the ideology of Islam.

3. *Religious orientation of other states*

Although Israel and Pakistan were unique in the twentieth century in that religion was the rationale for their coming into being as national states, the outlook and institutions in some other countries were more predominantly religious than in these. The traditional Muslim states of Saudi Arabia, Yemen and Afghanistan remained far more religiously oriented than the new Pakistan with its history of western contact and its inheritance of many western institutions. The ruler of Saudi Arabia, as Imam of the Wahhabi sect, combined a political and a religious role, while the Islamic authority, the *ulema*, continued to serve as his chief political advisers. In Yemen, law and custom remained within the prescription of traditional Islamic law.

Elsewhere in the Muslim world national self-assertion against western dominance was infused with a strong Islamic feeling which interacted with and tended to support these political movements. This was notable in the expression of Arabism, both in the Arab states of the Fertile Crescent and Arabian peninsula and in the Arabic-speaking areas of North Africa. Arabism was nourished by a sense of historic greatness based on the rise and spread of Islam and by the memory that the western powers against whom their current nationalistic aspirations were directed had once taken up arms against Islam in religious crusades. Throughout the Arab world three factors were interwoven: local nationalism in the form of attachment to a national unit such as Egypt, Iraq or Morocco, Arabism expressed in identification with the loosely related peoples from Morocco to the Persian Gulf who were linked by a common language and sense of history, and Islamic unity, of which the Arab segment of the Muslim world formed the religious, historic and linguistic core. In the charged climate of the twentieth century, especially its second quarter, these potentially competing identifications, unities and self-images tended to reinforce each other, especially when threatened from outside, and to intensify religious feeling, as well as to be intensified by it.

A somewhat parallel situation obtained in certain Buddhist areas, with Tibet, geographically and culturally isolated, preserving into the mid-twentieth century its religious structure and orientation, and with the reassertion of Buddhist principles and authority in the drive for liberation and the outlook of the new states of Burma and Ceylon. The absence of an authoritative scripture and body of law, however, and other basic differences between Buddhism and Islam, made religion in these modern Buddhist states more a factor affecting the temper of the society than a driving force for the shaping of political and social institutions.

VI. NATIONAL INDEPENDENCE IN THE FACE OF EUROPEAN EXPANSION

The few states of Asia and Africa that successfully resisted European dominance in the period of western expansion did so by a variety of means: Afghanistan and Ethiopia by isolation and resistance, Thailand and Iran by negotiation and by balancing off one European power against another, Japan by adopting western methods and competing with western powers in their own terms. In each case continuous independence and national integrity were central aims which coloured the otherwise diverse outlook of these countries.

Throughout its long, continuous history, the Coptic Christian kingdom of Ethiopia in the mountainous highlands of east Africa had had few contacts with Europe and had stood out against the spread of Islam from neighbouring areas. In the partition of Africa it was the only area on the continent, except the American-created state of Liberia, which remained unclaimed by the European powers. Its access to the Red Sea was cut off by Italian occupation of the coastal strip which formed the colony of Eritrea, but when Italy tried to move inland by force, her armies met defeat. From the time of the battle of Adowa in 1896, at which the Ethiopians turned the Italians back, Ethiopia became a symbol of successful resistance, the first sign that non-Europeans might stand against European aggression. Forty years later it again became a symbol when its emperor appealed unsuccessfully to the League of Nations for protection against Mussolini's imperial ambitions.

Ethiopia's independence was the independence of cultural as well as physical isolation. Its traditional priesthood retained a virtual monopoly of education and learning. Abyssinian herdsmen in the east and tribesmen from the Sudan in the western regions had little communication with the centres of priestly and aristocratic culture, and these in turn had few contacts with cultural currents in the outside world. Until after the second world war very few persons left the country to study abroad. Foreign trade was minimal. The Italian occupation of 1936–41 brought the country its first network of roads and the first beginnings of industry.

Like Ethiopia, Afghanistan maintained its independence by struggle and by isolating itself as far as possible from European influences. From the first half of the nineteenth century its independence was threatened by Britain, which sought to dominate the area in order to protect the north-west frontier of India through which invaders had repeatedly entered the sub-continent in the past. Britain's efforts, together with counter-moves by Russia, brought recurrent fighting to Afghan territory during the nineteenth century, destruction of forts and cities, the presence of foreign troops and intervention in the conduct of foreign affairs. The constant efforts of Afghan rulers to preserve or regain full control continued until 1919, when Britain finally recognized the full independence of Afghanistan.

Few modernizing influences entered the country during its years of isolation and the struggle to maintain its independence. Outside ideas and foreign investment were regarded with suspicion as a possible cloak for foreign domination. Conservative religious leaders opposed social change. Even after 1919 innovation was opposed and the ruler was forced to abdicate in 1929 because of the unpopularity of his educational and other reforms.

In the years after the second world war both Ethiopia and Afghanistan were eager to bring the benefits of modernization to their people. Both had to develop their economy and their basic services, such as education and health, virtually from the ground up, with an acute shortage of trained personnel and of capital. Ethiopia's emperor Haile Selassie undertook an ambitious programme of reform in government and administration, education, finance, social structure, the army and relations between church and state. Afghanistan launched a major programme of hydroelectric and irrigation development, aviation, road building, education and health services. But in both countries leaders working to bring about change sought to do so within the framework of their traditional societies. As expressed by the ambassador of Afghanistan addressing Afghan students in the United States in 1958, the ability of the educated leadership to integrate the new programmes into the national life would determine whether these measures would 'constitute progress or a mere superimposition of an alien culture'.

In contrast to the countries whose defence was associated with isolation, Thailand and Iran preserved their independence by negotiation rather than by armed resistance, and by taking advantage of the rivalry between European powers. For Thailand, her location between the French-dominated states of Indo-China and the region of expanding British control in Malaya and Burma brought her the support of both of these powers in her role as a buffer between their colonial interests. Similarly, the interests of Britain and Russia in Iran set limits to the influence which either would permit the other to exercise over that country. In both countries western influences were considerable and the process of modernization was well under way before the impetus for national development spread to all countries after the second world war.

From the time that the Thai monarchs began to open their doors to western contacts in the middle of the nineteenth century, they welcomed western ideas and knowledge while at the same time they reinforced and renewed their traditional Buddhist culture. During his long reign (1866–1910), King Chulalungkorn introduced western manners at the court, modernized the legal system, abolished slavery, reformed the state administration, police and army, and sent his many sons and competitively selected 'king's scholars' to study in Britain and on the European continent. His successor promoted westernization even more vigorously, in education, recreation, literature, law, and he led Siam to participate in international organizations. The royal patronage and example gave prestige to western practices, which then seeped down through the population. But these monarchs were equally zealous in promoting the Buddhist faith, they encouraged the development or revival of Siamese culture, and the traditional way of life was followed in the country-side. In the middle of the twentieth century Thailand continued to see itself in the process of developing a modern society in its own manner, with a minimum of stress, through the gradual integration of old and new.

Iran during the twentieth century took a succession of steps to raise both its internal conditions and external status from the depressed state and scarcely more than nominal independence to which the country had declined. The revolution of 1906 introduced parliamentary institutions. The *coup d'état* of

1921 was followed by reforms in government, education, public health, in public and private law, the position of women and the place of the religious courts, as well as by developments in transport, communication and industry. Oil, which was discovered in quantity in the Persian Gulf in 1908, brought wealth and foreign economic influences into the country. After the second world war Iran asserted its determination to control its own resources when it nationalized the oil industry and forced the foreign investors to accept terms for the exploitation and sale of Persian oil which would safeguard the national interest.

The non-European country which met the challenge of European expansion most vigorously was, of course, Japan. From the time of the forceable opening of the Island Empire to outside contact in 1853, Japan set out to learn from the West and to compete with it. In little more than a generation, it moved from an isolated, self-contained island to a vigorous position in world trade; it gained military superiority over its huge neighbour, China, and was ready to challenge successfully a great western empire, Russia. Then, becoming itself a conquering and colonial power, it took on the features of western imperialism, following the lead of a comparable island people, the British, who, with a smaller population, had demonstrated the possibility of acquiring and ruling world-wide dominions.

Japan accomplished this transition by mastery of western technology, introduction of universal education and the modernization of its economic and political structure along western lines. But it did not follow a single, direct course, for western ideas often involved divergent concepts. The relative strength of different Japanese leaders and power groups determined the influence of ideas of democracy as against military force, of capitalism or of its Marxian alternative, of racial superiority or of human equality and brotherhood.

Increasingly the military leaders gained predominance and made the drive which had started as Japan's effort to catch up with the western nations into a drive for the extension of Japanese power. They defined national aspirations in terms of an Asian empire under Japanese hegemony which would provide the raw materials and markets for her economy, would reduce her desperate dependence on foreign trade and would relieve the pressure of population in her crowded islands. They interpreted the ancient Shinto myth that the emperor was destined to rule the 'world' of the Japanese islands as promising his rule over the global world.

When the great gamble of the second world war failed, Japan in defeat had no alternative goal to which to turn or return. At mid-century the Japanese people were seeking to redefine their place in a world which had changed drastically in the half century since the aspiration to become a great military empire had been in line with the pattern established by the nations of the West.*

* See Chapter XXIX, pp. 1064–67, for cultural renaissance and adaptation of Japan.

VII. EMERGING NATIONALISM: AFRICA

Latest of the nationalist movements to emerge was that of the African peoples south of the Sahara. Rumblings of incipient nationalist feelings began to be heard after the first world war, with the formation of the National Congress of British West Africa by European-educated Africans, and these rumblings grew in volume during the following years. In West Africa, Nnamdi Azikiwe of Nigeria and Wallace Johnson of Sierra Leone published anticolonial articles, deemed to be seditious, in Azikiwe's *African Morning Post* (1936). In East Africa Jomo Kenyatta appeared before royal commissions to voice the protest of his people, the Kikuyu, against the taking of their lands for white settlers (1928–29, 1931–32), and he declared in his book on the culture of his tribe that: 'The African is conditioned, by the cultural and social institutions of centuries, to a freedom of which Europe has little conception, and it is not in his nature to accept serfdom for ever.'[*]

But it was only in the years after the second world war that African nationalism spread throughout the continent and assumed the proportions of a major movement. Then it gathered momentum rapidly. In the area of its first major triumph, the British West African colony of the Gold Coast, only ten years elapsed between Kwame Nkrumah's return from his studies in the United States and Britain to lead the struggle for 'freedom *now*' and his celebration of independence. In 1951 he was in prison on charges of attempting to coerce the colonial government; six years later his application for admission of Ghana to the United Nations was immediately accepted as the nations of the world hastened to welcome a new state from tropical Africa.

The focus of African nationalism was anticolonial. Whether leaders and nationalist groups aspired to a modern welfare state or reasserted the values of traditional African culture, whether at any moment they were seeking full independence, self-government or equality of political rights, all opposed foreign domination and made colonialism the centre of their attack. None of the nationalist movements reflected a traditional national unity, for the political divisions of the African continent in the twentieth century were the creation of the European nations which had carved up the territory without regard to those who occupied it, splitting some tribes and grouping others with their traditional enemies. Each movement developed pragmatically in its particular area, subject to many cross-currents of European and local origin. The broader identification was with Africa and fellow Africans, but Pan-Africanism remained a vague and relatively small component of African nationalism until after Ghana's independence.

African nationalism was a reaction to racialism as well as to colonialism. Pride of race which ran like a thread through most movements was a response to the discrimination and the implication of inferiority to which Africans had long been subjected.

[*] Jomo Kenyatta, *Facing Mt Kenya* (London, 1938), 1953 ed., p. 318.

The European impact on Africa set the framework within which the aspirations of African peoples were formulated and pressed. For the colonial powers the area was a vast region of physical resources to be exploited for trade, profit and the needs of the industrial economies. Tropical climate, malaria and the tsetse fly made the African continent far less suitable for European settlement than the continents of America and Australia where such settlement had spread. Certain areas, however, were attractive for settlement, most notably the veld of Southern Rhodesia and the highlands of Kenya, as well as the Union of South Africa. There European settlers pioneered farming communities and came to look upon the area as their own.

Everywhere, the relations of European to African was that of the 'superior' culture to 'inferior'—representatives of a technological society in contact with isolated, non-literate, tribal peoples for whose way of life they had only an anthropological concern. Cultural 'superiority' was reinforced in most areas by racial discrimination, uncompromisingly in the Union of South Africa, very generally in British areas, much less in French possessions and least of all in Portuguese territory, where there was considerable intermarriage and the sharp distinctions were cultural rather than racial.

Wherever European contact spread the effect was to undermine the structure of African society and the traditional pattern of African life. Commercial crops tended to supplant or intrude upon the subsistence economy of African communities, and not infrequently reduced the available food supply. Recruiting of African labour for mines and plantations drew men away from tribal villages. Taxes which had to be paid in cash forced them to seek employment for wages. The appropriation of African lands cut away the foundations of tribal life. Railways and roads opened up lines of communication and contact between areas and groups. The growth of urban centres around points of administration, mining or trade introduced Africans to an urban milieu where traditional relationships and controls were largely inoperative and the individual had to function under strange, competitive conditions without the extended family and group relationships which had defined his role and sustained him in carrying his responsibilities. As the twentieth century progressed, fewer and fewer of the African peoples remained undisturbed in their tribal life.

Few Africans however were entirely cut off from their tribal roots. Many of those who worked for wages returned to their villages each year as soon as they earned the cash which they required, and their places in mines or on plantations were taken by others for a temporary period. Wives and children remained in rural areas, or city-born children were sent home to relatives to be brought up. But the number remaining in permanent urban employment grew continually as cities expanded. Some enterprises made special efforts to create conditions which would hold a stabilized labour force, and education or personal or family circumstances intervened to cut off tribal contacts and to produce a detribalized urban population.

Even the detribalized Africans, however, rarely became incorporated in any complete way into European culture, for the conditions of European impact generally offered the African no version of European life which he could adopt in place of his own. Forced to labour in the white man's mines by the white man's taxes, required to carry a pass or observe a curfew and subject to arrest by the white man's police, excluded from the white man's buses and residential areas and from the white man's jobs, offered the principles of brotherhood by the white man's religion but refused them in practice, deemed by the white man to be 'unready' for responsibility, the African was in a position to admire and covet the white man's goods but hardly to see or appreciate the bases of his society and to make them his own. The outstanding exceptions, such as M. Félix Houphouët-Boigny of the Ivory Coast, a minister in three French cabinets, only served to underline the general situation.

In urban communities and centres of employment, Africans generally lived apart from Europeans in locations where housing and other facilities often met neither the African's standards for the village nor the European's standards for the city. Classification of 'European' and 'African' jobs placed a ceiling on ambition. Opportunities for secondary and advanced education were severely limited. Where Africans had an opportunity to observe the Europeans in their midst, what they saw was often far from representative of the manner of life which the same people would have followed within their own cultural milieu. Some Europeans in fact had chosen Africa in order to escape from the standards of social responsibility and democratic conduct which their own societies imposed. The gulf between European and African life was narrower and the barrier less complete in some areas than others. After the second world war the trend everywhere except in South Africa was to offer Africans increased access to the education, manner of life, occupations, status and values which Europeans enjoyed.[19]

The impact of European domination varied considerably, according to differences both in local conditions and in the policies and practices of occupying powers. Geographical conditions and natural resources produced such different types of economic development as copper mining, plantation cultivation of sugar and cotton, cocoa growing on individual farms, and the collection of palm oil and ivory from the bush. They also determined the vital question of white settlement. African tribes differed in their form of organization and manner of traditional life, and hence in the basis for their adaptation. Large Muslim populations in some areas had their distinctive outlook, organization and behaviour.

Quite different colonial policies resulted in distinct patterns of development in the areas ruled by each of the European powers.

Britain's policy of 'indirect rule' left much of the structure of African society intact and made local chiefs into agents of British administration. British law prevailed mainly in matters relating to trade. Missionaries provided education and health services, with government subsidies supplemented later by direct government services. A sharp division in status, occupation, area of residence and privileges distinguished the European from the African, but the growing number of educated Africans were conceded a considerable measure of responsibility and opportunity.

British policy was not uniform, however, as between the regions of West Africa and Uganda where climate and terrain offered few attractions to white settlers and the temperate regions of the Kenya highlands and Rhodesia where white settlement was encouraged and became extensive. Where the population was almost wholly African, Britain applied its generally stated colonial policy of preparing colonial peoples for self-government when they were 'ready', though up to the second world war the 'readiness' of African peoples was assumed to lie in the distant future and even in 1950 African leaders working for independence were being arrested and jailed. After the second world war the timetable was revised sharply, programmes of education, welfare and economic development were pushed vigorously, Africanization of the civil service was accelerated and the colonial administration made every effort to assist these regions to become independent African states.

In the areas where there were white settlers, however, Britain supported the settlers and followed a repressive policy toward the African population. In spite of the declaration by the Colonial Office in 1923 that the interest of the African population must be given first consideration, the best lands were made available for European development while Africans were confined to 'reserves' and were restricted in movement, employment, use of public facilities, educational opportunity and political participation. When this policy met violent resistance in Kenya after the second world war in the outbreaks of Mau Mau terrorism, while South Africa moved to strengthen its policy of *apartheid* and West Africans moved toward independence, colonial policy was caught between opposing pressures. Settlers in Kenya and Rhodesia sought independence for 'their' colonies from Britain, with the clear objective of maintaining the supremacy of the small European population over the vast African majority; Africans demanded equality of political rights. British policy in these areas was to resist both settler pressure for continued dominance and African efforts to achieve majority control, to try to develop a 'multi-racial' society in which there would be some sort of balance among racial groups, and to retain colonial authority until a pattern should be established which would prevent the white settlers from trying to follow the course of South Africa.

French colonial policy initially followed a different course from that of Britain, but after the second world war it moved in a similar direction. France viewed its large African domain as an area to be made French. The education which it introduced was identical with that provided in France—African children learned about 'Charlemagne, our great ancestor'—and the 'assimilated' African became a French citizen. African communities where such citizens were sufficiently numerous sent representatives to the National

Assembly in Paris. This French policy drew no racial lines. It produced a small group of highly cultivated 'Black Frenchmen', separated by a wide cultural gulf from the mass of the population most of whom acquired no education or training in even elementary technical skills. The policy did not look toward ultimate African self-government but to the incorporation of African areas into the French Union. As late as 1944 a formal resolution of the French Colonial Conference at Brazzaville stated: 'The attainment of self-government in the colonies even in the most distant future must be excluded.'

The French constitution of 1946 inaugurated a new policy, for it pledged France to lead her dependent peoples toward 'freedom to govern themselves and to conduct their own affairs democratically'. Under this policy facilities for general education were greatly extended and the *loi cadre* of 1956 provided for universal suffrage and a measure of self-government. Two years later, African territories were given the option of withdrawing from the French Union and Guinea was the first to choose independence.

Belgium's policy with respect to the Congo focused on the development of the area's resources rather than on the political development of the area's people. This vast resource-rich region in the very heart of Africa, originally brought under European domination by a private association headed by the king of the Belgians became notorious in the early 1900s for the way in which it was being exploited. Africans were deprived of their land, forbidden to leave their villages, and forced to work under conditions of virtual slavery.

When the Belgian government assumed jurisdiction over the territory in 1908, it abandoned these practices and adopted a paternalistic policy toward the Congo people designed to treat them humanely and to make them into efficient workers. Congolese were given technical training and were employed in skilled and responsible jobs in mines, transport and communication which elsewhere were reserved for Europeans. Living conditions for Africans in areas to which European influence extended were generally superior to those in neighbouring colonies, although racial segregation was clearly maintained. Health services were extended throughout the territory and community centres offered training to women in nutrition, home economics, nursing and child care. The people enjoyed no political rights, however, for the area was governed directly from Brussels by a centralized administration.

In the years after the second world war Belgian policy also changed. In the words of the governor-general addressing the government council of Belgian Congo in 1955: 'We have decided in future to substitute a regimen of trustee-ship for the paternalism which we have practised up to now'. The new policy rejected in principle both segregation and assimilation and adopted the concept of a 'partnership' with reciprocal rights and duties between the whites plus the *évolués*—assimilated Africans—on the one hand and the general population on the other. Wage differentials between Africans and Europeans were reduced by introducing common standards, the structure of the Belgian commune was adapted to urban communities and rural districts in order to permit local self-government, and training in administration was offered to the sons of chiefs and others destined to wield authority in tribal areas.

The policy of partnership on Belgium's terms was, however, short-lived. Faced suddenly with violence and demands for independence in 1959, Belgium responded swiftly with the offer of almost immediate independence. In 1960 this vast area, rich in resources, which had been regarded in purely economic rather than political terms, embarked on self-government, although its people had had practically no political experience and there was virtually no European-trained leadership comparable to the *élites* in French and British areas who had been educated in the universities of the metropolitan countries.

Portugal remained committed to a policy of assimilation, coupled with a restrictive policy in respect to political rights and labour which was even more repressive than the authoritarian system in force at home. Portuguese public law distinguished between fully responsible citizens and persons of 'colonial status' who were not subject to Portuguese laws and, in the language of the tribal populations statute, were 'not deemed liable to fulfil obligations which they could not reasonably have foreseen or have been deemed willing to accept'. 'Assimilated' individuals, who declared their intention of coming fully under Portuguese civil and criminal law and who met established qualifications of language, education, occupation, age and good character, enjoyed equality of Portuguese citizenship without racial or other distinction. Catholic missions were entrusted with full responsibility, aided by state subsidies, for such education as was provided to the African populations.

Persistent reports of the systematic use of forced labour led to efforts within the United Nations to require Portugal to report to the United Nations Trusteeship Council annually, as did other colonial powers, on the administration of their dependent areas. Portugal, however, maintained that under a law enacted in 1951 these were not dependent areas but full provinces of the Portuguese state, and the Portuguese government refused to report to the Trusteeship Council or to permit representatives of the United Nations to visit the areas.

In addition to the possessions of the four major colonial powers, the former German territories—Tanganyika, Ruanda Urundi, Togoland and Cameroons —were placed under mandate to Britain, Belgium and France at the end of the first world war and became United Nations trust territories administered by the same countries at the end of the second world war. The Trusteeship Council periodically evaluated their progress toward self-government in terms of: steps taken toward the exercise of the elective franchise; elimination of racial discrimination; extension of education; protection of the African population in their claims to their lands; and measures to increase economic potentials and to expand the base of the economies.

Within the broad framework of European domination and the distinctive pattern applied to each colonial area, a group of African leaders emerged who voiced a growing sense of Africanism. Educated Africans, studying abroad in London, Paris, the United States or India, became aware of world trends and formed African student associations. When they returned home they established organizations to voice the problems of their respective territories or of all Africa. African leaders everywhere aspired to freedom from foreign domination, but at first they differed in the process of African development which they envisaged.

African aspirations were formulated in terms of modern western life and values by Kwame Nkrumah as he led Ghana to independence. Educated in the United States and Britain, calling himself a 'non-denominational Christian and a Marxian socialist', detached from his tribal roots and rejecting the traditional authority of the chiefs as 'feudalism', yet very close to the masses of his people and able to speak directly to them, Nkrumah conceived of his new country as a modern welfare state, based on the principles and structure of parliamentary democracy and the use of modern technology. The leaders of the much more populous neighbouring state of Nigeria held the same view. The nationalist movements of the two areas were in fact closely linked from the 1920s on.

Nkrumah's speech to the legislative assembly in 1953 when he offered his independence motion expressed this position. Rehearsing the history of the region from the time of the ancient empire of Ghana which fell to the Moors in the eleventh century, he asserted that 'throughout our tortuous history, we have not been docile under the heel of the conqueror'. He recalled the resistance of the Ashanti nation to the British, the 'earliest manifestation of Gold Coast nationalism' in the Fanti Confederation of 1868, the National Congress of British West Africa which came into being at the end of the first world war in response to the wartime slogan of the Allies who declared that they fought for freedom, and the succession of organizations after the second world war leading to the formation in 1949 of his Convention People's party with its programme of 'freedom *now*'. His people, he said, knew 'that freedom is not something that one people can bestow on another as a gift. They claim it as their own and none can keep it from them.'

The task of an independent African state, he said, was to create a new society which would benefit from the technology and institutions of the West but would not 'sacrifice unheedingly in pursuit of material progress' the values of its pre-technological society. 'We have to work hard to evolve new patterns, new social customs, new attitudes to life, so that while we seek the material, cultural and economic advancement of our people, while we raise their standards of life, we shall not sacrifice their fundamental happiness.'*

Opposed to the goal of a modern western-oriented state was the traditionalist reaction against European ways. Jomo Kenyatta asserted most dramatically the superior virtues of tribal culture (*Facing Mt Kenya*, 1938); the Mau Mau terrorists in Kenya in the 1950s gave this view a distorted and violent form.

* Kwame Nkrumah, *Ghana: Autobiography of Kwame Nkrumah* (London, 1957), Chapter 17.

Educated in Britain, where he studied under the great British anthropologist, Bronislaw Malinowski, Jomo Kenyatta resented the condescension of European scholars toward tribal societies, and he was moved to present his own description of the culture of his tribe, the Kikuyu of east Africa. He described family and kinship, age groups and initiation ceremonies, religion, magic, warfare and, especially, the use of the land as vital institutions, providing a rich life for his people. This life would be destroyed by undermining any of its integrally related parts. 'It is all these different aspects of life together that make up a social culture. And it is the culture which he inherits that gives a man his human dignity as well as his material prosperity.'* He expressed only bitterness and contempt toward those who would break the integrity of this culture on the pretext of 'civilizing' the Africans and giving them 'the benefits of European progressive ideas'.

The feeling expressed by Jomo Kenyatta was shared by Africans of many sorts. Not only tribal chiefs whose position and authority were at stake, but educated Africans who had acquired western training or had embraced Christianity or had achieved a modicum of economic success in the white man's world, yearned for the 'good old days'. Out of a deep sense of chaos and frustration, their own society damaged or destroyed and no decent alternative anywhere in sight, they tried to renew the values and practices which their European contacts had taught them to reject and often to despise.

Throughout the continent, movements of Africans took a modernist or a traditionalist form, or some combination of the two. Prior to the second world war most of those who received western education were western oriented and sought African progress in terms of the development of a western-style society, while traditionalism was represented by some of the hereditary chiefs who continued everywhere to retain a very substantial measure of prestige and respect, from educated and uneducated alike.

In the years after the second world war the clear division between the western and traditional orientations was modified by the neo-traditionalism of some of the educated *élite* and the modernism of some of the tribal chiefs. In the Belgian Congo some of the western-educated elements began to seek to strengthen the authority of the traditional chiefs, to provide them with training for their expanded tasks, and to reorient cultural associations toward African lore and history instead of, or in addition to, European culture. Some of the traditional chiefs, in turn, sought westernization, especially those who had embraced Christianity. Some students and educated Africans from French West and Equatorial Africa, in contrast to their pre-second world war predecessors, turned against the French policy of assimilating Africans into French culture. They sought to revive African culture, exalting 'negritude' and affirming the existence of common Pan-African elements; they wished to reinterpret the history of Africa from the perspective of the African

* Kenyatta, *Facing Mt Kenya*, op. cit., p. 317.

people and to use the knowledge and insight which their western training and exposure was giving them to develop an African ideal. Some envisaged a process of cultural blending, such as that presented by an African dance troupe which toured Europe and the United States in the 1950s with a programme that combined traditional dances and songs, current popular music and dramatizations of such events as the introduction of a mulatto wife to the rites of the tribe.

The development of African trade unions gave the nationalist movements a new mass base. In the British and French areas where union organization was permitted, though often harassed, Africans and whites formed separate unions, and the African unions became strongly nationalistic. They formed substantial components of people's political parties, as in Ghana, and their leaders in West Africa, Kenya and the Rhodesian copperbelt became important political figures. It was the secretary of the Kenya Federation of Labour, Tom Mboya, one of the first group of Africans elected to the Kenya Legislative Council, who acted as chairman of the first conference of Africans from non-self-governing areas, held in Accra in 1958.

As African states moved toward independence, the positive goal of 'development' came to supplement the attacks against colonialism and racialism which had furnished the main emotional drive.

After Ghana's independence in 1957, the nationalist movement throughout the continent gathered great momentum. Everywhere the tempo of change was accelerated, moderate proposals were replaced by more drastic ones before they could receive full consideration or be carried out, and any alternative to independence became unacceptable. The *loi cadre* had been expected to satisfy French African demands for at least ten years, but in a short two years the march out of the French Community had begun. Timetables reckoned in months were set for the independence of one area after another—Nigeria, Uganda, the trust territories of Togoland, Somaliland, Cameroons. In the trust territory of Tanganyika, where the administering authority in 1955 had opposed the idea of even a twenty to twenty-five year target date for self-government, a commission appointed in 1959 to propose limited constitutional steps went beyond its instructions and proposed full-scale elections and responsible government in a matter of months, stating that it knew that if it stayed within the terms of reference which it had been given at the time of its appointment its report would be obsolete before it could be read.

For the areas which contained white settlement, intensified nationalism meant mounting tension and rejection by Africans of efforts to develop a so-called 'multi-racial' society. Proposals for restricted suffrage based on educational qualifications, which would severely limit the number of Africans eligible to vote while allowing the franchise to whites, were regarded by African leaders as a mere device for perpetuating white rule. So were separate voting lists for white, Asian and African voters and representation according to racial groups which gave an equal or smaller number of representatives to

Africans than to the tiny European minority and to the somewhat larger group of Asians. Racial 'parity' which took the form of an equal division of educational funds in Tanganyika between the three racial groups—25,000 Europeans, 70,000 Asians and 8,000,000 Africans—convinced African leaders that the intent of 'multi-racialism' was to maintain Africans in permanent subjection. They insisted that there was only one basis on which a genuine 'multi-racial' society could exist and a workable system for participation of non-Africans be developed: acceptance of the principles of democracy—one man, one vote—and recognition of the basic fact that these were African countries.

Within a short time nationalism invaded the areas where the possibility of future independence had not been contemplated by the colonial powers. The outbreak of nationalist violence in the Belgian Congo in 1959 came as a shock to those who had assumed that the Belgian system was proof against such anticolonial developments; a year later the issue was whether the nationalists would wait four months for elections or would insist on independence on the spot. Disturbances in neighbouring Angola indicated that the fire of nationalism was spreading even to Portugal's 'tribal provinces' where access to and from the outside world was severely restricted.

In the Union of South Africa, Africans who in spite of repression and discrimination had participated most extensively in urban industrial and modern agricultural life and were the most Europeanized of African populations, aspired to equality of status within the mixed society of which they were a part. But the success of nationalist movements elsewhere in the continent and the hardening of *apartheid* policies at home brought mounting tension and the threat of open conflict.

African nationalist movements took on a Pan-African tone. One of the objectives stated in the constitution of Nkrumah's Convention People's party at its inception, was 'to support the demand for a West African Federation and of Pan-Africanism by promoting unity of action among the peoples of Africa and of African descent'. Nkrumah himself lost no opportunity to press toward his vision of united African peoples; he acted as host to the first meeting of independent African states and to the first conference of representatives of the non-self-governing African territories in 1958. Immediately after Guinea became independent, the prime ministers of Guinea and Ghana announced a projected linking of their two countries to form a nucleus which other African states would be invited to join as they became independent.

African peoples, however, faced many problems and difficulties in realizing their aspirations. As the leader of the Tanganyika nationalist movement, Julius K. Nyerere expressed it in 1957: 'We do not seek freedom so that our people may remain in poverty and ignorance or revert to primitive savagery.'* But African economic life was almost wholly dependent on European capital and management. With a few exceptions, such as coffee growing in Tangan-

* Letter to M. Springer, n.d.

yika and cocoa in Ghana and the Ivory Coast, commercial agriculture was European-operated, as were mining, industry and trade.

Without capital, managerial experience and technical knowledge, neither African individuals nor African governments were in a position to exploit the continent's resources for the benefit of the African people. Economic colonialism threatened to remain after political colonialism was gone. Moreover, against the background of the traditional authority and wealth of the chief and with the example of European enterprises using low-paid African labour, there was a real temptation for those Africans who might gain some wealth and power to entrench themselves personally at the expense of the masses of the people.

Tribal rivalries complicated the development of self-governing, viable states, for ancient antagonisms did not disappear overnight and tribal boundaries rarely coincided with political divisions created by European powers and inherited by African nationalists. The difficulties of applying democratic principles were immense, especially on the part of those who had little experience in their operation. Nkrumah, who had shown himself a master of democratic principles and parliamentary processes during his struggle for independence, soon resorted to repressive measures to restrain opposition which he believed was endangering his new state.

The basic problem faced by all new states, the limited number of technically qualified and educated people on whom the burden of development rested, was nowhere so acute as in Africa, though the lack was much greater in some areas than in others. The situation was sharply illustrated in the French territories after the introduction of the *loi cadre* which provided for the partial self-government of the territories by local African ministries and a 50 per cent Africanization of the civil services. In one after another of the territories, the same man served as a member of the French National Assembly in Paris and as the chief minister in the colony or the mayor of the principal city, while scarcely a beginning could be made in the programme of Africanization of the civil services for lack of available personnel.

The rich resources of the continent were potential sources both of salvation and of danger. They provided a basis for productive economies capable of sustaining the African people, but in a resource-hungry world they were coveted by foreign governments and enterprises for their own purposes. Pressures were great to exploit the deposits of copper, uranium, bauxite, iron ore and other materials at a pace and in a manner dictated by outside forces and interests rather than by the tempo at which African society could make use of these sources of wealth. Vast, thinly populated parts of the continent, moreover, offered possibility for settlement, not only in the areas which enjoyed a healthy climate, such as Angola, but in regions which would become habitable as the tsetse fly and other disease carriers were brought under control.

Africans could not hope to be allowed to work out their destiny without interference, as the people of the Americas had been able to do in the years after their independence. They were caught at the moment of their emergence as independent peoples in the midst of a world in conflict, where distance no longer isolated or protected and where so rich a prize as a vast continent could not remain outside the world struggle for power. Though Africa could no longer be simply carved up without regard for the people, as it had been in the nineteenth century, it was the target of the many pressures which powerful states and groups had the resources and skill to apply. Africans might repeat their slogans of 'Hands off Africa', 'Free Africa We Keep', but these were scant protection against determined efforts to draw them into the orbit of one or another of the world's power groupings.

In this struggle the main protagonists were the communist and non-communist worlds. But a pull came also from Islam. A belt of Muslim people stretched from east to west along the border of the Sahara and down the Niger valley, making up more than half the population of the French territories and most of the people of northern Nigeria; substantial numbers of Muslims were also to be found in the east, not only in the Sudan but down the coast, and in most areas Islam was tending to spread. Addressing these populations, the Cairo radio sought to link African nationalism to Islam and to the nationalism of the Arabs, and to induce Africans south of the Sahara to make common cause with the Muslim peoples of North Africa. The Islamic revival of these years and the increased facility for Africans to join the pilgrimages to Mecca made Islam a factor of growing importance in determining the direction of African development.

Under the impact of the long struggle between French and Muslims in Algeria and the use of the Sahara for atomic tests, Muslim states of North Africa traditionally oriented toward the north and east made common cause with African states across the Sahara to the south. From one end of the great continent to the other, leaders began to talk of an African identity, an African personality, the future of Africa—not just of the individual states—and the place of Africa in the world.

At best the African's task of cultural integration between a non-literate, tribal culture and a modern technological one was as difficult a transition as any people had had to make. Under the most favourable circumstances it would place severe strains on the social structure and heavy demands on the creativity, stability and adaptability of the people. Africans brought to this task attitudes and experience built up in the face of colonial rule, racial dominance, and economic exploitation. Moreover, in the cultural atmosphere of the mid-twentieth century, they were exposed to no single accepted version of technological culture but to fundamental conflicts and many uncertainties among its representatives.

The African people, seeking to enter the modern world, faced heavy odds indeed in their struggle for self-realization and development.

NOTES TO CHAPTER XXVIII

1. Professor Radim Foustka (Czechoslovakia) considers that the survey of 'the self-image and aspirations of nations' given in this chapter shows the radical difference which exists between the authors' viewpoint and that of Marxist critics: The very term 'self-image' cannot but evoke an attitude of scepticism. . . . This concept, it would seem, reduces itself to the general idea that nations as a whole formulate their 'aspirations' and 'aims' and carry them into effect both at the political level (through their state and within it) and at the cultural level. This is a completely unscientific assertion and the authors themselves have been compelled to admit that 'in formulating national aims' there is always 'in some degree a reciprocal interaction between the people and the state even where a small element imposed its will on the majority and sustained it by dictatorial means'. How is it possible to discern any self-image of a nation in such a case ? . . .

The evolution of mankind in the twentieth century is seen solely from the angle of the ruling class of the bourgeoisie or its leaders . . . There is not the slightest allusion to the great struggle of the working class for democracy and no mention of the fact that on this issue the opinions of the workers were significantly different from those of the bourgeoisie. Of questions as important as this the authors make short work, mentioning only that the national self-image has been 'that of the dominant element which provided articulate leadership', and noting that there were other views 'shared by non-dominant elements'. Thus the artificial concept of 'national self-realization' was designed only to bolster up the ideology of the ruling bourgeoisie and to give a false notion of the general body of national aims and aspirations. . . . The concept is so artificial and unreal that quite naturally the term 'self-image' breaks down. . . . The authors would be in a position to eliminate the contradiction and offer a scientific solution to the problem only if they were to accept as a premise the class system of states and the class system of politics and culture as formulated and realized by the ruling class. Naturally it is impossible to ask for, or expect, from them such an approach to the question, and it is therefore evident that the resultant divergency of views cannot be resolved whatever comments are made on the text submitted by the authors.

The same viewpoint is upheld by A. E. Bovin who considers that people's ideals can find a real expression in life only when there is an effective socialist force behind them. In a class society this force is represented by classes, in other words by major groups of people having one and the same relationship to the means of production. The ideal embodied in the form and substance of a government is always a class ideal, the realization of the interests and requirements of the economically preponderant class.

A. E. Bovin also takes the view that the authors have passed over facts which give a pointer to the basic aspirations of the nations of the world in the twentieth century:

(1) More than a thousand million people in twenty-three countries have put an end to the exploitation of man by man and are building a classless society. These same aims inspire the workers' and communist movement which exists in all countries of capitalist civilization.

(2) Millions of people have definitely finished with colonialism. In the period since the second World War alone some forty independent states have come into existence in Asia and Africa.

(3) The movement of the partisans of peace has become a most important element on the contemporary stage and an active political force in all continents of the globe.

2. *The Author-Editors call the reader's attention to the exact language of the text, including the following statements: '. . . no single attitude permeated all sections, classes, occupations, ethnic elements and personal outlooks even in the most centrally administered or totalitarian states. . . . In each case, the national self-image which has been noted has been that of the dominant element which provided articulate leadership. . . . It must be remembered, however, that . . . the divisions and conflicts of view within nations were no less significant than the differences among nation-states . . . workers whose labour had been treated as a commodity sought bargaining power and status as human beings. . . .'*

3. In the opinion of Professor E. N. Anderson, the Author-Editors may be criticized for identifying the self-image with the national state. They are transferring to the rest of the

world an ideal which is essentially western in origin and general acceptance. Even in Europe, however, there exist minorities which lack all prospect of achieving independence in a national state and yet which have an image of themselves as national groups. The term nation is as yet scarcely applicable to the peoples of Asia and Africa, where national bonds have not subsumed or supplanted caste, religious, tribal or other loyalties. On these continents political unity does not imply cultural unity, and the major problem facing the new states of the world lies in the need to develop a common culture that will assure the continued independent existence of the political state, or that will at least make it possible for a people to decide what the political form and scope of their life should be. Upon the basis of present evidence one cannot assume that the peoples of these continents will follow the example of Europe and everywhere introduce the nation-state as standard. There are alternatives, for example, in federal structures like those of Switzerland and the United States, as Professor Lynn M. Case has remarked in a comment on the text of the Author-Editors, and there are many kinds of agreement among independent political units under the United Nations which offer prospects of a greater variety of self-images than the West has developed up to now.

4. Professor Radim Foustka notes that the authors ignore the fact that liberal democracy took shape in the progressive capitalist countries in the nineteenth century, i.e. in the period of pre-monopoly capitalism. Since then it has undergone, and is continuing to undergo, substantial changes in the direction of a limitation of the classical liberal (bourgeois) democracy. Typical examples of such changes are to be found in the USA legislation (the Taft-Hartley Act, the McCarran-Smith law, etc.) The authors regard faith in the reasonable basis of human nature as being an element only of the liberal democratic view of life ('to function more fully, more rationally and more humanely'). This is tantamount to tacitly denying that the ideology and practical activity of the socialist states is also based on this principle.

   See also Note 4 of Chapter XXIII.

5. *The Author-Editors' position has been explicitly stated in Chapter III, p. 64: 'They [the communists], too, viewed man as a rational being whose judgment, in the long run, could theoretically be trusted, and they regarded the state as the product of rational action, not as a mystical entity.'*

6. Candidate of Juridical Sciences F. M. Bourlazky notes that the assertion by the authors that communists when they come to power reject democratic rights and liberties is contrary to the facts. Socialist democracy not only does not reject, but on the contrary gets the best out of, the principles and forms which were elaborated by earlier types of democracy. Social justice and freedom, equality of citizens before the law, freedom of conscience, universal suffrage, the system of representation—all these ideals acquire a special value with socialism and are weighted with a real content. Thus the old principle of democracy—government not only for the people but by the people—gains a new significance in the context of the socialist system. The state makes it its aim to ensure that in the final analysis every individual should be able to take part in the administration of public affairs; and not only by participating in the election of deputies, giving them instructions and listening to their reports, but also directly in day-to-day life.

   One aspect of this is the new role assigned to voluntary organizations (of trade unions, young people and so on) and the gradual transfer to them of state functions.

   This role of the public organizations is all the more significant in that they have increased enormously in size so that to all intents and purposes they cover the whole population.

   The direct participation of the workers in the solution of state problems is achieved, among others, by such original methods as the preliminary discussion of laws and of plans for the national economy. Forty to fifty million people, more than half the adult population of the country, have been involved, for example, in the USSR in such consultations on economic planning. For more details on this point see F. M. Burlatzky 'Rastsvet sotsialisticheskoy demokratii' ('The Development of Socialist Democracy') in *Vestnik istorii mirovoi kultury*, 1961, No. 5.

7. Professors E. Gathier and G. Masson object to the minor role attributed to Christianity in the discussion of the self-image of western Europe. They state that the Author-Editors'

discussion of liberal democracy ignores the fact that the idea that 'man is rational, responsible and capable of exercising control over his own affairs' is also 'an essential part of the Christian message, Catholic as well, and very often asserted by the Popes, defended by the "social Catholics", chiefly in our century'. In general these scholars believe 'that the image of the Christian faith and of the Catholic Church which emerges does not conform to reality and would hurt Christian sensibilities'. They believe that the self-image of Western Europe should not be identified with liberal democracy but with the older Christian tradition still carried by the Catholic Church.

The comments of Gathier and Masson may be elucidated by citing, for example, the encyclical *Atheistic Communism* of Pope Pius XI (1937). It reads, in part:

16. If we would explain the blind acceptance of Communism by so many thousands of workmen, we must remember that the way had been already prepared for it by the religious and moral destitution in which wage-earners had been left by liberal economics.

29. . . . Society is for man and not vice versa. This must not be understood in the sense of liberalistic individualism, which subordinates society to the selfish use of the individual; but only in the sense that by means of an organic union with society and by mutual collaboration the attainment of earthly happiness is placed within the reach of all. In a further sense, it is society which affords the opportunities for the development of all the individual and social gifts bestowed on human nature. These natural gifts have a value surpassing the immediate interests of the moment, for in society they reflect the divine perfection, which would not be true were man to live alone. But on final analysis, even in this latter function society is made for man, that he may recognize this reflection of God's perfection, and refer it in praise and adoration to the Creator. Only man, the human person, and not society in any form is endowed with reason and a morally free will.

The following titles may be suggested for the liberal point of view:

John Dewey, *Liberalism and Social Action* (New York, 1935).
R. M. McIver, *Democracy and the Economic Challenge* (New York, 1952).
J. Roland Pennock, *Liberal Democracy: Its Merits and Prospects* (New York, 1950).
Karl G. Popper, *The Open Society and Its Enemies* (Princeton, 1950).
Massimo Salvadori, *Liberal Democracy* (New York, 1957).

8. Professor Radim Foustka notes that the section 'Marxist–Leninist Communism' gives a quite distorted idea of Lenin's development of Marx' teaching and of the reasons responsible for this. The authors consider that Lenin advanced the view of the possibility of revolution in industrially backward areas 'in the light of conditions at the opening of the twentieth century when the major capitalist countries were enjoying both rising productivity and profits from colonial areas, and workers in those countries were organizing to share to some extent the returns from these sources rather than to overthrow their regimes'. This assertion is absolutely divorced from reality. At the end of the nineteenth century the onset of the age of imperialism, characterized by an extremely uneven development of capitalism, made it apparent that under those conditions the socialist revolution could not be victorious simultaneously in all capitalist countries. Concretizing the general concept of Marx and adapting it to changed historical conditions Lenin, the leader of the Russian Marxists, came to the conclusion that the socialist revolution could and must triumph in one country, taken separately. Imperialism with its highly uneven development and its exploitation of less developed countries by more developed countries, of colonies by their possessors, brought with it a form of mutual dependence between the countries belonging to the world system of imperialism in which some capitalist countries succeeded in reducing their contradictions at the expense of others and temporarily reinforced their positions in the world. Lenin therefore drew the inference that in this new period the contradictions of capitalism might be aggravated precisely in the backward capitalist countries at whose expense the more developed ones temporarily alleviated (or, more correctly, 'repressed') their own economic and political conflicts. This means that there is every likelihood in the assumption that a revolution can and must begin in an economically more backward capitalist country on which its more fortunate competitors shifted part of the load of their contradictions and where, accordingly, capitalism was less solidly entrenched. These ideas found their most systematic development in Lenin's theory of imperialism and in his theory of proletarian revolutions in the age of imperialism which were fully confirmed by the triumph of the October revolution in Russia in 1917.

K. Marx and F. Engels, in equipping the proletariat with a most logical and coherent scientific philosophy, showed that the only way to arrive at a solution of the historic problem of the proletariat—the creation of a communist society—lay in the establishment of a dictatorship of the proletariat. Their teaching on the dictatorship of the proletariat was further developed by Lenin. After studying the experience of the struggle of the revolutionary class in Russia he reached the conclusion that the best form of dictatorship of the proletariat is not a parliamentary democratic republic but a republic of Soviets. He discovered Soviet power as the state form of the dictatorship of the proletariat and defined the dictatorship of the proletariat as a special form of the class alliance of the proletariat with the exploited masses of the non-proletarian classes, under the direction of the working class, and particularly emphasized the fact that the dictatorship of the proletariat and its highest principle was the alliance of the working class with the peasantry. His treatment of the peasant question, which is in effect the question of the allies of the working class in its struggle for power and for the construction of a socialist society, had already begun on the eve of the Revolution of 1905–7. The opportunist leaders of the Second International and the other enemies of revolutionary Marxism were indifferent in their attitude to this issue and claimed that the peasantry could not be an ally in the struggle of the working class for power. In combating the enemies of Bolshevism Lenin revealed the revolutionary potentialities of the peasantry and the possibility, and the need, for an alliance of the working class with the peasantry in its struggle for power and for the victory of socialism. Thus since it is a part of the general question of the dictatorship of the proletariat the peasant question represents one of the vitally important issues of Leninism.

Lenin's presentation of the national question differs radically from the way in which the problem was posed by the parties of the Second International who viewed it out of its context and divorced from the major issue of power and the proletarian revolution. He considered it to be a part of the general question of the proletarian revolution and of the dictatorship of the proletariat. Leninism first connected the national question with the question of colonies thus transforming it from a special intra-state problem into a general international problem, a world problem involving the liberation of the oppressed peoples of dependent countries and colonies from the power of imperialism.

9. The Soviet scientists think that the fascist regime is not the ideology of petty bourgeoisie, but that it is a reactionary and overtly terrorist dictatorship of the imperialist upper bourgeoisie. Its aim is to stifle completely and utterly the resistance of the working class and all progressive forces within the country.

10. Candidate of Juridical Sciences U. P. Ouryas objects to the authors' comparison of the Federal Republic of Germany and the German Democratic Republic in terms of struggle against Nazi ideology. In the German Democratic Republic the former Nazi may live and work only if he fully rejects the Nazi ideology: there are no social strata or groups which are interested in Nazi ideology. The situation is quite different in the Federal Republic of Germany where the Nazi and revanchist sentiments are rather strong—as has been acknowledged even by some official representatives of the government.

11. Candidate of Economic Sciences I. P. Yastrebova notes that in the section devoted to the Republic of South Africa the part played in the national life by the Africans who make up 67 per cent of the population is ignored. It is by their toil that all the wealth of the country has been created. A British publicist who has long been studying the country's problems takes the view that 'without Bantu labour the farms and factories of South Africa would become a desolation within five minutes'. (B. Davidson, *Report on Southern Africa*, London and Cape Town, 1952.)

The authors say nothing about the liberation struggle of the non-Europeans, particularly the African peoples. (See in this connection A. Luthuli, *Freedom in the Apex*, Johannesburg, 1959; W. Alphaeus Hunton, *Decision in Africa*, New York, 1957; and other works.)

The remark made by the authors at the beginning of the section advising reference to 'Emerging Nationalism: Africa' does not invalidate the criticism we have just made, more particularly since there is no mention of the liberation struggle of the Africans in the Republic of South Africa.

12. I. P. Yastrebova underlines that the policy of *apartheid* is not something entirely new or distinct in its nature from the policy practised towards the aboriginal population of the country both in the former English colonies of South Africa (Cape Colony and Natal) and in the former Boer republics (Transvaal and Orange Free State) which in 1910 were incorporated as provinces into the South African Union. Nor does it differ greatly from the policy pursued irrespective of party allegiance by the governments of the Union throughout its existence. All the bourgeois parties of the Union (later Republic) of South Africa, whatever their programmes, form a united front in the matter of their policy towards the non-European population. Here for example is what W. K. Hancock noted: 'Although native policy is the fundamental political question in the Union (or perhaps because it is so) it has not determined the party divisions in parliament and the constituencies. The leaders of all parties, including the Labour party, professed their allegiance to the principles of racial segregation.' (W. K. Hancock, *Survey of British Commonwealth Affairs*, London, 1942, Vol. II, Part II, pp. 12–13.)

13. I. P. Yastrebova calls special attention to the fact that at the moment when the Europeans arrived in South Africa the country was not an empty, uninhabited space. Even the first Portuguese travellers and later the Dutch found here a considerable African population. The earliest inhabitants of this area were Bushmen and Hottentots and later the Bantu tribes. The forward movement northward of the Boers and the English was accompanied by savage fighting with the African peoples not for 'empty land' but for the land held by the Africans. The 'native reserves' were not the result of a process of natural settlement of African tribes. They were transformed into special reservoirs of cheap manpower from which the Europeans drew the workers they needed and to which they sent them back when their labour was no longer required; thus the whole life of the Africans was subjected to innumerable restrictions and regulations.

14. I. P. Yastrebova underlines that the process of detribalization is not a consequence of the well-meaning educational activity of certain groups of Europeans but the objective result of the social and economic changes that have taken place in African society (growth of the urban population, process of differentiation in the African village, etc.). See also L. D. Yablochkov, 'On detribalization and urbanization in Africa South of the Sahara' in *Vestnik istorii mirovei kultury*, No. 3 (21), 1960.

15. I. P. Yastrebova considers it a great mistake to describe *apartheid* as a 'means by which the Afrikaners set themselves apart, defined themselves as a people and sought to guard their identity and their survival'. The South African nationalists in the Republic express the interests of the classes *who hold in their hands the levers of command in the economic and political life of the country*. In the first place apartheid is directed against the native African, i.e. against that part of the population which is exploited and deprived of its rights.

16. Professor Zurayk observes that 'Nowhere in this section ['States of Religious Origin or Outlook'] is it observed how this establishment of states on a religious basis runs contrary to modern ideas and tendencies. Although this chapter purports to describe the 'self-image and aspirations' of peoples—without consideration to their soundness or validity—is it right in a book whose subject is the twentieth century not to express a judgment on a phenomenon which is so much out of line with the basic tendencies of this century?'

17. Candidate of Historical Sciences V. B. Louzky in his works shows that the aspiration of the Jews for establishment of their national state was used by the Great Powers in their own interests. Thus, Great Britain from the moment of the proclamation of the Balfour Declaration (November 2, 1917) supported the Zionist movement to weaken the Arab national movement in Palestine which was turned into a British mandate in 1918.

18. Candidate of Historical Sciences L. R. Gordon-Polonskaya notes that in the first half of the nineteenth century the Muslims in fact suffered rather more from individual measures by the British authorities in India than the Hindus. However, after the insurrection of 1857–59, during which Hindus and Muslims waged a common struggle for the liberation of India, the British colonial authorities, particularly in the seventies of the nineteenth century, began to turn their main attention to setting the so-called Muslim revival against

the Hindu revival and strengthening the Muslim community in an endeavour to direct its activity towards resisting the Hindu domination with which it was allegedly threatened.

In this connection special significance attaches to the publication in 1871 of a book by Sir William Hunter, who was both a senior official of the British colonial service and an historian (W. W. Hunter, *Our Indian Musulmans*, London 1871), in which he analysed the course of British and Muslim interactions in India and came to the conclusion that it was necessary to build up support for British colonial power within the leadership of the Muslim community. The same ideas were expressed by another leading official of colonial India, W. S. Blunt (*Ideas about India*, London, 1885). In 1885 the colonial authorities took a decision to extend the participation of Muslims in the colonial administration. In the eighties the British instigated a series of clashes between Hindus and Muslims all over the country which culminated in 1893 in large scale Hindu-Muslim pogroms in which many lives were lost. From that time onward the fomenting of disputes between Hindus and Muslims became a regular element in the arsenal of the British policy of *divide et impera*.

19. Candidate of Economic Sciences I. P. Yasterbova underlines that the principal reason for the political changes in Africa after the second World War is the development of the mass campaign of the African peoples in favour of independence. It was this struggle, and not the general attitude of the colonialists, that induced the colonial powers to make concessions to the liberation movements.

Between 1945 and 1959 a series of local events reflected throughout Africa the agitation in favour of independence: there were strikes, demonstrations and protest movements in the Belgian Congo, Nigeria, Madagascar, the Gold Coast, Uganda, South Africa, Nyasaland, Northern Rhodesia, etc. repressed by the authorities. In Southern Rhodesia there was a strike by African workers employed in the building of the Kariba Dam. See also Kwame Nkrumah, *Autobiography* (Edinburgh, 1957), Sekou Touré, *L'action politique du Parti democratique de Guinée pour l'émancipation africaine* (Conakry, 1959, several volumes); Sekou Touré, *L'action politique du PEG-RDA pour l'émancipation et l'unité africaine dans l'independence* (Canakry, 1959); and other works.

CHAPTER XXIX

DRIVES FOR CULTURAL INTEGRITY AND RECOGNITION

THE self-image and aspirations of peoples were couched not only in political forms but also in terms of more or less articulate goals of cultural development.[1]

I. RENAISSANCE OF ANCIENT CULTURES

During the twentieth century the peoples of Asia and the Middle East reasserted the traditions of their ancient cultures and related them, in one way or another, to the cultural currents of the modern day. The process ranged from traditionalism to revolution; it involved both the revival of orthodoxy and the reform of religion; it brought a sense of history and a renaissance in the arts. In whatever form, there was a reawakening and a new vitality of cultural expression among all these peoples.[2]

1. *India*

The self-image of India as she struggled to nationhood and independence evolved during a century of interaction with the West. It was compounded of the rediscovery of a great national past, a newly forged sense of unity, a renewed religious spirit, the incorporation of western liberal ideas and institutions and a commitment to social reform. Alone among the peoples subjected to western colonialism, Indians were exposed to western liberal thought in sufficient numbers and over a sufficient period of time for them to make it their own, apply it to their own traditions and integrate it with the other elements in their view of life. In addition the long, active struggle for independence under the leadership of Mahatma Gandhi consolidated both goals and methods and gave a unique character to the Indian experience.

The absence of an Indian historical tradition had long prevented the emergence of a self-image glorifying the past political achievements of the Indian people. But the revival of Sanskrit studies in Europe in the nineteenth century and the recognition of Indian cultural achievement had helped to create the image of a golden age during which the Hindu mind had achieved a superiority over the rest of the world. 'Hindu superiority' was the theme of many writers who emphasized the spiritual qualities of Indian life and extolled her philosophers and her classical literatures and art. But the current weakness of Indian life and India's political subjection emphasized the unreality of this view.[3]

The result was a great movement for national independence, Hindu reformation, social reform and revival of cultural life which sought to make the facts of Indian life more nearly coincide with the image of its greatness. By the second quarter of the twentieth century the uncertainty and ambivalence had gone and independent India saw itself clearly as a modern state resting on a rich and vital tradition from the past.

The rediscovery and reassertion of Indian culture and its dynamic integration with ideas derived from the West was the fruit of the interaction during the nineteenth century of European scholarship, British administration and the work of Indian scholars, religious figures and practical leaders.

When British authority was established in Bengal at the beginning of the nineteenth century, Hindu society was freed from the Muslim authority which had dominated it for five hundred years, but it found itself confronted by a basic challenge from English civilization and culture. The first effect was astonishment in the face of a new world of ideas, forms of art and literature, new ways of thinking and great political and social doctrines. The youth of Bengal, overwhelmed by European civilization and appealed to by missionary tracts which derided the Hindu religion, were led to question the very foundations of their social and religious life.

A positive response to this situation came in successive movements for the reform of Hinduism.* These followed several courses: some elements of the Christian religion and of the thought and attitude of the West were Indianized by the Bramo Samaj; Ramakrishna reaffirmed the essential spiritual nature of Hinduism; the Arya Samaj, while insisting on the purity of primitive Hinduism, accepted the weapons and methods of its adversaries—sacred text, church organization, individual conversion; the English language gave unity to the revival. By the end of the nineteenth century the feeling of inferiority which Hindus had suffered at the opening of the century had entirely disappeared. In the following period, Hinduism not only developed with revived faith, but with a sense that all the problems posed by society could be resolved within its framework; a Hindu outlook inspired the national upthrust which India experienced in the twentieth century.

Among Indian Muslims, a similar movement centring around the Aligarh Muslim University brought revitalization and a modern outlook. Although in time the dominant Muslim view became separatist and led ultimately to partition and the creation of Pakistan, it played a part during most of the period in the modernization of the Indian view and contributed directly to the nationalist movement.

In the course of the nineteenth century the Indian people came to recognize that they possessed a common tradition, a common history and a common conception of life. The unity of the Indian people had long been apparent, as was reflected in the common terms used by Chinese, Persians

* See Chapter XXV, Religion, pp. 885–90.

and other neighbours for all Indians, regardless of the political divisions from which they came; but the idea of the unity of India as a nation did not exist. All historical works before 1800 were in the form of local chronicles or were written from a dynastic point of view by Muslim chroniclers for whom the history of India began with the Muslim invasions.

A series of discoveries created a sense of Indian history, beginning with the identification by European scholars at the end of the eighteenth century of the Sandro Cottus of the Greek historians with Chandra Gupta Maurya who founded the first Indian empire after the invasion of the north-west Punjab by Alexander the Great. This furnished a central point for dating other events. The next step was the deciphering in 1837 of the Asoka inscriptions which revealed a great monarch who reigned over the greater part of India for many years and whose proclamations reflected a great civilization and an efficient administration and form of government much in advance of that which existed in most countries.

The discovery of the reign of such a king, who sent missions to other identifiable kings, made it clear that there really was an Indian history; the subsequent publication of many documents and inscriptions provided a basis for viewing in detail the life of India through the ages. One of the results of these discoveries was to bring Buddhism back into the Indian tradition from which by the nineteenth century it had practically disappeared, as had the memory of personages such as Asoka. The effect of all these studies was to give to all Indians a sense of the continuity of their history, of an uninterrupted tradition and of the 'Indianness' of their life.

Moreover, the discovery that India had transformed the life of neighbouring countries came almost as a revelation. Documents which threw light on 'greater India'—Funan, Champa, Siam, Indonesia, central Asia—showed that Indians from all the great regions of the country had played a significant role in the expansion of civilization and the creation of national cultures. Archaeological discoveries in Afghanistan and central Asia brought to light a great and dynamic civilization, where Sanskrit was used not only for scientific and cultural purposes but in a simplified form for personal correspondence. The awareness that Indian influence had extended to many countries and that India represented, so to speak, a mother civilization gave to Indians great pride and a sense of their importance in the world.

European scholarship also contributed to the sense of Indian nationality through the study of Sanskrit. Sanskrit studies had always been carried on in India, but they had been limited to a small class, and even in this class certain books were regarded as secret and were accessible only to certain castes. It was the translation into European languages of the Vedas, the *Upanishads*, the *Bhagavad Gita* and the other fundamental texts of Hindu thought, and studies of them published in western universities, which permitted the new Indian middle classes, drawn from all the castes, to study the sacred texts. This extension of cultural traditions which had formerly been reserved to small groups permitted the Indian people to have the common feeling of being inheritors of Indian culture.

The same evolution took place with respect to Indian art. Up to the end of the nineteenth century the attitude of educated Indians was dominated by what they had learned of European art. It remained for Europeans to discover the caves of Ajanta and other treasures in the jungles and, with the Anglo-Tamil scholar Ananda Coomaraswamy, to bring a new appreciation of Indian art in the early twentieth century.

When Indians became interested in their own artistic tradition, they discovered that there was a unity of Indian art throughout the country and that this had spread to other countries. In the caves of the thousand Buddhas at Tan Huang in the heart of the Gobi desert, paintings were discovered which were clearly influenced by Indian thought and styles, as was true in central Asia, Indonesia, Cambodia and Siam. The striking unity of Indian art was not limited to a particular period; in all epochs the fundamental ideas remained the same, showing again that the Indian spirit possessed undeniable unity.

Thus through more than a century in this India which had formerly been divided into many kingdoms but which had only a single civilization, the sentiment grew that all Indians belonged to a single family, that they represented a single tradition, that they had the same artistic and literary heritage and that, in spite of past conflicts, they constituted a single nation.

The incorporation of western liberal thought into the Indian self-image was profoundly affected by the system of education introduced in 1835 by Thomas Babington Macaulay. Before that date India had had its own system of education which had produced scholars and thinkers in all periods. At first the East India Company thought of subsidizing the existing Indian establishments and of setting up others on the same plan, but this was opposed by the most progressive of the Indians of the period, such as Ram Mohan Roy.[4]

Macaulay, who came to India as minister of justice, insisted that instruction should be given in English and on subjects of European interest. He foresaw a time when Indians would have rejected their own ways of thinking and would have accepted what he regarded as the highest form of life, the culture and the civilization of nineteenth-century Britain. Although Ram Mohan Roy did not want to make Indians into Englishmen, he too desired that they should acquire a modern manner of approaching social and religious problems, cultivate a critical sense and appreciate the new ideas then reigning in Europe.

The subject matter taught in the Indian colleges was the history of England and Europe, political science and economics. Instruction in natural sciences came later. Whatever else may be said about this subject matter, one fact was of central importance: the English language was the language of freedom and independence. From Milton to the end of the nineteenth century, the great poets and the political and social thinkers all insisted upon freedom of thought and expression and the right of man to liberty. The study of these texts had consequences which the British had not foreseen, convinced as they were of the permanence of their rule.

This system was in force throughout the entire country for more than a century and it played a central role in creating the new life of the country. It brought a new dynamism into Indian thought and a new way of approaching problems of all sorts, as Indians began to call into question the validity of their own institutions in terms of the principles and doctrines which they had studied in schools and colleges. It produced in the whole of India an educated middle class which had the same outlook, spoke the same language and thought in a similar manner, and which formed the leading element in administration, politics, journalism and education.

A second major result of the new education was the expression of a new humanistic outlook in the Indian languages. While instruction at the university level was given exclusively in English, much instruction in the secondary schools was in the various Indian languages, and it therefore became necessary to write books in each of these languages which would transmit the new ideas. The Indian languages, which already possessed rich literary traditions, were transformed into effective modern languages and they came to reflect the feelings, ideas, doctrines and emotions which modern India was experiencing. Under the influence of a common education and common experience, the languages were used to express the same kinds of thought, they adopted the same forms and they created, even in their differences, a unity of Indian expression.

By the beginning of the twentieth century, a renaissance of Indian literature was in progress. New writers were appearing who were thoroughly imbued with European traditions and culture, but who turned more and more to the genius of their own languages and cultural traditions. The great figure of Rabindranath Tagore symbolized this synthesis. Up to the first world war inspiration came primarily from western Europe, but after the October revolution a strong and growing interest developed in the literature, doctrines and social ideas of the communists, and these additional influences were felt in literature and in humanistic thought. Indian humanism of the twentieth century was thus neither entirely western nor traditionally Indian, but a new product of the two.

One of the essential results of the critical spirit introduced by the new education was to separate the religious from the social. For the first time people realized that caste was not a religious institution, and that untouchability was not an integral part of Hinduism—that in fact all the great Hindus from the Buddha to Mahatma Gandhi denounced it. The separation of the merely social from the truly religious represented one of the most fundamental changes brought into India and made it possible to legislate on all sorts of social matters—marriage, inheritance, caste—since these institutions had lost their religious sanction.[5]

At the same time that Lord Macaulay introduced a system of modern education he introduced a penal code for India which embodied the basic principles of British jurisprudence, including the principles that all men are equal before the law, no one is held guilty until he has been judged so by a competent court, and procedures should be public. Indian law had never admitted the principle of equality, whether in Hindu law where different punishments were applied to different castes or Muslim law where the word of an unbeliever was not accepted as against the word of a believer; the principle of inequality had been in fact part of the structure of Indian society. Now the evolution which began with the introduction of the code of law had the effect of rooting the principle of equality in a permanent fashion in the Indian spirit. The fact that for more than a century all men had been equal before the law permitted the constitutional assembly of independent India to proscribe untouchability, and the parliament to make its practice a crime.

The Indian self-image of the twentieth century was imbued with the spirit of nationalism, which too had evolved through the nineteenth and early twentieth centuries, incorporating first political, then social and finally economic objectives.

The uprising of 1857 had been simply a protest against alien rule; the political ideas of the rebellious princes had been merely to restore the ancient régimes and re-establish the political anarchy of innumerable princedoms under a puppet emperor. By contrast the Indian National Congress established in 1885 was founded by a group of men who had been educated by western methods and who spoke the language of modern history and politics. These were members of a new class who cited the speeches of Mazzini, based their arguments on the logic of Burke and drew their inspiration from the Declaration of the Rights of Man. The national movement was not an association of the dispossessed. It was directed by lawyers, journalists, doctors, industrialists who were the fruit of the contact between East and West.

The first leaders of the Congress did not envisage a free and independent India, for they thought that continued British rule was essential for India to progress. They saw too many difficulties to think in other terms, and they contented themselves with trying to secure changes which would enable them to participate in government. But by the end of the century new ideas intervened and a new generation came to believe that a country cannot progress without independence and that the struggle for independence is one of the first duties of a people.

At the turn of the century Bal Gangadhar Tilak gave the nationalist movement a doctrine of political activism. He believed that the nation should draw its strength from its history and own traditions and not let itself be diverted by modern philosophy and foreign thought. He justified his call for direct action by his interpretation of the *Bhagavad Gita,* in the light of which revolution could be regarded as orthodox and sanctioned by religion itself.

But although Tilak began to give the national movement a mass base by identifying it with traditional religion, it did not become fully a mass movement until Mahatma Gandhi assumed the leadership.

Gandhi believed and declared that political liberty could not be separated from social emancipation.[6] He insisted that India should carry out a social revolution before attaining political independence; he maintained that the new national movement must be based on the whole people and not just an educated class; he associated himself with the activist section of the Muslims represented by the Khilafat movement and by leaders such as Maulana Abul Kalem Azad, and he made Hindu–Muslim unity one of the conditions of national development; he insisted on labour as the way of human redemption; he held firm to his fundamental principle that political action should avoid all violence and even hostility toward those against whom India was struggling.

Gandhi introduced into the Indian national movement the conception that national fulfilment involved not only political independence but basic changes in society itself—the abolition of untouchability, modification of castes, extension of rights to women, a secular state. He incorporated all these elements into the national struggle, strongly urging the participation of women in his non co-operation movement, obliging his followers to spin as a qualification for political work, encouraging inter-caste marriages and making the abolition of untouchability one of the great points of his programme. He developed the movement in the villages, carrying the doctrine of social integration to the masses of the people and arousing a new sense of national unity.

If Mahatma Gandhi had been able to achieve independence within five or ten years, his social objective might not have been realized. But the length of the struggle, which started in 1920 and did not end until 1947, ingrained his views. The entire country received the stimulus of thousands of people accustomed to work hard and to sacrifice and of the sense of unity created by this enormous movement; a whole generation grew up within the framework of a strict national discipline. The long struggle was itself an instrument for eliminating many customs and practices which had been blindly accepted in the past and for putting into effect the social ideas which the leaders had already grasped on an intellectual plane. By the end of the period a new outlook had been created among the masses of the people and the ideas which had been entertained only by the intellectuals became part of the Indian outlook.

Prior to the Soviet revolution nationalism in India was conceived in political terms, in relation to authority, power and the direction of the state. The basic modification brought to Indian thought by the October revolution was the idea that in order to avoid economic collapse and a peril to its future the state would need to intervene in the economic sphere. The Soviet experience played an important role for India in creating a conviction among the leaders that the ideas of political progress gained from contact with the West must be united with a doctrine of economic progress, founded on planning on a national scale.

Thus the contact between East and West in India may be regarded as a process of fertilization which gave a new life to a very ancient people, to transform it and to create a new and dynamic civilization based on its past. India had never had a prejudice against borrowing ideas from abroad. In every period of Indian history Indian humanism borrowed from and gave to others, never hesitating to receive what it thought enriching. If Indian writers formerly borrowed from the Persian language or the traditions of Persian poetry and in modern times borrowed European techniques and cast their works in the form of novels, sonnets or dramas, they did not thereby lose their Indian character. It was wholly within the tradition of Indian history to borrow from the USSR the idea of planning and of economic equality without taking over the idea of the dictatorship of the proletariat or limitations on individual freedom.

It was the inherent strength and flexibility of Indian civilization that permitted the adoption and assimilation of ideas coming from the West. And it was the force and the value of the ideas, social objectives, scientific outlook and economic conceptions of the West which played a part in bringing about the transformation of the Indian outlook.

In this amalgam which constituted the self-image of independent India, the several components had greater or less meaning for different segments of Indian society. For the Muslim minority which made up about a tenth of the population of independent India, the liberal component was the heart of the modern Indian self-image. The Muslim leaders who chose to cast their lot with a secular India rather than with an Islamic Pakistan expressed their confidence in the force of liberalism within the Indian synthesis. More, they thought that the principles of democracy and essential unity which they drew from their Muslim tradition, in combination with the liberal principles which they had imbibed, could make a positive contribution toward the evolution of the new India.

All elements in India saw the new nation as creating a new civilization, deeply rooted in its own past but renewed and modified by ideas from the West, a synthesis which should be of value to the whole world.

2. China

At the opening of the twentieth century China saw itself humiliated and impotent, a chained dragon able only to lash out in ineffectual fury at the foreigners who were extending their influence with force and arrogance further and further into the Celestial Empire. In the middle of the century its leaders could declare that 'bright new China stands like a giant in the East'.

The awakening of China and the reassertion of its historic place in the world followed a very different course from that of India. On the one hand

China had never lost its sense of identity as a nation and a people and it had retained a continuous record and knowledge of its long history. On the other hand China's contact with the West was of a different character. Western influences never entered into the structure and outlook of the entire country, as they had penetrated India through its uniform system of western education and law. Western culture in China remained apart from, and rarely integrated with, the Chinese tradition. Western liberalism neither revitalized the Chinese spirit as it had the Indian, nor stimulated the reassertion of a basic tradition stripped of the accretion of custom. Most of all, no social renovation had begun to modernize the basic structure of Chinese society until the communist forces built their strength on the revolutionary aspirations of the peasants and brought a radically new order of life to the Chinese people.

China's experience with the West during the nineteenth century had been most unfavourable to a synthesis of Chinese and western cultures. When in the 1830s British efforts to force the opium trade on the Chinese people had made it necessary for the Chinese empire to modify its age-old practice of treating the rest of the world as vassal states or as barbarians, the emperor's representative had appealed to Britain in terms of moral principles. The reply—armed attack, vandalism and the imposition of unequal treaties granting a privileged position to foreigners on Chinese soil—established the pattern of relationships which persisted for a hundred years.

In the course of the years the Chinese reluctantly concluded that it would be necessary to acquire western knowledge and to design western methods of defence. Throughout the nineteenth century, however, they did not see this as involving the adoption of western attitudes but only as applying western techniques to Chinese purposes, though there were those who thought the distinction between 'substance' and 'function' unsound since western techniques were in fact the foundation of their government.

In contrast to the Indians who acquired western liberal attitudes before they acquired western scientific techniques, Chinese interest was at first almost wholly in the technical aspects; four-fifths of all the works translated into Chinese in the second half of the nineteenth century were on scientific and technical subjects.

The acquisition and application of western knowledge for 'self-strengthening' was, however, half-hearted, for the ruling group of scholar-administrators, selected through the imperial examinations which had been used for two thousand years, were reluctant to admit new bodies of knowledge or to share their power with men educated in missionary institutions or abroad. Nor were they prepared to adopt an institutional structure which would facilitate the development of modern industry, and such industrial developments as were initiated were treated by the officialdom chiefly as a source of tax revenue and perquisites.

Through the nineteenth century Chinese society continued to be composed of a great mass of peasants and a small group of landowners from whose ranks the scholar-administrators were largely drawn. The imperial régime was weak, but the *literati* under the authority of the emperor still held a monopoly of power and organization. As in the past, however, popular unrest manifested itself in the form of peasant rebellions and in the activities of secret societies. In the middle of the century the Tai-Ping rebellion, led by Hung Hsu-chuan who had borrowed from the Christian missionaries the idea of a Messiah, aroused much of the interior of the country and for a period maintained a rival government until the rebellion was finally suppressed. At the close of the century the Boxer outburst directed against foreigners again revealed the presence of widespread unrest and the precarious base on which the central authority rested. A movement for reform was stimulated by the rivalry of Japan and the example of its modernization; many Chinese were attracted to Japan to learn new ways.

The first effort at social reform, the 'hundred days' of 1898, failed disastrously. At the insistence of a group of scholars led by Kang Yu-wei, the emperor was persuaded to issue a series of decrees designed to set in motion a process of modernization, but the dowager empress nipped in the bud this threat to the old régime, tightened the reins of power in her own hands, and consigned the leaders of the reform movement to exile or death. Yet Kang Yu-wei's vision of a new China was not blotted out. Though he lived in exile and died in obscurity in 1927, his pupils kept alive his concept of the successive stages through which China should progress toward 'the Great Commonwealth' in which there would be no distinction of high or low, rich or poor, race or sex, and in which all men would share property in common; they published after his death his design for a community where the state would assume responsibility for the livelihood and welfare of all, a design which bore a close resemblance to the communes actually established by the communist régime.

Two aspects of the reform movement, moreover, had immediate effect. The old examination system for public office was abolished, and with it the monopoly so long held by Confucian scholars in the leadership of the state. Education along modern lines was instituted with the establishment of the University of Peking, and later of other universities in the western style. From these universities, and from the students returning from study in Japan, the United States, western Europe, and finally Moscow, came a new leadership which first abortively and then decisively revitalized Chinese society and gave it new direction.

By 1911 the structure of Manchu rule was so weak that it was overthrown in 1911–12 almost without a struggle. But the republic set up in its place with Sun Yat-sen as its first president rested on no firm foundation of popular understanding and support. The years of imperial impotence and western penetration had left great social disorganization; missionary education had undermined the social structure and disparaged traditional values without providing an effective alternative, while the missionaries themselves had been identified with the extraterritorial and other privileges enjoyed by western economic interests on Chinese soil. There was as great popular bitterness against the West as against the Manchus, and although Sun Yat-sen drew his own inspiration from the West there was no general understanding of western constitutional principles on which to base a republican structure.

The revolution was carried out centrally and its principal effect was to destroy what remained of central authority while it inherited much of the weakness of the old régime. The provincial war lords only awaited the downfall of the emperor to strike out on their own. When the new government sought foreign loans to bolster its position, the foreign powers demanded further concessions in return. The new régime faced the opposition of military men who rallied many scholar-administrators of the old order. It had no mass support, for the gulf between peasants and intellectuals was unbridged and the traditional hold of the landlords over the villages remained unbroken.

When Sun Yat-sen saw the success of the October revolution in Russia and the fact that the other western powers, instead of supporting his revolutionary effort, continued to take advantage of China's weakness, he concluded that the Russian people were China's best friend and that their methods of revolution and organization had much to teach. To carry forward his own revolution, he organized the Kuomintang party, accepted communists as members and sent his lieutenant, Chiang Kai-shek, to Moscow to study the methods of the Red army. He formulated the steps by which his party was to transform China in terms of his Three People's Principles—*San Min Chu I*: Nationalism, to build China as a free, independent and equal member of the family of nations: Democracy, through a gradual process involving defeat of the warlords, tutelage under the Kuomintang party and finally an elective constitutional government; and People's Livelihood, through 'land to the cultivator' and capital development by the state.

But after Sun's death in 1925 Chiang Kai-shek expelled the communists from the Kuomintang and concentrated the efforts of his party more and more on the military unification of the country. He made no effort to enlarge the scope of democratic activity in order to bring to an end 'tutelage' by the party and to reach the stated goal of constitutionalism. Nor did he make any significant effort to carry out economic reform. By the time that the Japanese invasion began in 1937, the Kuomintang had lost its revolutionary direction and the revolutionary initiative had passed to the communist movement which tapped the energy of the peasants and set in motion a mass drive for social change.[7]

The political changes initiated by Sun Yat-sen were paralleled by a literary movement, the New Tide, which broke sharply with the traditions of Chinese society. Its principal leader, the dean of the College of Letters at Peking University, Chen Tu-hsiu, saw no meeting ground between Chinese and western methods, and he called on the new generation in China to choose 'independence not servility, progress not conservatism, aggressiveness not timidity, world-mindedness not narrow nationalism, practical attitude not ceremonies, scientific approach not speculation'.* The young intellectuals who took part in this renaissance rejected, as equally superstitious, traditional Confucian principles and Christianity which many of them had embraced.

The movement spread with great rapidity and vigour among the younger intellectuals, and it brought a first major step toward bridging the gap between the intellectuals and the people by insisting that books be written in the language of common speech, *pai hwa*, and not only in the literary language which no one spoke and only the educated could read. It focused the attention of Chinese writers on the actual conditions of contemporary Chinese life and developed a school of realistic writing which spared no institution of Chinese society.

The most scholarly of the leaders of the New Tide, Hu Shih, remained true to the liberal principles which had inspired the original movement, but more and more of the writers soon moved to the left. Chen Tu-hsiu together with Li Ta-chao, the earliest popularizer of Marxism–Leninism in China, and others founded the Communist party in 1920, and a series of leftist writers' organizations were established. As the communist movement grew in strength, these writers played an active part in giving the movement its Chinese form.

The communist movement in China thus developed in a society in which the age-old division between the masses of the people and the landowning, literate *élite* had not been bridged, and in which no substantial social measures had been taken to relieve misery and poverty, though these conditions were well-known and were constantly depicted by writers; the sanctioning institutions of Confucianism had fallen into disrespect under the impact of missionaries and Chinese liberals, but no alternative set of values had been incorporated into Chinese thought; the tradition of central authority remained strong but a hundred years of weakness had brought near-dissolution; hatred and scorn of the foreigner and an abiding sense of the unique greatness of the Chinese people had never been lost.

The achievement of the communists, under the leadership of Mao Tse-tung and with the support of many of the intellectuals, was to reach the peasants and to provide the means by which they could identify themselves with the nation. Wherever the communist armies appeared, they organized the villages until the Japanese invaders in the northern provinces found themselves no longer confronted merely by armies but by a people in arms; after the war the Kuomintang could offer no effective resistance to the communist forces based on wide popular support. Once in power, the communists rejected as a foreign intrusion the western liberalism which had always remained an island in Chinese life, and they provided the Chinese

* *La Jeunesse*, September 1915.

people with new terms in which to reassert and re-establish their greatness.

In the first decade of its existence the Chinese People's Republic moved with immense energy and great speed toward its goal—to make China once more one of the greatest, if not the greatest, of the world's peoples. It converted the corrupt bureaucracy which had long provided the structure of Chinese government into a highly centralized administration and it cut the ground from under potential war lords by the organization of the people's army. It set the people from one end of the country to the other at the task of making a great 'leap forward' on every front—in agriculture and industry, in irrigation and construction, in education and science, in transport and mechanization, in health and in the culture of the people.

As this effort was projected, all the resources of the people and the country were to be tapped, from the greatest to the least. Large-scale industrial organization and advanced technology must seek to equal and if possible outstrip the West, but local efforts were to be made to adapt traditional crafts and improvise forms of partial mechanization; hundreds of thousands of workers were organized to build canals and dams, while young people were sent into the mountains to hunt for springs which might supply water for local irrigation; in a land where famine had long been endemic and population was mounting, new methods of farming and farm organization were introduced in the effort to raise more food with less labour; schools were organized at all levels with whatever resources there might be at hand.

Although Marxism-Leninism furnished the theoretical guide to the creation of the new China, the Chinese People's Republic regarded itself as the inheritor of the wisdom of the Chinese sages, the inventiveness of the Chinese people and the greatness and unity of the Chinese empire. While the Confucian family system as it had been practised was discarded, leading Chinese scholars found a basis in the writings of Confucius for revolutionary and democratic principles. Alongside modern medicine, which was practised and taught, the practice of traditional Chinese medicine was encouraged. Operas on new themes were composed in the old Chinese style. People in all regions were urged to collect folk songs and to compose new songs in familiar manners. Newly literate people were stimulated to form writing groups and to tell the stories of their factories or farms. Famous Buddhist temples were restored and historical and archaeological discoveries were made widely known.

The task of modernization was gigantic and fantastically difficult. The hectic pace of change in the first years did not conquer the ancient ills of hunger and misery overnight and it brought new strains and problems in its wake. But in the new China nothing seemed impossible to a people of 600,000,000, with four thousand years of recorded history behind them, now that the interlude of weakness was over and they were once more on their way.[8]

3. Japan*

In Japan, the Asian country which most consciously and zealously sought to adopt western ways, new patterns of thought were incorporated into a basically different culture which nevertheless remained in many respects unchanged. The cultural orientation of Japan during these years was the result of the interplay between traditional habits and imported western attitudes and practices, under the conditions of self-assertion, national expansion and military defeat that made up Japan's history in the twentieth century.

More than virtually any other nation, Japan contained a homogeneous people sharing a common traditional culture. Self-contained, self-centred and at peace through the two and a half centuries of isolation before the opening of Japan by the West, it had been neither interfered with nor stimulated by alien ways, ideas or conflicts. The Japanese image of the world was the image of Japan.

In the closed and ordered Japanese society, basically feudal and familial, each person's status and every relationship was carefully defined and expressed in modes of speech and conduct. Compassion and benevolence were high virtues. Man's relation with nature, too, was clearly defined. It involved an intimate intuitive harmony with the fruitful earth, the gentle climate and the beauty of the changing seasons, together with helpless fear in the face of raging typhoons and calamitous earthquakes. Nature was not as in the West a challenger to be conquered and bent to the service of man. According to religious concepts which endowed living objects with spirit or souls, mankind was part of a natural continuum which included animals and gods. The individual's goal was to maintain self-discipline, fortitude and inner peace within an assigned status and in the face of the stresses and trials of life and death.

This was the cultural base upon which western culture, so fundamentally different in many respects, was eagerly superimposed. Not only did the Japanese people master western technology and put it to work; they imported and translated countless western books on all subjects, coined words to cover new materials and ideas, introduced western music, sports, dancing and other forms of recreation, and made western philosophical thought the framework for academic study.

Many intellectuals devoted themselves with such energy and ability to the study of western thought, literature, science and the arts that they came to be more at home in western ideas and ways of thinking than in those traditional to Japan. Listening to western music, discussing western philosophy, even celebrating such western holidays as Christmas, they began to feel that Japan belonged to the culture group of the West rather than with the 'backward' cultures of Asia toward which modernized Japan looked with scorn.

* For other aspects of Japan's development see Chapter IV, pp. 88–9, and Chapter XXVIII, p. 1032.

The masses of the people, for their part, saw daily life enriched by the fruits of industrialization which raised the level of living, although earnings remained meagre and major industrial efforts were directed to heavy industries and war production. Rapid economic expansion constantly broadened opportunities; no former class of handicraftsmen feared the machine for it largely replaced the labour of already overburdened housewives or entered new fields which were not a part of pre-industrial production. Confusions or conflicts between traditional and western ways seemed transitional, easily borne as part of the process of assimilating new knowledge and making it their own.

Yet western thought and practice did not wholly replace traditional Japanese cultural values and attitudes. Private life—the house and garden and the manner of living in them, the family structure and personal relationships—remained traditionally Japanese; chairs and western clothes were used at work, but straw-matted floors and kimonos in the home. Agriculture retained its traditional form, gradually improved by the pragmatic application of new knowledge. So also did the multitude of small family enterprises where a few machine processes supplemented or replaced handicraft methods. Large-scale industry, banking, commerce and merchant shipping created new institutions and ways, which were added to rather than substituted for older forms. In the arts and in recreation the same pattern prevailed. Western plays and movies flourished, alongside the rigorously maintained traditional drama; western music, dancing and baseball competed with traditional forms of entertainment.

Westernization, in short, meant the incorporation of western knowledge and ways into the existing structure and basic values of Japanese society. The ideal was often expressed as 'Japanese spirit, western talents'. Although the old feudal structure was replaced by political and educational institutions drawn from the West, the feudal texture of the social fabric remained. It continued to condition all relationships—between employer and workers, landlord and peasant, old and young, masters and servants, and superiors and inferiors in every professional, economic, social or family hierarchy.[9, 10]

Moreover, western institutions were modified in the process of being adopted. Although parliamentary forms were introduced, the Japanese government remained essentially an executive system, centralized in the emperor, and designed to carry out the process of rapid capitalist development and military build-up. The Japanese Diet, chosen by restricted suffrage to represent functional economic and social groupings, lacked many of the essential features of western parliaments—an effective party system, cabinet responsibility, full control of the purse, supremacy of civilian over military authority. Universal education was initially imbued with the western concept of equality of opportunity, but it was soon redirected to emphasize responsibilities and duties, on the basis of traditional principles: honour to Japan's historic past, the emperor system as the centre of Japan, Confucian ethics as defining the status relationships of a semi-feudal society.

The self-image and aspirations with which the Japanese people entered and fought through the second world war were thus compounded of western technology, military organization and educational methods, a traditionally Japan-centred view of the world, traditional patterns of loyalty and acceptance of status focused on the state and the emperor, and a traditional attitude toward death as man's last and greatest opportunity to meet the vicissitudes of life with courage and fortitude.

The great defeat brought this self-image down in ruins. Nothing coherent remained, neither the western nor the Japanese components, and least of all the amalgam into which they had been formed. In the years after 1945 the Japanese people, with the same self-conscious endeavour with which they had deliberately sought westernization seventy-five years before, turned their efforts to finding a new viewpoint, social structure and national goal. In the initial phase of this effort they were subjected to the anomaly of a conquering, occupying power attempting to introduce democratic institutions and concepts from the vantage point of its authoritarian position. They experienced too, for the first time in many centuries, large-scale intermingling with and exposure to an alien people. At mid-century the process of reshaping a new self-image and re-charting national objectives was still in flux, but some of the component elements were emerging.

The component of democracy, basic to many of the institutions adopted during or following the period of occupation, was much featured in the revised system of education and was being applied tentatively and experimentally in some areas of personal relationships. But it was not clear how far the concept of democracy would prove viable in this society. For people had been conditioned by tradition, language and experience to conform to prescribed rules and status relationships and they had not been called upon to assume the kind of individual responsibility for decision and choice that was basic to western democratic concepts and institutions.

As Japan faced the new world of the mid-twentieth century, she found to her surprise that the peoples of Asia whom she had formerly despised—India, Indonesia, China and others—were rising as nations. For the first time since the start of modernization, the Japanese could feel in good company among the peoples of Asia and no longer had to try to identify themselves with the West.

But more basic than their reappraisal of other peoples of Asia was the reappraisal of their own Asian heritage. In their process of reorientation, educated Japanese began to re-evaluate the non-western bases of the Japanese mentality and feeling which lay below the surface of conscious, westernized thought. The new self-image could acknowledge these qualities, seek their development and use them as a basis for selecting and incorporating whatever might come from abroad.

Among younger men and women—those who had been forced to rethink their attitudes toward their native tradition and toward the West during the war while facing death in suicide squadrons, or who as school children had seen all that they had been taught crash around them—the effort to rediscover a native base led them to explore popular Japanese culture. It seemed to them that neither rootless westernism nor formal intellectualized traditionalism possessed vitality for a new age. And so they sought to discover the outlook and values of the common people, the sources of their strength and endurance, the nature of their aspirations, and ways to release their potential creativity. This was their answer to the challenge which democratic principles offered to a society which had accorded the intellectual a place apart and had exacted self-discipline but not self-expression from the masses of the people.

4. South-east Asia and Korea.

Prior to the second world war the region of south-east Asia remained firmly under colonial rule, with the exception of Thailand which had maintained its independence and the Philippines which had received self-government in 1935 with the promise of independence in ten years. Korea, which had come under Japanese influence after the Sino-Japanese war, had been annexed in 1910 and made subject to direct administration by Japan. In the decade after the war, east and south-east Asia became a region of independent states and by the time that Malaya joined the family of nations in 1957 only a few small remnants of colonial authority were left in the area.

Compared to most parts of the world south-east Asia, which had been a great meeting-place and crossroad of civilization during most of its history and was the source of considerable wealth, remained relatively secluded and static up to the war though it was not untouched by the currents of thought which were arousing other peoples to self-consciousness and to action. Colonial administrations made few concessions toward self-government and extended western education to only a small fragment of the population. The traditional ruling groups had generally lost their power and position, except as they were sustained by the colonial power, as were some of the Indonesian princelings who served as functionaries for the Dutch.

Throughout the region economic enterprise and public administration were mainly in the hands of Europeans, while the local populations carried on subsistence agriculture and fishing, and worked as plantation labour or in the exploitation of forest and mineral resources such as teak, petroleum or tin. The economic and administrative direction by Europeans was supplemented in some areas by a class of Chinese merchants, Indo-European administrators or Indian moneylenders and technicians; Indian and Chinese workers supplied the labour for some plantations and mines. Though conditions varied within the region, they were nowhere favourable to the growth of effective nationalism.

Yet there were some stirrings of nationalist sentiment in the region and the beginning growth of a new class of potential leaders. Though the colonial atmosphere and social pressures tended to make the educated Burman,

Indonesian or Cambodian into an Englishman, Dutchman or Frenchman and to draw him away from his roots and his people, some with western training were taking on a national outlook.

In Indonesia from 1908 on, there were occasional demands for rights, chiefly for participation in activities reserved to Europeans. The first evidences of anything suggesting revolt came with communist-led disturbances in 1926, a mutiny of sailors in 1933 and the formation of a youth congress which pledged itself to work for 'one Indonesian nation, one Indonesian country and one Indonesian language'. The image of 'one Indonesia' extending for 1,500 miles over a sprawling archipelago, inhabited by people in every stage of economic and cultural development, speaking some 250 languages and dialects, was indeed a bold one; it seemed little short of fantastic when put forward by a group of young intellectuals whose number was very small and who lacked organization and support.

Burma, which was administered until 1937 as a province of India, benefited from the concessions of local self-government secured for India by the Indian National Congress. On the other hand technical posts not filled by Europeans were largely filled by Indians and the Indian army provided for defence. Under colonial administration the pattern of Burmese life based on Buddhist attitudes and institutions had been seriously undermined and disorder and confusion were widespread. The expansion of rice farming in the delta had led to the creation of large estates in the hands of absentee landlords, unstable tenancy and seasonal labour and the establishment of new villages many of which did not even have a pagoda. Indian and some Chinese immigrants supplied much of the labour for plantations, industries and mines; the greater part of the population of the larger towns before the second world war was non-Burmese. There was considerable unrest and repeated expression of opposition to British rule, especially in the 1930s.

The units which composed the loose federation which the French called Indo-China had distinct populations, religions and histories and were subject to different forms of administration. Signs of unrest were evident in the serious rebellion of 1930, which was violently repressed, and in the growth of religious sects which formed themselves into semi-military bodies under strongly nationalist leaders.

Fewer signs of nationalism were visible before the second world war in Malaya than elsewhere in South-East Asia. The Malay peninsula, with its resources of tin and rubber, contained a Malay population mainly engaged in farming and fishing, a large Chinese population many of whom worked in the tin mines owned by Europeans or Chinese, and Indian farm labourers who worked on the rubber plantations mainly owned by Europeans. Colonial policy favoured the Malays, especially the princely class. The people of this communally divided land, living under a colonial economy in the shadow of the great imperial naval base and entrepôt of Singapore, had little basis for a sense of national identity and unity.

The turning point in south-east Asia came swiftly and drastically with the Japanese invasion and rule during the second world war. The rapid collapse of the forces of the colonial powers destroyed in one quick blow the prestige which had sustained their authority in the area. There was no restoring colonial rule once the Japanese were driven back, though the Dutch tried desperately to do so, unable to believe that a people with so little experience could organize and hold together the vast and scattered Indonesian archipelago, and though the French waged a costly war for eight years to try to hold Indo-China.[11]

The Japanese occupation not only broke the hold of the colonial powers. In one way or another it contributed both to the creation of the new nations and to the disorganization with which these nations had to deal.

The Japanese set up a puppet régime in Burma to which they granted 'independence' in 1943 and one in Indonesia to which they promised 'independence' on the eve of their own defeat. They conducted their administration in Indonesia in Japanese, which the Indonesians did not understand, and in the Malay-Indonesian language which the Indonesian nationalists had hoped to make the national language, thus displacing Dutch. In Burma they trained and armed a contingent of Burmese to fight against the British, providing the Burmese with their first military forces. In time the Burmese army units turned against the Japanese and helped to drive them out, and then they became part of the people's movement which demanded freedom from Britain. Independent Burma, recognized by Britain in 1947, was the first of Britain's possessions to withdraw from the Commonwealth.

In these and similar ways the Japanese helped to launch as independent nations the countries of south-east Asia which they had sought to prepare for an 'Asian Co-prosperity Sphere' under Japanese hegemony. At the same time their occupation tended to disorganize the life of the region. The trail of physical destruction left in Burma made it difficult for the post-war Burmese government to re-establish communication and control the countryside or restore the economy. In Malaya, workers were conscripted at the rate of 20 for every 250 persons in the population; of 74,000 such workers sent to work on railway construction in Thailand, only 12,000 were reported as having returned to their homes. Some 300,000 people were shipped as forced labour from Java.

The new countries of south-east Asia, plunged thus swiftly into the responsibilities of statehood through the disorganizing experiences of war and occupation, saw themselves first of all as nation-states. In some the nation was identified with a pre-colonial unit, in others with an entity created by colonial rule. In still others divisions were imposed in terms of the conflict between major power groups. The small kingdoms which the French had brought together into Indo-China re-emerged as the states of Cambodia, Laos and Vietnam. By contrast, the multitude of islands over which the Dutch had exercised authority not only declared their common identity as a nation, but laid claim to Western New Guinea on the ground that it had been part of the Dutch empire and the Indonesian state was heir to all that had composed this unit, as well as to the thirteenth-century realm of Madjapahit.

The collapse of the Japanese empire also left Japan's own colony, Korea, free to join the family of nations. In spite of Korea's long history as an independent entity loosely linked to China by political and cultural ties, Japan undertook to extend Japanese language and culture to the area, as well as to develop its economy as part of her own industrial development. The Japanese surrender offered the Koreans the opportunity to reverse the process of incorporation into Japan, to restore the Korean language, replace the Japanese who occupied most posts of responsibility at all levels, and to reassert a national identity.

But all these countries were caught up, to a greater or less degree, in the global conflict to extend communism or to contain it, and their development was conditioned by their role in this contest. Before Korea had more than begun to establish its national identity, it found its soil converted into a battleground, and after three years of destruction it emerged as two states, divided along an arbitrary line drawn not by the Korean people but by the powers. Like Korea, Vietnam was partitioned by international agreement when the French were finally forced to leave Indo-China after defeat by communist-led armies supported by peasant guerrillas; a northern unit became a communist-controlled state while South Vietnam retained its non-communist orientation. The governments of the other new states of the region, often with outside assistance, resisted internal movements led by communist elements during the initial difficult phases of national organization.

With the exception of North Korea and North Vietnam, the new states all saw themselves in some way as liberal democracies and drew up their constitutions either as republics or as constitutional monarchies; Vietnam, which initially established itself under personal rule, voted almost immediately to do away with its monarchy and to create a republic. All faced immense difficulties in their task of achieving productive and viable economies. The region contained considerable natural resources, not only in the varied islands of Indonesia but in rice-rich Burma and Cambodia and in Malaya with its tin and rubber. Every country was, however, woefully short of the essentials for economic development—technical, scientific, administrative and entrepreneurial personnel, capital and organization. Yet they saw themselves, somehow, as creating modern societies and serving the welfare of their people.

In seeking a basis for their identity and existence, they drew on their traditions in various ways. Burma turned to the Buddhist tradition on which the stability and well-being of its society had formerly rested and it rededicated itself to the values which the Buddha had proclaimed. The personal conviction of its first premier, U Nu, made these values alive in public policy:

the great Buddhist conclave in 1955 in honour of the 2,500th anniversary of the Buddha's death lent them added prestige. The problem was whether this renewal could serve to invigorate and guide the new state and to provide adequate motivation and control, not only with respect to the non-Buddhist minorities but in the less stable of the rural areas and in the cities.

Buddhism was important, too, in Cambodia, Laos and Vietnam—it was in fact officially declared to be the religion of the state in the constitution of Laos—but the special sects, such as the Cao Dai, and the substantial numbers of Christians made the Buddhist tradition somewhat less central to the self-image of these states.

For Indonesia the problem was to achieve 'unity in diversity'. In a first effort to cope with this problem, the new government established a strongly centralized state, but it soon became apparent that the several islands had retained a strong sense of their individual identity and that the slogan of the youth of 1928—'one Indonesian nation, one Indonesian country, one Indonesian language'—would not become a reality overnight. Although Indonesia adopted the principles and forms of liberal democracy, the difficulties of organizing the country economically and politically were great and the wide gap between village and central government was bridged only by personal loyalty. President Sukarno, who commanded such personal loyalty from the early days of the struggle for liberation, looked for some form of 'guided democracy' in terms of which to design a workable state.

For Malaya the problem of 'unity in diversity' was also very real, for communalism was traditional, economic divisions were sharp, and at the time of independence the Malay, Chinese and Indian populations, the farmers, tin miners, rubber workers, mine and plantation owners and merchants, had a long way to go before they could subordinate their separate identities and regard themselves fully as 'Malayans'.

Thus, in all south-east Asia the swift conversion of dependent people into independent states created nations which faced great problems of political organization and economic and social change without having developed a common outlook through a long nationalist struggle, and without possessing a substantial group of educated and experienced men equipped to lead their technical and political development. Flanked on either side by the two giants of Asia, China and India, each driving with great energy to create a powerful modern society in its own terms, these smaller and less firmly established states had, perhaps, only one common guiding aspiration: 'Merdeka'—Freedom.

5. The Arabs

Arab nationalism in the twentieth century was the expression of a people who shared a common language and a sense of common identity with a great past, whatever the political units within which they were to be found. The sense of Arab identity and the aspirations of people who regarded themselves as Arabs were built up gradually through the century, reaching a high emotional pitch a decade after the second world war.

Arab nationalism absorbed or overrode other loyalties that offered alternative bases for identification and dedication among Arab peoples. It overshadowed emotional attachment to the nation-state and identification with other than the Arab phase of the long history of the ancient lands of the Middle East and North Africa. Although Egypt set up the gigantic statue of Rameses II in the centre of Cairo and made the most of tourist interest in the great pyramids and tombs, it was the Arab rather than the Pharonic tradition upon which modern Egypt built its sense of mission and identity. The effort to focus on Egypt as a nation-state rooted in the past of the Pharaohs declined as Arab nationalism rose. Finally the Arab identification triumphed with the creation of the United Arab Republic by the union of Egypt and Syria in 1958, and the abandonment of Egypt as a name, with the historic associations which it evoked.

Arab nationalism also transcended loyalty to Islam, though the sense of Arab greatness was bound up with the sense that Islam was authentically Arab. The centre of Islam, the holy city of Mecca, was an Arab city; Arabic was the language in which the Quran was written and continued to be read or recited by all believers; historically it was the Arabs who carried Islam to the East and to the West. Yet Arab nationalism served as a counterweight to the Pan-Islamic movement of the early twentieth century which sought to bolster the authority of the caliph, and the nationalist movement included among its leaders Christian and Druse Arabs who placed national identity above religious affiliation. Arab nationalism tended, too, to overshadow dynastic and other personal loyalties which had been the main form of affiliation known in the region and continued to characterize the relations within the Arab world to the middle of the twentieth century.

Arab nationalism drew much of its strength and emotional intensity from the fact that it became more and more a rallying point for antagonism against the colonial powers of the West. Nowhere was anticolonial sentiment stronger or more charged with resentment and distrust. Nowhere was there a more bitter sense of betrayal. In the climate of the mid-twentieth century, the efforts of western powers to protect their interests in the area seemed an especially intolerable affront to the dignity of a proud people, and Arab nationalism offered an outlet for this indignation.

The initial impetus for Arab nationalism came from the Islamic revival of the late nineteenth century, inspired by the nationalist, Pan-Islamic spirit of Jamal ad-Din al-Afghani and the liberalism of Mohammed Abduh, who believed that a purified Islam could assimilate modern technical and social ideas and could renew the strength of Muslim society. Ideas of secular nationalism, in the western sense, were stimulated by missionary education; some of the most vigorous members of the Arab nationalist movement were graduates of the American University at Beirut.[12]

The Young Turk movement of 1908, with its call for 'Liberty, Fraternity and Equality', appeared to the Arabs to offer an outlet for their awakening self-consciousness. In the multi-cultural Ottoman empire, where administration was carried on by Turkish pashas but the nationalities within the empire retained their identity, the Arabs supposed that they would gain greater autonomy under the constitutional government which the Young Turks proposed. But the Young Turks envisaged a nation-state which should be Turkish in culture and national loyalty, not merely in rule.

The Arabs came to realize that there was no place for them in a movement leading to Turkification, and they turned toward organizations of their own, forming a series of secret societies between 1908 and 1912. The aim of these societies was still not separation from Turkey, but full political rights and an effective share in the administration of the empire. The first all-Arab congress, called in Paris in 1913 on the initiative of a group of Arab students abroad, formulated similar demands.

The most practical encouragement to Arab nationalism came from the western powers who sought to use Arab ambitions to achieve their own military objectives in the first world war. As Turkey became involved in the war and it appeared that the Ottoman empire might be crumbling, the aspirations of the Arabs gradually shifted from participation within the empire to independence. Arab leaders sought and received Allied encouragement for their aims and in 1916 Husain, the sharif of Mecca, raised the standard of the 'Great Arab Revolt' against the Turks. In the name of Arab nationalism the Muslim Arabs thus turned against another Muslim power and hastened the downfall of the sultan who was also their caliph.

But the powers not only mobilized the Arabs and gave them a sense of their potentialities; they created among them a common sense of betrayal and indignation which gave new direction and a new bitterness to their nationalism. During the negotiations through which the British encouraged the Arabs to rise, the Arab leaders understood that they were being promised support for independence. When they joined the Allies' cause, they thought that it was their own battles rather than those of the Allies that they were fighting. But in the peace settlement which divided the Arab lands of the Fertile Crescent between Britain and France as mandatory powers under the League of Nations, they saw themselves as mere pawns in the game of European power politics.

From that time forward the emotional fervour of Arab nationalism, which had hitherto been vague, anti-Turkish or compounded with dynastic ambition, became passionately anti-western. The sense of betrayal was accentuated and the anti-western feeling exacerbated by the Balfour Declaration of 1917 which declared that Britain would look with favour upon the establishment of a Jewish national home in Palestine. A Jewish homeland appeared to the Arabs as an intrusion into what they regarded as *their* land, and in the context of alien rule imposed through the mandate system it took on the character of a beachhead for the colonially-minded West.

The discovery of oil introduced a new factor affecting the aspirations of the Arabs. From the opening up of the immense oilfields in Iraq in the 1920s and in the Arabian peninsula in the 1930s, the politics of the western powers in the Middle East became the politics of oil. The Arabs were subject to the effects of agreements among the powers and between the powers and Turkey which disposed of territory and carved out oil interests. But, as owners of the land where oil was pumped and across which it was carried by great pipelines they could exert pressure on the powers in their turn. Especially after the nationalization by Iran of the Anglo-Iranian oil properties in 1951, which led to a general raising of the share of oil profits received by local states throughout the Middle East from around 10–15 per cent to approximately 50 per cent, the undreamed-of riches which oil revenues brought to the treasuries of Iraq, Saudi Arabia and the sheikhdoms of Kuwait and Bahrein gave these governments the financial means to pursue their ambitions, either for themselves or for the Arab cause. In the years after the second world war their command over these coveted oil resources placed them in a position to play off rival power blocs against one another.

In the inter-war years the exercise of European authority in the Arab countries was vigorously and repeatedly resisted throughout the area. There were armed revolts against the establishment of British authority in Iraq in the early 1920s and even more violent resistance to French rule in Syria. In Palestine violence was almost continuous. Egypt succeeded in throwing off the British protectorate in 1922. The extension of European rule in North Africa had been resisted by tribal chiefs and religious sects during the nineteenth and early twentieth centuries, and such resistance continued to appear, as when the Riff in Morocco waged a five-year campaign from 1921 to 1926. Some of the resistance was Arab-oriented, some expressed tribal or dynastic ambitions, some focused on religion. Especially in North Africa, nationalism during these years was intensely religious; the strong revival movement for the rigorous adherence to orthodox Islam was often scarcely distinguishable from the nationalist movement against European domination. In one form or another nationalist movements became a driving force in the Arab lands.

As these movements grew in intensity, the common opponent—the western colonial powers—was clearer than the common bond of unity. Many factors tended to divide the Arab peoples and to stand in the way of transforming the sense of identity with others who called themselves Arabs into any more substantial form.

The level of social and economic development ranged widely, from Egypt and Lebanon, which had relatively high rates of literacy and a substantial middle class, to the Arabian peninsula where, outside the foreign oil installations, virtually all modern facilities for the population were lacking. Tribalism and nomadism were widespread; the strongest Arab tradition in fact was the nomadic one. Over half the population of the Arabian peninsula and the Fertile Crescent, and much of Arab North Africa was composed of

Bedouins or other nomadic peoples. With the development of modern transport and military weapons, many of the nomads lost their sources of livelihood as caravan drivers and fighters. But though their economic and military function declined, they remained oriented toward their traditional way of life; they were still, at least psychologically, men on horseback or camelback, men of the tents, not of the village or town. Their independence and pattern of personal loyalty tended to stand in the way of national integration, though the trends of the times were driving them towards a settled mode of life.

The peasant villages, in turn, were almost universally part of a feudal pattern, dominated by large landowners who rarely had any but a remote and limited concern for the welfare of 'their' peasants, or encouraged them to expect or seek social change. Arab nationalism, in contrast to the nationalist movement in India, was not fundamentally a movement for social reform.[13]

Dynastic rivalries continued to be a divisive factor. Constant petty wars among neighbouring rulers remained the pattern in the Arabian peninsula through the first quarter of the century, until Ibn Saud, head of the Wahhabi sect, overcame one after another of his rivals and extended his authority over most of the peninsula. In the course of establishing his rule, Ibn Saud displaced the Hashemite sharif of Mecca, Husain, who had led the Great Arab Revolt. When Britain placed Husain's two sons on the thrones of Iraq and Jordan respectively, the rivalry between the two dynasties shifted from control of the Holy City to leadership of the Arab cause.

In addition to the persistence of dynastic rivalries, the Arab peoples were divided into separate national states, more or less arbitrarily defined by outside powers. Iraq was established under British tutelage in a region containing nomadic tribes and urban centres, Sunni and Shi'ite Muslims, a majority of Arabs and a large minority of Kurds. France divided its mandate into half-Christian Lebanon where French influence had long been strong and Syria, where intense devotion to Islam became linked with national resistance. Britain, caught in Palestine on the horns of the dilemma it had created by professing support to the cause of both Arabs and Jews, carved out the desert kingdom of Transjordan as an Arab state.

In each of the mandate territories, as well as in Egypt which had been under British tutelage since 1882 and became a protectorate in 1914, and in North Africa, the nationalist struggle was carried on by separate political units which sought and gained successive measures of self-government, constitutional rights and finally independence. When a comprehensive movement for Arab nationalism reasserted itself during and after the second world war it encountered vested interests identified with the states which had come into being.

It encountered, too, competing claims to Arab leadership. Syria's location made it the keystone of the Arab arch and some of its leaders entertained the idea of a 'greater Syria' extending south-east and south-west from Damascus.

Iraq had the advantage of greater freedom during the inter-war period, and wealth derived from oil. Egypt had the largest population, published the newspapers read most widely throughout the region, and furnished teachers and technicians to other Arab countries.

The first concrete move toward some form of political unity came at the encouragement of the British early in the second world war when it was apparent that the Allies could not count on Arab support such as they had received in the first world war, and that in fact they might find the Arabs among the supporters of the Axis, as an abortive anti-British outbreak in Iraq showed. In May 1941, the British foreign secretary, Anthony Eden, declared that the British government would give full support to any scheme for Arab unity that might command general Arab agreement, for it seemed 'both natural and right that the cultural and economic ties between the Arab countries, and the political ties too, should be strengthened'.*

On the initiative of Egypt the League of Arab States was formed in 1944. But the separate nationalisms, the rivalries for leadership, the cultural disparities and other divisive factors made the league merely a loose organization of sovereign states. In the aftermath of the second world war it was the individual states of west Asia and north Africa that were the beneficiaries of the wave of nationalism which swept across the world. By 1957 ten separate Arab states were members of the United Nations; Sudan, with one foot in the Arab world and one in tropical Africa, might be counted as an eleventh.

But Arab nationalism was not submerged by the separate nationalisms of the Arab states, and it was soon called into new vigour by the continued intervention of the European powers, in one way or another, in the Middle East. As colonialism came to a virtual end in Asia, its remnants in the Arab lands appeared even more intolerable than when Arabs had shared with much of the rest of the world their subordination to European rule. Britain retained certain special rights in Iraq as well as its protectorate over Aden and some of the sheikhdoms of the Arabian peninsula; the Suez Canal was under foreign administration; Algeria was administered as part of metropolitan France. Above all, Israel appeared as a spear thrust by the West into the side of the Arab body.

The humiliation of the defeat by Israel in the Palestine war of 1948 stimulated the sense of Arab unity and of the need to stand together against a common threat. But it was not until a leader emerged who could focus Arab sentiment and harness it to his own ambition that Arab nationalism became more than a discontent, a binding attitude among the Arab states within the United Nations, and a constant threat to the continued existence of Israel.

Initially Gamal Abdul Nasser was the leader of an Egyptian revolutionary movement which threw out King Farouk in 1952 and launched a programme for economic and social reform. Within a short period he became the outstanding figure in the Arab world, voicing most uncompromisingly and per-

* *The Times,* May 30, 1941.

sistently the Arab hatred of Israel. When Britain and France intervened with force in Suez in 1956, Nasser became the target of the kind of gunboat diplomacy that had been the mark of colonial tactics in the past. Thereafter he was the symbol of the Arab stand against the colonialism of the West.

The constitution which Nasser promulgated for Egypt at the beginning of 1956 proclaimed that Egypt was both an Arab state and an Islamic state.

As an Arab state, Nasser saw Egypt as the centre of an Arab union or federation: the first step was to attempt to effect a union of Syria and Egypt. It was fully indicative of the triumph of Arab nationalism over the nationalism of the separate states that the name 'Egypt', with its long history and many associations, was discarded in favour of 'United Arab Republic'. As the champion of Arabs still in subjection to western powers, he offered support to the rebels in Algeria and a home to the Algerian nationalist government created in exile. In bidding for Arab leadership, however, Egypt faced rivalry from Iraq, and it was not immediately apparent whether the spirit of Arab nationalism could bring the various parts of the Arab world together on a political basis.

In proclaiming Egypt an Islamic state, Nasser sought to keep the centre of Islam with the Arabs as it had always been, in spite of the emergence of Pakistan as an Islamic state and the numerical proponderance of non-Arabs in the total Muslim population of the world. Yet this concern was secondary to the focus on Arabism, for the provisional constitution of the United Arab Republic (1958) proclaimed only that: 'The United Arab state is a democratic, independent, sovereign republic and its people are part of the Arab nation.' It made no mention of Islam.

Nasser also declared Egypt to be an African state, and entered a bid on behalf of the Arabs for the leadership of Black Africa as it emerged from colonialism and tribalism. Islam was strong in parts of the African continent and was spreading; the Sudan, though rejecting union with Egypt in favour of independence, announced itself as one of the Arab states; Cairo radio beamed its special programmes constantly to the south and south-west; representatives of the United Arab Republic were on hand to take as important a part as possible in any gathering of African states or groups.

These moves were part of the power politics of the mid-twentieth century, when politicians talked of a 'power vacuum' in the Middle East, oil was vital, the communist and non-communist worlds were at odds, and anyone who might succeed in organizing and modernizing the Arab area could play a strategic role. But beneath these hard political realities lay the vague dream of an Arab 'homeland' stretching from the Persian Gulf to the Atlantic and a strong emotional feeling of Arab identity. In spite of technical backwardness, lack of economic development, much poverty and ignorance, and every problem that beset the underdeveloped countries of the modern world, the Arab people had the sense that they were experiencing a spiritual renaissance and were standing on the threshold of a new era of Arab greatness.

II. CULTURES OF RECENTLY SETTLED LANDS

In contrast to the ancient societies which drew on their historic past to renew their life in the twentieth century, the countries which had been settled in relatively recent times—in the Americas, Australia, New Zealand—were culturally oriented toward the future. These new countries had been created by people who had deliberately turned their backs on the past and had ventured into a new life in an empty continent or a new society. They were based on hope and the expectation that the lot of the children would be different from that of the father, and better. The pioneer spirit of these countries was constantly renewed by streams of immigrant newcomers and by the recurrent movements of older settlers into new regions of undeveloped land or into new fields of endeavour.

In all these countries in the twentieth century there was some nostalgia for the 'old world', some seeking for roots in the cultural heritage of Europe and some sense of cultural inferiority which they were still striving to outgrow. But such backward pulls were more than balanced by the sense that these were peoples who had taken fate into their own hands and whose eyes were on the future, for their children and their children's children.

1. *The United States*

The familiar terms often applied to the United States reflect the orientation of its culture toward the future, 'the land of opportunity', the immigrant's dream of 'gold in the streets', the injunction 'go west, young man'. The legend on the Statue of Liberty in the harbour of New York proclaimed a land dedicated to a future to which all could aspire, whatever their past: 'Give me your tired, your poor, your huddled masses yearning to breathe free.'

From their beginnings as a nation, the American people were self-conscious about the historic experiment which they were living out. In their 'land of promise' they saw themselves as building a new kind of life and a new kind of society which would stand as a model for the rest of the world. They never ceased to take for granted that the United States was a unique experiment and suitable for imitation, that their approach to life in a society composed of all manner of men could well be used by all manner of men elsewhere.

The 'American dream'—the social myth which drew millions of Europeans to American shores—was compounded from the rationalism and optimism of the eighteenth-century Enlightenment and the rigours and rewards of peopling a continent; the heritage of British institutions provided the equipment and a Calvinist ethic much of the original drive. The dream rested on the basic assumption that man, by his own striving, could advance toward an earthly goal; he could overcome the obstacles presented by nature, which could be subdued, and by the faults of man, which could be remedied. Society could remake and renew itself and bring itself closer to the conditions for ideal life.

In this permanent revolution, where the individual's own striving was backed by the social conscience of the successful and the social effort of voluntary groups, work had supreme value, success was a measure of individual worth, material well-being was a social objective, and freedom the favourable condition. These were not purely materialistic goals, as they often appeared to others. At its core, the American drive for material well-being was an expression of the refusal to accept poverty and misery as the necessary condition of man. In the American view, material well-being, health and education freed men to lead lives of human dignity. Because Americans believed profoundly in men's potentialities, they insisted that opportunity should be open to all who would work to achieve a better life for themselves and for their children.

Throughout the American experience, this fundamental vision was taken for granted, however far it was from realization in practice. There were sharp conflicts over how it might be realized; the simple faith in automatic progress wore thin and came to seem naïve; the shibboleths of individualism, freedom and enterprise were abused and made to sanction corporate power; prejudice and discrimination, especially against Negroes, mocked the principles of equality of opportunity. The small, indigenous Indian population, displaced in the process of settlement and relegated to reservations, was largely forgotten. In the process of eliminating the contradiction of slavery from a society committed to democracy and equality, civil war during the 1860s tore the country apart regionally and left an aftermath of regional poverty, bitterness and nostalgia that still continued to act as a drag on the realization of national ideals in the middle of the twentieth century.

But only small groups of extremists seriously questioned the basic tenets, while the people as a whole clung stubbornly to the faith that had brought them or their fathers or grandfathers to American shores. Even in the depths of the depression of the 1930s, radical alternatives had small appeal. Although Marxism attracted a number of intellectuals and some workers' groups, and fascism rallied some 'hate' groups, the great mass of the people at all levels remained confident that a way would be found within the framework of the democratic constitution and the enterprise system to re-establish the conditions within which they could live progressively fruitful lives.

Historic experience gave substantial reality to the social ideal. Initially it rested firmly on an agrarian tradition built up in the process of settlement. The land and climate, by and large, were friendly to man. Though the forests were dark and the prairies wide, the hills stony and the rivers dangerous in flood, the soil for the most part was fertile, rainfall was sufficient, mountain barriers could be crossed and the climate included neither the cold of the Arctic nor the tropical heat of jungle or desert. In such a land men of sturdy courage, endurance and ingenuity could carve out a livelihood for themselves. With the aid of favourable provisions for landholding, families cleared the land, established homesteads and either stayed to farm or again moved on. From the 1840s squatters could buy the land which they occupied at a minimum price; from the 1860s, the settler could claim a homestead of 160 acres merely by living on it and cultivating it. By this process of land settlement, democracy and individualism were firmly grounded in an agrarian base; in fact some historians attributed the genius of American political and social life to the repercussions on the total society of this moving frontier.

Simultaneously with the settlement of the continent, industry took root and grew, under conditions which made labour scarce and placed a high premium on mechanical ingenuity and labour-saving techniques. Through most of the nineteenth century the urban population grew even more rapidly than the rural, and after 1870 industrial expansion proceeded at an accelerated pace. Both land and industry drew a constant stream of peasant immigrants from every part of Europe, to mingle and form the American population.

These and other conditions of American life combined to sustain the basic self-image. America had no feudal heritage, and although class differences were marked, such classes as developed were of recent origin, and anyone could aspire to enter them. The 'self-made man' was a favourite American stereotype; successful politicians, business men, writers and professional men pointed with pride to their lowly beginnings. The class system was in continual flux; the saying, 'from shirtsleeves to shirtsleeves in three generations' expressed the assumption that class position was not static, but could only be kept by constant effort.

Americans took it for granted that they were in tune with the times and an example to others because the major tendencies of the modern world—industrial technology, capitalist enterprise, democratic principles and institutions—were the basic ingredients of their tradition. These were held in check by no previous pattern or structure, nor was there the need to repudiate conflicting elements of tradition in order to establish them on a revolutionary basis. The 'American system' had the full and continuous sanction of the American tradition and could thus be assumed to be in its essentials beyond question or debate.

But a society built on the sense of promise was bound to fall short and there were always many gaps between the dream and the actuality. From the start Americans were self-critical, for denial of the basic principles brought a sense of guilt and failure. Self-criticism and defensiveness—even violent expressions of prejudice—were reflections of the discomfort that Americans felt over the contradictions between ideals and daily life.

Moreover, the individualistic, competitive, open society, with its emphasis on success and its constant influx of new people, placed heavy psychic demands on the individual. In the wilderness or in the world of strangers, each man had to make his own place; he could not simply accept it. Self-reliance was a hard and lonely precept. It is not surprising that those from whom it demanded too much should have projected their anxieties on to others. As successive groups of immigrants filled the lowest paid jobs and occupied the poorest housing, each in turn—Irish, French-Canadian, Italian, Mexican—

met a recurrent stereotype which attributed the conditions of poverty and ignorance to supposedly inherent characteristics; as each group became established, its members joined in applying the stereotype to the latest arrivals. From time to time demagogues exploited the anxieties that lay beneath the surface and turned latent fears into bursts of hate.

American society was, by choice as well as geography, self-contained. The American people, in emigrating, had rejected the lands of their origin and cast their lot in the New World. They might feel sentimental toward the 'old country' or send money to relatives, but they did not want to look back or to become involved in Europe's affairs. Isolationism was the expression of people who saw their 'manifest destiny' within their own continent and whose aspirations took the form of a future for their children, not a place of power in the world.

In the course of the twentieth century the American self-image was subjected to many strains. In the first decades the flow of immigrants reached a peak and placed a heavy burden on the process of integration. The traditional assumption had been that anyone who came with the intention to make the United States his home became an American as soon as he landed, or at least as soon as he had taken out his naturalization papers. But at the height of the mass migration it became apparent that the 'melting pot' had not worked as rapidly and completely as some people had expected, though millions of peasants from many different countries, quite unaccustomed to democratic processes and urban industrial life, had learned to function effectively within the institutions of American society.

A wave of anti-immigration sentiment led to restrictive legislation after 1920 which brought to an end a long chapter in the history of both Europe and the United States. This legislation set quotas which discriminated against south and east Europeans—the most recent immigrant groups—on the charge that they were less 'assimilable', attributing to them the familiar stereotypes of poverty and ignorance. The quota system was to prove embarrassing in later years, when many of the children and grandchildren of Italian and Polish immigrants had risen to positions of prominence and leadership, but it remained for decades on the statute books, a monument to the uncertainty that beset a mixed people striving to be one.

The persistent failure to accord full equality of opportunity and status to racial minorities and even to ensure to Negro citizens their elementary rights remained a thorn in the American conscience and a source of conflict whose bitterness was enhanced by the underlying sense of guilt. Systematic attacks on discrimination slowly reduced obstacles to employment, education, political participation and the enjoyment of the amenities. Negroes never ceased to believe that American principles would ultimately be applied to them. But racial discrimination remained the major blot on American life in the eyes of Americans themselves.

The two world wars drew the United States out of its isolation and into world affairs.[14, 15] After the first conflict, the old desire to reject Europe re-asserted itself with such strength as to prevent American participation in the League of Nations, though many people felt that the country was sufficiently mature to assume a share of world responsibility. But after the second world war the United States could not withdraw as it had before. Reluctantly the American people looked beyond their own preoccupations to world problems, taxed themselves to provide financial aid to other parts of the world, spent immense sums for military defence, and tried to play a role commensurate with the position in which they found themselves.

Economic development raised questions as to the adequacy of principles and methods formulated in other times. During the 1920s there was much self-criticism and discussion of the effects of machine civilization. Amid the speculative prosperity of the period, many people began to wonder whether equality, democracy and independence were compatible with the monotony and regimentation of factory life. The depression of the 1930s shook the faith in the American dream. Where was liberty, with no place to go? Where was the American standard of living, with no job? Especially, where was self-respect, with no work? Since success was the culturally established goal, its absence left people without a sense of direction and with the awful weight of failure. The experience was particularly shattering to the many children of immigrants who came of age in these years, for they had learned to identify Americanism with a high standard of living and success, yet they found the door of opportunity closed to them. It left a deep mark upon the American outlook and aroused the desire for security in a society which had hitherto been mainly concerned with opportunity.

But one of the most persistent components in the American tradition was the spirit of reform which kept Americans always working at the unfinished business of removing the injustices and imperfections in their society. The New Deal of the 1930s, which refashioned many institutions in response to the depression, was in this tradition. It was a pragmatic effort to make American institutions work better, not to discard them, and it sought to meet the problems of a modern capitalist economy within the framework of freedom and democracy. It restored to the American people the sense that their own fundamental principles and habitual approach to problems gave them the means to pursue their course under the new conditions of modern economic life.

The growth of large-scale organization brought further problems. Bureau-cracies in government, industry and labour organization replaced much of the individual enterprise which had had its roots in the small shop and family farm. In the years after the second world war, Americans became conscious of the 'organization man' and of a tendency for people to rely on others for their ideas and sense of direction rather than on themselves. Socio-logists found some signs of greater class rigidity, but under pressure of heavy progressive taxation lower economic levels rose faster than upper, closing the gap in patterns of living. Initiative and enterprise retained high cultural value and continued to be expressed in business and community life. The aspirations of people in all walks of life were increasingly defined in terms of common standards of consumption and welfare.

The continuing proof to Americans of their way of life was the success of the American experiment. Although they recognized that good fortune had brought a continent into their hands at a crucial time in world history, the American people nevertheless regarded their prosperity, the stability of their society in an unstable world and the progressive extension of their democracy as evidence of the validity of their principles. In the nineteenth century they had seen their experience as unique because they were engaged in establishing a democratic way of life in an untamed continent. In the twentieth century they still believed it to be unique, for they were the first to develop an economy of plenty on the basis of modern technology—the first major society which did not rest on a substratum of exploitable poor.

At mid-century many Americans were asking themselves whether, in achieving affluence, they were in fact attaining their goal. Did highways crowded with private cars, generously stocked supermarkets, ever extending suburbs, and countless forms of convenience, comfort and entertainment add up to the good life? Did the persistence of unresolved social problems—bad housing, over-crowded schools, water pollution—reflect too great a preoccupation with private satisfaction at the expense of public responsibility? Were people becoming soft and losing their sense of purpose? Yet even in asking themselves these questions Americans continued to assume that their way was not merely right for themselves but a valuable example to others.

Abraham Lincoln remained America's most authentic voice. The millions of Americans who climbed the steps of the Lincoln Memorial in the nation's capital to stand before the gaunt, compassionate figure of the Great Emancipator felt that here, more than anywhere, they were in the presence of America's spirit. It was Lincoln's vision of human dignity in freedom that they too, however awkwardly, sought to realize. And though they could accept intellectually the fact that other peoples in other cultures might pursue other values, in their hearts they believed, with Lincoln, that 'the spirit which prizes liberty' is the heritage of 'all men, in all lands, everywhere'.

2. *Canada*

Canada, which shared the continent with the United States, shared also the same pioneer spirit. It, too, was a democratic society on the upgrade devoted to work, committed to the principle of equality, composed of immigrants striving to make good, pragmatic in its approach to life and proud of its material achievements.

But Canada had much that gave it an outlook quite distinct from that of its more populous neighbour. Its land and climate were harder to tame and to endure. A large part of its vast territory lay north of the Arctic Circle, and in much of the rest the climate was severe. Only a narrow strip from east to west could be peopled by the kind of frontier settlement that spread across the United States. Canada's frontier lay to the north, and here advance depended on science and technology—on new strains of wheat that could mature in the short growing season, on magnetic aerial prospecting and the new demand for uranium and cobalt, on airlifts to sustain Arctic settlements.

Canada's was a bi-cultural society. The majority of its population was English-speaking and predominantly Protestant. Its French population had been allowed to retain 'the benefit and use of their own laws, usages and customs' when Britain acquired the area from France in the eighteenth century, and French Canada never ceased to insist on the right to its characteristic way of life. It was an essentially peasant society, conservative, and deeply devoted to the Catholic Church which played a central role in the community's life. The Canadian outlook and virtually every aspect of Canadian society were affected by the need to accommodate distinct cultural groups, to tolerate wide disparities and to maintain an atmosphere of mutual respect which would enable all elements to move forward together as Canadians. Canadians became masters of the art of creating and sustaining a working partnership.

The British empire provided the framework within which Canada worked out its difficult problems of geography and population. In this relationship, too, the key was partnership. Within the flexible structure of the empire, Canada moved toward autonomy and independence without ever breaking with the mother country and it made a nation out of small, widely separated islands of population. In the process, it had the effect of transforming the British empire into the Commonwealth, for each step in this transformation from the Durham reforms of 1838 to the Statute of Westminister in 1931, was worked out to accommodate the situation and meet the demands of Canada, the most politically developed and independent unit of the empire, and the other dominions became the beneficiaries of the process.

With a small and slowly growing population and an enormous, difficult terrain, Canada's schemes for development and her institutional structure generally ran ahead of the actualities. Whereas in the United States people were repeatedly breaking out beyond the bounds, in movement of population and in all manner of activities, so that formal institutions and orderly processes of government kept having to catch up, Canada repeatedly developed the institutional framework before the people were there to use it. The symbol of Canada's frontier was the Royal Canadian Mounted Police—the red-coated 'Mounty'—in contrast to the image of the 'wild west' in the United States. Individual initiative was prized, but Canadians took it for granted that public action was necessary to create the conditions where it could be exercised.

As the smaller partner in close working relations with the United States, Canada was at some pains to preserve her interest and identity. The sheer size of the United States and its prior industrial development made it a magnet attracting Canadians in search of opportunity. Large numbers of rural–urban migrants crossed the border to the growing cities of the United States. From 1850 to 1950 emigration from Canada practically equalled immigration into the country from abroad; nearly a million Canadian-born were living in the United States in 1950, as compared with a total Canadian population of 14,000,000. Canadians and Americans were linked through common organizations—labour unions, professional bodies, religious, business and voluntary groups—with Canadians, of course, habitually in the minority. Here again, Canada's ability to maintain integrity within a partnership relationship kept her identity and inner drive intact.

In the middle of the twentieth century Canadians saw themselves as just beginning to unlock the unlimited wealth of their frozen north, with the aid of science, with their capacity to develop the necessary institutions and with a people undeterred by hardship. As a leader within the British commonwealth and an increasingly strong member of the North American partnership, Canada was in a position to benefit and draw strength from both associations. On the basis of their success in accommodating a bi-cultural society and in adjusting their internal and external relations, Canadians believed that they had a unique contribution to make to a world in which nations and peoples desperately needed to find practical ways of living and working together.

3. *Hispanic American Countries*

The countries of South and Central America fall into two groups, those with a basically Indian and mixed population, such as Mexico, Guatemala, Ecuador, Peru and Bolivia and those which, like Canada and the United States, were essentially the product of European settlement, although minorities of indigenous populations might remain as islands or have contributed substantially to the racial composition of the general population. The latter countries included Spanish-speaking Argentina, Uruguay, Colombia, Chile, Venezuela, Paraguay, and some of the countries around the Caribbean, as well as Portuguese-speaking Brazil.

Each of the Hispanic countries had its distinctive history and character. They shared a common language and expression, a similar layout of their cities and towns according to the pattern prescribed by their Spanish ruler in the sixteenth century, and the beginning of their national histories in the period of liberation from Spain around 1820. The identity of the several countries after independence had corresponded in part to Spanish administrative jurisdictions, but boundaries were uncertain and conflicts between neighbouring states were part of the history of most countries during the first hundred years of their existence; the great statue of the Christ of the Andes, erected in 1902 on the border between Chile and Argentina, symbolized the termination of one of these long conflicts. The formation of the Organization of American States in 1948 with its mutual security system did much to reduce inter-American tensions and to promote co-operation in meeting common problems in the mid-twentieth century.

Most of these countries found the principal market for their products in the United States and this country was the major source of foreign investment, though much Argentine wheat and meat went to Britain. Inevitably they resented this dependence on their larger and richer neighbour while at the same time they felt a common bond with it, for the American republics from the start had maintained an identity of interest *vis-à-vis* any European power which might seek to establish or re-establish dominion in the western hemisphere. Culturally they looked to Europe rather than to the United States, except in respect to economic affairs. This ambivalent attitude toward the United States fluctuated with changing circumstances, changing leadership and changing policies on the part of the United States. In the nationalistic, anticolonial atmosphere of the mid-twentieth century, anti-United States sentiment was often an expression of the growing national aspirations of the Latin American peoples.

Among the individual Hispanic-American states, Argentina was the most economically developed and drew its population from the most varied European sources. During the first quarter of the twentieth century it became one of the world's important food producers, not only for the meat raised on its broad pampas but, as dry farming permitted the extension of grain cultivation into its southern plains, for wheat as well. Industrial development received a stimulus during both world wars and from the vigorous efforts of the régime of Juan Perón in the 1940s and 1950s to achieve economic self-sufficiency.

In time, the cattle-raising *gauchos* were overshadowed by the growth of large cities peopled in substantial part by Italian, German and other immigrants. Especially after the United States closed its doors to free immigration in the 1920s, Argentina was a principal destination for European emigration, and its rapidly growing population of varied European origins distinguished the country from those on the Pacific coast whose people remained predominantly of colonial origin, as well as from the countries which rested on a broad Indian base. Its size, wealth and vigour gave it a position of leadership among the Hispanic-American republics, not only in economic development but in intellectual fields through a lively press and publishing industry. This leadership was lost in the 1940s and 1950s when for a dozen years the country came under the only fascist-type dictator to rise in the western hemisphere, Juan Perón; but after Perón's fall in 1955 Argentina again took its place as a vigorous member of the Latin American family of nations.

Chile went far toward developing the features of a welfare state and provided both an example to other countries and trained personnel to man their services. From the 1920s it developed an elaborate system of social insurance which grew in the 1950s into one of the most comprehensive health services in the world. It took the lead in the training of social workers and in placing the expanding social services on a professional basis. It was in the forefront in national economic planning with the establishment of the Chilean Development Corporation in 1939 to provide an approach to overall national development.

Others of the Hispanic countries had their distinctive characteristics and roles. Uruguay proudly maintained a continuous record of stable democracy; it was so intent on guarding against one-man rule that it placed the executive power in a nine-man presidential council instead of in a single president. Colombia retained a particularly strong Catholic tradition and prided itself on the purity of its Spanish speech. Cut into a series of high plateaux and valleys and little affected by recent immigration, it developed strong regional differences focused in a number of vigorous urban centres. Partisan cleavages with deep historic roots, however, broke the political stability which the country had enjoyed until 1948 and created a state of uncertainty which stood in the way of efforts to take advantage of large, undeveloped territory and resources and to raise the economic and social levels of its people. Venezuela, rich in oil and minerals which were exploited mainly with foreign capital, drew on these sources to provide an ample public treasury, but long years of dictatorship left a backlog of limited social development which the country was vigorously striving to overcome in the late 1950s.

4. Brazil

Much the largest of the basically European countries of Latin America and one of the most rapidly growing was Brazil. With a territory equal to the entire continent of Europe or to the United States, and distinguished by its Portuguese language and colonial history from the Spanish-speaking republics, Brazil saw itself as a culture and people in the making.

Up to the middle of the twentieth century vast areas of the country remained unsettled, and the majority of Brazil's more than 50,000,000 people were still concentrated on the coastal plain and in the central coffee-growing and mining plateau regions. Much of the Brazilian terrain was unfriendly and difficult of access, with its untamable tropical jungles and immense menacing rivers. It was filled with dangers—from poisonous snakes and insects, tropical diseases and attacks by nomadic Indians.

Yet most parts of the country had already been penetrated by the end of the eighteenth century. At a time when North American settlers had spread only a sixth of the distance across their continent, Brazilian frontiersmen, *bandeirantes*, had been driving their herds from pasture to pasture or founding wilderness settlements in nearly every region. But unlike frontier settlements in the United States which retained contact with centres of population and culture and thus constituted the forward line of an advancing civilization, those of the Brazilian hinterland lived an isolated, self-sufficient life of their own, out of touch with the people of the coast.

The main segment of the Brazilian population, economy and society was made up of large estates, slave-owning until the last decade of the nineteenth century, devoted to sugar or coffee cultivation or to mining. Plantations—*fazenda*—raising sugar in the tropical areas and coffee in the uplands, with their patterns of big house and slave quarters, provided the basis for a rural aristocracy which furnished the wealth of the country and its patriarchal upper class. Considerable racial mixture partially bridged the gulf between Europeans and the Africans who continued to be brought as slaves until the middle of the nineteenth century and remained in slavery until 1888. In 1872 the mulattoes were estimated at a fifth and slaves at a seventh of the total population. In the middle of the twentieth century, a third of the population was estimated as of mulatto or Negro stock.

In no other country of the old world or the new was the process of racial amalgamation so fully achieved as in Brazil. The heritage of slavery continued to be reflected in the low economic status of the darker elements of the population; prominent persons of mixed ancestry seldom if ever boasted of their African heredity, though they might often point with pride to Indian elements in their background; immigration policy in the twentieth century encouraged European immigrants rather than those from the Caribbean or Africa—or, after a brief period when Japanese immigration was welcomed, from Asia. But the relatively little racial prejudice which Portuguese settlers generally displayed had laid a basis for racial amalgamation and for the racial attitudes of Brazil in the twentieth century.

The rural aristocracy of the coastal region constituted a small cultivated *élite*. This type of *élite* was characteristic of all the countries of Latin America, where a quasi-feudal economic system provided little or no means for the basic population to partake of the cultural life of the country.

The back country was another world. Here, neither big house nor slave, neither riches nor such wide social distance characterized the frontiersmen, herders, ranchers or the people of the small towns which served as market centres for the nuclei of population in the hinterland. Here, in the plateau of the back country, ethnic and social mixture went on constantly, and Brazilian popular culture gradually took shape during the years of colonial rule and of continued feudal dominion in the nineteenth century. It was from this popular culture and native base that much of the vitality for the definition of a distinctly Brazilian outlook and self-image emerged in the twentieth century.

The distinctive course of Brazil as a new country in process of defining itself was partly conditioned by the relations which had existed with the mother country in the period of colonial rule and the half-century after independence. In contrast to Spain, which had poured much cultural energy into its empire in the New World, designing cities, establishing universities and developing centres of rich living and high culture, Portugal's interest in her Brazilian colony had been chiefly economic. The first professional schools in Brazil were established at the beginning of the nineteenth century more than 350 years after the founding of the University of Mexico and the University of San Marcos in Peru. While many cities of the Spanish colonial empire had been centres of wealth and culture, Brazilian cities had been poor towns of petty merchants; the real wealth and culture had been centred in the big houses of the rural aristocracy. The small Brazilian intelligentsia had been trained in Portugal.

Separation from the mother country was achieved in 1823 without the kind of heroic struggle which characterized the Bolivarian wars of independence against Spain; the regent himself declared the country to be independent. And during much of the nineteenth century, while many of the Hispanic republics were experiencing great political instability, Brazil enjoyed the continuous fifty-year reign of her emperor, Dom Pedro (1840–89). Throughout the period, the old social structure remained virtually unchanged, while the available education perpetuated the traditional literary-juridical mentality and did little to develop the outlook and skills to cope with the Brazilian milieu.

The downfall of the empire in 1889, like the earlier separation from Portugal, was brought about from the top, by the very elements which had enjoyed prestige and power—the Church, the army and the rural aristocracy. The Catholic Church, which occupied the status of state church under the constitution of 1823, objected to the disciplining of clerics who were outspoken against the régime; the military resented the fact that they were kept out of politics; and the rural aristocracy turned against the régime when it replaced the gradual, compensated emancipation of the slaves by outright, unrecompensed abolition. A military coup established a republic and set Brazil on a course of modernization.

The republican constitution adopted in 1891 was modelled essentially on that of the United States in its provision for a federal system, a bicameral legislature and periodically elected president, the separation of church and state and the declaration of certain civil rights. Much of its spirit was provided by the positivist philosophy of Auguste Comte, whose words 'Order and Progress' appeared on the Brazilian flag. Although this political orientation and structure was repeatedly threatened by the military, which tried to intervene when the operation of the political system did not seem to its liking, it provided the framework for a vigorous approach to industrialization and to encouragement of economic development.

The doors to immigration were opened wide, and Brazil received a substantial portion of the great flood which poured out of Europe in the last decades of the nineteenth and early part of the twentieth century. Two-thirds of the white population in 1940 were of other than Portuguese stock, mainly Italian and other south European. Many of the immigrants were settled on the land in colonies established under the supervision of the government or on large estates, where they retained their language, educational institutions and cultural patterns, and mingled little with Brazilians of other origins.

After the formation of the republic the cultural ties with Europe were not broken, but the chief cultural link was with France. Paris, the 'city of light' which attracted so many painters, writers and students from Europe and the New World, became a main source of cultural influence on the intelligentsia of the new Brazil. Major economic ties were with the United States.

The first world war gave an impetus to Brazil's process of coming of age. Although its direct participation in military operations consisted only of a medical mission and a few ships, the decision to participate was a reflection of its sense of status, and it earned Brazil a place at the peace table and a temporary seat on the Council of the League of Nations. It thus, in a sense, marked the début of Brazil on the international scene outside the western hemisphere.

Brazil's new sense of identity was strongly reflected in the modernist movement in art and literature which began in 1922 with an exhibit of modern arts in São Paulo in that year. This movement was not simply an extension of the literary and artistic movements which had taken shape in Europe before the first world war and were being taken up throughout the occidental culture areas, including various movements in the Hispanic countries of Latin America which called themselves 'ultra-modernist' or 'vanguardist'.

The central characteristic of the Brazilian modernist movement was that it was bitterly and violently anti-European. However much it might owe to currents of thought and style which originated or were nourished in Europe, its spirit was one of rebellion and protest not simply against tradition but against European dominance. It was an intensification of the same spirit of Brazilian nationalism which had found expression before; at the time of independence it had taken the form of romantic treatment of native Brazilian themes—nature, the idealized Indian, the romantic figure of the *bandeirante*; after the establishment of the republic, it was reflected in the acclaim accorded to Euclides da Cunha for his novel dealing with a rebel fanatic of the back country—*Os sertões* (1902).

Up to the 1930s, however, the course of Brazilian development had still not broken through the old social structure and pattern of life, though the great new centres of urban society had already grown spectacularly. Rio, freed of yellow fever in the first decade of the century, became one of the world's great capital cities, and São Paulo, in addition to serving as the prosperous port for the coffee country, took on the characteristics of a thriving industrial centre. By the 1930s industrial production exceeded agricultural in value, although industrial activity was still largely limited to the processing of agricultural products in the food and textile industries. The prosperity of the country from the late nineteenth century on still flowed almost entirely into the hands of the old patriarchal upper-class *élite*, except for the largely self-contained agricultural prosperity of some of the colonies of immigrants, notably some of the German settlers in the state of São Paulo. Illiteracy remained widespread and poverty characterized the lot of the vast majority of the population, on the land and in the urban slums. Even in 1950 hardly more than half the children of primary school age were in school.

From the 1930s on, national efforts were directed toward the development of a distinctively Brazilian, modern society, capable of realizing the potentialities of the vast country, exploiting its material and human riches and building for Brazil a distinctive culture and place in the world. A series of educational reforms laid out an extensive system of primary, secondary, normal and university education. In the next two decades some twenty universities were established—public universities in the capitals of most states, and Catholic universities in five of the principal cities. Key members of some of the faculties were recruited abroad, chiefly in France, Italy and Germany.

Numbers of technical and specialized schools in all fields were set up with great rapidity, often in advance of the availability of teaching personnel. More than a third of all the schools of social work in the Latin American republics, for example, were located in Brazil in the 1950s. The first school of public administration in South America was instituted in Brazil in 1955. In one field after another Brazil, which had been late to start, forged ahead, proliferating institutions and organizations, initiating new efforts, giving vent to its ambitions during these years. Education and the related fields of publishing, press, radio, bookselling, and the beginnings of active social research were only a few of the directions in which Brazil showed the vigour of a young country shaping its outlook, its people and its culture.

The older policy of group settlement, which encouraged or resulted in the maintenance of national minorities with their own languages and institutions, gave way to a policy of Brazilianization. The educational reforms of the 1930s required all teaching of basic subjects to be carried on in the Brazilian language. Immigration policy was adjusted with a view to bringing in immigrants who would contribute directly to the building up of the country and the open policy of the early part of the century was modified to achieve this purpose.

A series of political changes were reflected in the revision of the Brazilian constitution to provide among other things for greater centralization and for the assumption of economic responsibilities by the state. Social legislation of an advanced character was enacted. Brazil was the first of the Latin American republics to attempt to extend the benefits of its social security and other welfare programmes on a large scale to the rural population. From the 1930s on, a strong national Catholic revival brought the Church more actively into the process of shaping modern Brazilian life, with the founding of a series of pontifical universities, a successful campaign for religious education in the schools and active participation in welfare programmes.

In the middle of the twentieth century Brazil was still in the process of defining itself, seeking to find its own ground in the midst of conflicting world tendencies. It was committed to democratic principles by its first republican constitution in 1891, but actual practice and later constitutional revisions revealed uncertainty as to the extent and nature of this commitment. The dictator, Getulio Vargas, seized power in 1930 in contravention of the constitution and held it with military support for fifteen years; eight years later, he was returned to power by a democratic election. In the constitutions of 1934 and 1946, individual rights were assured in less complete terms than in the constitution of the United States and of other democratic countries; freedom of speech, for example, was specifically limited. Voting was not universal, but was confined to those who could read and write, a substantial limitation in a country where, in 1950, adult illiteracy was still estimated at 52 per cent. In the economic sphere principles of capitalism and private enterprise were generally accepted and assumed; but the constitutions of 1934 and 1946 included specific statements of the power and responsibility of the state to intervene, not only in order to supply basic services, but to break any monopoly in private hands.

Brazil was clear in principle on the issue of racial integration and amalgamation; one of the constitutional limitations on freedom of speech was directed against the expression of racial prejudice. But even this wholehearted principle was qualified by the policy of encouraging European immigration and limiting that of other racial elements. Religious liberty was clearly established in principle, and the presence of a substantial Protestant minority attested to the reality of the religious guarantees; but the traditionally Catholic character of the culture, strengthened by the Catholic revival, tended to convert Catholic attitudes into public policies; in response to strong Catholic pressure the complete prohibition on divorce was retained in the constitution of 1946.

The conflict was still unresolved between the traditional society—aristocratic and personal, patriarchal, literary and juridical—and the modern trends toward a democratic, practical, scientific, industrial way of life.

As Brazil looked toward its role as a growing state and a potential large power, it sought to open up and exploit its remaining territory and to build an internally integrated economic and political structure—a far easier task in the modern days of motor roads, aeroplanes and the extension of railways than in the time of the *bandeirantes* whose frontier settlements had lost touch with the coastal areas. But it brought in its wake severe inflationary pressures that threatened to undermine efforts to lay the basis for economic expansion.

The ultimate evidence of the determination to base its national development squarely on its land and the masses of its people was the decision to move the seat of government away from the bustling, cosmopolitan coastal city of Rio de Janeiro and to build in brilliantly modern style a new capital, Brasilia, in the interior of the country.

With its vast territory and resources, its varied ethnic stocks, its rapidly growing population and its immense vitality, Brazil asserted its leadership increasingly within the system of American states and it looked forward to taking its place in the coming century as one of the major nations of the world.

5. Australia and New Zealand

Australia and New Zealand were outposts of the British empire. In contrast to the United States with its mixed population and Canada with its French minority, the lands 'down under' were British in population, in culture and in their dependence on the British empire for their existence. Until the second world war they assumed that the British empire was a permanent institution and the basis for their survival. Their identification with the empire and sense of dependence upon it were well reflected in their contributions to its preservation. In the first world war Australian casualties practically equalled those of the United States, although the population of Australia was hardly more than 5 per cent as great; in New Zealand some 40 per cent of men eligible for military service volunteered, and a large proportion failed to return.

It was not until after the second world war that these countries emerged as self-reliant entities. With the British empire in Asia gone, they found themselves on their own, small countries, far from the parent to which they had been linked. The role of Australia in the United Nations showed the change. In the early formative days of that organization it was the Australian delegate, Dr. H. V. Evatt, who led the movement to give a larger role to the Assembly in order that the voices of the small nations might be heard. Australia thus stood as a spokesman for the small nations, no longer merely as a segment of the British empire.

The history of Australia in the nineteenth century was the history of conflict among economic groups over the kind of society to be established on the continent. Because of the distance and the cost of emigration, most settlers came with governmental assistance rather than by the sort of free, undirected immigration which peopled the United States and Canada. Settlement, therefore, always involved public policy and the issue of what kind of country was being built, while the harsh, arid continent set severe limits to the kinds of settlement which were possible beyond the areas along the coasts.

For more than sixty years Australia was used as a penal colony, but before transportation of convicts was finally discontinued in 1853 free settlers had introduced sheep raising and had begun to make Australian wool famous. In contrast to the homesteaders who opened up the United States, Australian ranchers acquired large areas of arid terrain for grazing operations. Under a policy designed to keep a labour supply available by preventing the easy acquisition of land, lands were offered for sale with no limit on the size of the holdings and half of the proceeds were used for assisting further migration. When a short-lived gold rush in the 1850s left many diggers seeking homesteads after their diggings failed, there were pressures on behalf of small settlers. But measures to permit homesteading in the 1860s and after brought conflict with the ranchers and the climate made homesteading difficult if not impossible in all but a small part of the country.

Australia thus developed as a country not of small farmers but of large operators and labourers—of large ranchers, mining companies and shipping firms rather than of small enterprises, and of migrant sheep shearers and ranch workers, miners and maritime or other workers in the coastal cities rather than independent cultivators. In this situation strong labour unions were formed early. Men with union ideas and experience from Britain organized sheep shearers, miners and dock workers into large unions which extended beyond local political divisions.

In the second half of the nineteenth century the issue was joined as to whether the country should be developed for the big owners of ranches, mines, sugar-cane plantations and shipping companies or whether it should be developed for the workers. Owners sought to exploit the resources of the continent with whatever labour they could secure; workers insisted that the continent should be developed for the benefit of the common man under conditions which would offer a decent standard of living. The 'white Australia' policy emerged from this struggle, originally directed against the Chinese brought in to work in the mines and then broadened into a general opposition to the importation of labour from Asia and the Pacific. Organized workers fought and finally outlawed the system by which plantation labourers for the sugar-cane fields were being recruited from the Pacific islands under conditions closely approaching forced labour. In time the 'white Australia' policy came to be used as a broad limitation on the free immigration of Asians to Australia.[16]

During the 1890s the big owners scored a temporary victory when they beat down massive strikes of sheep shearers, miners and maritime workers by force and with the aid of the police and the courts. But their victory was short-lived, for labour, defeated on the economic front, turned to political action and formed the first Labour party to achieve power in any country. It set up a unique system of labour arbitration and enacted a body of social legislation which put Australia in the forefront of the movement toward the welfare state.

In the twentieth century Australia saw itself as a new society committed to maintaining for all the people, through organized effort, a high minimum standard of living which would give an opportunity for all, not to become rich but to live decent lives. Self-critics in the middle years of the century complained that Australia was not keeping up with other countries—Britain, the Scandinavian countries, New Zealand—in the welfare field which she had pioneered in the years before the first world war. But the system of minimum wages, union organization, social insurance and social services provided the means for absorbing large numbers of penniless immigrants after the second world war at the levels already established for Australians, without permitting their influx to undermine wage levels, place an undue burden on social services or disrupt the pattern of life.

Australia did not see itself as a land of individualism, in spite of the lonely sheep stations and the self-reliance of the people. Its very distance from Europe made it especially conscious of the importance of world ties. Its history of economic conflict made it conscious of the need for collective action. Its uncompromising terrain and climate, which required more than endurance and ingenuity to make headway against drought, soil deficiency, pests and disease, made Australians especially conscious of the dependence of man on the applications of science.

One scientific conquest after another changed the agricultural outlook on a grand scale. Intensive research developed drought- and rust-resistant strains of wheat which made Australia one of the world's great bread-baskets; the rabbit pest was conquered by the spread of a disease, the prickly pear cactus which was taking over land at the rate of a million acres a year was driven back by the release of a moth, and the identification of trace elements missing from the soil virtually doubled the land area which could be brought under cultivation. Equally spectacular results were envisaged in the development of mineral resources and industry.

In the mid-twentieth century Australia was still a land which was building a society in terms of a decent standard of living for all. But by then it could take for granted its old tools of labour organization and social security which had become permanent features of its social and governmental structure, and it was placing major emphasis on the contributions of science. The heart of its development programme after the second world war was a nation-wide organization for scientific research and development, and it was indicative of the light in which Australia saw itself that the young university at Canberra should seek to develop a centre for the physical sciences which would be second to none and would attract the ablest and most creative scientific minds that could be found anywhere in the world.

New Zealand's short history since the beginning of European settlement in the 1840s and its population of only 2,000,000 by the mid-twentieth century, made it very much aware that it was young and small in relation to the position in which it found itself in the world. Some of its spokesmen attributed to this situation New Zealand's great concern with education and welfare, for every individual counted and must be developed and protected —and also its special combination of individualism and governmental support.

On the basis of its favourable soil and climate, New Zealand attained a high level of productivity—it claimed the highest *per capita* agricultural productivity in the world—and a commensurately high level of living for its people. With few extremes of wealth or poverty, it could insist that its high *per capita* income more truly reflected the condition of all the people than did the high average incomes of some other countries which covered wider disparities. Its social welfare system was one of the most comprehensive in existence.

But as a small, isolated people, New Zealanders faced central problems which were driven home to them by the collapse of world markets in the 1930s, the war in the Pacific and the constant emigration of many of their ablest men. How far should New Zealand try to develop a self-contained life, and how far should it continue to produce meat and other foods for world consumption and depend upon imports for many of its needs? What was involved in sustaining its high living standards in a crowded world? And could so small a country develop a rich cultural life which would hold its highly educated people, or must it continue to expect its distinguished sons, such as the great atomic physicist Ernest Rutherford, to find better opportunities to make their contribution away from the land of their birth?

III. CULTURAL REORIENTATION OF MIXED SOCIETIES: MEXICO

In the regions of Central and South America once dominated by the great empires of the Aztecs, Incas and Mayas, a European overlay rested on a broad Indian foundation. Here, developments of the twentieth century took the form of a cultural reorientation and a movement toward integration which brought to prominence the Indian heritage. The process involved a social revolution through which depressed classes and isolated peoples moved toward full citizenship.

Mexico led the way in this process, which was still very far from complete at the middle of the century. The Mexican revolution of 1910 set in motion both a social revolution and what has been termed 'the reconquest of Mexico by the Indian'. The result was not only to alter the class structure but to change racial and cultural values until it was no longer a source of prestige to be 'European' but an expression of pride to call oneself 'Indian'. The impact of the new self-image which the revolution brought to the people of Mexico did not stop with the country where it originated but penetrated throughout the Indian-based societies of Central America and the Andean region.

The population of these countries was composed of three main elements, European, Indian and *mestizo*. The small European overlay consisted of the descendants of European conquerors and later settlers. Since much of the European migration had been of men alone, a very large proportion of the population was *mestizo*, of mixed Indian and European ancestry. But at the opening of the twentieth century large Indian populations in Mexico, Guatemala, Ecuador, Bolivia and Peru, and smaller ones in other countries had been barely touched by European ways and were isolated from the national life. In 1950 estimates placed this culturally Indian population still at 20 per cent in Mexico, 40 per cent in Ecuador and Peru, and 55 per cent in Bolivia and Guatemala.

In each of these countries, at the opening of the century, a small, wealthy Europeanized *élite* ruled over an illiterate and impoverished people, enjoying virtual monopoly of land and other wealth, political and military force and social prestige. Although the cities which had been great centres of culture in the colonial period had lost some of their imperial baroque splendour in the stormy years after independence, the old landowning families still made up an aristocratic society. They identified themselves culturally with Europe and lived a cultivated life in their town houses facing the central plaza or in the 'big house' on their estates, sending their sons to officer the army, to manage the sugar estates, to enter the liberal professions and fields of learning, and to man the upper ranks of the highly personal bureaucracy.

The masses of the people who remained outside this cultural milieu were divided into two main elements, those who continued to live as Indians within the structure of their traditional communal culture, geographically isolated, on islands within the Europeanized society, and those who lived and worked as peasant-labourers, often in a state of quasi-serfdom on the large estates, or in the mines, or as industrial workers in the towns. The small middle class of merchants, foremen and urban artisans were generally made up of *mestizos* and such special groups as Jews or Syrians, some of whom had recently immigrated to the area.

The racial, economic and cultural elements of this divided society were variously defined in different regions. The *ladino* might be distinguished from both Indian and white, as in much of Central America, or the general category of 'white' might embrace all who were not clearly Indian or Negro; 'Indian' might mean, specifically, those who lived within the Indian communal village structure, or it might simply mean 'poor, rural and backward' and be applied without limitation of race. Whatever the pattern, however, the Indian was depreciated as culturally inferior; 'European' carried prestige and these attitudes were everywhere reinforced by strong class feeling.

Although the constitutions of the Latin American republics, drawn up at the time of independence, were democratic in words and were generally modelled on that of the United States, the social reality was thus inconsistent with the political formulation. The wide gap which separated the upper *élite* from the mass of the people was bridged only by the paternalism of master or quasi-feudal landlord. The Catholic Church discouraged racial discrimination but sanctioned the class division and bade the lower classes accept their status and respect the authority of their masters.

The Mexican revolution which began in 1910 cut through this pattern. It was started by intellectuals with democratic ideals but little interest in social reform who attacked the political tyranny of Porfirio Díaz and the denial of democratic processes by his dictatorial régime which had been in power for more than forty years. In the years which followed the dictator's fall, it was joined by other groups who pressed the leaders to include their demands in the revolution's aims, and it became an economic and social revolution against the quasi-feudal structure of society.

The groups which rose to take advantage of the revolution and to make it the expression of their hopes were first of all the peasants, under Emilio

Zapata, who demanded land and an end to the *latifundia* system. They were joined by the urban workers whose unions took shape within political clubs and whose military battalions organized the workers in each town where they were victorious. Workers' participation in the revolution led to the inclusion in the Mexican constitution of 1917 of the most advanced labour law in the world at that time. Since most of the industrial expansion under Díaz—mines, transport, industries—had been developed with foreign capital, the workers' movement had a strongly nationalist, anti-foreign character and drew to it other nationalist elements.

The Mexican revolution was led by no disciplined party or group and followed no single ideology. Only after seventeen years did a National Revolutionary party take shape, secure election to office and undertake to institutionalize the revolution. The course of the revolution and the policy of its leaders veered in different directions from time to time, accelerating or slowing down the process of land distribution, intensifying or relaxing the antagonism to foreign investors, becoming anticlerical or tolerating the Church. But it never lost its popular methods and intent.

The direct effects of the revolution were many. It destroyed the *latifundia* system, releasing the peasants from their dependence on and bondage to the semi-feudal landlord. It reduced the position of the Church, excluding it from the field of education, nationalizing Church property and restricting the activity of the clergy. It initiated a wide range of social and educational reforms. It gave a place to organized labour. It brought a renaissance in the arts which combined the use of indigenous forms and the expression of modern social themes, to make Mexican mural painting one of the outstanding forms of creative expression in the twentieth century. And it made the Indian no longer a debased drag on Mexico's progress but an authentic representative of its people and its spirit.

At mid-century Mexico still had a long way to go to reach the goal of economic and social reconstruction and cultural integration. Although the incorporation of the Indian into Mexican national life was greatly accelerated by the revolution and much national effort was devoted to programmes designed to enable the Indian population to raise its living standards and move out of its isolation, an estimated quarter of the Indian population in the 1950s was still living in extreme poverty. Though the *latifundia* system had been broken, great contrasts of wealth and poverty persisted, and the rate of economic expansion barely kept ahead of population increase.

It was the new sense of dignity which Mexicans found in the reintegration of their Indian heritage which made the contribution of Mexico's revolution unique. The drive toward integration of cultures and peoples had appeared recurrently in Mexican history—initially in the attitude of the conquerors toward the Indian as a soul to be Christianized and the acceptance of intermarriage, at the time of independence in the concepts of political equality formulated by the *mestizo* leader José María Morelos, and in the mid-nineteenth century in the rise of the Indian, Benito Juárez, to be chief justice and then president of Mexico. Now Mexico offered to the world the first demonstration in modern times that a people could express its self-respect in terms which it had formerly despised. In a world where European superiority was still almost unchallenged, it was an assertion of human dignity for the mixed-blood to be able to boast that he was Indian instead of apologizing for being only partly white. At mid-century Mexico remained an outstanding example of the successful integration and reorientation of races and cultures.

The same reorientation of cultural values which accompanied the Mexican revolution was under way in all the countries with predominantly Indian and *mestizo* populations by the middle of the twentieth century. It had still not broken the hold of the old society in most countries; only Bolivia had effected a major social revolution involving the distribution of land. The Aprista movement in Peru had been repeatedly suppressed and in Guatemala, in spite of a start at land reform, the gulf between Indian and *ladino* was still wide. But the direction of movement was clear and the old *élites* were on the defensive or in retreat. The framework within which national policies were debated and shaped was provided by the Indian heritage and racial stock as well as by the European currents that continued to flow through the life of the continent.

The dynamic for the economic reorganization and cultural integration of these mixed societies, historically fragmented by class and ethnic divisions, came logically from the *mestizo* element. It could hardly come from the *élite*, for they had too high a stake in the preservation of the economic structure, and their own prestige was at issue. Nor could it come from those who continued to live as Indians in small, ethnocentric communities, for it was predicated on some form of participation in national life. But for the *mestizo*, his own status was bound up with a national image which gave equal place to the Indian and the European heritage and defined national well-being in terms of racial and cultural integration. So long as the national ideal was defined in terms of the racial and cultural characteristics of the European, white *élite*, the *mestizo* must take second place. But he need yield to none in a society where Indian blood was a cause for pride and Indian cultural values commanded respect.

The Mexican measures for land reform and education were outstanding examples of attempts at such integration. A unique form of land tenure, the *ejido*, was evolved by the revolution to meet the special tradition, mentality and needs of the landless peasant. It retained many of the elements of the indigenous communal land holding, but secularized and individualized, without the sanction and cohesion of the communal culture. It thus both involved a reinterpretation of the Indian's cultural patterns and permitted him to acquire new attitudes, e.g. an individual and secular instead of a communal and sacred relation to the land, which could enable him to accept change in other aspects of life.

The educational devices included rural cultural missions and rural schools which used the local crafts, customs and modes of expression as a basis for learning, and which encouraged their development. In these schools traditional wisdom and crafts were combined with literacy, arithmetic, and improved health and farming practices, to enable the peasant, whether Indian or *mestizo*, to better his lot in his own terms and also to follow an avenue into the broader society should he or his children have the initiative to do so.

The movement which made the most conscious effort to close the cultural gap and achieve a fusion which would respect the Indian's personal and cultural integrity defined itself as *indigenismo*. Originating in Mexico, it reached an international level by 1940, with the first Inter-American Indian Congress at Patzcuaro, Mexico, followed by the second and third such congresses in 1949 and 1954 at Cuzco, Peru, and La Paz, Bolivia. *Indigenismo* as a movement distinguished itself from *indianismo* on the one hand and *occidentalismo* on the other. It rejected the 'indianism' which occasionally took the form of a nativist movement of rebellion against the surrounding society, and it was equally out of sympathy with the romantic effort to preserve the Indian in his untrammelled state as a museum Indian. At the same time it rejected the glib occidentalism of both left and right, which saw the Indian as possessing no positive values and assumed that his only road to progress lay through accepting, at all costs, western material and intellectual values and patterns, either socialist or individualist.

Those who stood for *indigenismo* sought integration through interaction, reinterpretation and synthesis. They recognized that from the years of the Conquest the changes in Indian culture had been largely on the surface. But they also recognized that the penetrating force of industrial culture was not to be checked, and that it had the power, unless its impact was mitigated, to produce disorganization in Indian communities. They sought means which would be based on respect for the Indian personality and culture but would not hesitate to intervene to facilitate the adjustments inevitably produced by cultural change.

The principles of *indigenismo* were set forth in the declaration of the third Inter-American Indian Congress in 1954. Within the framework of the Universal Declaration of Human Rights, it claimed for the indigenous American the full exercise of his economic, political and social rights. These it defined as rights to land, liberty, suffrage and education; the right to properly remunerated work and the protection of social legislation; the right to organize on a communal, labour or co-operative basis; the right of freedom from racial discrimination and of respect for his cultural traditions, and the right to the incorporation of his cultural traditions with modern techniques.[17]

These claims for the indigenous American expressed the goals of the societies of which he was a central part.

IV. MINORITIES SEEKING CULTURAL AUTONOMY

In many parts of the world nation-states included populations which differed in culture from the dominant element and which yet sought to retain their identity as peoples. They generally comprised a minority in the population but, where the dominant element was itself numerically small, the majority of the people might be identified with groups which occupied the status of minorities.

The minorities problem in this sense was in large measure a by-product of nationalism. In traditional Asian societies, under the Ottoman empire, and to a degree under the Austro-Hungarian and Russian empires, many cultural groups submitted to a common rule and often lived for generations in neighbouring areas, while retaining their cultural identity, their language and customs, their distinctive dress, their religion, their system of education and sometimes their personal law. The growth of nationalism destroyed this situation, for it made all members of the state into nationals—Frenchmen or Dutchmen, Canadians or Mexicans, Brazilians or Lebanese. Wherever the population of a nation-state was not culturally homogeneous, nationalistic aspirations and a desire for self-determination on the part of non-dominant segments might conflict with the nationalism of the dominant group.

The minorities problem was already present before the opening of the twentieth century in the irridentist claims of nation-states to neighbouring territory inhabited by people of the same culture, such as the Italian claim to Trentino and Trieste and the French claim to Alsace-Lorraine. It was also present in the restiveness of the subject peoples of the Austro-Hungarian, Russian and Ottoman empires who sought the restoration of their former independence, as did the Poles, or demanded a measure of autonomy combined with full economic and political rights and opportunities. Where a minority was culturally related to another state or identified with it on the basis of religion, its aspirations might become an excuse for international intervention and it might find itself a pawn of international politics. The German minorities in eastern Europe and the Slavic populations in the Balkans were the bases for Pan-German and Pan-Slavic movements, and the Eastern Orthodox and other Christians within the Ottoman empire were brought under the 'protection' of Russia and France respectively. Where the minority was related to no outside state, its aspirations did not bring involvement in international politics; the Irish stood alone in their effort to secure autonomy from Britain, as did the Catalans in their similar demand from Spain; Jews in each country had the support only of their fellows who were also in a minority position in some other land.

During the nineteenth century the right of minorities to cultural autonomy had been recognized in principle by Austria, whose constitutional law of 1867 provided that every nationality had an inviolable right to preserve its national character and the use of its language in education, administration and public life. No such policy was followed, however, in the Hungarian part of the Hapsburg empire or with respect to minorities by Russia or Germany. Precedent for protection of minorities by international treaty had also been set by the treaty of Berlin in 1878 in respect to the newly established Balkan states, but there were no means of enforcement; Rumania, for example, continued to refuse citizenship to its Jewish population until after the first world war.

During the early years of the twentieth century the issue of the status of minorities was intensified by the mounting drive for national independence and self-determination and by the extension of suffrage, mass education and other pressures for the identification of all citizens with the state. The Irish pressed unremittingly for home rule; the effort to improve the position of minority peoples contributed to the Russian revolution of 1905 and to repeated disturbances within the Austro-Hungarian empire. At the same time the intensified nationalism of such groups as the Young Turks or the Prussians placed their minorities under new pressures designed to make Arabs into Turks or Poles into Germans.

In the peace settlement after the first world war the application of the principle of self-determination, 'as far as practicable', resulted in independent status for some of the former minorities of eastern Europe. The creation of new states, however, did not remove the problem of minorities and their status. Culturally distinct populations were so interspersed that boundaries could not be clearly drawn on ethnic lines. Furthermore, other factors, such as strategic boundaries or efforts to create viable economic units, left cultural minorities along several borders.

The Versailles Conference recognized the dilemma arising from the conflict between the principle of national self-determination and the presence of cultural minorities and undertook to deal with it in respect to the new and enlarged states. With these and with the defeated states of Austria, Hungary, Bulgaria and Turkey, the Allies concluded treaties requiring that minorities should enjoy full civil and political status and have the right to receive elementary education in their own language, to use their language for publication and before the courts, and to establish their own social and cultural institutions. The 25–30 million people covered by the minorities treaties made a fifth of the total population of the thirteen countries involved; in Czechoslovakia and Poland they were approximately a third and in Rumania a quarter of the population. Much the largest groups were Germans, Ukrainians and Jews. The treaty obligations with respect to these minorities were placed under the guarantee of the League of Nations. No similar internationally sanctioned obligations were imposed on other members of the League, however, with the exception of Iraq which agreed to them as a condition of admission to League membership in 1932.

During the twenty years when the principle of international protection of minority rights was in effect, the difficulties inherent in minority conflicts were well revealed. The several hundred petitions received by the League of Nations ranged from individual acts of violence to charges of systematic suppression of large groups. Some minorities did not dare appeal to the League for fear of reprisals; others tried to use the League machinery to resist social measures, such as land reform, which penalized the few for the benefit of the many. Some groups refused to accept their status as minorities and sought persistently to undermine the authority of the state or disrupt its operation. German and Hungarian groups, especially, regarded the Slavs to whom they were subject as inferior peoples to whose dominance they were unwilling to submit.

For the many cultural minorities in Russia which had been generally neglected under the tsars and in some cases suppressed, the October revolution brought a marked change. The USSR encouraged the cultural expressions of non-Russian groups, within the framework of the Soviet economic structure and administration, wherever these expressions were consistent with the overall purpose of the state. It developed written languages for peoples who had none, used the local languages for elementary education and for propaganda and promoted literary and artistic activity. In the 1930s educational materials were being published in 104 languages, as were technical instructions and literary works.

Where, however, the cultural patterns and nationalist traditions of certain ethnic groups were inconsistent with the interests of the larger society, they were overridden. The drive for industrialization, collectivization, and for uniform education stressing scientific subjects and Russian history and culture went on throughout the Soviet Union. The settlement of nomadic peoples put an end to their ancient way of life. The anti-religious basis of communist principles undermined the cultural integrity of groups whose traditions were strongly rooted in religion and in religious practices. Under the constitution of the Soviet Union a number of autonomous republics were set up on the basis of the cultural identity of the inhabitants. During the second world war, however, the German autonomous republic on the Volga was liquidated and its population removed to Siberia, and other autonomous republics in the Crimea, Caucasus and Volga disappeared. After Stalin's death, the national autonomy of several peoples was restored.

Over the years the atmosphere in many parts of the world became progressively less favourable to the status of cultural minorities. At one extreme, steps were taken to eliminate them as a group from within the body politic. This approach was first applied in Turkey and Greece under the treaty of Lausanne terminating the hostilities which had continued in the eastern Mediterranean after the first world war. In order to achieve cultural homogeneity, Greeks were expelled from Asia Minor, though many of their families had lived there from time immemorial, in exchange for Turks from Macedonia who had long been resident in that area.

The rise of dictators and the intensification of the kind of nationalism of which National Socialism was the most exaggerated example brought régimes to power which were prepared to go to any lengths to rid the state of minority elements or to bring them into conformity with the dominant group. Hitler's policy of ridding areas under his control of Jews and of displacing non-Germans from the Baltic provinces was followed after the war by the expulsion of hundreds of thousands of Germans from Poland and Czechoslovakia.[18] The resettlement in Israel of Jews who had survived in central and eastern Europe and of Jewish communities from Muslim countries —Yemen, Iraq, Morocco—was accompanied by the displacement of nearly a million Arabs most of whom remained for a decade or more as homeless wards of the United Nations relief agency. The exchange of populations in the partition of India brought the largest mass migration in history, although it still left large Hindu and Muslim minorities in Pakistan and India.

The change for the worse in the status of many minorities between the ends of the first and second world wars was reflected in the approach to the problem by the United Nations as compared to the League of Nations. Whereas the League had sought to guarantee the right of minorities to continued cultural existence and the enjoyment of civil rights, the United Nations was concerned with their physical protection. The League's efforts on behalf of minorities petered out before the League itself came to an end. Petitions on behalf of minorities dwindled from 204 in 1930–31 to 4 in 1938–39 and the minorities office in the League's secretariat was disbanded in 1939. The United Nations made no effort to revive this machinery. For non-self-governing territories, it established a Trusteeship Council, and through its Human Rights Commission it concerned itself with the rights of individuals. But when it approached the issue of minorities which wished to maintain their cultural autonomy and identity, it saw the problem not in terms of rights to be guaranteed, but in terms of threats to survival.

The United Nations' contribution was the concept of 'genocide'—acts committed 'with intent to destroy, in whole or in part, a national, ethnical, racial or religious group as such' (*Genocide Convention*, Article II). The United Nations Genocide Convention applied to such acts as killing, causing serious bodily or mental harm, preventing births and forcibly transferring children.

The conflict between the aspirations of minorities and the drive of the dominant elements to realize their own aspirations for the whole nation was a source of tension in the years after the second world war. There was scarcely a region where this problem was not present in some form. It was not a major problem in most of western Europe, in part because minorities were few and the non-repressive character of state institutions made for accommodation among people of different traditions, but there were unresolved tensions in such areas as Northern Ireland and Catalonia. The problem was most likely to be present in areas where peoples had lived interspersed for many centuries and where new states had been created or borders had changed; but the French minority in Canada was evidence of the persistence of cultural minorities in countries settled in the relatively recent past. In the tangled population pattern of eastern Europe, minority problems were further complicated by the displacement and resettlement of populations as a result of the second world war and its aftermath. In the Middle East the variety of tribal and religious loyalties added to the problems of integrating the several states, while throughout south and south-east Asia separate communities remained distinct. The issue of tribal identity could not fail to be of major importance in the emerging national states of Africa.

At mid-century, minorities which desired to retain their cultural identity found themselves in a variety of situations. In well-integrated, multi-cultural societies, where substantial harmony existed among elements, they occupied a more or less clearly defined and accepted position, though there might be competing efforts to increase the influence or extend the institutions of one or another group. French Canada, for example, remained almost a state within a state, yet its people participated in national life in ways which transcended the cultural separateness of the group.

In less integrated, multi-cultural societies, groups which composed the state maintained a precarious balance while they were in the process of developing institutions, attitudes and a body of experience which would cut across ethnic lines and lead toward a more integrated society. Lebanon, with its evenly divided Muslim and Christian populations, was such a country. Malaya offered a classic example of a precarious balance, for the Malays had been less aggressive than the almost equally numerous Chinese minority, and both the Chinese and Indian minorities could identify themselves with large and dynamic states of fellow-nationals if the process of integration should not become effective in the new state of Malaya.

Some minorities were in situations of active conflict, as were the Tamils of Ceylon who were determined to establish their language on a par with the official Sinhalese, or the Turks in Cyprus who resisted the efforts of the Greek majority to unite the island with Greece. Some found themselves subject to expulsion or suppression. Bulgaria offered its Turkish minority the opportunity to leave the country by a specified date or conform to conditions which the majority of Turkish inhabitants considered unacceptable, and they emigrated to Turkey.[19] East European Jews were alternately prevented from emigrating and encouraged to leave. Groups of foreign traders in a number of areas were the object of resentment by virtue of their economic position and were sometimes subject to attack on ethnic grounds, as were Chinese in south-east Asia and Indians in East Africa.

In parts of Asia and the Middle East where the shift from group to national loyalty was in its early stages, and especially in Africa, minorities were in a state of transition. The Karens whose semi-autonomy was recognized by Burma, the varied peoples of Indonesia who were not immediately prepared to accept centralized government, the tribal peoples of Iran and other tribal peoples throughout the Middle East, were relatively new to nationalism. They had only begun to experience the institutions of the nation-state and the impact of common education, modern thought and modern economic life.

A quite different situation existed where tribal enclaves remained in the midst of highly developed societies. Aborigines in Australia and New Zealand, North American Indians on reservations, hill tribes in north and central India, and indigenous Indian communities in Central America and the Andean plateau lived as islands within modern society and culture. The aspirations of these isolated tribal groups differed and were changing. Among North American Indians, for example, there was great ambivalence between the desire to retain their identity and live their own lives and their recognition that this was necessarily a narrow and limited prospect. Some, such as the Hopi, had such a deep conviction that their way of life was superior that they resisted all influences which might change it. Others, especially after many young men had participated in the second world war, saw their only future in integration into the larger society and the abandonment of tribal life. All such groups faced a radical choice between continued isolation and the virtual abandonment of their traditional culture.

For cultural minorities, whatever their status, a number of issues remained unresolved. The first was the nature and extent of cultural pluralism that was possible within national societies and cultures. There was a trend towards patterns of accommodation based on common national identity combined with acceptance of religious, linguistic and ethnic differences; but the counter-trend toward uniformity and intolerance had shown itself strongly in the 1930s and it could reappear in time of stress, as when Egypt turned against its age-old Jewish population at the time of the Suez crisis in 1956.

The second question was how much cultural diversity would survive the levelling effect of urban industrial culture, with its mobility, industrial discipline, effects of mass production and patterns of conformity. To the extent that cultural identity was associated with a nomadic or an agrarian way of life, industrialization tended to destroy it, though cultural groupings remained within the common urban environment. Identifying distinctions of dress were likely to disappear in the streets of the city, at the work bench and in offices. Movement in search of jobs broke down the isolation which made for cultural separateness, as did the roads which penetrated into remote areas and the common ideas that spread out over the air-waves.

Finally, there was the relation between the drive of individuals for opportunity to function as full-fledged citizens and the drive of minorities for recognition of their separate identity. Were these drives compatible? Or did the insistence upon cultural recognition so set apart the members of a group as to stand in the way of their full acceptance as individuals and therefore their full enjoyment of the citizenship which they claimed? And, conversely, did their acceptance as individuals on the basis of merit so attenuate their sense of identity with the group from which they came that they would no longer share the drive for the maintenance of cultural identity and minority rights?

NOTES TO CHAPTER XXIX

1. Doctor of Philosophy A. I. Arnaldov thinks that it is essential for the authors to stress the point of view of Soviet scholars that this chapter should include a special section on the development of *Communist culture* which has become a significant component of cultural evolution in the twentieth century.

The socialist reconstruction of society is inconceivable without profound changes in the field of culture, changes which can be classed as a true cultural revolution, and whose goal is the creation of a new, socialist culture. The cultural revolution, however, is not to be understood in a vulgar sense as the negation of all past culture. Socialist culture does not arise in a vacuum. It is the heir to the best that was created in the conditions of a society based on exploitation. V. I. Lenin said: 'It is necessary to take the entire culture left by capitalism and to build socialism from it. It is necessary to take all of science, technology, all knowledge, art. Without this we shall not be able to build the life of the communist society.' (V. I. Lenin, *Collected Works*, Vol. 29, p. 52.) Hence, one of the concrete tasks of the cultural revolution is to select from the cultural heritage of the past everything of lasting value and to discard everything that is unnecessary, that is contrary to the nature of socialist society, not to say harmful and reactionary. This is the basis for the development of a culture that is truly socialist in content, i.e. reflecting the life and ideals of the new society, pervaded by its ideology, by the urge to serve the people and to help them actively in the struggle for socialism, and subsequently for communism.

2. Doctor of Historical Sciences A. M. Dyakov underlines that the renaissance of the ancient cultures of the peoples of Asia is in the first place linked with the growth of the national liberation struggle and the creation of independent states. The October Revolution in Russia has had a decisive influence in this direction: 'The national movements in the countries of Asia which finally won their freedom were influenced, and in some cases inspired, by the existence of the Soviet State and the growth of Soviet power.' (K. M. Panikkar, *Asia and Western Dominance*, London, 1954, p. 248.)

3. T. Földessy (Hungary) and candidate of Historical Sciences L. I. Yurevich, noting that the study of India in Europe has undoubtedly played a definite part in arousing in the Indian people an interest in its past, however underline that the renaissance of Indian culture and the reformation of Hinduism were chiefly an expression of the growing national liberation struggle and of the new bourgeois ideology which came to the fore.

4. Dr Dušan Zbavitel writes: Many distinguished figures in Indian politics and cultural life have pointed out that English education in India was too one-sided. It stifled Indian traditions and also prevented Indians having any deep knowledge of Russian, French, German and other cultures. It is enough to refer to Rabindranath Tagore who in his famous letter to Miss Rathbone (1941) gave a fair appreciation of the influence of English education on Indian life. This point of view is shared by T. Földessy and L. Eötvös, who note that describing British policy in India particularly in the cultural and educational spheres, Mr Nehru wrote that the British 'deliberately tried to prevent change, except in so far as this was necessary to consolidate their position and help them in exploiting the country and its people to their own advantage. . . .

'Changes, and some changes in a progressive direction, did come, but they came in spite of British policy, although the impetus for that change was the impact of the new West through the British.

'. . . Even the British government, in spite of its dislike of education, was compelled by circumstances to arrange for the training and production of clerks for its growing establishment. It could not afford to bring out from England large numbers of people to serve in this subordinate capacity. So education grew slowly, and though it was a limited and perverted education, it opened the doors and windows of the mind to new ideas and dynamic thoughts.' (See J. Nehru, *The Discovery of India*, New York, 1946, pp. 312–13.)

5. Dr Dušan Zbavitel underlines that reformist trends for the abolition of the hierarchy of caste and even of the caste system itself existed in India long before the introduction there of English education. The Sikhs for example had very much earlier advocated the abolition of the caste hierarchy.

6. Dr Dušan Zbavitel underlines that Rabindranath Tagore expressed the view that political liberty could not be separated from social emancipation long before Gandhi; Tagore, moreover, declared that the social emancipation of the Indian people was the first condition for the political liberation of India from the British domination.

7. Doctor of Historical Sciences S. L. Tikhvinsky argues that the Kuomintang lost its revolutionary character not in 1937 but in 1927. From the moment that it came to power in 1927 all the progressive elements were excluded from it and its ranks were filled with bureaucrats and representatives of the semi-feudal military class who soon obtained an absolute majority in the party.

   A most important feature of the internal political life of China from 1927 to 1936 was the armed conflict between the reaction personified by the Kuomintang and the revolutionary democratic camp. The Kuomintang government deluged China with the blood of revolutionary workers and peasants. The report of the International Organization for Assistance to the Fighters of the Revolution for 1930 says: 'From the moment when the so-called period of hostilities came to an end in 1928 and up to the all-China session of the Kuomintang in 1929 approximately 450,000 workers and peasants were exterminated. During the last six months of 1930 the number of revolutionaries who lost their lives amounted to 140,000.'

   From the outset of the Japanese aggression against China in 1931 the government of Chiang Kai-shek pursued a policy of concessions to the aggressors: first Manchuria was abandoned to them and then the province of Jehol. And when in the summer of 1933 the Kuomintang forces in the province of Chalhar in defiance of the government's orders resisted the Japanese attack Chiang Kai-shek's crack divisions were sent against them. During the period from the end of 1933 to the beginning of 1934 the Kuomintang savagely suppressed the anti-Japanese uprising in the province of Fukien. In 1935 it admitted the occupation by the Japanese of the province of Hopeh and of the northern part of the province of Chahar. This view is supported by T. Földessy and L. Eötvös.

8. Professor Zurayk has commented: These pages seem to me to carry a eulogy of Communist China, underscoring the brighter aspects and omitting the grim ones. It not only portrays the aspirations and the self-image, but implies more or less an approval of them and of the achievements of the system.

9. Doctor of Economic Sciences H. J. Eydus considers that it is impossible to see the capitalist development of Japan as merely the result of the penetration of Western economic, socio-political and cultural influences into the country. Japan passed from a feudal to a capitalist structure in pursuance of the same objectively ruling laws of historical development as other countries. The survivals of feudalism conserved in Japan are a result of the development of Japanese capitalism and not emanations of the 'Spirit of Japan'.

10. *The Author-Editors call the attention of the reader to the discussion of Japanese industrialization in Chapter IV, pages 88-9.*

11. Dr Min Latt underlines that it is wrong to consider the Japanese occupation as a turning point for the liberation movement in South-East Asia. At the beginning of the war the peoples of South-East Asia already had great experience of the anti-colonial struggle, of which the most important landmarks were the national uprising against Dutch rule in Indonesia in 1926–27, the national insurrection in Burma in 1930–32 and others.

12. Candidate of Historical Sciences V. B. Lutsky underlines that according to the testimony of the missionary Al Smith (*Zeitschrift der deutschen Morgenländischen Gesellschaft*, 1854) the foundation of the first educational society in Syria was due to Arab initiative.

13. Soviet scholars believe that the authors are wrong in saying that Arab nationalism, in contrast to the nationalist movement in India, 'was not fundamentally a movement for social reform'. V. B. Lutsky, a research historian, has stressed the fact that social reforms

were introduced in Algeria, Tunisia, Morocco, Egypt, Syria and Iraq after the liberation of these countries.

14. Doctor of Historical Sciences L. I. Zubok notes that the assertion that the USA remained in isolation up to the first world war and did not participate in world affairs is not in accordance with the facts. See Note 5 to Chapter I.

15. *The Author-Editors call the reader's attention to the exact language of the text.*

16. Candidate of Historical Sciences L. A. Zak underlines that the catchword of a 'White Australia' designed to arouse racial antagonism among workers affected not only the interests of the workers but also those of certain circles of the bourgeoisie. See L. L. Sharkey, *An outline history of the Australian Communist Party* (Sydney, 1944), L. L. Sharkey: *The Trade Unions* (Sydney, 1959), and other works by leaders of the Australian Communist Party.

17. Candidate of Historical Sciences L. A. Zak underlines that the main problem confronting the population of Latin America in the sixties of the twentieth century is still the struggle against the oppression of foreign capital which has entrenched itself in the economic life of these countries. (See for example the work by the Peruvian journalist Yenaro Carnero Checa: *Ensayos latinoamericanos*, s.l., 1959.)

18. Tamas Földessy and Lorant Eötvös observe that there is nothing in common between the Hitlerite policy against the Jews and other nations, and the expulsion of the Germans from Czechoslovakia and Poland after the second world war:

   (*a*) The Hitlerite policy was directed against innocent people whilst the Germans in Poland and Czechoslovakia were deeply involved as a fifth column in the preparation of the war against the countries where they lived.

   (*b*) Hundreds of thousands of people lost their lives as a result of the Nazi crimes, but there was never any threat to the lives of the Germans evicted from Poland and Czechoslovakia. They were able to go on living and working in their new homeland.

   The expulsion of Germans from the territory of Poland and Czechoslovakia was sanctioned by the decision taken by the three allied powers—the United Kingdom, USA and USSR—at the Potsdam (Berlin) Conference in 1945. (See section XIII, of *Report on the Berlin Conference of the Three Powers*. 'Regularized transfer of the German population.')

19. Academician D. Kosev writes: After the establishment in Bulgaria of a People's Democratic Government the Turks intensified their propaganda among the Turkish population in Bulgaria in order to render them disaffected towards the Bulgarian nation and national authorities and to persuade them by demagogic promises to emigrate from Bulgaria. The Turkish mission and consulate played a special part in this agitation as did also some rich Turks who utilized the influence they had enjoyed among the people in the past.

   Influenced by many years of agitation and by the demagogic promises of Turkish propaganda, part of the Turkish national minority expressed a desire to emigrate to Turkey. In fulfilment of the wishes of these Turks, and in conformity with the Convention of October 18, 1925, between Bulgaria and Turkey on the exchange of population, the Bulgarian government, following the elimination of the consequences of the post-war economic situation, took steps to issue emigration papers to all Turks who wished to leave. Up to October 1950 about 120,000 Turks who had made declarations attesting their desire to emigrate had been given emigration passports.

   However, the Turkish government created a number of difficulties and hindrances for the emigrants and many of those who had sold their property did not manage to obtain Turkish visas but had to stay in Bulgaria. Those who went to Turkey found themselves in a very difficult situation there. Here for example are the impressions of one emigrant as reported by the newspaper *Gercek* on September 20, 1950: 'We thought that in Turkey there was a heavenly paradise. Now we are asking one another where is this paradise? . . . Even in a year or two's time we shall still not be able to find work. We just do not know what to do.'

CHAPTER XXX

DRIVES FOR INDIVIDUAL FREEDOM AND HUMAN DIGNITY

WHILE nations and peoples sought to realize their aspirations as total societies, elements in the population aspired to change their condition and status. Workers, peasants, women and members of minority groups sought to attain the status and opportunities promised for all people by the principles of the Declaration of the Rights of Man, but enjoyed only by the more favoured elements. Their drive was for individual freedom and human dignity, self-respect and the respect of others, first-class citizenship and full participation in the life of their societies.

I. LABOUR[1, 2]

Labour's drive for recognition, status and welfare was the most potent and widespread of these efforts. By the opening of the century 'labour' was well-established as a self-conscious entity in the industrial societies of Europe, America and Australasia. Though aspirations were variously defined and concepts differed as to how best to pursue objectives, labour was an element to be reckoned with in these countries. The major difference in aspirations was between those who hoped to overthrow the existing system and usher in a new social order by revolutionary means and those who sought an improved status within the existing society.

In the older industrial societies it was primarily craftsmen and industrial workers who thought of themselves as 'labour' and organized to secure their rights. Agricultural workers were minor elements in these labour movements, or were not organized at all; white-collar employees only slowly and partially came to identify themselves with labour. In some of the non-industrial and newly industrializing societies, however, almost the opposite situation prevailed in the labour movements which took shape there, for the principal groups of employed workers were frequently plantation labour and government or public utility workers. Moreover, in the very different conditions in which labour consciousness developed and industrialization was taking place, labour movements were often interwoven with nationalist movements and the aspirations of people as workers were linked with their desires for national integrity.

But whatever its form, a self-conscious labour movement was assumed by mid-century to be a normal and integral feature of modern society.

I. ASPIRATIONS OF LABOUR

Workers expressed their aspirations in many ways. In every industrial country, and in non-industrial countries as ideas or industrial practices spread, workers voiced their common interests through trade unions. Their aspirations were also expressed through political channels, by the formation of labour parties or the identification of workers with other political groups which offered promises of meeting their desires. Within organizations based on religious, welfare, racial or other common interest, workers formed sections to identify their aspirations and to enlist the support of the total group.

Workers also expressed their aspirations in many individual, unorganized ways—in the manner in which they spent their earnings, their response to job opportunities and incentives, their quest for education, the effort to give their children advantages which they themselves had not enjoyed, their participation or non-participation as citizens in community life.

The hopes and aims of labour were differently formulated in various countries in relation to the social structure, the manner and time of industrialization and the ideology which prevailed among workers and their leaders, but everywhere they reflected common desires for dignity and decency, for status and participation in the society of which they formed a part and a reasonable share in what it had to offer. In countries with the strong class traditions which characterized most European nations, workers focused on the desire to raise their class status and to function on a more nearly equal footing with other elements in society. Where class lines were less rigid, the objectives were more specifically economic. Where liberal principles had already been established by a vigorous middle class, labour sought the extension of these principles to themselves, and found many allies among middle-class people who saw in labour's aspirations a reflection of their own beliefs. Where they saw only exploitation in the existing order, they sought its overthrow in favour of a dictatorship of the proletariat. Under authoritarian rule they faced charges of insubordination and subversion, and they were suppressed.

Everywhere workers sought a fuller share in the fruits of industrial production and a more adequate income in order to support a higher standard of life. The central demand of labour for increased real wages, present in virtually every contract negotiation or labour dispute, expressed the workers' insistence that they should be the beneficiaries as well as the instruments of industry and be able to enjoy more of the good things of life as these were defined by the standard of living of other segments of society. They sought, too, to establish standards for decent and humane conditions of work, such as shorter hours and protection against accident and industrial disease. They wanted security in the face of the hazards of life and the uncertainties of industrial employment.

Most fundamentally, labour in all countries sought personal dignity—the status of human beings. Challenging the nineteenth-century *laissez-faire* economic concept of labour as a commodity to be purchased and used in the process of production, and also the traditional class attitudes as to what was good enough for workers, they asked to be treated as people and to enjoy the rights and dignity of free men. Towards that end they sought the right to form organizations, to speak with a common voice through representatives of their own choosing, and to withhold their labour through the strike. In a few countries they wished to share in the management of industry. In many they aspired to assume responsibility for the conduct of national governments through parliamentary forms, and to use these governments to take over and operate major segments of basic industry.

In many areas of the world organized groups of workers hoped to bring about a basic change in the economic, political and social structure by revolutionary means, and to substitute worker control for control by those who traditionally exercised privilege and power. In the countries where such revolutionary change did in fact occur, labour organizations assumed responsibility for achieving production goals and for administering protective regulations and social benefits.

In the course of these years the aspirations of labour expanded with the changing society, though the fundamental drive for full economic and social participation remained. In the early years of the century the labour movements were concerned to protect the workers against a variety of ills—low wages, instability of employment, danger of accident and disease and exposure to the unrestrained authority of employers. Unions sought to increase the workers' share in the fruits of industry and to reduce the relative power of the employer. Although these objectives remained central, they ceased to be the sole interest as workers acquired better conditions and greater power. By mid-century labour was also becoming concerned with the maintenance of a dynamic, growing, productive economy, as workers realized that their welfare was intimately bound up with increasing the fruits of industry through rising productivity and economic expansion, not merely with securing an adequate share.

A committee of the International Labour Organization noted this shift of emphasis during the second quarter of the twentieth century. Reviewing the role of its workers' and employers' representatives, it observed that 'the contribution to be expected from the representatives of the employers and the workers is more positive and less negative than it was at the beginning'. When the ILO had been formed in 1919, employers and workers had been represented separately 'very largely for the protection and defence of their respective material interests'. By 1956 this representation had 'taken on a wider content and now represents also a combined interest of the two elements in the productivity of industry and in the function or skill of management in industry'.*

* International Labour Office, *Report of the Committee on Freedom of Employers' and Workers' Organizations* (*McNair Report*) (International Labour Office, Governing Body, 131st session, Geneva, March 6–10, 1956. Mimeo), p. 200.

The broad economic and social changes in these years were at least partially responsible for the realization of many of labour's goals. The rising material level of living of the workers in industrial countries rested basically on the productivity which modern technology brought.[3] The relationship was a reciprocal one: increased wages which greater productivity made possible in turn stimulated employers to use labour more efficiently. Technical change, too, inevitably altered the status of the worker by eliminating much unskilled labour and requiring an educated, alert, technically competent labour force. It tended to create within the ranks of labour a worker-aristocracy of skill and competence, distinct from those who had nothing to offer but their physical effort. The interests of these two segments of labour did not always coincide.

The welfare and position of the worker at any particular time, moreover, was deeply affected by general economic conditions beyond the control of individual worker and organized labour alike. The contrast between the condition of workers at the depths of the economic collapse of the 1930s and in the prosperous decade after the second world war was far greater than any difference which the success or failure of labour's efforts during either of these periods could make. The change in the situation of North American labour in this period, for example, reflected primarily the shift from a desperately sick to a vigorous economy, although during these same years a weak and despised labour movement became a powerful, well-recognized force.

Changes in the place of labour in society, furthermore, were part of the whole process of social change during these years—the breakdown of class structures, the extension of responsibility and authority of the state, rising levels of general education, destruction of old privilege—all hastened by wars, taxation and shifts in political power. The achievement of many of labour's aspirations came about through the dissolution of the social structure which had assigned to labour a place from which it sought to emerge. Finally, the proletarian revolution in Russia provided the rest of the world with a new image which had a profoundly unsettling effect on the old concepts of labour's status.

Yet when the impact of these broad forces has been duly recognized, the part played by labour itself still remains a major factor in the history of the first half of the twentieth century. The struggles of labour unions, the exercise of political power and the constant efforts of countless individuals achieved for workers both material benefits and a new status.

2. METHODS OF SEEKING LABOUR'S OBJECTIVES

The organized ways in which labour formulated and sought its objectives differed from place to place, partly because of the historic shape of social and political institutions, partly in relation to the time of industrial development and its form, and partly because of the ideology prevailing among the leaders and rank and file of workers.

The major difference in ideology was between those who accepted the capitalist system and sought to improve the lot of labour within it and those who repudiated the system and saw their hopes realizable only through its overthrow. The distinction was not, however, clear-cut and simple.

The first group focused its efforts on using collective bargaining to secure higher wages, improved conditions of work, freedom of association and action, and various direct benefits. They generally looked to the state to establish minimum conditions of wages, hours and conditions of health and safety and to provide social security and welfare services, and they used their political influence to bring about legislation to this effect.

Those who rejected capitalism tended to concentrate upon disruptive measures designed to demonstrate labour's strength and ultimately to overturn the existing power structure. They were divided into several camps. Syndicalists and anarchists rejected the state as well as the structure of capitalist industry in favour of the concept of industries run by their workers. Revolutionary socialists sought the dictatorship of the proletariat and saw the labour movement as the instrument of the proletarian revolution and an arm of the dictatorship of the proletariat for the administration of industry.

A large middle group, including both non-revolutionary socialists who followed the Marxian analysis of the weaknesses of the capitalist system and others who accepted capitalism to some extent but distrusted the profit motive for different reasons, favoured the ownership of the principal means of production by the state or co-operatively and they sought to nationalize key industries.

In pursuit of its objectives, labour used both the economic power which it could command through union organization and the political force which it could muster through organized parties. The choice of method and the relation between the economic and political approach varied with the factors mentioned above.

Although the labour movements which resulted all expressed their common conflict of interest with employers in similar ways, they differed in emphasis and in the extent to which they used one or another of the techniques available to organized workers. In some countries, the character of the movement changed with changing situations over the years. The British labour movement was built on the basis of collective bargaining, but it developed in time as a strong political force. Similar movements with emphasis on collective bargaining took shape in the Commonwealth countries and the United States. On the European continent the orientation of labour from the beginning was political and revolutionary, as part of the socialist, anarchist or communist movements, but these labour organizations also engaged in collective bargaining to improve the economic condition of workers. The communist unions played a post-revolutionary as well as a pre-revolutionary role, while the potentialities of the labour movements in the newly industrializing countries in the mid-twentieth century were only beginning to be apparent and their direction was far from clear.

(a) British labour movement

The oldest substantial labour movement, that of Great Britain, evolved its form and method under the conditions which surrounded British industrialization. Britain was the first country to become industrialized; it had a well developed tradition of voluntary association and parliamentary democracy and a Protestant religious ethic which stressed individual and social responsibility; its feudal institutions had been disrupted though not wholly destroyed by an increasingly dominant commercial and industrial middle class.

Against this background British labour adopted the method of voluntary association for collective bargaining, first by crafts and then by industries; it established, in law and practice, its right to organize and to use its economic strength through the strike, peaceful picketing and other orderly practices; it entered political life and functioned through the parliamentary system. These methods were already well established by the opening of the twentieth century; they were guaranteed to workers when Parliament, dominated by the middle-class Liberal party, passed the Trades Disputes Act of 1906 at the instigation of the first Labour party member.

The approach of British labour was always pragmatic. As explained by Margaret Bondfield, first British woman cabinet member and minister of labour in the Labour party government of 1929: 'We learnt from facts and events. Doctrine played comparatively little part in the lives of most of us ... experience was the main thing.'*

Through the first half of the twentieth century labour extended its influence by these same methods until the Labour party, resting squarely on a trade union base but including in its membership individuals from outside the union ranks, achieved a majority position. At the close of the second world war it assumed office and carried through a programme of public ownership of certain key industries coupled with a widespread system of public social services and educational reforms supported by heavy, progressive taxation. The efforts of British labour played an important part in the modification of British society which resulted in very substantially reducing the gap in real income between rich and poor. British workers secured a new status, level of living, range of welfare services and a measure of power and responsibility.

(b) Labour movements on the European continent

The German labour movement grew up in a country with authoritarian rather than democratic traditions, where industrialization came later and more rapidly than in Britain, and where there was a strong class structure and many remnants of the feudal order. In this setting the German labour movement was the product of political organization.[4] The unions were the creation of the Social Democratic (Socialist) party, and functioned as an appendage to the party until the Mannheim declaration of 1906 placed them on an equal basis

* Margaret Bondfield, *A Life's Work* (London, 1948), p. 10.

of collaboration. Thereafter they continued to regard their political efforts to gain influence in government as of at least equal importance with collective bargaining. The goal of both unions and party, as stated in the Mannheim declaration, was 'the rise of the working class and its equality with the other classes of society'. German Catholic workers, similarly situated but unable to accept the Marxian concept of class struggle, formed separate unions, generally affiliated with the Catholic Centre parties, and following the ideology of the 1891 papal encyclical, *Rerum novarum*.

In most of the other countries of central and northern Europe labour followed the German pattern. Socialist parties sponsored trade union organization and acted as the workers' voice. Collective bargaining was secondary to political action. The central struggle was for elevation of the working class and the ideology was the Marxian concept of the class struggle. The political situation in these several countries largely determined the course of labour's development. Where there was a strong parliamentary tradition, as in the Scandinavian countries, labour organization and methods came to approximate closely those of Great Britain. Where, as in the Netherlands and Austria, a large Catholic population constituted a separate political force, Catholic trade unions corresponded to Catholic political parties. Where communist parties acquired strength, some of the unions passed under their political influence.

In contrast to the socialist labour movements elsewhere on the continent, French and Italian labour prior to the first world war followed an anarchist-syndicalist course. Confronting weak parliamentary systems characterized by a multitude of parties divided along minute ideological lines, labour in these countries called for revolutionary economic change by direct means rather than through political action or party affiliation. Revolutionary goals and direct-action methods made French and Italian workers resort to the general strike or other spectacular work stoppage as a favoured instrument to dramatize the plight and assert the demands and power of labour.

With the rise of international communism after the first world war the French and Italian labour movements were torn between those who thought that communism offered a way to realize their revolutionary hopes and those who tried to avoid the political approach which communism implied. In the years after the October revolution and again after the second world war, the struggle for and against communist control which took place within virtually all labour movements was particularly acute in Italy and France.

(c) Labour movements in newly settled industrial countries

In the countries outside Europe which achieved a high degree of development before the middle of the twentieth century, notably Australia, New Zealand, Canada and the United States, labour followed a course which was closer to that of Britain than to the labour movements of the Continent. In all these newly settled countries, however, the absence of a feudal past and the fact that effective manhood suffrage antedated industrialization profoundly affected the attitudes of labour, their goals and their methods. Workers did not have to fight to destroy long established class privilege or to establish political democracy. Their goals, therefore, were to secure for themselves in the economic field rights and privileges corresponding to those which they already enjoyed as citizens and to raise their level of living and of opportunities for their children to those of the comfortable middle class with which they felt themselves identified.

The labour movements of Australia and New Zealand, however, differed from those of the United States and Canada in their much greater use of legal machinery. In Australia a system of compulsory arbitration was established at the turn of the century after a series of widespread and disruptive strikes. Labour had to seek its practical objectives through this channel and to engage in litigation before arbitration tribunals in order to secure awards of wages, hours and terms of employment that would incorporate the principle of a living wage and security on the job. At the same time it formed its own political party, which held the balance of power in federal and state parliaments from the early years of the century and governed the country during the first world war, in the late 1920s and during and after the second world war.

Australian labour used its influence and power to secure protective factory and mine legislation, free compulsory education, and a comprehensive system of public social services. In addition, Australian labour shared the outlook of the rest of the population—a small, isolated people of European origin seeking to achieve and retain a European manner and standard of living—and vigorously supported the 'white Australia' policy and a protective tariff designed to keep out the products of low-paid Asian labour.

Labour in the United States, on the other hand, and also in Canada, focused its efforts on collective bargaining, first on a limited craft basis, then from the 1930s through mass industrial unions in mass-production industries. Its major struggle was for the right to bargain collectively and to use the weapons of economic power which would make such bargaining effective, without being victimized by employers for these efforts. North American labour evolved methods of negotiation, equipped itself with the necessary technical knowledge to meet employers on their own ground, and developed an elaborate voluntary union–management machinery for carrying out contracts and adjusting grievances or disputes under the contracts.

The main body of North American labour formed no political party. At first labour unions looked with suspicion on all political action and even on social legislation, fearing that government intervention might lead to governmental restriction on union activity, and preferring to keep the exercise of economic power free from political involvement. From the 1930s on, however, after federal legislation had protected the right of unions to organize, bargain collectively and engage in peaceful picketing, and after the impact of the depression had made clear the need for social security and other forms of protection, the labour movement shifted its position. It actively supported social legislation and became an important force in mobilizing public opinion and bringing pressure on legislators. In addition, unions threw their support to friendly candidates of one or the other of the major political parties, and organized committees for the political education of their members and to stimulate their political activity.

(d) Communist labour movement

The communist pattern of labour organization arose under the conditions of tsarist Russia where the rights and freedoms enjoyed by British and west European workers were absent and channels for political expression were closed. Though the concepts of class struggle, revolutionary overthrow and dictatorship of the proletariat owed their origin to Karl Marx, it was Lenin's scheme of organization which shaped communist trade unionism both in its pre-revolutionary and its post-revolutionary stages.

In both phases, the concept of the Party as the essential voice of the working class and the organizational plan of 'democratic centralism' defined the role and procedure of the labour movement. Any and every organization had to recognize the leadership of the Party and submit to it. 'Democratic centralism' meant that a disciplined Party membership, receiving directives from the central committee of the Party, would form cells through which to transmit central Party directives to trade unions under their control, while the unions in turn would extend this influence to workers at large.[5] In the pre-revolutionary state, the pyramid of tightly organized and centrally directed Party cells provided a means of developing and carrying out a strategy of revolution. Once the Communist party gained control and administered the state, this system provided the transmission belt for communicating central policy to workers' groups and for workers' opinion to reach the centre.

In Soviet Russia and the other communist states, the labour unions functioned as organs of government, responsible for carrying out economic policy, achieving production goals and administering social benefits.[6] The preamble to the statutes of the Soviet workers' organizations provided that they 'shall organize a socialist emulation of workers and employees to raise labour productivity to the utmost, to fulfil and overfulfil State plans, to continuously develop all the branches of industry, transport and agriculture, to improve quality and reduce production costs, to make full use of all the reserves of the socialist economy; to take part in planning and regulating wages . . . promote the introduction of progressive technologically substantiated production rates . . .'. The trade unions exercised some responsibilities in the fields of social security, industrial health and safety and labour inspection commonly carried by government agencies in other countries.

In these circumstances bargaining was inappropriate and the collective agreement did not serve the function of establishing wages or other basic conditions, all of which were determined by the planning agencies. 'The purpose of Soviet collective contracts is to ensure the fulfilling and exceeding of production plans, the continuous increase of output and improvement in the organization of labour and the strengthening of the responsibility of economic and trade union organizations for improving the material living conditions of the workers and of the cultural services made available to them.' The collective agreement, which must be in conformity with state plans and which was signed after full discussion within the plant, usually contained the following matters: commitments of the management and works committee in respect of the implementation of the production plan; remuneration; training and upgrading of workers, engineers, technicians and salaried employees; state and labour discipline; protection of labour; housing and living conditions; provisioning of workers and communal catering arrangements, and cultural services.

Differences of opinion between directors and factory committees were transmitted for decision to the competent ministry and central committee of the trade union, and thence to the Central Council of Trade Unions acting in agreement with the competent ministry.

According to the principle of democratic centralism all trade union organs 'from the base to the summit' were elected by the members of the trade union to which they reported on their activity, and all decisions were taken by majority vote. Trade union organizations settled all questions in accordance with the Statutes of the Trade Unions and the decisions of the higher trade union organs. 'Trade union organs of a lower level are subordinate to the organs of a higher level.' Soviet trade unions 'conduct all their activities under the guidance of the Communist party of the Soviet Union, the organizing and directing force of Soviet society'.

With respect to the right to strike, the Soviet government reported to the ILO in 1955 that: 'No provision is made, or has ever been made in Soviet legislation, to restrict or prohibit strikes. In practice, however, no strikes occur in the Soviet Union, because there is no reason for them in a country with a socialist economic and social régime, where the instruments and means of production belong to the workers themselves.' The reports from Bulgaria, Czechoslovakia, Hungary and Poland were similar.*

Although strikes *per se* were not illegal, anyone participating in a work stoppage might be guilty of other offences which carried severe penalties, such as counter-revolutionary activity, or of absenteeism which was punishable by correctional labour at reduced wages in the worker's usual job. Reports of anything resembling strikes were extremely rare, and it appeared that this institution was in fact virtually eliminated in the Soviet Union. Serious large scale strikes did however occur in 1956 in Poland, East Germany and Hungary; these were attributed by the authorities to mistaken leadership, the action of counter-revolutionary elements and the backwardness of certain parts of the working class.[7]

* International Labour Office, *McNair Report, op. cit.* pp. 194–5.

(e) Labour movement in Japan

The conditions of industrialization in Japan were not favourable to the spontaneous organization of workers and their independent expression. A strongly feudal and authoritarian society set its stamp upon both the large-scale enterprises set up with government support for the heavy industries, and the small, paternalistic light-industry shops where family-type relationships were extended to the relations between workers and employers. For many years the Japanese labour movement was less a movement of workers than of intellectuals who had read Marx and knew something of the labour movements in Europe, and who formed a succession of organizations, dividing and recombining over the central issue of whether to stand for the complete overthrow of the economic system or to work for reforms.

In the periods when the government was anti-democratic and militaristic, the labour movement was suppressed by law, and from the early 1930s to the end of the second world war its leaders were in jail. In the periods when the political climate was more favourable, leaders from among the Marxist intellectuals drew their following largely from the civil service, teachers and transport workers and some of the employees of larger factories. Since each union was generally confined to a single enterprise where paternal family attitudes continued to prevail and 'temporary' workers did not belong to the same union as those with 'permanent' status, no strong, worker-led, practical-minded trade unions developed. Some slight tendency toward practical unionism appeared after the second world war under the stimulus of the United States occupation and the co-operation offered by the International Confederation of Free Trade Unions, but the chief feature of the Japanese labour movement at this time was the contest for domination between communist and non-communist leadership. To the extent that the workers themselves were articulate, they tried mainly to protect at all costs their hold on their jobs in the difficult and uncertain conditions which beset the Japanese economy in the immediate post-war years.

(f) Labour movements in newly industrializing areas

As industrialism spread to other parts of the world, or even in advance of industrial development, labour movements arose in imitation of those already well-developed in the older industrial countries. These movements grew up in the framework of very different societies from those of Europe or of European settlement, under different economic conditions and in a different climate of local and world opinion. In consequence they played a different role in relation to the self-image and goals of the workers of these areas. As borrowed rather than indigenous institutions, they did not grow from local roots. Inheriting standards and ideology developed elsewhere and lacking the experience of slow growth, struggle and step-by-step achievement, they seldom developed a sturdy structure or a basis for realism and responsibility. They were even more dependent than European unions had been at a corresponding stage of their evolution on the leadership and participation of intellectuals. At the same time the weakness of the middle classes in these countries increased the importance of labour as a factor in the evolution of their societies.

In the non-industrial areas of Latin America, Asia and Africa where European and North American firms developed mines, industrial enterprises or factory-type plantations, inexperienced local workers were no match for the great corporations. In the early stages of the European labour movements, workers and industrialists had grown up together; many men of small means had emerged as entrepreneurs at the same time that workers entered and found their place in industry. But when workers in non-industrial areas experienced the sudden impact of highly organized enterprises, already fully developed in their home areas, they found themselves separated from the masters of modern industry by a wide gulf of power, knowledge and culture.

In the countries consciously and actively engaged in economic development, state enterprise or other large-scale operations led the way, and the drive for rapid industrialization left no time for the gradual development of labour organization.

Yet the workers and potential workers of these countries were aware of some of the conditions which their fellow workers in industrially developed countries enjoyed. They had before them the success of the 'workers' state' in Russia in achieving rapid industrialization, and much impetus for Asian labour organization came from communist sources, aided by Russia's Institute for Toilers of the Far East. They also saw the high living standards and political responsibility enjoyed by workers in such countries as Britain, Scandinavia, Australia and the USA and desired these benefits for themselves.

They looked to the government, however, rather than to their own direct efforts to define the obligations of employers and to establish standards and conditions of work. It was natural that they should do so. Internationally accepted labour standards were formally accepted by many of the non-industrial countries which ratified International Labour Organization conventions relating to such matters as hours of work, the labour of women and minors, industrial accident and disease. Even dictatorial governments which sternly repressed labour organizations, as in some countries of Latin America, adopted labour codes and social legislation for which European workers had long struggled, though such codes often remained unenforced.

In the older industrial countries labour unions had been formed in response to actual industrial experience and labour and social legislation had resulted from the long struggle of organized workers for decent working conditions, terms of employment and social benefits. In the newly industrializing countries the order was reversed. The first step was the enactment of labour and social legislation for which labour itself did not have to fight—legislation designed by governments to protect their people against foreign exploitation or to bring their countries in line with international standards. This body of legislation, covering such matters as hours of work, minimum pay, child labour, accident compensation, maternity leave, job tenure and social security, provided a very different framework from that within which industry had developed in Europe and America, and placed labour in a very different position.

In these new circumstances the role of labour unions and their appropriate methods of operation were far from clear. Collective bargaining was rarely their central function. In some countries, notably in Latin America, a major activity of the unions was to watch the enforcement of the protective legislation and to help workers to secure their rights under such laws.

In most newly industrializing countries, notably in Asia and the Middle East, labour leadership came almost wholly from outside the ranks of labour itself and was provided by intellectuals or other educated members of the middle class. Such leadership tended to be more preoccupied with ideology than with the day-to-day problems of workers in industry and to reinforce the political character of the unions.[8] Trade unions formed substantial parts of the various political parties, and each union group had its political affiliation. Trade unions played a special role in the emerging African countries because of the virtual absence of a middle class and because the unions offered virtually the only basis for mass organization and leadership outside the tribal structure.

As the young labour movements in these countries gained experience and increased their contact with labour leaders from other countries through participation in the International Labour Organization and the international labour federations, and through technical assistance and the mutual visiting of leaders under international aid programmes, they began to adopt some of the attitudes and procedures which the older unions had developed. It remained an open question at mid-century, however, how far the experience and attitudes gained in the already industrialized countries were relevant to the situations which the new unions encountered.

Among the major factors conditioning the role of the new unions was the level of productivity. In the older industrial countries increased real wages and standards of living for workers had largely reflected, and been made possible by, increased productivity. The success of organized labour in securing advances in real earnings had been achieved within limits set by the advancing level of productivity. In the communist countries the major function of trade unions was to help to achieve production goals and to raise the productivity of the workers as a means of ultimately raising levels of living. In the newly industrializing countries labour productivity was low; but many of the conditions that reflected productivity increases in other countries were claimed as a matter of political right. At mid-century the dilemma of low productivity and high aspirations remained unresolved in the labour movements of this segment of the world.

(g) *International labour movements*

From the early days of industrialism labour consciousness had a strong international component. This was particularly true of the politically oriented, ideologically dominated movements. The Communist Manifesto in 1848 had called upon the 'workers of the world' to unite, and Marx's followers of all shades of opinion, whether gradualists or revolutionaries, shared in some measure the sense of common destiny and common cause which he enunciated. The more pragmatic labour movements might be narrowly nationalistic in such matters as immigration restriction or tariff protection, but even they often recognized that their gains would in the long run be protected by the success of workers in other countries in raising their wages, and they expressed a common sympathy.

The First International (1864), and especially the Second International (1889) which was composed initially of the socialist parties of Europe and later included those from overseas, provided a meeting ground for the socialist-oriented labour movements. But labour's national loyalties proved stronger than its international solidarity when put to the test by the outbreak of the first world war. The Third International, formed in 1919, became the international centre for communist parties and, through them, for the trade unions which they controlled.

Meanwhile trade unions united internationally on the basis of separate crafts or industries such as miners, typographers, metal trades workers. The main function of these secretariats was to keep their members informed about trade conditions and disputes in different countries and to prevent workers in one country from acting as strike-breakers in another. In 1903 the International Secretariat of National Trade Union Centres was formed, composed of the principal trade union centre in each country; in 1913 it changed its name to the International Federation of Trade Unions. Its primary purpose was to furnish a meeting ground for the discussion of common problems. The national Christian trade unions, whose organization in several countries was stimulated by the papal encyclical *Rerum novarum* (1891), met in Zurich in 1908 to form the International Secretariat of Christian Trade Unions, with membership open to Protestant as well as Catholic unions. Much the largest membership, on the eve of the first world war, was in Germany.

Following the second world war, unions had to regroup themselves internationally after the European trade unions which had been destroyed or distorted by Nazi and fascist domination had been re-established. The communist unions took the lead in reviving international labour organization by joining with non-communist unions from a number of countries to establish the World Federation of Trade Unions in 1945, but four years later the non-communist unions withdrew to form the International Confederation of Free Trade Unions. The latter did not limit itself, as had the International Federation of Trade Unions, to a single federation or trade union centre from each country and so drew in unions with different political affiliations in Europe and Asia and different wings of the labour movements in the United States and Latin America. The International Federation of Christian Trade Unions continued to be composed chiefly of Catholic unions in France, Belgium, Austria and Canada, and both Catholic and Protestant unions in the Netherlands and Switzerland.[9]

3. RIGHTS AND RESPONSIBILITIES OF LABOUR

The manner in which the labour unions of the several countries were able to function depended not only on the form and intention of the unions themselves but on the legal framework within which they operated and the attitude of employers, government and the public. This framework involved: the right of workers to form labour unions, and of unions to conduct their own affairs; the right of labour to use its ultimate weapon, the strike; and the provision of machinery for carrying on labour–management negotiation, and requirements with respect to its use.

(a) Right of organization

In virtually every country labour had to struggle long and often bitterly in order to establish the right freely to form and join unions without interference by employers or government.

The British trade unions, among the earliest to achieve status and freedom from interference, fought for more than a hundred years to free themselves from legal restraints. They had been subject to prosecution, at first for their very existence and then for most of their acts, until the Trade Union acts of the 1870s gave them legal standing and the right to engage in activities essential to their effectiveness. Nevertheless, a court decision in 1901, the Taff Vale Railway Co. case, had the effect of virtually preventing strikes; the Trade Disputes Act of 1906 was then enacted to confirm this right. Again in 1909 trade unions were restrained from using their funds for political purposes, and it required the Trades Union Act of 1913 to lay down the conditions under which unions could seek political objectives. Australian labour in the 1890s fought bitterly for the right of collective bargaining against intransigent employers in the sheep raising and maritime industries; it was only able to consolidate its position and establish its rights when it entered politics and the Labour party became a political force in the early twentieth century.

The fascist and Nazi régimes of Italy and Germany made the free trade union one of their principal targets.

In the United States many large-scale industries bitterly resisted the formation of labour unions. A public investigation of violations of free speech and the rights of labour in the early 1930s disclosed that some large companies had acquired arsenals of tear gas and other weapons, violence and threats of violence were common, and associations of employers were systematically engaged in building up anti-union public sentiment, preventing labour from organizing, and breaking union strength. From 1934 to 1941 issues connected with labour's attempt to organize, gain recognition and bargain collectively were the most frequent single cause of strikes.

In the 1930s a series of laws enacted by the federal Congress gave labour a new legal charter within which to seek its objectives. These laws guaranteed to workers the right to organize and be represented by 'unions of their own choosing', defined 'unfair labour practices' in which employers were forbidden to engage, established the right of peaceful picketing and forbade the use of injunctions in labour disputes. They established administrative machinery to facilitate the choice by workers of the union through which they wished to be represented, to ensure that employers would bargain in good faith, and to provide an agency to which workers could appeal when they thought that the prohibitions against unfair labour practices were being violated. With these guarantees labour organizations grew rapidly in the mass-production indus-tries from which they had been largely excluded and union recognition and collective bargaining became established and accepted procedures in Ameri-can industry. In 1947 the new strength of labour organization was restrained by the Taft-Hartley Act, which limited certain union practices relating to the closed shop, boycotts and jurisdictional disputes and which provided that when, in the opinion of the president of the United States, a threatened or actual strike imperilled the national health or safety, workers might be en-joined from striking for a period of eighty days while the government sought to settle the dispute.

German trade unions had enjoyed a favourable legal position from 1890 on, after the expiration of Bismarck's anti-socialist laws which had been used to restrict their activity, and the German labour movement was one of the most vigorous on the European continent. But when the Nazis came to power, strong, independent unions had no place in a totalitarian state; their organi-zations were dissolved and their leaders persecuted. Under the principle of *Gleichschaltung* and the idea of military organization as the pattern of German life, the Nazi Labour Front was formed as a disciplined body of workers, obedient to the captains of industry and loyal to the régime.

Italian unions had never occupied a secure position; a number of proposed laws to give them legal status in the late nineteenth and early twentieth cen-turies failed of passage. Unions enjoyed a sort of *de facto* status by virtue of legislation which implied their existence by setting limits to their activity or authorizing their representation on certain bodies. The fascist régime liquid-ated the independent trade unions and substituted workers' organizations that functioned not as bargaining agents but as arms of the corporate state.

In the years after the war the German and Italian trade unions, and those in other Nazi-occupied countries, had to be rebuilt from the ground up.

Labour's right freely to associate was recognized as a principle internation-ally in the structure of the International Labour Organization. In this organi-zation, established in 1919, each member country was represented by separate representatives of government, workers and employers, and these delegates voted individually rather than as a national group. This form of tripartite representation permitted the workers' delegates from different countries to join in formulating the position of workers on specific issues. The Universal Declaration of Human Rights confirmed: 'Everyone has the right to form and to join trade unions for the protection of his interests' (Article 23). The International Labour Organization adopted conventions in 1948 and 1949 specifying in detail the conditions which constituted genuine freedom of association for labour. These included the right of all workers, without previous authorization, to form organizations of their own choosing, and the right of these organizations to function freely without control, supervision or danger of dissolution in such matters as drafting their constitution and rules, electing their officers, holding meetings, joining national and international federations and engaging in political activity.

By 1955 these principles of freedom of association were generally part of the legal structure of the industrial countries of west Europe, the United States and the British commonwealth. In these countries unions commonly enjoyed constitutional or legal guarantees of the right of association, not expressly subject to limitations by law. They were not required to register, although in a few cases certain privileges were reserved for registered unions, and there were no restrictions as to which workers were permitted to form labour unions, including those in public employment.

Unions in these countries were uncontrolled in respect to the formation of their constitutions, election of officers, meetings, right to engage in political as well as economic activity and right to join national or international federations. They enjoyed the legal right to strike as well as to engage in collective bargaining and enter into collective contracts. Apart from limitations relating to essential industries or public employees, only an occasional restriction remained, such as the prohibition against jurisdictional strikes in Denmark, sympathetic strikes in Canada or secondary boycotts in the United States.

Outside the industrial countries, however, the legal status of unions was usually more circumscribed. In a number of areas compulsory registration and a measure of government supervision was required and the right to strike was limited or denied.

(b) The strike

The ultimate weapon of the labour union was the strike—the ability of organized workers to withhold their labour. The right to strike was one of the basic rights which the free trade unions enjoyed, but there was a tendency to seek means other than painful and costly work stoppages to secure the benefits which labour sought. Lock-outs by employers to force labour to accept their terms and often to prevent organization were used extensively in the late nineteenth and early twentieth century, but became less frequent as unions gained more general acceptance.

The strike had a different character and served a somewhat different function where labour was oriented toward collective bargaining than where it was geared for political action. In all cases it was a test of labour solidarity and as such had an ethical and emotional meaning for workers who were called upon to make individual sacrifices for common objectives.

As the last resort in collective bargaining the strike represented the workers' ability to inflict direct economic injury on those from whom they were seeking bargaining concessions. Between stubborn bargainers, a strike was a test of endurance—of whether the employers could endure loss of production longer than workers could endure lack of wages. Such bargaining strikes tended to be long drawn out, for they were not usually entered into until the bargaining process had broken down and a difficult impasse had been reached.

Where labour was politically oriented, the strike served more as a demonstration or protest than as part of a bargaining procedure. The object was to impress, to embarrass, above all to dramatize the workers' case. A quick walk-out, a twenty-four hour stoppage was a public gesture, to demonstrate the power of labour or to cause public disorder rather than to injure employers economically or to pit the workers' capacity to sacrifice against the employer's capacity to forgo income. Political strikes tended to be very short, lasting only a day or two or even a few hours.

The general strike, designed to paralyse the economic life of the community was the most drastic of the workers' means of protest. In the early twentieth century the more radical unions regarded it as a principal weapon while the moderates opposed its use. The French anarchist-syndicalist, George Sorel, expressed the belief in his *Reflections on Violence* (1908) that the value of the general strike was not its actual use but its role as a 'social myth' to keep alive the sense of the class struggle.

The general strike was used for political purposes, notably in Belgium in efforts to secure manhood suffrage in 1893, 1902 and 1913. It was used to protest economic conditions, as in Sweden in a month-long general strike in 1909 to protest against the growing use of the lock-out, or in the British general strike of 1926 to protest against a national lock-out of coal miners. It was invoked for revolutionary purposes, notably in the Russian revolution of 1905 and in Germany in 1918.

General strikes were suppressed with great vigour, punitively and with heavy loss of life in the case of revolutionary and some political strikes and with economic and legal penalties when the objectives were economic. The British general strike of 1926 evoked a reactionary Trade Disputes Act which reversed the hundred-year trend toward liberalizing the position of trade unions.[10]

While the right to strike was generally accepted as a basic element in the freedom of workers to organize and seek their objectives, changes in the nature and structure of industry raised complex problems with respect to the exercise of this right. In addition, the development of other methods for securing labour's objectives tended to make the strike somewhat less central, as workers came to depend more upon political or legal action or economic research to press their cause. This was true both of industrially developed countries where the institutional structure for regulating labour relations became more elaborate, and for newly industrializing countries where workers' political influence often exceeded their ability to put pressure on their employers by withholding their labour.

In the course of these years the public sector of the economies of the non-communist countries expanded very substantially, both in response to practical considerations and under strong socialist influences in many countries. The ILO found in its survey of the economies of the seventy member countries in 1955 that the public sector was employing a large segment of the labour force of most countries, regardless of the political structure. In addition to the regular civil services, education, health and welfare, the areas of employment by units of government or by government corporations included generally some or all of the communications services—post, telegraph, telephone, radio; the utilities—electricity, water, gas; transport—railways, city transit systems, air, merchant marine, roads, canals, airport and dock facilities; banking and finance agencies; munitions industries; conservation and exploitation of certain natural resources, such as water power, forests, mines and petroleum; atomic energy; and frequently some government participation in basic chemical, steel, electrical, shipbuilding or automobile industries and in major development programmes such as the TVA in the United States or the Snowy Mountains scheme in Australia. In these circumstances, where as much as 20 per cent of the labour force was in government employ in a country like Australia or 10 to 13 per cent in Canada and the United States, the question of the rights of workers *vis-à-vis* the government became involved.

In addition, the great growth of cities and the extreme interdependence of industrial activity made the entire community acutely dependent on the continuous operation of many industries and the continuous maintenance of central services. Cities of millions of people with only a few days' supply of food were exposed to disaster if transport services were interrupted for a long period; shut-downs in basic materials such as steel or in fuel supply or electric power could paralyse whole areas or economies. Health and safety could be menaced by the cessation of essential services. It was immaterial whether these industries and services were provided by public or private operations; their interruption menaced the public.

In these circumstances the industrial countries where the right of free association and resort to the strike were generally recognized hedged the strike about with limitations designed to protect the public while leaving the basic rights and freedoms of labour unimpaired. At mid-century nearly every industrial country placed some restraints on the workers' freedom to strike when such a strike would result in danger to health or safety or hardship to the community, or when it involved an 'essential' industry or public employees. The only west European industrial countries without one or another of these limitations in 1955 were Denmark, Sweden and Italy. In non-industrial countries restraints on the right to strike were more general. Strikes were permissible only for the purpose of direct economic or social benefits in several Latin American countries and all strikes were prohibited in Turkey, Spain and Portugal.

The line was not an easy one to draw, however, especially in view of the tendency for governments to enlarge the areas of their activity and thus to bring a larger proportion of workers into the category of public employees. To deny to these workers the rights enjoyed by those in comparable types of work in private industry appeared to penalize them for being public employees. Equally difficult was the effort to draw the line between 'essential' and 'non-essential' services or industries.

(c) Machinery for adjusting labour–management relations

The unresolved dilemma was made less serious in most countries by the development of positive means for adjusting labour relations which would reduce the likelihood of resort to the strike. Some form of machinery to facilitate negotiation and collective bargaining was set up in practically every country; in some a strike was legal only if the established procedures had been followed.

Mediation services were generally offered by government where negotiations threatened to break down, and their use was made compulsory in some countries. In the Scandinavian countries the negotiation of industry-wide contracts was set up on a national basis with a fixed schedule for annual preliminary negotiations, the referral of points of disagreement to government mediators, the settlement of remaining unresolved issues by government wage boards in Norway and a joint employer–union board in Sweden, and the adoption of the new agreement at a uniform time each year. Only in the rare instances where agreement was still lacking after the procedure had been followed would there be the possibility of a strike. The principle was also well established that disputes arising over the interpretation or execution of the labour contract were not to lead to work stoppages and labour courts were established to adjudicate such disputes in Denmark in 1910, Norway in 1915 and Sweden in 1928.

In most west European countries works councils were provided for by law and their elections, conducted by secret ballot, were carried on under government supervision. Within the general framework of laws and broad collective agreements, these works councils had responsibility for developing the detailed terms of the work contract and assuring its observance. The most binding structure for the conduct of labour relations was the system of compulsory arbitration established in Australia, New Zealand, the Union of South Africa and Northern Ireland.

4. ACHIEVEMENT OF LABOUR'S GOALS

By mid-century many of the goals which had looked far distant to workers at the opening of the century had been at least partially achieved or had come within sight—in terms of material standards, rights as workers and status as citizens.

As a consequence both of better wages and working conditions and of the social provisions of the welfare state, workers had come to take for granted many of the material benefits of which their predecessors of 1900 had hardly dared to dream—greatly increased real wages, leisure, social security, social services, housing, travel, holidays, pensions, medical services, the education of their children. Such benefits were not enjoyed equally by the workers of all the industrial countries nor by all workers in each country, for great differences in productivity continued to be reflected in differences in levels of living, the gap between rich and poor had been narrowed more sharply in some countries than in others and disadvantaged groups remained. But with all these qualifications, most of the workers of the industrial countries enjoyed a material standard of living well above that of fifty years before, and in the most advanced industrial countries the difference was great. The struggle for higher wages and other benefits continued unabated, however, for the rising aspirations of workers more than kept pace with the rising productivity of industry.

The rights of labour freely to associate and to seek their objectives had become well established in the major industrial countries. In most countries machinery for the conduct of negotiations and the settlement of labour disputes enabled representatives of labour and management to deal with each other without the need for constant militancy or intransigence; in fact it sometimes appeared to the union rank and file that their officials had become so preoccupied with the mechanics of labour–management adjustment that they no longer provided vigorous leadership, and 'wildcat' strikers protested against their unions as well as against their employers.

Yet the memory of the destruction of labour organizations by the fascist and Nazi régimes was still vivid; labour's rights were still limited and trade unionists imprisoned under some of the ruling dictators. Anti-labour sentiment was in fact far from dead even where labour organization was a well-established institution. Labour movements continued to act as the guardians and promoters of labour's rights and to serve as the means through which workers struggled within the social and political framework of their several societies to secure for themselves and their children the status, opportunities and conditions of life which the principles of western society made the goal of all people.

Labour's political role was also generally well-established. Through political parties or pressure on legislatures, labour continued to work for social legislation and it participated responsibly through the International Labour Organization in the formulation of world-wide standards for labour's status and welfare.

In their individual response to widening opportunities, moreover, workers demonstrated both the determination and the capacity to move into a new place in society. Many sent their children to secondary schools and some to universities; they acquired and enjoyed decent homes, travelled, read, enjoyed cinema and radio, developed hobbies and accepted community responsibilities.

By the mid-twentieth century the worker in the industrial countries had thus achieved a status as a human being and a citizen. He enjoyed, for the most part, decent conditions of work. He was far less distinguished than in the past by dress and speech, by the poorness of his housing and his lack of education, by his poor health and that of his children. Nor was he expected to keep his place and to accept as his due inferior standards that were deemed good enough for him. In the words of the report sponsored by the welfare ministers of the northern European countries: 'By joining with his fellows the wage-earner has found a powerful means not only of furthering his economic interests but also of enhancing his general status and dignity as a useful member of the community. The downtrodden labourer of former days standing in wooden shoes and cap in hand before his employer is now but a memory from the bygone past.'*

Nevertheless, the very nature of all industry continued to make the status of the individual worker dependent and insecure. His job was often monotonous and conditioned by the machine; changing technology offered a constant threat to his mastery of his job and to the value of his skills; many factors beyond his control—automation, economic fluctuations, changes of product or plant location—might leave him without work and require him to find a new job or move to a new place; in the calculations of management he remained an item of cost. In their continuing struggle for status, workers made a constant effort to reduce their dependence on the employer's whim, through such devices as seniority and guaranteed annual wages; they sought positive measures to facilitate necessary changes, such as provisions for retraining and the costs of moving to new jobs; they endeavoured to secure a share in determining the manner in which changes affecting workers, such as automation, would be introduced.

The place which labour occupied had become a key to the character of industrial states. In the democratically oriented states labour became a major power element, extending its influence and active participation step by step throughout the period, assuming the political leadership in some countries for periods of time. The status and rights of labour served as symbols of democratic liberalism in constitutions and national policies. In countries where authoritarian forces were strong, labour was a rallying point for challenges to authority and the suppression of the right of workers to organize and express their grievances was a symbol of dictatorship. In the communist countries the interests of labour organizations were bound up with the interests of the

* *Freedom and Welfare, op. cit.*, p. 503.

government and they were responsible for carrying out economic policy, achieving production goals and administering social benefits.

In the newly developing countries labour's self-conscious effort to secure status was inextricably bound up with the political awakening of the people, with their national aspirations and with their efforts to find their identity as citizens in the new societies that were replacing the static and status-bound societies of the past. The conditions which workers faced were often worse and their problems more formidable than those which had confronted labour in the early days of western industrialization. But the workers of Asia, of Latin America and of Africa had before them, in the achievements of the workers of industrially developed countries, a standard of aspiration which their predecessors had lacked.

II. PEASANTS AND FARMERS

While labour was achieving a large measure of success in its struggle for status in industrially advanced countries and a growing self-consciousness elsewhere, the rural masses remained generally less articulate and less successful in their more sporadic efforts to improve their lot.

Both in regions of advanced agriculture and in underdeveloped areas, farmers occupied a relatively disadvantageous position as compared with those engaged in industry and trade. In both types of societies farm incomes were generally below those of corresponding elements in the city. In underdeveloped areas primitive techniques and insufficient land meant low productivity and, consequently, low returns to the cultivator. Where agricultural technology was advanced, the farmer's very efficiency tended to depress his income by bringing a constant threat of glutted markets and falling prices. Rural populations everywhere had higher birth rates than those in the city and the expanding needs of industry for workers were met from the extra hands not needed on the farm. Differential wages in favour of industry reflected this process.[11]

In dealing with other segments of the population, farmers were generally at a bargaining disadvantage, for many small, competitive units often confronted a few strong suppliers of equipment, storage, transport, processing and marketing services. Where cultivators did not own their land but were required to give a substantial portion of their crop to absentee or feudal landlords, they were at an additional disadvantage. Where they were also in debt to their landlords, they might be in a state of virtual peonage.

For his lesser income, the farmer generally worked long and hard, as his crops or his stock might require, rarely able to restrict his hours to a fixed number as did the urban worker. He might be idle in slack seasons and overworked in others. With the high rural birth rate, the cost and burden of childrearing fell disproportionately on the country people. In addition rural life in many areas lacked the amenities of the town—conveniences such as electricity and running water, facilities such as schools and health services, shops, sources of entertainment.

Though the rural dweller was at an economic and social disadvantage as compared with the city dweller, and though the city exerted a strong pull to attract rural migrants by virtue of jobs and urban attractions, there were aspects of rural life which farmers cherished and wished to maintain. The aspirations of rural folk as they found expression during these years were mainly for means to enjoy these positive rural values. Farming as a way of life contrasted favourably with the kind of life available in the city in that it was geared to the rhythm of the seasons to which men through the centuries had been attuned. It offered to the farmer a measure of self-direction, subject only to the demands of nature, and, except where he worked for another, freedom from the dictates of other men. Although rural tasks were often laborious and of a sameness, they were much more varied than the monotonous jobs which urban workers were often called on to perform, repetitively, day in and day out. Land, in the rural tradition, meant security; the alternative of city employment at the pleasure of an employer meant hazard.

The rural person wanted first and foremost the security which was part of the rural way of life—albeit full of hazards from nature—enhanced by security of tenure or ownership in his land. Secondly, he wanted access to the means of exploiting his land effectively, and in such a way that it could yield him a decent living. This meant access to knowledge, to markets and sources of supply on favourable terms, and to credit for development. Thirdly, farmers aspired to enter fully and freely into the cultural life of the broader society, through access to education, through communication and through the opportunity to enjoy the amenities which had become part of city life, such as labour-saving appliances in the farm home and enlarged social contacts made possible by modern transport and communication.

The situation of the farmer and the character of farmers' movements differed radically from one area to another, but all shared two basic, common aspirations: to reduce the disparity, both economic and cultural, between farm and city, and to realize the positive values of rural life.

Where, as in western Europe, North America, South Africa, Australia and New Zealand, the typical farmer produced crops for market on a family farm which he owned or held in secure tenure, farm organizations were composed of independent producers who banded together to provide themselves with common services, for economic bargaining or to use their political power to gain public facilities or legislation favourable to agriculture. Some organizations were primarily economic in their emphasis, others essentially political and some included social activities, but all sought to strengthen the farmer's hand within the existing structure of agriculture and the existing social order. Where there were class distinctions between well-to-do, middle and poor farmers or farm labourers, farm organizations generally represented the middle and upper groups.

In the very different conditions of essentially feudal landholding in east Europe, Latin America and the Middle East, where tenants or farm labourers were only one step removed from serfdom and lived in poverty and ignorance at the mercy of their landlords, peasant movements had a more or less revolutionary aim. They were composed of the poor or landless peasants who made up the vast majority of the peasant population in areas where the middle-level farmer, so typical of western Europe and North America, was almost non-existent. They sought to recast the structure of agrarian society to give the peasant rights in the land which he tilled and to break the landlords' power.

After the second world war a third type of movement among rural people began to take shape in Asian countries and in other underdeveloped rural areas under the outside stimulus of community development programmes. The objectives of such programmes were to raise the economic and cultural level of backward and often isolated rural areas as a part of the effort for national development; their method was to stimulate self-help among the people themselves. The vigour with which people in many areas responded to these stimuli—in India, Pakistan, the Philippines, Jamaica, Puerto Rico, Africa—indicated that community self-help had the potentialities of a major movement for the reconstruction of rural life.

I. FARMERS' MOVEMENTS IN COUNTRIES OF ADVANCED AGRICULTURE

Farmers of western Europe, North America and Australasia were not a depressed class but were entrepreneurs with a middle-class outlook. Though their status was generally below that of the urban middle class, it was nevertheless that of property owners and business men. There were, however, profound differences in attitude between the farmer in young countries such as Canada, Australia and the USA and peasant owners who were more deeply rooted in the land which had been in their family for many generations. For the former, land was a resource to yield him a living and, although he was often strongly attached to his particular acres, his main interest was in the income which the use of the land might bring. His immediate forebears had moved from one farm to another in the course of a lifetime seeking better opportunities, and many twentieth-century farmers continued to look for additional acres or better land.

In contrast, the European peasant-owner was almost a part of the land which he farmed. He was the temporary custodian of a terrain which had sustained his ancestors and which was his to cherish and to hand on as a heritage to his children, richer if possible but certainly no poorer. The peasant who lived within a family–land continuum could not willingly exploit and exhaust the land, as the farm entrepreneur often did, careless of the morrow. He must practise good husbandry, for his own future and that of his children were bound up with preservation of the fertility of the soil.[12]

Farm organizations in countries where independent farming and commercialized agriculture predominated grew out of technical societies for such purposes as stock breeding, out of scattered fraternal or social unions, and out of sporadic protest movements against conditions unfavourable to agriculture. They tended to become the means through which farmers engaged directly in co-operative economic activity, for agricultural credit as in Germany and Italy, or for co-operative marketing as in Denmark, Switzerland, Canada, New Zealand and the United States. They engaged in political action, sometimes through an agrarian party, more often by political pressure within parties and on governments as in Canada and the United States. As government services to agriculture were extended and countries adopted economic measures to support farm incomes, farmers' organizations frequently became the medium through which these programmes were carried out. Agricultural extension services, for example, were provided in Denmark by government grants to farm organizations and were partially supported by farm organizations in the United States; local farmers' committees participated in the administration of acreage allotment and soil conservation programmes in the United States and much responsibility for the British farm programme rested with local farmers' councils.

Farm organizations tended to be dominated by, and to reflect the interests of, the more substantial farmers, sometimes to the point where the smaller farmers formed a separate organization, as in Denmark. The principal international association which linked national farm organizations, the International Federation of Agricultural Producers formed in 1946, spoke for these substantial groups.

On broad social and economic issues organized farmers tended to be on the side of social reform when issues directly affecting farming were involved; they opposed the power of banks, public utilities and large corporations and called for anti-monopoly measures; they supported cheap power, easy credit, rural electrification, public ownership or regulation of transport, storage and marketing facilities and the extension of roads, education, health and other services to rural areas. On other issues they tended to be more conservative; some farm organizations went to the extreme of being anti-labour and of opposing the various social protections of the welfare state; others made common cause with labour in support of broad social programmes.

In general, farm movements of the twentieth century in the technically advanced countries reflected the efforts of independent farm entrepreneurs to withstand the pressure of, or to get in step with, the modern industrial economy and to make a secure and prosperous place for themselves in it.

2. PEASANT MOVEMENTS

The most articulate and well-organized movements of peasants on feudal estates were those of Russia and eastern Europe. Here, at the opening of the century, land was still held in *latifundia* on essentially feudal terms; the abolition of serfdom in the 1860s had left the peasantry scarcely better off than before, for they were burdened with payments for their land and often lost it to the richer landlords. Within the feudal structures, different peasant traditions survived, the village community or *mir* in Russia, the extended family or *zadruga* in some of the Balkan areas and individual proprietorship elsewhere. But everywhere the aspirations of the peasants were the same—to own their land.

Peasant movements of protest and reform had gathered momentum during the late nineteenth century. The Populists in Russia envisaged an agrarian society based on the *mir*, and from 1900 on their successors, the Social Democrats, retained this as their goal for the rural sector while adopting a revolutionary socialist view for industry. Peasant unrest was a major element in the abortive Russian revolution of 1905, and the Stolypin reforms were adopted thereafter in a belated effort to quiet peasant discontent. These reforms were designed to create independent peasant proprietors rather than to strengthen the village community.

Peasant parties and movements in eastern Europe pursued the goal of individual ownership of the land. A number of such movements took shape around the turn of the century, the Czech peasant party, formed in 1896, being one of the strongest and most practical. The movement in Rumania led to a peasant uprising in 1907 which was not suppressed until some 10,000 peasants had been killed.

As against the aspirations of the peasants for an agrarian society of peasant proprietors, Marx and his followers insisted that the proletarianization of the peasants was inevitable and that fundamental improvement in the lot of the peasants could come only as the lower peasants joined the class war and as agriculture was reorganized on a collective basis into large producing units. The socialist parties thus stood opposed in principle to the populist aspirations and movements of peasants.

Lenin, however, saw that the revolutionary thrust of the peasants could be used as a practical aid in bringing the proletarian revolution and that it was in fact essential to the success of the revolution in predominantly agrarian societies such as Russia. His slogan 'land for the tillers' linked the uprising of the peasants to the proletarian revolution and brought under his leadership the peasants who moved on their own initiative to dispossess the landowners once the revolution of 1917 got under way. The October revolution was thus a victory for peasants as well as for workers, and the distribution of land to the peasants was one of its most immediate fruits.

The revolution in Russia gave a tremendous impetus to the peasant movements of eastern Europe. Taking advantage of the extension of the franchise under the new constitutions of the east European countries, peasant parties rose to power in the 1920s throughout the area.

These peasant parties were entirely composed of poor peasants, for there was no peasant middle class comparable to that in west European countries, and they were directed against the landlords. Their programmes reflected peasant aspirations. They stood for the individually owned family farm, both as an economic unit and as a way of life. They supported democratic principles of government.

They were anti-capitalist as far as the ownership and exploitation of large units of land and of large-scale industry were concerned. They favoured state ownership of public services and basic industries and the scattering of small, individually owned industries through the countryside to spread the benefits of industrialization and share them with the peasant proprietors. They favoured the organization of co-operatives where larger operations of either rural industry or agriculture were desirable. They wanted education, health and the other services of the modern state extended to the villages and they opposed what they regarded as the privileged position of the towns. Their image was that of a rural society, based on an educated, independent, landowning peasantry, which would use co-operation as the means of combining the advantages of small property with those of large enterprise.

Although the peasant parties shared a common outlook, they varied considerably from country to country. The well-organized Czechoslovak party was successful in pushing through the most extensive of the programmes of land reform and for introducing the eight-hour day for agricultural labour. Polish peasants formed no single organization but a number which ranged from radical to conservative and from anti-clerical to clerical. In Rumania the peasant party constituted the political opposition until it came to power in 1928 and established the first parliamentary government which the country experienced. The Bulgarian party, in existence since 1901, received a majority of the votes in 1923. The Croat peasant party which became a dominant element in Yugoslavia in the 1920s combined Croatian nationalism with a clearly defined rural ideology.

Moves to link peasant movements internationally came from both right and left. After the first world war a conservative element in Bavaria and Austria attempted to initiate an international organization but failed. A Russian-sponsored Communist Peasant International held its first congress in 1925, but it had relatively little influence on east European peasant movements during the inter-war years. On the initiative of the Bulgarian peasant party, a bureau for agricultural research was established in Prague in 1921 with Czech, Bulgarian, Polish and Serbian peasant parties as members, joined later by some west European groups. The peasant movements never attained a degree of international organization comparable to that of the socialist and communist parties.

Except in Hungary, where the landowning class retained its hold, a very considerable measure of land distribution was carried out throughout east Europe in the inter-war years. Although the agrarian reforms varied greatly in their completeness, in the size of holding left to the former landlord, in the proportion of the poor peasants who acquired land, and in the ability of the peasants to command the necessary means of cultivation, the landlord class was virtually eliminated and a major social revolution was effected. And though the peasant holdings were small, their freedom from obligations to landlords and the opportunity to raise more subsistence crops instead of grain for market enabled numbers of peasants to make some improvement in their condition and to take a step toward their ideal of a prosperous agrarian society.

The tenure of power by the east European peasant parties was, however, short-lived. Reactionary elements, displaced from the land, reasserted themselves politically and broke down the democratic procedures which had enabled the peasants to rise. The murder of the Bulgarian peasant party leaders in 1923 broke up that party; the Croat peasant leaders were imprisoned and some killed; Rumanian leaders were persecuted and the party denied the power it had earned at the polls; in Poland some leaders were imprisoned and others fled. Suppression of the peasant parties ended in dictatorship for most countries of eastern Europe.

Meantime in the USSR private peasant proprietorship of the means of production was replaced by co-operative ownership. At no time did the Communist party accept peasant aspirations to the individual ownership of land as anything except a practical device to get rid of the landowners and to create a partnership between peasants and industrial workers. Collectivization was always the goal. An initial period of collectivization was followed in 1921 by the period of the New Economic Policy when individual peasant operations were permitted; but this was declared from the start to be a temporary slackening of pace, not a basic change in direction. When collectivization was resumed in 1928 it was carried through rigorously, in spite of the opposition of certain categories of landowning peasants.[13, 14]

In the years leading to the second world war and during the war the peasants of eastern Europe were strong elements in the anti-Nazi resistance movements of their countries. When these countries regained their independence at the close of the war, urban-led communist minorities with strong backing from the international communist organization contended for power with the more loosely organized peasant majorities. When the communist parties came to power they expropriated the remaining estates and divided the land with great rapidity, and they organized communist peasant parties in Poland, Bulgaria, Rumania, Hungary and Czechoslovakia in the effort to orient the peasants toward collectivization.[15]

In the face of strong traditional aspirations to individual landownership among the peasants, the communist leaders in each of these countries moved somewhat cautiously toward this avowed goal, in Poland halting and even reversing the process in 1956. But the leadership of the people's democracies was committed to the Marxian view that socialization of agriculture was essential. A socialist society had no place for the vision of a rural democracy of peasant proprietors to which the east European peasant movements aspired in the years when they offered a means of expression to the peasant masses of these areas.[16]

Peasant risings played a part in revolutionary movements in Latin America and Asia. The aspiration of peasants changed the character of the Mexican revolution which began in 1910. Under the long dictatorship (1877–1911) of Porfirio Díaz, more than 90 per cent of the Mexican peasants were landless; in many states the proportion exceeded 95 per cent. Their real income fell steadily, especially in the decade after 1900 when the decline was variously estimated at between 33 and 75 per cent. Meanwhile the mounting wealth of the country flowed into the hands of a small class of rich landholders, the Church and foreign investors. In its initial phase, the revolution, inspired and led by middle-class intellectuals who sought an end to political tyranny and concessions to foreign exploiters, was not a movement for agrarian reform. But when the agrarian leader Emilio Zapata raised the cry of 'land for the landless' and urged his followers to demand and take over lands belonging to landlords and the Church, this became its central drive.

The demand of the Mexican peasants for land expressed two distinct ideologies with quite opposite origins, the traditional Indian concept of communal lands held and worked by the village, and the North American concept of individual ownership of his own land by each farmer. From both points of view the peasants and their leaders rejected the authority of the 'patron' or landowner and the admonition of the Church that they should submit to this authority as from God. Nor were they guided by Marxist principles as a basis for collectivization.

In the successive stages of the continuous Mexican revolution, the peasants achieved freedom from submission and debt-peonage to the landlords and secured the distribution of a large proportion of the agricultural lands—all of the lands in the most populous regions. They combined their traditions of communal holdings and their desire for individual possession in a system of *ejidos* owned in common by the village, but parcelled out to each villager or *ejiditario*, who was entitled to possession of a portion of the land so long as he cultivated it. More than forty years after the beginning of the revolution, the economic condition of the Mexican peasant remained low and the claims of many *ejiditarios* were still unmet for lack of sufficient available land to provide all with farms which would yield an adequate livelihood. But the agrarian basis had helped to keep the Mexican revolution essentially democratic in its values and orientation.[17]

Elsewhere in Latin America, the aspirations of the peasants—*campesinos*—were the basis of revolutionary movements, but with little success in changing the *latifundia* system which prevailed so generally throughout the area. The Apra party of Peru, formed in the 1930s by urban intellectuals, drew its mass support from the rural areas and couched its demands in terms of land for the landless. The movement, however, was suppressed, its leaders were jailed or exiled, and in the 1950s the peasants of Peru, as of most other Latin American countries, had as yet found no means of breaking the hold of the landowners. In other countries the undercurrent of land hunger rose to the surface briefly or locally from time to time, as in Guatemala in the early 1950s. In Bolivia, however, the peasants' aspirations for land achieved fulfilment when, in 1952, a government pledged to redistribute the land took power by force and proceeded to make good its pledge; and land reform was a principal plank in the platform of the revolutionary leader who ousted the dictator in Cuba in 1959.[18] No popular leader could be unaware of the Latin American *campesino*'s desire for land or fail to recognize that, in a world where the remains of feudal landholding had been or were being swept away, agrarian reform in these areas was already overdue.

All over Asia peasants became aroused to seek new rights in the period after the first world war. In most areas, notably India, Indonesia and Burma, the peasant awakening contributed to the nationalist movements. After independence the reconstruction of rural life was part of the process of national development.

In China the communist leadership built the revolutionary movement squarely on the peasants' aspirations for land, for Mao Tse-tung insisted that the peasant, not the urban worker, must provide the revolutionary base in an essentially agricultural country. Under the actual conditions of Chinese agriculture, holdings were infinitesimally small and insufficient to provide a living, even when worked by intensive and often skilful methods.

When the communist leaders, after first redistributing the land, used persuasion, inducements and pressure to encourage co-operative or collective farming, they found Chinese peasants less insistent than Russian and east European peasants had been on retaining individual ownership. Within ten years of the initial land distribution, they were able to take the further step of placing landholding and the whole of rural life on a communal basis.

3. COMMUNITY DEVELOPMENT

In the years after the second world war efforts to raise the peasant masses in all parts of the world came not only from the peasants themselves but from national and international agencies seeking to promote economic and social development. To the men who led these countries in their struggles to function as modern states, peasant populations isolated from the currents of the modern world appeared as a drag on their efforts. The national leaders knew that unless the level of productivity and participation among the rural people could be raised, the economies of their countries could not advance substantially and their political and social structures would rest on shaky foundations. In each of these countries, therefore, means were sought to stimulate the peasants not only to change their agricultural methods but to engage on their own behalf in efforts to improve their lot. This process went under the general term of 'community development'.

Community development meant organized efforts to raise the level of rural community life, primarily through self-help and co-operative activity on the part of the rural community itself, stimulated and provided with technical aid in such a way as to cultivate self-reliance, initiative and common effort. Community development programmes had their antecedents in a variety of related activities: in agricultural extension services, community programmes of health education, co-operative organization, community schools or cultural missions, and various forms of welfare activity. As they took shape in different countries they varied considerably in form and emphasis, but all in one way or another represented a partnership between government and people.

At one end of the scale, in the Philippines where all government was highly centralized, the programme was administered from the office of the president of the republic and was set up as a means by which public services could be carried to remote regions which they had not previously reached. A 'village worker' represented all government services at the neighbourhood level and acted both as a liaison to the combined government agencies to which he was responsible and as an awakener of initiative and guide to village and neighbourhood self-help. At the opposite extreme, the programme in Jamaica, West Indies, took the form primarily of assistance to volunteer effort provided by personnel of what was originally a non-governmental organization, the Jamaica Welfare Commission. It operated only in the communities which sought assistance in carrying out some common effort. The main task of its workers was to advise, assist and train volunteer local leaders and to act as consultants to the groups which gave democratic expression to the interests of the locality.

Between these two extremes were a variety of community development programmes, differently designed to fit different areas. The ambitious programmes undertaken in India and Pakistan aimed to reach all of the more than half-million villages in that vast sub-continent within ten years. The Indian programme grouped approximately one hundred villages in each 'development block'; appropriate rural services were provided at the block centre—veterinary services, health clinics, vocational education, agricultural extension, co-operatives, small industries. A 'village-level worker', living in one of the villages which he served, acted as stimulator and consultant to a group of villages within the area. Government offered a certain amount of financial as well as technical assistance to projects undertaken by the villagers, providing some of the materials for the construction of roads, wells, schools, latrines, drainage pits, or furnishing fertilizer and seed for agricultural demonstrations, or materials and equipment for vocational training.

The Egyptian programme, designed for the large crowded villages of the Nile valley, emphasized the establishment of centres serving several villages where a range of services and activities were united—hospitals, schools, adult education, vocational workshops, co-operative enterprises, social centres. The objectives were both to overcome the disparity between rural and urban areas in respect to services which had been almost wholly confined to the cities and, by bringing these services close to the people, to stimulate their use. In a number of countries, special 'aided self-help' housing programmes provided technical guidance and materials at low cost to enable groups of families, by their co-operative efforts, to provide themselves with improved rural housing.

The philosophy which ran through all the community development programmes was well expressed in the law establishing the community education programme in Puerto Rico in 1948: 'The community should not be civically unemployed. The community can be constantly and usefully employed in its own service, in terms of pride and satisfaction of the members.' While the emphasis in some places was on concrete results—acres planted by improved methods, miles of roads constructed with village labour, wells dug, bridges built, schools built, land reclaimed, and community centres in operation— these were only the outward signs of the change in outlook and habits of rural people.

Community development was, in a sense, imposed on rural people from the outside and was designed to bring them into line with the values and practices of the broader society. Yet wherever such programmes were carried on with vigour and skill, their effect was to release latent energy and uncover latent desires and interests. Those who had started in the role of stimulators soon found themselves facing demands for further aid from villagers whose initiative often far exceeded what the technicians and leaders had been prepared to expect. Governments were hard pressed to make good on the promises of technical and material aid with which they had undertaken to supplement local efforts. Although some efforts to stimulate village initiative were abortive, the picture of apathetic rural people hard to arouse and tenacious of old ways had to be rapidly revised. Lack of energy often turned out to be merely the prevalence of malaria, malnutrition or internal parasites; lack of ambition reflected the long-existing hopelessness of the peasant's lot, and ignorance and conservatism the absence of the opportunity to learn. Ancient peasant societies were not being transformed overnight, for the heavy burden of poverty and ignorance presented a problem of staggering dimensions in all the newly developed countries, and the distance to be travelled was very great. But the impulse to change was unmistakably there. In the mid-twentieth century the peasant peoples of Asia and the Middle East, of Latin America and Africa were beginning to glimpse a new life toward which they were prepared to strive and were beginning to find their voices and means of action as they moved toward participation in the life of the modern world.

III. WOMEN

Many of the major changes of the twentieth century had their sharpest bearing upon the lives of women, who not only shared the new experiences and outlook which affected the whole society but found their own position altered. Every aspect of urban industrial life invaded and modified women's traditional domain, the home, removing most of its economic functions and making its former responsibilities, such as health, housing, sanitation and education, into matters of community concern. Inescapably these forces changed the activities of women, their sphere of operation and their place in society, drawing them into employment and public life, altering their relationships both within and outside the family group, and giving them a new status, new roles, new opportunities and new responsibilities. In large measure the new position of women was an incidental result of broad social trends. But to a considerable degree it was brought about by the conscious efforts of women themselves.

Prior to the twentieth century women in all parts of the world lived within social systems which assigned to them an inferior position and a restricted role. Law, religion and custom in western countries had combined to sanction complete subordination of women to men, though in practice women had always found means to make their influence felt. Under the Anglo-Saxon common law, married women enjoyed no independent legal rights—to property, guardianship of their children, use of their own earnings, determination of their own domicile. In the systems derived from the Roman law via the Napoleonic Code, property and parental rights were almost wholly enjoyed by men, and a married woman could not take legal action or engage in business and enter into contracts, or could do so only with her husband's consent. Religion sanctioned the duty of obedience. With few exceptions women enjoyed no political rights and had very limited access to education.

In eastern countries the position of women was somewhat less restricted by law than it was in the West, but it was far more limited by custom. Under Muslim law women enjoyed independent rights of property, guardianship and legal personality; in practice, except in Indonesia, the system of seclusion was general, women were veiled if they emerged from the home—except as they worked in the fields—and education and political rights were limited to men. Hindu women lived under severe legal and social restrictions, their scope of activity defined by their place in the extended family system. Seclusion was common, child marriage frequent, permanent widowhood the rule and education rare. Buddhist principles permitted general equality in property and personal status, but the strong patriarchal family in China left women little independent scope and the highly structured Japanese society reinforced the subordinate status of women by language, gesture and every detail of life.

I. THE GOALS OF WOMEN'S ASPIRATIONS

In the twentieth century increasing numbers of women throughout the world aspired to a new status and a new life. The status which they sought was one of personal identity as individuals; the new life was one of full opportunity. They wished to share the rights enjoyed by men and to be able to take part in the same political activity, receive the same education, engage in the same professions or other types of work, and be governed by the same code of social behaviour. But they wished, too, for the opportunity to give full expression to their differences without the implication of inferiority. Such aspirations were generally voiced by educated women; it was not always clear that they were wholly shared by others. They were achieved in large measure during the first half of the century by the women of the industrialized countries but were only beginning to be realized at mid-century by most women elsewhere.

In each country women couched their common goals in terms of the ideologies and conditions of their societies. European women had begun to agitate for a change in status at the time of the French revolution when they sought to extend to women the concept of the 'rights of man'. But they had met little sympathy for such expressions as Mary Wollstonecraft's *Vindication of the Rights of Woman* (London, 1792), or the proposal of a group of Frenchwomen that the National Assembly of 1789 adopt a 'declaration of the rights of women'. Nor had anyone taken seriously the warning of Abigail Adams to her husband in the Continental Congress of the rebellious American colonies in 1776: 'If particular care and attention is not paid to the ladies, we are determined to foment a rebellion, and will not hold ourselves bound by any laws in which we have no voice or representation.'* Such ardent exponents of the rights of men as Jean Jacques Rousseau and Thomas Jefferson insisted that these rights did not include women.

In time, however, the concept that 'all men are created equal and are endowed with certain inalienable rights' worked as a leaven until the concept 'man' took on the meaning 'human'. It was no accident that the founders of the movement for women's suffrage in the United States should have been leaders in the anti-slavery crusade, or that the classic text for the women's rights movement in Britain and on the European continent, *The Subjection of Women* (1869) should have been written by the great exponent of liberalism, John Stuart Mill.

These principles of liberal democracy furnished the driving ideology for the women of Britain, the Commonwealth nations and the United States, for many of the women of the European continent and for most of the articulate women of Latin America and the eastern countries. Their concept of themselves and their objectives was based on a view of the individual personality as the ultimate social value. The basic ideological drive toward individualism was bolstered by economic trends, but it often had to contend with the traditional view of the priority of the woman's duty as wife and mother in a patriarchal family and with the new emphasis on the role of the mother brought by twentieth-century psychiatry.

Marxian socialism provided the ideology for women workers who took part in the socialist and communist political movements and in the labour organizations associated with them. In this view equality between the sexes was an integral aspect of a society in which the exploitation of one individual by another would have been eliminated.

Karl Marx regarded the subjection of women as a form of exploitation and an evil of capitalist society, and declared that 'social progress can be measured

* Quoted in C. A. Beard, *The Republic* (New York, 1943), p. 5.

with precision by the social position of the female sex'.* Equality of the sexes was in fact so basic to the socialist concept of a new society that it ceased to be a separate issue. Women enjoyed the same rights and duties as men in common activities within the political parties formed by the working class. Many women such as Rosa Luxemburg (1870–1919) and Clara Zetkin (1857–1933) in Germany, Louise Michel (1830–1905) and Laura Lafargue (1846–1911) in France, and Nadezhda Krupskaya (1869–1939) and Alexandra Kollontai (1872–1952) in Russia played a prominent part in the revolutionary movements. The second International Conference of Socialist Women, held in Copenhagen in 1910, instituted an 'International Women's Day', March 8, as a day of international solidarity of women in the struggle for economic and political equality, preservation of peace and the well-being of children. The principle of equality between men and women was automatically incorporated into law upon the establishment of the USSR.

Some agitation for changes in the position of women had begun in Asian countries before the close of the nineteenth century as a result of contact with the liberal thought of the West. In Japan a few women had been trained abroad and had founded higher educational institutions for women and organizations to seek women's rights. They received little support, however, from the men who led the movement for westernization, even though a freer and more equal status for women was recognized as a feature of western society. In China the influence of missionaries had affected a limited number, especially among the merchant classes whose contacts with the West were greatest, and had set a few women on the path of education. Reform movements in India stimulated by contact with the West, such as the Bramo Samaj, had included emancipation of women from Hindu customs as a cardinal point in their programmes, and Indian women were among the active participants and leaders in nationalist agitation. In Muslim areas there was as yet little sign of movement.

During the twentieth century women's movements grew in nearly all parts of Asia. After the October revolution the equality of men and women in the USSR became an inspiration and stimulus to women in Asian countries, for they saw in this example the first society where women were expected to function according to their capacities and potentialities.

Once the breach had been made in the wall of seclusion and subordination by the impact of either liberal democracy or Marxian socialism, Asian women invoked the equalitarian principles of the Quran and Buddhism and the basic assumptions of Hindu thought to attack the body of customs by which these had become overlaid. Muslim women called attention to the fact that the Quran gave them property rights not enjoyed by the women of the West, that the Prophet had encouraged women's political participation, and that the limitation to four wives with the injunction to take only one if justice could not be done to more had been a great step forward, designed to enhance the

* Letter to Kugelmann, 1868.

position of women. Hindu women had the support of Hindu reformers who regarded such traditional practices as permanent widowhood and child marriage as distortions of Hindu principles. Even in Africa, westernized African leaders began to recognize that their efforts to modernize their countries could be continually dragged down unless women shared the education and the concepts with which they themselves were working.

Women's aspirations were often closely linked with other movements, such as national liberation or the rights of labour, though the efforts of working women to achieve equal pay for equal work did not always receive the full support either of the trade unions or of other women's groups more intent on political rights. By sharing in the struggle against colonial rule, women in India and in Indonesia became part of common efforts and received as a matter of course the same voting rights as men when their countries became independent nations. Similarly it was the participation of Egyptian women, still veiled, in the movement for national liberation in 1919 that gave the initial impetus to their emancipation and brought support to their cause.

In the second quarter of the twentieth century international organizations gave strong endorsement to the aspirations of women. The fifth Inter-American Conference of 1923 recommended that the governments of the American republics modify their constitutions and laws 'in order to obtain for the women of the Americas the same civil and political rights enjoyed by men'. Women of the communist countries and related groups elsewhere worked together internationally through the Women's International Democratic Federation, formed at the first International Women's Congress in Paris in 1945. They joined in celebrating International Women's Day, and in initiating the first World Peace Congress in 1949 and the annual celebration of June 1st as 'Defence of Children Day'.

The Charter of the United Nations affirmed faith in the 'equal rights of men and women' and declared among its purposes the encouragement of respect for human rights without distinction of race, sex, language or religion. The Universal Declaration of Human Rights formulated a clear vision of women's status in the kind of society which the Declaration implied, declaring that 'men and women . . . are entitled to equal rights as to marriage, during marriage, and at its dissolution', that 'everyone' has the right to 'free choice of employment' and, 'without any discrimination, has the right to equal pay for equal work', the 'right to education' with higher education 'equally accessible to all on the basis of merit', the 'right to take part in government' and 'freely to participate in the cultural life of the community'.

By mid-century the women of the world thus had formal world opinion on their side, though a wide gulf remained between the goal envisaged by the Declaration of Human Rights and the actuality of the day. As a goal, it was rarely challenged openly, however much it might be rejected in thought and feeling.

2. METHODS OF SEEKING OBJECTIVES

In the initial stages of the women's movement in each country, outstanding women came forth as leaders, and their names became by-words in their own countries and sometimes around the world. Much of the movement for women's rights in the nineteenth and early twentieth centuries in Europe and America centred in the activity of individual women, such as Susan B. Anthony (1820–1906), Elizabeth Cady Stanton (1815–1902), Lucretia Mott (1793–1880) and Lucy Stone (1818–93) in the United States, the trade unionist, Mary MacArthur (1880–1921) and the militants Emmeline (1857–1928) and Sylvia (1882–1960) Pankhurst in England, Frederika Bremer (1801–65) and Ellen Key (1849–1926) in Sweden, Nina Bang (1866–1928) in Denmark, Louise Otto-Peters (1826–95) in Germany and Aletha Jacobs (1849–1929) in Holland. By the time of the first world war the women's movements in these countries had passed beyond the phase of individual leadership, though distinguished women continued to break ground, as did Margaret Bondfield (1873–1953), first British woman cabinet minister, whose career as a leader of labour rather than of women brought her to political office in 1929.

In the non-western countries individual women exercising personal leadership launched vigorous movements on behalf of women in their countries during the twentieth century. Madame Sarojini Naidu (1879–1949) of India, Madame Saraawi (–) in Egypt, Halide Edib Adivar (1875–) in Turkey, Baroness Ishimoto (1897–) in Japan, Mme Sun Yat-sen (1890–) in China, by their personal courage, sacrifice and ability to dramatize the cause of women, focused attention and drew support. They surrounded themselves with followers whom they developed into leaders in their turn and to whom they handed on their role and responsibility.

Outstanding women in every country sought higher education and the opportunity to enter the leading professions which carried prestige and the highest status in the society. They sought these opportunities for their own self-development and the personal satisfactions of professional work, but at the same time they believed that they were demonstrating that women as a class were not the inferior beings they had been assumed to be. Those who achieved distinction and were able to compete successfully with men at the highest level of professional activity, science, scholarship or artistic creation were symbols of their sex. By their achievements they hoped to wear down the prejudice of men and enhance the self-confidence of other women.

From the nineteenth century on, women formed organizations to promote their cause. One of the earliest objectives of their organized efforts was to make higher education freely available for women as a road to the professions and to economic independence and leadership. Institutions for the higher education of women were established in several countries, in the United States in the 1830s and in England in the 1840s; the London Medical School for Women was set up in 1874. In the last quarter of the nineteenth century

European and American universities began to admit women, either in special cases or freely. The first Dutch woman was admitted to university study by special permission of the prime minister in 1870, and selected women secured permission to enter universities in Russia and Switzerland. The publicly supported state universities established in the United States from 1862 on were open to both men and women, as were, generally, the British municipal and dominion universities. Mexico graduated its first woman physician in 1887 and first lawyer in 1898. By the opening of the twentieth century momentum had been created for the full extension of higher education to women.

In the non-western countries where the movements for women's rights did not take shape until after the first world war, the right to enter higher educational institutions was not the important issue which it had been for western women at a corresponding stage of their organized effort. The principle had already been established and the western-style universities which were being founded in these areas generally had no specific bars against admission of women.

Everywhere the main focus of organized movements for women's rights was on securing the right to vote; such an emphasis was natural in the democratically oriented societies of the West which had gone through a long struggle to establish manhood suffrage and had couched their statements of the rights of men in essentially political terms. It was an integral part of the socialist movement for both economic and political equality.

The women's right movements, which drew their leadership and main support from the middle and upper classes, generally involved two groups: a militant element, such as the British suffragettes, who staged mass demonstrations, chained themselves in public to dramatize their cause, courted arrest, went on hunger strikes or engaged in other forms of aggressive behaviour, and a more moderate element who felt that such tactics would not advance their cause but were more likely to alienate the men upon whom they had to depend for legislation. The moderate group urged patience, reason and the demonstration of what women could do as workers and citizens, rather than resort to spectacular behaviour.

The movements for women's rights which emerged later in other parts of the world engaged in a similar struggle for the suffrage, had a similar upper- and middle-class composition, and showed the same division. In Egypt in the 1950s, where women still had no vote, the leader of the militant element went on a hunger strike and courted imprisonment as the Pankhursts had done in their day in Britain, while the more moderate women's organizations worked to encourage women to enter the professions, called attention to their achievements, and tried to secure the implementation of the positive rights of women provided in the Quran. In Indonesia, where suffrage was not an issue, the broad women's organizations were devoted to general welfare, while a small group focused on the promotion of women's legal rights.

Some women sought political office and figured as political leaders. In Europe this was chiefly as candidates of the socialist parties which were almost alone in welcoming women candidates. Elsewhere women candidates were less likely to be confined to particular parties. Rarely, however, did women organize as a political bloc to support candidates of their sex.

Only the most ardent elements in the women's rights organizations of the western countries attacked the legal disabilities of married women with the same zeal that they brought to the struggle for higher education and suffrage. Since the inability to dispose of property, enter into contracts, establish domicile or exercise guardianship of children became important only in time of family conflict or crisis, these matters seemed vital chiefly to those women who had suffered directly and those concerned as a matter of principle. In the United States a militant group sought to prohibit all legal discrimination on the basis of sex by means of an amendment to the federal constitution but they encountered strong opposition from other organized women who feared that the measure would undermine protective labour legislation which the latter regarded as more important than gains in legal status. For organized Muslim women, however, greater rights in respect to marriage and divorce and the application in practice of their stipulated rights of property and guardianship were of central importance.

As women became active in community life they organized for other purposes than to advance their own status, and the group dedicated to women's rights became a small fragment of the whole, either maintaining a separate organization or representing a special interest within broader groups.

In virtually all countries women organized for purposes of social welfare. Religious congregations of nuns had long provided hospitals, orphanages, homes for unmarried mothers and other institutions. Along with teaching, social welfare was one of the earliest types of activity undertaken by women outside the home. In some places it remained the principal way in which women participated in community life. Voluntary organizations took the initiative in establishing welfare services where they were lacking, providing milk stations for babies, clubs, nurseries, playgrounds, homes and hospitals for children, homes for unmarried mothers, settlement houses and a multitude of other services. Women in Pakistan formed an organization to provide schools, handicraft employment and other services to refugees; Turkish women undertook to establish the first institution in the country for juvenile delinquents; women of Thailand supported services for the blind; women in Colombia set up and sustained community centres, clinics, kindergartens and schools; voluntary groups in the United States supported pioneer projects in dental hygiene, travelling libraries, children's dramatics. Where services were already provided by the state or by organized private agencies, women's organizations supplemented professional services, supplying volunteer nurses' aides to hospitals, recreation aides to community centres and filling a host of other posts under professional direction.

These voluntary organizations were chiefly composed of women of the middle and upper classes who had leisure to devote to such activity and were in a position to donate or raise funds. Leadership was often supplied by a prominent figure such as the wife of the president, governor or prime minister, a member of the royal family or of the aristocracy, or a woman of wealth. Participation in such activities was frequently a mark of social prestige. A leading organization in the United States composed of the socially *élite* admitted to membership only those who would dedicate several hours a week to voluntary service in social welfare agencies.

The voluntary welfare activities led by prominent women were particularly characteristic of the early stages of women's organized efforts, although they continued along with other lines of activity. As women extended their activities they formed a wide variety of organizations with many purposes and bases for membership. Some organizations were formed for self-entertainment, mutual improvement or pursuit of a common interest such as gardening. Others were based on religion, nationality or race and sought to promote the interests of their group in the total society, to provide a basis of social solidarity, to engage in welfare activity, or to support broad social objectives in line with the principles of their group or their responsibilities as women. Women's auxiliaries of men's organizations, such as fraternal organizations, professional or labour groups, gave support to their husbands' interests and provided a social group on the basis of their husbands' occupations.

Still others were formed to provide means for the social, educational and recreational activities of women and girls, as through the YWCA, Girl Scouts and Girl Guides, or the Countrywomen of the World. Some were dedicated to a specific social cause, such as temperance, peace or birth control. Others were the women's arms of political parties, or were non-partisan organizations dedicated to a proper use of the suffrage. University women organized to support fellowships and promote education. Women in business and the professions formed associations to strengthen their position, especially where they were still struggling to break down occupational barriers.

All these organizations reflected the active interest and concern of women outside the home. While they drew their membership most heavily from middle-class elements, they included a wide social range and utilized the energies, training, intelligence and time of both employed women and housewives.

Whatever their basis and purpose, most of them developed programmes of study, some form of democratic organization and the means of voicing the views of their members on public issues. They supported legislation and other public measures in line with their objectives, engaging in campaigns of public education, persuading legislators and getting out votes. They worked especially for such things as maternal and child health and the suppression of prostitution, civic improvements, the extension of social services, adequate inspection of food and drugs, better schools. Through these organizations, women's activities came to be more and more directed toward the welfare of the total community rather than the direct championship of the rights of women.

Although women's organizations continued to flourish up to the middle of the twentieth century, both in those countries where they had been in existence for many years and in those where they expressed the new role of women emerging from seclusion, there was a growing tendency for women to function in bodies composed of both men and women rather than in separate groups. As members of professional associations, trade unions, political parties or interest groups, on governing boards of community agencies, in associations of parents and teachers composed of men and women, and in countless other groups, women participated as full members without regard to their sex and performed functions determined by their individual capacities. Where this kind of participation existed and women were accepted on their merits as individuals, they felt that they had achieved the fundamental goal envisaged by the pioneer champions of women's rights.

3. ACHIEVEMENT OF GOALS

In each of the fields in which women aspired to a changed status, their conscious efforts or the broad social and economic developments of the period brought them toward their goals. The United Nations Commission on the Status of Women, reviewing in 1955 the progress toward realization of the status envisioned in the Universal Declaration of Human Rights, found a marked extension of women's political rights, some changes with respect to the legal status of married women but many limitations still to be removed, continued inadequacy of facilities for secondary and higher education as compared with those available for boys, and only a beginning toward implementing the principle of equal pay for equal work. It noted that the rights of women on paper were far more numerous than those in actual practice and that a major task ahead was to help women to become aware of their rights and to exercise them.

(a) Political rights

At the opening of the century women had the right to vote only in New Zealand, in two Australian states and in four states of the USA. By the middle of the century they had secured the vote in nearly all countries. Suffrage advocates achieved few successes before the first world war, adding only Norway, the rest of Australia, Finland and eight more of the states of the USA, plus municipal franchise in Britain and a few other places. But the impact of the war brought large numbers of women into the labour market and gave the suffrage movement the momentum for victory. During and immediately after the war, the British Parliament capitulated and granted the vote to women over 30 (1918), the United States constitution was amended to forbid any state to deny the right to vote on the ground of sex (1920), women's suffrage was included in the new constitutions of the USSR, the states which succeeded to the

Austro-Hungarian empire, and the Weimar republic of Germany, and women were enfranchised in the remaining Scandinavian countries, the Netherlands, Canada and the Union of South Africa.

Elsewhere in Europe, as well as in Latin America, resistance to women's political participation continued up to the second world war, especially where democratic liberalism was weakest and the influence of the Catholic Church was most strongly felt. The first of the Latin American countries which took formal action to give women the vote was Ecuador (1929), followed within the next five years by Brazil, Uruguay and Cuba. In the East, Turkish women who had been agitating for the franchise since 1908 secured it as a result of Ataturk's reforms, but not until 1934, more than ten years after he came to power. During the 1930s Britain extended the right to vote to women in Ceylon, India and Burma, and the United States did the same in the Philippines. Thai women were successful in being included as voters when their country became a constitutional monarchy in 1932. Japanese women, however, failed in their efforts to get women's suffrage written into the Japanese constitution of 1920.

The impact of the second world war and the declaration of the 'equal rights of men and women' in the United Nations Charter helped to bring political rights to the women of most of the remaining independent nations of the world, though in a few cases subject to qualification or limitations not imposed on men. France and Italy enfranchised their women, leaving the Swiss as the only European women still disfranchised in 1955. All of the Latin American republics except Paraguay had granted suffrage by that time. Women were fully entitled to vote in the newly created states of Asia, in China and under the post-war constitution of Japan. Liberia was the first African state to give its women the franchise, followed in 1955 by Ethiopia, and African women voted in the elections leading to the establishment of the Gold Coast as the independent state of Ghana.

In the Middle East, the enfranchisement of women was still in process at mid-century, as the Muslim women who had started in the 1920s to work for political as well as social rights were beginning to achieve success. Women with education received the franchise in Syria in 1949 and Lebanon in 1952. But the eight remaining Muslim countries in the region made up the bloc of states where women in 1955 were still without political rights; besides Switzerland and Paraguay, the only other such states were the tiny territories of Liechtenstein and San Marino. Egyptian women, however, were promised the vote at the time of the adoption of the constitution of 1956, and when Tunisia became independent in 1957 its women received the right to vote in municipal elections.

Although the franchise was sought as a means to secure other things which women desired, there appeared to be little tendency for women to vote as a bloc. Their political behaviour closely resembled that of men, expressing a similar range of opinion and of local, group or class interests. How far their presence in the voting population contributed to the trend toward an increasing volume of welfare legislation could not be readily assessed, since the trend to enact such legislation was strong everywhere.

The number of women holding public office generally remained small, even after the franchise had been enjoyed for some years, except in a few countries, notably the Soviet Union where they made up more than a quarter of the members of central and local soviets. Most countries, including those where the vote had been recently granted, could point to a few examples of women elected to national legislative bodies, serving as cabinet ministers, appointed to diplomatic posts, chosen mayors of cities or serving as judges. In a few instances a certain number of places in legislatures were specifically designated for women in order to ensure their representation, as initially in the provincial legislatures of Pakistan or the system of group representation in the Diet of Japan after the second world war.

Women were rather more likely to be appointed to responsible posts, especially in education, social welfare, labour and cultural affairs, than to be elected to office, and women's organizations often made it their business to see that the names of qualified women were placed before appointing officers when a position was to be filled. The presence of women in high office was not, however, an accurate reflection of the general level of public participation, for some women were appointed to responsible public positions even in countries which had not yet accorded them the franchise. The middle ranks of the civil service offered a better indication of such participation, and women served in great numbers in those countries where they had been most fully incorporated into public life.

(b) Education

Women were generally successful in securing access to higher education. The principal European universities opened their doors in the first decade of the twentieth century, as did those of Turkey and, generally, in Latin America. By the second quarter of the twentieth century the opportunity for higher education was no longer an issue in western countries, although some professional faculties were slower to admit women than others, and subtle forms of discrimination often continued to make women feel unwelcome. In Japan women were effectively barred from the universities in fact, though not in theory, until after the second world war because the higher schools through which the student had to pass on the way to the university admitted only boys, but they attended a number of institutions of higher education for women.

Women were more readily admitted to the higher institutions which prepared for the arts and sciences and the liberal professions than to the technical vocational schools that trained for skilled occupations. A review of the Latin American countries in 1953 found that whereas women were everywhere admitted to universities on an equality with men, they were effectively excluded in every country but one by custom, prejudice or regulation from vocational training for skilled tasks other than those relating to home making, sewing and other traditionally feminine skills.

In the countries where basic education reached the entire population, it included both sexes equally. But where illiteracy remained high, elementary education was usually less available to girls than to boys. Girls made up only 14 per cent of the primary school pupils in India in 1937, 24 per cent in Egypt and 35 per cent in Turkey; by 1950 the proportions had risen to 27, 35 and 38 per cent respectively.

There was a general tendency for school systems to adopt co-education, both as a matter of principle and for practical reasons, although opposition from conservative Catholic and Muslim sources remained strong. Co-education was supported in principle by most of the pedagogical literature of the period, and it was made necessary in practice by the difficulty of duplicating for boys and girls the increasingly complex and extensive facilities which modern education required.[19]

(c) Legal status

The legal disabilities of married women with respect to property, guardianship, domicile, legal personality and the right to contract and engage in business were only partially and slowly removed. Where they were modified, it was often as the result of measures designed to limit rights formerly enjoyed by men or to protect the interests of children.

Married women in England in the 1870s and 1880s acquired the right to hold property in their own names, retain their own earnings and share with their husbands in the guardianship of their children, though equal guardianship was not established until 1925. The individual states of the USA began to accord some or all of these rights in the middle of the nineteenth century and by the mid-twentieth century only a few states retained some limitations on guardianship and rights over property. The German civil code of 1900 placed single women on the same basis as men, but for married women the husband retained virtually complete authority over property, children and domicile. These provisions remained unchanged under the Weimar republic, and were not modified until the code was revised in the 1950s to bring it into conformity with the basic law of 1949 which established full equality of men and women before the law and prohibited discrimination on the ground of sex.

The French civil code which gave married women no right to dispose of their property, enter into a contract or sue in court without their husbands' consent remained unchanged until 1938, and these same provisions, in whole or in part, were still in the codes of the majority of the Latin American countries in 1955. Eight of the Latin American countries, however, revised their laws to remove or modify these limitations and several enacted legislation, primarily in the interest of the child, which restricted the authority of the father to dispose of family property and increased the rights of the mother over the children. In the Soviet Union all legal disabilities were removed by the first Soviet constitution, and the constitutions of the people's democracies of eastern Europe also provided for complete equality of legal status.

Except where the principles of the Roman Catholic Church were supported by law, as in Ireland and in some of the countries of Latin America, divorce laws in western countries were generally liberalized and inequalities in the conditions for divorce as between men and women were removed. The viewpoint underlying many of these revisions corresponded to that of the divorce laws of Sweden, Norway and Denmark, enacted between 1915 and 1920 after extensive study by a joint commission. These Scandinavian laws were expressly designed to preserve the ethical character of marriage as a union based on mutual sympathy, love and confidence, and they made mutual consent the basic ground for marriage dissolution where deep and constant discord exists.

In Muslim areas the legal status of women remained unchanged, except in Turkey where the civil code of 1925 replaced Muslim law and put men and women on an equal footing, including the abolition of plural marriage and the equalization of the conditions of divorce. Proposals were made in Indonesia and Pakistan for marriage laws within the framework of the Quran which would safeguard the wife by specifying the conditions in which divorce or second marriage was acceptable and requiring court procedure before either would be legal, but as late as 1956 no such law had been enacted in any Muslim country. The constitution of India and subsequent legislation established complete legal equality for Hindu women in matters of property, marriage rights, parental responsibility and authority.

(d) Economic rights and opportunities

The crux of women's changed position lay in their economic role, since without potential means of independent support their status in industrial society could not be other than that of a dependent. Their employment involved three issues: the chance to train for and enter those occupations which required skill, paid well and carried prestige; equality of pay and absence of discrimination in employment at all levels; and suitable conditions of work and freedom from abuse.

Pioneer women, often at the cost of great personal struggle and sacrifice, succeeded in entering one occupation after another that had been regarded as the exclusive domain of men. In Europe and North America vigorous women paved the way during the nineteenth and early years of the twentieth century. At the middle of the twentieth century distinguished Asian women similarly pioneered by representing their countries diplomatically, serving in their countries' ministries, and practising medicine, law or engineering. These were outstanding individuals who overcame obstacles and gained the inner satisfaction and the outward recognition that comes to the pioneer.

As the initial phase passed, however, and professional women increased in number, their position often became ambiguous. Prejudice and negative social attitudes hung on, and many women found that they had to work doubly hard to achieve the recognition readily accorded to men, without enjoying the status or satisfactions of pioneers. Women's organizations, which had supported and cheered the first women in their fight to break through initial barriers, were indifferent to the difficulties which women continued to encounter in securing favourable employment or promotion. Neither men nor women looked upon the aggressive woman as a desirable personality type.

Professional women themselves became less ready than the pioneers had been to struggle for a career if this meant the sacrifice of marriage and a home, and they generally tried to combine both. At best the professional woman with a home and family carried a double load and required exceptional stamina to be able to give to her career the same intensity of effort that her male counterpart could devote to his. If her husband regarded her success as a competitive threat to his status, her career might endanger her marriage. Often she could not count on servants to look after her home and children as the pioneer women had generally been able to do, for domestic help was no longer plentiful and cheap. Many women with professional training found it necessary to interrupt their careers while their children were young, only to encounter great difficulty in re-entering the field after a lapse of years. Potential employers, in their turn, hesitated to offer the best opportunities to young women because of the expectation that they would remain active for only a brief period. The basic problem of how to combine a professional career with the responsibilities of a home had not been solved by the women of the western countries by mid-century.

In the USSR, where women constituted nearly half of the work force in factories and offices and a still larger proportion of trained specialists and professional workers especially in medicine, various aids and services provided by the state lightened the home burdens of employed women. A system of canteens was steadily extended to lessen the need for housework, and nurseries and kindergartens were available for pre-school children. Increased numbers of boarding schools as well as after-school provisions for supervised study and play reduced the working mother's direct responsibilities. All these facilities made it somewhat less difficult for Soviet women than for those elsewhere to meet the demands of both profession and home. In the Chinese People's Republic the commune system went still further in relieving women of household responsibilities and enabling them to devote themselves to work outside the home.

In all industrial countries, the tendency for a large and increasing proportion of all women to engage in work outside the home during at least some period in their lives was accelerated by labour shortages during the wars. The first world war opened up new fields to large-scale employment of women and the impact of the second world war was even more pronounced. Conditions of full employment during the decade after the second war confirmed new patterns of employment which might have been abandoned if there had been a post-war slump.

In the non-industrialized countries employed women fell into two main groups, a small number of professionals drawn from the educated *élite*, and a large group of factory workers drawn from the poorest and most necessitous elements in the population. The former were pioneers; the latter were often the product of social dislocation—refugees, widows, unmarried mothers or members of a depressed group. The mass of women in respectable homes were not permitted or expected to work or to move freely in the broader society. Only as this last group began to emerge did signs appear of an approximation to the employment pattern which had developed in the industrialized countries.

Except in the Soviet Union and the people's democracies, where equal pay for equal work was a standard policy, women often received lower pay than men. In part, they worked in traditionally low-paid employment—in industries such as textiles with relatively low wage scales, in lower paid unskilled tasks, often excluded from skilled trades by discriminatory apprenticeship rules or lack of access to training, and rarely promoted to supervisory positions. In addition, pay scales established for public employment in European countries and agreed upon by collective contracts between employers and trade unions commonly specified differentials on the basis of sex. Formal pay differentials were rare in the United States, as they never existed in the civil service and were infrequent in collective contracts with trade unions, but they were not uncommon in practice. The rationale of such differentials was that male workers were assumed to have dependents to support but females not. Yet studies of employed women consistently showed that a large proportion of them were supporting children, parents or other relatives.

Change toward greater equality of pay came slowly in European countries. The Swedish civil service accepted the principle of equal pay in 1925 but it was still in the process of removing inequalities thirty years later. Collective bargaining contracts in European countries quite generally continued to provide for differentials. The British government in 1955 initiated gradual steps to eliminate pay differences in the civil service and for teachers by 1961. By 1955 nine countries had adopted the convention on equal pay prepared by the ILO in 1951, and legislation had been enacted by fourteen states of the USA and three Canadian provinces. But French employers complained that France's acceptance of the ILO convention put them at a competitive disadvantage with other countries where inequality of women's wages continued to prevail.

The countries where women were only beginning to enter the labour market in large numbers toward the middle of the century tended to adopt the principle of equal pay but often did not achieve the practice. The experience in Latin America was indicative of the problem. Although a number of Latin American countries had laws requiring equal pay for equal work, the actual earnings of women in industrial employment ranged from 20 to 50 per cent below those of men. Limitations on employment opportunities and technical training, depressed wages in jobs regarded as typically 'women's work', inadequate inspection or lack of a proper system for evaluating what constituted 'equal work' contributed to this situation. Similar factors were at work elsewhere.

Most of the labour codes enacted and extended during this period contained provisions designed to protect women workers against hazardous employment; many required the granting of maternity leave. ILO conventions covering maternity protection (1919), prohibition on the employment of women in mining or other underground work (1935) and prohibition on night work for women (1941, revised in 1948) had been ratified by 18, 35 and 16 countries respectively by 1957.

The largest single group of working women was composed of those employed in domestic service. Traditionally, this was the occupation in which women received the lowest pay, worked the longest hours, were least protected from their employer's caprice and abuse, and were most often excepted from provisions of labour laws and social security guarantees. In the industrial countries the development of alternative fields of employment offered new opportunities which freed many women from the necessity of working in other people's homes and the withdrawal of large numbers to factory or other work improved the bargaining position of those who remained as domestics. Although household workers generally continued to work longer and more irregular hours and to receive less pay than those in other employment, wages rose, hours declined and conditions became more standardized. In the course of time the social legislation which applied to other workers was extended to domestic workers, including social security benefits and minimum wages, and they joined trade unions.

For middle-class women this generally meant the loss of household help since they could no longer have someone at their beck and call for a small sum and they could not afford to pay a decent living wage for a regular day's work. But for millions of other women it meant a chance to live their own lives and take care of their own homes. The progressive elimination of the cheap household servant was one of the most democratizing influences of the century for the women of the industrialized countries.

(e) Maternal health

In human terms the change in the conditions of child-bearing was the most revolutionary development in the lives of women in the twentieth century. For centuries mankind had lived under the assumption that women would bear children, often with great frequency, in pain and danger of death, and that a large proportion of babies and a considerable number of mothers would die. Even during the nineteenth century graveyards were filled with infants' headstones and often the graves of women who had died in childbirth.

Advances in medical knowledge and the spread of maternal and child health services removed most of the risk and much of the pain of childbirth and greatly reduced the likelihood that the child would die. By the middle of the twentieth century women in cities and most rural areas of the West, and wherever modern health facilities existed around the world, could count on a safe pregnancy, barring illness or accident from other sources, and could experience a delivery under hospital conditions which ensured protection from infection and emergency medical aid to save the life of mother and child in case of complications. They had access to knowledge of safe and reasonably sure methods to avoid pregnancy and were thus in a position to plan the spacing of their children and the number that they would undertake to bear and rear. In some areas, such as Japan, they could interrupt an unwanted pregnancy by safe means, although in most countries the practice of abortion was discouraged or forbidden by law and thereby rendered unsafe. With these developments went a change in attitude which brought maternity within the scope of scientific control and removed the process from the realm of fate.

The combined effect of the small-family system and the increased likelihood that children born would survive greatly reduced the number of years which women spent in child-bearing and thus made a larger part of their lives available for other activities. This helped to make possible their wider economic role as well as their participation in other areas of social life.

(f) Social status

All these changes brought women a new social freedom and blurred the lines between the social worlds of women and men.

The early feminists attacked as a major source of indignity the sharp division which made all social activity outside the home exclusively the affair of men, reserving to them the coffee houses, taverns, sports and clubs and permitting them to seek sexual gratification outside the home, while women were limited to home-bound activity and were held to a rigid code of sexual morality. But it was not so much the feminist attacks or their aping of masculine appearance and behaviour that affected women's social status. Rather, it was the schools and the jobs which took women out of the home, the general loosening of formal manners and conduct based on status, a freer attitude toward sex and the narrowed scope of the home.

With the achievement of social freedom and relative equality of status, however, Western women found themselves in an ambivalent situation. The principle of equality was firmly established in the context of democratic individualism. A common system of education oriented girls and boys to the same idea of developing their own capacities and interests to the fullest; the open doors of higher education invited the girl to pursue this development as far as her abilities would lead; employment opportunities offered a choice of occupation and the chance to earn her living; she was expected to understand public issues, vote and take part in public life as an independent person; she associated freely with boys and could choose her mate, or choose not to marry.

But she was expected to marry and to raise a family. The impact of Freudian psychology strengthened the idea that the woman who sacrificed marriage to pursue a career was failing to lead a normal life, and stressed the role of the mother and the importance of the early experience of the child. She was expected to give to her children the love, security and intelligent upbringing that she had learned was their due, and she was far more conscious than earlier generations had been of the damage which she could do to the personality of the child if she bungled her maternal role. She was expected to take her status from her husband's occupation and position and to help sustain it; to further his advancement was one of her first responsibilities.

The inner conflict and uncertainty as to values which this dichotomy set up manifested itself in a frequent cleavage or tension between the career woman and the housewife, each tending to look down on the other in order to express her inner jealousy and both jealous of the women who successfully combined the two roles. For the women who maintained both a career and a home, the double burden was heavy. Opportunities for part-time employment were generally few and there were insufficient child-care centres, housekeeping aides, community kitchens or other devices which might lighten the home part of her task; the inadequacy of such services often reflected the idea that mothers should remain in the home. The conflict and problem were brought out sharply in the 1955 meeting of the United Nations Commission on the Status of Women where statements by some of the non-governmental consultants to the commission precipitated a discussion of whether working mothers could be good mothers and drew from members of the commission a plea for measures to make it less difficult for women to cope simultaneously with their duties as mothers and workers.

For women in eastern countries in process of modernization, the inner conflict was no less sharp than for women of the West, for their problem was how far to follow the pattern of western social behaviour and how far to conform to the pattern traditional to the East. They experienced in a most intense and personal form the cultural ambivalence common to societies in transition. Men in these countries could adopt many western attitudes and ways without seriously modifying their attitudes or behaviour relating to the home, their relations with women of their own culture and their concept of women's position. Many externally westernized men maintained non-western values in their homes, marrying the girl selected by their parents, never taking their wives with them when they went out socially, and keeping intact the traditional pattern of masculine authority and the separateness of the life of men from that of women. Women, however, could not adopt western values without becoming involved in the issue of their own position.

Their dilemma was apparent in every eastern country. In Japan it appeared to some observers that the most durable effect of the changes inaugurated during the period of occupation after the second world war might be a new status for women, yet ten years after the close of the war that change was still very unsure. There was great uncertainty in the relations between boys and girls and considerable reaction against the free association which was encouraged in the immediate post-war period. Co-education at secondary and university levels was still working itself out. Highly trained women were still not readily accepted in responsible posts. Social workers found themselves dealing with family situations in which basic conflicts of values and alternative concepts of family structure and duties underlay family disorganization. The most popular Japanese films, radio programmes and novels were devoted to such themes as the conflict between romantic love and filial duty, the right of the daughter *vis-à-vis* the mother-in-law, the right of the woman to her own decisions and her own life.

For Indian women traditional and Western practices were in direct conflict. Arranged marriages were the rule, with careful consideration traditionally given by the families to caste status, family reputation and economic position and to the horoscopes of the couple, and with no close association between the young people prior to marriage. The Indian woman who aspired to the social independence of the Western woman and the pattern of romantically based marriage was in broad defiance of traditional *mores*. Mahatma Gandhi lent powerful support to those who wished to break through custom by encouraging inter-caste marriages and accepting the individual choice of mates. Nevertheless, many educated women were unsure as to whether to remain with the old, to adopt new ways, or to seek some compromise between basically opposed systems.

On the surface, at least, the easiest transition to a modern social status for women seemed to be taking place in the Buddhist countries of south-east Asia and in Indonesia, although the traditional protected status retained a nostalgic appeal. By the second quarter of the twentieth century women of Thailand enjoyed access to education, easy freedom of movement, varied employment and free choice in marriage. Women leaders were undertaking to make equality of status a reality in practice through a broad programme of social and cultural development designed to enable women to keep pace with their husbands and stimulating their participation in welfare and other activities within their communities. Women in Ceylon formed a larger proportion of the school population than in Hindu and Muslim countries and were the first of the Asian women to vote. Indonesian women inherited traditions of equality and participation, and those with education entered a labour market where trained people of all sorts were few and their services were in great demand.

In some of the Muslim countries the issue of women's social position at mid-century continued to centre around the question of seclusion. In Pakistan a small group of women from educated homes who had themselves enjoyed personal freedom sought by gradual means to further the steady process by which women were emerging from purdah, making the matter an issue at one point and avoiding the issue at another. In the early 1950s the director of the newly established department of social work at the University of the Punjab refused to allow the curtain down the middle of the classroom which separated the sexes in some of the other departments of that university, preferring to recruit only those students who could associate freely with men, while near by the director of a new school for training in home economics had a wall built around the grounds in order to enrol girls who otherwise would not attend.

The Arab states at mid-century ranged from a strongly Westernized pattern in Lebanon, half-Christian and half-Muslim, where free social movement was the general rule and large numbers of women had been educated in local French and American schools, to the complete seclusion which prevailed in Saudi Arabia and Yemen. Many educated Egyptian women had come to move freely in the society of the principal cities in the course of the thirty years after their prominent leader first discarded her veil, but Egyptian feminists were still complaining that the political leaders who talked about the rights of Egyptian women did not appear in public with their own wives. Families were expected to arrange suitable marriages for their daughters; even for girls who were receiving professional training, choice was usually limited to the chance to say 'no' to their parents' selection.

The women of Turkey experienced a drastic change in social status by a revolution from above at a time when the educated *élite*, already Westernized, was ready for it. At mid-century many of the rest were still catching up. Leading Turkish women were occupying important positions and had many achievements to their credit. A larger proportion of the members of university faculties in Turkey were women in 1948 than in any country reporting this information to Unesco except the United States, 15 per cent as compared with 24 per cent in the United States and 3–5 per cent in European universities. But thoughtful Turkish women were reconsidering the meaning of the westernization which they had experienced, determined to be 'western' but wishing to avoid mere imitation. Some saw signs of reaction—a religious revival which might threaten their position, the resumption of the veil in some villages, the possibility of general political reaction. To others it seemed that the revolution had been less complete than had appeared on the surface and that the process was still going on.

Among the Asian women who experienced the most drastic change were those of China. In the first part of the century Western-educated Chinese women found themselves caught between their new aspirations and the strength of the Chinese family system with the filial obligations which it entailed. The conflict was sharpened as the attacks on the Confucian family grew following the New Tide movement. When the communists came to power, they made the liberation of the Chinese women from family tyranny a central objective; personal choice in marriage, independence, education and comradely participation were the declared programme. By rapid steps they relieved women not only of their family subordination but of many of their family responsibilities. The women of the Chinese communes represented as radical a change in status as had been experienced by any large body of women during the course of the twentieth century.

By mid-century women nearly everywhere had thus attained many of the goals which the articulate among them had expressed and their leaders had sought. But their status, role and self-appraisal were still in flux, for throughout the world many of the strains and uncertainties of industrial society impinged inexorably upon their lives.

IV. RACE AND CASTE GROUPS SUBJECT TO DISCRIMINATION

The drive for individual freedom and human dignity in the twentieth century involved groups in many countries who were the object of discrimination because of race, caste or other social disability and who were frequently accorded less than the full privileges of citizenship. Unlike other minorities who desired cultural autonomy within multi-cultural societies,* members of these groups sought the removal of social stigma and legal restrictions which stood in the way of individual and group acceptance and advancement.

A variety of historic situations had resulted in the presence of such elements and had produced the patterns of relationship with the dominant populations which existed in the twentieth century. Negroes in the Americas were still handicapped by the long aftermath of slavery. Native Africans in South Africa had been subjugated in the unequal contest with European settlers for land, and the other non-European populations of that country—Coloureds and Indians—shared the disabilities imposed by the European element in its efforts to keep the Africans in subordination. Untouchables of India were the product of the long history of migration by the warring peoples in the Indian sub-continent, for whom the Hindu caste system had provided a mechanism for establishing and perpetuating superior-inferior relationships; they had been assigned the most unpleasant work, and the disabilities to which they were subjected were a means of ensuring that tasks necessary to the life of the villages would be performed. The Eta of Japan, descended from a class of untouchables in feudal times, had acquired the legal status of commoners in 1868, but were the object of prejudice and social discrimination. North American Indians had been relegated to reservations in the United States and Canada in the expansion of European settlement, whence some had emerged to seek status as individual citizens while others pressed their claims as tribal groups. Jews had lived for centuries as non-Christians in Christian-organized societies and as enclaves in Muslim areas, and although in Europe they were generally free from former legal restrictions, they faced attitudes generated in earlier times.†

The patterns of advance followed by two such groups, Negroes in the western hemisphere and untouchables in India, are presented here as illustra-

* For a discussion of such groups, see Chapter XXIX, pp. 1101–7.
† See Chapter XXV, pp. 871–9, Judaism, and Chapter XXVIII, pp. 1019–25, Israel.

tive of some of the many forms which the struggle for full and effective citizenship took in various parts of the world. These two groups were selected for their size, for the differences as well as the similarities surrounding their status and its change and because world-wide interest in their fate was felt and expressed during these years.

Under the impact of the world-wide trend toward equality, all such groups pressed their efforts to achieve first-class status within their societies. With the tragic exception of European Jews and of the dark-skinned peoples of the Union of South Africa,* they generally made substantial headway toward this goal during the first half of the twentieth century.

1. NEGROES

The people most subject to discrimination, whose aspirations everywhere took the form of a desire for status on a par with other citizens—'first-class citizenship'—were Negroes. Virtually nowhere outside Africa did they aspire to cultural identity and separateness on the basis of race. Where they developed separate institutions and expressions of identity it was because they were forced to do so, or as a means of working toward full equality, and these institutions, such as churches, press or legal and welfare organizations, took their form from the corresponding institutions of the broader society.

The great majority of the Negro people outside Africa lived in the Americas —North America, the Caribbean islands, and Caribbean littoral of Central and South America, where they had originally been brought as slaves. Their status at the opening of the twentieth century reflected their history in each of these areas.

(a) Caribbean and Latin America

In the islands of the Caribbean, Negro slaves had constituted the mass labour force for sugar plantations worked under the direction of a handful of planters and administrators. In the twentieth century the bulk of the population of most of these islands was made up of direct descendants of Negro slaves and mulattoes of combined Negro and white ancestry. This was most true of Haiti, which forceably threw out its French masters in 1798 and therewith its white population. Here a mulatto élite confronted the black masses, and virtually the only whites were Syrian traders who had entrenched themselves in the island's economy. On the other islands, which continued under colonial status, a dominant white element remained; as the islands moved toward and acquired self-government, leadership passed to representatives of the predominantly Negro majority.

In the islands of Cuba and Puerto Rico which had been part of the Spanish empire, the European element had not been confined to a few planters but had immigrated in sufficient numbers to make up a large part of the population. Since racial exclusiveness had never characterized the Spanish, there had been

* See Chapter XXVIII, pp. 1011–18, South Africa.

considerable intermingling of white and Negro elements until, by the twentieth century, these populations ranged in colour from black to white with no sharp line of distinction. The darker element, for historical reasons, tended to predominate in the plantation areas of the coast and in the lower economic ranks, while the lighter were more numerous in the interior and generally predominated at the higher economic levels.

The situation was similar in the countries of Central and South America which bordered the Caribbean. From Mexico to Brazil the coastal regions were largely inhabited by dark-skinned people who traced their origin to slavery on local plantations or who had come over as plantation workers from the Caribbean islands in post-slavery times. In some areas people in the interior were predominantly European, as in Costa Rica; elsewhere they were predominantly Indian, as in Guatemala. More generally they were *mestizo*—mixed Indian and European—as in Mexico, or mulatto—mixed white and Negro—as in Panama.

In none of these areas was a sharp line drawn between white and coloured. Either there was simply a gradation or three groups were identified, white, mulatto and black. Colour prejudice was present, expressed in minor and often subtle ways—exclusion of dark-skinned people from the most select clubs, a tendency to show job preference to the lighter of two candidates for the same post, special comment, open or whispered, when dark-skinned persons achieved prominent positions. Venezuela put up a bar against immigrants from the Caribbean islands, and Brazil showed preference for European immigrants. But in none of these areas of Spanish and Portuguese background was the Negro population subject to specific forms of discrimination; nor was it self-consciously engaged in seeking first-class status in the society. Whatever racial and cultural self-consciousness existed in these countries was identified with the indigenous Indian, not the Negro, elements in the population.

(b) Negroes in the USA

Historic position of American Negroes. The situation was very different in the United States where a sharp colour line defined the Negro minority. Here, during the twentieth century, the Negro people carried on a conscious struggle for first-class citizenship. The framework for this struggle was provided by the historic circumstances of their entrance into American life, the legal and ideological basis of American society, the impact of American economic development, and a racial dogma which was originally formulated to reconcile the contradiction between slavery and democracy and which continued to sustain an arbitrary colour line.

In contrast to the situation on the Caribbean islands, Negro slaves brought into North America never constituted a large body of workers managed by a handful of white owners or overseers. Except in a few limited areas—small islands off the south-east coast and, later, some of the rich land of the Mississippi delta—Negro slaves were interspersed with white settlers. They worked farms adjacent to others worked by indentured white labourers, and when the latter completed their term of service they acquired land and, in time, often one or two slaves. At the time of the Civil War in 1860 only a quarter of the slave population was living on plantations worked by fifty slaves or more, while an equal number were on farms with less than ten slave workers. Of the total population of the United States in the twentieth century, Negroes constituted roughly 10 per cent. In no state did they comprise more than 30–40 per cent of the population.

Scattered in small groups, the slaves imported into the North American colonies had no basis for retaining the relationships, language or culture of their African past; on the larger plantations it was generally customary to secure slaves from different regions so that they could not build up solidarity against their masters on the basis of common language or old ties. There was no such transplanting of African culture as among the people of Haiti whose songs and voodoo practices in the twentieth century still recalled their homeland of Dahomey, although some few African traces were found by anthropologists in the speech and superstitions of some areas. American Negroes were culturally the products of the American environment; they took their ideas, values and patterns of behaviour from their white masters and neighbours and adapted them to their own experience as an exploited minority within a democratic society.

The Negro people in America never looked upon slavery as part of the order of nature or a permanent condition. Though for more than 200 years the majority were unable to escape their lot as slaves, though many exhibited strong personal loyalty to individual masters, and though many patterns of outward subservience were developed as protective behaviour, the indignities of slavery never became an accepted part of their outlook on life. They sang of the 'children of Israel' emerging from bondage in Egypt to seek the 'promised land', singing of themselves. And when freedom came individually to the manumitted or collectively with emancipation they grasped it as their birthright and sought to make it fully real.

The obstacles which they confronted, however, were many. Chief among these was the racial dogma developed during slavery to rationalize the existence of that institution in a basically democratic society. Had slavery been an acceptable institution, it would not have been necessary to ascribe natural inferiority to those who happened to be slaves. But in a society which proclaimed that 'all men are created equal and are endowed by their Creator with certain inalienable rights' it was necessary to consider those held in slavery as somehow less than 'men'.

The dogma as developed had two major parts. On the one hand it attributed the dependence, poverty, ignorance and other effects of the conditions imposed upon the Negro to his inherent inferiority. On the other hand it assumed the ethnic integrity of the 'white race'.

Although intermarriage was not countenanced, as it was in the Spanish and Portuguese colonies, much intermingling took place, until the American 'Negro' as a physical type came to range from black to a colour indistinguishable from that of many so-called 'whites'. Since during slavery children took the status of their mother, the slave population came to include many children of white masters. These and all others of mixed ancestry became 'Negro', no matter how closely they resembled whites in appearance or how preponderantly white their ancestry. In contrast to the Latin American countries where the mulatto either represented a part of the gradation from dark to light or a defined middle group, a sharp colour line was drawn between the whites and all who could be identified as having any Negro ancestry. The illogic of this colour line was made ironically plain by the opposite treatment of white-Indian mixtures, for in the latter even a small proportion of white forebears enabled a person to call himself 'white'.

After emancipation, in 1863, the doctrine of Negro racial inferiority and white racial purity, devised to justify the institution of slavery, became a rationale for continued prejudice. Its psychological value in assuaging troubled consciences and permitting behaviour inconsistent with the principles by which other aspects of life were governed embedded the dogma of racial inferiority deep in the popular mentality. Only slowly did it give way to the impact of contrary evidence produced by scientific investigation, to day-by-day experience in a society where mounting numbers of Negroes functioned ably in positions requiring high levels of responsibility and skill, to the broadening concept of liberalism, and to the shifting world situation with its changed relationship between Europeans and darker peoples. Even at mid-century a Negro writer could conclude that 'it still offers more resistance to the Negro's progress than all the practical difficulties of social advance combined'.*

The practical obstacles faced by ex-slaves were, however, also very real. In the Civil War which brought emancipation to the Negroes, an essentially agrarian society sought to resist one that was becoming more and more industrially oriented. The two regions, south and north, clashed over the basis upon which the new lands to the west should be developed and on the policy of protective tariffs to encourage industry versus free trade to maintain markets for agricultural products abroad. The victory of the north meant the triumph of industrialism. The agrarian south came out of the war defeated and impoverished.

The southern milieu into which the Negro people emerged from slavery was, consequently, both economically and psychologically unfavourable to their effective integration. The great majority of the Negroes stayed on in the areas where freedom found them, farming the land on shares for owners who were often too poor to pay cash wages, in communities too poor to support good schools, and among people resentful and sensitive in defeat and determined to regain and reassert their self-respect.

* Margaret J. Butcher, *The Negro in American Culture* (New York, 1957), p. 18.

Nor did the expanding industries of the north offer an alternative, for workers for the factories were recruited among the peasant immigrants from Europe, not the freedmen of America's rural south. The people of the north who had fought to abolish slavery as an institution gave little thought to those whom they had made their fellow-citizens. Some northerners supported missionaries who went south to establish schools for the freedmen and their children, but most were much too preoccupied with the rapid industrialization of their region and the rapid growth of the western states to worry about what was happening to three and a half million ex-slaves. After a brief attempt to impose conditions favourable to the Negroes, they abandoned the effort in favour of political reconciliation and reunion of the divided country. Left to deal with the situation in their own terms, the southern states took whatever measures they could to recreate a subordinate and restricted status for their Negro populations.

The legal basis of the Negro's position was laid down in the constitution of the United States which stated the rights of citizens in terms of the basic concepts of eighteenth-century liberalism. After emancipation, former slaves as well as those born free acquired full citizenship; an 1856 declaration by the Supreme Court that citizenship rights were not meant to apply to persons of colour even when free had been erased by the Civil War. Additional amendments to the constitution in the following years explicitly forbade denial of the right to vote on grounds of 'race, colour, or previous condition of servitude', and forbade the states to deny to any citizen the 'equal protection of the laws'.

The federal structure of the United States, however, greatly complicated the legal problem of ensuring full citizenship rights to Negroes, since the general police power, most kinds of authority over the conduct of individuals, control of education, determination of qualifications for voting, and regulation of conditions of employment fell within the domain of the states. Attempts by the federal Congress after the Civil War to assure to Negroes the unrestricted use of public facilities such as inns, eating places and transport were held by the Supreme Court to be beyond the scope of federal legislation in so far as they applied to the acts of individuals rather than those of official bodies.

Even within the scope of federal authority, moreover, there was the crucial question of whether separation was compatible with equality. The constitution specified 'equal'; it did not specify 'same'. Over the eloquent dissent of one of its members, the Supreme Court in 1896 held that the constitutional requirement of equality might be satisfied by the provision of separate facilities if these were equal in quality to those provided for other citizens. For nearly sixty years this decision enabled the southern states to practise segregation in their systems of education, public parks, public health facilities and the like, and to require that separate facilities be provided in public transport and other services.

By the opening of the twentieth century it was apparent that the struggle for full citizenship would be more complex than it had at first appeared. The elaborate design of subordination developed by the white south confronted the Negro with a pattern of expected and enforced behaviour which placed many practical and psychological blocks in the way of his advance. Southern whites adopted toward all Negroes the manners and attitudes used toward children or servants, always calling them familiarly by their Christian names even, for example, when a school inspector spoke to a teacher in the presence of his pupils, and expecting or excusing childish behaviour, irresponsibility, petty thievery or buffoonery but resenting and even punishing outward evidence of self-respect which could be interpreted as an assertion of equality, such as a well-painted house or a non-servile manner. They established job ceilings which closed most of the middle range of skilled, factory and clerical occupations and supervisory positions and generally restricted professionals to service to other Negroes. Under the pattern of segregation, Negroes had to sit in coloured waiting rooms, travel in coloured sections of trains, use service lifts, walk in coloured parks, read in coloured libraries and attend coloured schools.

In the north segregation was not a matter of principle, but Negroes were simply expected to live in the poorest slums and to fill the lowest jobs. By unsystematic but effective job discrimination, refusal to let or sell housing space, and exclusion from public eating places, Negroes in northern cities were backed into a ghetto-type of existence. And always, south and north, they had to be prepared to meet the stereotype of the lazy, easy-going, irresponsible person of inferior mentality whose slum living, poverty and lack of education were attributed to his 'racial characteristics'. The most industrious, responsible, moral, educated or wealthy Negro individual was not free from the stereotype applied to the group.

The struggle for full citizenship. (i) *Education.* Education seemed to offer the open door to progress. All testimony agrees that the freedmen exhibited an unquenchable zeal for the schooling which had been denied them as slaves and, in some states, as freed Negroes. The thousands who took refuge behind the Union lines during the Civil war begged to be taught; more thousands streamed to the schools established by missionary societies. In the brief period immediately after the war when Negroes enjoyed political power under the protecting guns of the victorious Union forces, they spent public funds on education with what their former masters regarded as financial irresponsibility. Throughout the following years, education continued to be an indispensable element in the struggle for full participation, both on the part of millions of Negroes as individuals and in the organized expression of their aspirations. Institutions of higher education were established for Negroes by the private efforts of missionaries, churches and public-spirited citizens, by the southern states, and in the nation's capital with the aid of the federal government. They played a central role not only by providing a body of educated leaders but by serving as focal points for the formation of opinion, for mutual support and for the development of a Negro middle class.

In the early years of the century two opposing tactics were advocated by Negro leaders. One view, for which Booker T. Washington was the spokesmen, held that Negroes should concentrate on developing their practical skills and earning capacity in order to equip themselves as a mass to function above the lowest economic level of American society. Up from slavery himself (see his autobiography, *Up From Slavery*, 1900), he thought that Negroes should, as a tactical matter, accept for the moment the pattern of segregation, which he compared to two fingers of the same hand. In line with his philosophy, he founded an educational institution devoted especially to vocational training and means to improve living conditions—home economics, public health, nutrition—among the Negroes in the south.

An opposing viewpoint, associated initially with the name of W. E. B. DuBois who came of northern free Negro stock, held that there should be no acceptance, even tactically, of the pattern of segregation and no differentiation of the Negro's education from that received by whites, for to emphasize manual skills in the training of Negroes only played into the hands of those who regarded the Negro as intellectually inferior. According to this view, the most important task was to break down the image of the Negro as inferior, to destroy the habits of segregation and discrimination, and to establish the Negro's legal rights. Negroes should seek nothing less than the best, in their own educational institutions if necessary, or by entering the institutions of the majority, and should distinguish themselves as individuals in the professions and occupations which carried prestige in the society and would earn them respect. This approach came to be referred to as the 'talented tenth'—i.e. the advance of the Negro group through the success of its outstanding individuals. Numbers of able individuals entered the leading universities in the country and distinguished themselves as students and in their subsequent professional careers. In addition, several of the major institutions of higher education for Negroes strove valiantly to offer a level of liberal education on a par with the best in the country, and many less well-equipped colleges did their best to follow suit.

Although these two approaches were advocated as alternatives, they were in fact followed simultaneously. In time Booker T. Washington's viewpoint lost much of its support as new generations of Negroes with more education and wider experience became impatient with the pattern of accommodation to the imposed indignities and felt that a more militant attitude was in line with the times. They rejected the 'Uncle Toms', who knew how to exploit the stereotype of the respectful, subservient Negro in order to secure from whites financial support for education, health services, welfare institutions and other things which the Negro community needed; the younger generation preferred to receive less, but with dignity and as a matter of right, rather than to beg successfully for more.

(ii) *Legal status.* While education remained fundamental to the Negro's striving for equal status, his effort to secure his legal rights was the most dramatic aspect of the struggle. Once freed, his rights as a citizen were those of any other man. Even the 'separate but equal' doctrine was not designed by the courts to be discriminatory in principle, since theoretically it applied equally to whites. In entering the legal battle to achieve in fact what the constitution and the common law guaranteed in principle, the Negro lawyers and their white collaborators knew that eventual victory would come to their side so long as American democracy endured, but that the necessity of combating discrimination point by point and state by state, often community by community and subterfuge by subterfuge, meant a long, discouraging fight. To meet this situation the National Association for the Advancement of Coloured People was formed by whites and Negroes together in 1910 to protect and promote Negro rights. It first sought to secure protection against direct maltreatment, whose most extensive form, mob violence and 'lynching', had too often gone unpunished; then it marshalled legal talent and made it available wherever Negro citizens were prepared to make a test case out of the denial of their legal rights.

Through the years, cases brought by Negroes, generally argued by lawyers supplied by the NAACP, led the Supreme Court to interpret in detail the meaning of the constitutional provision that no state might deny to any citizen the 'equal protection of the laws'. It held that a Negro was entitled to be tried by a jury from which Negroes were not excluded, and that state courts could not enforce private agreements to exclude Negro residents from an area, since such exclusion by direct state action would be unconstitutional. It outlawed one subterfuge after another by which Negroes were prevented from voting—declaring invalid state laws which specified that only those whose grandfathers had been eligible to vote could be enrolled, and the claims by some states that political parties were private organizations whose primary elections to choose candidates did not involve 'voting' in the sense meant by the constitution.

It soon became apparent that 'separate but equal' in fact meant unequal, and the courts so ruled in one specific situation after another, finding the 'equal protection of the laws' denied by unequal pay for teachers, unequal physical facilities for schools, or by the provision by a state of scholarships for Negroes to study in another state instead of admitting them to the state's own institutions of higher education. Finally, after a series of decisions in which it recognized that 'equality' had intangible as well as material aspects, the Supreme Court in 1954 arrived at the conclusion that enforced separation in education, in and of itself, meant inequality, and it reversed the decision which had established the 'separate but equal' doctrine fifty-eight years before. The constant legal struggle not only achieved specific gains in breaking down discriminatory practices, and finally the doctrine of 'separate but equal' itself, but made the Negro people conscious of the law as their potential ally.

(iii) *Equal economic opportunity*. While some Negro leaders and their white associates worked aggressively on the legal front, others directed their efforts toward achieving equal economic opportunity and modifying the social and economic handicaps under which masses of Negro people lived.

The first world war swelled to a flood the trickle of Negroes moving from the rural south to northern cities. With the supply of immigrant labour cut off and industry expanding to meet war needs, factory recruiting agents turned to the south and set in motion a mass migration to northern industrial communities which continued in the following decades. But as they entered northern industry, Negroes encountered negative and discriminatory attitudes on the part of both employers and fellow workers, built up during the years when most factory employment was closed to them and only the unskilled, heavy or menial tasks were regarded as proper 'Negro jobs'.

In the effort to meet some of the problems of inexperienced and often confused people from the backward rural areas of the south who moved into the worst slums, were offered the lowest paid jobs and were subjected to the competitive atmosphere and discriminatory attitudes of northern cities, Negro leaders and white citizens joined to set up welfare organizations dedicated to the promotion of equal opportunity. Such organizations, which by the 1950s had been formed in some sixty cities and were affiliated since 1911 in a national association known as the National Urban League, worked to change the discriminatory habits of their communities. They laboured patiently to modify patterns of employment, prying doors open through negotiation, finding competent workers for new positions, stimulating schools and parents to encourage their children to train for occupations which were not yet available to them, and combating the depressing conditions and frustrations which tended to undermine the Negro's sense of himself and destroy ambition. Prior to the second world war, these efforts produced only limited openings at higher levels of employment, generally much more slowly than people were prepared to fill them.

The extreme shortage of labour in the second world war forced employers to set aside their preferences and prejudices and use any workers they could get—older workers, women, handicapped, as well as Negroes. Even then it required pressure from the government, which adopted a wartime policy of non-discrimination in order to use manpower efficiently, to facilitate the opening up of skilled, technical and clerical jobs on any large scale. By the close of the war the employment pattern had been radically changed. Although in some communities many occupations remained difficult for Negroes to enter or virtually closed, in others Negroes were unprepared and untrained to take advantage of new opportunities as fast as these opened up. In the years after the second world war those who had been working for equality of economic opportunity turned their efforts in two directions, to eliminating job discrimination by securing the enactment of state and municipal laws making such discrimination illegal, and to stimulating the masses of Negro children and young people to raise their occupational sights as the abler and more determined among them had done long before.

In their contacts with organized labour, Negroes found themselves at first on the outside, excluded from most craft unions and, from time to time, brought into mines or mills as strike-breakers by anti-labour employers. As their numbers in northern industry grew, it became apparent to some Negro leaders that the fate of the great majority of the Negro people as workers was closely bound up with the fate of labour. Unions composed of Negroes existed in trades traditionally carried on by them, notably sleeping car porters and baggage carriers, and the leaders of these unions undertook to stimulate unions in other fields to recruit Negro members and helped to build a favourable attitude toward unionization among Negro workers.

A change in the character of American trade unionism facilitated this process. The strength of the craft unions which dominated the American labour movement until the 1930s lay in their monopoly of a particular skill, and restrictions on admission to membership were therefore a part of the union strategy. But when union organization was extended into the mass-production industries, unions formed on an industrial basis virtually had to adopt an inclusive policy on membership, since their strength depended upon complete organization within the industry rather than monopoly of a limited skill. As Negroes entered these industries they became members of the mass unions. Some of the local craft unions still refused to lower their bars, and some anti-union employers in the south successfully appealed to the racial prejudices of their white workers in their effort to prevent labour organization. But on the whole the labour movement in the 1940s and 1950s made an important contribution to the Negroes' economic advancement. Unions insisted on equal pay for equal work, they offered an opportunity for many Negroes to function as responsible members of the organization without having their leadership activity restricted to their own racial group, and the labour movement as a whole could generally be counted on to support the efforts of Negroes to extend their rights in other areas.

The net effect of the broad economic forces, the growth of labour organization and the special efforts to expand employment opportunities for Negroes was marked by a rise in the economic level of the Negroes relative to the whites. Although Negroes remained at mid-century predominantly in the lower economic ranks, the average wage received by Negro workers increased from 38 per cent of the average received by whites in 1939 to 61 per cent in 1958, a period during which the real incomes of whites were rising rapidly.

(iv) *Housing*. Discrimination in housing remained one of the most stubborn obstacles to full integration into American society. As rural Negroes migrated in ever larger numbers to industrial cities, they moved into the slums which those who could afford better homes were leaving. But when they in turn acquired the means to move out of their slum ghettoes as their predecessors had done, they found the way barred by a multitude of restrictive practices— unwillingness of builders, real estate brokers and lending institutions to build, sell or finance except in areas where non-whites already predominated, and agreements among white neighbours not to sell to non-whites. The suburban areas into which cities were spreading were especially hard to enter.

The result of these restrictions was generally poor housing, crowding and higher rents than white families had to pay for similar accommodation. Most seriously, they meant isolation from the broader community, for limitation of housing led in effect to segregation in neighbourhood facilities such as schools or parks. As Negroes made headway in their efforts to break down discrimination in other areas, the right to live wherever their means and tastes might permit became an increasingly central issue in the struggle for equality. In time they began to score some successes in this difficult field.

The Supreme Court of the United States in 1917 forbade as unconstitutional municipal ordinances which sought to designate residential areas on the basis of race. In 1948 the Court further held that restrictive covenants entered into by white neighbours were not legally enforceable if one of the group should choose to sell to a Negro. Practices of the federal government's housing agencies which had tended to reflect restrictive patterns were discarded in the 1950s in favour of a policy of open occupancy. One by one, states and municipalities began to enact laws directly forbidding various forms of discrimination in housing; sixteen states and fifteen cities had taken some official action by 1957. Even with these measures, however, the road to equality in housing was long and difficult and a commission on race and housing aptly reported its findings in 1958 under the title *Where Shall We Live?*

(v) *Political influence*. Political power had been a weapon for Negro advance during a brief period immediately after the Civil War, when the Negroes in the south had been forcibly enfranchised. But as one device after another effectively kept the majority of southern Negroes from the polls, political action ceased to afford a recourse. In spite of successful legal efforts to outlaw many of these devices and of substantial gains in the number of Negroes registered and voting in the southern states, the combined effect of many obstacles up to mid-century left Negroes in the south still politically weak. In the northern cities, however, large numbers of Negro voters went to the polls. They sent only a handful of Negroes to the federal Congress and a limited number to state legislatures, but increasing numbers were elected to city councils, and many persons elected to federal, state and local bodies who were not themselves Negroes were very conscious of the votes of their Negro constituents.

It was never the policy of Negro leadership to try to stimulate or organize bloc voting by Negroes; to have done so would have implied that Negroes constituted a separate community. For many years most Negroes identified themselves with the party of Abraham Lincoln—the Republican; the dominant white element in the south was almost solidly of the opposite party—the Democratic. In the northern cities, they found most of their neighbours Democrats, and under Franklin D. Roosevelt a large proportion of them swung to his party, the Democratic, because of the liberal labour and welfare policies of his administration. In the succeeding years, both parties recognized that the votes of Negroes could be decisive in many closely contested elections and were thus under pressure to identify themselves with the accelerating pace of Negro advance rather than with indifference or with die-hard opposition.

With a single brief exception, Negro chauvinism did not provide a basis for political or other form of organization up to the middle of the century. At the end of the first world war a dynamic West Indian Negro, Marcus Garvey, launched a movement which declared that there was no hope for the Negro in the white man's country, and called for a return to the homeland of Africa. He exalted everything black, proclaiming a black God and black Christ. He conducted mass demonstrations, set up co-operative stores, restaurants, laundries and other businesses for the separate life of black people, formed uniformed corps of Black Cross nurses and military units, and sponsored the organization of a Black Star steamship line to Africa. Appealing to the black masses, and condemning the middle-class Negro leadership as vehemently as they disclaimed him, he raised substantial sums of money and enlisted large numbers of followers—he claimed 6,000,000 while his opponents insisted that he had less than 1,000,000. But after a life of only about three years the movement collapsed, with business failures, legal entanglements and loss of membership. Its main contribution was to demonstrate the unrest in the Negro masses and their readiness to respond to vigorous leadership which offered a basis for self-respect even when combined with a counsel of despair.

During the 1930s the Communist party made a strong bid for Negro members, and some, especially among younger intellectuals, were attracted by the Party's ardent championship of Negro rights, though its proposal of 'self-determination' or a separate state for the area where the Negro population was densest had little appeal. Many Negroes became disillusioned, however, when the Party line shifted. After Hitler invaded Russia the 'imperialist' war became an 'anti-fascist' crusade, and the Party urged them to forget their grievances during the war. Meantime the more conservative Negro leaders told them to press their wartime advantage at the same time that they supported the war effort. After the war the Communist party resumed its support for the Negroes' struggle against discrimination, but it played an insignificant role in the strategy of racial advance.

The full force of Negro political influence was rarely brought to bear on the national government, but its potential effect was demonstrated during the second world war. When it seemed to Negro leaders of all types—labour, legal, clergy, educational, professional—that the government was not taking adequate steps to incorporate Negroes into the war effort, they organized what would have been a nation-wide 'March on Washington' to impress the government with the unanimity and strength of Negro feeling. Under the threat of such a march the president issued an executive order forbidding discrimination in war industries and government agencies and set up a special wartime agency to see that the order was carried out. After the war the policy of non-discrimination was continued in the government service, and extended to the armed forces and to private industries doing work on contract for the federal government.

(vi) *Literature, the arts and sport.* The battle against the stereotype of the inferior Negro was waged on the literary and artistic front, especially from the 1920s on. In 1925 Alain L. Locke, a graduate of Harvard University and the first Negro to have been a Rhodes Scholar at Oxford, published a book which included writings by Negro authors under the title *The New Negro.* In the following decades both white and Negro readers were introduced to a range of talent among Negro writers and to books by both Negro and white authors in which Negro characters were deeply and vividly revealed. These books helped to make Negro Americans as individuals an integral part of the national American image, as other books were doing for other Americans—pioneers on the western prairie, small farmers on worn-out mountain land or children of immigrants in the urban jungle.

Because the arts were loosely integrated into the prestige and economic structure of American life, they were less beset by prejudice and discrimination than most other avenues to success. Especially in the arts of entertainment, many Negroes showed great talent and received recognition, although it required persistent efforts on the part of Negro leaders and liberal whites to overcome the motion picture industry's reluctance to portray Negroes in any roles except those which would seem fitting to southern audiences.

Sports also were relatively open, and Americans became accustomed to cheering Negro sport stars and to being represented internationally by Negroes as Olympic runners and jumpers and world boxing champions. Professional baseball was slow to lower its bars, but once Negro players began to be hired in this highly competitive and popular sport, they pitched, caught and batted their way to distinction. In making their marks in entertainment, arts and sports, Negroes were taking advantage of the same avenues by which other disadvantaged groups such as the children of poor immigrants often found a pathway to the top.

Meantime Negro folk expression was becoming part of the American literary and artistic tradition, along with the lore of other folk elements such as 'hill-billies' and cowboys. Spirituals—religious songs composed in slavery—were first introduced to audiences around the country by singers from Negro colleges who went on tour to raise money for the support of their schools. Work songs, humour and slave biographies were brought together during the 1930s when unemployed writers and musicians were set to work collecting

American folk materials from all sources. Jazz music and dance not only became the basis of America's popular music, especially from the 1920s on, but achieved popularity in many other parts of the world.

The pattern of Negro life. As they struggled to make an honourable place for themselves in the full range of American life, Negroes developed a series of institutions and a range of attitudes that were in part products, in part instruments, of their struggle. Although their objective was to be able to function as ordinary citizens, the circumstances of discrimination led to the development of separate institutions paralleling those of the broader society, not only in the officially segregated south but generally in the north as well.

Oldest and most central of these institutions were the Negro churches which came into being in part because of exclusion from white churches in the south after the Civil War and in part because the church, as a sanctioned institution, provided an opportunity for Negroes to congregate without arousing the fear of the whites and inviting their interference. The church provided a rallying place, training ground and centre of mutual aid and social intercourse; much of the leadership in local communities was provided by Negro ministers.

Within the pattern of segregation, the Negro school became an important institution of the group, even though it was under the supervision of the white school administration and was generally handicapped by poor equipment as well as by the isolation resulting from segregation. Teachers made up the largest group of professionals in the southern Negro communities and hence formed the core of the Negro *élite*. They did much to insulate Negro children from the depressing effects of their environment and to keep alive their ambition and determination in the face of heavy odds.

The Negro press served two functions, as an organ of protest and as a news service, reporting to the Negro community news of its members and of events of importance to it which did not find their way into the pages of the general press. As the one agency which reached out beyond the bounds of local church or school and carried news from all sections of the country, the press conveyed a sense of the total national Negro community and provided an image in terms of which the Negro people could see themselves.

In addition to these major organizations, Negroes formed duplicates of many bodies from which they were excluded—associations of doctors, lawyers, or business men in those communities where local medical societies, bar associations, or chambers of commerce did not admit Negro co-professionals to membership. They also organized a multitude of social and interest groups and fraternal bodies, as did other elements of the population in the typically heterogeneous American communities.

The sharply drawn colour line had the effect of solidifying the Negro group in spite of itself, of forcing its advanced members to identify themselves with the Negro masses and become their leaders instead of simply trying to enjoy personal success, and of keeping dark and light together instead of prizing off a privileged mulatto element. It created the presumption, both within the Negro group and without, that each individual must be preoccupied with the fate of the race—he must study the health of Negroes if he were a doctor or their incomes if he were an economist, he must act as a spokesman if he found himself in a mixed group, and be regarded as a symbol, a test case, a representative of his race wherever he went. By thus taking away the private character from the Negro's life it forced all to participate, willy-nilly, in the common struggle for equality of status and for the right to function as unqualified Americans.

The steady advance in education and economic status produced a growing Negro middle class which by mid-century had assumed substantial proportions. Between 1940 and 1950 the proportion of Negro men who were engaged in professional, clerical, managerial, skilled or supervisory occupations increased from 10 to 17 per cent and the proportion of Negro women in these occupations increased from 7 to 13 per cent. While these percentages were still far below those of the whites, more than half of whom were in these occupations, they reflected a considerable expansion of the middle-class group.

Originally the Negro middle class was drawn principally from those who already enjoyed superior advantages at the time of general emancipation and thus had a head-start over their fellows in the process of integration into American life. These were the descendants of free Negroes who made up an eighth of the Negro population in 1863, of the children of white masters and Negro slaves whose fathers had seen to it that they were given special training as craftsmen, or were assigned to preferred tasks, or occasionally were given land, and the other personal retainers or household slaves whose position set them apart from ordinary field-hands. During the second world war and after, the basis was greatly broadened by the combination of wartime wages and benefits from labour gains which enabled many more families to keep their children at school and the educational benefits for war veterans which enabled large numbers of Negro veterans to attend universities and technical schools at government expense.

Although the Negro middle class was far more privileged than the Negro masses, it was in some ways subjected to greater psychological strains. Because of its precarious status it felt the need to conform to middle-class standards of conduct, morality and patterns of consumption even more rigorously than did other members of the American middle class. It was under great pressure for success and could not, as could members of the lower class, accept defeat from the start in the unequal battle. Members of the middle class, unsure of acceptance in the broader society, were ambivalent in their own attitudes. Struggling desperately to erase the 'Negro' stereotype from the minds of the whites with whom they had to deal, they were under pressure both to dissociate themselves from the masses whose poverty and its accompanying manifestations confirmed the stereotype, and to defend and aid them since they could never wholly escape identification with the total Negro group.

The colour line took its psychological toll in other ways. In a society where 'white' carried prestige, colour prejudice was reflected within the Negro group; the darker child soon learned that in many subtle ways his less dark fellows were likely to receive more favoured treatment—to be cast as hero in a school play, be more popular if a girl, or find the teacher expecting better performance and more ready to recognize it. Constant reminders that he was held in low esteem by others gnawed away at the Negro's own self-respect. Studies during the second quarter of the twentieth century revealed the depth of self-hate which frustration, combined with the negative evaluation of society caused many Negroes to turn in upon themselves. Other psychological studies began to call attention to the equally devastating effect of colour prejudice on the personality of the white person, and the added burden imposed upon the Negro by displacement upon him of the white man's sense of guilt.

The accelerating rate of change in status. By the mid-fifties the groundswell towards full participation had become broad and deep. With each passing year it became less possible for those who resisted the full acceptance of Negroes as fellow citizens, workers and neighbours to maintain that they were not ready for full citizenship, that they preferred to remain apart, or that agitators were stirring up a people who were generally content. When in 1955 a tired seamstress riding home on a bus in the southern city of Montgomery, Alabama, was arrested for refusing to surrender her seat to a white passenger and move to the crowded rear of the bus, the entire Negro population of the city remained off the buses for months, until separate seating of whites and Negroes was discontinued by court order. Led by a young minister, meeting in churches and prefacing their meeting with prayer, they organized an orderly, steady passive resistance.

Before the Montgomery demonstration, the idea of passive resistance as a weapon in the struggle for racial equality had been used only by small interracial groups who sat together patiently in restaurants which refused to serve them; economic pressure had only occasionally been used, as in campaigns under the slogan 'don't buy where you can't work' to force the employment of Negroes in neighbourhood stores. It remained for this episode to establish beyond a doubt that the masses of the people, south as well as north, had decided that the time for patience in the face of discrimination was over, and were capable of spontaneous disciplined expression in ways which could dramatize their cause and have a major impact on the economic interests of the communities of which they were a part. Passive resistance and boycott were used increasingly in the following years, not only to overcome the opposition of die-hards who sought to block execution of the order of the Supreme Court to end segregation in the schools, but to open up all manner of facilities and to tear down the structure of segregation and discrimination wherever it remained.

In the north, meantime, Negroes and their collaborators were using political power to secure legislation making discrimination on grounds of race, religion or nationality illegal in employment, public facilities, education and housing. By 1957 fifteen states had expressly prohibited discrimination in employment, six states had extended the prohibition to all housing which received any form of public aid, and New York City had made it applicable to purely private housing as well. At the same time individual Negroes in all walks of life, especially those in kinds of jobs or responsibilities which few of their race had formerly filled, strove to demonstrate by their competence the ability of Negroes to perform whatever tasks their individual training and capacities had prepared them for. However modest their outlook and however much they might wish to lead personal, anonymous lives, they knew that they could not yet escape the burden of being symbols and champions of their race.

In the changed climate of American society and the altered world situation, the rate of change in the status of the American Negro was greatly accelerated. The transformation of Africa from the dark abode of primitive people into the home of independent nations whose representatives sat shoulder-to-shoulder with the great powers in the United Nations could not fail to have repercussions on the status of Negroes throughout the world. Many American Negroes who had dissociated themselves from their distant African past found the new African states a source of racial pride and self respect, while more and more whites came to realize that the treatment of the Negro minority in the United States was not a purely domestic matter but one which had a major impact on the foreign policy of the country and the nation's place in world affairs.

The very rapidity of change and mounting evidence that the day was past when it was possible to 'keep the Negro in his place' evoked a burst of massive resistance and of typically counter-revolutionary violence from the defeated but die-hard element in the south. As the extremists captured the initiative in reaction against the Supreme Court's school integration decision of 1954, it appeared that the momentum of change was for the moment checked in the southern states. But only the die-hards regarded the set-back as more than temporary. And in the face of renewed indignities the Negro people remained self-disciplined. The vast majority continued to struggle for an integrated society in line with American principles and Christian doctrine, but the growth of a bitterly anti-white organization calling itself 'Black Muslims' showed that white intransigence could evoke a corresponding response.

In spite of violent reaction the process of integration gathered momentum. In the 1950s Negro engineering school graduates had their choice of jobs in major industrial corporations which, little more than a decade before, had refused employment to Negro applicants; there was thorough integration in the armed services, which had been completely segregated at the opening of the second world war, and in civilian branches of the government; Negroes served in growing numbers in the diplomatic service, occupying such responsible posts as that of cultural attaché in Rome or Rangoon; they were appointed as professors in the faculties of major American universities; they were active as rank and file and in many leadership posts in the labour movement and other voluntary organizations; the job aspirations of the nine Negro boys and girls who entered the famous Little Rock, Arkansas, high school in 1957 under the protection of federal troops were representative of any group of high school students—engineer, atomic scientist, dress designer, lawyer, teacher, ballet dancer.

Most important of all, more and more Americans who happened to be Negroes were able to function as individuals outside traditionally Negro roles on the basis of their interest and training, without having to preoccupy themselves with Negro problems alone, or be limited to serving members of their own group, or stand always as a spokesman or symbol of the race.

Throughout the years the struggle to integrate Negro Americans as full citizens and participants in American life was not a struggle of Negroes alone, but of the people of the United States, for it was part of the overall American effort to realize the full meaning of democracy. In the words of one of the dynamic Negro leaders of the 1950s, describing what she called the 'epic achievement' of the Negro in the United States since 1863: 'The Negro's progression from chattel to freedman, to legal citizenship, to increasing equality of rights and opportunities, to accepted neighbor and compatriot represents a dramatic testament to democracy's positive and dynamic character.' Wherever undemocratic inconsistency exists 'the majority stakes in its progressive solution are fully as great as those of the minority'.* The 'American dream' of freedom and equality, of the rights of each individual as a citizen, of his worth and dignity as a person and of his entitlement to equal opportunity to pursue his well-being and development remained basic to American life and thought, however much these principles might be violated in practice. As the Swedish social scientist, Gunnar Myrdal, concluded, after an extensive study of the position of the American Negro in the 1940s: 'The whites have all the power, but they are split in their moral personality. Their better selves are with the insurgents. The Negroes do not need any other allies.'†

2. UNTOUCHABLES

Among the largest groups subject to the most extreme forms of discrimination were India's untouchables, who numbered 50,000,000 according to the census of 1931. These classes were segregated, denied elementary civil rights and confined to occupations like scavenging which were considered unclean. They were present in all parts of India, for every village and town depended on them to do the necessary tasks which no other Hindu would perform; they in turn were wholly dependent, for they could not even draw water from the village well and must wait for their water jars to be filled by others.

Untouchability dated from time immemorial—it existed at the time of the

---

* Butcher, *The Negro in American Culture, op. cit.*, p. 22.
* Gunnar Myrdal, *An American Dilemma* (New York, 1944), p. 1004.

Buddha, for he attacked it—and it was entrenched in social custom. To many it had the support of religion, for the belief was widely held that the untouchable person had come to his present status as a result of his sins or failures in a previous life. Many untouchables held this view of themselves. They thus found themselves held down by strong sanctions that were practical, religious and psychological.

The revolutionary change in their status, to the point where the practice of untouchability was made a penal offence, was brought primarily by the forces which liberated the country and were reforming the broad structure of Indian society. The efforts of untouchables themselves played only a minor part in the alteration of their position from that of outcast to citizen with full legal rights.

By the end of the nineteenth century movements for the reform of Hindu society brought untouchability under attack. Swami Vivekananda, one of the major figures of the Hindu Reformation, denounced it root and branch. A number of Brahmins and other high-caste persons began to work individually among the untouchables. A few maharajas took steps within their domains. The maharaja of Baroda attempted to abolish untouchability in his state, but was unable to give full effect to his intention; the maharaja of Travancore appointed untouchables as judges and to other public office. These were, however, isolated attacks, and although they grew in number they represented the special interest of individuals rather than a broad movement. Nevertheless, together with other aspects of the reform movements of the time, they began to undermine the public attitude which took untouchability for granted as a permanent, unchangeable institution.

Some outside pressures contributed an impetus toward a change in the treatment of untouchables, notably the danger of large-scale conversion to Christianity or Islam. Christian missionaries in the nineteenth century first appealed mainly to the Brahmins and attracted a number of educated persons, especially in Bengal where British interests were centred and western ways were gaining prestige. But with the movement to reform Hindu society from within, Christianity lost much of its appeal to those whose reason for leaving the Hindu faith had been the rigidity of its social customs. Thereafter many of the Christian missionaries shifted their approach and appealed to the untouchables, to whom they offered equality of status within the Christian community. Especially in certain regions, missionaries were successful in attracting substantial numbers of untouchables, and Hindu leaders saw a threat of large-scale defection unless the lot of the untouchables within the Hindu community could be improved. In addition, there was the ever-present attraction of casteless Islam.

It was Mahatma Gandhi, however, who made the abolition of untouchability a vital national issue. When he returned to India from South Africa in 1915, he visited the families of the untouchables who had provided the main support for his passive resistance in South Africa and, to the dismay of his friends who had endowed an *ashram*—or retreat—for him, he welcomed untouchables to stay with him in the same house. From that time on he made it clear that the eradication of untouchability was one of his primary missions.

Under Gandhi's leadership the national movement committed itself to the abolition of untouchability as a central objective. The 1920 session of the Indian National Congress passed a resolution stating that the removal of untouchability was necessary for the attainment of freedom, and thenceforth the Congress never veered from this position. In 1929 it set up an Anti-Untouchability Committee which worked to get temples, schools and wells freely open to untouchables. Where the Congress party secured control of provincial governments under the constitution of 1935, it secured the enactment of measures on behalf of untouchables, such as free education from primary school through to university in Bihar or the opening of some of the temples in Bombay.

Gandhi himself lost no opportunity to keep the 'sin of untouchability' in the public mind. He insisted that the workers of the Congress party go into the villages and actually practise equality with the people who had so long been considered outcasts. In his own tours all over India he stayed with untouchables in their colonies. For the untouchables themselves he sought to build up their own self-respect. Considering the name 'untouchable' objectionable and likely to confirm a sense of inferiority, he renamed them *harijans*, children of God. He encouraged them to seek their own self-improvement, to adopt conduct, such as not drinking, which would command respect, and to participate actively in the Congress party. To assist them in their efforts at self-improvement he founded and served as president of a society for the service of *harijans* —*Harijan Seva Sangh*—with funds and personnel devoted to education and welfare services.

The *harijan* community itself became active in its own behalf in some places and produced some outstanding leaders, the most notable of whom was Dr Bhim Rao Ambedkar, a lawyer and sociologist educated in London. As the nationalist movement began to use the method of passive resistance against the British administration, *harijans* adopted the same technique for their own ends. In Travancore, for example, a passive resistance movement led to a proclamation in 1932 permitting *harijans* to enter Hindu temples. *Harijan* movements for self-improvement were local and were mostly centred in urban communities, except for a state-wide movement in Travancore which sought to raise the whole community. With the help of local units of the Congress party, there were repeated local efforts to remove disabilities, but in British India these came up against the law courts which upheld local custom in such matters as access to village wells. Even where there was no legal change, custom did break down to some extent in a number of places.

These piecemeal efforts, however, appeared entirely inadequate to Dr Ambedkar, who saw no future for the Depressed Classes within the Hindu fold. He therefore began to organize a political movement with the object of gaining recognition for untouchables as an entity separate from the Hindus, entitled to separate political rights and representation as were other non-Hindu communities, notably the Muslims. The movement received recognition from the British government, whose policy was to encourage separatist tendencies among groups in the Indian sub-continent, and Ambedkar was invited to attend the Round Table Conference in London in 1931 as a representative of the untouchables. But the move to make the untouchables into a separate community was opposed by Gandhi in the strongest terms, and he conducted a 'fast unto death' when the British proposed to put the plan for a separate community into effect in 1932. His fast resulted in a compromise providing for special seats for *harijans* but election from joint constituencies.

Dr Ambedkar's efforts received little mass support from *harijans*, for the majority of them were devout Hindus by religion and they did not respond to his anti-Hindu appeal; those who were ready to dissociate themselves from Hinduism were more likely to seek identity with the Christian or Muslim community than with a community of outcasts whose identity was defined in Hindu terms. More importantly, since what the *harijans* desired was to enjoy the full rights of citizens, their goal was assimilation into the total community and the removal of barriers rather than the perpetuation of a separate identity.

By the time of independence the Hindu public had come to recognize untouchability as an evil and to accept the necessity of eradicating it. More than twenty-five years of Gandhi's propaganda, the commitment of the Congress party, and the awakening among the *harijans* themselves had prepared the ground for a radical solution.

In independent India the legal position was clear. According to the constitution: ' "Untouchability" is abolished and its practice in any form is forbidden. The enforcement of any disability arising out of "Untouchability" shall be an offence punishable in accordance with law.' The Untouchability (Offences) Act of 1955 spelled out in detail types of discrimination and imposed penalties. In addition the Indian government recognized that centuries of disability had placed *harijans* at such a competitive disadvantage even where they were no longer barred that special provisions were necessary to ensure them the opportunity to secure an education and to participate in public life. Accordingly, special scholarships were earmarked for *harijan* students and a proportion of vacancies in public appointments were reserved for *harijan* appointees. Meantime the ablest among them held cabinet offices in the central government and in the several states.

The habits and attitudes of centuries did not vanish overnight in the more than half a million Indian villages and towns, and legal rights did not immediately become social practice. But democratic processes were making the abolition of untouchability effective. The adult franchise brought political power to former untouchable classes in local, provincial and central governments, and the recruitment of *harijans* to all branches of public service helped to give reality to the revolutionary change in status of this most disadvantaged segment of Indian society.

NOTES TO CHAPTER XXX

1. Corresponding member of the Academy of Sciences Ludvik Svoboda (Czechoslovakia) thinks that the section devoted to the workers' movement does not contain a thorough and comprehensive exposition of the problem. It only enumerates facts but does not bring out the essential and definitive phenomena. . . . The main reason for this is that the authors do not grasp the underlying economic realities of the problems. . . . It is characteristic that the authors sympathize only with the economic struggle of the working class and repudiate the political and ideological struggle. It can be inferred from a reading of the text that the authors consider the strike an admissible means of pursuing the struggle only when it does not go beyond the limits of economic demands and that they condemn the political strike. In the authors' view the ideological struggle is something that has been introduced into the workers' movement from outside mainly by the intelligentsia. It is not surprising therefore that the situation of the working class in Western Europe seems to the authors to be quite satisfactory. This point of view is supported by Dr János Jemnic (Hungary), who notes that the authors devote attention mainly to those aspirations of the workers which were directed towards improving the situation of the working class within the framework of the existing social system. Such a narrowing of the field of investigation has brought with it the result that the workers' movement as a whole has been represented in a distorted way: the false impression is created that the welfare of the popular masses can in the main be assured by a reformist movement in the framework of the existing social system. In two places in the text the authors make a brief reference to the revolutionary movement of the working classes in the West, but not nearly enough is said about it.

2. *The Author-Editors wish to draw the attention of the reader to the language of the text, notably to the discussion of the communist labour movement, pp. 1118–19, and of revolutionary unionism in western Europe, p. 1116.*

3. Dr János Jemnic and K. Baginyan underline that the expansion of power resources and mechanization, the rational organization of industry and the growth of labour productivity under conditions of the predominance of private property do not lead to higher living standards for workers, but are mainly exploited in the interests of employers. See Lewis Mumford, *Art and Technics* (New York, 1952), Lewis Mumford, *In the Name of Sanity* (New York, 1954), and other works. The worker gains nothing unless he wins concessions by struggle (for example the strikes in the iron and steel industry in the USA in 1959).

4. Doctor Baginyan notes that it was no mean achievement of the German workers that they were able to utilize the very limited constitutional legality to set up their own organizations—the trade unions, the co-operatives and the party. This latter exerted a great influence on the activity of the trade unions until a resolution was carried at the party's Mannheim session in 1906 which laid down the principle of 'equality of rights' between trade unions and party, and so undermined the position of the revolutionary wing in the trade unions (see Farwing: *Der Kampf um die Gewerkschaften*, p. 219).

5. Dr Baginyan underlines that 'democratic centralism' means not only strict discipline but also the giving of extensive democratic rights to all local organizations and to each member of the party and the exercise of control over the elected organs by the whole mass of the party. Here are the provisions laid down in this connection in the Statutes of the Communist Party of the Soviet Union as confirmed at its twenty-second session in 1961:

The guiding principle of the organizational structure of the party is democratic centralism which implies:

    (*a*) the elective character of all the controlling organs of the party from the lowest to the highest;

    (*b*) a periodic rendering of accounts by party organs to their party organizations and to their superior organs;

    (*c*) a strict party discipline and subordination of the minority to the majority;

    (*d*) the unconditional mandatory force of decisions by higher organs for lower organs. (See *Ustav KPSS* ('Statutes of the Communist Party of the Soviet Union'), Moscow, 1961, p. 12).

6. Drs János Jemnic and K. Baginyan write: In Soviet Russia and the other socialist countries the workers' unions have received very extensive rights. Their interests fully coincide with those of the government. The trade unions are not only called on to defend the interests of the workers but they have been given the function of handling social insurance funds and are responsible for occupational health, safety in factories and protection of labour. Under these conditions collective agreements have become bilateral obligations binding both on the administration and on the trade unions, and designed to promote common aims. See for example *Ustav professionalnykh soyuzov SSSR* (Statutes of the Trade Unions in the USSR) as confirmed at the twelfth session held on March 27, 1959 (Moscow, 1959).

7. Candidate of Juridical Sciences A. Bovin underlines that organically strikes cannot take place in the USSR and in the people's democracies as when power is in the hands of the working class strike action loses all meaning. The events which took place in 1956 in Poland, in the German Democratic Republic and in Hungary have nothing at all to do with the struggle of the workers for their rights. These were attempts at counter-revolutionary insurrections directed towards the overthrow of the socialist structure in those countries and were organized by internal counter-revolutionary forces with the active support of international imperialism. The working class in Poland, the German Democratic Republic and Hungary very quickly liquidated those expressions of hostility to socialism since they had not the slightest roots in the working masses. See Note 12 to Chapter II.

8. Dr Baginyan writes: In most newly industrializing countries the struggle for freedom and independence against foreign intervention is of vital importance. Therefore in comparison with political issues the everyday problems of the workers at times temporarily recede into the background.

9. Dr Baginyan underlines that the leaders of the International Confederation of Free Trade Unions took up a schismatic attitude and refused to collaborate with the World Federation of Trade Unions in the struggle for peace. See for example W. Z. Foster, *Outline History of the World Trade Union Movement* (New York, 1956) and also Labour Research Association, *Labour Fact Book 12* (New York, 1955).

10. Dr János Jemnic notes that the Trade Disputes and Trade Unions Act of 1927 paralysed trade union activity in the United Kingdom for many years.

11. Candidate of Economic Sciences V. P. Tikhomirov calls attention to the fact that the peasantry in itself does not represent a homogeneous mass and therefore the position of the various strata of farmers and peasants in the class society is different.

12. Professor A. N. den Hollander writes: 'The difference between "peasant" and "farmer", as made chiefly by American authors, remains as indistinct in this manuscript as it is in whatever other publication I have ever read.' Although the Author-Editors use the term 'farmer' for the essentially capitalistic type of agriculturalist in Western Europe, North America, Australia and New Zealand, and 'peasant' for the subsistence farmer or farm tenant of Eastern Europe and Asia, a further analysis of criteria may be of use. The distinction between peasant and farmer is cultural, and the difficulty of defining the one type and the other arises from the fact that in modern times, especially during the present century, the transitional stages between the one and the other become so numerous as to blur the outline of each.

The concept of peasant, at least as understood in the West, derives from the caste society of the feudal age and its continuation in the Old Regime, when the peasant as an agriculturalist was stationary. He worked the land in an almost self-sufficient economy; he did not see or think—except in religion—much if at all beyond the limits of his locality, and he was a member of a family as the primary working unit and of the village as a compact, co-operative group. He found little value for his kind of existence in learning, even to the extent of knowing how to read and write, and he had the habits of behaviour of one accustomed to working the soil and associating with livestock as much as with human beings. Whether he owned the land which he worked or had the status of serf did not affect the essential characteristics of the cultural type; in either case he was a peasant.

Whether and to what extent these characteristics persisted into the recent period depended largely upon the availability of alternatives to this way of life for members of the peasantry. Alternatives first became possible on a significant scale with the rise and spread of industrial society, which changed market relations for the agricultural population and thereby brought about a transformation in the attitude of the peasants toward change and time and toward the quickest means of adjusting to the new opportunities, those of education. The process of adaptation to the industrial society included learning something about commercial, scientific agriculture and cost accounting, and these interests entailed the adoption of many social and political mores and interests of the urban population. Rate and extent of adaptation varied according to circumstances, and often in the same region according to personal qualities; but as individuals adjusted to the new society, they acquired characteristics very different from those of the peasantry. In lieu of a better term to refer to the new type of agriculturalist, one may employ the word developed in the United States, where, in the absence of a traditional caste or legally fixed class or status structure, the new type predominated and set the norm. The new type was referred to as 'farmer', a person with middle-class characteristics, whose occupation, a capitalistic enterprise, was not industry or commerce but agriculture. As this occupation became increasingly mechanized and subject to scientific discipline, the agriculturalist tended more and more to share even the habits of work and of thought of the industrial technician, and the distinction between rural and urban society has rapidly faded. At this stage working the soil ceased to be synonymous with the way of life of the peasantry and became a means of earning a living which would enable the practitioners to be as much like the members of urban society as the occupation of agriculture would permit. In the process involved Europe has offered many examples—one thinks of Denmark among others—of the type 'farmer', but most of the agricultural population remains at various stages in the movement from peasantry to farmerhood.

Important reading for this subject is the article 'Farmer' by Professor Rudolph Heberle in the *Handwörterbuch der Sozialwissenschaften*, volume III (edition 1961), pp. 478 ff. (The article and Professor Herbele's bibliography are in German.) Especially to be recommended is the report of a symposium of French scholars in various fields held in Paris in March 1951 on the theme *Villes et campagnes. Civilisation urbaine et civilisation rurale en France*. The report, edited by Professor Georges Friedmann, was published by the University of Paris, École des Hautes Études, at the Librairie Armand Colin (no date).

13. V. P. Tikhomirov notes that the authors give a distorted view of the policy pursued by the Communist Party of the Soviet Union on the peasant question and of the collectivization of agriculture which was carried out in the Soviet Union. At the end of the twenties agriculture in the USSR was lagging very far behind the growth of socialist industry. Industry was centralized and operated on a large scale. Agriculture had remained on a small scale and fragmented. Heavy industry was based on communal, socialist ownership of the means of production whilst private ownership of the means of production was the rule on the small peasant farms. Socialist industry was subordinated to the principle of planning. The small peasant holding was at the mercy of market fluctuations. Large-scale socialist industry could rely all the time on the newest technical advances and was developing at a rapid tempo in obedience to the principle of reproduction on an extended scale. The small peasant holding, based on primitive techniques and manual labour, had no possibility of using up-to-date machines, and was developing slowly, often so slowly as not to ensure even simple reproduction.

By 1927 the small fragmented peasant holding had basically exhausted its potentialities for further increase of productivity. The process of splitting up peasant holdings was continuing in the countryside. These yielded only a minimum of marketable produce, particularly grain. Whilst the gross output of agriculture for 1926–27 exceeded the pre-war level the gross yield of grain, the basic farming crop, amounted in that year to only 95 per cent of the gross output for 1913; the marketable part of the grain harvest was 13·3 per cent against 26 per cent in the pre-war period.

Under those conditions the grain harvest could not satisfy the country's bread requirements which were increasing in proportion to the growth of the urban population and the working class. The backwardness of agriculture was putting a brake on all socialist construction.

In the interest of the construction of socialism it was urgently necessary to liquidate the backwardness of agriculture and to effect a transition from the small privately owned peasant holding to the large-scale socialist farm. In order to build socialism all land had to be transferred to public ownership as socialism could not successfully be constructed if two forms of economy—the socialist economy in the urban sphere and the petty goods economy in the rural sphere—continued to coexist.

The socialist reconstruction of agriculture is based on Lenin's co-operative plan. Lenin had pointed out that co-operation is the most easily accessible way to the socialist reconstruction of agriculture, that in the conditions of the dictatorship of the proletariat the mere growth of co-operation is identical with the growth of socialism, and that when there is state ownership of all the major means of production, and an alliance of the proletariat with the masses of the toiling peasantry, and when the proletariat plays the directing role in this union all the conditions are fulfilled for using co-operation as a means of building the socialist society. Leninism teaches that the peasantry must co-operate on a strictly voluntary basis, and that they must be gradually convinced by practical illustrations, initially in those spheres of co-operation which relate to supplying and selling and then in the sphere of agricultural production, so that there is a progression from the lowest to the highest forms of production co-operation. The creation of a solid industrial basis is an essential prerequisite for the mechanization of agriculture and contributes to the socialist reconstruction of the countryside.

By putting agriculture on a co-operative basis three important problems were at one solved: (a) the units of agricultural production were transformed from small and frag-mented peasant holdings to large-size collective farms; (b) the last exploiting class—that of the kulaks (rich peasants) was liquidated; and (c) the conditions required for a decisive rise in agricultural production were created.

In the first years of Soviet rule, the Russian peasantry acquired by personal experience the conviction that only if agriculture were put on a co-operative basis could there be any possibility of raising the standard of living of the peasants as a whole and of liquidating exploitation in the countryside. That is why the overwhelming mass of the poor peasants and middle peasants voluntarily adhered to the collectivization of agriculture.

In the place of twenty-five million small peasant holdings in the USSR there now exist seventy thousand collective farms. The peasantry of the Soviet Union has become a homogeneous class in the socialist society. See also Note 11 to Chapter XXI.

14. *The Author-Editors refer the reader to the chapter on Agriculture (Chapter XIV) and to the references provided in Note 1 to that chapter.*

15. Academician D. Kosev thinks that the assertion that the peasant parties in the countries of Eastern Europe were organized by the communist parties is at variance with the historical facts. Such parties were in existence even before the second world war. Already during the war against fascism a *rapprochement* had begun between the peasant parties and the communist parties and was later transformed into a fighting alliance.

16. Dr János Jemnic thinks that the views expressed on the development of the Eastern European countries since the war proceed from a mistaken concept. The characteristic feature did not lie in the divergencies between the peasant parties and the communist parties. On the contrary the communist parties everywere played a major role in carrying out land reform; and they defended peasant holdings from the big landowners (there is no mention of this).

V. P. Tikhomirov agrees with him and notes that the authors give a wrong idea of the process of collectivization in the people's democracies of Europe. A solid alliance of the working class and the peasantry under the leadership of the communist and workers' parties was established whilst the war for liberation from foreign and domestic reaction was still going on during the second world war. After the collapse of Nazi Germany at the end of the war, people's democracies, which were the expression of a system based on the alliance of workers and peasants, were set up.

The communist and workers' parties were able to adjust their relations with the peasant parties. In regard to the mass peasant parties whose leadership was at the outset strongly under the influence of the rural bourgeoisie the communists began by adopting a policy of unmasking and isolating the reactionary leaders from the masses.

They supported the left wing of the peasant movement and helped to bring about the advancement of genuine representatives of the peasants. The peasant parties expelled the bourgeois elements from their leadership and recognized the directing role of the working class.

Democratic agrarian reforms which did away with the landlord class were carried out in all the European people's democracies between 1945 and 1947.

In Poland and Hungary half of all the cultivated land belonged to the landlords, in Czechoslovakia and Roumania one-third and in Albania the majority. It was only in Bulgaria where at the time of the Russo-Turkish War of 1877–78 the landlords—all Turks by nationality—had fled the country, leaving no more big estates in the hands of their owners, that the agrarian reform was from the outset of an anti-capitalist character. In the people's democracies only a small part of the arable land was nationalized; as the mass of the peasants wanted to get the estates of the big landlords into their private ownership, these were in the first place divided up between peasants who had little or no land.

The masses of the peasantry themselves took part in the appropriation and distribution of the landlords' properties, in securing which they were assisted by the working class. When in 1945 the government of General Radescu in Rumania began to sabotage the land reform the workers called upon the peasants themselves to divide up the land and their advice was followed. At the end of 1944 commissioners were sent by the Polish Workers' party into the villages to apportion the estates, who were assisted in their task by teams from the factories.

The division of the big estates strengthened the union of the workers and of the peasants. Material conditions in the countryside were somewhat improved and in a few years most poor peasants raised their holdings to the economic level of the middle peasants. However this was not a radical solution of the peasant problem. In course of time the peasants convinced themselves by personal experience that there was very little likelihood of a major improvement in the great mass of peasant holdings and that large-scale collective farms must therefore be set up.

By the beginning of 1962 almost all the peasants in the European people's democracies, including even the former kulaks, had voluntarily joined productive agricultural co-operatives. The incomes of the production co-operatives in the European socialist countries are distributed basically in proportion to work done and partly also in proportion to land.

17. V. P. Tikhomirov notes that actually it was only the Cárdenas government (1934–40) that began to implement the agrarian reform in Mexico but this reform was not carried through to the end. The struggle of the peasants for the land still continues in Mexico. Thus in 1958 there was peasant agitation in the north-west part of the country.

18. V. P. Tikhomirov notes that the land reform in Cuba was not just a 'plank in the platform of the revolutionary leader'. On May 17, 1959, a law for agrarian reform was adopted in Cuba. When it was put into effect in 1960 it resulted in the complete elimination of the *latifundia* which represented the main obstacle to the consummation of the Cuban revolution. As stipulated by the agrarian legislation about 125,000 peasant families, mainly selected from among those who previously had been tenants of the big landowners, received plots of land. One special feature of the agrarian transformation was a mass movement for the creation of co-operatives (production co-operatives with joint cultivation of the soil) to which more than half the area of cultivable land was allotted. The co-operatives have been mainly aligned on the sites of the big landed estates which had been granted to the agricultural workers and peasants who previously possessed little or no land.

19. Candidate of Economic Sciences Z. M. Pashetkina notes that the constitution of the Soviet Union specifically lays down that women have an equal right to education. A case in point is the vocational training of women. In 1960–61 out of the total number of pupils in intermediate vocational schools 47 per cent were women. In the 1960–61 session, women formed 43 per cent of the students in higher educational establishments, and 63 per cent of those in higher educational institutions for training teachers; they made up 56 per cent of students in institutions for training staff for the public health service and for the sports and cultural departments. (*Narodnoye khozyaistvo S S S R v 1960 g. Statisticheskiy sbornik* ('Statistical annual of the national economy of the USSR for 1960'), Moscow, 1961, p. 779.)

21   PAINTING I

Pablo Picasso, 'Les demoiselles d'Avignon', 1907. New York, Museum of Modern Art

PAINTING II

*Fernand Léger,
'Three Women'
(Le grand
déjeuner), 1921.
New York,
Museum of
Modern Art*

PAINTING III

Georges Braque,
'Still Life with
Grapes', 1927.
Washington,
Philipps Collection

24 PAINTING IV

Kasimir Malevich, 'Matinée à la campagne après la pluie', 1911. New York, Guggenheim Museum

25 PAINTING V

Piet Mondrian, 'Composition in Red, Yellow and Blue', 1921. Amsterdam, Municipal Museum

26 PAINTING VI

Paul Klee, 'Zwitscher Maschine' (Twittering Machine), 1922. New York, Museum of Modern Art

27   PAINTING VII

Pablo Picasso, 'Guernica' (Mural), 1937. New York, Museum of Modern Art

28 PAINTING VIII

Käthe Kollwitz, Portrait (charcoal), 1943

29   PAINTING IX

   Alexander A. Deyneka, 'The Defence of Petrograd', 1927–28

30

PAINTING X

Ben Shahn,
'Handball', 1939.
New York,
Museum of
Modern Art
(Abby Aldrich
Fund)

31   PAINTING XI   Jackson Pollock, 'Number 1', 1948. New York, Museum of Modern Art

32 PAINTING XII

José Clemente
Orozco, 'Zapatistas',
1931. New York,
Museum of Modern
Art

33 SCULPTURE I

(a) *Auguste Rodin, Bronze figure from 'L'enfer', c. 1900. Poitiers, Musée des Beaux Arts*

(b) *Aristide Maillol, Bronze, c. 1905–10. Poitiers, Musée des Beaux Arts*

[Giraudon   (a)

(b)

[Giraudon

(a)

(b)

(c)

(d)

(e)

34 SCULPTURE II

Henri Matisse, 'Head of Jeannette' (Jeanne Vaderin), 1910–12. New York, Museum of Modern Art

(a) *Jeannette I* (1910)   (c) *Jeannette III* (1910–11)

(b) *Jeannette II* (1910)   (d) *Jeannette IV* (1910–11 ?)

(e) *Jeannette V* (1910–11 ?)

[*Modern Art*]

(b)

[*Modern Art*]

(a)

35   SCULPTURE III

(a) *Umberto Boccioni, 'Unique Forms of Continuity in Space', 1913. New York,*
     Museum of Modern Art
(b) *Antoine Pevsner, 'Developable Column', 1942. New York, Museum of Modern Art*

36 SCULPTURE IV

Alberto Giacometti, 'Chariot', 1950. New York, Museum of Modern Art

37   SCULPTURE V

Henry Moore, 'Family Group', 1945. New York, Museum of Modern Art

38 SCULPTURE VI

Reg Butler, 'The Unknown Political Prisoner' (project for a monument), 1951–53. *New York, Museum of Modern Art*

39   SCULPTURE VII

*Alexander Calder, 'Lobster Trap and Fish Tail' (Mobile), 1939. New York,
Museum of Modern Art*

40   SCULPTURE VIII

V. I. Mukhina, 'Industrial Worker and Kolkhoz Labourer', 1937

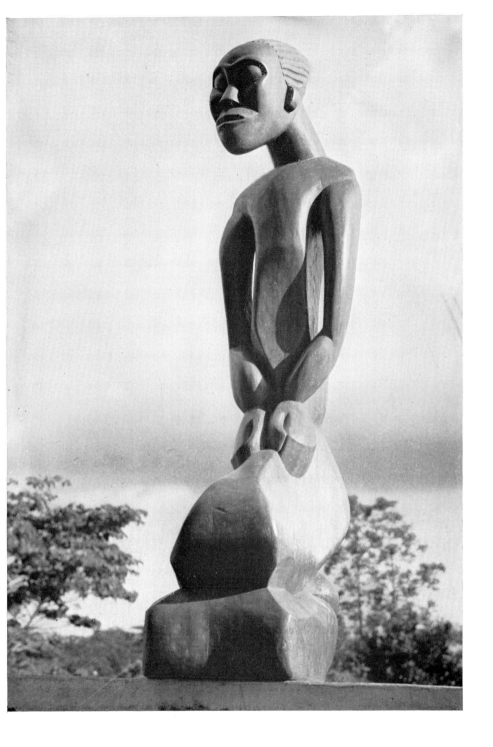

41 SCULPTURE IX

Oku Ampofo, 'Animist Slave', Accra, Ghana

42   SCULPTURE X

Isamu Noguchi, Modern Garden in Japanese Style, 1958. Unesco House, Paris

43 ARCHITECTURE I

Walter Gropius, The Bauhaus, Dessau, 1925–26

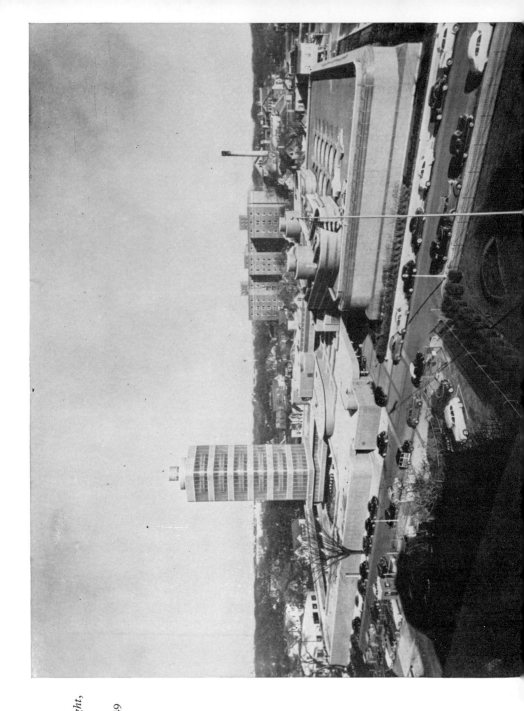

44 ARCHITECTURE II

Frank Lloyd Wright,
Johnson's Wax
buildings, Racine,
Wisconsin, 1936–49

[NHC/*Photo Cloetingh and Deman Studios*

45 ARCHITECTURE III

   (a) *Individual homes in a suburban development, South Bend, Indiana, USA*
   (b) *Le Corbusier, 'Unité d'habitation', Marseilles, France, 1952*

[*Le Corbusier*

46   ARCHITECTURE IV

United Nations Headquarters, New York, 1947–50

47 ARCHITECTURE V

(a) *P. L. Nervi, The Palazzetto dello Sport, Rome, 1956–57*
(b) *University College, Ibadan, Nigeria, 1961*

(a)

48 ARCHITECTURE VI

(a) *Oscar Niemeyer, Cathedral, Brasilia, Brazil,* 1960
(b) *Oscar Niemeyer, Supreme Court, Brasilia, Brazil,* 1960

(b)

[*Georgia O'Keefe*

49 PHOTOGRAPHY I

Alfred Stieglitz, 'The Steerage', 1907. New York, Museum of Modern Art

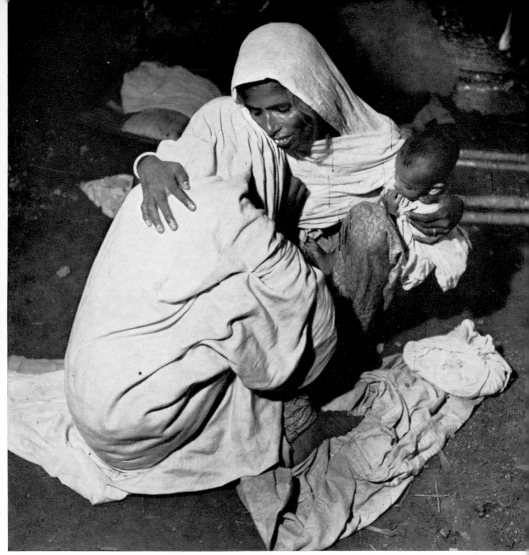

50 PHOTOGRAPHY II

Margaret Bourke-White, 'Grief', India, 1953

51 PHOTOGRAPHY III (opposite)

Henri Cartier-Bresson, 'Shanghai', 1

[*Mag*

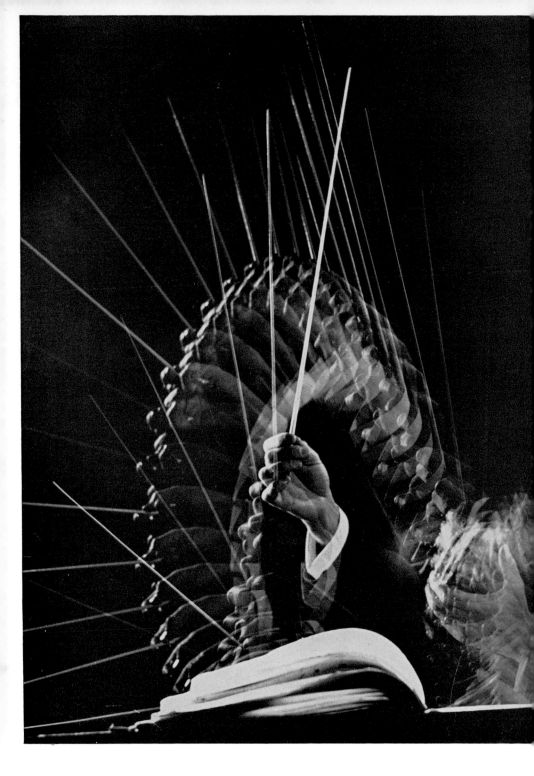

52   PHOTOGRAPHY IV

Gjon Mili, '3/4 Beat', c. 1942

53 PHOTOGRAPHY V

The Interior of the Heart

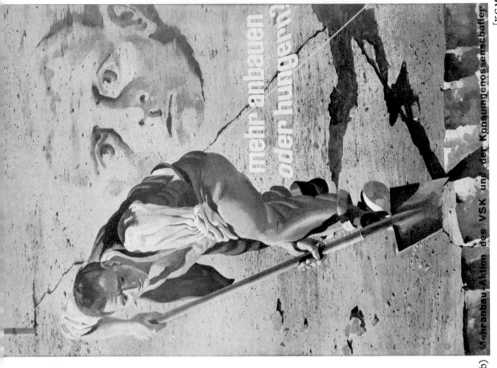

(b)

mehr anbauen
oder hungern?

Mehranbau-Aktion des VSK und der Konsumgenossenschaften

[KGM]

[AP]

(a) *News photography: F. Durdin, Bombing in Chungking, China, 1941*

(a)

(a) [*Photo Chevojon*

55 THE THEATRE I

    (a) *Auguste Perret,*
    Champs Elysées
    Theatre, auditorium
    under construction,
    Paris, 1911–13

    (b) *Gerhard Weber, The*
    State Opera,
    Hamburg, 1955

(b)

[*German Embassy*

(a)

56 THE THEATRE II

   (a) *Constantin Stanislavsky, scene from Act IV of* The Lower Depths *by Gorky.*
     Moscow Art Theatre, 1902

   (b) *Elwin Piscator, scene from* Flüchtlingsgespräche *by Bertolt Brecht. Munich,*
     1962

(b)

57 MOTION PICTURES I

    (a) *D. W. Griffith, scene from* Intolerance, 1916
    (b) *Sergei Eisenstein, scene from* Battleship Potemkin, 1925

(a) [c

58 MOTION PICTURES II

    (a) *Charlie Chaplin, scene from* Modern Times, 1936
    (b) *Walt Disney, scene from* Snow White and the Seven Dwarfs, 1938

(b) [c

59   EASTERN ART I

Abanindranath Tagore, 'Dacca Stripes'

60   EASTERN ART II

Jamini Roy, 'Southal Dancers'

[*Modern Art, Delhi*

61 EASTERN ART III

    (a) *Amrita Shergil, 'Brahmacharies', 1959. New Delhi, National Gallery of*
        Modern Art
    (b) *Zainul Abedin, 'Sharing the Meal', 1943. Dacca*

[*Photo Kafil Uddin Ahmed*

62   EASTERN ART IV

George Keyt (Ceylon), 'Nayika'

(b)

(a)

63 EASTERN ART V

(a) *Shunko Mochizuki, 'A Lotus', 1957*
(b) *Tano Rigen, 'Old Style Exhibition', 1955*

[*Skinner*

(a)

64 EASTERN ART VI

(a) *Chi' Pai-shih, 'Composition',*
    London, F. Skinner Collection

(b) *Siu Pei-hong, 'Water Buffalo*
    and Snake'. Paris, Musée
    Cernuschi

(b)

[*Cernuschi*

PART FOUR

EXPRESSION

INTRODUCTION

THE literary and other arts which gave expression to the developments of the twentieth century reflected the struggles of men all over the world to make order out of the new experiences and conceptions brought by the scientific theories and technological applications, and by the social changes, political upheavals and catastrophes that determined the direction of their lives and moulded their hopes and fears.

In western industrial society the process involved an examination and re-evaluation of society, consideration of the nature of man and his place in the universe and psychological exploration of man's hidden motivation. During the first half of the century all the movements in the arts could in one sense be interpreted as carrying to their logical end forms started in the late eighteenth or nineteenth century. They could be regarded too as negating or dissolving all style and common modes of expression in favour of a multitude of individual, almost private, idioms. Yet in a more profound sense they expressed fundamental re-evaluations of the meaning of life in the face of accelerated, drastic, world-wide social change, and they produced recognizably different, even revolutionary, artistic and literary forms.

When neither scientists nor statesmen, nor yet religious leaders, were clear about the potentialities of order in the universes opened by science, artists alone could not make a complete poetical statement for the new world comparable to the *Divine Comedy* or the cathedral of Chartres for the mediaeval order. But though the outlook and styles of western writers, painters, sculptors, architects and composers remained up to the middle of the century still experimental and often chaotic, they were as different after Marcel Proust and James Joyce, Picasso, Le Corbusier, Debussy and Schönberg as was the outlook of science after the work of Planck, Einstein, Heisenberg, Mendel and Freud.

The centres from which changes in literary and artistic expression radiated were in Europe, but after the first world war the offshoots of European civilization, especially the United States and Latin America, were developing their distinctive forms of expression which interacted with the European but asserted an identity of their own. After the October revolution, revolutionary experience and intent gave new direction to the literature and arts of the USSR and to the interaction of western and non-western cultures within the Soviet Union.

In other parts of the world artistic expression involved a variety of reactions to the aggressively expanding culture of the West, the revitalization of traditional cultural forms and, drawing on both sources, the quest for modes of expression appropriate to the new national experiences which these countries were undergoing.

Most conspicuously in the West, but to a large and increasing extent in non-western culture areas as well, the technology of mass communication, together with mass education, altered the milieu, changed the audience and blurred the distinction between the popular and fine arts. The secular orientation of much of twentieth-century life, the spread of leisure and the development of the entertainment industries shifted artistic expression away from the religious area where much of it had originated into the realm of entertainment or information. Yet the search for poetic truth beyond any single religion, and the function of the arts in revealing human possibilities, opening visions of order, and redeeming pain and failure, remained no less necessary than in the past.

The new tendencies affected the place of the artist in society and broadened the social strata from which artists were drawn. The artist's place, in turn, affected the tendencies taking shape. He might be aloof from the main currents of his society, as were many in the West; he might be drawn into direct contribution to social change as in the revolutionary societies of Russia and China and the active nationalist movements in colonial areas; he might be the guardian of a traditional art such as the No plays of Japan; he might be one of many individuals scattered through many different cultures who combined a functional participation in modern life with the attempt to find and express its meaning. Increasingly he depended upon one or another form of public support for the arts.

By mid-century artists all over the world had begun more self-consciously to recognize that whatever their own culture they had common aspirations and problems. Intensification of nationalism influenced many of them in their experiments with materials and form, yet both in the West and in the East they refreshed themselves by drawing on forms from many parts of the world. More and more, in spite of national feeling, barriers of language and other idioms, and of conflicting political ideologies which extended to different conceptions of the function of the arts in society, they and their audiences became aware of each other on a world-wide scale. Films had a world-wide audience, and were shown at international festivals; the International Society of Contemporary Music presented works of new composers in different countries; international writers' congresses were held frequently. American and Siamese dance troupes appeared simultaneously in Rangoon, while Balinese, Kabuki and Indian dancers were popular on Broadway and elsewhere, and the Chinese Theatre and Russian Ballet played to full houses in London and other capitals, both West and East. An occasional writer, such as the Indian poet Rabindranath Tagore, was able to achieve a unique synthesis which made him an integral part of other cultural traditions as well as his own. With the aid of modern photography André Malraux drew on the ancient and modern arts of many cultures and parts of the world to convey in *Les Voix du silence* (1951) his conception that 'all art is man transcending his destiny'.

Yet expression remained infinitely varied in terms of the multitude of languages and of visual and musical idioms which embodied the world's manifold cultures, and of the individuality of the creative artist. The tendencies during these years cannot begin to be encompassed within the limits of the pages which follow. The works of numbers of writers and artists of first quality have necessarily been passed over, most especially those written in the less widely used languages; only a few have been mentioned to exemplify the trends discussed or because their influence was widespread and profound.[1,2]

CHAPTER XXXI

TENDENCIES IN LITERATURE AND THE ARTS IN THE WESTERN CULTURE AREAS[3]*

I. AT THE OPENING OF THE TWENTIETH CENTURY

BY the opening of the twentieth century the social changes brought by industrialism and the intellectual changes engendered by the spread of science and technology were already finding expression in the arts.

The classical Graeco-Roman and the Judaeo-Christian traditions, which had provided the principal formulations for western artists and writers in the pre-scientific, pre-industrial age, had ceased to be satisfactory vehicles for thought and expression.[4] Nineteenth-century theories of the origin of the species made man a part of nature instead of a special creation and turned attention to his actions as expressions of biological drives while questioning the concepts of conscience and sin which were the basis of traditional morality.

Extremes of wealth and poverty, the dehumanizing tendencies of aristocratic landowning, the helplessness of individuals in war, the revelation that serfs were men, the conflict of rationalism, the Church and Christian brotherhood had produced crises of conscience and social changes which were embodied in Tolstoy's *War and Peace* (1864–69) and Dostoevsky's *Brothers Karamazov* (1879); Tolstoy himself had turned his back on his previous way of life and his *Resurrection* (1899) augured a new order and kind of man.

In Britain a line of realistic novelists and critics like Thomas Hardy (1840–1928), William Morris (1834–96) and John Ruskin (1819–1900) had detailed the disintegration of rural society, the ugliness of industrial cities, the loss of craftsmanship and the experience of factory hands as men. The genteel tradition of bourgeois respectability had been relentlessly unmasked by the realism of French novelists after Gustave Flaubert's (1821–80) *Madame Bovary* (1857). It had been shaken to its foundations by the Norwegian dramatist Henrik Ibsen (1828–1906), whose dramas of social criticism and protest revealed the harshness of middle-class domesticity. The life of the slums had been grimly delineated by Émile Zola (1840–1902) in *Les Rougon-Macquart* (twenty volumes, 1871–93) and by the Russian Maxim Gorky's (1868–1936) glimpses into the *Lower Depths* (1902). The coming revolt of workers and their assertion of their right to life was the heart of Zola's *Germinal* (1885) and Gerhardt Hauptmann's (1862–1946) *The Weavers* (1892).

The Dutch painter Vincent Van Gogh (1853–90) had expressed the explosive energy in simple workers and in nature even in its apparently most

* Dr. Helen D. Lockwood collaborated in the preparation of this chapter.

ordered aspects. Paul Gauguin (1848–1903) had offered the French world of art an escape to the freshness of primitive life. The Danish critic and essayist Georg Brandes (1842–1927) had brought Nietzsche to world attention and introduced Scandinavian and Russian authors in western Europe.[5]

In poetry, eloquent descriptions of feeling were replaced by concentrated forms designed to evoke directly the feeling of a unique experience by the use of symbols and new metaphors. The influence of Stéphane Mallarmé (1842–98) and Jean Arthur Rimbaud (1854–91) spread. Mallarmé had sought to purify language of dead metaphors and discursive meanings, and to attain pure music of words. Rimbaud had sought to find forms so free and packed with associations that the full chaos of inner conflicts could be expressed.

In the visual arts, Auguste Rodin (1840–1917) had by 1900 turned sculpture from the static, draped figures of conventional decoration approved by academicians to dynamic characterizations. His combination of strength and mind, of faith in humanity and closeness to nature made him influential. His brilliant reinterpretation of motion and of surfaces related to the inner centre opened the way for the movements of the next decades, even though these movements—neo-classicism (Aristide Maillol, 1861–1944; Charles Despiau, 1874–1946), then Cubism and organic abstraction—broke away from his ruggedness and love of nature. (Pl. 33a, 33b.)

New forms in painting had begun to replace the naturalistic representation and the visual illusion of perspective characteristic of western art from the time of the Renaissance. A succession of French painters from Édouard Manet (1832–83) to Claude Monet (1840–1926), Georges Seurat (1859–91), Paul Cézanne (1839–1906) and others after them approached the problem of form by studying the relationships of impressions made on them by objects; others probed their own inner feelings directly, as did Edvard Munch (1863–1944) in Norway and Ernst Ludwig Kirchner (1880–1938), Vasily Kandinsky (1866–1944) and others in Germany. Whichever the approach, they were all trying to present not the outer appearance but their view of essential reality. Their interpretation thus became itself the object. They moved away from literal imitation to abstracting particular factors—light, lines, colour, planes, symbols of feeling. Thus during the last decades of the nineteenth century the ground was laid in philosophy and practice for the development of abstract art and new interpretations of the human image.[6, 7]

In music Richard Wagner (1813–83) and Johannes Brahms (1833–97) had loyal followings. The nineteenth century symphony was modified and new forms began to emerge. Brahms upheld the classical tradition but enriched the form with a sensuous lyricism partly drawn from delight in German folk-songs and gypsy songs and partly affected by the atmosphere of Vienna where he was living. The influence of Wagner's operas spread over the whole of the musical world—his conception of the unity of the arts, his large orchestra, his complex texture of *leitmotivs* making a continuity of psychological association, his bold freedom in harmony. Indeed it even affected the later orchestration of Nicolai Rimsky-Korsakov (1844–1908), a leader in the rising Russian national school. Opera itself was further varied under the stimulus of nationalism to include national history, legend, folk-song and -dance and to express these with orchestral originality and directness (Modest Mussorgsky: 1839–81: *Boris Godunov*, 1874; a succession of operas by Rimsky-Korsakov). Italian opera modified its traditional form to express first romantically and then more realistically the loves and hates of ordinary people (Pietro Mascagni, 1863–1945: *Cavalleria Rusticana*, 1890 and Giacomo Puccini, 1858–1924: *Madame Butterfly*, 1904); in Giuseppe Verdi (1813–1901) it reached high dramatic skill and clarity of orchestra in interpreting Shakespearian subjects (*Otello*, 1887; *Falstaff*, 1893).

The symphony had developed in magnitude, expressing boundless personal sorrow (Peter Tchaikovsky, 1840–93: *Sixth Symphony*, 1893) or ecstasy of mysticism (Alexander Scriabin, 1871–1915: *Third Symphony—The Divine Poem; Fourth Symphony—Poem of Ecstasy*). Scriabin's radical use of harmonies gave fresh effects to an essentially classical structure. Gustav Mahler (1860–1911) expanded it to include double choirs of instruments and of voices and new percussion instruments in a gigantic effort to convey religious significance (*Eighth Symphony*, 1907). Symphonic poems and rhapsodies of Franz Liszt (1811–86), romantic tone poems and operas of Richard Strauss (1864–1949) using even larger orchestras than Wagner, eastern tales of Rimsky-Korsakov, Finnish legends by Jean Sibelius (1865–1957), lyrical suites by Edvard Grieg (1843–1907) introduced new subjects, precipitated debates about the validity of programme music and fostered national self-expression; they continued a movement toward freeing music from tonal harmonies and introduced changes in structure.

The basis for new architectural styles had been laid with the use of some of the materials that industry had made available. The Crystal Palace which housed an international exhibit in London in 1851 had introduced the possibilities of iron and glass and the first 'skyscrapers' had thrust their heads above city roofs in the 1880s and 1890s. By 1900 Louis H. Sullivan (1856–1924) and Frank Lloyd Wright (1869–1959) in the United States had begun to design office buildings and houses that would change the face of the rising industrial cities.

As literature and the arts broke out of their traditional moulds, they took two main directions which presaged the courses which would be followed in the succeeding years. Many writers adopted a rational approach. George Bernard Shaw (1856–1950) accepted the technological, money-based milieu as the given raw material that had to be civilized and he brought to bear the study of history, economics and biology in developing his conception of social change and human evolution. Anatole France's (1844–1924) interest in philosophy led him to religious scepticism and belief in human progress without intervention of any mythical personal deity. Painters such as Seurat and

Cézanne made experiments applying the physics of light and principles of geometry.

In contrast to these rational efforts to find and express natural truth, varied tendencies gathered up into a trend toward romanticism. In the decades before 1900, under the influence of the English arts and crafts movement started in 1870 by William Morris, a style known as *Jugendstil* (in France *Art Nouveau*, in Britain *Modern*) expressed a conscious revolt against historical styles and the ugliness of industrial technology and rationality. It took many forms in striving for a contemporary vocabulary and for originality, especially in the graphic arts, architectural ornamentation and interior decoration; its decorative element was felt widely in paintings of such men as Van Gogh and Gauguin, Pierre Bonnard (1867–1947) and Jean Edouard Vuillard (1868–1940) and in some architecture.

Similar revolt in literature expressed itself by escape into a world of fantasy or colourful bygone ages and in the exaltation of writers as a separate *élite* having no connection with ordinary society (Maurice Maeterlinck, 1862–1949; Hugo von Hofmannsthal, 1870–1929; Stefan George, 1868–1932; Alain Fournier, 1886–1914; Ricarda Huch, 1864–1947). Other writers who also turned their backs on natural science and rationality but were more concerned with truth of actual life probed unexplored realities of emotion and actions of men in situations of crisis or madness or under the impact of primitive cultures. They sought modes of expressing directly the emotions of men cut off from their social roots and subject to chance and weakness (Joseph Conrad, 1857–1924), or seeking renewal of life by following instinct (D. H. Lawrence, 1885–1930), or oppressed by the sense of perversity, decadence or madness in Europe itself (André Gide, 1869–1951; Jacob Wassermann, 1873–1934; Gustav Meyrink, 1868–1932; Franz Kafka, 1881–1924).

All kinds of literary and artistic expression—books, pictures, serious music—continued to find their audiences among the cultivated bourgeois class of patrons who could afford the arts. It was they and the *nouveau riche* who bought pictures to hang in their homes and supported museums. They bought and read the books and magazines. They made up the audiences and provided the support for concerts, opera, ballet and theatre.[8, 9]

Artists and writers themselves generally came from the same bourgeois class. As in all periods, they performed a number of different functions: as artists in the classical sense of 'fine arts' and 'literature'; as designers of physical objects from cathedrals or skyscrapers to clothing or toys; as entertainers at all levels from grand opera to circuses; and as reporters and interpreters of information, which might range from on-the-spot news to a popular presentation of a scientific theory.

Those who identified themselves with the tradition of the fine arts thought of themselves as dedicated professionals whose sense of calling and skill distinguished them from members of other professions and from amateurs in the arts. They saw their role as that of seekers who must therefore be free to probe and express the reality behind the appearances in any way that they could. The artist as a free spirit was a kind of ultimate in a free society. Society could take the results of his quest, gaining enlightenment and providing him with a living; or it could disregard or reject them, leaving him to make his living by teaching his art, doing journeyman's work in it or engaging in some unrelated work, or else to remain poor and lonely.

Those who functioned as designers, entertainers or interpreters had to relate themselves directly to their society, for their expression found its outlets through the agencies engaged in production, entertainment or the spreading of information.[10]

II. THE YEARS OF INNOVATION

The early years of the twentieth century, especially the decade from about 1905 to the first world war, were distinguished by an outburst of experimentation in all the arts. In these years the trends present at the opening of the century were carried forward and virtually all the principles which resulted in distinctively twentieth-century forms of expression were explored.

Until the first world war shattered men's faith in unbroken movement toward peace and progress, the tempo and sense of change brought hope more often than confusion or despair to the artists and writers of Europe and America. The advancement of technology at first seemed to reinforce the faith in progress. It was now possible to conceive a standard of living for all people which should mean that they could have opportunity to use their human qualities and become fully developed free beings, who might even evolve biologically into higher forms of life, more adequate, especially, in the use of reason.

When writers and painters came to look closely at their society, to be sure, they found that great contrasts of wealth and poverty remained and that success itself tended to bring conformity, mechanization, preoccupation with property, deadening fatigue and compensating sensuality rather than freedom of the spirit. Production and machines appeared to be worshipped as new gods while owners, managers and bench workers alike were driven by the tempo required for the market rather than by direct human need. Artists began to feel that science and technology were not great liberating agents after all, and to revolt against the stifling of imagination for the sake of efficiency. Yet playwrights like George Bernard Shaw and novelists like H. G. Wells (1866–1946) believed that educated men would use their intelligence to remedy social ills, once these were exposed, and that creative evolution was part of the process of the universe. In this they expressed a widely held view.

But as changes accelerated and deepened, there was widespread consciousness of loss of standards and need of some vital reassertion of imaginative truth. From the seventeenth century, artists had been in a Europe changing through experimental science, and they had had to discover ways to express an enlarging and shifting variety of orders. There was no longer a leading style, such as Gothic or Baroque or heroic drama.

When in the twentieth century the discoveries of Planck and Einstein brought an even profounder revolution in science, people recognized that something momentous had happened that could shake the world, though they knew that they did not understand it. While physicists were coming to treat their generalizations not as true absolutely but as true within a certain frame of reference, artists were already seeking ways to convey the shiftings of relationships. 'Relativity' became a concept to apply to nearly everything. The apparent implications of the new theories and the confusion of standards pushed artists to ever more revolutionary expression. Time was a dimension to be included in many different ways and needed a relevant language. Motion and lines of force were more important than mass. Values were tested by experience, itself breaking the bounds of tradition.

In psychological relationships, writers and artists continued to follow the line of Jean Jacques Rousseau, William Wordsworth and Feodor Dostoevsky who, by direct, self-conscious observation and imagination, had revealed many aspects of man's nature, from delicate sensing to depths of hidden motivation. Their understanding that knowledge comes by way of sense experience and that environment influences people's behaviour was now beginning to be confirmed by experimental psychology with its demonstrations of conditioned reflexes. Their own psychological probings received further impetus from Freud's evidence that this conditioning goes on at very early stages of life, and that a basic creative drive, the libido, expresses itself in various symbolic ways in daily life and in dreams.

Yet in these times no Leonardo da Vinci or Goethe could comprehend the whole scientific and human revolution of his age, could both experiment scientifically and make great works of art. Artists and writers sensed the impact of scientific thinking, but few were themselves students of the sciences. There were important exceptions, such as the sculptor Naum Gabo (1890–   ) and the painters Vasily Kandinsky and Paul Klee (1879–1940). But the principal influence of the new science was through the climate of change rather than the direct application of scientific knowledge.

Artists of all sorts were caught up in the atmosphere of change. They tried one experiment after another, confident that they would find ways to penetrate to new realities and gain their own fresh vision of life, and they sought evidences of human dignity and man's identity in folk cultures, new strata of society and new psychological depths. Conscious as they were of different kinds of reality, they felt the need for new forms. Cubist painters analysed shapes that could be seen with the naked eye; constructivists looked for the scientific law behind specific observations and derived abstractions mathematically; expressionists abstracted feelings directly without reference to external images. But all selected some essential quality and contemplated it in its own separate context, which was no longer defined, as in the old perspective, by the visual illusion of distance but rather by the field of force and time.

Writers intent on probing immediately and swiftly to the essence of experience rejected the long-winded eloquence of romanticism and its vague feeling of the infinite; they rejected descriptive realism and naturalism. They were preoccupied with techniques for evoking sense impressions freshly, the blurring of senses into each other, and all sorts of fleeting feelings as interest shifted from the actual world to dreams and hallucinations. They used elliptical forms that could be intense and fresh. In the new forms of the novel they aimed to evoke experience rather than to describe or comment on it.

Gifted and energetic young poets, composers, painters and architects knew each other, formed societies, wrote manifestoes and produced their works in the midst of lively interchange of ideas. True, they scorned the *bourgeoisie* which had to be their audience and they did not discover an audience in the industrial masses. Many had difficulty in being heard and at times in subsisting. While some gloried in the possibilities of the age, many felt that the creative imagination was under attack; expressiveness for them became an end in itself. Already overtones of neurosis were present. Some of the most seminal originators saw worlds that had no hope in them. Marcel Proust (1871–1922), who started writing of personal identity eternally alive in memory, came to be more and more deeply disgusted by the decaying upper class among whom he lived, until in the end he saw that even love among them brought only destruction and finally their own oblivion in death and absence from anyone else's memory; the only value left was relentless uncovering of their vanity in a work of art.

The atmosphere for most of the younger men of these years, however, was one of possibility and they engaged with positive vigour in the battle for expression and acceptance. Even the powerful middle class itself was more ready to accept change and to listen to new voices than it had been, partly because it was caught up in the momentum of industrial progress and partly because the conscience of its more enlightened members forced them to see the misery and ignorance of masses of people.

The struggles of artists and writers to find new forms of expression and to reach new levels of reality were dominated by two opposing concepts of man's nature, the rational and the irrational, with correspondingly distinct approaches to life and art.

In these years, as in the previous decades and those to follow, one line of artists and writers grasped the tools which science put in their hands, adopted the scientist's objective viewpoint, applied rigorously a more relevant and psychologically deepened analysis, and sought to find and express new order and relationships beneath and beyond traditional institutions and forms. The systematic experiments of the cubist painters were of this order, as were the plays of social criticism, the theories of such composers as Arnold Schönberg

(1874–1951) and Paul Hindemith (1895–   ), and the work of sculptors and architects who called themselves 'constructivists'.

In the other line were writers and artists of many schools who denied the existence of the rational or saw it submerged by man's irrationality. They rejected the method of science as well as the kind of life which science and technology had produced. They saw man responding to inescapable irrational forces acting within the individual to produce his emotions, and to bring romantic or mystical unity with the universe or regression to a primitive state. They tried to convey such responses in language, colour, tone or shape.

The two viewpoints persisted side by side and interacting in the expression of the twentieth century, one view or the other becoming dominant in a particular place or time, in one or another of the arts, or in the work of a specific artist. The greatest artists, as in the past, combined both views, as did some groups, most notably in the Bauhaus of the 1920s where sculptors and painters of both schools joined architects to develop buildings and furniture, theatre design and display which should be modern in design and human in intent. But generally the two tendencies operated separately and in counterpoint with each other, the contrast between them sharpened and their interplay made more dramatic by the intellectual development of the time which carried both the rational and the irrational to new heights and depths—the magnificent achievements of the scientific mind and imagination and the appalling brutality of war and terror.

Artists and writers in this decade of experimentation used the tools which they were fashioning chiefly to unmask society, to tear away every sort of convention, and to probe for inner meaning and experience. Carrying forward the line of the nineteenth-century realists, writers and artists assaulted one after another of bourgeois society's best established institutions and most cherished values. They attempted to bring the detachment of the natural scientist to their scrutiny of society, as historians were examining the past by means of 'objective' history. Treating all old conceptions of value and ways of describing life as mere conventions, dead and irrelevant, they brought everything under microscopic search for some new interpretation which would coincide with reality and evoke it. They assumed that for man to attain his full development as a human being he must be able to express his full nature, including his biological drives, and they regarded any morality which was not based on these needs as contrary to their conception of human values.

As they looked at their society, they saw two worlds of the poor and the rich, those whose fate was unremitting, repetitive toil, misery and early death, and those who rose to success or enjoyed the fruits of industry and trade. And they saw that this industrial society not only presented grave problems of wealth and poverty but raised serious doubts as to the life values of the successful. So they examined critically the bourgeois family, relations between parents and children, monogamy, prostitution, the professions and the courts, religion, property, women, the masses. They detailed the texture of life in

drab industrial towns (Arnold Bennett, 1867–1931); they exposed the posses-
siveness and sturdiness of men of property in the upper middle class and their
complete failure to understand love or the creative imagination (John
Galsworthy, 1867–1933: *Man of Property*, 1906; Thomas Mann, 1875–1955:
Buddenbrooks, 1901); they looked for and found redeeming human values in
those whom society scorned, the lowest drunkard, the pitiful failure; they
found the nobility of work among peasants tilling the soil (Knut Hamsun,
1859–1952: *Growth of the Soil*, 1917) and factory workers, and also the
potential tragedy and grandeur in the rising revolt of these workers (Maxim
Gorky, *Mother*, 1907); and they showed up the superficiality of those engaged
in social reform who did not recognize the relation between the basic structure
of society and human need (G. B. Shaw, *Major Barbara*, 1905).

George Bernard Shaw expressed the point of view which underlay this
scrutiny in commenting on the meaning of his play about prostitution, *Mrs
Warren's Profession*:

'I must, however, warn my readers that my attacks are directed against themselves, not against my stage figures. They cannot too thoroughly understand
that the guilt of defective social organization does not lie alone on the people
who actually work the commercial makeshifts which the defects make
inevitable ... but with the whole body of citizens whose public opinion, public
action, and public contribution as ratepayers alone can replace Sartorius's
slums with decent dwellings and Mrs Warren's profession with honorable
industries guarded by a humane code and a "moral minimum wage".'*

Yet Shaw believed in life and the evolution of man; his sure comic sense,
devastating as it was, did not undermine certainty and open the way to
neurosis as did Thomas Mann's classic novel *Buddenbrooks*. For here the
child of the decaying German bourgeois family is the one who himself
becomes the critic and challenger of his own world, which he sees as crushing
creative vitality and artistic sensitivity. With similar disillusionment, Thomas
Mann's brother, Heinrich (1871–1950), grimly satirized the fatal German
adoration of authority in military, civil and home life (*Professor Unrat*, 1905;
Der Untertan, 1918).

The conventions which artists and writers attacked most aggressively were
the taboos around the subject of sex. What had been the special province of
the *risqué* French novel in the nineteenth century became a main focus of
attention. Samuel Butler (1835–1902) had not dared to publish his autobiographical novel, *The Way of All Flesh*, when he wrote it from the 1870s on,
and it appeared only in 1903 after his death. But in 1891 Frank Wedekind
(1864–1918) had broken the silence about sex with his drama *Frühlingser-
wachen* and in the decade before the first world war the stories and plays of
Arthur Schnitzler (1862–1931), who brought a Viennese doctor's detachment

* G. B. Shaw, Preface to *Plays Pleasant and Unpleasant* (London, 1898).

to the subject of sex, became famous all over Europe, and D. H. Lawrence's *Sons and Lovers* was an immediate literary success when it appeared in 1913.

In their exploration of sex a succession of novels, poems, plays and musical compositions analysed the relationship between father and son into its hidden hatred and unrelenting battle; they looked at the relations between husbands and wives, treated marriages as breakable when they had become conventional and hampered the free expression of creative impulse, and assumed that women as well as men were struggling to be free of frustration and were active in pursuit of their need; they viewed the 'eternal triangle' from every angle except that of traditional morality—lyrically, realistically, in terms of new frustrations when lovers found that the satisfaction of their physical attraction shut them off from other relationships. D. H. Lawrence sought always the positive expression of sex and its resulting freedom enhancing all life; he found it, not in people bound up by success, power and high position, but in workers such as miners or gamekeepers, and he searched for this freedom to the ends of the earth.

As they unmasked the face of their own world, a number of writers and artists thought that they saw in primitive society vitality and beauty which civilization had overlaid or destroyed. Stimulated by publications in the growing field of anthropology and aided by the ethnological museums founded in the last quarter of the nineteenth century where African masks and other examples of the art of primitive peoples could be studied, they looked for evidence of the deepest human values among people unrepressed by modern civilization. Sir James Frazer's study, *The Golden Bough* (1890) furnished materials to writers and artists and stimulated their imagination. French and German painters used African masks to convey what they saw in the human face; Igor Stravinsky (1882–   ) drew inspiration from the primitive, ancient Russian folk ways for his *Le Sacre du printemps* (1913); D. H. Lawrence, in *The Plumed Serpent* (1926), glorified the unity of man with nature through the symbols and rituals of the Indians of Mexico.

In their recourse to primitivism, artists and writers borrowed external forms and projected their own longings into their image of primitive life. Few if any in this period, or indeed in later years, recognized the rigorous discipline, rigid traditionalism and complex symbolism of primitive expression or learned to share the vision and emotions of its creators.

When they contemplated the place of man in the universe, they confronted the necessity of accepting emotionally what since the time of Copernicus men had known intellectually, that the pre-Copernican view of a man-centred universe was false and that the heavens did not revolve around man's planet, guided by a beneficent providence ready to intervene on man's behalf or to order the spheres in relation to his welfare.

Faced with the problem of man's place in an indifferent universe, some such as Thomas Hardy saw man as helpless, tossed about like a cork, buffeted by chance and blind fate, overpowered by nature and destroyed by his own passions. In such a world, tragedy reigned. Others, like Maxim Gorky or Martin Andersen Nexö (1869–1954) who followed Karl Marx, saw the destiny of man as inseparable from the society of which he was an organic part, and society itself as the product of inevitable forces operating dialectically to produce successive patterns of action, reaction and synthesis. Those who accepted the concept of the philosopher Henri Bergson that there was a vital force making the world evolve creatively, saw man as an individual part of this *élan vital*.

While most writers and artists found the Christian synthesis inadequate for the twentieth century, a minority of distinguished and eloquent Catholic writers, such as Paul Claudel (1868–1954) in France and others elsewhere, reasserted the continuing validity of the Catholic view. As others became disheartened in their search for a satisfactory new view of man's place in the universe, the sureness of these writers helped to keep their influence alive.

The great upthrust in experiment during these years went on in all the capitals of Europe, and along similar lines in all the arts.

In Paris, which came to be known as the 'city of light' because so many movements of the arts were centred there, an exhibition of new painters in 1905 marked the beginning of twentieth-century painting. These painters were known as *Les Fauves* ('the wild beasts') because of their startling and dramatic use of brilliant colours instead of perspective as forces determining the composition of their paintings. Their use of colour was an example of the principle which was to dominate all twentieth-century painting. Painters were not imitating nature, they were conveying their own awareness. The picture itself thus became the object. They distorted parts for emphasis; they filled the canvas with large blocks of colour to make designs rather than to convey distances and produced an emotional impact by the colour relationships within the design.

The most gifted of this group, Henri Matisse (1869–1954) Georges Braque (1882–   ), Georges Rouault (1871–1958), André Derain (1880–1953), Maurice de Vlaminck (1876–1959), went far beyond the first stages of violent colour. Each created a succession of experimental works in painting or sculpture, exploring the human figure, religious passion and nature. Matisse loved life and expressed it always in harmonious patterns which he worked to make more and more fundamental, as in the five forms of 'Head of Jeannette' (1910–12). In his *Notes to a Painter* (1908), which were read by many young painters, he said: 'What interests me most is the human figure. It is through it that I best succeed in expressing the nearly religious feeling that I have toward life.' He explained that he studied a face until he found 'lines which suggest the deep gravity which persists in every human being'. Rouault, profoundly religious, used the new techniques and principles to make compositions resembling mediaeval stained glass and to probe to depths of hypocrisy, suffering or spiritual insight. Braque became a leader in a new movement which grew out of the feeling of a need for more structure. (Pl. 34a–e.)

The need for structure was crystallized by the retrospective exhibit of Paul Cézanne (1839–1906) in 1906 which presented twenty years of his unknown work. At once he became a central influence, decisive in turning painters to consider planes, cylinders and spheres. A new group emerged who analysed the geometry of objects—a breakfast table including its newspaper, a nude descending the stairs, a machine. They abstracted the crossing and recrossing of planes and the projections of them into space beyond their immediate mass; they minimized the factor of colour and separated it from the structure. They came to be known as Cubists. Braque and Picasso were the leaders and by the 1920s every young artist had to understand their principles if he was to be of his time.

Pablo Picasso's (1881–   ) 'Les Demoiselles d'Avignon' (1907) embodied the new attitude. Here he abandoned the rounded and slender shapes and delicate bluish colours of the acrobats and clowns whose inner sadness he had painted compassionately, and instead he now painted angular, distorted women, their harsh faces turned two ways at once or shaped like the African masks which he had been studying. Braque began to paint many facets of an object seen at the same time. Juan Gris (1887–1929) developed a style which maintained geometric severity. Fernand Léger (1881–1955), who loved machines and the common vitality of the new age, enlarged and simplified human figures to the lines of force of machines and strongly outlined their bold colours; he thus at once simplified and revealed with arresting clarity such daily rituals as women at lunch ('Le grand déjeuner', 1921). (Pl. 21, 22.)

These painters were rejected by the salons at first, but they exhibited their paintings independently and gradually became a major influence upon the main currents of twentieth century art. They laid the foundation for the new architecture and industrial design.

Similar movements, each claiming its own special principles, flourished in other countries. In Italy a group led by the poet Filippo Tommaso Marinetti (1876–1944) and the sculptor-painter, U. Boccioni (1882–1916) called themselves 'Futurist' and sought an idiom appropriate to modern cities. They came out with manifestoes and works expressing the conception that the dynamic of motion was the essential reality of modern life. Their *Manifesto*, (February 20, 1909), said: 'Everything moves, everything runs, everything is being rapidly transformed.' Boccioni in his sculpture experimented with analysis of the relationship of time and space in his 'Development of Bottle in Space' (1912) and his bronze 'Unique Forms of Continuity in Space' (1913). (Pl. 35a.)

In Germany, as in France, the years 1905–6 were key years in which artists paralleled *Les Fauves* in their insistence that the picture is not a copy of things but an entity in its own right made out of the artist's reactions. Various groups formed in different parts of Germany were influenced, not only by French symbolist poets and post-impressionist painters, but by the expression of passion in the Norwegian painter Edvard Munch whose works were exhibited in 1907, and the stimulus toward intuitive probing of inner experience from such dramatists as Ibsen and August Strindberg (1849–1912), the philosopher Friedrich Nietzsche, and the Viennese school of psychoanalysts.

By 1912, the group known as *Der Blaue Reiter* had formulated and expressed with passionate intensity (*Spiritual Art*, 1912; *Der Blaue Reiter*, 1912) the principles known as German Expressionism, to be applied to painting, music and drama, and Vasily Kandinsky had applied them in the first abstract water-colour. Kandinsky, Franz Marc (1880–1916), August Macke (1887–1914), Alexey Jawlensky (1867–1941) and Paul Klee were the painters who formed the core of the group; Arnold Schönberg spoke for music. Marc was killed in the first world war but Kandinsky and Klee continued as leaders in the movement of abstract painting, Kandinsky relying on intuition and Klee combining with intuition more observation and rational analysis.

These artists had a religious feeling of unity with the universe and conceived of their paintings, in Marc's words as 'pictorial allegories expressing the underlying mystical design of the universe'. They believed that the inner world of feeling could be made immediately visible without resort to the images of the outer world, i.e. that the abstract power of pure colour paralleled the psychological effects of musical tones, and they thought of abstract paintings as symphonic movements. They found in the physicist's conception of fields of force the basis for their forms of kinetic motion and they thought that the new evidence from psychology and biology confirmed their belief that human perceptions are valid reflections of reality. Therefore they conceived of their pictures not as anarchical or disordered violations but as new expressions of the creation of the universe.

In Russia, too, from 1907 on, various groups of young artists were turning away from naturalism. They studied French art and also old Russian ecclesiastical art which interested them because of its tendency to abstraction, its use of line and the way its perspective suggested motion. Their major tendency was toward pure mathematical abstraction, 'the expression of non-objectivity' as the 'suprematist' Kasimir Malevich (1878–1935) described his 'Black Square' on a white background (1913). In 1913 the suprematist group, Malevich, Vladimir Tatlin (1885–   ), and the brothers Antoine Pevsner (1886–   ) and Naum Gabo, with a group of architects, engineers and painters in Moscow, introduced principles of 'constructivism'. Pevsner had worked alongside the cubists in Paris. His brother had gone all over Europe studying art forms, but also he had studied mathematics, physics and engineering at the University of Munich and had made three-dimensional models of mathematical formulae. The constructivists considered both cubists and futurists limited because not scientific enough. They believed that pure representation of beauty could not be found by means that were merely personal and subjective. They aimed for abstraction based on mathematics and an underlying scientific law, and for forms relevant to the expressive qualities of the machine, which they recognized as dominant in the new world. They made constructions in space; they used steel as their medium; the forms were dynamic and partly functional.[11, 12] (Pl. 24.)

Pioneer architects in many countries, such as Victor Horta (1861–1947) and Henry C. Van de Velde (1863–1957) in Belgium, H. P. Berlage (1865–1934) in Holland, Charles Rennie Mackintosh (1868–1928) in Scotland, Peter Behrens (1868–1940) in Germany and Frank Lloyd Wright in the United States, revolted against the false overlay of imitated Renaissance and Baroque decoration on steel structures and began to construct office buildings with smooth walls, and houses fitted to their sites and their human use. Peter Behrens in Berlin insisted that the shape of the building must match the new materials, demonstrating the principle in a turbine factory of steel and glass in 1908 for the Allgemeine Elektrizitäts Gesellschaft. He insisted, too, that the quality of industrial design must be as high as that of the best craftsmen of the past. The three most important European architects of the twentieth century, Walter Gropius (1883–   ), Ludwig Mies van der Rohe (1886–   ) and Le Corbusier (1887–   ), all began by working with Behrens. The Cubist painters' studies of planes, rectangles, cubes and flat colours contributed to development in architecture, especially through the part played by the Dutch cubist painter, Piet Mondrian (1872–1944), in forming and guiding the *de Stijl* group, and through Le Corbusier's association with Léger and his own experiments in painting along cubist lines.[13] (Pl. 25.)

Experiments with musical forms paralleled those in the visual arts. Though they started somewhat later, the new musical idioms of the early twentieth century had much in common with the impressionist painting and the symbolist poetry of the preceding generation. Claude Debussy (1862–1918) renewed music for France and thence for all Europe by bringing into it the techniques of impressionism. His opera *Pelléas et Mélisande* in 1902 marked the end of the dominance of Wagnerian opera, and his tone poem *La Mer* (1905) evoked changes of the sea, the ground-swell, the counterpoint of light and winds playing over the surface and the dark mysterious depths. He used a new scale and rhythms such as those of Javanese gamelans; his open ninths and unresolved chords gave an atmosphere of freedom and his successions of chords conveyed iridescence and shifting motion. He gave music an idiom for expressing directly subtle, evanescent sensations and veiled feeling hitherto inaccessible to it. Other composers learned from him—Maurice Ravel (1875–1937), whose strong sense of structure and astringent dissonance made him most influential among the young French composers, Stravinsky, Bela Bartok (1881–1945), Ralph Vaughan Williams (1872–1958), Gustav Holst (1874–1934) and Jean Sibelius.[14]

Igor Stravinsky showed the influence of Debussy's innovations in his early music; he added a vast orchestra and his own emancipated rhythms based on Russian tradition. He was brought to Paris by the Russian choreographer, Sergei Diaghilev (1872–1929) where he wrote *L'Oiseau de feu* in 1910 and

Petrushka in 1911. These ballets established a new form in which the music and the pantomime of the dance were an integral structure. The brilliant originality of the music combined with the luxurious virtuosity of Diaghilev as director made them a sensational success. *Le Sacre du printemps* shocked its audiences when first performed in 1913 by its daring, barbaric rhythms and the primitive fierceness of the story, but by the end of the first world war it seemed, especially to young people, the very expression of western Europe's regression to blood sacrifice in 1914–18.

In Hungary Bela Bartok was drawn to Debussy in 1907, for he thought his music resembled folk songs. This helped to free Bartok from some conventionality and he wrote an opera (*Duke Bluebeard's Castle*, 1911–18) which was considered an Hungarian *Pelléas et Mélisande*. But then he went on his own way, studying and using the folk songs of Hungary, Yugoslavia and the Middle East, living among the people in order to collect their songs. He transcribed these songs and evolved harmonies for them; he combined them and art music in his major choral work *Cantata Profana* (1930) and made his own melodies for them. He experimented with various ancient modes and with atonalism. By the time of the first world war the direction of his style was clear, though it was not until the 1930s that he emerged as the composer of quartets comparable to those of Beethoven.

Gustav Mahler, composing in Vienna in the line of Brahms and nineteenth-century romanticism, originated the symphonic poem. In *Das Lied von der Erde* (1908) orchestra and voice dramatically interplay with subtle psychological shadings in a series of six episodes based on ancient Chinese poetry and covering the whole destiny of man to the final profound resignation before death. More experimentally, Arnold Schönberg, who had understood and used Wagner profoundly and who had grown beyond him to the need for new principles of composition, composed *Pierrot Lunaire* (1913) using atonality and striking contrasts to express the tension and anxiety that became the characteristic mood of the century. He belonged to the German Expressionists and wrote in *Der Blaue Reiter* along with Kandinsky. He introduced a radically new system of composition with a highly complex, mathematical musical language based on twelve notes used in series. This system came to be influential with composers later in the century and was brilliantly used by his two pupils, Alban Berg (1885–1935), who made it psychologically descriptive, and Anton von Webern (1883–1945) who made it more spare and abstract.

Musical awakening extended to Finland, Czechoslovakia, England and other countries. Sibelius in a series of symphonies from 1900–24 brought Finnish music into the classical line and made significant modifications of symphonic form. In England for the first time in centuries original English music flourished again. It was based on old English themes, folk songs, use of ancient modes and closeness to the temper of the country. Vaughan Williams in *Fantasia on a Theme from Tallis* (1909) took England away from imitation of continental music by his use of modal development of a sixteenth-century English theme, by his original rhythms and by a serious, aspiring splendour and orchestral richness. He and Gustav Holst were leaders in bringing new idioms to many kinds of choral and orchestral compositions. Choral societies and music festivals encouraged young composers who experimented with orchestral instrumentation, cross-rhythms of old madrigals, dramatic choral music, symphonies and opera. Among these Benjamin Britten (1913–   ) was especially successful in bringing into use the traditional English gift of melody.

Writers, not less than painters and musicians, felt the need of new forms. In trying to find ways to strip away the layers of convention and traditional connotation and to express new depths of consciousness that had not previously been exposed, they needed tools to explore the irrational. Marcel Proust, writing his search for identity in memory, analysed parts of a pattern of feeling that would be set off again and again later by recurrence of its key theme. Poets tried free verse and sought newly living possibilities in language itself, either stripping away all ornament and finding the word which conveyed the exact image, or seeking fresh comparisons used as private symbols and aiming at musical effect rather than meaning. Like the painters, symbolist novelists and poets insisted that since there was no reality except that interpreted through their perceptions, the form of the novel or poem was the reality; they too were demonstrating 'art for art's sake', as in the work of Paul Valéry (1871–1945), Proust, William Butler Yeats (1865–1939) or Rainer Maria Rilke (1875–1926).

Artists in all fields, convinced of the unity of the arts, explored together their interrelationships. The musicians set the works of the symbolist poets to music while the painters illustrated the texts. Several of the cubist painters designed the décor for Diaghilev's ballets.

The audiences for the artists' work remained up to the first world war essentially what they had been in the late nineteenth century, and the artists' relation to them continued to be based upon the cash nexus between the detached artist and the middle-class concert and theatre goers, museum visitors and purchasers of easel paintings and books.

The big orchestras in the capitals of Europe, organized to give the public serious music of the great tradition, tended to provide programmes of music that was already known and accepted. Many who attended did so as a sort of ritual to which they exposed themselves while remaining undisturbed. It rested with the conductor, who had emerged as one of the most important figures in making music, and to some extent with the virtuoso, to determine what music would be played.

Some conductors were interested in the new music and either commissioned or found works which they played occasionally, well surrounded with safer pieces, but gradually accustoming the audiences to newer sounds. Choral societies in cities, choirs in churches and musical festivals used new music in similar small amounts, but did provide some outlet and stimulus. But the difficulty of developing their own audience and of earning a living beset all pioneering composers now that the patronage of church and court was gone. Bartok's music began to be played extensively only after his death, and Schönberg never achieved popularity, though his theories kept increasing in influence among younger composers.

Painters and sculptors were in an even more difficult situation, for the middle class which could afford original works wanted paintings for the walls of their houses that were easily recognizable, decorative and pleasant to live with. Neither the artists' view of life nor their experiments with form fulfilled these requirements. Although portrait-painting continued to flourish at the richer levels of society where having family portraits was a snobbish symbol or to honour public figures, the new photography made portraiture less essential to preserve likenesses. In buildings constructed according to either functional or organic principles, decorative features which had been furnished by wall painting and sculpture were provided by the ways in which the structural materials themselves were used. Churches were largely imitative of old styles, conforming to tradition and conventional taste.

So easel-painting and independent sculpture became something personal to the artist, in which he felt himself free to say whatever he could find out about reality. His audience was neither present nor of concern to him. Museums or private collections were the principal repositories of his work. Salons and art dealers acted as intermediaries between artist and owner. Some rising men of property adopted the aristocratic tradition of connoisseurship, partly as a hobby and partly as a sign of success. Some museums showed, and began to buy, new works by contemporary artists. Within this special world, art became a sort of cult for its own sake, the museum a place where works were enshrined, and the artist a dedicated seeker guided by his own inner light.

Writers for their part retained a more direct relationship with those who read and saw their works, the middle-class readers and theatre-goers who saw their own lives depicted and dissected. Audiences were at first shocked by George Bernard Shaw, not knowing whether to take him as a clown or a prophet, but gradually he became popular. The reading public initially repudiated and then came to accept each new level in the uncovering of sex drives. They protested against free verse as well as free love. But they were losing their sense of certainty in the rightness of their own place and the beneficence of their society, and were ready to respond with acceptance and even eagerness to the exposures and insights which writers had to offer.

An increasingly important link between the reading, listening and viewing public and those who produced works of art was furnished by the critics whose dicta filled the columns of many new journals devoted to the arts and appeared increasingly in journals of opinion and the daily press. The critics' judgments often meant for the artist the difference between acceptance with the promise of present or future income, and failure. The less cultivated and independent-minded public learned to take its cue from their views. But sometimes the artists found them ruthless and lacking in understanding; Schönberg at one time founded a society to play new music which should be closed to all journalists.

III. THE 1920S AND AFTER

The first world war brought to a tragic close the period of creative experimentation in the arts and the hope for social regeneration with which the century opened. It shook European society to its foundations and made a mockery of what remained of traditional values. It broke up the groups of artists, writers and musicians who had known each other and worked together. Although Paris remained a magnet which drew artists and writers to its Left Bank, the image of the 'city of light' gradually dimmed. From the time of the first world war on, European artists and writers felt themselves caught in a cultural crisis, heirs of a sick society, uncertain of man's nature but confronted with terrible evidences of its irrationality.

Outside of western Europe, most notably in North and South America, countries which had remained culturally dependent long after they had gained political independence emerged from cultural colonialism during these years. The shock of the war and the European crisis stimulated tendencies already present in the United States and the Latin American countries to explore and voice the richness of their land, their people and their historic traditions and the qualities of their emerging national cultures. The USSR, intent on building a new society established by revolution, enlisted its writers and artists as workers to help accomplish this task, and, on the basis of the Marxist-Leninist conception of society, evolved principles of socialist realism to guide their work. What had been a more or less common western cultural evolution up to the war thus tended to become a series of related but distinctive national developments, which by the 1950s had acquired recognizably different qualities.

1. WESTERN EUROPE

(a) The crisis of European culture

For western Europe the dominant note from the 1920s onward was one of deep uncertainty. Few artists and writers, except those who dedicated themselves to the new architecture or the spread of information or some of the forms of mass entertainment, found ways to relate themselves positively to the main currents of modern life. But in their expression of conflict, absurdity or chaos they often voiced the confusions and anxieties which beset many of their contemporaries. Their honesty took away sham glories and supports and readied the ground for new growth.

Against the background of violent and drastic change wrought by the war and the October revolution, the artists' pre-war attacks on convention which had seemed daring and radical appeared tame, and their new forms became accepted and even popular. They now had the war itself to interpret. Even from the beginning of the fighting, a novelist such as Romain Rolland (1866–1944) protested against it in a series of articles published in 1915 as *Au dessus de la mêlée*. In 1916 Henri Barbusse (1874–1935) dissected the process of war in *Le Feu* and shocked his readers by taking them to the very smell of its destruction. In the decade after the war, novels, plays and poems, based on the invincible dignity of the common soldier, exposed the violation of all human values by trench warfare and revolted against the traumatic division of will in supposedly civilized men engaged in war (Arnold Zweig, 1887–   : *The Case of Sergeant Grischa*, 1921). Titles such as *All Quiet on the Western Front* (Erich Maria Remarque, 1929), *What Price Glory?* (Maxwell Anderson and Laurence Stallings, 1924), *Journey's End* (Robert Cedric Sherriff, 1929) and *Farewell to Arms* (Ernest Hemingway, 1928) came into the common language of the people as ironical comments on the human cost of war.

In the decade following the war, many of the pre-war experiments were put to use in a wide range of expression—in architecture, in the founding of literary magazines and the flowering of criticism, in a flood of novels and dramas, and in the mature work of some of the outstanding composers and painters of the pre-war decade. Freedom to experiment was no longer an issue but a condition so complete as to leave the artist in a state of virtual anarchy in which the burden of freedom could be as unbearable as the restraints of convention.

In the 1930s and 1940s whatever sense of direction the post-war burst of expression contained was again shattered by the collapse of the capitalist economies, the rise of totalitarian states and the horrors and dislocations of the second world war. Writers and artists, cast on to the waste-heap of unemployment or fugitives from the Nazi terror or the dictatorships of Italy or Spain, found the society which they faced ever more confused and intolerable and their isolation from it more complete; more and more of the voices of western European artists and writers were the voices of exiles. After the second world war, the terrible menace of the nuclear age added further evidence of chaos, brutality and madness on an ever more gigantic scale.

(i) *The sickness of society*. As writers and artists looked at the world about them, they saw it as a basically sick society. Many accepted the dictum of Spengler that they were witnessing *The Decline of the West* (1918–22). They wrote war novels which took away all glory and reason from war and left it as only a futile assault on human dignity. They wrote intimate biographies of great men revealing their all-too-human qualities and their feet of clay (Emil Ludwig, 1881–1948; Lytton Strachey, 1880–1932). Rejecting the assumption, which such writers as George Bernard Shaw and H. G. Wells had expressed, that educated man would reform his society, they delineated man's forlorn state with deep pity, as did Käthe Kollwitz (1867–1945) (Pl. 28) or, like George Grosz (1893–) mercilessly depicted man's cruelty to man and hit out at society angrily, contemptuously, with a sense of indignity or despair.

They attacked the fragmentation and confusion of city life and showed mass production and the machine as taking away all craftsmanship, subjecting workers to an unnatural, deadening rhythm and turning men into 'robots' (Karel Čapek, 1890–1938: *RUR*, 1920); they aimed their shafts at sophisticated upper-class and complacent bourgeois society (e.g. Aldous Huxley, 1894– : *Chrome Yellow*, 1921; Jacob Wassermann, *Der Fall Maurizius*, 1928; François Mauriac, 1885– : *Thérèse Desqueyroux*, 1927); they viewed with irony and horror the prospects for a *Brave New World* (Aldous Huxley, 1932) opened up by science. They adopted T. S. Eliot's (1888–) term for the whole cultural scene, *The Waste Land* (1922). In the classic statement of the sickness of European society, Thomas Mann symbolically chose a tuberculosis sanitarium as the milieu in which to conduct his diagnosis, and to point to the unsympathetic, materialistic figure of the engineer as the emerging authoritarian of the future (*The Magic Mountain*, 1922).

Many of the artists and writers felt themselves threatened by the instruments of mass communication—radio, motion picture, telecommunication, recording, the popular press—which created vast new audiences, and broke the boundaries between the serious and the popular arts. They agreed with the Spanish cultural philosopher José Ortega y Gasset (1883–), who saw that they faced a *Revolt of the Masses* (1929) and thought that the mass audiences could only degrade taste and debase the arts from the standards called for by the *élite* audiences of the past. The human predicament was epitomized by the German playwright, Ernst Toller (1893–1939), in his play *Man and the Masses* (1929), where the thrust of the masses to power and the ruthlessness of revolution overrode the individual human values which the symbolic woman tried to defend, and where both masses and individual stood against the existing society.

(ii) *The inner search*. Faced thus with uncertainty, irrationality, an oppressive sense of the sickness of society and the threat that the rising masses would overwhelm their world, artists and writers sought anxiously, sometimes even desperately, to find meaning in life. The artist in the classical tradition had always expressed a search for an integrated view of man's identity, his place in the universe and the social values within which he worked out his destiny. Now his quest became nervously intense and it led him in many directions.

The spread of Freudian concepts, which became part of the intellectual climate in the 1920s, stimulated intensive search into man's inner nature. Although some, such as D. H. Lawrence, rejected Freud along with all attempts to substitute scientific inquiry for intuition, most writers and artists used his ideas as they understood them to reinforce their tendency to seek reality in psychological depths, and to concentrate their search on the ramifications of sex. Freud himself had sought to bring rational observation and analysis to bear on the irrational behaviour of men, and to find ways to re-direct irrational impulses. His concept of 'sex' as a central drive was much broader and more general than the narrow physical meaning of the term. But the public at large, and most of the artists and writers, took from Freud only his discovery of irrational behaviour, not his rational approach to it, and they looked for the basis of human action and of man's creativity in the drive for physical gratification of sexual impulses.

Writers and artists, from the 1920s onward, thus carried to further depths the psychological probing and exposure of sex which had been part of the search for reality in the preceding decades. Whereas the earlier works had stripped off the mask of gentility, had shown society hiding its lusts under the institution of prostitution, had attacked conventional marriage and had revealed the shams and inner tensions of the bourgeois family depicted as the enemy of love and art, these had generally been in the nature of social com-mentary, though they were often couched in psychological terms.

Under the influence of Freud, the psychological novel, play, painting or music now sought motivation in deep layers of experience, especially the frustration from repressions in earliest childhood or, for those who followed one of Freud's disciples, Jung, in inherent archetypes provided by a sort of racial memory. Family conflict, especially the relation of father and son, was viewed and explored over and over again in terms of the 'oedipus complex' by writers and artists who either retold the classic Greek story with modern overtones (e.g. Jean-Paul Sartre) or cast in modern guise the son's love for his mother and murderous feeling toward his father (e.g. Eugene O'Neill, 1888–1953). James Joyce (1882–1941) was but the most gifted and extreme of the many writers who delineated the physical relation between man and woman to the last detail and related this sex drive to his character's whole personality. Proust, Gide and others explored homosexuality until it became commonplace to treat this once-taboo subject. Emphasis on, or pre-occupation with, a deep sexual urge infused much of the painting of Picasso and many others whose work bore the marks of his influence. Alban Berg in his opera *Wozzek* (1923) gave his listeners a direct sense of mad jealousy when he used a structure resembling psychoanalysis to show a military doctor and an officer treating a simple man as sick and uncovering his uncertainties, frustrations and capacity for violence until he is goaded by jealousy to kill his wife and drown himself.

The Dadaists (1916) chose their very name to express their sense of the absurd meaninglessness of life. André Breton, (1896–   ) who led the sur-realist movement which followed them, was introduced to Freud's work as a trained medical student, and saw the relevance of psychoanalysis to the chao-tic expressions of the Dadaists and to a possible fruitful use of automatic association of images in liberating the human spirit.

(iii) *Search into the lives of other men.* The quest for meaning led some writers and artists to look at the lives of many different kinds of people in different places, strata of society, and circumstances: rural people on the farms of Norway, peasant villages of Poland, the olive fields of Spain, the hills of Sicily; in industrial towns and cities as workers, business or professional men; in areas of cultural conflict and under stress of social change; in primitive societies and others of which the West had been largely unaware. Many found frustration, dullness, futility and pettiness in the lives which they explored, but others saw essential dignity, vitality and compassion. Not many, however, examined the imagination, vision or personality of the most dynamic elements in modern society, the scientists, engineers, industrialists, labour leaders or modern statesmen.

A few novelists began to see with prophetic insight and sympathetic imagination the clash of cultures and the inevitable human tragedy that augured the breakdown of nineteenth-century empires, as in Joseph Conrad's *Heart of Darkness* (1909) where white men were pulled to destruction in central Africa, and in E. M. Forster's (1879–   ) *A Passage to India* (1924) and André Malraux's (1901–   ) *La Voie royale* (1930); Malraux went on to delineate the beginnings of the revolutionary struggle in China in *La Condition humaine* (1933). Joyce Cary (1888–1957) saw similar conflicts in Africa in *Mister Johnson* (1939).

When the economic depression of the 1930s revealed capitalism in an apparent state of collapse and when the rise of totalitarian states threatened all liberties, many writers and artists believed that they had no recourse but to choose between fascism and communism. Only a very few chose the former except as they were forced into acquiescence. A number chose communism, or at least sympathized with it. Some, such as Ignazio Silone (1900–   ) in Italy (*Fontamara*, 1930) and Anna Seghers (1900–   ) in Germany (*Der Aufstand der Fischer von Sankt Barbara*, 1928) became convinced communists. Not a few of the prominent authors and journalists in Germany took sides against fascism, either because they recognized and fought it as the enemy of humanism and culture, as did Carl von Assietzky and Kurt Tucholsky in their *Weltbühne*, or because Hitler's seizure of power struck them like lightning and drove them into emigration. Lion Feuchtwanger's (1884–1958) novels *Erfolg* (1930) and *Die Geschwister Oppenheim* (1933) were revealing attacks on the system. Stefan Zweig (1881–1942), a typical representative of the intellectual *élite* of pre-war Vienna, wrote a series of historical novels as reflections of contemporary developments (*Fouché*, 1931, *Castello gegen Calvin*, 1936). Anna Seghers, a refugee in Mexico during the second world war, published a harrowing tale of escape from a concentration camp (*Das siebte Kreuz*, 1947).[15]

Those who inclined to communism did so in part because it seemed the road to bring them closer to the masses who, they felt, must be more real than their own middle class which they despised; in addition it appeared to offer an alternative to bourgeois capitalism in which man might perhaps find a basis for more humane relations with his fellows. But a number of these

writers and artists became disillusioned as they discovered the police methods
of the Stalinist state and saw in the Soviet purges of the mid-thirties new
means for breaking the human spirit by the state and subjecting the individual
to authority (e.g. *The God that Failed*, by Arthur Koestler, Ignazio Silone,
Richard Wright, André Gide, Louis Fischer, Stephen Spender, edited by
Richard H. S. Crossman, 1950).[16]

(iv) *Search for roots.* Some hoped to find answers to their anxious search in
a renewal of tradition. Once they had shaken off the shackles of the immediate
past, they reached into their cultural background for roots. For some
this meant a return to religion. The poets, T. S. Eliot and W. H. Auden
(1907–   ), turned their backs on the 'waste land' and found meaning in the
Anglo-Catholic church and the traditions associated with it. The Norwegian
novelist, Sigrid Undset (1882–1949) became a convert to Roman Catholicism
and wrote warmly of mediaeval life (*Kristin Lavransdatter*, 1920–22) and the
French writer, Jacques Maritain (1882–   ), also a convert, was a leading
exponent of the values of mediaeval Christian society.

For others the search for roots involved exploration of folk culture. The
interest in folk song which had influenced composers from the early romantic
period and was part of the growth of nationalist movements, now led to large-
scale systematic collecting, the founding of folk song societies, and devoted
search by such composers as Bela Bartok and R. Vaughan Williams. For many,
especially in France, it meant renewal of identification with the classical tradition of Greece and Rome (e.g. Jean Giraudoux, 1882–1944: *Tiger at the
Gates*, 1935; André Gide, *Theseus*, 1946). Stravinsky moved from the primitive theme and rhythms of *Le Sacre du printemps* to the classic myths of
Persephone (1927) and *Orpheus* (1948). Schönberg found his roots in the old
Jewish tradition and left as his last work the unfinished opera *Moses and
Aaron* (d. 1951). Thomas Mann, likewise, after dissecting European society
turned to the Jewish story of Joseph, conscious that his probing into the past
was a search for man in the present, for 'the essence of life is presentness'
(*Joseph and His Brothers*, 1934).

Those who rescrutinized the past in order to find some living form to which
they could hold sometimes found only fragments, which they expressed nostalgically but could not put together into a meaningful whole, and which they
used, in T. S. Eliot's phrase, to shore up their ruins. Sometimes they wholly
reinterpreted myths in ways that both renewed the past and interpreted the
present.

(v) *Existentialism.* The search for meaning which drew writers and artists in
many directions led some who had faith in neither God nor reason to a final
sense of nothingness or absurdity. In their view, the only possible attitude of
mind must be to confront existence without self-deception.

This attitude of mind had been developing through a line of writers from
Sören Kierkegaard and Feodor Dostoevsky (*Notes from Underground*, 1864)
through Friedrich Nietzsche and Martin Heidegger. New literary for-

mulations were sought by Franz Kafka and later by Jean-Paul Sartre and Albert Camus (1913–1960), two of the leading novelists and dramatists of the 1940s and 1950s, who became the main literary exponents of existentialism.*

Kafka expressed the ambiguity of existence in *Die Verwandlung (Metamorphosis,* 1916) and in the unfinished work, *Der Prozess (The Trial)* published after his death (1925). In *Metamorphosis* the schizophrenia of the man turned insect was written with complete lucidity to bring out the logic of each situation. In *The Trial* a little man was accused of something—he was not clear what—tried in what court he did not know, assumed he was condemned but was not clear for what, accepted it all as natural, went on eating, loving and reading his paper, was one day invited by two gentlemen into a wretched suburb where they put his head on a block and executed him.

Jean-Paul Sartre believed that man is what he wills, that he is responsible and that he must understand what his nature is that makes him capable of self-deception. He formulated systematically in *L'Être et le néant* (1943) the vague uncertainty which many others felt, and he expressed it in a series of novels beginning with *La Nausée* (1938). Unlike Kafka's people, his were always aware of the incomprehensibility and loneliness of their existence, and their search for fullness of life was expressed in various, often lurid, ways. But they were not freed of obligation, for they must engage themselves actively as the only liberation possible, without knowing the meaning of their acts in any universal context, but being wholly self-conscious in making their individual personalities.

The writings of Kafka led directly into Camus's interpretation of the human condition as absurd and the only possible attitude towards it that of the rebel who knows. Camus found the myth of Sisyphus relevant to today—the man who passionately loved life, condemned to eternally unfinished work but, each time that he began over again, suddenly experiencing a moment of consciousness in which he knew the whole of the human condition; this lucidity was his torture but it was also his crown of victory for he could scorn his fate and revolt (*L'Étranger,* 1942; *L'Homme révolté,* 1954). In his novels, dread, death, tyranny, conformity and capacity for renewal were gravely explored. *La Peste* (1947) dealt with the isolation of a community smitten with plague and men tested in face of mass death; integrity and decency between friends and devoted and conscientious work, however unavailing it might be, kept the dignity of the individuals authentic.

This general view of life came to be the dominant outlook among a large proportion of the writers and artists of western Europe in the mid-twentieth century. Although it did not define the terms of 'engagement' which would allow the reflective consciousness to be free, it was a view of life which could give courage and strength to those who had survived the horrors of war and concentration camps and must live with the knowledge that men had designed instruments of destruction which could extinguish life on earth. It contained

* For the philosophy of Existentialism see Chapter XX, pp. 665–6.

neither joy nor hope, nor yet the dramatic struggle of tragedy, the detachment of comedy, the irony or exaltation which had been the gift of great artists of other ages to their fellowmen. It was popular, especially in France and Germany, for the honesty with which it tried to face the whole of existence.

While the existentialists were concerned with the chaos of existence, other writers were oppressed by its excessive order. George Orwell (1903–50), in *1984* (1949) delineated an over-organized, inherently authoritarian world in which freedom of the human spirit could not exist. Some young men of the 1950s, inheriting both the existentialist recognition of incomprehensibility and Orwell's sense of the menace of ever increasing organization, refused to become involved, and they made a point of disengagement and of preoccupation with their private worlds and private lives.[17]

British writers and artists did not adopt the existentialist view as generally or completely as did their neighbours on the European continent. Although they had much in common with them, a persistent strain of compassion and sense of human dignity prevented most British writers and artists, for example E. M. Forster or Joyce Cary, from sharing fully the irrationality and nihilism which dominated so many of their fellows across the Channel. The feeling for the English countryside and a lively sense of the continuing past never wholly lost its capacity to renew the spirit. The composer Vaughan Williams could express the horror and nothingness of war, but he could still invoke the healing quality of the land. Some British painters and sculptors rivalled those of the Continent in the nightmares of violence which they called up (Francis Bacon, 1910–   ), and in their experiments with abstract form (Ben Nicholson, 1894–   ) but many persisted in seeing nature (Barbara Hepworth, 1903–   ) and in evoking its meaning even in their abstractions. Writers such as Virginia Woolf (1882–1941) tended to hold to some joy in their surroundings; though she saw life as a stream of sense impressions without purpose or direction, she nevertheless loved London's red buses and crowded streets and respected the people whose inner lives she relentlessly explored. And in 1956 the sculptor Jacob Epstein (1880–1959), a Jew, could create a suffering, transcendent 'Christ in Majesty' for the cathedral of Llandaff, Wales, as a testimony of his own sense of common humanity. Among those of the generation of the 1950s who tended to share the Continent's judgment that they lived in a sick society, there was more likely to be compassion, anger and even a call to reawakening rather than despair.

(b) Developments in artistic form

By the 1920s experiments in all the arts had freed artists and writers, as craftsmen, from old forms and had provided tools to express the complexity and immediacy of hitherto unclarified experience. In the decades which followed, the new tools were applied in many new works. Where the vision flagged and only experiment remained, the works came to be esoteric and barren. But where the artists had genius in using their skills to grapple with their need for some concept of the relationship of the individual and the universe and of the individual and society, they produced living works that added to the great tradition of the arts.[18]

For most there was no longer God or Platonic perfection or Kantian imperative; but artists faced and tried to interpret eternity and death, the uncertainties and ambiguity of changing processes of youth and age, love and hate, the relationship of the individual to the universal, the oscillations between the static and the creative, violence and order, light and dark, and men's consciousness of all these. Dread, anxiety and anguish accompanying the consciousness gave a characteristic tone to the expression, and abnormal manifestations were often anatomized as ways to understand the depths of what was usually called the normal. But the vitality of some artists in struggling for form enabled them to transcend chaos and gave them freedom from the authority of a deadening society. They interpreted their personal experience as a type of the universal. Making the work of art and watching the process were inseparable.

For those artists in all fields who felt themselves most out of tune with the world around them and isolated from their fellow men, the forms of their art became a compulsive expression of themselves. Among easel painters and sculptors especially, but also among writers and musicians, there were those for whom form became an end in itself and the world of 'art for art's sake' became the artist's private world, where others might perhaps penetrate but from which the artist made little effort to communicate. Some even made a cult of not being understood. Their audiences were small groups of connoisseurs who read the little magazines or frequented private galleries and workshops.

Meantime, the forms which had been radical a generation before became part of the common mode of expression. Commercial artists used abstraction, surrealist juxtaposition, simplification and stylization of sculpture and geometrical design in their advertising, store displays, furniture or textiles. Even some of the paintings which had been shocking when they were painted became familiar to the point of seeming commonplace. Writing with stream of consciousness technique came to be expected and music which did not use dissonance, new scales and irregular rhythms seemed dull. (Pl. 6.)

(i) *The novel.* In literature this was the end of a long line of exploration of sense experience, association, memory and imagination which had begun with Rousseau and which Wordsworth and Coleridge had turned into great poetry. The new features were the language, the symbols and the attitude.

With the increasing interest in psychology, in unwinding complexes to the last particular, and in varieties of tension in feeling, the novel became more and more the appropriate form. It was used both as direct expression of experience and as illustration of philosophy; it ranged from the discursive to the poetical; it became so varied as to be almost indefinable. It was supplemented by numbers of biographies and autobiographies which were written almost in novel form.

In Henry James's (1845–1916) works at the opening of the century, the interrelationships of inner feelings and the outer world in a stream of consciousness were still expressed by the all-observing author outside the novel or at times by a character who acted as observer. The sentences still kept to the traditional grammatical structure, but they had become involuted and elaborate.

Marcel Proust took the next steps in his *la recherche du temps perdu* (1914 *seq.*). Here the artist had become the work of art. The whole novel is a symbol. The characters have no existence in themselves but are the feelings which they set off in the observer, the 'I' who is the writer imprisoned in his sick-room watching himself in the act of creation. They stand for his desires as they reveal themselves in frustrated love and the social vanities of upper-class society, both among the *nouveaux riches* climbing and the aristocrats declining. They are developed in variations of great complexity, starting with the first volume in which all the main themes are announced as in an overture —the main characters, the places, the patterns of relationships which will recur with mounting complexity of meaning and shifting changes as the adolescent who first experiences them re-experiences them in other times and places. Here they are set against his childhood family background with its kindness and moral values, every one of which will be violated in the course of the development. In the beginning there are intricate sentences of interwoven strands of perception, event and feeling, making patterns that will be touched off as living memory again and again later. But gradually the motion becomes staccato, and the images become harsh and dissociated as the patterns are broken into ultimate disillusion.

Other novelists wrote staccato narrative, sought words for their sound as much as their sense, and conveyed action, motion and tension by breaking the structure of sentences in many different ways or trying to use different words. James Joyce made his own syntax in three novels and explored its possibilities to the limit. In his autobiographical novel, *Portrait of the Artist as a Young Man* (1916), the artist grows up from the beginning of consciousness, expressed in the language of a baby's perception, to his maturing logic of thought, expressed in the language of a Jesuit debate on aesthetics. In *Ulysses* (1922) he used a more complex structure to express the eternal search of man for home and self, and extravagant language to convey its irrationality. In *Finnegans Wake* (1939) he explored the language of sleep in the story of guilt, death and resurrection, and made up words out of syllables from many languages to express his concept that European man's deeply hidden consciousness was drawn from the archetypes of all Europe.

Virginia Woolf made the novel essentially poetry in *The Waves* (1931). She worked with sense impressions much as the painters did, and she used many of their techniques in making time and place and shifts of mood and psychological level.

Writers in the realists' line, interested in the structure of society, were by the 1920s using the techniques of fragmentation and sudden juxtapositions of unlinked detail in conveying the many kinds of experience present in a single outer situation. John Dos Passos (1896–   ) in *1919* (1932) gave the tone of confusion which is the intent of this novel by juxtaposing without explanation or transition the daily slang and other speech of ordinary people, the lofty eloquence of President Wilson, reportorial biographies of famous people, screaming newspaper headlines. André Malraux in *L'Espoir* (1937) used the interruptions of the radio to give what was happening all over Spain at a given moment of the revolution. In the 1940s Joyce Cary wrote two trilogies each delineating a single person in the round by viewing him in different situations through the eyes of three different characters.

In the later decades, shorter forms of narrative became more important. Ernest Hemingway's (1898–   ) concentration and action, and his swift, simple sentences were influential not only in his native United States but in Europe. Delight in concentration, together with the needs of magazines, made short stories increasingly popular both with writers and with readers. The form had been chiselled to masterpieces by de Maupassant and Chekhov in the nineteenth century. Now it took on all the varieties of language and mood that characterized novels. Only one rule continued to hold it together: it must make a single effect.

(ii) *Verse*. Verse in the twentieth century was not as important as in earlier centuries, for it was mainly lyrical, to be read privately, and indeed it came to be more and more special with meaning only for the few. Even verse drama approached popularity only a few times, as in the works of J. M. Synge (1871–1909), T. S. Eliot, Christopher Fry (1907–   ) and W. H. Auden. Younger poets paid tribute to Yeats by commenting that he kept the spirit of poetry alive and gave them courage to be poets by the magic of his music, his starkness in accepting the full range of passion and by his steadfastness in remaining a poet even into old age. Actually many experiments in imagery, cadence and rhythm did find new areas of awareness, and as poets struggled toward an imaginative expression of the shifting sense of reality they extended the bounds of poetry.

The intense poets of pure form carried the exploration of individual feeling, begun by the revolutionary romantics of the early nineteenth century, to a kind of ultimate, for they were not concerned with the interaction of their feeling and their fellowmen, but with the process of their own self-awareness. The subject matter of art was to be found in this process, and giving it shape by making works of art was itself the meaning of life. Such works were written by poets as different as the brilliantly intellectual Paul Valéry in France and the sensuous, passionate Rainer Maria Rilke in Austria. Valéry thought that consciousness was a flaw in the infinite. Thus the form even of pure poetry was a shadow on the vision of infinity and therefore to be rejected as imperfect; but after years of silence following his first poems, he did make exquisitely proportioned musical structures to express the subtle movements of his own disturbing awareness as he watched it in himself. Rilke, starting with a painter's observation of things, felt them always transformed into human meaning; he repudiated science and the mechanical age, rejected responsible social relationships lest his individual creativeness be killed, and dedicated himself to keeping it alive by probing changes in love, sickness and death until the fear and anxiety and pain became endurance of the self alive in infinity expressed in *Duineser Elegien* (1912–22) and *Die Sonette an Orpheus* (1923).

These poets and others freed verse from the traditional alexandrines, heroic blank verse and folk song. They renewed ancient Greek and Latin accents or verse forms of pre-Renaissance writers in their own language, for they were in revolt from the Renaissance. They tried *vers libre* with its varied length of line and freedom from rhyme to give, not the incantation of spells, but the shifting colours of mood and the swift, terse point of an image or movement. They left out links in order to maintain the concentration. Paul Claudel was almost alone in keeping the great dithyrambic effects in *L'Annonce faite à Marie* (1912) and *Christophe Colomb* (1933). When poets used traditional forms as Valéry did in *La Jeune Parque* (1917) or Rilke in *Die Sonette an Orpheus*, they filled them with such freshness of metaphor, starkness of statement or new pauses and rhythms that they made cadences sounding quite different from the past and indeed conveying the universal in twentieth-century terms.

Poets, except those who were defending the disappearing and still loved order by some traditionally descriptive verse (Robert Bridges, 1844–1930: *Testament of Beauty*, 1929) followed one of two lines, the imagist or the symbolist. The imagists laid down the principles that a poet could write about anything he chose, that the exact word for the image was to be used, and that the writing should be 'hard, clear, never blurred or indefinite' (*Imagist Manifesto*, 1913). They tended to limit themselves to separate impressions and, as they refused to evaluate these, in the end diminished into triviality. But their precision was used with skill by the other school of experimental verse, the symbolists. Their influence extended the poetical expression of the senses to include taste, touch and smell, and they were gifted in suggesting subtle transformations.

Since Mallarmé, the symbolists had tried to free language of discursive meaning and use it as pure music. They were preoccupied with the special moment of life, a moment unique to the individual and containing more than external images; they therefore sought fresh symbols to stand for it. Accepted symbols like the Cross were inadequate because they had become stereotypes expressing social conformity and were no longer historically relevant. But the poets of the 1920s and later needed symbols of this magnitude that would either order the chaos of hitherto unexplored reality or bring them closer to the source of life.

Indeed whether writers sought to convey experience directly as the imagists did, or metaphorically as the symbolists did, their problem of language was real. Yeats pointed out its implications when he said that every man has his own symbol. His most ambitious one was a 'Great Wheel' as explained in *A Vision* (1926), his better-known one 'Byzantium' in *Sailing to Byzantium* (1928). Rilke's symbols came from many sources—nature, the arts, Biblical tradition, classical myth, especially Orpheus. In *Die Sonette an Orpheus*, his resolution of fear and pain became finally a gracious music of acceptance and praise; like Orpheus he too was making temples out of the wilderness. He wrote a poetry of intensity and elegance new to Germany. He used a language of new shadings and overtones. French writers accepted him as bringing needed profundity to complement their essentially intellectual expression, and they regarded him as a truly European poet. He himself translated Valéry into German. He was read not only in Europe but in the United States and Russia.

Valéry, basically conceiving of the Creation as a flaw in the universe bringing change into the perfection of its unity, chose symbols of purity of vision: Apollo, the sun which in its brilliance could make men forget the flaw, the dazzling sea at noon, the diamond—a perfect focus of light, its facets reflecting the light back through the same lines as it entered. He symbolized the dark sources of creative energy by forest, trees, the Pythoness.

Such symbols were special to each writer and did not have meaning for the general run of people who still thought of the infinite in terms of the traditional sacred texts or did not think about it at all in their increasingly secularized lives. Indeed these poets of pure form could have meaning only for a literary audience specially ready to accept them on their own terms.

Other poets were searching for new symbols of social struggle or of national life. One of the first of these was Herman Gorter (1864–1927), a gifted Dutch poet who spoke for the heroic phase of European social democracy before the first world war in his *Pan* (1916), a poem in the form of an epic, attempting to reconcile the poetry of nature and Marxian political philosophy even as, centuries before, Lucretius had made poetry of Epicureanism. In Spain Federico García Lorca (1899–1936) used the traditional forms of Spanish folk song and Spanish classical drama to give modern expression to the humanity of the little people of the earth in the face of organized cruelty and to their bitter, tragic dignity in the face of the inevitable frustration of fate. W. H. Auden and Christopher Isherwood (1904–　) in *The Dog Beneath the Skin* (1935) and *The Ascent of F6* (1936) dramatized the implications of Marxism and of Freudian psychology. Auden gave a name to his time in the poetry of *The Age of Anxiety* (1947). But Gorter wrote in Dutch, a language accessible only to the people of a small nation; a popular poet such as García Lorca had meaning only within his own Spanish tradition; and Auden became an exile who turned to Christianity and wrote poetry historically.

It was outside of western Europe itself that the poetry of the individual showed its continuing vitality. In America, Robert Frost (1874–   ) found his images and symbols in the daily life about him. From India came the voice of Rabindranath Tagore, whose poetry and plays were eagerly and widely read in Europe and America and who was recognized as bringing to the poetic expression of the West an added quality from his eastern background. And in the Soviet Union the lyric poet, Boris Pasternak (1890–1960), who dedicated his autobiography (*Safe Conduct*, 1931) to Rilke, asserted the essential inner creativeness of individual self-awareness and the necessity that this be kept alive whatever the social and political structure. His poetry was read and loved in Russia, although his lyrical novel *Dr Zhivago* (1957) was rejected as failing to show an understanding of the great social effort of his countrymen and the meaning of their sacrifices, and it found publication and a wide audience only abroad.[19]

But there was no language in the developing urban cultures of the West in which poets could speak to their people. Even if writers tried to bring their language close to the spoken language of the people, they were confronted with the fact that only a highly educated few spoke the traditional literary language and that forces making new language tended to flatten it out as much as to enliven it. In western Europe and America the Bible was the last great body of literature in which the literary and the popular language were combined. The complications and specializations of industrialized society brought out special vocabularies, from the '$E = mc^2$' of the mathematical physicist to the plumber's 'bushings'. Industries, professions, departments of learning all had their own vocabularies, so specialized that they were unintelligible to even highly educated people outside their specific boundaries. Also, these vocabularies were filled with dead or synthetic metaphors, like the sociologists' 'underpriviliged', or the psychologists' 'adjustment', so that if a poet or novelist tried to draw his language from them, it had no freshness of life and tended to call up only classification. The statistics of life expectancy had no resonance such as 'men are as the grass' of the Bible; but the range of experience included in them was no less needing poetical expression.

The language of ordinary use became equally lifeless. Many forces made a babel of the spoken language among the rootless urban populations. Moreover, the common language of general literacy tended to become synthetic, a mixture of that used by mass newspapers, magazines and radio and what people learned in schools attended by everybody, and everywhere debased by advertisers and propagandists who, in the process of identifying their objects with desires, deliberately emptied language of its meaning.

(iii) *Music*. The new tools available to European composers—ideas of harmonic structure, rhythm, melody and tonal colour—enabled them, also, to express new dimensions of feeling. By the time of Debussy's death in 1918 they were free to use melody or not; to break out of tonality and use dissonances juxtaposed for special emotional effects; to leave chords unresolved, and to use successions of them, not in a structure but to give independent harmonic sensations; to draw on oriental scales or ancient modes; to develop the intricacies of chromaticism in series. Debussy himself, having experimented with modulations and chords to give shifting sensory effects, returned in his last works to the traditional dramatic form of the sonata and gave it new force. The way was indeed open to renewal of more sustained structure, with flexibility of expression now taken for granted.

Composers continued to write symphonies, quartets, cantatas and operas. But the symphonies might unfold on a succession of themes rather than dramatize two and develop them symmetrically; they were made more flexible by compressing or rearranging the four movements, the use of dissonances, the use of modes and by experiments with orchestral effects and the addition of voices; they might reflect varieties of national origin as in the works of Jean Sibelius, Vaughan Williams, Sergei Prokoviev (1891–1953) and Dmitry Shostakovich (1906–   ). The quartets used extreme ranges of sound on the stringed instruments, as Bartok's *Third, Fourth* and *Sixth*. The opera limited the range of intonation in the singing and either extended the potentialities of music-drama to express horror, madness and direct characterization or restored the classical tradition of opera with arias, recitatives, choruses and ensembles. Gian Carlo Menotti (1911–   ) used such unfamiliar subjects as *The Medium* (1946) and *The Consul* (1950) and Benjamin Britten dramatized traditional English materials. Stravinsky, in *The Rake's Progress* (1952), gave the classical opera form a new texture by using ambiguous tonality, delicate shifts to fit the exact syllables of the verse and skilfully interwoven quotations from a whole range of traditional music.

Modern ballet, which Stravinsky and Diaghilev had popularized as a form in its own right—an integrated combination of classical ballet, folk dance, pantomime and music with rich orchestral effects—was further developed by some of the French composers in ironical and masterly expression of men as puppets in a meaningless post-war existence (Erik Satie, 1866–1925: *Parade*, 1917; Francis Poulenc, 1899–   : *Les Biches*, 1924). Stravinsky himself changed its character after the first world war by the introduction of a chorus to sing elements of folk song as part of the orchestra (*Les Noces*, first performed 1923), by re-asserting Italian melodic line and classical dancing drawn from French dances of the seventeenth century (*Apollo Musagetes*, 1927; *Orpheus*, 1948), by a mixture of ballet and scenic oratorio (*Persephone*, 1934). Finally, in 1957, he constructed *Agon* in a complicated, highly original, abstract pattern. It was a dance competition with no story and no setting, but pure music and pure dance complementing each other, and a large orchestra, not for crashing blows but for intricate variety, attained by using parts of it in succession so that the music was always light and clean-cut.

Composers were fascinated with problems of the relationship of words and music, and composed music to series of poems (Hindemith's *Marienleben* of Rilke; Webern's songs of Rilke; Stravinsky's *Symphony of Psalms* and *Mass;* Arthur Honegger's (1892–1955) and Carl Orff's (1895–   ) scenic oratorios). Many wrote religious choral works (e.g. Vaughan Williams, Stravinsky).

In the course of the century, music tended to become both more abstract and more emotionally intense. The disquiet of the century went far beyond the pale shimmering of light of Debussy's music or the dim vagueness of doom of his *Pelléas et Mélisande* to the terrifying ominousness of some marches in Bartok's quartets, their sardonic humour, ribaldry and, at the other pole, profound tenderness.

Bartok wrote in the main line of the experience of his people. In the mountains and plains of the Carpathian basin where he lived among them making his collections of their songs, he found them still living as they had for centuries, while war continued to go over them. When he used their folk songs or made his own in similar vein, his curious mixture of East and West came straight from their present and not merely from their history or his own. His originality of form and understanding had a depth of expressiveness transcending any national interest and fruitful for all western music. His works might suggest the transparent mystery on the very edge of the audible as in his 'night music', or the sturdy assertiveness of loud dances; but they were not pictorial music. New forms, such as his *Music for Strings, Percussion and Celesta*, contained the range of feeling within a short, strong architectural form, shaped by concentrated use of every note of the themes, by symmetrical repetition of themes with varied relationships and swift complexity, by the variety and emphasis of the percussion instead of orthodox instruments, and by using five parts in dramatic contrast to each other in rhythm and tempo and mood. Most of the younger composers adopted Schönberg's system of the twelve notes of the chromatic scale used in series, although not all agreed with him, even in theory. Paul Hindemith worked out an opposing theory in his *Unterweisung im Tonsatz* (1937); he suggested a logical revision in tuning the tempered scale and outlined a system of musical construction based on scientific acoustical principles. Among them all there was less tendency to gather monumental orchestras with double brass and more to thin out the sounds and to use new combinations of various instruments.

By the 1950s Anton Webern in Germany stood out as the most influential composer using Schönberg's abstract theories. He wrote short concentrated forms ordered in a rigorously perfected symmetry and used the chromatic series in various groupings, working them out in canon and mirror canon. He separated the notes of the melody and let one instrument after the other trace and retrace them through the orchestra. The individualizing of notes, combined with complex use of long, silent intervals and rapidly changing tempos made a spare, subtle effect. Webern heightened it by new combinations of traditional orchestral instruments or by introducing popular instruments such as guitar, mandolin, harmonium and bells. This music was the expression of a man of great culture and balance of mind, of searching imagination and sensitive ear, and such works as his *Variations for Piano*, *opus 27* and *String Quartet, opus 28* were especially influential. But in less able hands his methods could produce very dry results.

In France the influential composer with whom most of the younger men studied was Olivier Messiaen (1908–). His organ and piano music was not abstract, but often very lofty and mystical in character. He was influenced by Debussy, especially in the use of unresolved chords. He explored new effects of polyrhythms, notable for the use of pauses and subtle variations in the lengths of tones.

One of the recurring questions through the first half of the century was what was to be the relationship of jazz with the traditional art forms of music, however revolutionized, for jazz was the widespread popular form. It originated in the USA and after the first world war became popular in Europe. It was even taken up by some of the most advanced composers in Europe and used within their own idioms; Stravinsky quoted jazz along with Vivaldi and Bach in the same piece.

Its mood was always ambiguous—sad under apparent gaiety, sometimes maliciously satirical, sometimes full of longing, and always beating the deep rhythms that reach to the crude nerve centres, thus releasing immense vitality. Its effects were attained by flatting the thirds, fifths and sevenths in the melody and playing it against a straight tonal accompaniment, beating with syncopated rhythms against the continuum. It was especially exciting because of improvisation. Gifted solo instrumentalists in small bands could take one theme after another and improvise unexpected and varied patterns on it, letting their temperaments go freely with the feeling of the moment. They borrowed from old songs or from whatever classical or popular music they knew and treated them all with complete freedom. The principal instruments were trumpet, saxophone, clarinet, piano, xylophone, double bass and drums. The musical tones were closely related to the quality of voices, especially the resonant voices of Negroes among whom jazz started. Some of the mutes in the wind instruments were used to give the effect of the voice in different moods. Many of its outstanding later performers were urban Jewish musicians, and jazz thus came to be expressive of some of the special tensions of twentieth-century urban life.

In the early decades people danced to this music; but gradually it became music to listen to and even took shape in a few concert pieces. In the middle of the century the question was whether it would serve to give new life to the abstract experiments that, in the hands of highly skilled composers who were detached from the stream of popular life, were tending to become purely technical.

(iv) *Visual Arts: painting, sculpture, theatre, photography.*

Painting. The main direction of the visual arts was toward abstraction. Once the picture had become the object with its planes carefully marked out, its space filled with the projections of these planes, painters began to make many modifications of pure Cubism, and by the 1950s had developed new forms of abstraction involving the texture of paint and colour as such and the use of symbols.

The two great leaders of Cubism, Braque and Picasso, developed in separate ways. Braque painted many canvases, always refining his own unique style. He was occupied with subtle aspects of space that Cubists had started to explore; he used more and more complicated techniques of shadows, colour and even representational aspects of objects, of planes overlapping and interlocking to convey the volume of the space he lived in and the quality of life in it. This led to a famous series of large decorative paintings of his studio in which he ordered all the dimensions of a professional painter's life—his tools, his unfinished canvases, his collection of *objets d'art* from all ages of Europe used as models, an image of a bird escaping from one of the canvases and suggesting a free flight of the imagination. It was the artist's experience made universal. (Pl. 23.)

Picasso experimented with many styles. In 1921 he combined Cubism, heightened colour and classical proportion in 'Three Musicians'. In 'Guernica' (1937), a large mural in whites, greys and blacks, he created the drama of brute power symbolized by the man-bull trampling helpless masses of people and a horse; their anguish of unavailing flight he conveyed by extreme distortion of every part of the bodies. In his many paintings characterizing different women and his own children, he drew simplified, heavy outlines of great vigour, often making the features grotesque and giving a fierce, penetrating realism without being literal. (Pl. 27.)

Among the expressionists, Paul Klee sought symbols of the unity of man, the earth and the cosmos, in his words (*On Modern Art*, an address in 1924) 'the one essential image of creation itself rather than the image of nature as a finished product'. He disciplined his mind and his technique to a point where he reconciled the objective with the abstract, the generative process and forces of nature with contemplation of their changing relationships and with free association of dream, fantasy and idea welling up from his subconscious. He was always trying to penetrate to the place 'where primaeval power nurtures all evolution'. His technique was fine-spun and subtle. His shapes were sharply drawn but were wholly non-representational. His backgrounds of colour were shaded delicately to convey the atmosphere of the world in which the figures existed. The figures were composed in precise, humorous caricature ('Zwitscher-Maschine', 1922) or tragic simplification of fear or captivity ('Maske Furcht', 1932; 'Gefangen', 1940), or complex rhythms of colour and motion ('Revolution des Viaduktes', 1937). His vigour and keenness as an original seeker into the relationships between clear exposition, poetical feeling and objective experience made him one of the most sought-after artists in the early periods of experiment. By the 1950s his stature was more and more appreciated. (Pl. 26.)

The surrealists, revolting from science and institutions, talked about the explosion of beauty and painted the explosions of their subconscious as discoveries of this beauty. Two unique painters who belonged to no movements but who fascinated their contemporaries by the new dimensions of their work opened the way for the later explorations of worlds of fantasy and dreams by the surrealists. Marc Chagall (1889–   ), who went from his native Russia to western Europe, startled and delighted the experimental artists there by painting his feelings in free combinations of realism and dream imagery shifting in an imaginary world always wholly his own and always essentially that of a village boy loving home, always original in colour and endearingly lyrical. Giorgio de Chirico (1888–   ) fascinated the same generation by pressing beyond the confines of ordinary dream images to a metaphysical unknown. He used recognizable Italian scenes with well-known forms of classical architecture and traditional Renaissance perspective, but turned them into strangeness by a light unknown on land or sea, by unexpected proportions of buildings, and occasionally by anonymous figures wandering as if lost.

Surrealism itself started as a literary movement with André Breton, Louis Aragon (1897–   ) and Paul Éluard (1895–1952). André Breton and Philippe Soupault (1897–   ) established a review, *Littérature*, in which to practise a new instrument, automatic writing, and they gathered other writers and painters around them. In 1924 in *First Surrealist Manifesto*, Breton wrote his definition of surrealism:

Pure psychic automatism by which it is intended to express whether verbally or in writing, or in any other way, the real process of thought. Thought's dictation, free from any control by the reason, independent of any aesthetic or moral preoccupation . . . . Surrealism rests on a belief in the superior reality of certain forms of association hitherto neglected, in the omnipotence of dreams, in the disinterested play of thought. It tends to destroy all other psychic mechanisms and to substitute itself for them in the solution of the principal problems of life.

In this view, surrealism would liberate the individual spirit. Initially many of these men, surrounded with social chaos and violence, not only rejected bourgeois art but believed that there must first be a change in society and that the proletarian revolution was necessary. Although their revolutionary faith did not survive, their artistic attitude expressed itself for twenty-five years in the works of groups in France and other countries—the United States, Belgium, Czechoslovakia, Yugoslavia, Denmark, Japan, England. Many painters and sculptors were led to extremes in juxtaposing all sorts of objects or fragments in fantastic, incongruous, shocking or apparently meaningless relationships. They attached physical objects—bits of bone, newspaper, rope, cloth—to their canvas and substituted for formal sculpture conglomerations of materials—roots, twisted wire, cement blocks, feathers. They dredged up from the subconscious images of experience hidden deep in the nervous system and exalted whatever behaviour would allow these images to swim to the surface—dreams, drink, drugs, madness, infantilism, identification with primitive people. The visions which resulted often conveyed the sense of a nightmare.

Painters like Max Ernst (1891–   ), André Masson (1896–   ) and Joan Miro (1893–   ), and sculptors such as Hans Arp (1888–   ) who exhibited with the surrealists, used their mastery of technique to reveal a reality with more meaning. Arp's polished marble expressed simple biological life. Exquisitely observed shapes of nature were designed into contrasts or angry battle by André Masson or by Max Ernst into fantastic mysteries of cosmic relationships or grotesque and sensual nightmares of human temptations. The witty Joan Miro carried out his own saying that 'one must go beyond form to poetry' in different moods, always with elegance, variety and proportion. 'Catalan Landscape: Hunter' (1923–4) expressed the hallucinations of hunger, the pink sky and yellow sea making an infinite space in bright light in which a little man with a gun larger than himself hunted a still larger rabbit stretched in flight; these were just suggested by finely drawn triangles, circles, open rectangles, solid cones and spheres, and their proportions of size and mass of colour brought the impact of their emotional implications.

After the second world war young painters, influenced by the surrealists and again compulsively seeking something new, became more and more interested in abstract patterns of colour for their own sake, sometimes relationships of coloured squares, sometimes calligraphy, sometimes undefined irregularities of shapes. They liked the grand scale and were preoccupied with the texture of paint itself. They were known as *tachistes* (Nicholas de Stael, 1914–55), 'activists' or as 'action painters'. A group of Americans of this school, most notably Jackson Pollock (1912–56), for the first time interested the Europeans in American painting in terms of pure art by reason of their vitality and brilliance of colour, boldness of technique and confident atmosphere of discovery. Other artists such as the English John Bratby (1928–   ), in some revolt against these abstractions, painted enormous canvases of ordinary commonplace life more or less symbolically. In London in 1957 a full-scale exhibit of works by the Australian Sidney Nolan (1917)–   ) opened a real and mythical world of untamed, cruel desert and jungle and of heroes and criminals struggling with it. (Pl. 31.)

Sculpture. In sculpture, abstractions were organic and constructivist. Sculptors of organic forms selected the single essential of motion or growth, elaborated surrealist fantasy by dreamlike juxtapositions, and expressed qualities and relationships by simplified or distorted representation. Constantin Brancusi's (1876–1957) 'Bird in Space' (1919) in polished bronze stripped the form of all detail to give the essential lift of the bird into the air. Alberto Giacometti (1901–66) made tiny surrealist structures in which dreamlike figures moved strangely as if affecting each other by their presence but not communicating ('Palace at 4 a.m.', 1932–33). His tiny bronze men were elongated shadows standing alone ('Man Pointing', 1947) or isolated from each other ('City Square', 1948). Henry Moore (1898–) made monumental reclining figures based on observation of people sheltering in the Underground during the second world war and on primitive Mexican sculpture, using holes of space to dramatize the primitive power in the massive solid bronze parts. His 'Family' (1945) was a classical expression of a central conception of husband and wife holding the child high and cherishing it together, made dynamic not by distortion but by simplification expressing deep acceptance of nature. At the other pole Reg Butler's (1913–) project for a monument, 'The Unknown Political Prisoner' (1952) gave tragic symbolical power to the large mass of stone making the base, and the cage-like mechanism of stairs and ladders suggesting a relentless threat of execution and insurmountable walls within which little men, both prison guards and prisoner, are trapped and anonymous. Ossip Zadkine (1890–) combined elements of cubism, surrealism and primitive art to achieve an expressionistic style; his monument to a destroyed town found a suitable place in Rotterdam. (Pl. 36–38.)

The more geometrically minded constructivists moved from plans for monumental buildings in the early 1920s to smaller statements like Antoine Pevsner's 'Developable Column' (1942), a bronze column using mathematically developed curves. Naum Gabo made many pieces of transparent celluloid, often called 'Construction in Space' (1932; 1951). Alexander Calder (1898–) made mobiles—mathematically proportioned abstractions of shapes in nature, delicately hung together so as to move always in balance and throw shadows of the forms in regular ways. He thought of his form as reflecting the system of the universe, with many detached bodies of different qualities floating in space, in motion or at rest, some near, some immensely distant. In the 1950s other sculptors tried to express astronomical conceptions in such intricate works as Richard Lippold's (1915–) 'Variations on Full Moon' (1949–50), space caught within fine aluminium wires marking planes.

The younger sculptors were all working in metals, using the resources of these materials to express extravagant harshness and satire, or mathematical harmony and strength. Some were seeking a vocabulary through which to communicate the brotherhood of common destiny.[20, 21] (Pl. 35b, 39.)

Theatre. In Europe and the United States the theatre expanded or diminished with the vicissitudes of war and competition with the cinema, radio and television. At times, flourishing repertory theatres took drama to towns far away from the great capitals; at others, only a small percentage of the people had seen a live play. In Russia the revolution in the theatre preceded the October revolution and the theatre was ready as a powerful instrument for interpreting a new world to new audiences.

Serious drama of the liberation of the human spirit, expressing itself in appropriate scenic design and action, had to struggle with the commercial theatre's notions of amusement. Numerous new theatres were organized in revolt, such as the Moscow Art Theatre (1898), the stylized Kamerny Theatre of Tairov (1914), the Deutsches Theater in Berlin (1905), the Abbey Theatre in Dublin (1904), the Vieux Colombier in Paris (1913), the Court Theatre in London (1904), the Provincetown Theater (1916), and Washington Square Players (1911) in New York. Amateur groups in many places were resources for new actors and new beliefs in the theatre. Directors established schools of theatrical training, explaining that the best amusement is akin to the best instruction and that the noblest theatre both amuses and instructs (E. Gordon Craig, 1872– : *On the Art of the Theatre*, 1911; *The Mask* (magazine) 1908 ff.; School for the Art of the Theatre, established at Florence, 1913).

Under the influence of Vaslav Nijinski (1890–1950) and Diaghilev, the dance ceased to be limited to classical ballet; various schools of modern dance followed in Germany and the United States. Composers wrote for the stage— Stravinsky, Prokoviev, Darius Milhaud (1892–), George Gershwin (1898–1937), Virgil Thomson (1896–) Kurt Weill (1900–50) and others. New scenic art emerged. A succession of styles challenged the concept of the unities in drama and even the tragic catharsis.

Up to the first world war the theatre was essentially realistic, in the manner of Ibsen and the Russian drama, producing the plays of Chekhov and the early Shaw. In the 1920s various bold experiments in symbolism, expression- ism and constructivism accompanied the exploration of the psychology of the subconscious and of myths, as in the plays of Eugene O'Neill, and were used in pacifist propaganda by Ernst Toller and in the drama of the masses in the USSR. In the 1930s political and anti-war drama took many forms, especially introducing new ways of interpreting vast social movements and making new demands on the audience.

At the beginning of the century great plays determined theatrical pro- ductions. Ibsen's drama continued to be staged all over Europe. Anton Chekhov's slices of life, with their psychological insight into the sadness and the comic aspects of the decaying and frustrated middle class, determined Stanislavsky's special style in the Moscow Art Theatre. Effectively presented in the Court Theatre by Harley Granville-Barker (1877–1946), Shaw's plays made the modern stage in England with his drama of discussion in which ideas became dramatic forces, intelligence became a dimension of human character and wit unmasked the pretensions of conventional moral complacency.

Before the October Revolution, Constantin Stanislavsky (1863–1938) had brought the Moscow Art Theatre—founded by him and V. Nemirovich- Danchenko (1858–1943) in 1898—to such perfection of realism, in the line from Pushkin and Gogol, that all over Europe it was the symbol of excellence and his method was an influence everywhere; indeed it was significant even into the 1950s in Europe and America. He ranged over different epochs and styles—a play of Gogol, a Russian verse play, Alexey Tolstoy's *Tsar Feodor*, or *Tartuffe* and *Le Mariage de Figaro*. He insisted that the actors live the parts, not merely act them; they must dedicate themselves to the theatre and constantly work on self-development so as to know every human emotion and how to control it. They must be able to execute the physical action of the play perfectly. Stanislavsky invented endless individual and group exercises to bring out the actor's hidden resources and he rehearsed meticulously over and over again until the depths of meaning were exactly expressed in a fused and living work of art. After the Revolution he showed Soviet projects and victories. He gave special attention to the youth who must make the new culture and organized studios for their training. (Pl. 56a.)

In the 1920s the theatre became a director's theatre and remained so through the 1950s. It was true that expressionist plays, such as those of O'Neill and Pirandello, lent themselves to directors' experiments. O'Neill's people in *Great God Brown* (1920) put on and took off masks startlingly as different relationships emerged; in his *Strange Interlude* (1928) two structures were presented visually at the same time, the outside gestures and direct speaking between the characters, and the thoughts accompanying them. Luigi Pirandello (1867–1936) staged the tragic impossibility of anyone's getting outside himself and showing himself to another in his own reality in *Six Characters in Search of an Author* (1921). But the understanding between these dramatists and the directors was never adequate, and the plays were not dominant.

Gifted men, influenced by the new painting rather than by plays, experimented with new forms and audiences and technology, using any plays available—Gordon Craig, Max Reinhardt, Elwin Piscator, Gaston Baty, Louis Jouvet, Jean-Louis Barrault, the futurist and constructivist Vsevolod Meyerhold (1874–1943). Edward Gordon Craig, whose influence had already been effective throughout Europe, looked to the renewal of the theatre through a director who would understand the true nature of the theatre and maintain a high standard, not as literature or as imitation, but as vision—a fusion of action, spoken words, music and scene. The modern theatre restored to its origins in the dance, its scene controlled by changing light creating an ever shifting maze of colour, form and motion, should enchant its audience into a beautiful mental and physical ease. (Pl. 56b.)

His work directly affected Max Reinhardt's (1873–1943) Deutsches Theater in Berlin. Reinhardt created the new stage proposed by Gordon Craig and made it dynamic with his own observation of great national or religious processions and festivals, his own love of the colourful and fantastic, and his own driving power and imagination. His repertory ranged over the whole of the world's dramatic literature, both classical and contemporary. Before and after the first world war he made the expressionist theatre of Germany. Among others he staged plays by August Strindberg (1849–1912) with their sense of unknown and evil power working in the life of man and their search for salvation (*Nach Damascus*) and by Franz Wedekind asserting man's drive for sexual power as an active force in the world (*Erdgeist*). He

used every new technical resource—the revolving stage, searchlights to bring
out expressionistic shadings, all-embracing masses of actors or small groups
bursting out from the audience, and he had a genius for bringing out actors'
ability so that they transcended themselves. Exiled in 1933, he went to the
United States where his spectacular technique was popularized in plays such
as *The Miracle* which he had made famous in Europe and America and
he remained an influence during the decade.

In the 1930s, with the depression and the ominous gathering of forces
leading to the second world war, a new kind of theatre emerged in western
Europe which moved still further away from traditional dramatic structure.
Bertold Brecht's (1898–1956) 'Epic Drama' was designed not to enchant the
audience or to produce catharsis but to encourage the modern scientific attitude to society, to make an unsophisticated audience aware of conditions
causing tensions and ready to apply its understanding reasonably in improving
society. He revolted from all the traditional dramatic unities and used episodes,
parables, narrative, folk ballads, free movements in space, expression by
speech, music, dance, pantomime, slogans motion-picture sequences to make
a drama fusing realism and poetic imagination, balancing the effect so that the
audience remained interested but not immersed. His genius as writer and his
control made these *Lehrstücke* far more than pieces of propaganda for dialectical materialism. His stinging comment on *laissez-faire* in *Threepenny Opera*
(1928) with a musical score by Kurt Weill, the outstanding musical comedy in
central Europe when it was first produced, ran several years in New York in
the 1950s. Exiled from Germany and writing from Finland, he bitterly showed
the very victims of war trying to profit by it and sharing responsibility for it in
Mother Courage and Her Children just before the second world war. He
understood the revolutionary force of vital people beyond any specific social
structure and at the same time their inescapable human weakness, their
malice or even alienation, whether it was the peasant girl struggling to keep
the governor's child she had saved and a fantastic judge deciding her case in
The Caucasian Chalk Circle (1944–45) or the brilliant scientific discoverer in
Galileo (1938–39).

Other original attempts to dramatize vast structures of power, social
relationships or scientific discovery were made by the Federal Theater,
1935–39, in the United States under the direction of Hallie Flanagan Davis
(1890–   ). It made a form, the Living Newspaper, in which dramatic lines
leading up to a climax of human interest were combined with statistical narrative to show *Power* (the struggles which led to the Tennessee Valley Authority), *One Third of a Nation* (the need of housing), *Spirochete* (the discovery of
the tubercular bacillus); $E=mc^2$. These plays went out across the country to
people who had never seen live theatre before.

During the 1920s in the USSR the documentary theatre presenting social
problems and building socialism produced a flood of plays. In 1927 in celebration of the tenth anniversary of the October revolution, the Moscow Art

Theatre produced *Armoured Train 14–69*, a dramatization of Vsevolod Ivanov's (1895–) novel of peasants who captured a train sent by the Whites to destroy them. One of the Moscow plays of the 1930s, *Oil*, set in a realistic scene of machinery for producing oil, showed the sacrifices necessary for this industrial expansion. At the end the players cried to the audience, 'Comrades, will you make this sacrifice,' and the audience roared back its willingness. Other plays celebrated the Revolution, such as *Chapayev* which later was made into a popular motion picture.

After the second world war the theatre retreated from documentation and the poetic drama emerged again briefly in England, France and the United States. In the main, the *élan* of experimental staging had settled into the gloss of theatre in the big capitals; no great dramatist was needing a stage. Little theatres reproduced earlier experiments, some romantic outbursts of angry young men and plays of the existentialists (Sartre, *Les Mouches*, 1943; Camus, *Caligula*, 1944). It was significant that Shaw's *Major Barbara* was filmed with Shaw co-operating with the director. The theatre was actually in competition with the motion picture and plays were often interchanged.

Photography. Photography developed rapidly as an art form which could express not only interpretations of mood and social realities similar to those of painters, sculptors and writers, but could penetrate other worlds. The swift accuracy of the camera could fix events that the human eye could not record— quick motion, momentary emotion, distant, inaccessible or tiny objects.

In the first enthusiasm for the new photography as art, not as the mere mechanical result of clicking a shutter, photographers thought of their compositions as paintings. The technology of the camera and of processing plates and film with the possibilities of using double exposures, retouching, distortions and other manipulations, led them to try angle shots, atmospheric effects, surrealist images, collages and photograms. They were able to suggest hidden mysteries and varied relationships—Alfred Stieglitz (1864–1946), *Venerable Trees*; Frederick Sommer (1906–), *Max Ernst*; Arnold Newman (1918–), *Igor Stravinsky*; Edward Steichen (1879–), *Rodin: Thinker*; Moholy-Nagy (1895–1946), photograms; Man Ray (1890–), *Raygrams*. (Pl. 49.)

Such varieties of composition were specially effective in posters for advertising, for they had the necessary instantaneous effect. Moholy-Nagy in the influential group of artists at the Bauhaus during the late 1920s and early 1930s and later as the head of the New Bauhaus in Chicago, taught the use of these devices and himself experimented. The photographic engraving process made production of prints of any size and quantity possible. Advertisers found these compositions especially effective in suggested relationship of desires and by the 1950s they were using a vast range of photographs, at first in black and white, and then in colour as fast as technical development of colour photography allowed.

But romanticism in using effects like painting gave way to use of the special resources of the camera in untouched, unmanipulated photographs. The pioneering Alfred Stieglitz himself and many other photographers aimed at precision of image and richness of texture brought out by light and by exact timing. The beauty and penetration of the picture depended on the special sensitiveness of the artist's perception and swift, sure technique in using the camera. The pictures might be dramatic or abstract; but they were neither decorations nor illustrations. They were records of the meaning of experience made by the artist as seeker. So Eugene Atget (1856–1927) recorded Paris and Walker Evans (1903–   ) and Margaret Bourke White (1905–   ) captured the face of the USA (*You Have Seen Their Faces*, 1937), Russia during war *Shooting the Russian War*, 1942), and the new India (*Halfway to Freedom: Report on the New India*, 1949). (Pl. 50.)

High-speed photography with exposures of a millionth of a second, developed in 1930 as a scientific tool for critical observation of rapidly moving (machine parts, permitted a series of exposures on one plate to trace the path of swift motion. This technique, used imaginatively, gave a quite new aesthetis experience of hitherto unseen shapes and patterns of motion, as in Gjon Mili'c (1904–   ) photographs of a factory worker's hands moving in assembling parts of bolts, his *Ballet Dancer* and his 3/4 *Beat* (Pl. 52). These and other techniques made it possible for the camera to reveal biological shapes hidden under the sea or processes like hatching an egg, or even to capture in a motion picture the working of the valves of the heart (Dr G. Keith Hargett and Edwin C. Udey, *Red River of Life*.) (Pl. 53.) By mid-century, wide-angled astronomical cameras not only gave astronomers an image of the universe far beyond anything previously possible, with which to seek answers to the question of whether the universe is expanding and what is its age, but enabled ordinary people to glimpse the scale and order of the universe and its continuing processes of creation, and to take aesthetic delight in the photographs.

Pictures used in conjunction with writing to increase the impact were the basis of photographic journalism which expanded rapidly after 1936. (Pl 54a.) The big publishers of the photographic journals sent photographers all over the world to cover wars, national crises, ordinary daily lives of remote peoples or of their own people; they published 'photographic essays' by juxtaposing single pictures in a series to make interpretative patterns. Governments made pictures to educate their people, or to interpret their country abroad (e.g. Farm Security Administration in USA and Empire Marketing Board in Great Britain), and many books were made by individual photographers or by editors selecting from far and wide—Walker Evans, *American Photographs*, 1938; Henri Cartier-Bresson (1908–   ), *D'une Chine a l'autre*, 1954; Donald C. Peattie and George Aymer, *This is Living: A View of Nature with Photographs*, 1938. (Pl. 51.)

The scale and development of the art and its possibilities in poetical communication were demonstrated in a photographic exhibit, 'The Family of

Man', 1955, made by Edward Steichen for the Museum of Modern Art in New York, later sent to many cities in many parts of the world, and also reproduced in both a cheap and an expensive book form. The exhibit contained 503 photographs made by 273 photographers in 68 countries, and selected from over 2,000,000 prints. It was conceived as a mirror of the essential oneness of mankind throughout the world as seen 'in the universal elements and emotions in the everydayness of life'; the photographs ranged from birth to death and included the daily relationships of ordinary men to themselves, their families, their communities and the world they live in. The American poet Carl Sandburg (1878–) wrote the prologue, and quotations from great poems, proverbs and sacred texts of many races and peoples defined the structure and pointed the meaning. Crowds of people attended the exhibit wherever it went. Here was a dynamic and popular art.

(v) *Architecture.* Architecture became in the 1920s the outstanding form of modern art and the one which most boldly carried forward the experiments which had gone on before the war, both the rational line of development and the exuberant organic school. The nature of architecture, to meet a practical need, required direct involvement in the society which it served and in the use of the new materials and processes which industry was developing. Under the leadership of a group in Holland known as *de Stijl* (1917–25), the Bauhaus in Germany (1919–33), and Le Corbusier's *Esprit nouveau* in France (1921 on), architects and painters evolved what came to be called the 'international style', although the leading architects themselves deprecated the label as suggesting fixed ideas.

Frank Lloyd Wright in the United States established the principles of organic architecture by a long series of buildings, plans for communities, and writings, and his influence spread in Europe and his own country. The Bauhof was started in Europe on the same principles.

Wright in his *Testament* (1959) defined the principles of organic architecture:

Amidst turbulent changes a way of building has brought to our society a new integrity. . . . These simple buildings themselves show architecture to be an *organism*, based upon 'part is to part as part is to whole'. Only such entity can live. Inevitably this nature-concept was individual in architecture as it was individual in the Declaration of Independence and characteristic of the nature of man himself. Wholeness of human expression in architecture is now assured. Never again could successful building be otherwise. 'Such as the life is, such is the form.'

Lao-tze expressed this truth, now achieved in architecture when he declared, the 'reality of the building does not consist in the roof and walls but in the space within to be lived in'. I have built it. When Unity Temple was built, this sense of interior space began to come through: 1906.

Whether the new architect belonged to the organic school or the European international, the essence of twentieth-century style was engineering honesty in the use of material—what looked like supports must actually be supports, not decoration—and 'functionalism' in design of the building. Architects worked in terms of the potentialities of mass production and of the new materials—steel, glass, concrete, aluminium, ceramics, plastics. They constructed houses which should not be boxes but homes or 'machines for living', and schools, office buildings, factories or banks which should provide ample light, efficient arrangement of space, and economy of construction and look like what they were instead of like pseudo-Greek temples, Gothic cathedrals or Baroque edifices.

The first group to be formed, *de Stijl*, led by the painter Mondrian and the architect Jacobus Oud (1890–   ), worked strictly with cubes, rectangles and flat planes, experimented with the effects of colour—varying the colour of the walls of a single room—and designed furniture to harmonize with their rectangular houses, using new materials such as steel.

In 1919 Walter Gropius established the Bauhaus in Weimar by reorganizing and combining an art academy (the Grand Ducal Saxon Academy for Pictorial Art) and a school for arts and crafts (the Grand Ducal Saxon Academy for Arts and Crafts). As he explained in his *Theory and Organization of the Bauhaus*, he sought to break down the hierarchy which had divided the fine from the applied arts:

The Bauhaus strives to co-ordinate all creative efforts, to achieve in a new architecture, the *unification of all training* in art and design. The ultimate, if distant, goal of the Bauhaus is the *collective work of art*—the Building—in which no barriers exist between the structural and the decorative arts.*

At first every student was taught by a theoretical artist and a craftsman until gradually people were trained who could combine the necessary factors. In spite of bureaucratic indifference and the hostility of an uncomprehending public, Gropius succeeded in bringing together as teachers some of the most outstanding painters, designers and architects of Europe. Students came from a number of countries, besides the main group from Germany. They not only studied theory of design but worked creatively in a range of workshops—carpentry, stained glass, pottery, furniture, metal, weaving, stage design, display and typography. When they moved the Bauhaus to Dessau in 1925, they illustrated both the new style and the principle of a creative group working together in the structure which they designed and the interior which they decorated and equipped. After the rise of Hitler caused the Bauhaus to close in 1933, its influence was dispersed throughout Europe and America as its students and teachers returned home and its directors, Gropius and his

* Museum of Modern Art, *Bauhaus 1919–1928*, ed. by H. Bayer and W. Gropius (New York, 1938), p. 22.

successor, Mies van der Rohe, went to the United States to head schools of architecture at Harvard and the University of Illinois and to become, with Frank Lloyd Wright, the architectural leaders in that country. (Pl. 43.)

The objectives of the Bauhaus were not only technical but social. Gropius insisted that if the development of industry had economic effects alone, the results would be dehumanizing; there must be some principle of human dignity, freedom, and satisfying relationships fostered by the environment in which people lived. Oud's row houses for workers in the Hook of Holland in 1924 were among the first to give effect to this principle through functional architecture.

Le Corbusier went even further, to think in terms of density of population, of articulating transport, work and living, and of planning whole cities that should be on a human scale and free of the confusion, crowding and gigantism all too prevalent as industry expanded and populations increased. He rejected the romanticism of modern suburbs, for they appeared to him only half city and half country and to solve none of the basic problems of living. Instead, he designed tall, slender flats, set in open spaces so that no family would be without light and air, oriented so that every family should have some sunlight during some part of the day, or be shaded from excessive sun in tropical or semi-tropical climates. He outlined possible plans for individual cities (Paris, 1925; Rio de Janeiro, 1929–30) and for types of cities which he called the Concentric City (1922), the Radiant City (1930), the Co-operative Village (1934), the Linear Town (1942). Areas were classified according to function; factories and homes were spaced so that workers could walk to work. Streets were planned in accordance with man's relationships to the automobile and shopping centres; recreation and education were provided for populations of specific sizes. Plans were open so that if the city expanded new integrated units could be worked out for different sizes of population. (Pl. 45a, 45b.)

Le Corbusier's influence spread widely, through the buildings which he constructed and plans which he laid out in many countries, through the spread of his idea for urban towers set in open spaces which was taken up by builders and housing agencies in such places as New York, Paris and Marseilles, through the leading role which he played in international congresses of architects and of city planners and through his students, many of whom occupied influential posts on planning commissions. His concept of the team of engineers and other technicians within which the architect must work was reflected in the organization of great building firms, which might number several hundred architects, engineers, city planners, designers, economists and other specialists. One such US firm in the 1950s was composed of 9 partners and 322 others, with offices in New York, Chicago and San Francisco.

During the second quarter of the century the new architecture was remaking the face of cities, and simplicity of style and forms adapted to the nature of the new materials became increasingly characteristic of furniture and household goods, the equipment for factories and offices, the layout of the printed page, and all manner of displays. Initially taken up by a few rich individuals who dared to build homes of 'advanced' design, the style came to be applied more and more to the functional purposes inherent in modern life for which the architects had conceived its value—streamlined factories to conserve workers' energy and speed; office buildings lifted from the ground on mushroom pillars, the walls serving only as screens and the interior space capable of being divided flexibly according to needs and easily changed; schools and flats with ribbons of windows rising vertically or cutting horizontally to give full sides of light; theatres with perfected acoustics and cantilevered balconies to be free from blinding posts; and parks designed as playgrounds for city children and adults. Because of its extensive use of glass and the tendency to make the inside of the building and its outer surroundings flow into each other, the style was especially well adapted to tropical and semi-tropical climates, and was adopted very widely in such places as Rio de Janeiro, Caracas, Cuba, Puerto Rico and southern California. (Pl. 55a, 55b.)

As the style matured in the hands of many architects, engineers and designers, it came to be used with increased flexibility. In its initial phase it had no place for decoration, depending for its beauty wholly on the proportions of the building and the panels of flat colour which might be part of the building design, and it clung rigidly to rectangular shapes. By the 1950s buildings began to make use of sculpture and painting as an integral part of the building's design and some curved lines were no longer taboo. Mies van der Rohe designed a fountain for a green space in front of one of his New York office buildings, and used paintings to decorate the executive suites on the top floors. Gropius in his building for the Harvard University Graduate School, used coloured tiles, abstract brick bas-relief, and a tall, tree-like construction. The United Nations Assembly building was decorated by Scandinavian, French and Spanish frescoes and tapestries. (Pl. 42, 46.)

During this process the organic school had considerable influence in emphasizing the human aspect of building and the relation of urban design to social forms; it did battle with gigantism or too narrow functionalism. Frank Lloyd Wright's influence rose and fell, but in the 1940s and 1950s it was high all over the world. His buildings were famous and each was unique—the Robie House (1909) in Chicago, horizontal like the prairies it belonged to, the earthquake-proof Imperial Hotel in Japan (1915–23), the models for Broadacre City designed in 1932, the most extended use of the cantilever principle in the tower of the Johnson Wax Co., in Racine, Wisconsin, the flowing space of the Guggenheim Museum (1959) in New York. He was critical of European architecture as still framing a box. Meanwhile the line of organic architecture was carried on in Europe by the Bauhof from 1920, and by 1951 there was a movement among Dutch and English architects to explore ways of drawing the two schools together, to spread the recognition of the function of form in society so that, without losing the gains of functionalism, more human elements could be included and the community could be beautiful. Neither school could be said to be dominant, and indigenous forms were emerging in different countries combining different elements. (Pl. 44.)

As architects sought to meet the new needs of the industrial age, they found their place in society changing and their scope determined by considerations quite outside of the world of art. They had to work not only in functional terms laid down by the prospective user and in a team with a variety of technical specialists, but within an economic and political framework. They were called on to design large units—whole city blocks, new towns, rebuilding war-shattered cities and obsolete sections of others, new capitals like Chandigarh in the Indian Punjab and Brasilia in Brazil, workers' suburbs, housing estates. They had to think in terms of large-scale construction methods involving prefabrication of standard parts and their assembly at the site. They worked within limits set by government plans for development, building and zoning regulations, real estate and financial practices, the organization of the construction industry and the readiness of those in power to carry out their plans.

At mid-century, although the influence of new architectural ideas appeared in many parts of the world, vast suburban developments around rapidly spreading cities were all too often laid out without reference to the architects' concepts of community design and were filled with trite, conventional dwellings built without regard for standards of excellence or honesty and imagination in the use of materials. Some of the finest buildings lost their effectiveness because of the construction of unrelated buildings around them and some of the most functional housing threatened to turn into new slums as a result of regulations as to who should live in it and the manner of its administration. Some buildings reflected preoccupation with materials for their own sake. (Pl. 47a, 47b, 48a, 48b, 20b.)

Yet architecture remained up to the middle of the century the most vigorous of the traditional arts, and the most fully a part of industrial society.[22]

2. EMERGING NATIONAL CULTURES IN OTHER WESTERN CULTURE AREAS

Outside western Europe three principal new lines of expression were developing within the western culture area in the decades after the first world war. The emerging national cultures of the USA, Latin America and the USSR grew from European roots and continued to be affected by European currents, but during these years they became more and more distinctive and self-conscious in spirit and form. By mid-century similar trends toward distinctive modes of expression were appearing in other young countries of European origin, Canada, Australia, New Zealand, South Africa.

In one form or another the developments in all these countries involved self-awareness as a nation and a people, discovery and assertion of the distinctive quality of national life and the social forms and personal experiences that were part of the shaping and maturing of new societies. These drives for cultural integrity and independence within the western culture area were no less a feature of the twentieth century than the drives for political independence from European domination by subject peoples.

Such movements did not, however, take place in isolation but in constant interaction with developments in Europe. During these years interaction was greatest in the case of the United States by reason of its stage of development, its world position, the constant flow of European immigrants and refugees to the United States and of American writers and artists to Europe, the wealth in the United States available for publication and the arts, the fact that American society was representative of the mass culture toward which European societies were tending and American writers were coming to grips with aspects which Europeans had not yet faced; American names inevitably appear among the representatives of major European trends discussed in the preceding pages.

With respect to Latin America, the distinctive forms of expression that were emerging had not yet entered the main stream of western literature and the arts, with a few noteworthy and distinguished exceptions—the poetry of the Nicaraguan Rubén Darío (1867–1916) and the Chilean Gabriela Mistral (1889–1957), the mural painting of the Mexicans José Clemente Orozco (1883–   ), David Alfaro Siquieros (1898–   ), Diego Rivera (1886–1957), the music of the Brazilian Heitor Villa-Lobos (1887–1959). (Pl. 32.)

The USSR lived largely as a closed community during these formative years, using its arts to help develop its revolutionary society and to discover and release the creative potentialities of a broad range of its people; apart from the influence of pre-revolutionary figures such as Stanislavsky, Eisenstein, or Prokoviev, who continued to function within the Soviet Union, especially in drama, films, music and ballet, the literature and arts of the USSR were little known beyond its borders.

In all these areas, and in the other countries of European origin from which an occasional writer or painter was beginning to be heard or seen, writers and artists conceived of themselves not as set apart but as contributing to a stream which would in time flow back into the common pool to add to the richness and variety of the great literature and arts of the West.

(a) The United States

When the USA at the close of the first world war found itself thrust into a central position in the world, its arts and expression had only begun to reflect a native view and to use native idioms. Predominantly they remained identified with Europe, mainly nineteenth-century England in literature, the classic and Renaissance art of Italy and France, and German and Italian music. The word 'culture', in fact, meant the European fine arts. The novelist Henry James, who finally became a British subject, revealed this attitude as he analysed the subtleties of inner feeling of Americans searching for refinement in the art centres of Europe and confronting aristocracies in decay.

The close cultural ties with Europe were maintained mainly by the middle class of the eastern seaboard who were educated in the classical tradition and, like their counterparts in Europe, read the books and magazines, supported the orchestras, bought pictures and endowed museums. But beyond them, stretching across the continent, lay vast areas of newly settled land, big, growing industrial cities, large, newly literate immigrant populations, and Negroes only a generation away from slavery.

Before the USA became involved in the war, young critics, such as Van Wyck Brooks (1886–   ) in *America's Coming of Age* (1915) and Randolph Bourne (1886–1918) (*History of a Literary Radical*, edited by Van Wyck Brooks, 1920) called on American writers to grow up out of cultural colonialism, to develop the wide range of new expression needed to convey the variety of the North American continent and mixed cultures, and to speak to other audiences than those for whom Henry James had meaning. They saw in the vigorous native tradition represented by such nineteenth-century American writers as Walt Whitman (1819–92), Ralph Waldo Emerson (1803–82), Herman Melville (1819–91) and Mark Twain (1835–1910) an authentic statement of the dignity of each man and of self-reliance as a part of the vast harmony of nature, viewed lyrically, philosophically, in terms of tragic conflict with evil, or humorously. They saw the expanding country, the wilderness, the forging of new forms of government in the terms defined by Abraham Lincoln 'of the people, by the people and for the people', the problems of industry, the many kinds of people learning to live together.

Some writers and artists had in fact already begun to express the broad American scene. The audiences that read Henry James had been shocked by the ruthless realism of Theodore Dreiser (1871–1945), whose *Sister Carrie* (1900) was at first refused publication. He showed Carrie, full of imagination and vitality, refusing to accept respectable poverty and the factory job that represented 'opportunity' in Chicago, but finding only emptiness in her relations with the successful men who were ready to give up their hard-won respectability for her. The two poets who became authentic voices of the new America, Robert Frost and Carl Sandburg, had published their first volumes in 1915 and 1916; in the 1950s they were still writing out of the lives of the people they knew and were still read and loved. Frost's poetry from *North of Boston* (1915) to *The Masque of Reason* (1945) and *The Masque of Mercy* (1947) had the sharp-edged humour, hard-bitten realism, and terse, bare understatement of his neighbours who farmed stony, infertile land; he wrote of them with love and with sensitiveness to both the terror and exquisiteness of nature, catching the sound of their speech in the distinctive cadence of his pentameter. Sandburg's *Chicago Poems* (1916), *Cornhuskers* (1918), *Smoke and Steel* (1920), *Good Morning America* (1928) voiced the sorrow and joy, the vulgarity, vitality and dreams of the masses of the people, whether in a new sprawling metropolis in the heart of the continent or on the open prairie.

In painting, a group known as 'The Eight' had exhibited their works in

New York in 1908, interpreting the crude forces of cities, the human struggle in villages on the prairie, men wresting a livelihood from the sea, the western desert. Their styles were distinctive and non-derivative; some indeed were in outright revolt from the new Paris. John Sloan (1871–1951) and others like him insisted on baring the harshness of city life ('Roofs: Summer Night', 1906) and were scornfully labelled the 'ash-can school'. The most authentically American among them, John Marin (1873–1953), developed between 1912 and 1922 an original style to express his faith in the turbulent energy which was thrusting up skyscrapers and spanning rivers with suspension bridges and his feeling that these structures were alive. Like Frost and Sandburg he continued through the following decades to express the vitality of the United States.

Two gifted and influential young American writers, the poets Ezra Pound (1885–   ) and T. S. Eliot, however, had turned away from the American reality to the European tradition in which they had been trained. Believing that the only way to cope with the disillusioning present was to recapture the riches of the past, they explored neglected aspects of European literature and also the literatures of the East. Pound published translations of Chinese poetry. Eliot studied Sanskrit and wrote about Dante. He became the high priest of a cult of the seventeenth-century English metaphysical poets, especially John Donne; he rationalized, in terms of a theory of order transcending the natural world of science, nostalgia for a society based on an *élite*, not yet corrupted by egalitarianism or the Rights of Man and the emptiness of increasingly secularized life. The skill and brilliance of both Pound and Eliot in experimental verse-forms fascinated young American writers eager to be in the *avant garde* and turned many of the next generation away from their own people; at the same time they made them aware that the United States was not isolated but was part of a world.

The first world war and the disillusioning peace shocked the people of the United States into realization that they must see themselves more clearly and also that they were in a larger world where their own position of power needed new attitudes. The writers who searched America itself and those who explored the experiments in the arts in Europe, especially in the school of Paris, became parts of interacting movements in the next decades. Unprecedented numbers of fearless, well-made novels, plays, poems, stories, debates in criticism, autobiographies, biographies, books of reporting, magazines and films were published and read and seen. They made the decade of the 1920s and the years that followed a revelation of new self-consciousness, while the new mass audience provided broad support for a wide range of artistic expression.

Americans now expressed themselves as distinct from Europeans. They were more consciously aware of Europe and often more critically. They used the experiments in form and techniques as they liked, and they drew on the tools of both continents provided by the social sciences and by the translation of Freud. They shared the general European trends—toward abstraction, psychological probing, preoccupation with sex, social criticism—but in terms of their own experience.

Yet while American writers and artists struggled for an authentically American expression, they continued to feel the pull of Europe. After the war, T. S. Eliot and Ezra Pound went to live in Europe, and their verse became part of current European expression. Throughout the 1920s American writers and artists flocked to the Left Bank in Paris, trying to turn their backs on the commercialism of society, and lured by the irresponsibility of the 'art for art's sake' school. But in the 1930s the depression forced most of them home and awakened them also to the realization, in the words of the returned poet Archibald MacLeish (1892–   ), that 'here we must live or live only as shadows' (*American Letter*, 1930).

The self-consciousness that now found expression took many forms. A long list of regional novels detailed the varied lives of ordinary people in the middle west, the south, New England, the isolated mountain hollows of the Appalachian ridge, the south-western desert, the mill towns and the mining communities, and made these all part of a common heritage.

Many writers saw the harshness or emptiness of life, as their counterparts did in Europe: the dull materialism of the small prairie town of *Main Street* (Sinclair Lewis, 1920), the flatness of success in the business of real estate in *Babbitt* (Sinclair Lewis, 1922), *An American Tragedy* (Theodore Dreiser, 1925) in which society was accountable for a bell-hop's becoming a murderer, the urban dweller buffeted by *A World I Never Made* (James T. Farrell, 1904–   : 1936, the families of displaced, migrant farm labourers with no home but the roadside in John Steinbeck's (1902–   ) *Grapes of Wrath* (1939), the meagre or decadent personalities with which William Faulkner (1897–   ) peopled the imaginary county in the deep south where his novels were laid.

Behind this criticism was the assumption that America ought to be the country envisioned by Whitman and Lincoln, and faith that if Americans would just see, they would bring its true destiny into being. Babbitt believed that it would be better for his son, and in *Grapes of Wrath* the character of Ma had the earthy vitality to survive and make another home, and her son found hope in the organization of workers in trade unions. Except for Faulkner, these writers were angry that Americans were blindly betraying their own ideals; they did not fundamentally despair of the human condition or believe in the inevitable violence of revolution.

The search for national self-awareness found roots which would give an historical dimension to a fast-moving culture. The western pioneers in their covered wagons, who had stood as symbols of limitless opportunity in the dreams of the American people, became the subjects of a succession of novels which used psychological approaches to deepen the understanding of this part of the epic of America. Conrad Richter's (1890–   ) trilogy took one pioneer woman and her family through successive stages of settlement, *The Trees* (1940), *The Fields* (1946), *The Town* (1950); O. E. Rölvaag's (1876–

1931) story of Norwegian immigrants, *Giants in the Earth* (1929) called up
the fears, heroic courage and knowledge of the earth with which men and
women faced the limitless stretches of lonely prairie which they were trying to
bring to fruitfulness and which could wipe out a man and his work with bliz-
zard, drought, locusts or undefinable chance; Willa Cather (1876–1947) told
how death came to the cultivated, sensitive Spanish archbishop at his lonely
outpost among simple Mexican and Indian people on the edge of the desert
(*Death Comes to the Archbishop*, 1927). The cost of taming the wilderness
was reflected in the poetry of Edwin Arlington Robinson (1869–1935).

The Civil War of 1861–65 was exploited in every conceivable manner,
most sensitively in Stephen Vincent Benét's (1898–1943) dramatic poem of the
lives of people on all sides in the war (*John Brown's Body*, 1929), but also
romantically, in careful historical studies, in biographies and in countless
novels built around episodes or individuals. Intimate biographies of men who
shaped the nation were written from hitherto unnoticed source materials and
in a manner to evoke the period and the milieu in which they lived.

The masses of the people were accepted and celebrated in their own idiom,
which was becoming a distinctly American speech (Carl Sandburg, *The
People, Yes*, 1936). An ever wider range of voices was heard—immigrants
speaking through their autobiographies (e.g. Ludwig Lewisohn, 1882–1955:
Upstream, 1922) and through the picture of life given by their children
(e.g. Jerre Mangione, 1919– : *Mount Allegro*, 1942), Negroes in their poetry
(Sterling Brown, 1902–   Langston Hughes, 1902–), autobiographies, novels
(Richard Wright, 1908–60: *Black Boy*, 1945, *Native Son*, 1940) and family
history (Pauli Murray, 1910– : *Proud Shoes*, 1956). The range of kinds of
people, their interrelations and their personalities widened as the process of
cultural integration went on and those who wrote came from more varied
backgrounds; all brought to their writing an awareness of other elements in
the mobile, fluid American society quite outside the scope of American writers
at the beginning of the century.

Painters, too, saw and commented upon the cities and the prairies, industry,
the desert and the sea. They were not originators of new styles, though each
painted with his own special language. Whatever their differences they all
conveyed the clear atmosphere and sharp bright light of the American continent by their use of strong colour. Together they made Americans more at
home with their country and the ways of the people—the harshness and loneliness of cities, but also the homeliness of the little houses lighted for workmen to come home to; the tough solemnity and endurance of man and wife
who had brought civilization to the wilderness frontier, the harvests, the tree
planting, the grand sweep of the land that were all part of converting the wild
and dangerous prairie into a bread-basket of the world; they saw machines
and industry wittily, lyrically and realistically; they satirized the pompous
oratory of their senators. Among them all Ben Shahn (1898–) had an especially original way of simplifying themes, a brave imagination and love of

people and cities that threw a clear, strong light on the play of boys in the slums bounded by walls, the fantastic nightmare of devastation of war and, in a mural done for a trade union hall, a better world possible through the organization of workers. (Pl. 30.)

American music showed less development and originality than the other arts, although a few composers drew from American sources and developed styles which lifted their compositions to the level of universal art. Aaron Copland (1900–), writing the music of the ballet *Appalachian Spring* (1944) for the American dancer, Martha Graham, used his own idiom in interpretation of regional rhythms. Roy Harris (1898–) used thematic material from folk songs of both cowboys and Negroes; his *Symphony for Voices* (1935) written to passages from Walt Whitman expressed Whitman's robust vigour with grandeur, austerity and simplicity. Several composers based operas upon the rhythms, tunes and language of the people, using evangelical hymns, political oratory and the cadence of daily speech and frequently employing American themes, such as the pioneer of women's suffrage in Virgil Thomson's *Mother of Us All* (1947).

The most distinctive American music came not from the composers of 'serious' music, but from the new popular musical idiom of jazz. From its origins in the Negro cafés of New Orleans, jazz spread in the 1920s until people throughout the country were dancing freely and excitedly to its nervous, syncopated rhythms and the wild improvisations of drums, trumpets, piano and saxophones. Famous band leaders became enormously popular, and led a series of changing jazz fashions which were followed by lesser bands. Mounting numbers of jazz enthusiasts became connoisseurs of the different jazz modes, developed a vocabulary of their own, and treated jazz as music to be listened to and not simply for dancing. By the 1950s serious jazz music festivals were being held, attended by appreciative audiences from all walks of life—one of the leading jazz music critics was a Catholic priest—and jazz compositions were being written, not merely improvised. The first serious composer to grasp the jazz idiom as the basis for a distinctive, American musical style was George Gershwin (1898–1937), whose *Rhapsody in Blue* (1923) and his folk opera of Negro life, *Porgy and Bess* (1935) established this new mode at the level of musical art.

In the effort to understand the quality of their emerging society and to define Americans to themselves, writers brought a range of approaches to the meaning of technology, abundance, mass literacy, the accompanying mass culture, the tensions of modern American life. Thorstein Veblen analysed respectable ways with brilliant irony in *The Theory of the Leisure Class* (1899, much read in the 1920s) and introduced the concept of 'conspicuous consumption' into current thought. Henry Adams (1838–1918), after analysing in his influential *Education* (privately printed 1906, published 1918) his immediate and unsatisfying heritage of eighteenth-century Enlightenment and Protestant Christian morality, turned to the cultural synthesis of the twelfth century; but he saw that there was no escaping to the past and that the Virgin of Chartres, the focus of that culture and symbol of compassion, only served to heighten the problem of modern man, who must find a basis for compassion and morality in an age of science, technology and accelerating social change. Walter Lippman's (1889–   ) classic examination of *Public Opinion* (1922) broke ground in exploring the relation of the mass culture and new media to the processes of democracy. The far-ranging news reporter, Lincoln Steffens (1866–1936), traced his efforts to understand crime and corruption in American cities and the men involved until he saw how they were bound up with efforts of people to meet their human needs (*Autobiography*, 1931).

Lewis Mumford (1895–   ) was one of the few writers in any country who analysed comprehensively the impact of science and technology on architecture, literature, painting and the culture of cities and tried to chart new directions (*Technics and Civilization*, 1934; *The Culture of Cities*, 1938). Vernon Louis Parrington (1871–1929) reviewed the quality and range of American expression in politics, press, popular novels and belles lettres, as related to the social and economic history of the continent (*Main Currents of American Thought*, 3 vols. 1927–30). Lillian Smith (1897–   ) brought a fearless understanding of Freudian principles to bear on the back-door sex relations between white men and Negroes, to uncover the nature and sources of racial prejudice and hate (*Killers of the Dream*, 1949).

During the depression of the 1930s the federal government, which had not been a patron of the fine arts as were the governments in European countries, gave great stimulus to the arts on a mass scale by including artists, writers, musicians and actors in its programme of work for the unemployed. Thousands of painters did wall paintings for public buildings or canvases which became available to schools or other public institutions; musicians formed municipal orchestras and played new compositions; experimental theatres tried out new forms; writers collected the life stories of all manner of people, and gathered a wealth of historical records and folklore. Although this aid to the arts was short-lived—a purely temporary depression measure—and was undiscriminating in extending support to unemployed artists without regard for the quality of their work, it uncovered a large reservoir of talent, made the arts a part of daily life outside the metropolitan centres to which they had tended to be confined, and left a residue of continuing interest and municipal or private support when federal funds were withdrawn.

About 1942 a group of young painters in New York turned against the realism and description of the land and people which the Federal Art Project during the years of the depression had encouraged. They adopted the principles of surrealism. They saw themselves as paralleling the discoveries of psychoanalysis. In emotion they felt that the basic fact of the United States to be interpreted was violence. They filled large canvases with great blocks of often subtle colour in dramatic contrasts, with shifting biological shapes and intricate confusions of lines. Although a number of such painters got into the museums in the United States during the 1940s and 1950s and began to be influential in Europe, this painting remained foreign to the general run of people. Alexander Calder's constructivist abstractions—his mobiles—however, were popular in the United States, and he was well known in Europe also.

It was of the essence of American expression during these years that it was the work of people from many lands and many backgrounds, immigrants and the children of immigrants who represented the interaction of two cultures, and older Americans, most of whom traced their cultural roots to Britain but some in the south-west to Spain, some in Louisiana to France, some in Pennsylvania to Germany, and some throughout the country to Africa. Outstanding writers, painters and musicians, who were completely identified as Americans, had been born in or were only a generation removed from Russia and Japan, Italy, Yugoslavia, Germany, China, France, Greece, Poland, Ireland, Czechoslovakia. In addition, the USA during these years was a principal haven for the many European artists and intellectuals who chose exile from the régimes which they could not accept at home. Although still identified culturally with their country of origin, writers such as Thomas Mann, architects such as Gropius and Mies van der Rohe, musicians such as Stravinsky and Hindemith and sculptors such as Naum Gabo and Pevsner lived, worked and taught in the United States.

From these varied and sometimes conflicting trends, in constant interaction with contemporary currents in Europe and among Europeans in exile, no single national style emerged. Europeans tended to identify American expression with violence and primitivism, and to enjoy it for this feature—not only the 'wild west' stereotype of the second-rate movies, but the sophisticated violence of Hemingway or Faulkner or the elemental passion of Steinbeck's barely civilized men. They recognized that the American language had taken on a character of its own, and French translations began to specify on their title page 'translated from the American' or 'translated from the English'. By the middle of the century the American vision and the American idiom had become distinct and had produced a body of works which were taking their place in the great tradition of the West.

(b) Latin America

The literary and artistic expression of Latin America was in some ways closer to Europe than was that of the United States and in other ways more distinct. The difference arose from the nature of the Latin American societies —quasi-feudal in structure, based upon *latifundia* worked by poor and illiterate rural masses and mines or other extractive industries largely exploited with foreign capital, the benefits accruing to the small upper class of landowners and the foreign entrepreneurs. In a number of countries—notably Mexico, Guatemala, Ecuador, Peru and Bolivia—large Indian communities, amounting to from 20 to 55 per cent of the total population, lived on the margin of westernized society, maintaining their language, social organization and cultural values. In Brazil the people of the hinterland were for a long time out of touch with the life on the coast.

Although the constitutions of Latin American countries since their independence in the first quarter of the nineteenth century had established the principle of democratic citizenship, the economics of the *latifundia* system, the cultural isolation of the Indians and the physical isolation imposed by the wilderness, perpetuated a very different reality. Neither rural masses, nor Indians, nor yet the men of the back-country, participated fully in the national life. During the twentieth century the struggles to achieve a fusion and integration of these fragmented societies provided the political and social milieu for the arts and letters of the period.

But while the societies of Latin America offered a less integrated national base from which to develop their forms of expression, they contained elements far more distinct and independent of European origin than any that were native to the United States. In the great pre-Columbian cultures of the Mayas, Incas or Aztecs and in the living continuity of the cultural traditions of the Indian populations lay rich resources quite outside the European line of influence. This substratum of Indian culture was evident in the archaeological remains, the large Indian populations, and the Indian blood in the *mestizos* who constituted a majority of the westernized populations in most countries. In Brazil the popular folk culture drawn from a combination of African, Indian and European origins developed during 300 years of isolation. As these indigenous influences came to the surface, they interacted with European elements to give Latin American expression in the twentieth century its unique quality.

The geography of the continent provided a second major factor shaping a mentality distinct from the European. Far more than in North America, where moderate rainfall, controllable vegetation and traversable terrain invited settlement and permitted the advancing frontier to remain in contact with centres of population, the violence and rigour of nature in many parts of the South American continent constantly challenged those who penetrated beyond the coastal strips.

Especially in Brazil, much of whose immense territory was made up of dense jungles traversed by huge, fierce rivers, man had to learn to live with untameable nature. In the words of the Brazilian writer, Euclides da Cunha (1866–1909), whose novel of the wild, rebellious life of the back country *Os sertoes* (*The Back Country*, 1904) became a classic, 'To conquer the land, we even had to produce a man capable of fighting it—bred in its image with its crudity and its energy in revolt.'* In isolated, self-contained pockets of settlement or wandering as herdsmen from one pasture area to another, the frontier *bandeirantes* and their descendants were deeply conditioned by their physical surroundings.

* Quoted in F. de Azevedo, *Brazilian Culture* (New York, 1950), p. 35.

Elsewhere, men had to come to terms with the limitless pampas of Argentina, to adjust to the rugged, domineering Andes with their steep slopes, isolated valleys and the thin atmosphere of their windswept plateaux, to cope with the *llanos* or plains where engulfing floods alternated with searing droughts, or with unyielding deserts in regions of Mexico, Peru, Chile and northern Brazil. Although parts of Latin America enjoyed a comfortable climate, manageable terrain and adequate rainfall, vast areas presented a constant menace to man. Nearly all were impressive in their majesty, richness and beauty.

In the late nineteenth century Spanish-American writers initiated the Spanish modernist movement which lightened the classic Spanish syntax and introduced a lively rhythm and impressionist style more appropriate to the spirit of the times. The leader and most influential poet of this movement was the Nicaraguan, Rubén Darío. Its precursors had been the Cuban poets José Marti (1853–95) and Julián del Casal (1861–93), the Mexican Manuel Gutierrez Nájera (1859–95), the Colombian José Asunción Silva (1865–96). Darío carried the movement to Spain when he went to live and work there during the early years of the twentieth century.

Modernist writers rejected both classic rhetoric and romantic eloquence and sentimentality. In the manner of the French Parnassians and symbolists, they sought clarity and purity of imagery and used a precise vocabulary enriched from the language of daily speech. They introduced great variety of metric forms in place of the limited number of classical metres.

During the first two decades of the twentieth century poets and writers in most Hispanic American countries followed the general direction set by Rubén Darío, who was recognized as the outstanding contemporary poet in Spain as well as in the New World. Leopoldo Lugones (1874–1938) in Argentina represented the left wing of the modernists; like Stravinsky and Picasso, he remained an experimenter, adopting new stylistic modes every few years. The Uruguayan, José Enriquez Rodó (1872–1917), outstanding among the prose writers, contributed to the positive sense of identity among Latin American writers; like other prose writers, who wrote mainly essays, articles or narratives of travel rather than fiction, he was best known for his critical essays, including his evaluation of the work of Rubén Darío, and especially for *Ariel* (1900) in which he set the idealism and spiritual character of the Hispanic heritage against what he saw as materialism and reliance on force in the culture of North America.

In their reaction against romanticism, with its idealization of the Indian and of local life, the modernist writers at first turned away from American materials and drew on a wide cultural heritage for inspiration—Greek or Scandinavian mythology, Christian legends, Japanese modes. Soon, however, they returned to native materials and themes. The Peruvian poet José Santos Chocano (1875–1934) called the poems which he published in 1906 *Alma América* (*Soul of America*). Lugones's *Odas seculares* (1910) were on native themes. Darío himself, after vigorously rejecting his American surroundings as unpoetical, used American scenes, legends and history in his later work. Short-story writers created distinctively South American characters, and though they patterned their stories on those of de Maupassant, they developed them in local terms.

The major renascence of arts and letters in Brazil did not come until 1920. Cultural relations between Brazil and Portugal had never been as close as those between Spain and her former colonies, for Portugal had done little or nothing to further cultural development during the colonial period. In the early nineteenth century, when the Portuguese government and royal court, fugitives from Napoleon, had been transferred to Rio de Janeiro, the king had imported a French cultural mission to offer instruction in the arts, and thereafter France supplied the chief European cultural inspiration to Brazilian artists and writers. Local literary and artistic traditions remained weak during the nineteenth and early twentieth century; they lost what little support they had had when the fall of the Brazilian empire in 1889 removed the principal source of patronage, the court.

The Latin American writers of the first quarter of the twentieth century constituted a more or less self-contained group, far removed from the general population. A number of them lived for a time in Europe, chiefly in Paris or Spain. Except in Buenos Aires, they could count on neither a well-developed publishing industry not a periodical press; Brazilian publications prior to 1920 were put out in editions of not more than one to two thousand copies. They were more concerned with style than with social content or impact. Their audience was a devoted circle of initiates drawn from the *élite* class to which they also belonged, for a broad public was yet to be developed.

The Mexican revolution which began in 1910 set in motion a major process of cultural reorientation whose effect extended not only to the countries where Indians made up a large proportion of the population but to other areas as well. In the years after the first world war, writers in Argentina, Chile, Colombia, Venezuela and Cuba joined those of Mexico, Ecuador and Peru in drawing their inspiration and their material from pre-Columbian and current Indian sources. Archaeological research brought to light during these years much new evidence of the very great antiquity and the amazing richness of early American civilizations. The influence of the archaeological remains was reinforced by a continuity in identity and in feeling from prehistoric times to the present where Indian populations lived on, tenacious of their way of life.

To this renewed appreciation of the Indian was joined a spirit of social protest. The tone was set by the poem '¿ *Quién sabe* ?' (Who knows ? 1913), written by Chocano while accompanying the Mexican revolutionary army: 'Indian, you who labour to till the lands that others own, do you not know that your blood and your sweat should make them yours?' The famous novel by the Mexican writer, Mariano Azuela (1873–1952), *Los de abajo* (1916, translated as *The Underdogs*) was one of many which dealt with the exploitation of the Indian.

In Brazil the major cultural movement dated from 1922 when a Week of Modern Art in São Paulo brought together poets, critics, novelists and artists. The movement which got its impetus from this event, well represented by the strongly nationalist poet, Mario de Andrade (1893–1945), was vigorously anti-European. Although it derived many of its technical characteristics from European sources, its spirit was that of revolt from tutelage to the older cultures. It marked the efforts of Brazilian writers and artists to speak as representatives of an independent culture, rooted in the physical surroundings, popular spirit and intense vigour of a people struggling to find itself in modern terms.

In the second quarter of the twentieth century Latin America produced clearly defined forms. In spite of local differences, writers and artists who did not know each other personally and were separated by great distances corresponded through the pages of reviews to shape among themselves a common Latin-American culture. There were strongly nationalistic novels and a wide range of interpretations of the essentially American in anthropology, philology, folklore, history and philosophy.

The most distinctive and best known of these forms were in the field of painting. Inspired by the revolutionary struggles of the people and by the forms and feeling expressed in ancient Indian monuments, Mexican painters, most notably Diego Rivera, José Clemente Orozco, and David Alfaro Siqueiros, gained world-wide renown for the quality of their murals. The exteriors of the University of Mexico buildings with their huge, brilliantly coloured figures and designs displayed a modern adaptation of pre-Columbian styles. The work of Cándido Portinari (1903–   ) in Brazil, was comparable in type and quality. Both in murals for public buildings and in single paintings representing ethnic and social types—Indian, *mestizo*, Negro, sharecropper's wife, family group, village at work—he conveyed a sense of the vitality, strength and endurance of the Brazilian people.[23] (Pl. 32.)

Musical expression, too, took on a distinctive character. In this field, it was the popular expression rather than ancient, indigenous styles which provided the basis for the best known work. The most widely known and prolific of the twentieth-century Latin American composers, the Brazilian Heitor Villa-Lobos, drew much of the style and feeling of his work from popular music and dance in which African and Iberian rhythms were ingrained.

Poetry had always been the most characteristic form of literary expression in the region. During these years poets experimented widely. Both the writers in Spanish, who called themselves 'ultraists' or 'vanguardists' and their Brazilian counterparts identified as 'modernists', made free use of metre and syntax, turning to free verse or reverting to archaic forms at will; they called up a great variety of associations by their images; some sought the utmost purity of form while others retained a feeling for the objectively real and specific.

In the poetic movements and expression of these years, the tendencies toward the abstract and toward the essentially native were intertwined. The Chilean poet Vicente Huidobro (1893–1948), representative of those whose search was for new forms of expression abstracted from reality, called himself a 'creationist' to denote the freshness of his approach. The Peruvian poet, César Vallejo (1895–1938) was known as 'essentially Indian' in spirit, for the sense of ancient, enduring sadness which his poems conveyed. Argentine writers named one of their leading literary magazines, established in 1925, after the protagonist in a famous novel of gaucho life, *Martín Fierro* (by José Hernandez, 1872). In this magazine, both native and abstract poetry appeared side by side, each equally a part of the quest for a native idiom, free from dependence on Europe— a quest which had been going on with more or less intensity from the time of independence.

In prose, some writers chose to use the psychological novel, others the novel of social import. The social novels which appeared in mounting numbers revealed not only an identification with the indigenous element but the struggles for the integration of society. They contrasted with European novels in giving nature a determining role; conflicts appeared more environmental and earthy than psychological. They revealed collective tensions between hostile and incompatible groups in great economic and social disequilibrium—Indians and rural masses versus the urban minority, or the spiritual and economic conflict between the native worker and the foreign enterprise. When the protagonist was not struggling against indomitable nature in the form of tropical jungle, forbidding Andes, empty desert or raging rivers, he was caught in the turmoil of societies in the process of fusion.

Novels of Indian life, which had been idyllic in the romantic period of the nineteenth century, became brutally realistic; Ecuadorian writers in particular depicted the Indian's lot as intolerable. The literature of the social underworld peopled by Indians dispossessed, debased and subjected to all manner of frustrations and injustices recalled the bitterest literature of tsarist Russia such as Gorky's *Lower Depths*.

The incorporation of indigenous elements, both human and environmental —even the revolt against European cultural dominance—did not however mean isolation from Europe and its intellectual and artistic influences. Whatever intellectual currents were sweeping Europe also swept the Americas— positivism, Marxism, psychoanalysis, existentialism. Works in other European languages were quickly translated into Spanish or Portuguese and circulated; the cultivated circles of Latin America discussed the same philosophers, playwrights, novelists or poets as were being discussed in the literary circles of Europe and North America. Europe's literature of crisis, failure, resentment and social rebellion had its repercussions on the Latin American literature of social protest. Such techniques as stream of consciousness, explorations of the subconscious and surrealist imagination gave the works of Latin American writers their modern flavour. The influence of Picasso was visible in the works of many painters.

These very currents of modern European thought and art, in fact, made it easier to understand the ancient cultures and to incorporate their spirit. The Venezuelan critic, Mariano Picón-Salas, noted that the

indigenous heritage would not have had so much validity if the spiritual attitude of twentieth century man and certain deep currents in the psyche and the art of the times had not prepared us—better than in other epochs—to comprehend these ultra-archaic forms. The neo-classicists and rationalists of the eighteenth century would not have understood the monumental art of Chichén-Itzá and Palenque, of Mitla, Tula and Teotihuacan as the contemporaries of Picasso could feel and revitalize them. Monsters, symbols, dreams and forms of our anxious and full age are related to those of distant times. As a result of our immersion in the mysteries of ethnology, of the symbolic enigma of the most ancient human cultures, of the terrible cosmic vitality of the germinal myths, of the depths in the subconscious to which contemporary psychology probes, the great sculptures of the Aztecs or Olmecas seem now nearer and more comprehensible. Compared to these, what a banal vision of life would be offered by the contrived portraits of the Rococo or the lightly hedonistic sensuality of the figures of a Renoir.[*]

Thus, in perhaps no other part of the world did so many diverse currents come together. The ancient Indo-American was still alive and also renewed; the Spanish and Portuguese represented a continuous European tradition; the cosmopolitan immigration of the twentieth century brought other European elements, especially to Argentina, Uruguay, Brazil and Venezuela; the major African influence was on music and dance, but spread thence to painting and literature; the impact of the physical surroundings was always present. In the emerging cultures of the region, the most modern European trends interacted with old traditions; the culture of the cultivated élite met the popular culture of the masses. The Spanish and Portuguese languages and the Catholic Church were unifying factors. Economic and social revolution, well under way in Mexico and barely initiated in many other areas, was in process of converting feudal, paternalistic societies into more democratic ones. The literature and arts of Latin America were coming to reflect the complex dynamics of these emerging societies.

(c) The USSR

The USSR inherited the literary and artistic traditions of western Europe, of which the Russian component was a major element during the nineteenth century. The works of the great Russian novelists, Dostoevsky and Tolstoy,

[*] 'El aire cultural en América Latina', *Journal of World History*, I (1954), p. 701 (translated).

the plays of Chekhov and the realistic stories of Gorky were among the works which had the greatest influence upon western writers when they were translated into German and French in the nineteenth century and into English in the early twentieth century. The major Russian composers of the nineteenth century, Tchaikovsky, Mussorgsky, Alexander Glazunov (1865–1936), Rimsky-Korsakov, shared with the German romantics a central place in the musical tradition of the West. The brilliant and creative Russian theatre and ballet were the inspiration of producers and choreographers on both sides of the Atlantic.

In the years before the first world war Russian artists and musicians shared the experimentation in which their western European contemporaries were engaged, in a free flow and interchange of influence and experience; Diaghilev's Russian Ballet used the work of foreign artists and in turn influenced them. Russian artists were prominent among those who carried experimentation with form the farthest, notably Kandinsky in his use of colour alone to express mood and the constructivists with their mathematically based abstractions. The Moscow Art Theatre under Konstantin Stanislavsky took the lead in experimenting with dramatic techniques for making the stage express inner psychological realities. Symbolist poetry was represented in the work of Alexander Blok (1880–1921) and Andrei Biely (1880–1934).

The October revolution gave impetus to these experimentations and an opportunity for pre-revolutionary writers and artists to apply their ideas of freedom from classical traditions to the making of the new Soviet culture. Kandinsky returned from Germany to join Pevsner, Gabo, Malevich, Tatlin and others in replacing the old Academy of Art. Members of the group started a new Higher and Technical Art Workshop which integrated architecture, sculpture and painting.

From 1917 to 1920 their movement expanded. They developed their ideas of art in the new Soviet world and designed projects to express them—a 'Monument to the Third International', to be an office building and a symbol of the new synthesis of art, learning and technical knowledge (Tatlin, 1919), a project for a radio station and a design for a textile town prepared by Naum Gabo. In 1920 they issued a *Constructivist Manifesto*, declaring that art is based on space and time; kinetic and dynamic elements are necessary to express time; art should not imitate but discover new forms, for reality is constantly changing. Vsevolod Meyerhold applied constructivist principles to the theatre and experimented with stylized forms, in staging, acting and the massing of performers until the play became essentially a design created by the producer.

Experimental writers, too, identified themselves with the Revolution. Vladimir Mayakovsky (1894–1930) welcomed the revolutionary spirit which discarded traditional values, and threw his energy into propaganda verse, epigrams on topical subjects in the style of popular factory songs, verse dramas glorifying the Revolution, and poems epitomizing the national aspirations as in *150,000,000* (1920), a poem in which the peasant stands for 150,000,000 Russians. Alexander Blok expressed the spirit of revolutionary Leningrad in his classic poem *The Twelve* (1918), using popular language and rhythms. Musicians formed an Association of Contemporary Music to encourage musical experimentation and to perform works of new, anti-bourgeois west European composers.

After 1920 the climate of free experimentation began to change. The movement of constructivist artists broke up, chiefly on the issue of whether art should reflect a definite ideology. Tatlin accepted the principle that art is an instrument of the socialist state, and remained to take part in the development of the USSR. Gabo, Pevsner and Kandinsky, believing that art must keep itself free of political influence, left Russia and became part of the movements of art in western Europe and the United States. A number of artists in other fields who wished to remain individual and experimental, including the composer Stravinsky, also left, as it became clear that those who remained would be called upon to participate directly in the building of the socialist society, and would be governed by the principles of style deemed appropriate to this purpose. But the theatre, still in the hands of Stanislavsky and Meyerhold, and the cinema under the creative leadership of Sergei Eisenstein, continued through the 1920s to experiment boldly. And some who emigrated, such as Alexey Tolstoy (1882–1945) and Ilya Ehrenburg (1891–   ), returned to their homeland.[24]

The pre-revolutionary writers, painters, musicians, sculptors and architects who remained in Russia or returned, and who went through the difficult process of having to reconsider their artistic doctrines, dedicated their efforts to helping in the struggle to remake Soviet society, to creating a popular art comprehensible to the working people, and to interpreting for them the heritage of the past. Their energies found outlets in dramatic, satirical and rousing political posters which raised propagandist art to a high technical level, as in the pictures and rhymes of the famous ROSTA windows by the poet and artist, Mayakovsky; in monumental propaganda sculpture to honour great revolutionary figures of the past; in the design of hydroelectric stations, factories, public buildings and workers' housing or the laying out of whole communities and new towns; in novels such as those of Alexey Tolstoy who wrote of the decay of the pre-revolutionary society and of his own childhood (*Nikita's Childhood*, 1921) and created fantasies into which he wove revolutionary ideology.

In the years immediately following the Revolution there were those who took a narrow view of the problems and paths of the new art. The group which organized Proletkult in 1917, to train gifted workers in the arts, maintained that the new culture could be created only by the hands of those directly linked with the working class, rejecting the possibility that men stemming from the old intelligentsia could take part; they repudiated Russian and world classics, declaring them to be bourgeois literature and hence utterly alien to the people. Other groups proposed that 'Pushkin be cast overboard from the ship of modernity' or insisted on the purely utilitarian mission of art. Lenin took a definite stand against these views of vulgar simplification, stating that 'proletarian culture must appear as a logical development of those resources of knowledge which humanity had amassed under oppression in capitalist society'.*

Some writers and artists did indeed emerge from peasant or partially peasant backgrounds; more, whatever their background, had participated actively in the revolutionary struggle and wrote with realism and insight drawn from direct experience. Men and women from many different walks of life brought to literature and the arts new material, new problems and new characters. Mikhail Sholokhov (1905-   ) hailed from a Don Cossack village, participated in the struggle against the kulaks, and after gaining world fame as a novelist continued to live and work in the same village, both as novelist and deputy to the Supreme Soviet. In his epic novel *And Quiet Flows the Don* (vol. I, 1938) he gave full expression to the vitality of the peasant as it showed itself in every relationship—to his land, his horses, his wife and children, his village, the whole Don River basin, and the confusion of armies passing over the land. Alexander Fadeyev (1901-56), who took part in guerrilla warfare in the Far East, showed the civil war in terms of the individual psychology of those who fought in it in *Razgrom* (*The Rout*, 1927). Dmitry Furmanov (1891-1926) was commissar of the legendary Chapayev's division, of which he wrote (*Chapayev*, 1923). Isaac Babel (1894-*c*. 1938) in *Cavalry* (1926) portrayed the civil war with grim realism.

With the first five-year plan in 1928, artists and writers were involved more directly in the work of socialist reconstruction, for the plan provided for the utilization of their talents, as of other human and material resources, and required their training, development and organization. Many writers belonging to diverse groups set out together for various parts of the country and produced works on the great changes that were being wrought in central Asia, in the north, in central Russia and in the Far East. The Russian Association of Proletarian Writers (RAPP) under Leopold Averbakh (1903-39) became the instrument for enlisting writers in the programme of industrialization and collectivization. In 1932 a more inclusive organization, the Union of Soviet Writers, in which Maxim Gorky, Sholokhov and Fadeyev were influential, brought together writers of all social origins, including many not members of the Party.

The role of writers and artists was, in Stalin's phrase, that of 'engineers of human minds'. As set forth in the statute of the Union of Soviet Writers, they were to create 'works of high artistic significance, saturated with the heroic struggle of the world proletariat and with the grandeur of the victory of socialism, and reflecting the great wisdom and heroism of the Communist

* Quoted in T. Trifonova, 'Soviet Literature', *Journal of World History*, VII (1962), p. 101.

party'. A common creative method, known as 'socialist realism', was approved for all forms of expression. (Pl. 29.)

This style, designed to create understanding, support and a favourable climate for national efforts, called for realistic presentation which would show things not only as they were but for what they represented in the building of a socialist society—figures which were both individuals and social types, such as portraits of 'The Delegate' (1927) and 'The Chairwoman' (1928) by the painter Georgy Ryazhsky (1895–1955), 'The Worker' (1922) and 'The Red Army Man' (1923) by the sculptor Ivan Shadr (1887–1941), or 'Peasant Girl' (1927) by Vera Mukhina (1889–1953); stories in which those who took an active part in the battle for production—workers, peasants, scientists, engineers—played the hero's role; historical scenes which identified valour in the present with the grandeur of the past; the Russian landscape lyrically seen and felt; warmly sympathetic sketches of peasant and industrial life.

In this vein, writers depicted the heroic struggles against nature, in the building of a paper mill in the remote forest of north-east Russia (Leonid Leonov, 1899–   : Sot, 1930), the drama of mechanization on a massive scale in the huge Magnitogorsk coke-chemical combine (Valentin Katayev, 1897–   : Vremya, vperyod—Time, Forward!, 1933), the vision and inescapable tragedy in collectivization (Mikhail Sholokhov, Virgin Soil Upturned, 1931). Whereas the works of the 1920s had been mainly devoted to the revolutionary struggle and the civil war, with such notable exceptions as F. Gladkov's (1888–1958) Cement (1925), major attention was now directed to the labour and efforts of the Soviet people who had become masters of their land and were transforming it. Painters produced documentary representations of the new way of life, the elemental strength of peasants, the vitality in scenes of labour. Sensitive to the human drama and recognizing that their task was to help create the new Soviet man, some writers dealt with the psychological conflict within the individual between the old and the new, and with the coming of age of the new man, as did Konstantin Fedin (1892–   ) in First Joys (1945) and No Ordinary Summer (1947–48).[25]

In the 1930s Maxim Gorky's influence was strong in relating new art to the classical tradition and in encouraging the cultures of the national republics. Proletarian writers were stimulated to study the great classics, though not to adopt the negative tone of Dostoevsky. The Union of Soviet Composers, organized in 1932, included in its purposes a reassessment of the classical and romantic heritage and it formed sections in the different republics to develop special national characteristics and the use of folk songs.

A distinctive type of historical novel emerged, devoted to the historical destinies of the people. Thus Alexey Tolstoy's Peter the First (Book I, 1929), although named after a tsar, reflected a whole epoch in the development of Russia, embracing all the strata of the Russian society of the time including the unpropertied masses. Novels such as Olga Forsh's (1875–   ) trilogy devoted to the eighteenth-century revolutionary Russian writer Radishchev

(1954) and A. Chapygin's (1870–1937) story of Stepan Razin (1926–27) depicted individual destinies, recreated decisive periods in the history of the people and showed widespread popular movements.

Writers of the many nationalities which make up the Soviet Union followed a course similar to writers in Russian, treating modern themes, producing regional historical novels such as Mukhtar Auezov's (1897–   ) *Abai* on nineteenth-century Kazakhstan, or drawing on personal experience as in Sadriddin Aini's (1879–1954) memories of youth, *Bukhara* (1948). By the 1950s Soviet literature was being produced in the languages of more than seventy nationalities, some of which had had no written language of their own, and was being translated into all the languages of the USSR so that wide masses of readers in all corners of the land could become familiar with a multi-national socialist literature as a whole.[26]

Continuity with musical tradition was also evident and was maintained into the 1950s in the works of the leading composers. Sergei Prokoviev, who returned to the USSR in 1933 after fifteen years in western Europe and America, made subtle and skilful use of classical forms as well as popular dances and tunes in his ballets, symphonies, concertos and sonatas ranging in theme from lyric to heroic and in mood from witty and gay to dramatic or grand. His music was much loved and played both in the USSR and in western Europe and America. Dmitry Shostakovich, whose work also became well known outside Russia as well as inside, drew freely on the whole classical tradition of European music and used its forms ingeniously and originally in his prolific output of symphonies and other works to celebrate great national efforts of the Soviet people. His *Symphony of 1905 Revolution* (1957) for the fortieth anniversary of the founding of the Soviet state incorporated the revolutionary songs of the people into a symphony in the classical form, combined with a great fugue to give a massive, cumulative effect. Folk themes were used in combination with traditional Russian modes by the Armenian composer Aram Katchaturian (1903–   ): *Gayna Ballet*, 1943; *Spartacus Ballet*, 1954).

Ballet, one of the most popular of the arts, also retained the form which had made it famous before the turn of the century. The dozens of ballet schools (thirty-two in the mid-1950s) taught the classical techniques, and troupes performed both traditional ballets, such as *Swan Lake*, and new ones on modern themes such as the story of the Chinese revolution in *The Red Poppy* (1927, by Reinhold Gliere, 1875–1956), danced in the classical style. Operas also used both legendary and folk materials.

The tone of all the arts was heroic—the five-year plan novels, monumental sculpture, such as Vera Mukhina's huge 'Worker and Collective Farm Woman' (Pl. 40) made for the Soviet pavilion at the 1937 Paris Fair, decorative painting to adorn façades and interiors of public buildings, Shostakovich's solemn and eloquent *Fifth Symphony* (1937), Prokoviev's music for Sergei Eisenstein's (1898–1948) spectacular film of the national hero, *Alexander*

Nevsky (1938). The heroism of the tsarist past was recalled with such figures as Ivan the Terrible. Writers drew inspiration from the personalities of outstanding leaders of the Revolution, most notably Lenin, of whom Mayakovsky created a profoundly human and at the same time monumental image in his poem *Vladimir Ilyich Lenin* (1924). The search for the Soviet hero led to such popular novels as N. Ostrovsky's (1904–36) *That's How Steel was Tempered* (1935), the story of the formation and growth of a young communist of working-class origin.

With the second world war artists and writers were mobilized even more completely than before for the common national purpose. In devoting themselves to arousing patriotic fervour and war efforts they were aware that they must reach deeper psychological levels than had been touched in much of the literature dealing with the struggle for production in the preceding years. The conference of the Union of Soviet Writers in 1942 expressed the view that only through 'psychological realism' and a humanistic and patriotic approach could Soviet literature preserve its most valuable asset: its ties with the masses. Amid the great volume of war reporting, historical and other novels, war plays and biographies of national heroes, some works of literary quality stood out, such as Fadeyev's *The Young Guard* (1945) and Leonov's prize-winning play, *Invasion* (1942).

Socialist realism had been conceived as a form which, while demanding truth and historical concreteness, a clear Party tendency and active participation in the life of the people, would not restrict artistic exploration; the statute adopted at the first Writers' Congress in 1934 stressed that socialist realism gives wide range to creative seekings. But during the Stalin era, literature and the arts suffered from the no-conflict theory and tendencies toward pompous depiction which all too often prevented the reflection of difficulties and contradictions involved in the building of the new society.

After the second world war writers and artists were subjected to a more restrictive interpretation of the state's demands upon them and of the limits of socialist realism than at any time since the early years of the first five-year plan. By resolution of the Central Committee of the Communist party in 1946, two of the leading literary magazines were denounced for publishing ideologically harmful works and one of them was suppressed. The theatre, which retained great vigour and popularity—some thousand theatres played to enthusiastic audiences composed especially of young people—was severely censured for failure to reflect the life of Soviet socialism and was directed to 'train youth in cheerfulness and joyousness, in devotion to their country and in confidence in the victory of their cause'. Under the stern direction of the Party's propaganda chief, Andrei Zhdanov, writers were required to be Party-minded and anti-cosmopolitan.

Following the death of Stalin a number of writers sought to free themselves from what they felt to be the narrowing and deadening effect of these policies, and in their congresses they expressed the hope that they might be allowed more leeway for lyric and personal expression. The veteran critic and writer, Iiya Ehrenburg, ventured a novel, *The Thaw* (1954), in which he treated the human problems of artists forced to choose between their vision and success, a dedicated doctor and teacher whose devotion did not bring full social rewards and a factory manager motivated by bureaucratic self-seeking.

Especially after the twentieth Congress of the Communist party in 1956, there was a marked revival of literary life. A number of new magazines and literary newspapers came into being. Problems such as literature's close touch with modern times, the hero in literature, lyric poetry, were animatedly discussed in the press and in All-Union Writers' congresses (1954, 1959). Stereotyped presentations had given way to more intricate portrayals of individualized heroes with deep roots in the masses, rich spiritual life and complexity of character. Socialist realism remained the method; the arts retained their essentially educational role; works were not acceptable which tended to undermine or disparage the common effort. But Soviet writers and artists were fulfilling their mission in increasingly varied and versatile ways.[27]

The literary and artistic expression of the USSR thus presented a contrast in many respects to that of western Europe. While west European writers looked upon themselves as special and apart, Soviet writers and artists were proud to regard themselves as fellow-craftsmen with those who followed other trades in the interest of society and the state. They functioned as did other workers through their trade unions, which served as channels for receiving the plans and aims of the state and for expressing their views and which were guided by the Party nucleus. Leading artists enjoyed high social status and prestige and some, such as the composer Shostakovich, and the prima ballerina, Galina Ulanova, served as delegates from their districts to the Supreme Soviet. Some of the most politically prominent of the Party leaders at different times headed the ministry of culture which administered the cultural components of the national plans.

Many of the experimental currents so prominent in western Europe were absent in the USSR. The ballet preserved its traditional romantic styles, performed with great skill, and its traditional décor. Architecture retained its massive character and use of decoration, adapted to the technology of cement and the prefabrication of structural elements.[28] Realism prevailed in all the arts in contrast to the European tendency toward abstraction. There was no Freudian probing of the unconscious, or deeply psychological poetry, though sensitive writers did not fail to capture and reveal their characters' inner life; in fact, Soviet expression came closest to that of western Europe, and especially of the United States, when it took the form of imaginative presentations of varied people in human terms.

Doubt and inquiry were discouraged and joyousness prescribed. The note of despair was absent; optimism, heroism or constructive criticism were the pervasive tones. The certainties of Marxist–Leninist ideology provided basic assumptions, in marked contrast to the west European's uncertain search for the meaning of life and the nature of man. In the words of Nikita Krushchev: 'We are against those who hunt only for the dark sides of life and gloat over them, trying to disparage and blacken our Soviet ways of life. Likewise we are against those who create sugar-coated pictures of life, offending the better senses of our people who scorn and cannot tolerate any falsehood.'*

Soviet leaders had no doubt that the literature and arts of the Soviet Union, as integral expressions of the new society, would make as significant a contribution to the world as had the great Russian writers and composers of the past.

IV. THE NEW MASS MEDIA AND THE ARTS

In the course of the twentieth century, and especially from the 1920s on, the media of mass communication greatly expanded the scope of the popular arts, provided the means of mass entertainment, and brought all manner of new information and knowledge within the reach of the common man. They also brought undreamed of means of influencing him by propaganda.

The media of mass entertainment—film, radio and television—offered employment to many more writers, designers and producers than ever before and gave them devices of hitherto unknown possibilities and the opportunity to reach vast new audiences. Many artists of only moderate gifts earned their living by their art in these industries, but artists of first-rate ability could also find new outlets. While many of the serious artists and writers scorned these new tools and left their exploitation to those whose only aim was to entertain, persuade or inform, some saw the film and the press, TV and radio as media of art and eagerly grasped the new instruments.

I. THE CINEMA AS AN ART

Once the Lumières in France had patented their first projection machine and showed a two-minute film to a Grand Café public in 1895, and Edison and Armat had projected narrative scenes for audiences in New York, the new art of the cinema was possible, an art close to the masses of the people and potentially expressive of the new scale of world-wide interests, revolutions of people and scientific discoveries. It began with Georges Méliès, the first poet of the cinema. His *A Trip to the Moon* (1902) was one of a long line of films that he made with inventiveness, technical audacity and careful workmanship; he made scenes of a fantastic world of motion, fairy tales, miracles of speed and the new science. His successors were the makers of animated cartoons which began in 1908.

At the same time the film telling a story appeared in France (Ferdinand Zecca's *History of a Crime*, 1901) and in America (Edwin S. Porter's *Great Train Robbery*, 1903, which ran twelve minutes), using from the start the melodrama of crime and violence that proliferated through the next fifty years. Both kinds of film developed rapidly into more sustained forms with varied

* Quoted in Trifonova, 'Soviet Literature', *op. cit.*, p. 107.

themes. In Italy and France a succession of historical dramas based on literature (*Quo Vadis* 1912; *Cabriria* 1914) sustained the story through several reels, were staged as grandiose spectacles and played by great actors like Sarah Bernhardt (*Queen Elizabeth*, 1912); but the production was limited by being treated as theatre.

D. W. Griffith (1875–1948) in the USA freed the cinema from the theatrical tradition and from literary sources. He told his story by scenes which he made from life. He moved his camera freely from place to place; he moved his characters about so that their motions were not stage-bound but natural; he had a scale of camera shots for focusing on special aspects of the players. Especially, he anatomized each scene into a succession of shots which he then edited by cutting so as to give the intensity required by his taste for melodrama. It was the delicate use of various kinds of motion in this editing that made a new aesthetic medium. Actually the aesthetic pleasure from the patterns of motion might be quite separate from the substance of the narrative material, and this became standard in later films from Hollywood which developed extraordinary technical resources in use of motion, even when the narrative content was immaturely extrovert.

As gifted directors and writers worked in the medium, the combination of story and moving pictures produced increasingly powerful works of art. D. W. Griffith's *The Birth of a Nation* (1915) and *Intolerance* (1916) were the first in the United States to show the possible magnitude of a feature film. *The Birth of a Nation* was hailed far and wide for its beauty of style, in spite of the fact that its narrative content was attacked in the United States and other countries lest it have the effect of renewing the racial hatreds of the Civil War. (Pl. 57a.)

The great Russian director Sergei Eisenstein (1898–1948) appreciated Griffith's successions of shots and his editing. He wrote: 'It is a question of creating a series of images composed in such a way that it provokes an affective movement which in turn awakens a series of ideas. From image to sentiment, from sentiment to thesis. . . . I think the film alone is capable of making this great synthesis, of giving back to the intellectual element its vital sources, both concrete and emotional'* His *Potemkin* (1925), the masterpiece of this kind of film, was a story of revolt of sailors against injustice, brilliantly photographed and using dramatic juxtapositions—the contrasts of calm scenes and the ruthless military; close-ups of a doctor inspecting the food which caused the revolt and of a horrible, squirming mass of worms occupying the whole screen—the symbol of evil and wrong that makes revolt inevitable; long lines of people on the quay passing the bier of the sailor killed in the skirmish; the soldiers' boots marching in relentless order down the steps toward peaceful people's outstretched hands and a common, fragile perambulator left after they had passed. (Pl. 57b.)

* Quoted in Maurice Bardèche and Robert Brasillach, *History of the Film* (London, 1938), p. 273.

During the first world war the Swedish director, Victor Sjöström (1879–1960) created the film of atmosphere—beautiful, poetical compositions closer to painting and music than theatre, such as *The Outlaw and his Wife* (1917) and adaptations of novels of Selma Lagerlöf. He understood the principle of keeping his stories and characters simple and of building up the incidents of ordinary daily scenes to an emotionally moving visual image of the whole life of the people and the nature around them.

The cinema after the first world war developed a variety of forms. The directors of the Soviet Union, confronted with the problem of interpreting the Revolution to the people, crystallized theories and made memorable films in the true-to-life line. The Kíno-eye Group, founded by Dziya Vertov in 1921, worked on the principles of documentation, use of unrehearsed scenes, selection of actors from among ordinary people according to the types needed, and scientific editing, cutting and putting together of the footage of each sequence to make a rhythm in relation to the total length of the film.

Eisenstein was the master of this technique, working mainly from life and in epic narratives (*Alexander Nevsky*, 1938, *Ivan the Terrible*, 1944). V. I. Pudovkin (1893–1953) carried the technique into the studio with controlled setting and light, professional actors trained to realism so severe as to approach life, and use of Vertov's theory of rhythm. He originated a school of films of individual human interest within society. His *Mother* (1926) made from Gorky's novel showed an ignorant, beaten-down peasant woman becoming socially conscious and, in the end, full of new faith, radiantly leading a procession of workers in revolt. The Ukrainian producer, A. P. Dovzhenko (1894–1956), interpreted the themes of nature and the peasant's love of life in *Earth* (1931).

Comedy, derived from the circus and its technique of pantomime, developed through a line of screen actors gifted in the use of symbolic gesture. American burlesque and parodies were translated into visual humour by Mack Sennett. His pupil, Charlie Chaplin (1889–   ) working in this line had by 1917 evolved for the silent screen a film language of great precision. It was, in his phrase, 'the poetry of movement'. His unique genius as actor and producer, and as an observer of life close to the people, lifted the film from vulgar buffoonery to great comedy expressing the grief and bitterness of the universe and bringing release through laughter. He was the little tramp with the bowler hat and cane making the ordinary gestures of life in a world which he did not understand, who always brought startling trouble and always met it with unfailing kindness and gentle courtesy and the detachment of the pure comic. He became the universal hero of his time, in the end always going down the road and out of the picture with dignity intact whatever the defeat or loss.

Chaplin was sensitive to the crises and climate of feeling of his time and expressed them sharply in *Shoulder Arms* (1918), one of the boldest war films, *The Kid* (1921), *The Gold Rush* (1925) parodying sentimental films of covered wagon days, *City Lights* (1931), and the more severe *Modern Times*

(1936) taking the monotony of machine industry to its logical extreme. *The Great Dictator* (1940) demolished the image of Hitler by ridicule. Even after the coming of sound his films kept his great art of pantomime and used sound only sparingly and in well understood relation to the gesture. (Pl. 58a.)

A conception of the aesthetics of motion pictures according to which scenes were treated as successions of paintings or as ballet determined many of the French and German pictures. The Germans especially were interested in the painterly aspects of settings and made films distinguished for these. Emotionally they were preoccupied with the macabre and the occult mixed with science, as in Paul Wegener's romantic *Prager Student* (1913) and Robert Wiene's *The Cabinet of Dr Caligari* (1919), one of the first horror stories and one which used every resource of expressionism. In both countries in the 1920s films were produced by poets and other experimental writers who often used surrealist symbolism; they found the medium especially flexible in conveying dreams, fantasy and in moving from one world to another. René Clair (1898–   ) made a witty, poetical world of his own where delicate irony played over enchanted and absurd romance and stylized characters danced through the vulgar incidents of daily life in ballet form. He might evoke an atmosphere of complete gaiety as in *Le Million* (1931), or he might create a sense of pointed irony in *A nous la liberté* (1931) by setting his romance in a fantastic amusement park and making the monotonous rhythms of industrial workers into those of prisoners walking up and down in the court of their prison.

More popular and widespread use of this conception produced animated cartoons—a series of paintings or drawings of figures in different positions photographed against a moving background. In 1923 Walt Disney began these and used them in a wide range of comedy; his Mickey Mouse was popular all over the world. His first long feature film, *Snow White and the Seven Dwarfs* (1938) dramatized a fairy story with grotesque humour and considerable horror. (Pl. 58b.)

In this development of motion pictures as story and drama, the need of sound was implicit from the beginning; lines of dialogue flashed on the screen had usually been necessary. Yet when it was introduced in 1926 (*Don Juan*) in synchronized music and in 1927 in combined singing and dialogue by Al Jolson in *Jazz Singer*, it seemed at first to divert attention from the natural suitability of film for expression by gesture and motion and to turn film drama into mere spoken dialogue. Regardless of old skills in acting, it called for new actors with voices effective on the sound track. New theories were expressed and practised. In the manifesto *Sound Film* by Sergei Eisenstein, V. Pudovkin and Grigory Alexandrov in 1928, the writers underlined the immense significance of sound and the danger that it might be misunderstood and used in mere 'speaking films' of a theatrical nature, and then defined the positive principle: 'Only utilization of sound in counterpoint relation to the piece of visual montage affords new possibilities of developing and perfecting the montage. The first experiments with sound must be directed towards its pronounced non-coincidence with the visual images. This method of attack only will lead in course of time to the creation of a new orchestral counterpoint of sight images and sound images.'*

A few of the directors of silent films made creative use of sound. René Clair used sound in imaginative counterpoint; the German director, G. W. Pabst turned from psychoanalysis to realistic social drama in *Kamaradschaft* (1932). Walter Ruttman made sound the substance of *Melody of the World* (1929), using screams of mechanical saws, panting of railway engines, howling of derivishes, voices of American orators, African war drums.

Colour introduced new complications of perception and its technology brought various theories for its use in the art of the cinema. Many experimenters delighted audiences who came to demand technicolor more and more, from the first three-colour feature, *Becky Sharp* (1938) to the brilliant subtleties of the Japanese *Gate of Hell* (1956), which combined the sureness of Japanese artistic taste with the technical excellence of film manufactured in the United States after the war.

Sound and colour led to wide use of novels and stage plays—these always in simplified form to make their unconfused impact within the less than two hours' time for their showing—e.g. *War and Peace* (1956), *Henry V* (1946). Among the significant productions made originally for the screen, Italian films in the 1940s and 1950s were outstanding for their neo-realism. Their *Open City* (Rossellini, 1946), *The Bicycle Thief* (De Sica, 1949) and *The Roof* (De Sica, 1958) were stories of the devastation of war and poverty and the struggle for a home. The directors used ordinary people living in the cities where these pictures were shot and thus obtained the authenticity of realism. But the lack of full expressiveness remained, and they found it necessary to experiment with using professional actors to speak the dialogue on the sound track.

By the 1950s a few films were presenting complex themes with penetration and sophistication, such as *Breaking the Sound Barrier* (1952), whose theme was the passionate drive to extend and apply new scientific knowledge and the tests of character involved, or *The Bridge on the River Kwai* (1957), popular wherever it was shown around the world, which told a mature story with complicated inner motivations and counterplots leading to the final irony of self-destruction in war.

Documentary films interpreted actual happenings in the world by direct use of the camera eye and their makers concentrated on photography itself. Robert Flaherty (1884–1951), the father of the documentary, in a series of studies of the daily lives of simple people living far from urban centres, depended directly on his camera for his form. He lived with the people sometimes several years until he knew their lives the year round and they were his friends. Then he shot his story through from beginning to end, studied the pictures, retook them and came out in the end with the poetry of man in his struggle

---

* Quoted in Bardèche and Brasillach, *History of the Film, op. cit.*, pp. 354–5.

with nature (*Nanook of the North,* 1922; *Moana,* 1926; *Man of Aran,* 1932–34; *Louisiana Story,* 1948). Flaherty's influence was in all the documentaries which followed, whether directly in similar poetical form as in Steinbeck's *The Forgotten Village* (1941), in which modern science comes into conflict with ancient ways in Mexico, or in the works of the group set up under public auspices by John Grierson (1898–   ) in the 1930s to make informational films in Britain.

The members of this group were trying to interpret the reality beneath the surface no less truthfully than Flaherty interpreted the people he knew; but they worked with large and complex ideas and environments—cities, industries, trade, war. Grierson wrote that 'human dignity is easier to see in the "noble savage". But the realist documentary, with its streets and cities and slums and markets and exchanges and factories, has given itself the job of making poetry where no poet has gone before it, and where no ends, sufficient for the purposes of art, are easily observed.'*

The school of gifted young men and women whom Grierson gathered around him worked in different ways, some analytically, some symphonically. Alberto Cavalcanti, from France, in *Rien que les heures* (1926) viewed the city around the clock; Joris Ivens from Holland, in *Zuyder Zee,* (1930) showed the struggle to repair the broken dike and turn back the sea; Basil Wright's *Song of Ceylon* (1934) depicted the life of one member of the British commonwealth and its trade. These and other makers of documentaries were called on by governments, industries, educators and scientists to produce interpretive films on many subjects, which gave them opportunities to experiment. In 1956, in one of the most artistic and scientifically revealing films of all, *The Silent World,* a crew of French scientists sailing through the tropical seas of the world told for the first time the story of underwater life as viewed by their colour cameras.

The cinema by the 1950s had matured into a complicated pattern of production by a skilled team of workers. It was the director who brought into harmony the screen play, the staging of the action, the camera work, editing and cutting, music and sound. Every new technical development involved new possibilities of interplay of these factors. The screen play had developed from the sketchy notes of the director to a completely detailed scenario worked out by the script writer. He and the director gave the substance of originality, meaning and proportion to the final form. The director had to be not only an imaginative artist conceiving his work of art; he had to be a leader of people able to convey shadings of his intent to them so that working together they would produce the unified whole.

Writers had begun to find the screen play a satisfying outlet for their experience of twentieth-century tensions. A few painters found the dynamics of motion more satisfactorily expressed in film than in two-dimensional canvases. Some of the best composers made the accompanying music. Critics

* John Grierson, *Grierson on Documentary,* ed. Forsyth Hardy (London, 1946), p. 84.

wrote seriously in newspapers. International festivals in Cannes, Venice, and in Asia selected prize-worthy films for originality and artistic excellence rather than popularity. Little theatres were outlets for works of genuine artistic quality.[29]

Although the finest films did not always require lavish expenditure to produce, at best the cinema was an expensive medium. Films required sponsors, and governments, educational bodies, research organizations, industries and arts councils were increasingly ready to support the development of films within the limits of their interests. The needs of the new audiences were only just beginning to be explored. Much remained to be found out about the camera itself. The TV screen brought new problems of motion-picture composition designed within its terms, specifically the restriction in width, the necessity for motion back into the picture and forward, the effect of diminution of size of figures and the fact that television reaches private audiences at home. But vast possibilities of aesthetic satisfaction were open beyond the forms demanded by audiences and producers thinking only of an evening's entertainment at a theatre.

2. THE ARTS OF PURVEYING INFORMATION

The arts of expressing information through the press, film and radio were extended for new mass audiences at a level of mass literacy never before reached. The scale of world consciousness and the needs of people to understand the forces and events that were changing their society demanded a new kind of writing that should convey accurately and understandably knowledge about happenings among men.

Reporters, seeking to express the reality within the appearances, faced complex problems of communication, for they had to imagine two worlds simultaneously and write in terms of both. If they described events in the terms and with the patterns of expression of the place from which they were reporting, people at home would read with their own presuppositions in mind and might miss the actual human meaning of the report. Writers therefore tried to send news or interpretive reporting in images that would at once conform with the reality at the point of happening and translate it for audiences with preconditioned patterns of thought, who were absorbed in their own lives, often given to quick response to stereotypes and only superficially touched by remote happenings. Public interest in events and the appearance of newspapers daily gave central importance to 'spot news', successive fragments of observation and information with which the public was bombarded day after day, and which *in toto* added up to the images of reality in terms of which masses of people reacted to public policy and to human beings in other parts of the world. Newspaper and radio reporters and commentators sought ways to help their audiences to make intelligible structures out of these fragments while keeping within their responsibility to report the facts.

As purveyors of information, writers and artists had to find ways to express both the magnitude of experiences and their alive, human significance. When they reported such events as the carrying of the mail across a country, the destruction of a city or the struggles of a vast army in the African desert, they were dealing with both individual and national effort or tragedy. Documentary films could show individual workers as representative of all the jobs in the intricate organization for carrying the mail, and could convey the tempo and duration of movement at successive points on the long train journey. They could show marching columns and parades of tanks over the limitless desert contrasted with close-ups of anxious faces as men prepared for immediate battle and with people at home in an ordinary factory listening to the news of battle action. The documentary film of climbing Mt Everest (1953) took the audience through this experience by means of mathematical diagrams, long-view shots of ice-masses and close-ups of their structure and of footsteps chopped in ice, successive scenes of individual climbers struggling to put one foot after the other, conveying the sense of duration, size, danger and the limits of endurance, and by tracing the stages by which the leader first conquered his objective mentally and then, with the others, physically achieved his goal. Writers, too, succeeded in translating overwhelming events into human terms. John Hersey's account of the bombing of Hiroshima (1946) told by taking six survivors through the whole day of the bombing was a classic of such reporting. (Pl. 54a.)

The mass media also brought new forms of mass propaganda which had as far-reaching ramifications for the arts as for politics. Propaganda itself is as old as religion; its new features in the twentieth century were its scale, its widespread use and the techniques which it could employ. Since the aim of propaganda is to produce an attitude or action in line with a preconceived point of view, its central principle is the identification of the audience's desires with the propagandist's goal. New knowledge of psychology—of conditioning and motivation—enabled the propagandist to develop techniques for manipulating attitudes and feelings—by repetition, association playing on hidden fears, evoking acknowledged or unacknowledged aspirations. In the complexities of the modern world, individuals who were constantly exposed to generalizations which they could not check against their own direct experience were vulnerable to emotional manipulation by these means.

Propaganda always required artists to give it form. They often wrote the speeches which public leaders then delivered or articles carefully placed in leading magazines; their painting and photography made the posters, billboards and advertising pages; their songs, their theatre, radio and television productions filled the air; they knew the rituals of mass ceremonies. Whatever the medium or the outlet, the artists' task was to make compositions that had immediate emotional impact leading in the direction the propagandist intended. The compositions therefore always had some images that would appeal to the audience, slogans that pointed the desired meaning of the pictorial or other images and finally the imperative 'do this', with the implication that doing it would satisfy the dreams and aspirations now aroused. Governments, industries which depended on mass advertising to market their products, and public and private bodies which undertook campaigns to promote such causes as improved agricultural or health practices, all used these skills of the artists. (Pl. 54b.)

This was at once an opportunity and a danger to the artists. The demand for their skills and the pay that went with it enabled them to live by their talents in their chosen art and to be successful members of their society. Some of the outstanding artists and writers did such work, not only in totalitarian countries where they were major contributors to national efforts, but elsewhere. Picasso, for example, decorated a salesroom for the Italian typewriter manufacturer, Olivetti; Salvador Dali (1904–   ) designed store window displays in New York. Writers and artists of all sorts contributed to wartime propaganda during the second world war. Many of the art forms developed by the leading artists and writers were taken over by those who were wholly engaged in commercial and propagandist art, and became familiar to wider publics. But there was always the crucial question: how free were artists to carry out their essential task of interpreting the human condition? Their form was determined by the purposes of the propagandist and the medium and outlet to be used. The men controlling both acted with certain assumptions about people, that they were either self-respecting individuals capable of making choices and having a right to know the nature of the choice, or a vast ignorant mass able to respond only to the simplest slogan hammered in by countless repetitions and as ready to respond to lies as to the truth.

The artists found symbols to fit these purposes and assumptions about people. If the purpose and assumptions were also their own, as for example in the documentary film *The River* (by Pare Lorentz and Virgil Thomson 1938), sponsored by the US government to promote flood control, there was freedom and the sincerity and insight which gave the work artistic value as interpretation. But often enough the artists worked insincerely, jaded by the product they were promoting or not believing in the goal of their propaganda, sometimes despising an audience that might respond to false appeals. Those who created the torrential output of vapid or dishonest advertising or propaganda appeals, dividing life into black and white categories and whipping up blind feeling, could only revolt under such conditions or become cynical.

In general the forms of conveying information through the mass media and of persuading people were not conceived of as 'art'. They were produced by men and women working at daily tasks, within large organizations, meeting deadlines, compressing their works into an allowed three or five or ten minutes of radio time, held down by the requirements of events and audiences. Much 'copy' was the merest routine. The purpose was, ordinarily, temporary, an observation of the moment, recorded in the ephemeral press or the still more ephemeral air waves. Yet these practical limitations were not unique to this age, for artists in all societies have worked within the framework of the conventions and pressures of their times. And when these efforts to convey information or attitudes were at their highest, they had the essential qualities of works of art, for they penetrated to realities behind the surface appearances, they sought and communicated deeply human meanings and deeply rooted human values, and they had form.

Most important for twentieth-century expression, those who used the mass media approached reality in contemporary terms, and they spoke not to the traditional, limited middle-class audiences or groups of connoisseurs but to broad masses of people. At mid-century these forms appeared to be the beginning of new modes of expression which opened vistas for the future at a time when self-centredness, rejection of society, uncertainty as to man's nature and preoccupation with form were bringing to a dead end many of the tendencies which had characterized western poetry, painting, sculpture, serious music, and even architecture in the previous fifty years.

NOTES TO CHAPTER XXXI

1. Doctors of Philological Sciences R. Samarin and A. Elistratova think that the text of Chapters XXXI and XXXII requires some preliminary notes:

Belles-lettres and art constitute an important element in the culture of the twentieth century. Being an original form of the reflection of reality they help to give a vision of the world. A rich variety of aesthetic feelings and emotions are generated from the wealth of man's practical experience and as this develops new forms of art such as the cinema for example evolve and display themselves, giving in their entirety a picture of objective reality. The failures, the anxieties and the sickness of our century, its desires and seekings, its discoveries, joys and triumphs, seen through the eyes of the contemporary artist and translated into imagery give a knowledge which cannot be replaced from any other source. But the works of literature and art do not only help us to know the world about us, they exert an influence on it by fashioning a social conscience and through this have an impact on reality. And it is here—in the ideological and aesthetic effect on society, and in the education of society—that the main social function of literature and art lies. People go to the artist to learn what man really is and what are his inner forces and potentialities. The propagandist effect of progressive ideas and moral standards makes art a progressive social force and contributes to its successful development just as, for example, very fine civic virtues such as patriotism, respect for the rights of other nations and deep humanism were inculcated into people by classical Russian literature, wherein lay one of the causes of its profound and universal influence. If we look at the literature and art of the twentieth century from this angle we must admit that there are two cultures in the world: one bourgeois, reactionary and to a considerable extent decadent, and the other democratic and progressive. 'Modern man'—his relation to the world, to society and to himself, the rhythm of his life, his aspirations and hopes—is in both cases the centre of interest but there are differences in the representation of this figure and his pressing problems. In the bourgeois world bourgeois culture rules whilst democratic culture finds itself in an oppressed state: under the conditions of a class society the thoughts and ideas of the ruling class are dominant also in the field of culture. On the other hand the oppressed classes, hostile to this social structure, create their own artistic culture which reflects their conditions of life and expresses their aims and interests. In a socialist society, a democratic culture prevails. In the West there are a number of theories which try to elucidate the essential problems of modern man. The major influence on literature and art comes (as is clearly indicated in Chapter XXXI) from the psychoanalytical school of Sigmund Freud and his followers, and from Existentialism.

In the twentieth century the influence of all the bourgeois schools taken together pales before that of Freud and, compared with it, represents a declining force. Freudian ideas have penetrated into the novel and drama and are now making strong inroads into the cinema. Freud translated into psychological problems all social conflicts; be exteriorized the unhealthy nature of man, declaring it to be the fundamental expression of his entire being. He consequently made what could be called a pessimistic apologia of existence. 'Alas, this is bad but it cannot be otherwise.' This creates a suitable attitude of psychological pessimism as a way of coming to terms with evil reality; and at the same time there is endless prating about a feeling for what is new and about intellectual intrepidity.

At the basis of Freud's theory lies the doctrine of egoism—the psychological emanation of all that is sensual, carnal, biological and erotic in man—which always remains an irrational embodiment of the anti-social principles of personality. Freud rejected the result of preceding historical development—that a higher type of man, a man of lofty principles, could come into existence—since in his view the process of cultural development does not eliminate the wild and primitive in man, it only represses it into the sphere of the subconscious. The rationally human is superimposed on the biological, predatory element, it does not replace it. It is only by constraint that the energy of the sexual urge can be directed towards work and people led to create the conditions for their own material well-being. Everything irrational, vicious and incomprehensible in social life has thus been placed within the individual, within the empire of the subconscious. Only by separating the sexual desires from the whole circle of human interests was Freud able to discern the flow of the impulses which originate in the innermost part of our being and clash with social impacts. But in reality the sexual desires do not possess the full autonomy which he attributed to them.

The realistic novel (L. Tolstoy, J. Galsworthy) showed that any form of egoism in whatever layer of the spirit it may lie, is the result of the social education of the individual, a projection of social relations into his subjective world. When life is viewed through the murky glass of utility and calculation, and a mood of utter tedium spreads abroad, there are far-reaching consequences in the realm of the carnal appetites; desires which are evidence of perversion are aroused. The further we penetrate into the twentieth century the more often we go through the entire gamut of psychological abnormalities, and the realistic novel convincingly illustrates the whole process by which passion is transformed into 'sex' (as a result of the alienation of sexuality from the high motives of spiritual life). The realistic artists regard these pheomena as the specific result of capitalist development. Thus the views of Freud are not a mere invention. They have given expression to that decadence of bourgeois society where love becomes impossible. This is why Freud delivered an attack on art asserting that it reflects only prettified reality, that poetry and real life are not compatible, that genuine pleasure is anti-aesthetic, and so on. To all the other ways devised for providing a basis of legitimacy for the bourgeois order Freudianism added the psychological motivation and therein lies the reason for its popularity.

The popularity of existentialism on the other hand is to be explained by the fact that it poses with unusual clarity the problem of human personality, displaying rather than concealing the crisis of bourgeois culture. No other trend shows so plainly that even the existence of personality is becoming impossible in bourgeois society which is strangling the culture it has generated. In this philosophy of despair and pessimism there is no room for faith in progress, in humanism or in the beneficial role of science and education; it connotes a disparagement of reason, of history and society; and going still further, it leaves no place even for society. The hope of existentialism is real personality, the lone individual opposed to all and to each. Whether the existentialist appears as a critic of the ideas of humanism and democracy (M. Heidegger) or of faith in science and enlightenment (K. Jaspers)—he always criticizes the concept of reason (and particularly the system of Hegel because it does not devote attention to the human personality and insists on the cult of reason). The dominance of this way of thinking—so the existentialists contend—has meant that man in the contemporary world has come to be felt as merely one thing among a number of other things. The actual idea of the depersonalization of man in capitalist society, of his transformation into a cog in an enormous mechanism is quite right but by no means new. As early as in the middle of the nineteenth century Karl Marx had brought this truth to light and had pointed out the inference—that a state of society which does not give full play for the development of personality must be changed. It is along this path that a third of mankind are now proceeding. Existentialism proposes another solution. Not the reconstruction of the social system which has man in thrall, but a realization that reason and science, instead of emancipating him, enslave him—this is the way out offered by the existentialists. 'Reason is the killer of human freedom, the killer of personality', is the dictum of Kierkegaard. In order to free himself man must be conscious of himself in another way. Only the realization of life as 'existence' opens to him a real way of being. He is not content to endure his freedom and responsibility, he endeavours to rid himself of them by flight into commonplace workaday life and seeks to become like others. There exists, however, a means of liberation from the bonds of this workaday life. It is the decision to look death in the face; to evaluate everything from the threshold of the final parting with life. 'Genuine existence' is in effect the structure of thought, the spiritual condition, the assessment of his own place in life that characterize a man 'in the face of death'. Genuine freedom can thus be attained only in the face of death and happiness lies in an awareness of the senselessness of existence. 'There exists no fate which could not be overcome by scorning it' (A. Camus in *The Myth of Sisyphus*). Although this philosophy no longer satisfies a number of existentialists (for example J.-P. Sartre) the idea that knowledge cannot be equated with the liberation of man has penetrated deeply into belles-lettres and art.

Against the background of the twentieth century, a century of wars, destruction and catastrophes (as it is frequently considered in the West) there is a sense of divorce from society and nature, an ever increasing isolation of the individual and a growth of subjectivity. Even the fantastically rapid advances in technology are often regarded as offering yet one more motivation for a pessimistic evaluation of the epoch as a whole; for is not this very technology threatening to turn against humanity? Given such views and the constant, obtrusive reiteration that man is unable to change anything, all that reflects the perdition of humanism, the twilight of reason and the subordination of man to impersonal and inhuman forces, or expresses a mood of scepticism and bitter irony, despair and perplexity, seems to be contemporary. The spirit of innovation in literature and art is regarded by the authors of Chapter XXXI as an aesthetic expression of irrationalism, and spiritual confusion. It is identified with the disintegration of human character, the break-up of language, the atrophy of basic literary genres, the effacement of the picture of reality, the dehumanization of art and the rupture with tradition. But of course there is another view of life—as seen through the eyes of a member of the socialist society—which is in flagrant contrast with it. In this, too, anxieties and complications have their place, but the outlook on the world and its future is joyous; man realizes himself to be a free and equal member of a society in which humanism has reached its zenith and the relation of man to man is that of friend, comrade and brother. The harmonious fusion of the personal and the social magnifies many times an individual's strength: he can and must do much to beautify the world, to improve people's lives and to bring about his own happiness. Literature and art are called on to give a true and historically concrete representation of reality in its progressive revolutionary development. The works of art and literature must provide knowledge, offer a source of joy and inspiration to millions of people; express their determination, feelings and thoughts, and serve as a means of ideological enrichment and moral enlightenment. To fulfil these complicated major tasks the links with the life of the nation must be reinforced in every possible way and there must be a deep penetration into the essence of the contemporary world, a true and highly artistic representation of the rich and many-sided practical aspects of life, an inspired and clear reproduction of something new and genuinely communist, and an unmasking of everything which thwarts the onward movement of society. These ideals serve as an orientation for the method of socialist realism, the main creative method of writers and artists in the socialist countries which, together with critical realism and neo-realism, also finds expression in the creative works of many progressive art workers in the capitalist countries. Its most important principles are its partisanship and strong links with the people, and a spirit of innovation which is connected with the applying and developing of all progressive traditions in world civilization. Interest in, and careful observance of, national form is inherent in the method of socialist realism and is a manifestation of its links with the people. Usually a socialist revolution with its wealth of ideas gives to art a clear, alert, inspired content, and has the significant effect of removing all obstacles that had previously existed between the artist and the nation.

The Stalin cult did a certain amount of harm to the development of the popular spirit in art; it deflected writers and artists from concentrating on the representation of ordinary Soviet people. The popular spirit manifests itself with particular clarity and appropriateness whenever professional art is closely linked with anonymous artistic creation and the mass development of amateur art. One of the most important professional, social and moral obligations of the leaders of culture in the USSR and other socialist countries is to show an interest in new talents and to seek out, develop and train them. Of course it is no mere chance that many significant artistic manifestations in the USSR have owed their origin to amateur art.

The popular character of art goes hand in hand with its partisanship (steady promotion of the communist ideals). Under present-day conditions in most countries it is impossible productively to serve the nation without taking an active share in the conversion of communist plans into living reality. Communist partisanship implies a repudiation of subjectivism in all its manifestations and of the deformation of reality. The 'theory of the absence of conflict' which existed for years under the cult of personality had a baneful influence on the creative work of a number of writers and artists who frankly devoted themselves to embellishing reality and representing in a saccharine, idealized way the complicated processes of the re-education of people.

Adherence to the party spirit demands from the writer or artist profound concern and emotion, and a sympathetic attitude to the individual human being: naturalism and formalism are incompatible with it.

A determination of the outlines of what is new in society and in man, which is required by partisanship and the popular spirit in art, are not only indivisible from the search for new forms and means of expression but directly stimulate them. But one can and must write in a new way not by destroying realism but by developing and renewing it. Finally there comes the problem of traditions, in the break with which many today in the West see the creative strength of modern art. What a profound delusion! Marxist–Leninist theorists have always emphasized the significance of inheritance in the development of culture: only by critical adaptation of all that is best in the legacy of humanity is it possible to achieve progress. The maintenance of genuine standards of beauty on which to build for the future is the most important requirement of the method of socialist realism. But 'conserving the inheritance does not mean restricting oneself to the inheritance' (V. I. Lenin: *Collected Works*, 4th Russ Ed., Vol. II, p. 494). Progressive leaders of culture are therefore confronted with the urgent problem of effecting a reappraisal of traditions. So literature and art must not kill the human features in man but on the contrary must cultivate in him whatever is fair and lovely and humanistic and human.

Professor Svoboda, taking the Marxist stand, makes a similar criticism of the text and considers that the arts are seen from the point of view of the so-called middle class, or to be precise from a section of the middle-class intelligentsia. There is a tendency to write about the 'modern' which caused some sort of sensation but not about the fundamental phenomena which are of a lasting value. As far as the social situation is concerned, it is also seen through an 'intellectual's eyes', from the point of view of those who show a tendency 'from naturalism toward abstraction' . . . Consequently it is clear that the author sees everything from a narrow, bourgeois point of view and evaluates everything accordingly. He prefers of course a non-political attitude in arts.

2. *The Author-Editors draw the attention of the reader to the fact that the chapters on Expression, which come at the end of the volume, are set in the context of the scientific and social revolutions of the period which have been discussed in the rest of the volume. As noted in the text, all the movements in the arts during these years expressed 'fundamental re-evaluations of the meaning of life in the face of accelerated, drastic, world-wide social change' (p. 1193), and reflected 'the social changes brought by industrialism and the intellectual changes engendered by the spread of science and technology' (p. 1196). For trends other than psychological exploration and abstraction which were only two among many tendencies, the reader is referred to sections dealing with 'Search into the lives of other men' (pp. 1216–18), and 'Search for roots' (p. 1218), to developments in Theatre, Photography and Architecture (pp. 1233–43). For the influence of Freud, see pp. 1215–16 and Chapter XVI, pp. 537–9, 546–9, Note 3, p. 567.*

to sections on literature and the arts in the USA, Latin America, and the USSR (pp. 1243–65), and to the discussion of 'The new mass media and the arts' (pp. 1265–74).

3. Commentators differ widely as to whether the major trends have been correctly identified and presented in this chapter. Professor Mario Praz fails to find a 'masterly synthesis', a 'clear outline', a tracing of phenomena to 'their origins', a 'logical trend' in the 'mass of facts'. Professor Jacques Presser, on the other hand, considers it a 'competent and trustworthy guide' to the cultural and artistic developments of the world, in which 'the main currents of modern times as manifested in men and in artists who represent them' are revealed and all the 'principal movements' of this half century are discussed.

With respect to the selection of material, Professor Praz thinks that the space allotted to the United States, Latin America and Russia is 'entirely out of proportion with the other countries' and results in neglect of many important European authors in favour of minor American writers. Professor O. Halecki states that the literature and art of the nations of east central Europe are neglected; Professor Edvard Bull suggests the addition of several Norwegian authors. Professor Presser recognizes that the selecting of persons to be included is 'precarious, especially in territories inaccessible to the authors' and that 'the reality will always be more nuanced than the best reproduction'.

Some commentators question the Author-Editors' evaluation of the main currents of aesthetic development which they discuss. Professor Presser asserts 'not without some scruple and reserve' that

'the text shows us the great currents of our century on the whole in their pessimistic aspects. The forces of disorganization, of decomposition, of dissolution are described here with more lucidity and more detail than the others, giving the reader the impression of a world balancing itself almost constantly on the brink of a precipice. The artists, in expressing the feeling of the life of this period, equally constantly mirror this precarious position—an imminent Last Judgment, expressed in words, sounds, painting, sculpture, architecture, in the theatre, film, and ballet by the most sensitive men of their generation. I wonder if this picture of our age, destined, if I am not mistaken, for all mankind, does not contain an element of too great subjectivity, is not, perhaps one must say, too "occidental".'

Professor E. N. Anderson adds:

In reading the chapters on Literature and the Arts one must bear in mind the authors' purpose of portraying the character of society as expressed in these media. Thus the chapters are not intended to be brief histories of literature and the arts; rather they are to relate literary and artistic expression to the socio-economic developments and currents of thought of society, and their method and approach are of such a kind as to enable the relationship to be clarified. Whether a 'logical trend' as demanded by Professor Mario Praz can be found depends upon whether one is looking for formal development and thematic analysis or whether one is concerned with the nature of the experience which writers and artists have portrayed. If there is one criticism to be made of the volume as a whole, it might be that the emphasis upon constructive action and achievements in the earlier chapters does not prepare the reader for 'the pessimistic aspects' mentioned by Professor Presser as revealed in the literature and the arts. The later chapters, especially the one about the western culture area, afford an essential balance to consideration of the total life of the period portrayed. This period was the most destructive in the history of the world; it was the most upsetting to mores, the most revolutionary in its conception of nature, man, society, and transcendental powers. The Author-Editors rightly emphasize the expression of these profound changes by the members of society most sensitive to spiritual and moral forces, writers and artists. Both those who were aesthetically creative and others as well were searching more or less consciously for identity, for a social order and for a place in that order, and the Author-Editors in their writing offer the results of this search by creative personalities.

It is another question whether the Author-Editors in discussing western culture gauge properly the relative importance of the several forces in it. They introduce them all, but they regard science and its technological expression as fundamental. They bring out the fact that many writers and artists, although aware of and influenced by currents of scientific thought and new technology, tended to reject this main stream of social development. They note that this tendency was by no means universal, that it was less strong in the United States and, of course, in the Soviet Union than in western Europe, and that it was not generally shared by architects, photographers and theatrical producers. They point to the potentials for new and positive developments in the arts offered by the new mass media and new forms of communication.

Although any discussion of degrees of influence quickly becomes subjective, or an exercise in semantics, it may be said with some confidence that aesthetic creators knew far less about science, except at a very popular level, and even about technology than, from personal experience, they did about the effects of power politics, war and revolution, social problems arising in an industrial urban society—crime, delinquency, poverty, pogroms, unemployment and the like, political disturbances, emotional insecurity, or of the profound change in the structure of society since the eighteenth century. These data are those about which writers and artists are concerned, and the question may be legitimately asked whether the aesthetes respond to and express in their work all aspects of experience. That Surrealism was no more fantastic than a Nazi concentration camp or an atomic explosion seems evident. As the Author-Editors point out, new experience evoked new ways and new themes for aesthetic expression, and, one might add, it stimulated some of the finest writers and artists to employ old themes and methods to express their novel experience. In these chapters the illogicality, the variety, the wealth of forms, subjects, methods and materials of aesthetic experience are richly employed in detail to reflect the life of the half century.

The synthesis of the Author-Editors is all the more remarkable because of the absence of monographic literature with the kind of approach they use. Wylie Sypher's excellent book, *Rococo to Cubism in Art and Literature* (New York, 1960), for example, does very little with the social aspects of the history of literature and art, and Pierre Francastel's volumes, *Peinture et société* (Lyon, 1951), and *Art et technique aux XIXe et XXe siècles* (Paris, 1956) are similarly strong in respect to intellectual and ideological analysis and weak respecting social analysis. Sigfried Giedion's volume, *Space, Time and Architecture* (Cambridge, Mass., 1956) has many revealing conceptions, but this work covers only architecture and town planning and is mainly concerned with the preceding century. There is no work which one can recommend as an expansion of the Author-Editors' attempt in these chapters to explore the relations between literature and the arts and society in this period.

4. Professor R. G. Villoslada remarks: To state that social and intellectual transformations have been (only or mainly) engendered by industrialism and scientific progress, will be of course challenged by those who admit in the march of history other more spiritual causes. But what cannot in any way be admitted is that Christian ideology is no longer, for western writers and artists, a satisfying vehicle of thought and expression.

5. Doctors of Philological Sciences R. Samarin and A. Elistratova assert that the development of realism in literature and art continued in the twentieth century in the form of critical realism (Anatole France, Romain Rolland, Roger Martin du Gard, George Bernard Shaw, Thomas Mann, Ernest Hemingway, B. Kellerman, Hans Fallada) and of neo-realism (Alberto Moravia, Vasco Pratolini, Renato Guttuso, the film directors Roberto Rossellini, Vittorio de Sica, Giuseppe de Santis, Federico Fellini, Lucchino Visconti and others).

During these years the method of socialist realism was also evolved (M. Gorky, V. Mayakovsky, M. Sholokhov, A. Tvardovski, M. A. Nexø, Pablo Neruda, Louis Aragon, Bertolt Brecht, Lu Hsün, Henri Barbusse, M. Sadoveanu, V. Mukhina, I. Shadr, S. Eisenstein, A. Dovzhenko, and others).

V. D. Dneprov: *Problemy realizma* ('Problems of realism') (Leningrad, 1960).

Problemy sotsialisticheskogo realizma ('Problems of Socialist realism') (Moscow, 1961).

Sotsialistichesky realizm v zarubezhnikh literaturakh ('Socialist realism in foreign literatures') (Moscow, 1960).

A. Ivashchenko: *Zametki o sovremennom realizme* ('Notes on contemporary realism') (Moscow, 1961).

T. V. Balashova *et al.*, *Sovetskaya literatura za rubezhom, 1917–1960* ('Soviet Literature Abroad, 1917–1960') (Moscow, 1962).

'Khudozhnik i sovremennost' ('The artist and contemporary problems') in *Akademiiya khudozhestv Ezhegodnik* Vol. I (Moscow, 1960), Vol. II (Moscow, 1961).

6. Candidate of arts V. M. Polevoy underlines that the text characterizes only one of the trends of art in the twentieth century, a trend which by no means encompasses all the processes taking place in the art of the time. At the turn of the nineteenth century the realistic trend entered a new stage of development in which it drew closer to social problems and political struggle. As a result, the realistic form acquired a new, pertinent and active content and became more expressive (for example, the work of K. Kollwitz in Germany, political satire in Russia during the revolution of 1905–7, etc.). Thus, the realistic and abstract trends represent two poles in the theory and practice of art in the twentieth century.

Sovremennoe izobrazitelnoe iskusstvo kapitalisticheskikh stran ('Contemporary pictorial art in the capitalist countries') (Moscow, 1961).

S. Mozhnyagin: *Abstraktsionism—razrushenie estetiki* ('Abstract art, the ruin of aesthetics') (Moscow, 1961).

7. *The Author-Editors call the reader's attention to the treatment of realism, pp.* 1196, 1202–6, 1214, 1247–8, 1260–61.

8. Doctors of Philological Sciences R. M. Samarin and A. A. Elistratrova assert that it was in the twentieth century that for the first time in history there came clearly to the fore the aesthetic questions of the wide masses who find satisfaction in those elements of democratic and socialist culture which have arisen both in the countries of Western Europe (the works of Romain Rolland, Henri Barbusse, M. A. Nexø, Sean O'Casey, Louis Aragon, Bertolt Brecht, M. Sadoveanu, V. Nezval, A. Seghers, Alberto Moravia, H. Bell, A. Tvardovski, A. Fadeyev, L. Leonov, K. Fedin and many others) and in America (works of Jack London, Sinclair Lewis, Theodore Dreiser, John Reed, Pablo Neruda, Jorje Amado and others).

In artistic culture for example there are the Mexican monumental painting, the graphic schools of South America and Italian neo-realism which are characterized by forms possessing specific national traits; this art is firmly linked with popular national life and is, in one or another way, based on the tradition of the national artistic schools.

9. *See pp.* 1216–18 *and* 1265–74, *also Chapter XXVII for a discussion of the mass audience and the use of material drawn from broad elements of the population.*

10. Candidate of Philological Sciences T. K. Trifonova asserts that the artist is confronted with the dilemma of whether he is to be a 'free spirit', a 'solitary artist' or a 'journeyman', but there is also at third road which he can choose, that of service to the people; this is the potentiality which is realized in the creative works of a large number of contemporary writers and artists—Romain Rolland, M. Gorky, Rabindranath Tagore, P. Picasso, K. Stanislavsky, G. Ulanova and many others.

11. Candidate of Arts V. M. Polevoy notes that pp. 1206–8, as well as the preceding text, reduce the entire development of the fine arts to the evolution from Les Fauves to abstractionism. This is not true to the facts. In reality, the twentieth century witnessed the appearance of many realists (the Belgian Masereel who worked in France, Kolbe in Germany, Manzu and Guttuso in Italy, Aaltonen in Finland, Epstein and Kent in the USA, Despiau, Bourdelle and Marquet in France, etc.). Whole new schools sprang up, for which the realization of the social significance of art was the basis for the adoption of the realistic method. At times these schools were of a national or international character. Moreover, the history of art in the twentieth century furnishes many an example of artists rejecting their abstract-aesthetic stand in favour of realistic art related to life. This is the natural development of twentieth-century art, contrary to the evolution which, on the above-named pages of the text is presented as the only and all-encompassing trend.

12. *The reader's attention is called, by the Author–Editors, to the pages referred to in Note 7 supra and to the sections on Theatre, Photography, Cinema, and Reporting, pp.* 1233–39, 1265–74.

13. V. M. Polevoy stresses that in his opinion between the creations of Horta, Van de Velde, Berlage and Mackintosh, on the one hand, and those of Gropius, Mies van der Rohe and Le Corbusier on the other hand, despite their continuity, runs an important demarcation line. It is not only of a stylistic nature, but also involves the social problems of architecture, its functional character, a new approach to city planning, the wide utilization of reinforced concrete, the artistic comprehension of new constructions, etc. It is probably in place here

to mention the 'national romanticism' of architecture in the countries of Northern Europe, which was one way of overcoming the eclectic imitation of historical styles.

14. Candidate of Arts B. B. Granovsky supposes that the silence about the creative works of Enescu, Rachmaninoff and some other composers is connected, it would seem, with the authors' basic tendency to regard the history of music in the twentieth century as merely the history of modernism in music. This is the only reason which can explain the relatively detailed description they give of the works of A. Schoenberg, A. Webern and O. Messiaen. For reasons which we fail to understand they have passed over in silence the influence of Rimsky-Korsakov on the young Stravinsky. See Y. Keldysh: *Istoria russkoy muzyki* ('History of Russian music'), (Moscow and Leningrad, 1947–54), parts 1–3; *Istoria russkoy sovetskoy muzyki* ('History of Russian Soviet Music') in four vols.: Vol. I, 1917–34, (Moscow, 1956); Vol. II, 1935–41 (Moscow, 1959); *Enescu* (Bucharest, 1961).

15. Candidate of Philological Sciences T. K. Trifonova thinks that it is necessary to underline that of great importance for the history of civilization in the thirties of the twentieth century are the collective statements made by writers and other exponents of culture as part of the struggle against the threat of fascism and war. Examples of these are to be found in the activity of the international group of writers *Clarté*, in Gorky's address *S kem vy mastera kultury* ('Whom do you side with, masters of culture?'), in the appeal launched at the initiative of the writers Henri Barbusse, Romain Rolland and Jean-Richard Bloch, in the series of anti-war and anti-fascist congresses (in 1932 in Amsterdam, in 1934 in Chicago, in 1935 in Paris, in 1937 in Valencia, in Madrid, in Paris) and in many other movements.

16. Doctor of Philological Sciences R. M. Samarin notes that whilst discussing writers who left the communist camp (they list the names of Arthur Koestler, André Gide, Louis Fischer amongst others) the authors prefer not to enumerate any of those who went over to the side of communism. Neither Dreiser nor Romain Rolland are mentioned here. But the fact that individual writers became disappointed and abandoned communism only proves that communism was never a conviction with them and that they had sworn fidelity to the ideas of communism only in words and could not grasp the difference between the existence of a new order of things and the distortions which occurred in Stalin's time. The practical experience of life shows that the disappointments and recantations are insignificant in comparison with the successes of the communist movement, the numerical growth of the communist parties, and their influence on the peoples as a whole.

17. Candidate of Philological Sciences T. K. Trifonova underlines that considerable attention is devoted to George Orwell, A. Koestler, F. Kafka and some other writers whilst at the same time the works of such outstanding personalities as Roger Martin du Gard, S. Maugham, Käthe Kollwitz and F. Masereel have not been described.

18. Candidate of Arts V. M. Polevoy notes that the strong ties between the artist and the life of society, and the task of creating works of art that would play an essential role in the spiritual life of society are advanced as the fundamental problems in the art of the socialist societies which emerged in the twentieth century.

19. Candidate of Arts V. M. Polevoy thinks that there are no grounds for including Pasternak in this section. Soviet poetry should be represented first and foremost by Mayakovsky. Mention should also be made of Alexander Blok. The reference in the text is not even to the poems of Pasternak (mention might have been made of the poem *Lieutenant Schmidt*, 1926) but only to his prose. This appears irrelevant in a chapter on poetry.

20. Candidate of Arts V. M. Polevoy underlines that on pages 1229–33 the evolution of the fine arts in the twentieth century is given a one-sided interpretation. Again, only one line of development is shown; phenomena in the history of art are regarded in isolation, unconnected with the important events in the history of countries and peoples. In distinction to the section on the theatre, for example, no account is taken of the new phenomena in the art of Europe evoked by the socialist revolution in Russia.

In the twentieth century, under the conditions of aggravated social and political conflicts, art has reacted keenly to the upheavals of two world wars; it is transformed under the influence of revolutionary outbursts, establishes stronger and more direct ties with social movements. The evolution of forms and the changes in aesthetic views are an expression of this process, which changed the relations of art to life in their broadest aspect and gave birth to new forms of the fine arts, to their new functional trend, etc.

As a result of the 1917 Revolution in Russia a new art was born, which was closely linked with the needs of the popular masses. This led to the strengthening of realism as the method best suited to the social tasks of art, and also to the wide development of such mass forms of art as political posters, book illustrations, etc. A most important indication of the new contacts which were established after the revolution between art and the public was the sharp rise in the number of visitors, mostly workers and peasants, to art exhibitions. The art of Europe was affected by the influence of mural paintings, meant for the masses, which arose in Mexico, partly on the basis of the idea of the revolution. The 1920's saw both the process of isolation of a number of art trends within a range of aesthetic ideas divorced from life; and also the attempts of certain trends—e.g. expressionism —to find points of contact with life. The subjective revolt against the repugnant aspects of life, so characteristic of expressionism, acquired a definite anti-militaristic shape in post-war Germany. The affirmation of humanism, the protest against war and fascism were traceable in the creative work of many artists, and formed the social and political basis of the poignant and intense aesthetic experience of many outstanding artists. One of the most striking examples of this is Picasso's *Guernica*, inspired by protest against the fascists' barbarous bombing of that Spanish city.

The second world war and the Allied victory over fascism freed the art of Germany and Italy. The socialist transformations in the countries of Eastern Europe led to the development of an art whose form and content are determined by its interrelations with the life and requirements of the popular masses. Side by side with the spread of abstract art, and to a considerable degree counterbalancing it, we witness the development of trends based on the affirmation of the value of life, the people, the ordinary man with his thoughts and feelings. The aesthetic value of these categories is expressed by realistic means, making them accessible to the millions. Among these trends, completely untainted by hermetism, mention must be made of neo-realism in Italy and France. Many artists of these trends made the transition to realism from expressionism (Renato Guttuso in Italy), from abstractionism (Cremer in Germany, the creator of the memorial to the Nazi victims in Buchenwald, with its profound plastic and emotional appeal).

21. *The reader is referred by the Author-Editors to pp. 1257–65 for a discussion of Soviet art and literature.*

22. Candidate of Arts V. M. Polevoy considers it necessary to point out that the radical changes in architecture in the twentieth century, brought about by the evolution of styles, the introduction of new materials and designs and their aesthetic comprehension are also connected with major changes in city planning. Among the novel aspects one can mention the construction of satellite towns to solve the problem of urban overpopulation, the zonal development of cities, the construction of neighbourhood units according to a general plan, the creation of building ensembles related to the natural environment, the reconstruction of cities to solve traffic and other problems, etc.

At mid-century the architectural appearance of Europe was greatly changed as a result of the widespread reconstruction of cities and towns destroyed during the war. The crying need for housing led to the development of industrial methods of construction, which in turn affected architectural solutions.

Architecture and building in the socialist countries opened new paths in town planning. The absence of private land ownership, the planned nature of the economy made it possible to solve on a large scale the problems of urban reconstruction, the building of new cities, the development of industrial and public buildings and of housing construction in accordance with the needs of society as a whole.

23. Candidate of Arts V. M. Polevoy notes that another form of the fine arts which rose to prominence in the countries of Latin America with world-wide repercussions was work in black-and-white. In its ideas and imagery it is closely related to mural painting, but it is generally more expressive and dramatic and is practically uninvolved with the renascence of the motifs of pre-Spanish culture. The *Taller de Gráfica Popular* in Mexico (founded in 1937) is the outstanding centre of this form.

24. Candidate of arts V. M. Polevoy points out that the description of the work of Tatlin and other artists on this page should not be separated from the data on the development of the poster and monumental sculpture (p. 1259). A wrong impression is created that first there was a period characterized by the works of Tatlin and Chagall, and then in the 1920's Mayakovsky and a number of other artists began to create posters and sculptors to make monuments. Actually, this occurred at the same time (monuments began to be erected in 1918). These were two simultaneous trends, of which the latter proved promising and enduring.

25. Doctor of Philological Sciences R. M. Samarin notes that the authors of this chapter are very much inclined to stress the break with tradition rather than the succession in the development of culture. 'I therefore should like to observe that in the art of socialist realism based on principles of strong links with the people and the party bold innovation in the artistic representation of life goes hand in hand with the use and development of all progressive traditions of world culture.' See also T. Trifonova: 'A Note on Socialist Realism', *Journal of World History*, VII, 1 (1962), p. 108.

26. Candidate of Arts V. M. Polevoy adds that similar phenomena also characterized other forms of art: music, the theatre, the fine arts. As in literature, new creative forms arose among the many peoples of the USSR: for example, opera, painting and sculpture in Soviet Central Asia, etc.

27. Candidate of Philological Sciences T. K. Trifonova in her papers asserts that the right understanding of innovation is of immense importance for socialist realism. A genuine spirit of innovation is connected in the first place with the ideological content and social tasks of literature and art and with the capacity of the writer and artist to understand and perceive the new in life. What is new in life and in activity determines the new content and the new social role of Soviet literature and art and creates continually new forms for the expression of a new content.

28. Candidate of Arts V. M. Polevoy asserts that from mid-1950's architecture was dominated by the striving to achieve aesthetic comprehension of mass industrial construction, as well as new materials and designs, free from decorative elements.

29. Candidate of Arts V. M. Polevoy says that mention should also be made of the international film festivals in Karlovy Vary and Moscow, where special prizes are awarded to films which promote ideas of humanism, friendship among the nations, the struggle for peace.

CHAPTER XXXII

DEVELOPMENTS IN EASTERN
LITERATURES AND ARTS

I. NATURE OF THE WESTERN CULTURAL IMPACT
AND TYPES OF REACTION

I. *General features*

THE development of literature and the arts in the East during the twentieth century was intimately bound up with the awakening of national self-awareness and with the reaction to cultural contact with the West. Few forms of expression were untouched either by direct influence from the West, or by the stimulus to the development of indigenous arts in response to such contact. By mid-century a similar process of interaction was beginning to be evident in Africa, chiefly in the visual arts, music and dance since traditional African expression was oral and visual rather than written. (Pl. 41.)

The tendencies to assimilate new cultural influences and at the same time to revive old cultural traditions in a period of national awakening both reinforced and competed with each other. Where traditional forms had great vitality, either because they were an integral part of the life of the community, as for example, Balinese dancing, or because they were in the hands of a responsible professional group, as were the No, Bugaku and Kabuki drama of Japan and the Chinese opera, they remained relatively unaffected by western contacts. Where the idiom or spirit of a classical form was incompatible with that of the West, as for example in much eastern music, there was no western impact, or else one form was substituted for the other form, or both continued in competitive co-existence. Where there was a measure of compatibility, as in the literary expression of many countries, notably China, or in the consonance between traditional Japanese architecture, painting and flower arrangement and western functional architecture, abstract painting and surrealist 'collages', a process of synthesis took place in which western forms were used as vehicles for expressing an eastern spirit, or traditional forms became vehicles for ideas and attitudes derived from contact with the West.

Where a form of expression was wholly absent, either because it had never been a part of the cultural tradition of the country or because it had disappeared, western forms were adopted and adapted to provide means for the expression of new attitudes and experiences. This was the case with most forms of prose, and the realistic drama of contemporary life. The coming of the cinema and radio added new and powerful media for the introduction of new forms and for the perpetuation or revival of some traditional modes of expression, such as music and the dance. These media, together with the spread of education, enlarged the audiences and altered their character.

Although the response to European cultural contact differed widely according to the indigenous culture, to the nature of the contact and to the period of maximum interaction, certain broad lines of development appeared in most areas.

The initial effect of the western impact was to stimulate enthusiasm among the western-educated *élite* for the literature and arts of the West. Western works were translated into local languages. Writers and artists began to follow western modes, using their native idioms. In a second phase, they re-emphasized their own classic forms. As the process continued, these countries developed and refined their national literature and arts, making such blend of western and traditional forms and themes as would reflect their emerging life and the role of their artists and writers in it.

The process began in different countries at different times, according to the time and form of western impact. The types of western literature and art which had most direct influence in different areas depended upon their source —British, French, German, Russian—and the time of their penetration. The manner of adaptation was affected by the local idiom and traditional forms and by the social development which accompanied the literary and artistic revival. The quality of the result ranged from weak and imitative stories, novels, poems or paintings to works of power and skill which reflected the genius of their authors and maturity of literary or artistic development. But everywhere interaction produced new vigour, and its effects were not limited to the western-educated elements who provided the initial channel. In fact, the writers and artists who made the most creative use of new concepts and forms were often, and increasingly, those who remained within their national cultural milieu rather than those whose education made them bi-cultural.

On first consideration, it would seem improbable that western expression could exert general influences upon eastern cultures in view of the changes in western literature and art during the period. Many of the problems which most concerned western writers and artists were quite irrelevant to the East, such as the disorders of a once-dominant European society, the impossibility of continuing to think in terms of a man-centred universe—a concept which the East had never entertained—or the liberation from a kind of representationalism in art which had not characterized the arts of the East. Nevertheless, there were enough broad differences between the western and eastern forms of expression for the general impact of the former to produce similar tendencies throughout the very different societies of the East.

While the impact of the West introduced new forms and content and broke the hold of traditional literary and artistic conventions, it simultaneously spurred interest in these same traditions, both by stimulating an awakened national consciousness and by arousing a reaction against the pretensions of the West.

The scorn with which some colonial administrators, missionaries and teachers viewed many aspects of traditional cultures, asserting the superiority of all things western, brought an initial turning away from the forms of local cultural expression by some of the western-educated. At the same time the western scholars who studied and translated the ancient classics, penetrated forgotten areas of history and brought to world attention the archaeological record of Angkor Vat, Mohenjo-daro, the Ajanta caves or the ancient cities of the Tigris-Euphrates valley, aroused a sense of history among the peoples of these areas and brought their cultural traditions alive. Many who had been indifferent or negative toward their cultural heritage reacted vigorously against the western sense of superiority and became determined to reassert traditional values.

2. *Interaction in specific areas*

The circumstances surrounding the western cultural impact in different countries, as well as the distinctive characteristics of the traditional forms of expression, determined the course taken in each country by the process of interaction during these years.

In the Indian subcontinent the process was long, gradual and complex. Literatures of high quality existed in a number of the Indian languages when English education, in the middle of the nineteenth century, brought the educated element in contact with English literature and the European classics in English translation. Western influence aroused its first strong response in Bengal, where in the late nineteenth century, Michael Madhusudan Dutta (1824–73) introduced the sonnet and the European epic forms and B. C. Chatterji (1838–94) introduced the novel. There the poet Rabindranath Tagore achieved a unique integration of western and Indian literary and musical qualities and his nephew, Abanindranath Tagore (1871–1951) made a similar synthesis in painting. In time, other regions experienced comparable developments.

The developments in all fields were closely linked with the political struggle and reflected its successive phases—first enthusiasm for things western; then romantic reconstruction of India's past; then, as the movement for self-rule gained momentum from 1919 to 1936, vigorous realism, optimism and zeal for reform together with the revival of classical arts; a growing spirit of social criticism and the rise of so-called 'progressive' writing from 1936 on; and, after independence, strong public support for the traditional arts, a wide range of individual expression, and the growing influence of popular forms which were developed and spread through the cinema.

In China the impact of western arts and letters came more suddenly, as a part of revolutionary movements. Traditional literary and artistic forms persisted into the early twentieth century scarcely touched by movements elsewhere, although more than fifty European novels were translated into Chinese. Following the political revolution of 1911–12, a literary revolution led by the scholars Chen Tu-hsiu (1879–1942) and Hu Shih (1891–1962), and the writer Lu Hsün (1881–1936), introduced western literary forms and the use of the vernacular, though Chinese painting continued to retain its traditional form.[1]

The leaders of the literary revolution insisted that there must be a clear and complete choice between old Chinese and new western ways, and that the Chinese literary language was completely dead and must be replaced by a comprehensible language based on common speech. Realistic novels and plays of social criticism focused attention on social ills. When the communist régime came to power in 1949, 'socialist realism' in literature and drama produced stories and plays which conveyed the optimism and vigour of social reconstruction and, in painting, provided a new idiom for propagandist art. At the same time traditional Chinese opera was revived and used as a vehicle for new ideas, while interest in folk music and art was stimulated.

Japan's Meiji restoration and self-conscious westernization set in motion two distinct tendencies in the arts, one to study and imitate western modes, the other to purify and reassert traditional forms, notably the formal literary language. In the arts, as in much of Japanese life, the two tendencies remained side by side, the western strong in the public sector and the traditionally Japanese dominant in the private sector of life. Changing political emphases had little reflection in the arts. Choice of western or traditional modes and efforts to integrate them on one basis or another remained largely an individual matter. Completely western types of expression existed parallel to completely traditional plays, music, painting, and flower arrangement, and readers enjoyed independently both western literature and Japanese classics. After the defeat and occupation following the second world war, pressure to find a valid integration and a modern, native idiom became extremely strong and led young writers to explore the popular ethos for a base to which to relate whatever they might draw from the classic Japanese tradition and the varied forms from the West.

Elsewhere in Asia a small western-educated group, by mid-century, had barely begun to reflect western influences in their native idioms. In Indonesia after 1925 an extensive programme of translation began to make western literature available in the local languages, and a small group of writers, using both Dutch and the Malayan which was being consciously developed as a national language, tried out western literary forms, especially the novel of social comment and psychological insight, to explore the problems of the day. Meantime, the rich gamelan music and dramatic dance of Bali and Java retained their vitality and integrity, to be discovered by the West and admired as one of the most highly developed stage cultures in the world, and Balinese painting and sculpture experienced a renaissance in the 1930s.[2]

Western-educated Thais acquired tastes in western literature and the arts, and provided appreciative audiences for western music; a few experimented with these western forms. Some of the most popular of the modern Thai novels revealed the Europeanized to themselves and confronted them with their problem of cultural integration. At the same time traditional literary forms such as short topical verses were put to current use, and the traditional arts of the dance, music and floral creations flourished and received strong official support. In the states which composed French Indo-China a few French-educated writers conveyed a sense of their ancient land in exquisite French verse and a few artists used essentially western forms of visual expression while others refined the traditional modes.

In the Arab countries the impact of western literature and arts resulted neither in as great an assimilation of western forms as in Asian countries, nor so strong a stimulus to the revival of traditional expression. Especially in Egypt, the principal centre of Arab cultural developments during these years, the educated element became familiar with western literature, music and painting, and much western literature, including some modern works, was translated into Arabic. Modern journalism and the prose essay were developed as vehicles for expression, but the western novel, short story and social drama, which were important vehicles of modern expression elsewhere, had not by mid-century overcome the handicap of the literary language, while the traditional Muslim prohibition on representing the human form tended to condition the development of pictorial art.

By the time that western influences became strong in Iran, the rich tradition of Persian literature and exquisite miniature art had lost its vitality, though there were always individual writers of distinction. In the early twentieth century much of modern Persian writing, including a number of magazines, was published outside the country, in Istanbul, London, Calcutta and Berlin. From the time of the revolution of 1905-8 the national movement gave a new impetus to literary expression. Actual forms were often shaped by journalists, for the press provided an important outlet for Persian writers and helped to make the written language simpler, more flexible and closer to popular speech. Historical novels in the western style, drawing on Persian materials, began to be attempted after the first world war and some poets turned to contemporary and public themes as well as to the lyric subjects and forms which were traditional.

One of the results of the changed position of Turkey in the nineteenth century was an effort to develop a national Turkish literature, freed of customary Persian forms ill-suited to the Turkish language, and in tune with Turkey's desire for westernization. The movement became intensified with the nationalism of the Young Turks in the early twentieth century. Drawing both on western sources, mainly French, and on classical Turkish forms and historical themes, writers sought to develop genuinely Turkish modes. Two of the most influential poets in the first quarter of the century, Yahya Kemal Beyatli (1886-1958) and Ahmet Hasim (1885-1933), found their main inspiration respectively in classical Turkish sources and in French Impressionism.

The decisive turning point in Turkish literary development, however, came at the time of the Ataturk revolution of 1923, when the Arabic alphabet was discarded in favour of the Roman script in the conviction that the language of common usage could thus find freer and more accurate expression. The reform turned Turkish students away from Arabic and Persian sources and augmented to a flood the translation of western classics of all sorts—French, English, Russian, German, Italian, Latin, Greek—making the major literary traditions of the West a part of the Turkish heritage. Under this stimulus, Turkish writers refined the vernacular language for poetic purposes and experimented with various verse forms. Novelists such as Halide Edib Adivar and Resat Nuri Güntekin (1892–1956) developed the novel along realistic, social and psychological lines, and many writers, such as Refik Halit Karay (1888–   ) became adept at using the short story to convey the rich variety of the Turkish country and people.3

Until the middle years of the twentieth century, literary and artistic interaction among the countries of the East was less pronounced than with those of the West. However, there was some cultural interaction between China and Japan, and the painting of these countries had a certain influence on the styles of modern painting in India. Only after independence were there the beginnings of literary exchanges among Asian countries and conferences of Asian writers, chiefly under 'progressive' auspices, as at Delhi in 1956 and Tashkent in 1958. There was some effort to bring modern Indian and Chinese literary and artistic circles into communication with each other. Indian writers, both classic and modern, were translated into Chinese. Indians had access to the Chinese classics in English translation; some current Chinese writing was published in English and became available to Indian readers. Visits of dance troupes between Asian countries and the distribution of films were other points of exchange.4

II. INTRODUCTION OF NEW LITERARY FORMS

The first aspects of western expression to be absorbed were literary forms—the novel, short story, Ibsen-style drama, essay, lyric poetry, such verse forms as the sonnet. New content came later, once the forms had become naturalized. Where traditional forms required strict adherence to elaborate and complex canons of expression, the western forms released the writer from traditional rhetoric, permitted direct expression and opened the way to new types of writing.

The traditional forms of eastern literature, drama and dance were predominantly poetical. The main body of literature used classical literary languages distinct from the language of speech. Its themes were traditional, telling stories of the gods or heroes, singing praises or invoking God or the gods, or expressing love in the conventionally established manner. Drama was stylized according to the canons of the No or Kabuki plays of Japan, the classical opera of China or the religious dance-drama of India and Bali.

Alongside these dominant forms of expression, however, most countries also had a secular literature which might use less stylized language or forms.

India had a non-religious dramatic tradition; vernacular literatures, using traditional forms and dealing with the familiar epic subjects, had developed in several of the major Indian languages. In these literatures the rigid formalism of classical Sanskrit had never wholly prevailed and their great masterpieces had long discarded many of the canons of Sanskrit poetry. Japan's non-classical literature took the form of semi-popular prose tales, written in the more informal language, and read primarily by women and the merchant class rather than by the samurai and literati. The Meiji restoration, however, had required the use of formal language and strengthened the more classical literary tradition. Prose fiction had been created as a genre in China some centuries before, so that the western novel was a less alien form there than elsewhere. Persian and Arabic literatures were largely devoted to religious and love poetry and some prose tales but did not include the various forms of drama that were central parts of the literatures of other Asian countries. Turkey had no strong literary tradition, for Persian influences predominated until the eighteenth century and by the middle of the nineteenth century efforts to follow French literary forms had counteracted tendencies toward a distinctive Turkish style.

Some form of folk expression was alive in most areas, as in the puppet plays of Indonesia or Turkey or the village dancing and extensive folklore in India, but it had little relation with the more formal literature and the other arts.

The western literary forms most easily and widely adopted were various types of prose, for there was usually less conflict of style in prose than in poetry or else the western prose forms were wholly new and distinct. They were suitable vehicles for realistic expression and social analysis and as such were appropriate to express the process of social change.

The short story and the novel were perhaps the most generally accepted. For the short story, the influences of de Maupassant and Chekhov were paramount. In China and Japan, India and the Arab countries, story magazines were established and flourished. Novels followed several styles. They appeared in large numbers in Japan; they became a popular mode of expression in China after the New Tide movement of 1917 and, with renewed vigour, after the establishment of the communist régime; Indian writers developed distinct styles for novel writing in the several Indian languages. After the first world war Arab writers, mainly located in Egypt though often originating in other Arab areas such as Syria and Lebanon, began to add original novels to the translations of western works which they had been introducing to Arabic readers for a generation. Turkish novels and short stories, drawing their material mainly from the life of the people, were numerous and varied; a bibliography of Turkish women writers in 1955 listed no less than seventy-eight women who had published novels since 1923. Although the numbers of original novels in Indonesian, Siamese, Persian and other non-western languages varied and the quality was uneven, the novel was accepted virtually everywhere as a modern literary form.

In all these areas writers also experimented with the modern drama, chiefly along the lines of the Ibsen-type modern social problem play. The one-act play, used as a vehicle for social commentary, was also popular. In China, Japan and India modern drama took its place alongside the quite different traditional dramatic forms which continued to be played in their classical manner and to retain their great popularity. Western plays in translation or western-style plays by local authors were produced under separate auspices and with an altogether different tone and intent. Some few attempts were made to recombine traditional elements into something closer to the western dramatic form, or to use old forms to present new content, notably in India with some adaptation of the dance-drama and the introduction of some political commentary into traditionally religious plays. Script writing for movies, a completely modern form, drew some of the outstanding writers in countries where extensive movie industries developed, notably Japan, India and communist China.

In countries which lacked the play-going traditions of China, Japan or India, western-style plays were not so generally written or produced. Among the Arabic-speaking countries modern drama was developed only in Egypt, where in the second quarter of the century it took the form of poetic plays, popular comedies and a few serious prose works. In Indonesia, where traditional puppet plays and dancing remained the great sources of popular entertainment, few attempts were made to compose plays in the western form, but new ideas were conveyed through the old medium. In Iran popular semi-religious dramas, traditional or spontaneous, continued to be performed during the month of Muharram, but formal dramatic writing was used primarily for political pamphleteering, in the form of satirical comedies to be read rather than played. Although some Turkish novelists and poets also wrote plays, the dramatic form achieved little popularity in that country during these years.

The growth of journalism was a major factor in changing literary style, for in many countries it was the principle vehicle for modernized prose. It required flexible expression in place of the old, formal, puristic writing limited by the kind of vocabulary permitted and the conventions surrounding its use. Literary journals had already appeared and were beginning to assume importance in India in the nineteenth century. In the twentieth century they proliferated in vernacular languages throughout the country. In the Arabic-speaking countries the press was one of the major vehicles for the modern literary movement, and the prose essay the principal form of modern literary expression. The movement for the nascent modern culture and expression of Indonesia centred in the 1930s in a review, *Pudjangga Baru* ('The New Writer', 1933 ff.), which published essays on such subjects as the significance of traditional literature for the modern generation, the conflict between traditional gamelan music and modern popular music influenced by the West, the aims of education, art for art's sake versus art with a social purpose, and the ever recurring question of the antagonism between East and West. The prose essay lent itself especially to social commentary and analysis of the problems which concerned the writers in these rapidly changing societies.

Although in all eastern countries poetry was the traditional form of most literary expression, and poetic forms were firmly established and very distinct, the western impact had a substantial effect on poetry also. Just as the western poets abandoned established forms in order to experiment with language, cadence and rhythm, eastern poets freed themselves from the far more rigid verse forms which their literary canons required, and in addition broadened the range of poetical themes beyond the prescribed subjects. For some, notably the Chinese after 1917, experimentation meant a sharp break with the past; for others, notably poets writing in the Indian languages, Arabic and Persian, traditional forms were modified through experimentation rather than being discarded.

Everywhere, the western impact, together with the spread of education and the growth of literacy, raised the problem of what language to use. The trend toward realistic writing about the contemporary scene meant a tendency, if not a necessity, to use the language of speech. India enjoyed the advantage of possessing vernacular languages which had already been used as literary vehicles and were well adapted to realistic subject matter. As Japanese writers in the late nineteenth century began to follow western models, they used the less formal language of speech rather than the prevailing literary language (e.g. Futabei Shimei, *The Drifting Cloud*, 1887–89).

In China, by contrast, it was only after the literary revolution of 1917 that a language appropriate to the western style of realism, the spoken vernacular *pai hwa*, was accepted as a literary medium; novels and plays using the vernacular in earlier periods had not been regarded as literature. This movement for the use of the vernacular was intensified with the measures taken by the communist régime to facilitate the use of a popular Chinese idiom and to develop a simplified script. Arab writers, for their part, found themselves hampered in attempting to write realistic novels or stories by the difference between the classical, literary Arabic and the common speech. All movements toward the use of the spoken languages for literary purposes up to the middle of the twentieth century proved abortive, and in all Arab countries the literary language continued to be used for press and radio, schools and mosques and all literary expression.

Whatever the obstacles, however, the same factors which led western writers to experiment with language and sentence structure in order to convey their meaning pushed writers in the East toward a freer use of language and toward efforts to bring the written work closer to the terms of everyday speech.

Many of the western-influenced writers were well grounded in their own classic literature and continued to use its forms while also following western lines. The Indian Malayalam poet, Vallathol (1879–1958), for example, started in the early twentieth century as a writer in the classic style. Under western influence he adopted a realistic approach, and then became one of the 'progressive' writers. Yet at the same time he translated one of the Sanskrit class-ics, the *Rigveda*, into traditional-style Malayalam. One of the leaders of the Chinese literary revolution of 1917, Hu Shih, was a thorough scholar of the Chinese classics and even the Chinese communist leader, Mao Tse-tung, did not feel it necessary for the Chinese to be limited to the forms of 'socialist realism' but set an example to his followers by writing and publishing poems in the classic Chinese style.

As writers drew on their native heritage for themes and forms of expression, they found two distinct sources, the literary tradition preserved by an edu-cated *élite*, and a folk tradition more or less alive among the people. Between the two, the gulf was often wide.

Various factors tended to enhance the folk aspect. The new realism focused attention on the common people and their forms of expression. Western interest in folk cultures as repositories of common human experience, myths and symbols further tended to elevate folk art. The folk tradition, couched in the idiom of the people rather than a literary language, was often more in line with the modern temper and with what modern writers were trying to express than was the classical. This was most vividly illustrated in communist China, where the traditional, popular picture-broadsides furnished a more usable base for the development of pictorial and written realism and material with didactic and propaganda intent than the traditional artistic and literary media. The combined effect of westernization, the revival of interest in local culture and practical objectives thus tended to narrow the gap between literary and folk expression.

III. MODIFICATION OF LITERARY CONTENT

New content followed the adoption of new forms. Western writing was real-istic; it dealt with contemporary society and with live people, living their ordinary daily lives; it was concerned with the personality of many different individuals. It was in sharp contrast to the content of classical eastern writing which treated mythological or historical figures and bygone or imaginary ages in a symbolic, allegorical or stylized manner and presented characters as types, defined by their position in society or in the hierarchy of the gods. It was not so markedly different, however, from the secular or popular writing.

Since western literature differed so markedly from the predominant types of literature in the East, its impact upon content as well as form carried eastern writing in a clearly defined direction. However great the differences among the novels of Scott, Goethe, Dickens, Dostoevsky, Zola, Aldous Huxley, Sartre or Hemingway, the short stories of de Maupassant, Chekhov, Gorky or Thomas Mann, and the plays of Ibsen and George Bernard Shaw, their in-fluence was similar. It strengthened whatever secular literary trends were already present and it stimulated the writers of China and Japan, of India,

Indonesia, Egypt, Lebanon or Turkey to look at the social world around them and to try to depict and analyse its people and its institutions.[5]

Since much of the literature of the West was associated with social change, it offered appropriate models to writers whose own societies were marked by even greater extremes of wealth and poverty and were experiencing even more drastic social upheavals.

The aspects of western literature which appealed in each area and at each period varied with changing conditions. The relation of successive influences to the stages of the political struggle in India has already been noted. Scott and Dumas rather than Dickens or Thackeray provided models for the first of the western-style Indian novels in the latter part of the nineteenth century, for the social urge of the time was to recreate history. Indian nationalism was drawing on the rediscovery of India's past; the historical romanticism of Scott was therefore a welcome model to follow in casting this nationalist historical urge into literary form. The Bengal novelist, Bankim Chandra Chatterji, provided the model for the heroic Indian novel. Modern Indian drama of this period, too, as initiated by the Bengal playwright D. L. Roy (1864–1913), used Indian historical characters.

At a second stage, in a period of self-criticism, Indian writers found models in the western novels and plays of social criticism. Along these lines, Tagore's novels in Bengali revealed the weaknesses of Indian society, and S. C. Chatterji (1876–1938) exposed social evils of Indian life with insight and ruthlessness. Prem Chand (1881–1936), writing in Urdu and Hindi, dealt with village life and the problems of rural India. Similar tendencies appeared among writers in other Indian languages. For Indians in this mood writers such as Dostoevsky had immense appeal. The social drama in the manner of Ibsen and Shaw was used by the leading writers in Marathi (Mama Warerkar), Kannada (T. K. Kailasam, R. V. Jagirdar), Malayalam (C. V. Raman Pillai), Tamil (P. Sambandha Mudaliar) and other languages to examine and expose mercilessly various aspects of political life, formal religion and all manner of social evils.

Then, with the rapid social changes that preceded and followed independence, and with the influence of communist writers reinforcing the realism of the literature of the non-communist West, many Indian writers adopted a 'progressive' approach, writing social comment and criticism in the manner which they regarded as 'socialist realism'. Dramas, short stories and one-act plays were used as vehicles for mass propaganda to depict the breakdown of feudal society, the exploitation of the workers, the misery of landless peasants and the conflict between old and new.

But though these successive influences were followed by leading writers they never produced a uniform trend, for Indian writers at all times drew their inspiration from a wide range of sources, ancient and modern, local and foreign and produced a variety of styles which reflected the complexity of Indian life

China, on the other hand, where the main impact of western literary influence came after the literary revolution of 1917, went through no period of western-influenced historical romanticism, but plunged directly into self-criticism. Lu Hsün's *Diary of a Madman*, which was published in 1918 in the *New Youth Magazine*, introduced the Chinese reading public to vernacular prose, sharp satire and a bitter attack on Chinese social life, and his *True Story of Ah Q* (1923) pilloried the passivity and gloom in the character of ordinary Chinese people resulting from centuries of feudalism, the callousness to suffering and the misery brought by the self-deception of 'saving face'. Virtually all the writers after the literary revolution wrote bitingly of the misery, oppression, chaos and disorder of Chinese society. Yeh Shao-chun (1893–), a follower of Dostoevsky, drew his characters from the oppressed and downtrodden; Mao Tun (1896–), in his novel *Midnight* (1923) and trilogy *Disillusion, Agitation*, and *Pursuit* (written in 1927–28, later issued as *Eclipse*) portrayed the mental processes of different classes of people in the face of national disorder, economic collapse, the evils of landlordism and foreign aggression; the dramatists Tsao Yu (1905–) and Tien Han (1899–) dealt with the breakdown of the family system and the effects of the semi-feudal social structure and rising capitalism and dramatized the misfortunes of the common folk as a result of the civil war.

Western literature was of less direct influence in China than in either India or Japan, and of less interest to Chinese writers. Nevertheless, Hu Shih's defence of Ibsenism ushered in the social drama, Dostoevsky provided the inspiration and model for novels dealing with the poor and oppressed, Lu Hsün found inspiration in the works of Gogol and Chekhov and most of the leading writers were also prolific translators; the leading modern poet, Kuo Mo-jo (1892–), translated works by such varied authors as Goethe, Tolstoy, Turgenev, Upton Sinclair, J. M. Synge, Shelley, Galsworthy, and the *Rubaiyat* of Omar Khayyam. Once the western influence had broken the traditional Chinese literary mould, writers turned less to western models than to Chinese examples and their own experimentation. The literary renaissance established as respectable the old Chinese novel, such as the fourteenth-century masterpiece, *All Men Are Brothers*, and therewith provided a realistic vernacular model which modern writers could follow.

The close association of Chinese writers with revolutionary movements and the continual political conflict, civil war and foreign intervention which racked Chinese society led them to form a succession of literary organizations which reflected their respective positions. A few remained outside the political currents, such as the essentially romantic Yu Ta-fu (1896–1945), who wrote of the personal confusion of individuals caught in the uncertainties of the changing pattern of marriage and family life, Pa Chin (1905–), who pictured the decay of the Confucian family, and Hu Shih, who continued to press for freedom of literary experimentation. But most writers turned increasingly to the left and became spokesmen for the communist cause.

With the coming to power of the communist régime in 1949, writers who had been part of the original literary revolution came to occupy positions of leadership in the new régime; the novelist Mao Tun became minister of culture, the poet Kuo Mo-jo, vice-premier of the Chinese People's Republic. The tone of the writing changed drastically, though the realism, irony, homely characters and social themes remained. Preoccupation with suffering, despair, chaos and decay was replaced by confident assertions of social progress. Such a writer as Lao Shê (1898–   ) moved from the realism of extreme poverty and despair in *The Horned Moon* (written in the 1930s) and *Rickshaw Boy* (1946) to his propaganda plays during the Japanese war when he headed the National Writers' Anti-Aggression Association; after the establishment of the communist régime he wrote a proletarian play, *The Dragon Whisker Drain* (1951) about the construction of Peking's new sewage system to beautify the capital and improve the living conditions of the workers.

Peasants' struggles against landlords, and their own transformations in learning to work in cadres and expand production in the agrarian revolution were described in novels such as Ting Ling's (1907–   ) *The Sun Shines Over the Sankan River* (1948) and Chou Li-po's *Hurricane* (1948–49), both of which received the Stalin prize in 1951. Chao Shu-li (1905–   ), a writer whose knowledge of peasants and capacity to write their language with realism, humour and zest made him an outstanding popularizer, showed in his *Rhymes of Li Yu-tsai* (1946) the new will among the peasants as they dealt with the landlords and with each other. The theme appeared in many short stories, new forms of traditional opera and new adaptations of folk songs. More and more efforts were made to bring writers to live among the masses and to encourage workers and peasants to become writers

Japanese writers, by contrast, read avidly any and all western literature and followed many different styles. From the 1880s they were stimulated and influenced by English, German, French and Russian authors. Among them, Tsubouchi Shoyo (1859–1935), one of the first promoters of western views of literature in Japan and a reformer of Japanese drama, translated all the works of Shakespeare; Mori Ogai (1862–1922), translator of *Faust*, introduced continental European literature; Natsume Soseki (1867–1916), a student of English writing, became a satirical novelist; Shimazaki Toson (1872–1946) was first influenced by romanticism in his poetry and later, under the influence of naturalism, became a realistic novelist writing of social problems.

Twentieth-century European writers were translated as they appeared. After 1920 some Japanese writers leaned toward Marxism in philosophy and proletarian novels in writing. Many found the doubt and uncertainty of the European writers a basis for their own doubts about their efforts to assimilate western ways, as in Tanizaki Junichiro's (1886–   ) *A Fool's Love* (1925, Nagai Kafu's (1879–1959) *The Tale of America* (1908) and *The Tale of France* (1909). As their own inner struggle reached a crisis, the European cultural crisis took on meaning. At mid-century the existentialists seemed to express their mood, and the writings of Sartre became popular.

The extensive Japanese literature of the twentieth century followed no line. In most instances it was characterized by some form of realism, often meticulous detail of daily life; it did not generally attempt to explore emotional depths; it might or might not express a social attitude; it usually retained the traditional Japanese imagery, which remained alive. Japanese writing reflected both the currents of the West and the vicissitudes of Japanese life. In one sense it might be regarded as an extension of the literature of Europe; in another sense, it was an emerging national expression which by mid-century was still in process of taking shape.

At different periods, in differing atmospheres, and in the hands of people of different political beliefs, social criticism thus took a variety of forms. It was used to expose the misery of rural peasant or urban shopkeeper, to pillory the well-to-do, to portray the class struggle, or to show the efforts of nationalists, revolutionaries or others working for social change. The experience of the writers themselves determined the closeness and realism with which they could enter into the lives of those about whom they wrote. Some, notably in China after the New Tide movement, shared the life of village or market place and knew the peasants or other common people; others were limited by their class position and western education, and could write at first-hand mainly of their own social group.

On the whole, western-influenced writing tended to deal with progressively broader and lower social strata, starting with essentially upper-class material in the early years of the century, and dealing by the second quarter of the century more and more with the peasant, the rickshaw boy, the shrimp fisherman or the pearl diver. Western-influenced writers in the main were in the vanguard of social change and often followed a style of writing and thought strongly influenced by communist philosophy and canons of expression even where communist political influence was not dominant or strong.

Such writing, too, tended to be secular in tone. Much, if not most, of the traditional expression of the East had been religious in origin and some, such as temple dancing in India, retained a religious function. The spirit of modern western literature and art was strongly secular. Whether western forms were adopted or imitated, or whether traditional forms were revived, existing secular aspects were strengthened and the predominant tone and use became secular.

The romantic emphasis in western writing, relating as it did to a society which encouraged the expression of individual preferences and beliefs and in which romantic marriage was the general form, introduced a new set of values to societies where behaviour was closely prescribed by situation and status, and marriage was a matter of family arrangement. Romantic themes, and especially the conflict between romantic and traditional values in marriage and family life, became prominent in the literature of India and Japan. In

communist China marriages arranged in the interest of the family were
brought under attack and the western-style romantic marriage was given
support.

The western literature and art which probed the subconscious, however,
found little acceptance and exerted much less influence than did romantic
writing or realism and social criticism, although there was experimentation
in this area by some of the younger writers. There was no such widespread
interest in psychology as in the West, the subject matter of western psychological novels seemed often remote and the attitudes revealed by these writings
often incomprehensible or offensive, while the style and vocabulary of writers
such as James Joyce acted as a barrier to understanding and acceptance.

Of less influence, too, was the literature which expressed the quest for
meaning in the universe and man's place in it. To the Asian mind, the western
malaise in the face of the implications of modern science, the need for
reassurance, or the despair of meaninglessness were strange reactions. On a
different plane, however, the acute conflict of values to which western-
influenced easterners were exposed stimulated a quest for new values or a
new synthesis.

Up to the middle of the twentieth century distinctive literary forms that
drew from both traditional and western sources and were modern in spirit
had nowhere fully emerged. But some combination of revival, adaptation,
and experimentation in every country reflected the national awakening, the
cultural interaction, and the cultural vitality of each area. When the Indian
poet Rabindranath Tagore received the Nobel Prize for Literature in 1913, it
was in recognition of his creative assimilation of western influences combined
with a genius for expressing depths of the Indian spirit in forms which could
not only be loved and absorbed by the Indian people but understood effectively
in other parts of the world.

IV. THE VISUAL ARTS

The impact of the western visual arts upon artistic expression in the East was
much more limited than the influence of western literary expression. Whereas
the western-educated element everywhere was more or less familiar with
western literature, and modern literary expression in eastern countries was
intimately bound up with the process of social change, western arts were
known to a much more restricted group and played no such general part in
the cultural adaptation through which eastern societies were passing. The
character of the traditional idiom and the place of the visual arts strongly
influenced the manner in which western influences were felt.

In the nineteenth century the traditional visual arts of the Indian sub-
continent were in disrepute with the western-educated element which had
imbibed the negative attitudes of the puritan-minded British toward art
forms which were often sensuous and which they did not understand. The

revival of Indian art came at the turn of the century, largely as the result of the researches of an Anglo-Tamil, Ananda Coomaraswamy and the work of an Englishman, E. B. Havell (1861–1934), who headed the School of Art at Calcutta and expounded the beauties of Indian art, and Abanindranath Tagore, who became the founder in Bengal of the first modern style of Indian painting. Trained in western techniques, and also influenced by the techniques of visiting Japanese artists, Abanindranath derived his style from the miniature paintings of the Mogul period, the sculpture of Hindu temples, and the wall paintings from the caves of Ajanta and Ellora. His pupils carried the Bengal style, with its eclectic Indian manner and traditional themes, to many parts of the country, where they directed or taught in the principal art schools. At Bombay, however, a school of art under the direction of western painters remained a centre of western training and influence. (Pl. 59.)

A few individual artists developed their own special idioms. M. A. Rahman Chughtai (1897–), who came from a family of artists in the Persian tradition, developed his delicate, flowing, romantic style from Mogul miniature painting; after partition he became a sort of painter-laureate of Pakistan. Jamini Roy (1887–) turned to the folk tradition and developed his manner wholly on the basis of the stylized forms, bright, flat colours, and visual conventions of folk art. Amrita Sher-Gil (1912–41), most influential painter after Abanindranath Tagore, freed Indian painters from the effort to conform to the Bengal school or to imitate western modes, by using her thorough western training freely and flexibly to evoke the feeling of the Indian people and scenes which she depicted. (Pl. 60, 61a.)

The most distinctive characteristic of Indian painting as it emerged in the 1940s and 1950s was its eclecticism. With few exceptions, young painters experimented with many modes; in a collection of paintings, often even the paintings of a single man, some element from nearly every school, East and West, could be seen integrated into the painter's personal idiom and used with whatever sensitivity, brilliance, mere derivativeness or lively originality he could achieve. (Pl. 61b, 62.)

In Japan, by contrast, a painting tradition based on an elaborate artistic vocabulary used with great flexibility and economy was very much alive when western influences began to enter Japan, and it continued to flourish along traditional lines. When Japanese artists became interested in western painting, they found themselves confronting a completely alien idiom, oil paint with its opacity and shadings, rounded figures, large canvases, external perspective. These were the complete antithesis of the transparent water-colours, the always decorative, two-dimensional, delicate and small paintings of Japanese art. Japanese painters learned to use the western media and to paint in the western manner, imitatively, sometimes skilfully, but without incorporating any of the feeling or the technique of their own style. Some art scholars who visited Europe after the Meiji restoration (1868) had urged their compatriots to stick to their traditional styles, and had exerted their leadership in this direction. But numbers of Japanese artists studied in Paris or under French influence, and painted French nudes and still-lifes, landscapes and distorted figures that would have been indistinguishable from the work of their fellow students in a European art class. (Pl. 63a, 63b.)

For those who stuck to the traditional medium and essential forms, exposure to western art had a more creative effect. Abstraction could be, and was, successfully absorbed into their works—in designs of decorative papers, textiles, posters, screens; new abstractions could be incorporated into the traditional artistic vocabulary to give flexibility and variety to compositions in the traditional mode. Freedom of line and in the use of colour could give warmth and a less formal atmosphere without destroying the essential quality. All manner of constructions, whether surrealist compositions, constructivist designs or balanced mobiles, could be elaborated by people trained through the art of flower arrangement to apply principles of harmony to the juxtaposition of objects. In contrast to dull imitativeness in the use of oils, the western influences which could be assimilated to the Japanese style itself became part of the idiom and were used with ease and brilliance.

Until the Communist revolution Chinese painters were not seriously influenced by western styles of painting.[6] Modern Chinese painters followed the old masters in their technique—their calligraphy, their inner rather than outer perspective, and the intent of the picture to speak with an inner voice. Under the communist régime art was enlisted as a means of propaganda, and artists were encouraged to paint in the style of socialist realism. Portraits of leaders, scenes depicting the vigorous and happy work of building a socialist state, posters to exhort and inform were turned out as needed, and artists learned to use the unfamiliar medium of oil for this purpose. In the initial stages this work was quite unrelated to the traditional manner in which the artist expressed himself; it was much closer to the popular broadsides which made no pretence to art but which had long served to entertain, and sometimes to inform, the villagers.

Interest in traditional Chinese culture was however great. Study and reproduction of the early Buddhist paintings in the Tun Huang caves of north-west China brought these works to public attention; some of the most distinguished painters in the traditional style were honoured; people throughout the country were encouraged to collect and preserve folk materials of all sorts and to experiment with their own forms of expression. Thus elements were present for a possible integration of traditional and new forms in the expression of a renewed national spirit.[7] (Pl. 64a, 64b.)

V. ARCHITECTURE

Until after the second world war public buildings, commercial structures and factories followed closely the undistinguished styles current in the West, whether they were built by colonial governments or western commercial interests or by local agencies. The main streets and public buildings of Tokyo, Shanghai, New Delhi and Cairo became hardly distinguishable from those of western cities, except where a colonial government tried to adapt some local motif as, for example, when the British in India built railway stations or post offices in a pseudo-Mogul style, as irrelevant as the Greek columns or Gothic windows that were the hallmarks of their public buildings at home.

As the new international style of architecture began to remake the cities of the West, it spread to the East. In Japan it was much more in keeping with the architectural traditions of the locality than earlier European styles had been, for light and space, simple lines, clean surfaces and the union of the interior with its outdoor surroundings were principles of Japanese architecture. Elsewhere it was introduced in eastern cities in occasional buildings, frequently hotels. When the partition of India and Pakistan left the capital of the Punjab, Lahore, on the Pakistan side of the line, the Indian government invited Le Corbusier to construct a new capital for the East Punjab, Chandigarh, and features of Le Corbusier's style began to appear in new buildings all over India. (Pl. 20b.)

By the 1950s the international style had become the symbol of modernism— as much for the main street of Bangkok as for the main street of small cities in the United States. It did not have the same technological *raison d'être* as in the West, for steel and glass were not readily available and mass production did not provide materials for building construction and decoration. It was primarily for stylistic and social reasons, and because its features of lightness and space made it suitable to the tropics, that the international style was being adopted in the cities of the East.[8]

VI. MUSIC AND DANCE

Even more than the visual arts, music and dance in the East retained their traditional form, unaffected by contact with the West. Musical idioms so distinct as to be incompatible prevented the interaction of most eastern music with the music of the West, although the gamelan music of Java, which used intervals not unfamiliar to the West, had been the inspiration for some of the musical innovations introduced by Debussy. Music and dance were integral parts of highly traditional institutions associated with religion, with the court or with carefully preserved artistic forms. As such they were largely insulated from the currents that were modifying others forms of expression. If they were touched at all it was through the stimulus to the revival of cultural traditions which came as an indirect, but powerful, response to the impact of the West.

The revival of the dance in India offers a striking example of such a response. At all times dancing had been a highly developed art in India, closely associated with religious practices, but in the nineteenth century it had come under widespread disapproval among the educated classes, influenced by

British puritanism and the zeal of social reformers. Without patronage, both the temple dancing of south India and the court dancing in the north had fallen into a state of decay and abuse.

The leader of the movement to revive interest in Indian dancing in the second decade of the twentieth century was the poet Rabindranath Tagore, who brought the Manipuri dance form, which he found in a flourishing state in the north-east province of Assam, to his school, Santiniketan, in Bengal. Others followed, establishing schools for the teaching of other forms—the classical Bharata Natyam temple dance of south India, taught by expert masters at a school in Madras (Rukmini Devi, Kalakshetra); and in Travancore the elaborate Kathakali dance-drama, revived and popularized at the centre established by the poet Vallathol (Kerala Kalamandalam). Dancers began to appear on the stage, at private performances and before the numerous dance societies which were formed to arrange dance showings. By the 1930s the dance had not only regained its place within India, but outstanding dancers such as Uday Shankar and Ramgopal had brought the beauty and complexity of Indian dance to European audiences.

Where the dance remained an integral part of the life of the community, it retained its vitality within its own cultural milieu and gained appreciation from outside. Balinese village dancers and gamelan orchestras continued to develop new dances and music and to adapt traditional modes. Siamese dance troupes received government patronage and not only performed for important occasions at home but were sent abroad as a gesture of official courtesy and good will. These and other eastern dancers inspired a few choreographers and artists in the West, and troupes visited western capitals, where their beauty and style became more widely known. Within the Soviet Union, the Asian republics were encouraged to develop their indigenous dance forms, and the participation of performers from these areas in national festivals made their styles familiar in other parts of the USSR.

VII. EFFECT OF MASS MEDIA

The literature and arts of the East, as those of the West, were profoundly affected by the new media—radio, cinema and, in later years, television. These means of mass communication provided vehicles both for the rapid and widespread introduction of new forms and ideas, and for the preservation of traditional forms and their dissemination to the masses of the people. In countries with extensive local motion-picture industries, most notably Japan and India, the new medium was used to convey traditional themes and traditional art forms, such as the music and dance that filled most Indian films.

The cinema also became a vehicle for social commentary, with a far wider audience than the modern play or novel. In rare instances, notably a few outstanding Japanese and Indian films, it became a new and powerful art form. At the same time foreign films, often 'B grade' productions featuring violence or romance rather than those of literary and artistic merit, were widely shown both where a local industry flourished and where none had been developed. Their impact was more widespread and direct than was that of western literature and art. By affecting standards of taste, the cinema stimulated the development of popular art forms in these countries. The so-called 'movie music' in India, scorned by those who cherished the purity of classical Indian music, and also 'movie dancing', offered examples of such popularization, based on traditional forms but reduced to a popular idiom for the new mass audiences which the cinema brought into the literary and artistic milieu.

VIII. REACTION OF WEST TO CULTURE CONTACT WITH EAST

Although the relation between western and eastern forms of expression was chiefly a one-way flow from the West to each of the eastern countries, it was not wholly one-sided. As world communication grew and western peoples lost some of their ethnocentrism and sense of superiority, western writers and artists showed increased interest in, and appreciation for, the arts of the East. Painting, sculpture and the dance were most readily understood without the barrier of language.

With the aid of modern photography, the ancient art revealed by archaeological discoveries and the arts of new cultural areas were brought into world consciousness, such as the paintings in the Ajanta caves and other examples of the art of mediaeval India, the art of Tibet, or the Khmer art of south-east Asia. The artistic expression of Egypt or Persia, Cambodia, China, India or Africa might be seen not only in museums but in articles in popular magazines or text-books for schoolchildren. Only in the twentieth century would it have been possible to discuss the art of the world, past and present, as a common expression of human striving, as did André Malraux in Les voix du silence (1951).

Translation set up a two-way flow, also, as Chinese, Japanese, Indian and Arabic classical writings were increasingly translated into western languages. Already in the nineteenth century, eastern philosophy, especially the Hindu classics, was affecting philosophical thought in the West, notably in Germany in the latter part of the nineteenth century, and in the outlook of American thinkers such as Ralph Waldo Emerson and Henry Thoreau. The Rubaiyat of Omar Khayyam achieved immense popularity, while The Arabian Nights furnished the most common picture of the 'East' in western minds.

In the twentieth century a number of western writers were influenced by the literature of one or another eastern country. Arthur Waley's sensitive translations of Chinese classics into English made these works widely accessible. In time, modern Chinese, Japanese and Indian writings also began to be translated into European languages. Expressions of eastern thought reached a wider and wider range of people in the West. By mid-century almost any news-stand where cheap books were sold offered translations of the *Bhagavad Gita*, the *Analects* of Confucius, the words of the Buddha, or the *Holy Quran*. The poetry of Rabindranath Tagore helped to prepare the way for acceptance in the West of India's right to independence and to enable the West to begin to understand and welcome India's belief that its development could bring to the world a fresh vision of the creative human being.

The images of eastern culture which reached the West, however, were sometimes far from authentic, for what the West liked to think of as the 'wisdom of the East' was often only a romantic projection of a desire to escape from its own *malaise*. In the effort to build a more accurate, fuller and deeper basis for mutual understanding, Unesco set up an 'East–West' programme of mutual interchange in the 1950s and made it an increasingly central part of its international activity.

Yet it still may be questioned whether, up to the middle of the twentieth century, familiarity with non-western forms of expression had more than a superficial influence on the thought and expression of the West.

NOTES TO CHAPTER XXXII

1. Candidate of Arts V. M. Polevoy makes the following addition: However, a number of painters seek for ways of broadening the possibilities of the traditional style, drawing on the experience of European art (Hsü Pei-hung, known under the pseudonym of Shu Peon); the traditional ink painting is undergoing a definite rejuvenation. But it is in the field of engraving that the traditional art makes the most telling effort to break through the medieval imitations and come closer to life. The decisive role here was played by the Lu Hsün Academy of Arts, set up in the 1930's in the Red districts of China. The artists of this Academy made an extensive study of Soviet engraving and created works reflecting the life and struggles of the people.

2. Candidate of Arts V. M. Polevoy thinks special interest attaches to the lacquer painting of Vietnam, which has revived in a new form the traditional medieval techniques. A group of masters in Northern Vietnam have succeeded in raising it to the level of genuine art, combining realistic solidity of image with amazing decorative colourfulness.

3. Corresponding member of Tadjik Academy of Sciences J. S. Braginsky thinks that it is necessary to point out that one of the major writers of Turkey in the twentieth century is Nazim Hikmet (1902–63). His creative work in which brilliant innovations are associated with profound mastery of a number of the best classical and popular traditions of Turkish literature is widely known in many countries. (See R. G. Fish: *Nazim Hikmet*, Moscow, 1960.)

4. See *Tashkentskaya konferentziya pisatelei stran Azii i Afriki Materialy* ('Tashkent Conference of the writers of Asian and African countries—Materials') (Tashkent, 1960).

5. Candidate of Arts V. M. Polevoy thinks that here and in the other pages treating of the influence of European authors on the writers of Asia, the enormous influence of the work of Tolstoy is unjustly passed over. Yet this influence was quite profound by virtue of the ethical-educative impact and depth of socio-psychological penetration into life characteristic of Tolstoy.

6. In this connection Candidate of Arts V. M. Polevoy points out the exception of wood-cutting as observed above in Note 1.

7. Candidate of Arts V. M. Polevoy makes the following addition: Especially striking is the development of the arts among the peoples inhabiting the Soviet part of Asia. After the Revolution of 1917 major changes in cultural life occurred here. The people freed from the double burden of class and national oppression devoted themselves with new energy to the development of literature, music, theatre and fine art in their traditional forms. Folk art received state and public support. Of especial significance was the birth of new forms of art, in which the possibilities of the realistic method developed in the West are applied to the national art forms. Thus, professional painting and sculpture have arisen among the peoples of Central Asia, where they were formerly non-existent; national music drama, ballet and other forms are developed. These innovations are called for by the growing scope of spiritual life, by the necessity for developing those art forms which by virtue of their method are capable of reflecting the people's contemporary life.

8. Candidate of Arts V. M. Polevoy underlines that the new needs of social life in the newly-independent countries of the East stimulate the development of new branches and idioms of architecture. The development of a national industry, public education, the tasks of raising the standard of living—all promote the development of new forms of architecture and building, the destruction of the sharp contrast between the living conditions in the European and native sections, so typical of the colonial countries.

CONCLUSION

CHAPTER XXXIII

THE CHANGING SHAPE OF THE LIFE
OF MANKIND

BY the middle of the twentieth century the scientific and cultural developments that had taken place in the past fifty years had already radically altered the life of mankind and trends then apparent were in process of bringing further revolutionary changes.

The dramatic advances in scientific knowledge, the methodical application of such knowledge, and the resulting changes in material conditions were exerting a vast and ever increasing influence on the economic, social and political life of man, as well as on his cultural, ideological and moral development. Within the span of fifty years man's knowledge of the universe had increased beyond all previous experience; power generated from many sources had been harnessed and nuclear energy was further increasing man's control; the ability to break down matter and recombine it had permitted the creation of new materials to serve man's purposes; men travelled at speeds beyond the speed of sound; they had placed satellites in orbit around the earth and sent rockets beyond the earth's gravitational pull to circle the sun, and they were preparing to travel into space themselves.

An unprecedented growth in medical science had brought new and potent means for the control of disease and the virtual eradication of such scourges as plague, malaria, smallpox and cholera which had taken heavy toll of human lives over large areas, while preventive medicine had diminished infant deaths, extended the life span and raised the general level of health. The people of the world had available to them an abundance of riches and a level of well-being which no previous society could have even imagined, much less provided.

The new potentialities were becoming the heritage of all mankind, not merely of the privileged few. The sense of equal entitlement to the means for a decent life had taken hold of all manner of men, within nations and throughout the world community, whether in industrially developed or newly developing countries, in centres of old empires or among peoples emerging from colonialism, in socialist or free enterprise societies, and whether under communist, democratic or even dictatorial rule. Equality of status had become an accepted principle in most of the world, as monarchical, aristocratic and other systems of rank and class had been discarded, disabilities imposed on women had been removed, and measures to implement concepts of equality were being applied with some effectiveness within different social systems. An ever widening range of education, opportunities for recreation, facilities for the welfare of children and the handicapped, and a multitude of other services and amenities were being provided for the entire population in many areas. Remaining limitations on universal suffrage were being withdrawn. Virtually every state was using its taxing power to bring about greater equality by deriving tax revenue from those able to pay and dedicating it to services for the benefit of all.

Racial superiority, so dominant a feature of human society in the past, was declining sharply through all but a very small part of the world. The European white man no longer dominated the darker peoples of the earth. Although in a few places groups fought desperately to hold a superior position on the basis of race, the principle of equality of status was being extended, both within mixed societies and in the world community. The one issue on which there was near unanimity in the United Nations was opposition to racialism.

Literature and the arts were no longer the cultural inheritance of an educated *élite*. They were reaching the people as a whole, who made up the mass audiences and were beginning to participate in creative activity. Men had not yet however found the means to give full expression to their new experiences and the new social forces that were taking shape. They had broken through traditional conventions and forms of expression, to explore new psychological depths, new social forces and man's new relation to the physical universe. The period had been rich in experimentation, but new styles had not yet been developed which would permit a flowering of expression comparable to that which had occurred in great ages of the past.

Cultural expression throughout the world, however, was taking on a quality of universality. Before the twentieth century the literature and arts of each culture area had been set off in compartments; the cultural expression of China and India and of the Islamic peoples was little known or shared by the people of the West, and although the political dominance of the West gave to other peoples a certain superficial knowledge of the culture of Europe, only rarely did this make a deep or lasting impact. By the middle of the twentieth century peoples of all parts of the world were aware of other cultures, and although their understanding and appreciation was limited they recognized that each culture had values of its own which were important for mankind as a whole. Nearly everywhere there was a double tendency—to foster indigenous expression and to seek to understand, appreciate and embrace the expression of others.

A new world society was in fact emerging in which many different people were all playing an active part. The first half of the twentieth century brought to an end four centuries of European expansion and world dominance and reduced Europe to the position of only one among several dynamic centres of culture and of power. At the middle of the century, western Europe was flanked by two great areas, America and Russia, continental in size, with fast growing populations and still unexploited resources, which were developing new, dynamic societies. On the continent of Asia, ancient, populous and historically civilized societies, most notably China and India with a population between them of a thousand millions, were taking their place in the world, impelled by vital urges and mastering and utilizing the new scientific knowledge and its technologies to build up social and industrial strength. Within the Americas the growing importance of the Latin American states gave evidence of their great potentialities, while the stirring of new life on the continent of Africa made it clear by the middle of the century that the emergence of the African people into the world community was a new and vital fact in the history of mankind.

The reduction in the relative position of Europe and the reinstatement of other regions as units in world history restored a balance among societies which had been destroyed by the extension of European power. But now the several centres of dynamic power in Asia, Europe, America and Africa were not self-contained and cut off from each other as they had been in the days before Columbus and Vasco da Gama linked Europe with the West and the East. They were interrelated and interacting one upon the other, for distance was no longer a divider and no society was isolated from the vital currents which flowed from all parts of the world.

Mankind thus enjoyed immeasurably greater prospects for the enrichment of life than ever before, and the benefits of man's new powers over nature were being extended to all manner of men and to all peoples. Yet man also faced graver dangers than ever in the past: on the one hand, a rate of population increase such as even Malthus had not imagined; on the other hand, powers of destruction which could bring annihilation.

The conquest of diseases and better preventive measures had already raised the life expectancy of men in progressive societies to double that of less developed communities, and the spread of medical knowledge was rapidly extending the same trend to other areas. As death rates fell sharply, population mounted ominously in areas which were struggling to shake off their age-old burdens of hunger and poverty. On a world-wide basis, calculations of the earth's potential for producing food gave no cause for concluding that food supply could not keep pace with population growth, and the actual threat of famine had been reduced by increased agricultural productivity and improved transport. But the political organization of the world was not such as to bring together hungry peoples and the vacant lands which remained on the globe, and the anomaly of food surpluses in some areas and chronic hunger in others continued to confront mankind. And even more serious than the question of food was the burden of a rapidly expanding population on all manner of facilities in countries scarcely able to provide the barest minimum in education, housing, water supply, transport and other necessities, especially when they were trying to devote their energies and resources to expanding the base for their economic development.

The explosive force of rapidly expanding population was a factor in the world situation which mankind in the middle of the twentieth century had hardly begun to face. Differential rates of growth were expanding the newly developing areas, not only absolutely but relative to the areas which had been economically dominant, altering relationships among peoples. At the rate at which world population was then increasing, the world would be filled to its maximum capacity, by any system of calculation, within measurable time.

Few nations, within themselves, had made successful efforts to adjust the relation between their people and their resources. Among nations, population pressures were a continuing source of tension. The demand for *Lebensraum* had ceased to be the basis for colonial expansion when colonialism came into disrepute, but the pressure behind the claim had not abated. The open doors of the New World through which millions of immigrants from Europe had poured in the nineteenth and early twentieth centuries were closed and only a trickle of the old stream continued to flow, but an emigrant potential was present in many parts of the world.

Mankind in the middle of the century was more conscious of the threatened destruction of human life than of dangers from its multiplication, for from the moment when the first atomic bomb was dropped on Hiroshima men knew that this was but a portent of the capacity for self-destruction which man had discovered and let loose. No previous generation ever faced the danger to humanity itself inherent in the new weapons of ever greater and more incalculable power. Knowing that wars in the past had been unleashed by men in their pride without counting the cost to humanity, mankind could find little assurance in the often expressed hope that the very magnitude of the danger would act as a deterrent to the use of the terrible weapons and would save man from destroying himself.

The drama of the mid-twentieth century was thus projected on a new scale of almost unlimited hopes and unlimited threats, of high possibilities for the realization of human potentialities and of supreme dangers, of immense powers in the hands of men, far beyond the forms of power known in the past. The power of modern science to alter the conditions provided by nature for the earth changed the situation of mankind as radically as did the discovery of fire, or the movement from the stone to the metal age. The environment within which man lived became increasingly man-made. Man himself had the power to determine whether this environment would increase his survival or terminate it, whether it would foster his physical, emotional, intellectual and spiritual development or restrict and menace it, and which of his many potentialities it would favour and which suppress.

The unprecedented power of science created a new priestly caste, the scientists, who alone could exercise the ultimate power which scientific knowledge conveys. Mankind had become dependent on this class, beyond the dependence of earlier societies on the priests who knew the mysteries. It was deeply affected by the character of the scientists and technicians, their distribution through society, the structure through which they functioned and the factors which determined the uses to which their knowledge would be put.

As among the peoples and societies of the earth, those which rested upon a base of developed science held power over those which did not command scientific knowledge and processes, whether or not they enjoyed political independence and national status. Europe's dominance in the nineteenth century had rested on such a base. In the twentieth century the disparity between the scientific and non-scientific societies increased immeasurably, while at the same time the command of scientific knowledge spread from old centres to new ones, altering in a major way the balance among nations and peoples. The contest among the world's peoples for status or dominance had become inexorably a contest to command this power. Concepts of freedom, independence, sovereignty and status had come to have meaning fundamentally in terms of the mastery of scientific knowledge.

States of continental size, with large populations and with natural resources covering essential requirements had obvious advantages in the technological age over smaller units, however progressive and advanced they might be. Although the twentieth century saw the break-up of the few great empires which had dominated the world and the birth of a multitude of independent, sovereign nations, the tendency was toward the emergence of a few states of great size and power—the USA and the USSR in dominant positions at mid-century, China and India rising, Brazil seeing itself as a future great state of continental proportions—and toward the grouping of smaller units into blocks or closer federations—the Common European Market, the Arab states, the Organization of American States, the moves toward Pan-African unity. In the middle years of the century these trends were pulling the world into parts —communist, anti-communist and neutralist—and the contest among these great divisions was becoming more and more a test of strength through the command and application of the resources of science.

The power which science had placed at the disposal of man could be utilized only with immense and increasingly complicated organization—political, industrial and technical. Without a very great measure of direction, on a scale rarely attempted in the past, the new forces opened up by science could not be harnessed effectively. The entire shape of economic life underwent revolutionary changes, in capitalist as well as in communist and mixed economies. The mammoth corporations which alone could command the resources, technical skills and capacity for continuing scientific research had become huge centres of scientific inquiry, social life and economic dynamism. Over a larger and larger part of the world these vast industrial complexes were coming to constitute the units of which society was composed. The state, in turn, could not fail to assume more and more power, for even if it did not wish to organize production activities itself it had to exercise control in relation to the use of such great powers by others.

Great organizations were thus inescapable and dominant factors in the life of mankind, whether in the form of giant industrial corporations or of the all-pervasive state, or of lesser associations through which men sought to organize their lives and to cope with the new forces. These were the new

Leviathans, and the magnitude of the power with which they confronted the individual far exceeded that which he had faced in the past. Earlier societies had been composed of scattered and more or less isolated units—villages, tribes, cities, regions—separated by distance and geographical barriers, where effective power was confined and limited by lack of communication. Now there was no spot on the globe where men lived in self-contained isolation, beyond the long arm and the insistent voice of power, organized on a gigantic scale.

The inevitable concentrations of power could not fail to affect the status of the individual. The supreme value of the individual, which had been proclaimed in the revolutionary doctrine of 'liberty, equality and fraternity', remained a vital part of the heritage of the twentieth century and a dynamic concept in the political evolution of those years. The modern state, based on universal suffrage, was committed to the welfare of all the people and it offered its citizens a vast array of services and protections which earlier states had not thought it necessary or appropriate to provide. At the same time, the relation of the individual to society was inescapably changed as the modern state entered into every sphere of life, equipped with powerful instruments to compel or induce conformity to its policies and purposes.

There were basic differences in the position of the individual within different systems of organization and authority. Where all power rested in an all-embracing, centrally administered state, the individual derived his role from the policies of the state. These might call for his self-improvement and his active participation in planning and achieving common goals, or at the other extreme they might require his unquestioning acquiescence in the judgment of those in command, devoted subjection to their authority, and sacrifice of individual ends. In all cases the scope of individual initiative was defined by the higher authority and all roles and responsibilities were ultimately related to a common purpose.

Where, however, a number of organizations acted in some measure as independent centres of power, their countervailing forces tended to balance each other and to leave the individual with latitude to exercise a wide range of choice and initiative. The individual retained a considerable measure of freedom and scope in societies where labour organization confronted organized management, corporations competed one with another, religious organization counterbalanced secular authority, military organization was subject to civil powers, organized farmers could influence public policy, an entrenched civil service was secure against political interference, an independent judiciary could apply accepted principles of law, and political parties could compete freely for political control. Yet here also it was through organized groups that the individual must generally function in order to make a place for himself in modern society.

The power of science and the power of organization brought both an intellectual and a moral crisis in the life of mankind. Intellectually, the question was whether men had the capacity to understand the complexities of the forces which they had loosed and to imagine new kinds of order which would replace the orders of nature which they had learned to manipulate or destroy. Morally, the crisis arose from the collapse of many values and the conflict among those which remained, and from the disparity between the power which men held in their hands and the weakness, uncertainty or contradiction in the guides to its use. These had become the great issues of the second half of the twentieth century.

The enormous complexity of the forces which men had let loose defied man's understanding. Patterns of air traffic became so complex that human observation and calculation no longer sufficed to keep speeding jets out of collision paths; electronic devices operating more swiftly and precisely than human senses and thought, were taking over the control of the air from the men in the control towers and the men at the controls of the planes. But these electronic brains in turn depended upon men's ability both to feed them the right information and to keep them in perfect operation. Expanding cities and proliferating highways encroached on each other and on the countryside, creating more problems for every one that they solved. Agricultural surpluses piled up in some areas while hunger stalked in other parts of the world. The conquest of disease and the resulting increase in survival and lengthening of the life span impinged on many institutions. To grasp these complexities, to foresee the impact of each change, to calculate the interaction of innumerable factors demanded knowledge and thought far beyond that demanded by former societies where a much smaller part of life was subject to modification by the actions of man. And it demanded knowledge and thought by more people, for complex forces played upon individuals in all walks of life and few could limit their understanding and guides for action to matters within their direct experience as most men had done in the past.

The changing world conditions challenged men's capacity to envision the desirable and the possible when the old orders would no longer suffice to contain the new powers and potentialities The institutions, relationships and social ideas of the period of the first industrial revolution could not be expected to absorb the changes wrought by the atomic age. New patterns must be conceived. What concepts of the good life were compatible with the new situation and took advantage of the new potentialities? What relations among peoples, nations, groups and individuals could be sustained and could foster the development of human potentialities? What balance of countervailing forces could maintain an essential degree of stability and yet keep open the door of freedom and opportunity for individuals, groups and peoples? What controls could hold in check destructive or overweening forces? Without the vision of new order, man could only fumble with old forms.

The moral issue was whether a new morality for a scientific age was to be found in science itself, or whether any of the historic formulations of moral values and sanctions were sufficient in the new situation. Scientists themselves faced an ethical dilemma. Science had its own morality for the pursuit of knowledge—relentless search, freedom of mind, utter honesty in observing and reporting, mutual co-operation in the common quest for truth. But scientists did not traditionally extend these values to the application of knowledge, for in this area it was not the values of science but those of the society that reigned. Other professions had their ethics for the use of scientific knowledge—the medical profession for healing, the military profession for destruction. But with the terrible possibilities that had been unleashed, scientists began to question their own neutrality in relation to the application of their knowledge and to ask whether they did not have a special responsibility, at least to make the potential effects of their discoveries known to the public and to those concerned with policy.

Value systems inherited from the past were embedded in the social fabric of all societies and they inevitably formed a part of the approach to new situations. In respect to each of these systems, two issues presented themselves: what values might have validity, and who would decide which should serve as guides.

Each of the great religions was asserting itself with renewed vitality in the middle of the century, but it remained a question whether any or all of them furnished a basis for making the kinds of decisions that men were called upon to make in the new age, and whether they offered sufficiently powerful sanctions to give effect to the moral judgments which they might prescribe. The morality of socialism was being invoked in large parts of the world; yet it had been formulated by Marx in the age of early technology and elaborated by Lenin in the beginning period of the scientific revolution of the twentieth century.

In the value system of liberal democracy, the basic principle of individual worth was implemented by dependence upon the self-direction of the individual and the collective wisdom of the people; but however appropriate the concept *vox populi, vox Dei* might have been in pre-technological days when decisions related to things about which people could have direct knowledge, it seemed less likely that wisdom would reside in the collective will in respect to problems of the atomic age. At the opposite extreme the 'leadership principle' placed full responsibility for moral judgment upon an individual whose intuition and personal conviction, whatever its basis, would provide a guide for his followers and relieve them of the moral burden; but the danger in this principle had been revealed by its main twentieth-century proponents, and this danger grew with each increase in potential power over the material universe and the minds of men. Collective leadership by a dedicated group might provide some of the technical knowledge which the people as a whole lacked and avoid the caprice of a single leader; but such leadership, too, required a basis for responsible decision.

Perhaps the central moral challenge to a world in which all people professed adherence to the Universal Declaration of Human Rights was whether man could find human terms in which to build a system of values, whether dedication to the cause of mankind could provide sanctions for such a system, and whether human values could be related to the order found in nature. In a society where great power was inherent and pervasive, what would sustain human compassion and respect for the essential dignity of every man? Once the old, limited concept of 'natural order' had been destroyed, could science yield insight into a deeper level of natural order where unifying principles and relationships might be found which would favour human development and could act both as guides and as sanctions for conduct?

These had become momentous issues for mankind—not for one race or one nation or group of nations, not for one class or one creed, but for all the earth's people.

Faced with these issues, men in the second half of the twentieth century had a new view of progress. Through much of human history men did not think in terms of progress but of fixed orders, timeless and eternal, the stage on which man lived his brief life and other men would lead theirs after him. The fixed social order continued to provide the image of man's life on earth in the societies of Asia and in the tribal societies elsewhere in the world even up to the twentieth century.

In the western world, from the time of the Renaissance, and especially from the scientific revolution of the seventeenth century, men no longer saw society as fixed but as capable of progress—of change for the better. In the eighteenth century progress involved the removal of imperfections which kept human society from the state of perfection inherent in the natural order. With the enunciation of the theory of evolution, progress itself was seen as part of the natural order. In the view put forth by Karl Marx, progress occurs through a dialectical process in which the struggle of two contending systems of production always leads to the victory of the higher one—the feudal form being essentially higher than the form based on slavery which it superseded, the capitalist form higher than the feudal, the socialist than the capitalist, and the ultimate and highest form, communism. When the twentieth century opened, western society saw progress, whether evolutionary or revolutionary, as inevitable; it might be accelerated or retarded by the conscious efforts of man, but it was the sure direction of human development.

The concept of the static society and the concept of automatic evolutionary progress were destroyed by the events of the first half of the twentieth century. Formerly static societies glimpsed the possibilities of change and set themselves on new paths. In Europe, however, there were many people, representative of a wide range of viewpoint, who saw that new powers could be evil as well as beneficent in effect and came to believe that the idea of automatic progress was worse than an illusion. They saw it as a dangerous superstition which prevented men from recognizing the awful threats in scientific and technical development uncontrolled by a parallel development in morality. In part this view was a reflection of the decline in the position of Europe as a result of the shift of power. But in part it was a cry of danger, a warning that men were not fearing atomic destruction enough because they were spellbound by the traditional idea of progress.

Yet outside western Europe the idea of progress remained as living a concept as it had ever been. It lived in the United States and in other parts of the New World, not so much as an elaborated theory but as the outlook of young societies in the process of achieving material well-being and with great resources at their command. It lived, also, in the new nation-states of Asia and Africa as the mental counterpart of their determined drive for industrialization and modernization. But its stronghold was in the communist orbit, wherever Marxism was a living force, for it was the corner-stone of Marxian thought. Since, in this view, the superstructure of society always follows the basic system of production, man is bound to grow with his self-shaped forces of production and, to the extent that he lives up to the task put before him by history, progress is assured.

In the outlook of mankind at the middle of the twentieth century, progress thus appeared as a possibility which man might grasp. The challenge was one of choice. No society in the past had even begun to give full scope to the potentialities of all its people, and only the great figures of all ages and cultures had shown by their intellectual power, their sensitivity of perception, their spiritual force and their capacity for human relationships some of the possibilities inherent in the human species. Man's new powers had given him some of the means to create a social and physical environment favourable to the richer development of human life on a broader scale than ever before—if, and only if, he would use them to that end. Man might fall by the way or scale new heights, but whichever his destiny he would bring it about by his own use of his new powers.

BIBLIOGRAPHY

The scope of the subject matter treated in this volume precludes the inclusion of a systematic bibliography. Even when limited to the language of the text, any comprehensive and balanced list of references would be monumental and any list of references dealing with contemporary history is bound to become out of date even before it is in print. Furthermore, since material relating to individual countries has been used in the text mainly to illustrate broad tendencies rather than for its own sake, and since technical subjects have been considered in relation to general scientific and cultural developments in non-technical terms for the non-technical reader, bibliographical references may appropriately be limited to these same purposes.

With these considerations in mind, the author-editors have selected items for each chapter as follows:

1. The general bibliography is confined to guides and to world histories which include a substantial consideration of the recent past.
2. Books relating to the general political development of these years are listed with chapters I—III, and those relating to general economic and social developments with chapters IV and V.
3. Books relating to individual countries and specific social movements are listed in connection with chapters XXVIII, XXIX and XXX.
4. Publications relating to scientific thought, the development of knowledge and various forms of expression are mentioned in the text of the chapters dealing with these subjects. Bibliographies for these chapters, VI, VII, VIII, XIII, XVI, XX, XXXI, XXXII, merely add a few works of general reference, where such are available.
5. Chapters on the application of scientific knowledge—IX-XII, XIV, XV, XVII-XIX—and on the transformation of social institutions—XXI-XXVII—are supplemented by brief lists of works which treat the subjects in comprehensive or comparative terms or which approach a limited area or aspect in a manner to illumine the broader field.
6. In general, books referred to in the text are not repeated in the bibliographies.
7. With a very few exceptions the following are excluded:
    (a) Books published since 1960.
    (b) Magazine articles and pamphlets.
    (c) Books not available in English.

BIBLIOGRAPHY—GENERAL

A substantial body of material dealing with cultural and scientific developments on a global scale is contained in the reports, studies and other publications of international organizations, both official bodies, i.e. the United Nations and its specialized agencies, and non-official. The official agencies publish lists of their publications. For the publications of unofficial agencies, consult the *Directory of International Scientific Organizations* published by UNESCO, Paris, which describes the scope of these organizations and lists their publications.

AMERICAN HISTORICAL ASSOCIATION, *Guide to Historical Literature* (New York, 1961).

AMERICAN UNIVERSITIES FIELD STAFF, *A Select Bibliography: Asia, Africa, Eastern Europe, Latin America* (New York, 1960).

MONTAGUE F. ASHLEY MONTAGU, (ed.), *Toynbee and History: Critical Essays and Reviews* (Boston, 1956).

GEORGES BALANDIER and J. F. M. MIDDLETON, (eds.), *International Index of Social and Cultural Anthropology* (New York, 1958).

ERICH H. BOEHM, (ed.), *Historical Abstracts*, 1775–1945 (Vienna, 1955–), quarterly

MAURICE CROUZET, (ed.), *Histoire générale des civilisations* (Paris, 1953–59), 7 vols.

LUIS DIEZ DEL CORRAL, *The Rape of Europe* (trans. by H. V. Livermore, London, 1959).

ALOIS FISCHER, *Neue Weltstatistik: Zahlen, Daten, Karten,* (2nd ed., Vienna, 1952).

PATRICK GARDINER, (ed.), *Theories of History* (Glencoe, Illinois, 1959).

A. GRANDIN, *Bibliographie générale des sciences juridiques, politiques, économiques et sociales de* 1800 à 1925–26 (Paris, 1926–   ), 3 vols, with annual supplement.

S. HOFSTRA, (ed.), *Eastern and Western World: Selected Readings* (The Hague and Bandung, 1953).

INTERNATIONAL COMMITTEE OF HISTORICAL SCIENCES, *International Bibliography of Historical Sciences* (Paris, 1926–   ), annual.

INTERNATIONAL INSTITUTE OF DIFFERING CIVILIZATIONS, *International Guide to Study Centers on Civilizations and their Publications* (Brussels, 1955).

ANNA et ANDRÉ LEJARD, (eds.), *Cinquante années de découvertes: Bilan* 1900–1950 (Paris, 1950).

GOLO MANN and ALFRED HUESS, (eds.), *Propyläen Weltgeschichte* (Berlin, 1960–62), 10 vols.

New Cambridge Modern History (Cambridge, 1957–62), 10 vols.

ROBERT R. PALMER, (ed.), *Atlas of World History* (Chicago, 1957).

ALEXANDER RUESTOW, *Ortsbestimmung der Gegenwart: eine universalgeschichtliche Kulturkritik,* (Erlenbach and Zurich, 1950–57), 3 vols.

ARNOLD J. TOYNBEE, *A Study of History,* (New York and London, 1948–1961), 12 vols.

UNESCO, *International Bibliography of Sociology* (Paris, 1952–   ), annual.

UNESCO, *International Bibliography of Political Science* (Paris, 1953–   ), annual.

UNESCO, *International Bibliography of Economics* (Paris, 1955–   ), annual.

UNESCO, *International Political Science Abstracts* (Paris, 1951–   ), quarterly.

UNITED NATIONS, *Statistical Yearbook* (New York, 1948–   ), annual.

BARBARA WARD, *The Interplay of East and West: Elements of Contrast and Co-operation* (London, 1957).

CAROLINE F. WARE, (ed.), *The Cultural Approach to History* (New York, 1940).

WALTER P. WEBB, *The Great Frontier: an Interpretation of World History since Columbus* (Boston, 1952).

W. S. WOYTINSKY, *Die Welt in Zahlen* (Berlin, 1925–28), 7 vols.

EUGENY M. ZHUKOV *et al.,* (eds.), *Vsemirnaia Istoriia* (Moscow, 1955–   ), 10 vols.

CHAPTER I

THE SHIFT IN WORLD POWER

RENÉ ALBRECHT-CARRIÉ, *A Diplomatic History of Europe since the Congress of Vienna* (New York, 1958).

G. L. ARNOLD, *The Pattern of World Conflict* (New York, 1955).

MAX BELOFF, *The Foreign Policy of Soviet Russia,* 1929–1941 (London and New York, 1947–49), 2 vols.

SAMUEL F. BEMIS, *The United States as a World Power: A Diplomatic History, 1900–1955* (rev. ed., New York, 1955).

MORITZ J. BONN, *The Crumbling of Empire* (London, 1938).

DENIS W. BROGAN, *The Era of Franklin D. Roosevelt* (New Haven, 1950).

EDWARD H. CARR, *The Bolshevik Revolution, 1917–1923* (London, 1950–53), 3 vols.

EDWARD H. CARR, *The Soviet Impact on the Western World* (New York, 1947).

WINSTON S. CHURCHILL, *The Second World War* (London and Boston, 1948–53), 6 vols.

GORDON A. CRAIG and FELIX GILBERT, *The Diplomats, 1919–1939* (Princeton, N.J., 1953).

DAVID J. DALLIN, *The Rise of Russia in Asia* (New Haven, 1949).

FOSTER R. DULLES, *America's Rise to World Power, 1898–1954* (New York, 1955).

ERIC FISCHER, *The Passing of the European Age* (rev. ed., Cambridge, Mass., 1948).

GEOFREY M. GATHORNE-HARDY, *A Short History of International Affairs, 1920–39* (4th ed., London and New York, 1950).

CHARLES DE GAULLE, *War Memoirs* (trans. by J. Griffin and Richard Howard, New York, 1955–60), 3 vols.

ERNEST B. HAAS, *The Uniting of Europe: Political, Social and Economic Forces, 1950–1957* (Stanford, 1959).

S. WILLIAM HALPERIN, *Germany Tried Democracy: a Political History of the Reich from 1918 to 1933* (New York, 1946).

HENRY V. HODSON, *Slump and Recovery, 1929–1937: a Survey of World Economic Affairs* (London and New York, 1938).

HAJO HOLBORN, *The Political Collapse of Europe* (New York, 1951).

YAMATO ICHIHASHI, *The Washington Conference and After: A Historical Survey* (Stanford, California, 1928).

JOHN H. JACKSON, *The Post-War Decade: a Short History of the World, 1945–1955* (London, 1955).

OSZKÁR JÁSZI, *The Dissolution of the Hapsburg Monarchy* (Chicago, 1929).

BRUNO LASKER, *Books on Southeast Asia: a Select Bibliography* (rev. ed., New York, 1959).

C. A. MACARTNEY, *Hungary and Her Successors: The Treaty of Trianon and its Consequences, 1919–1937* (London, 1937).

FRANZ H. MICHAEL and GEORGE E. TAYLOR, *The Far East in the Modern World* (New York, 1956).

K. M. PANIKKAR, *The Afro-Asian States and Their Problems* (London and New York, 1959).

K. M. PANIKKAR, *Asia and Western Dominance: a Survey of the Vasco da Gama Epoch of Asian History, 1498–1945* (London, 1953).

HARRY B. PRICE, *The Marshall Plan and its Meaning* (Ithaca, N.Y., 1955).

JAN M. ROMEIN, *The Asian Century* (London and Berkeley, 1962).

ROYAL INSTITUTE OF INTERNATIONAL AFFAIRS, *Atlantic Alliance: NATO's Role in the Free World*, compiled by Donald McLachlan (London and New York, 1952).

HUGH SETON-WATSON, *Eastern Europe Between the Two Wars, 1918–1941* (2nd ed., Cambridge, 1946).

HUGH SETON-WATSON, *Neither War nor Peace: The Struggle for Power in the Postwar World* (New York, 1960).

WILLIAM L. SHIRER, *The Rise and Fall of the Third Reich* (New York, 1960).

IVAR SPECTOR, *The Soviet Union and the Muslim World, 1917–1956* (rev. ed., Seattle, 1958).

LEON TROTSKY, *The History of the Russian Revolution* (trans. by Max Eastman, Ann Arbor, Mich., 1947), 3 vols.

DIXON WECTER, *The Age of the Great Depression, 1929–1941* (New York, 1948).

PATRICK G. WILSON, *Government and Politics of India and Pakistan, 1885–1955: A Bibliography of Works in Western Languages* (Berkeley, Calif., 1956).

GUY A. WINT, *The British in Asia* (rev. ed., London and New York, 1954, 1955).

MAURICE ZINKIN, *Asia and the West* (rev. ed., London and New York, 1953).

CHAPTER II
THE IMPACT OF NATIONALISM AND TREND TOWARD INTERNATIONAL CO-OPERATION
Nationalism

ALFRED COBBAN, *National Self-Determination* (rev. ed., Chicago, 1948).

KARL W. DEUTSCH, *Interdisciplinary Bibliography on Nationalism* (Cambridge, Mass., 1956).

KARL W. DEUTSCH, *Nationalism and Social Communication: An Inquiry into the Foundations of Nationality* (Boston and New York, 1953).

RUPERT EMERSON, *From Empire to Nation: The Rise to Self-Assertion of Asian and African Peoples* (Cambridge, Mass., 1960).

CARLTON J. H. HAYES, *Essays on Nationalism* (New York, 1926).

HANS KOHN, *Nationalism, Its Meaning and History* (Princeton, N.J., 1955).

ROYAL INSTITUTE OF INTERNATIONAL AFFAIRS, *Nationalism: A Report by a Study Group* (London and New York, 1939).

PHILIP W. THAYER, (ed.), *Nationalism and Progress in Free Asia* (Baltimore, Md., 1956).

International Co-operation

ROBERT E. ASHER et al., *The United Nations and Promotion of the General Welfare* (Washington, D.C., 1957).

HANS AUFRICHT, *Guide to League of Nations Publications: A Bibliographical Survey of the Work of the League, 1920–1947* (New York, 1951).

ROBERT BERKOV, *The World Health Organization* (Geneva, 1957).

CHARLES G. FENWICK, *The Inter-American Regional System* (New York, 1949).

LELAND M. GOODRICH and EDVARD I. HAMBRO, *Charter of the United Nations: Commentary and Documents* (second ed., Boston, 1949).

HESSEL DUNCAN HALL, *Mandates, Dependencies and Trusteeship* (Washington, D.C., 1948).

GOVE HAMBIDGE, *The Story of FAO* (New York, 1955).

MANLEY O. HUDSON, *The Permanent Court of International Justice, 1920–1942* (rev. ed., New York, 1943).

INTERNATIONAL LABOUR OFFICE, *The International Labour Organization: The First Decade* (London, 1931).

WALTER H. C. LAVES and CHARLES A. THOMSON, *UNESCO: Purpose, Progress, Prospects* (Bloomington, Ind., 1957).

OLIVER J. LISSITZYN, *The International Court of Justice: Its Role in the Maintenance of International Peace and Security* (New York, 1951).

ANDREW MARTIN, *Collective Security: A Progress Report* (Paris, 1952).

AMOS J. PEASLEE (ed.), *International Governmental Organizations: Constitutional Documents* (The Hague, 1956), 2 vols.

WILLIAM E. RAPPARD, *The Quest for Peace since the World War* (Cambridge, Mass., 1940).

WALTER SCHIFFER, *The Legal Community of Mankind: A Critical Analysis of the Modern Concept of World Organization* (New York, 1954).

FREDERICK L. SCHUMAN, *The Commonwealth of Man: An Inquiry into Power Politics and World Government* (New York, 1952).

JULIUS STONE, *Aggression and World Order: A Critique of United Nations Theories of Aggression* (Berkeley and Los Angeles, Calif., 1958).

CHARMIAN E. TOUSSAINT, *The Trusteeship System of the United Nations* (London and New York, 1956).

UNITED NATIONS, *Everyman's United Nations: The Structure, Function and Work of the Organization and Its Related Agencies During the Years 1945–1958* (New York, 1959).

FRANCIS P. WALTERS, *A History of the League of Nations,* (London and New York, 1952), 2 vols.

QUINCY WRIGHT, *Mandates Under the League of Nations* (Chicago, 1930).

ALFRED E. ZIMMERN, *The League of Nations and the Rule of Law, 1918–1935* (2nd. ed., London, 1939).

CHAPTER III

THE NEW ROLE OF THE STATE AND ITS COMPETING FORMS
(See also Chapter XXIII)

The Inclusive State

WILLIAM H. BEVERIDGE, *Social Insurance and Allied Services: Report* (London and New York, 1942).

SOLOMON FABRICANT and R. E. LIPSEY, *Trend of Government Activity in the United States since 1900* (New York, 1953).

MARY P. FOLLETT, *The New State: Group Organization the Solution of Popular Government* (New York, 1918).

HAROLD J. LASKI, *Authority in the Modern State* (New Haven, 1919).

HAROLD J. LASKI, *Liberty in the Modern State* (London, 1930).

ROBERT M. MACIVER, *The Modern State* (Oxford, 1926).

THOMAS E. UTLEY and J. STUART MACLURE, (eds.), *Documents of Modern Political Thought* (Cambridge, 1957).

Liberal Democracy

CARL L. BECKER, *Modern Democracy* (New Haven, 1941).

JOHN DEWEY, *Freedom and Culture* (New York, 1939).

WILLIAM Y. ELLIOTT, *The Pragmatic Revolt in Politics* (New York, 1928).

THOMAS G. MASARYK, *The Making of a State* (New York and London, 1927).

T. ROLAND PENNOCK, *Liberal Democracy: Its Merits and Prospects* (New York, 1950).

Challenges to Liberal Democracy

G. D. H. COLE, *A History of Socialist Thought*, (London, 1953–56), 4 vols.

G. D. H. COLE, *Fabian Socialism* (London, 1943).

E. F. M. DURBIN, *Politics of Democratic Socialism* (London and Toronto, 1940).

JOSEPH A. SCHUMPETER, *Capitalism, Socialism and Democracy* (3rd. ed., New York, 1950).

GEORGES SOREL, *Reflections on Violence* (trans. by T. E. Hulme, New York, 1914).

Fascism

WILLIAM EBENSTEIN, *The Nazi State* (New York and Toronto, 1943).

HERMAN FINER, *Mussolini's Italy* (London and New York, 1935).

GUY STANTON FORD, (ed.), *Dictatorship in the Modern World* (2nd ed., Minneapolis, 1939).

CARL J. FRIEDRICH and Z. K. BRZEZINSKI, *Totalitarian Dictatorship and Autocracy* (Cambridge, Mass., 1956).

ADOLF HITLER, *Mein Kampf* (trans. under direction of Alvin Johnson, New York, 1939).

BENITO MUSSOLINI, *The Corporate State* (2nd ed., Florence, 1938).

FRANZ L. NEUMANN, *Behemoth: The Structure and Practice of National Socialism, 1933–1944* (2nd ed., New York and Toronto, 1944).

GAETANO SALVEMINI, *The Fascist Dictatorship in Italy* (New York, 1927).

Communism

CENTRAL COMMITTEE OF THE COMMUNIST PARTY OF THE SOVIET UNION, *History of the Communist Party of the Soviet Union* (New York, 1939).

MILOVAN DJILAS, *The New Class* (New York, 1957).

KARL KAUTSKY, *Social Democracy vs. Communism* (ed. and trans. by D. Shub and J. Shaplen, New York, 1946).

V. I. LENIN, *Collected Works* (authorized trans., New York, 1927).

MAO TSE-TUNG, *The Chinese Revolution and the Chinese Communist Party* (Peking, 1954).

ROYAL INSTITUTE OF INTERNATIONAL AFFAIRS, *The Soviet–Yugoslav Dispute* (London and New York, 1948).

HUGH SETON-WATSON, *From Lenin to Krushchev: The History of World Communism* (New York, 1960).

JOSEF STALIN, *Leninism* [*Foundations of Leninism; Problems of Leninism*] (trans. by E. and C. Paul, London, 1928–33), 2 vols.

SIDNEY and BEATRICE WEBB, *Soviet Communism: A New Civilisation?* (London and New York, 1935).

CHAPTER IV

THE TRIUMPH OF INDUSTRIALISM

(See also Chapters IX and XXI)

PAUL ALPERT, *Twentieth Century Economic History of Europe* (New York, 1951).

JULIUS H. BOEKE, *Economics and Economic Policy of Dual Societies, as Exemplified by Indonesia* (New York, 1953).

WILSON BRAND, *The Struggle for a Higher Standard of Living: The Problem of Underdeveloped Countries* (Glencoe, Ill., 1958).

NORMAN S. BUCHANAN and HOWARD S. ELLIS, *Approaches to Economic Development* (New York, 1955).

J. H. CLAPHAM, *An Economic History of Modern Britain:* Vol. III, *Machines and National Rivalries* (1887–1914) *with an Epilogue* (1914–29) (New York and Cambridge, 1938).

COLIN CLARK, *The Conditions of Economic Progress* (3rd ed., London and New York, 1957).

HENRY DAVID *et al.*, (eds.), *The Economic History of the United States* (New York, 1945–), 9 vols.

J. FREDERIC DEWHURST, *et al.*, *America's Needs and Resources: A New Survey* (New York, 1955).

J. FREDERIC DEWHURST *et al.*, *Europe's Needs and Resources: Trends and Prospects in Eighteen Countries* (New York and London, 1961).

MAURICE H. DOBB, *Soviet Economic Development since* 1917, (London and New York, 1948).

S. HERBERT FRANKEL, *The Economic Impact on Under-Developed Societies* (Oxford, 1953).

SIMON G. HANSON, *Economic Development in Latin America* (Washington, D.C., 1951).

EIJIRŌ HONJŌ, *The Social and Economic History of Japan* (Kyoto, 1935).

LLOYD J. HUGHLETT, (ed.), *Industrialization of Latin America* (New York, 1946).

PETR I. LIASHCHENKO, *History of the National Economy of Russia to the* 1917 *Revolution* (trans. by L. M. Herman, New York, 1949).

WILLIAM W. LOCKWOOD, *The Economic Development of Japan: Growth and Structural Change,* 1868–1938 (Princeton, N.J., 1954).

GUNNAR MYRDAL, *An International Economy: Problems and Prospects* (New York, 1956).

SERGEI N. PROKOPOVICH, *L'industrialisation des pays agricoles et la structure de l'économie mondiale après la guerre* (trans. by N. Nicolsky, Paris, 1946).

WALT W. ROSTOW, *The Process of Economic Growth* (2nd ed., Oxford, 1960).

FRED A. SHANNON, *America's Economic Growth* (3rd ed., New York, 1951).

EUGENE STALEY, *The Future of Underdeveloped Countries* (New York, 1954).

INGVAR SVENNILSON, *Growth and Stagnation in the European Economy* (Geneva, 1954).

W. S. WOYTINSKY and E. S. WOYTINSKY, *World Population and Production* (New York, 1953).

GEORGE WYTHE, *Industry in Latin America* (New York, 1945).

MAURICE ZINKIN, *Problems of Economic Development in Asia* (rev. ed., New York, 1954).

CHAPTER V

THE CHANGING SOCIETY

Industrial Society

CYRIL E. BLACK, (ed.), *The Transformation of Russian Society* (Cambridge, Mass., 1960).

G. D. H. COLE, *World in Transition* (New York, 1949).

GEORGES FRIEDMANN, (ed.), *Villes et campagnes: Civilisation urbaine et civilisation rurale en France* (Paris, 1953).

ERIC FROMM, *Escape from Freedom* (New York, 1941).

KAREN HORNEY, *The Neurotic Personality of our Time* (New York, 1937).

SEYMOUR M. LIPSET and REINHARD BENDIX, *Social Mobility in Industrial Society* (Berkeley and Los Angeles, Calif., 1958).

KARL MANNHEIM, *Man and Society in an Age of Reconstruction: Studies in Modern Social Structure* (London, 1940).

ELTON MAYO, *Social Problems of an Industrial Civilization* (Cambridge, Mass., 1945).

DAVID M. POTTER, *People of Plenty* (Chicago, 1954).

PRESIDENT'S RESEARCH COMMITTEE ON SOCIAL TRENDS, *Recent Social Trends in the United States* (New York, 1933), 2 vols.

ARNOLD M. ROSE, (ed.), *The Institutions of Advanced Societies* (Minneapolis, 1958).

UNITED NATIONS, *Report on the World Social Situation* (New York, 1957).

ERNEST WATKINS, *The Cautious Revolution* (London, 1951).

WILLIAM H. WHYTE, *The Organization Man* (New York, 1956).

Changing Non-Industrial Societies

GEORGES BALANDIER, *Sociologie actuelle de l'Afrique noire: Dynamique des changements sociaux en Afrique centrale* (Paris, 1955).

SYDNEY N. FISHER, (ed.), *Social Forces in the Middle East* (Ithaca, N.Y., 1955).

BERTHOLD F. HOSELITZ, *The Progress of Underdeveloped Areas* (Chicago, 1952).

MARGARET MEAD, (ed.), *Cultural Patterns and Technical Change* (Paris, 1953).

MARGARET MEAD, *New Lives for Old: Cultural Transformation—Manus, 1928-1953* (New York, 1956).

WILBERT E. MOORE, *Industrialization and Labor: Social Aspects of Economic Development* (Ithaca, N.Y., 1951).

JEROME F. SCOTT and R. P. LYNTON, *The Community Factor in Modern Technology* (Paris, 1952).

EDWARD H. SPICER, (ed.), *Human Problems in Technological Change: A Casebook* (New York, 1952).

UNESCO, 'Social Factors in Economic Growth: A Trend Report and Bibliography', *Current Sociology*, Vol. VI (Paris, 1957).

WILLEM F. WERTHEIM, *Indonesian Society in Transition: A Study of Social Change* (The Hague, 1956).

TAYA ZINKIN, *India Changes* (New York, 1958).

Population Movements and Changes (see also Chapter XV)

HARRISON S. BROWN, *The Challenge of Man's Future: An Inquiry Concerning the Condition of Man During the Years that Lie Ahead* (New York, 1954).

ALEXANDER M. CARR-SAUNDERS, *World Population: Past Growth and Present Trends* (Oxford, 1936).

H. A. CITROEN, *European Emigration Overseas: Past and Future* (The Hague, 1951).

OSCAR HANDLIN, *The Uprooted* (Boston, 1951).

PHILIP M. HAUSER, (ed.), *Population and World Politics* (Glencoe, Ill., 1958).

DUDLEY KIRK, *Europe's Population in the Interwar Years* (Princeton, N.J., 1946).

EUGENE M. KULISCHER, *Europe on the Move: War and Population Changes, 1917-1947* (New York, 1948).

POLITICAL and ECONOMIC PLANNING, *World Population and Resources: A Report* (London, 1955).

DONALD R. TAFT and RICHARD ROBBINS, *International Migrations: The Immigrant in the Modern World* (New York, 1955).

JACQUES VERNANT, *The Refugee in the Post-War World* (New Haven, 1953).

CHAPTER VI
THE NEW SCIENTIFIC THOUGHT

JACOB BRONOWSKI, *The Common Sense of Science* (London, 1951).

HERBERT DINGLE, (ed.), *A Century of Science, 1851-1951* (London and New York, 1951).

GERALD W. ELBERS and PAUL DUNCAN, (eds.), *Scientific Revolution: Challenge and Promise* (Washington, D.C., 1959).

PHILIPP FRANK, *Modern Science and Its Philosophy* (Cambridge, Mass., 1949).

EDWARD HUTCHINGS, (ed.), *Frontiers in Science: A Survey* (New York, 1958).

International Encyclopedia of Unified Science (Chicago, 1955–   ).

JOSEPH NEEDHAM and WALTER PAGEL, (eds.), *Background to Modern Science* (Cambridge, 1938–   ).

ALFRED NORTH WHITEHEAD, *Science and the Modern World* (New York, 1925).

LORANDA L. WOODRUFF, (ed.), *The Development of the Sciences* (New Haven, and London, 1941).

CHAPTER VII
MATHEMATICS AND LOGIC

NICOLAS BOURBAKI (pseud.), *Éléments de Mathématique* (Paris, 1940–1960), 6 vols.

ALONZO CHURCH, *Introduction to Mathematical Logic* (Princeton, N.J., 1956).

RICHARD COURANT and HERBERT ROBBINS, *What is Mathematics? An Elementary Approach to Ideas and Methods* (London and New York, 1941).

HOWARD EVES and CARROLL V. NEWSOM, *An Introduction to the Foundations and Fundamental Concepts of Mathematics* (New York, 1958).

WILLIAM FELLER, *An Introduction to Probability Theory and Its Application* (2nd ed., New York, 1957).

GODFREY H. HARDY, *A Mathematician's Apology* (Cambridge, 1940).

DAVID HILBERT, *The Foundations of Geometry* (trans. by E. J. Townsend, Chicago, 1902).

STEPHEN C. KLEENE, *Introduction to Metamathematics* (Amsterdam, 1952).

CLARENCE I. LEWIS and HAROLD L. COOPER, *A Survey of Symbolic Logic* (2nd ed., New York, 1959).

PAUL ROSENBLOOM, *The Elements of Mathematical Logic* (New York, 1950).

BERTRAND RUSSELL, *Introduction to Mathematical Philosophy* (London and New York, 1919).

EDWARD C. TITCHMARSH, *Mathematics for the General Reader* (London and New York, 1948).

BARTEL L. VAN DER WAERDEN, *Science Awakening* (trans. by A. Dresden, Groningen, 1954).

ALFRED NORTH WHITEHEAD and BERTRAND RUSSELL, *Principia Mathematica* (Cambridge, 1910–13), 3 vols.

RAYMOND L. WILDER, *Introduction to the Foundations of Mathematics* (New York, 1952).

CHAPTER VIII
THE ELABORATION OF THE PHYSICAL SCIENCES

FRANK D. ADAMS, *Birth and Development of the Geological Sciences* (Baltimore, 1938).

RITCHIE CALDER, *Science in our Lives* (East Lansing, Michigan, 1954).

CARL T. CHASE, *The Evolution of Modern Physics* (New York, 1947).

ARCHIBALD and NAN CLOW, *The Chemical Revolution: A Contribution to Social Technology* (London, 1952).

PETER DOIG, *A Concise History of Astronomy* (London, 1950).

ALBERT EINSTEIN and LEOPOLD INFELD, *The Evolution of Physics* (New York, 1942).

JAMES K. FINCH, *Engineering and Western Civilization* (New York, 1951).

ALEXANDER FINDLAY, *A Hundred Years of Chemistry*, (2nd ed., London, 1948).

GEORGE GAMOW, *Matter, Earth and Sky* (Englewood Cliffs, N.J., 1948).

J. ROBERT OPPENHEIMER, *Science and the Common Understanding* (New York, 1954).

EDMUND T. WHITTAKER, *A History of the Theories of Aether and Electricity* (London and New York, 1951–54), 2 vols.

CHAPTER IX
INDUSTRIAL PRODUCTION

Materials and Energy

SAM H. SCHURR and JACOB MARSCHAK, (eds.,) *Economic Aspects of Atomic Power* (Princeton, N.J., 1950).

DEMITRI B. SHIMKIN, *Minerals, A Key to Soviet Power* (Cambridge, Mass., 1953).

UNITED NATIONS, ECONOMIC COMMISSION FOR ASIA AND THE FAR EAST, *Relationship Between Industrial and Power Development* (New York, 1951).

UNITED NATIONS, INTERNATIONAL CONFERENCE ON THE PEACEFUL USES OF ATOMIC ENERGY, *Proceedings* (New York, 1955–58), 17 vols.

UNITED NATIONS, *Proceedings of the United Nations Scientific Conference on the Conservation and Utilization of Resources, 17 August to 6 September, 1949* (Lake Success, New York, 1950–53), 8 vols.

UNITED STATES PRESIDENT'S MATERIALS POLICY COMMISSION, *Resources for Freedom*, (Washington, D.C., 1952), 5 vols.

ERICH W. ZIMMERMANN, *World Resources and Industries: A Functional Appraisal of the Availability of Agricultural and Industrial Materials*, (rev. ed., New York, 1951).

Technology

AMERICAN MANAGEMENT ASSOCIATION, *Automation and Other Technological Advances* (New York, 1953).

PERCY DUNSHEATH, (ed.), *A Century of Technology, 1851–1951* (London and New York, 1951).

PAUL EINZIG, *The Economic Consequences of Automation* (London, 1956).

ROBERT J. FORBES, *Man the Maker: A History of Technology and Engineering* (London and New York, 1958).

GREAT BRITAIN, DEPARTMENT OF SCIENTIFIC AND INDUSTRIAL RESEARCH, *Automation* (London, 1956).

FREDERICK POLLOCK, *Automation, A Study of Its Economic and Social Consequences* (trans. by W. O. Henderson and W. H. Chaloner, Oxford and New York, 1957).

DICKSON RECK, (ed.), *National Standards in a Modern Economy* (New York, 1956).

ABBOTT P. USHER, *A History of Mechanical Inventions* (rev. ed., Cambridge, Mass., 1954).

A. A. ZVORIKINE, *Sosdanie Materialno-Teknicheskoi Basi Kommunisma v SSSR* (Material and Technical Foundation of Communism) (Moscow 1959).

Management and Labour Utilization

JAMES C. ABEGGLEN, *The Japanese Factory: Aspects of its Social Organization* (Glencoe, Ill., 1958).

A. ARAKELIAN, *Industrial Management in the U.S.S.R.* (trans. by E. L. Raymond, Washington, D.C., 1950).

DAVID GRANICK, *Management of the Industrial Firm in the U.S.S.R.* (New York, 1954).

G. B. HURFF, *Social Aspects of Enterprise in the Large Corporation* (Philadelphia, 1950).

INTERNATIONAL LABOUR OFFICE, *Higher Productivity in Manufacturing Industries* (Geneva, 1954).

INTERNATIONAL LABOUR OFFICE, *International Comparison of Real Wages: A Study of Methods* (Geneva, 1956).

INTERNATIONAL LABOUR OFFICE, *Minimum Wages: An International Survey* (Geneva, 1939).

INTERNATIONAL LABOUR OFFICE, *Payment by Results* (Geneva, 1951).

INTERNATIONAL LABOUR OFFICE, *Unemployment Insurance Schemes* (Geneva, 1955).

ABRAM T. JAFFE and CHARLES D. STEWART, *Manpower Utilization* (New York, 1951).

HENRY A. LANDSBERGER, *Hawthorne Revisited. Management and the Worker: its Critics, and Developments in Human Relations in Industry* (Ithaca, N.Y., 1958).

THOMAS M. LING, (ed.)., *Mental Health and Human Relations in Industry* (London, 1949).

FRITZ J. ROETHLISBERGER and WILLIAM J. DICKSON, *Management and the Worker: An Account of a Research Program Conducted by the Western Electric Company, Hawthorne Works, Chicago* (Cambridge, Mass., 1939).

SOLOMON M. SCHWARZ, *Labor in the Soviet Union* (New York, 1952).

FREDERICK W. TAYLOR, *Principles of Scientific Management* (New York and London, 1915).

S. HERBERT UNTERBERGER, *Guaranteed Wage and Supplementary Unemployment Pay Plans* (Chicago, 1956).

LYNDALL URWICK and E. F. L. BRECH, *The Making of Scientific Management* (London, 1945), 2 vols.

CHAPTER X
TRANSPORT

REGINALD M. CLEVELAND and SAMUEL T. WILLIAMSON, *The Road is Yours* (New York, 1951).

CHARLES E. GIBSON, *The Story of the Ship* (New York, 1948).

ADAM W. KIRKALDY and ALFRED D. EVANS, *Transport: Its History and Economics* (6th ed., London, 1946).

OLIVER J. LISSITZYN, *International Air Transport and National Policy* (New York, 1942).

HARRY O. MANCE et al., *International Transport and Communication* (New York, 1943–47), 7 vols.

CARL E. MCDOWELL and HELEN M. GIBBS, *Ocean Transportation* (New York, 1954).

P. HARVEY MIDDLETON, *Railways of Thirty Nations* (New York, 1937).

JACOB SCHENKMAN, *International Civil Aviation Organization* (Geneva, 1955).

LESLIE A. SCHUMER, *The Elements of Transport* (Sydney and London, 1954 and 1955).

CHARLES E. R. SHERRINGTON, *A Hundred Years of Inland Transport, 1830–1933* (London, 1934).

CHAPTER XI
COMMUNICATIONS

EDWARD L. BERNAYS, *Crystallizing Public Opinion* (New York, 1923).

GEORGE A. CODDING, *The International Telecommunication Union: An Experiment in International Co-operation* (Leiden, 1952).

COMMISSION ON FREEDOM OF THE PRESS, *A Free and Responsible Press: A General Report on Mass Communication: Newspapers, Radio, Motion Pictures, Magazines, Books* (Chicago, 1947).

GOVERNMENT OF INDIA, *Report of the Press Commission* (New Delhi, 1954).

ALEXIS INKELES, *Public Opinion in Soviet Russia: A Study in Mass Persuasion* (Cambridge, Mass., 1950).

WALTER LIPPMANN, *Public Opinion* (New York, 1922).

ROBERT K. MERTON, *Mass Persuasion: The Social Psychology of a War Bond Drive* (New York and London, 1946).

VANCE PACKARD, *The Hidden Persuaders* (New York, 1957).

POLITICAL and ECONOMIC PLANNING, *Report on the British Press* (London, 1938).

FRANK S. PRESBREY, *The History and Development of Advertising* (Garden City, N.Y., 1929).

WILBUR L. SCHRAMM, (ed.), *Communications in Modern Society* (Urbana, Ill., 1948).

BRUCE SMITH, HAROLD D. LASSWELL and RALPH D. CASEY, *Propaganda, Communication and Public Opinion* (Princeton, N.J., 1946).

UNESCO, *News Agencies: Their Structure and Operation* (Paris, 1953).

UNESCO, *Press, Film, Radio: Reports on the Facilities of Mass Communication* (Paris, 1951), 5 vols.

UNESCO, *Tentative International Bibliography of Works Dealing with Press Problems* (1900–52) (Paris, 1954).

UNESCO, *World Communications: Press, Radio, Film, Television* (3rd ed., Paris, 1956).

UNITED NATIONS, ECONOMIC AND SOCIAL COUNCIL, *Freedom of Information, 1953: Report Submitted by Salvador P. Lopez, Rapporteur on Freedom of Information* (New York, 1953).

FRANCIS WILLIAMS, *Transmitting World News: A Study of Telecommunications and the Press* (Paris, 1953).

CHAPTER XII
MEANS OF DESTRUCTION

RALPH NORMAN ANGELL, *The Great Illusion: a Study of the Relation of Military Power in Nations to Their Economic and Social Advantage* (London, 1910).

RAYMOND ARON, *The Century of Total War* (Garden City, N.Y., 1954).

JAMES P. BAXTER, 3rd, *Scientists Against Time* (Boston, 1946).

ELIS BIÖRKLUND, *International Atomic Policy During a Decade* (London, 1956).

PATRICK M. S. BLACKETT, *Atomic Weapons and East–West Relations* (Cambridge, 1956).

LIONEL M. CHASSIN, *Histoire militaire de la seconde guerre mondiale* (Paris, 1947).

CYRIL FALLS, *The Nature of Modern Warfare* (London, 1941).

JOHN F. C. FULLER, *A Military History of the Western World* (New York, 1954–1956), 3 vols.

JOHN F. C. FULLER, *The Second World War: A Strategical and Tactical History* (New York, 1949).

VICTOR WALLACE GERMAINS, *The 'Mechanization' of War* (London, 1927).

EDGAR J. KINGSTON-MCCLOUGHRY, *War in Three Dimensions: The Impact of Air-Power upon the Classical Principles of War* (London, 1949).

HENRY A. KISSINGER, *Nuclear Weapons and Foreign Policy* (New York, 1957).

BASIL H. LIDDELL HART, *A History of the World War, 1914–1918* (London, 1934).

WALTER MILLIS, *Arms and Men: A Study in American Military History* (New York, 1956).

JOHN U. NEF, *War and Human Progress: An Essay on the Rise of Industrial Civilization* (Cambridge, Mass., 1950).

GERALD WENDT, *Atomic Energy and the Hydrogen Bomb* (New York, 1950).

QUINCY WRIGHT, *A Study of War* (Chicago, 1942), 2 vols.

CHAPTER XIII
THE DEVELOPMENT OF BIOLOGICAL SCIENCES

RALPH W. GERARD, *Unresting Cells* (New York, 1940).

RICHARD S. GOLDSCHMIDT, *Understanding Heredity* (New York, 1952).

JULIAN S. HUXLEY, *Evolution, the Modern Synthesis* (New York, 1943).

ALEXANDER OPARIN, *The Origin of Life on the Earth* (trans. by Ann Synge, 3rd ed., New York, 1957).

CHRISTIAAN P. RAVEN, *An Outline of Developmental Physiology* (trans. by L. de Reiter, London and New York, 1954).

GEORGE G. SIMPSON, *The Meaning of Evolution* (New Haven, 1949).

GEORGE G. SIMPSON, COLIN S. PITTENDRIGH and LEWIS H. TIFFANY, *Life* (New York, 1957).

CHAPTER XIV
FOOD AND AGRICULTURE

Agriculture

Agriculture in the Twentieth Century: Essays . . . Presented to Sir Daniel Hall (Oxford, 1939).

MURRAY R. BENEDICT, *Farm Policies of the United States 1790–1950: A Study of Their Origins and Development* (New York, 1953).

FOLKE DOVRING, *Land and Labour in Europe, 1900–1950: A Comparative Survey of Recent Agrarian History* (The Hague, 1956).

FOOD AND AGRICULTURE ORGANIZATION OF THE UNITED NATIONS, *Inter-relationship between Agrarian Reform and Agricultural Development* (Rome, 1953).

FOOD AND AGRICULTURE ORGANIZATION OF THE UNITED NATIONS, *The State of Food and Agriculture: Review of a Decade and Outlook* (Rome, 1955).

FOOD AND AGRICULTURE ORGANIZATION OF THE UNITED NATIONS, *So Bold an Aim: Ten Years of International Cooperation Toward Freedom from Want* (Rome, 1955).

LEONARD E. HUBBARD, *The Economics of Soviet Agriculture* (London, 1939).

NAUM JASNY, *The Socialized Agriculture of the U.S.S.R.: Plans and Performance* (Stanford, Calif., 1949).

CHARLES KELLOGG, *The Soils That Support Us* (New York, 1941).

FAIRFIELD OSBORN, *Our Plundered Planet* (Boston and London, 1948).

HOWARD S. REED, *A Short History of the Plant Sciences* (Waltham, Mass., 1942).

ROYAL INSTITUTE OF INTERNATIONAL AFFAIRS, *World Agriculture: An International Survey* (London, 1932).

EDWARD J. RUSSELL, *World Population and World Food Supplies* (London, 1954).

US DEPARTMENT OF AGRICULTURE, *Science in Farming: The Yearbook of Agriculture, 1943–47* (Washington, D.C., 1947).

DOREEN WARRINER, *Land Reform and Development in the Middle East* (London and New York, 1957).

DOREEN WARRINER, *The Economics of Peasant Farming* (London and New York, 1939).

PAUL LAMARTINE YATES, *Food, Land, and Manpower in Western Europe* (London and New York, 1960).

Forestry

FOOD AND AGRICULTURE ORGANIZATION OF THE UNITED NATIONS, 'Ten Years of Forestry in FAO', *Unasylva* II, 2 (Rome, 1957).

STEPHEN HADEN-GUEST, JOHN K. WRIGHT and EILEEN M. TECLAFF, (eds.), *A World Geography of Forest Resources* (New York, 1956).

US DEPARTMENT OF AGRICULTURE, *New Knowledge in Forestry: Report of the Chief of the Forest Service, U.S. Department of Agriculture, 1948* (Washington, D.C., 1949).

ROBERT K. WINTERS, (ed.), *Fifty Years of Forestry in the U.S.A.* (Washington, D.C., 1950).

Fisheries

CHARLES L. CUTTING, *Fish Saving: A History of Fish Processing from Ancient to Modern Times* (London, 1955).

FOOD AND AGRICULTURE ORGANIZATION OF THE UNITED NATIONS, 'Improving the Fisheries Contribution to World Food Supplies', *FAO Fisheries Bulletin*, VI 5 (Rome, 1953).

MICHAEL GRAHAM and G. L. KESTEVEN, 'Biological Possibilities in World Fisheries', *FAO Fisheries Bulletin, VII*, 1, (Rome, 1954).

HAROLD A. INNIS, *The Cod Fisheries: The History of an International Economy* (rev. ed., Toronto, 1954).

G. L. KESTEVEN and G. E. R. DEACON, 'The Contribution of Oceanographic Research to Fisheries Science', *FAO Fisheries Bulletin*, VIII, 2, (Rome, 1955).

JAN-OLOF TRAUNG, (ed.), *Fishing Boats of the World* (London, 1955).

UNITED NATIONS, *Papers Presented at the International Technical Conference on the Conservation of the Living Resources of the Sea, Rome, 18 April to 10 May, 1955* (New York, 1956).

UNITED NATIONS, *Report of the International Technical Conference on the Conservation of the Living Resources of the Sea, Rome, 18 April to 10 May, 1955* (New York, 1956).

Nutrition

FOOD AND AGRICULTURE ORGANIZATION OF THE UNITED NATIONS, Committee on Calorie Requirements, *Calorie Requirements: Report. 12–16 September, 1949* (Washington, D.C., 1950).

FOOD AND NUTRITION BOARD, National Academy of Sciences—National Research Council, *Recommended Dietary Allowances: Revised 1953* (Washington, D.C., 1953).

ANCEL B. KEYS *et al.*, *The Biology of Human Starvation* (Minneapolis, 1950), 2 vols.

JOHN BOYD ORR, *Food, Health and Income* (London, 1936).

MARJORIE L. SCOTT, *School Feeding: Its Contribution to Child Nutrition* (Rome, 1953).

HENRY C. SHERMAN, *The Nutritional Improvement of Life* (New York, 1950).

HAZEL K. STIEBLING and MEDORA WARD, *Diets at Four Levels of Nutritive Content and Cost* (Washington, D.C., 1933).

CHAPTER XV
HEALTH AND POPULATION

Health

BRITISH MEDICAL ASSOCIATION, *Fifty Years of Medicine: A Symposium from the British Medical Journal* (London, 1950).

ARTURO CASTIGLIONI, *A History of Medicine* (trans. and ed. by E. B. Krumbhaar, 2nd ed., New York, 1947).

RENÉ and JEAN DUBOS, *The White Plague: Tuberculosis, Man and Society* (Boston, 1952).

MIKE GORMAN, *Every Other Bed* (Cleveland, 1956).

L. FABIAN HIRST, *The Conquest of Plague* (Oxford, 1953).

DONALD HUNTER, *The Diseases of Occupations* (London, 1955).

JOINT ILO/WHO COMMITTEE ON OCCUPATIONAL HEALTH, *Second Report* (Geneva, 1953).

GEORGE ROSEN, *A History of Public Health* (New York, 1958).

PAUL F. RUSSELL, *Man's Mastery of Malaria* (London and New York, 1955).

RENÉ SAND, *The Advance to Social Medicine* (London and New York, 1952).

RICHARD H. SHRYOCK, *The Development of Modern Medicine: An Interpretation of the Social and Scientific Factors Involved* (2nd ed., New York, 1947).

JAMES S. SIMMONS, (ed.), *Public Health in the World Today* (Cambridge, Mass., 1949).

LUDWIG TELEKY, *History of Factory and Mine Hygiene* (New York, 1948).

NIKOLAI ARKADEVICH VINOGRADOV, *Public Health in the Soviet Union* (3rd ed., trans., Moscow, 1952).

C. E. A. WINSLOW, *Man and Epidemics* (Princeton, N.J., 1952).

C. E. A. WINSLOW, *The Cost of Sickness and the Price of Health* (Geneva, 1951).

Population (see also Chapter V)

F. G. BOUDREAU and CLYDE V. KISER, (eds.), *Trends and Differentials in Mortality* (New York, 1956).

ANSLEY J. COALE and EDGAR M. HOOVER, *Population Growth and Economic Development in Low-Income Countries* (Princeton, N.J., 1958).

RONALD FREEDMAN, P. K. WHELPTON and A. A. CAMPBELL, *Family Planning, Sterility and Population Growth* (New York, 1959).

FRANK LORIMER and F. OSBORN, *Dynamics of Population* (New York and London, 1934).

WILBERT E. MOORE, *Economic Demography of Eastern and Southern Europe* (London and New York, 1946).

GUNNAR MYRDAL, *Population: A Problem for Democracy* (Cambridge, Mass., 1940).

JOSEPH J. SPENGLER and OTIS D. DUNCAN, (eds.), *Population Theory and Policy* (Glencoe, Ill., 1956).

UNITED NATIONS, *The Determinants and Consequences of Population Trends* (New York, 1953).

WILLIAM VOGT, *People: Challenge to Survival* (New York, 1960).

UNITED NATIONS WORLD POPULATION CONFERENCE, *Papers of the World Population Conference, Rome, 1954* (New York, 1955).

WORLD POPULATION CONFERENCE, Geneva, 1927, *Proceedings* (ed. by M. Sanger, London, 1927).

CHAPTER XVI

THE SCIENTIFIC APPROACH TO HUMAN BEHAVIOUR AND HUMAN RELATIONS

FRANZ G. ALEXANDER and HELEN ROSS, (eds.), *Dynamic Psychiatry* (Chicago, 1952).

STUART F. CHAPIN, *Social Science Research: Its Expanding Horizons* (Minneapolis, Minn., 1953).

GLYN E. DANIEL, *A Hundred Years of Archaeology* (London, 1950).

WAYNE DENNIS *et al.*, *Current Trends in Psychology* (Pittsburgh, 1947).

HOWARD S. ELLIS and BERNARD F. HALEY, (eds.), *A Survey of Contemporary Economics* (Philadelphia, Pa., and Homewood, Ill., 1948 and 1952), 2 vols.

Encyclopaedia of the Social Sciences (New York, 1930–1935), 15 vols.

LEON FESTINGER and DONALD KATE, (eds.), *Research Methods in the Behavioral Sciences* (New York, 1953).

JOHN CARL FLÜGEL, *A Hundred Years of Psychology, 1833–1933* (2nd ed., with developments 1933–47, London, 1951).

GEORGES GURVITCH and WILBERT E. MOORE, (eds.), *Twentieth Century Sociology* (New York, 1945).

Handwörterbuch der Sozialwissenschaften (Stuttgart, Tübingen, Göttingen, 1952–).

PHILIP L. HARRIMAN, JOSEPH L. ROUCEK and GEORGE B. DE HUSZAR, (eds.), *Contemporary Social Science, Volume I; Western Hemisphere* (Harrisburg, Pa., 1953).

R. F. HARROD, *The Life of John Maynard Keynes* (London, 1952).

H. STUART HUGHES, *Consciousness and Society: The Reorientation of European Social Thought, 1890–1930* (New York, 1958).

ERNEST JONES, *Life and Work of Sigmund Freud* (London and New York, 1953–57), 3 vols.

FELIX M. KEESING, *Culture Change: An Analysis and Bibliography of Anthropological Sources to 1952* (Stanford, Calif., 1953).

CLYDE KLUCKHOHN and HENRY A. MURRAY, (eds.), *Personality in Nature, Society and Culture* (2nd ed., New York, 1953).

ARTHUR L. KROEBER, (ed.), *Anthropology Today: An Encyclopedic Inventory* (Chicago, 1953).

DANIEL LERNER, (ed.), *The Policy Sciences: Recent Developments in Scope and Method* (Stanford, Calif., 1951).

GARDNER LINDZEY, (ed.), *Handbook of Social Psychology* (Cambridge, Mass., 1954), 2 vols.

KARL MANNHEIM, *Ideology and Utopia: An Introduction to the Sociology of Knowledge* (trans. by L. Wirth and E. A. Shils, New York, 1936).

FRITZ MORSTEIN MARX, (ed.), *Elements of Public Administration* (2nd ed., Englewood Cliffs, N.J., 1959).

NATIONAL BUREAU OF ECONOMIC RESEARCH, *Economic Research and the Development of Economic Science and Public Policy*, Twelve Papers presented at 25th Anniversary Meeting (New York, 1946).

TALCOTT PARSONS and EDWARD A. SHILS, (eds)., *Toward a General Theory of Action* (Cambridge, Mass., 1951).

MASSIMO SALVADORI *et al.*, (eds.), *Contemporary Social Science, Volume II: Eastern Hemisphere* (Harrisburg, Pa., 1954).

BRIAN SIMON, (ed.), *Psychology in the Soviet Union* (trans. by J. and M. Ellis *et al.*, Stanford, Calif., 1957).

SOCIAL SCIENCE RESEARCH COUNCIL, COMMITTEE ON HISTORIOGRAPHY, *Theory and Practice in Historical Study* (New York, 1946).

SOCIAL SCIENCE RESEARCH COUNCIL, COMMITTEE ON HISTORIOGRAPHY, *The Social Sciences in Historical Study* (New York, 1954).

SOL TAX *et al.*, (eds.), *An Appraisal of Anthropology Today* (Chicago, 1953).

UNESCO, *Contemporary Political Science* (Paris, 1950).

UNESCO, *International Repertory of Social Science Documentation Centres* (Paris, 1952).

UNIVERSITY OF MINNESOTA GRADUATE SCHOOL, SOCIAL SCIENCE RESEARCH CENTER, *The Social Sciences at Mid-Century: Papers Delivered at the Dedication of Ford Hall, April 19–21 1951* (Minneapolis, Minn., 1952).

MAX WEBER, *On the Methodology of the Social Sciences* (ed. by E. A. Shils and H. A. Finch, Glencoe, Ill., 1949).

MAX WEBER, *The Theory of Social and Economic Organization* (trans. by T. Parsons, rev. ed., New York, 1947).

LEONARD D. WHITE, (ed.), *The State of the Social Sciences* (Chicago, 1956).

BARBARA WOOTTON, *Testament for Social Science: An Essay in the Application of Scientific Method to Human Problems* (London, 1950).

CHAPTER XVII

THE HOME

JULIET LITA BANE and MILDRED R. CHAPIN, *Introduction to Home Economics* (Boston, 1945).

ISABEL BEVIER, *Home Economics in Education* (Philadelphia, 1924).

JOHN BOWLBY, *Maternal Care and Mental Health* (Geneva, 1951).

LEONARD CARMICHAEL, (ed.), *Manual of Child Psychology* (2nd ed., New York, 1954).

HAZEL T. CRAIG, *The History of Home Economics* (New York, 1946).

PAULINE NICKELL and JEAN M. DORSEY, *Management in Family Living* (New York and London, 1942).

WILLIAM D. WALL, *The Adolescent Child* (London, 1948).

HELEN L. WITMER and RUTH KOTINSKY, (eds.), *Personality in the Making: The Fact-Finding Report of the Midcentury White House Conference on Children and Youth* (New York, 1952).

CHAPTER XVIII
THE ENVIRONMENT

NELS ANDERSON, *The Urban Community: A World Perspective* (New York, 1959).

RICHARD K. BEARDSLEY et al., *Village Japan* (Chicago, 1959).

LE CORBUSIER (C. E. JEANNERET-GRIS), *Concerning Town Planning* (trans. by C. Entwistle, London, 1947).

DAVID and ISABEL CROOK, *Revolution in a Chinese Village* (London, 1959).

ROBERT E. DICKINSON, *The West European City: A Geographical Interpretation* (London, 1951).

RONALD P. DORE, *City Life in Japan* (Berkeley, Calif., 1958).

SHYAMA CHARAN DUBE, *Indian Village* (Ithaca, N.Y., 1955).

OTIS D. DUNCAN et al., *Metropolis and Region* (Baltimore, 1960).

ORLANDO FALS-BORDA, *Peasant Society in the Colombian Andes* (Gainesville, Fla., 1955).

HERMAN FINER, *The T.V.A.: Lessons for International Application* (Montreal, 1944).

ROBERT M. FISHER, (ed.), *The Metropolis in Modern Life* (Garden City, N.Y., 1955).

FOOD AND AGRICULTURE ORGANIZATION OF THE UNITED NATIONS, *Essentials of Rural Welfare* (Washington, D.C., 1949).

ARTHUR B. GALLION and SIMON EISNER, *The Urban Pattern: City Planning and Design* (New York, 1950).

PATRICK GEDDES, *Cities in Evolution* (London, 1915).

PAUL K. HATT and ALBERT J. REISS, Jr., (eds.), *Cities and Society: Revised Reader in Urban Sociology* (Glencoe, Ill., 1957).

JOINT UNITED NATIONS–UNESCO SEMINAR, *Urbanization in Asia and the Far East: Proceedings*, (ed. by Philip M. Hauser, Calcutta, 1957).

PAUL H. LANDIS, *Rural Life in Process* (2nd ed., New York, 1948).

MAHMUT MAKAL, *A Village in Anatolia* (London, 1954).

LEWIS MUMFORD, *The City in History: Its Origins, Its Transformations, and Its Prospects* (New York, 1961).

LEWIS MUMFORD, *The Culture of Cities* (New York, 1938).

ROBERT E. PARK, *et al.*, *The City* (Chicago, 1925).

WILLIAM A. ROBSON, (ed.), *Great Cities of the World: Their Government, Politics and Planning* (London and New York, 1957).

PITRIM A. SOROKIN *et al.*, (eds.), *A Systematic Source Book in Rural Sociology* (Minneapolis, 1930–32), 3 vols.

UNITED NATIONS, *Second Report on the World Social Situation* (New York, 1959).

UNITED NATIONS, *Urban Land Problems and Policies* (New York, 1953).

CHAPTER XIX
PREVENTION AND TREATMENT OF SOCIAL BREAKDOWN

ERNEST BARKER, *The Development of Public Services in Western Europe, 1660–1930* (London and New York, 1944).

WILLIAM H. BEVERIDGE, *Voluntary Action: A Report on Methods of Social Advance* (London, 1948).

ANNE BOURDILLON, *Voluntary Social Services, Their Place in the Modern State* (London, 1945).

LUCIEN BOVET, *Psychiatric Aspects of Juvenile Delinquency* (Geneva, 1951).

ERNEST W. BURGESS, (ed.), *Aging in Western Societies* (Chicago, 1960).

EVELINE M. BURNS, *Social Security and Public Policy* (New York, 1956).

CYRIL BURT, *The Young Delinquent* (rev. ed., Brickley, Kent, 1944).

ALBERT DEUTSCH, *The Mentally Ill in America* (rev. ed., New York, 1949).

INTERNATIONAL LABOUR OFFICE, *International Survey of Social Security: Comparative Analysis and Summary of National Laws* (Geneva, 1950).

INTERNATIONAL LABOUR OFFICE, *International Survey of Social Services, 1933* (Geneva, 1936), 2 vols.

INTERNATIONAL ASSOCIATION OF GERONTOLOGY, *Old Age in the Modern World* (London, 1954).

GEORGE R. NELSON, (ed.), *Freedom and Welfare: Social Patterns in the Northern Countries of Europe* (Denmark, Finland, Iceland, Norway, Sweden, Ministries of Social Affairs, 1953).

MADELINE ROOFF, *Voluntary Societies and Social Policy* (London, 1957).

CLIFFORD R. SHAW and HENRY D. MCKAY, *Juvenile Delinquency in Urban Areas* (Chicago, 1942).

DAVID STAFFORD-CLARK, *Psychiatry To-day* (Harmondsworth, Middlesex, 1952).

RICHARD TITMUSS, *Problems of Social Policy* (London, 1950).

UNITED NATIONS, *International Survey of Programmes of Social Development* (New York, 1955).

UNITED NATIONS, *Social Progress Through Local Action* (New York, 1955).

UNITED NATIONS, *Training for Social Work: An International Survey* (New York, 1950); *Second International Survey* (1955); *Third International Survey* (1960).

UNITED NATIONS, *Economic Measures in Favour of the Family* (New York, 1952).

BARBARA WOOTTON *et al.*, *Social Science and Social Pathology* (London, 1959).

CHAPTER XX
MAJOR TRENDS IN CONCEPTS AND IDEAS

I. M. BOCHENSKI, *Contemporary European Philosophy* (trans. by D. Nicholl and K. Aschenbrenner, Berkeley, Calif., 1956).

ROBERT N. C. HUNT, *The Theory and Practice of Communism* (rev. ed., New York, 1957).

THOMAS A. JACKSON, *Dialectics: The Logic of Marxism and Its Critics* (London, 1936).

WALTER KAUFMANN, (ed.), *Existentialism from Dostoevsky to Sartre* (New York, 1956).

HERBERT MARCUSE, *Soviet Marxism: A Critical Analysis* (New York, 1958).

JACQUES MARITAIN, *The Degrees of Knowledge* (New York, 1938).

CHARLES A. MOORE, (ed.), *Essays in East-West Philosophy* (Honolulu, 1951).

F. S. C. NORTHROP, (ed.), *Ideological Differences and World Order* (New Haven, 1949).

F. S. C. NORTHROP, *The Meeting of East and West* (New York, 1946).

JOHN P. PLAMENATZ, *German Marxism and Russian Communism* (London, 1954).

SARVEPALLI RADHAKRISHNAN, (ed.), *History of Philosophy, Eastern and Western* (London and New York, 1952–3), 2 vols.

DAGOBERT D. RUNES, (ed.), *Twentieth Century Philosophy* (New York, 1943).

BERTRAND RUSSELL, *A History of Western Philosophy* (London and New York, 1945).

JEAN WAHL, 'Philosophie', in *50 Années de Découvertes: Bilan 1900–1950* (Paris, 1950).

MORTON G. WHITE, (ed.), *The Age of Analysis: 20th Century Philosophers* (Boston and New York, 1955).

PHILIP P. WIENER, *Evolution and the Founders of Pragmatism* (Cambridge, Mass., 1949).

CHAPTER XXI
ECONOMIC INSTITUTIONS
(See also Chapters IV and IX)

SOLOMON ADLER, *The Chinese Economy* (London and New York, 1957).

WILLIAM ASHWORTH, *A Short History of the International Economy, 1850–1950* (London and New York, 1952).

S. S. BALZAK *et al.*, (eds.), *Economic Geography of the U.S.S.R.* (trans. by R. M. Hankin and O. A. Titelbahn, New York, 1949).

ALEXANDER M. BAYKOV, *The Development of the Soviet Economic System: An Essay on the Experience of Planning in the U.S.S.R.* (New York and Toronto, 1947).

BURNHAM P. BECKWITH, *The Economic Theory of a Socialist Economy* (Stanford, Calif., and London, 1949).

ABRAM BERGSON, (ed.), *Soviet Economic Growth: Conditions and Perspectives* (Evanston, Ill., 1953).

ARTHUR R. BURNS, *Comparative Economic Organization* (New York, 1955).

ROBERT W. CAMPBELL, *Soviet Economic Power* (New York, 1960).

THOMAS C. COCHRAN, *The American Business System: A Historical Perspective, 1900–1955* (Cambridge, Mass., 1957).

JEROME B. COHEN, *Japan's Postwar Economy* (Bloomington, Ind., 1958).

ROBERT I. CRANE, *Aspects of Economic Development in South Asia* (New York, 1954).

DAVID J. DALLIN and BORIS I. NICOLAEVSKY, *Forced Labor in Soviet Russia* (New Haven, 1947).

HAROLD U. FAULKNER, *The Decline of Laissez-Faire, 1897–1917* (New York, 1951).

PHILIP SARGENT FLORENCE, *The Logic of British and American Industry* (London, 1953).

DHANANJAYA R. GADGIL, *The Industrial Evolution of India in Recent Times* (4th ed., London, New York, Bombay, 1942).

JOHN KENNETH GALBRAITH, *American Capitalism: The Concept of Countervailing Power* (Boston, 1952).

GOVERNMENT OF INDIA PLANNING COMMISSION, *The New India: Progress through Democracy* (New York, 1958).

GEORGE N. HALM, *Economic Systems: A Comparative Analysis* (New York and Toronto, 1951).

GEORGE W. HOFFMAN and FRED W. NEAL, *Yugoslavia and the New Communism* (New York, 1962).

CALVIN B. HOOVER, *The Economy, Liberty and the State* (New York, 1959).

TREVOR JONES HUGHES and D. E. T. LUARD, *The Economic Development of Communist China, 1949–1958* (New York, 1959).

K. WILLIAM KAPP, *The Social Costs of Private Enterprise* (Cambridge, Mass., 1950).

JOHN MAYNARD KEYNES, *The Economic Consequences of the Peace* (London, 1919).

JOHN MAYNARD KEYNES, *The General Theory of Employment, Interest and Money* (London, 1936).

EDWARD S. MASON, (ed.), *The Corporation in Modern Society* (Cambridge, Mass., 1959).

NATIONAL RESOURCES COMMITTEE, *The Structure of the American Economy, Part I: Basic Characteristics* (Washington, D.C., 1939).

RAGNAR NURKSE, *Problems of Capital Formation in Underdeveloped Countries* (Oxford, 1953).

WILLIAM A. ROBSON, (ed.), *Problems of Nationalized Industry* (London and New York, 1952).

WILHELM RÖPKE, *A Humane Economy: The Social Framework of the Free Market* (trans. by Elizabeth Henderson, Chicago, 1960).

HARRY SCHWARTZ, *Russia's Soviet Economy* (2nd ed., New York, 1954).

W. SOMBART, *Das Wirtschaftsleben im Zeitalter des Hochkapitalismus* (Leipzig, 1927) Part III of *Der Moderne Kapitalismus,* 2 vols.

NICOLAS SPULBER, *The Economics of Communist Eastern Europe* (New York, 1957).

GEORGE A. STEINER, *Government's Role in Economic Life* (New York, 1953).

GEORGE W. STOCKING and MYRON W. WATKINS, *Cartels in Action: Case Studies in International Business Diplomacy* (New York, 1946).

JOHN STRACHEY, *Contemporary Capitalism* (London and New York, 1956).

C. N. VAKIL and P. R. BRAHMANAND, *Planning for an Expanding Economy* (Bombay, New York, 1956).

HENRY C. WALLICH, *Mainsprings of the German Revival* (New Haven and London, 1955).

MAX WEBER, *Wirtschaft und Gesellschaft* (4th ed., Tübingen, 1956).

CHAPTER XXII

SOCIAL INSTITUTIONS
(See also Chapter V)

'AFRICAN ELITES', *International Social Science Bulletin*, VIII, 3 (Paris, 1956).

FREDERICK L. ALLEN, *The Big Change* (New York, 1952).

RUTH N. ANSHEN, (ed.), *The Family: Its Function and Destiny* (New York, 1949).

SHMUEL N. EISENSTADT, *From Generation to Generation: Age Groups and Social Structure* (Glencoe, Ill., 1956).

ERIK H. ERIKSON, *Childhood and Society* (New York, 1950).

DAVID V. GLASS, (ed.), *Social Mobility in Britain* (London, 1954).

INTERNATIONAL AFRICAN INSTITUTE, *Social Implications of Industrialization and Urbanization in Africa South of the Sahara* (Paris, 1956).

INTERNATIONAL INSTITUTE OF DIFFERING CULTURES, *Development of a Middle Class in Tropical and Sub-tropical Countries* (Brussels, 1956).

JOHN J. JOHNSON, *Political Change in Latin America: The Emergence of the Middle Sectors* (Stanford, Calif., 1958).

MARION J. LEVY, *The Family Revolution in Modern China* (Cambridge, Mass., 1949).

REUBEN LEVY, *The Social Structure of Islam* (Cambridge, 1957).

DAVID LOCKWOOD, *The Blackcoated Worker: A Study in Class Consciousness* (London, 1958).

C. WRIGHT MILLS, *The Power Elite* (New York, 1956).

C. WRIGHT MILLS, *White Collar: The American Middle Class* (New York, 1951).

MARY MORRIS, *Voluntary Organizations and Social Progress* (London, 1955).

ALVA MYRDAL, *Nation and Family: The Swedish Experiment in Democratic Family and Population Policy* (London, 1945).

ALICE C. PERCIVAL, *Youth Will be Led: The Story of the Voluntary Youth Organizations* (London, 1951).

UNITED NATIONS, *Slavery* (New York, 1955).

ROBERT VAN NIEL, *The Emergence of the Modern Indonesian Elite* (The Hague and Chicago, 1960).

SIDNEY and BEATRICE WEBB, *The Consumers' Cooperative Movement* (London 1921).

GERHARD ZIEMER and HANS WOLF, *Wandervögel* (Bad Godesburg, 1962).

CHAPTER XXIII

POLITICAL INSTITUTIONS
(See also Chapters III, XXVIII)

Democratic and Authoritarian

HAROLD E. DAVIS, (ed.), *Government and Politics in Latin America* (New York, 1958).

MAURICE DUVERGER, *Political Parties: Their Organization and Activity in the Modern State* (London, 1959).

MAURICE DUVERGER, *The French Political System* (Chicago, 1958).

HERMAN FINER, *Theory and Practice of Modern Government* (rev. ed., New York, 1949).

WOLFGANG FRIEDMANN, *Law in a Changing Society* (Berkeley and Los Angeles, Calif., 1959).

HAROLD R. G. GREAVES, *The Civil Service in the Changing State* (London, 1947).

RICHARD HOFSTADTER, *The American Political Tradition and The Men Who Made It* (New York, 1948).

LIONEL CECIL JANE, *Liberty and Despotism in Spanish America* (Oxford, 1929).

GEORGE M. KAHIN, (ed.), *Major Governments of Asia* (Ithaca, N.Y., 1958).

CARL LANDAUER, *European Socialism: A History of Ideas and Movements from the Industrial Revolution to Hitler's Seizure of Power* (Berkeley and Los Angeles, Calif., 1959), 2 vols.

HAROLD J. LASKI et al., for the Inter-parliamentary Union, *Development of the Representative System in Our Times* (Lausanne, 1928).

HAROLD D. LASSWELL and ABRAHAM KAPLAN, *Power and Society* (New Haven, 1950).

HERBERT LUETHY, *France Against Herself* (trans. by E. Mosbacher, New York, 1955).

HERBERT S. MORRISON, *Government and Parliament: A Survey from the Inside* (London and New York, 1954).

FRANZ L. NEUMANN, *The Democratic and the Authoritarian State* (Glencoe, Ill., 1957).

SIGMUND NEUMANN, (ed.), *Modern Political Parties: Approaches to Comparative Politics* (Chicago, 1956).

AMOS J. PEASLEE, (ed.), *Constitutions of Nations* (2nd ed., The Hague, 1956), 3 vols.

WILLIAM E. RAPPARD, *The Government of Switzerland* (New York, 1936).

WILLIAM A. ROBSON, *Justice and Administrative Law: A Study of the British Constitution* (3rd ed., London, 1951).

HERBERT A. SIMON, *Administrative Behavior: A Study of Decision-Making Processes in Administrative Organization* (New York, 1947).

CARL B. SWISHER, *American Constitutional Development* (2nd ed., Boston, 1954).

Communist

JOHN A. ARMSTRONG, *The Soviet Bureaucratic Elite: A Case Study of the Ukrainian Apparatus* (New York, 1959).

CONRAD BRANDT, BENJAMIN SCHWARTZ and JOHN K. FAIRBANK, *A Documentary History of Chinese Communism* (Cambridge, Mass., 1952).

ISAAC DEUTSCHER, *Stalin: A Political Biography* (London and New York, 1949).

MERLE FAINSOD, *How Russia is Ruled* (Cambridge, Mass., 1953).

VLADIMIR GSOVSKI, *Soviet Civil Law* (Ann Arbor, Mich., 1948–49), 2 vols.

JOHN N. HAZARD, *Settling Disputes in Soviet Society* (New York, 1960).

JOHN N. HAZARD, *The Soviet System of Government* (rev. ed., Chicago, 1960).

CHARLES P. MCVICKER, *Titoism: Pattern for International Communism* (New York, 1957).

LEONARD B. SCHAPIRO, *The Communist Party of the Soviet Union* (New York, 1960).

DEREK J. R. SCOTT, *Russian Political Institutions* (London and New York, 1958).

S. B. THOMAS, *Government and Administration in Communist China* (rev. ed., New York, 1955).

JULIAN TOWSTER, *Political Power in the U.S.S.R. 1917–1947: The Theory and Structure of Government in the Soviet State* (New York, 1948).

Colonial Systems

NTIEYONG U. AKPAN, *Epitaph to Indirect Rule* (London, 1956).

GEORGE BENNETT, (ed.), *The Concept of Empire: Burke to Attlee, 1774–1947* (London, 1953).

THOMAS E. ENNIS, *French Policy and Developments in Indochina* (Chicago, 1936).

JOHN S. FURNIVALL, *Colonial Policy and Practice: A Comparative Study of Burma and Netherlands India* (Cambridge, 1948).

PAUL KNAPLUND, *Britain: Commonwealth and Empire, 1901–1955* (London, 1956).

FREDERICK J. D. LUGARD, *The Dual Mandate in British Tropical Africa* (London, 1922).

HERBERT I. PRIESTLEY, *France Overseas: A Study of Modern Imperialism* (New York and London, 1938).

KATHLEEN M. STAHL, *British and Soviet Colonial Systems* (London and New York. 1951).

JOHN STRACHEY, *The End of Empire* (London, 1959).

AMRY VANDENBOSCH, *The Dutch East Indies: Its Government, Problems and Politics*, (3rd ed., Berkeley, Calif., 1942).

GEORGES VAN DER KERKEN, *La Politique Coloniale Belge* (Antwerp, 1943).

CHAPTER XXIV
MILITARY INSTITUTIONS

WALLACE CARROLL, *Persuade or Perish* (Boston, 1948).

RICHARD D. CHALLENER, *The French Theory of the Nation in Arms, 1866–1939* (New York, 1955).

FRANK P. CHAMBERS, *The War Behind the War 1914–1918: A History of the Political and Civilian Fronts* (London, 1939).

JEROME B. COHEN, *Japan's Economy in War and Reconstruction* (Minneapolis, 1949).

GORDON A. CRAIG, *The Politics of the Prussian Army, 1640–1945* (London, 1955).

D. FEDOTOFF WHITE, *The Growth of the Red Army* (Princeton, N.J., 1944).

RAYMOND L. GARTHOFF, *Soviet Military Doctrine* (Glencoe, Ill., 1953).

CHARLES GIDE, (ed.), *The Effect of the War upon French Economic Life* (Oxford and London, 1923).

WALTER GOERLITZ, *History of the German General Staff, 1657–1945* (trans. by B. Battershaw, New York, 1953).

W. K. HANCOCK and M. M. GOWING, *British War Economy* (London, 1949).

ELIOT JANEWAY, *The Struggle for Survival: A Chronicle of Economic Mobilization in World War II* (New Haven, 1951).

EDGAR J. KINGSTON-MCCLOUGHRY, *The Direction of War: A Critique of the Political Direction and High Command in War* (London and New York, 1955).

HAROLD D. LASSWELL, *Propaganda Technique in the World War* (New York and London, 1927).

BASIL H. LIDDELL HART, (ed.), *The Red Army* (New York, 1956).

ALBRECHT MENDELSSOHN-BARTHOLDY, *The War and German Society* (London and New Haven, 1937).

WALTER MILLIS *et al.*, *Arms and the State: Civil–Military Elements in National Policy* (New York, 1958).

JAMES T. SHOTWELL, (ed.), *Economic and Social History of the World War* (New Haven, New York and London, 1922–1936).

HANS W. SINGER, *The German War Economy* (Manchester, 1943).

HANS SPEIER and ALFRED KOEHLER, (eds.), *War in Our Time* (New York, 1939).

ALFRED VAGTS, *A History of Militarism: Civilian and Military* (rev. ed., New York, 1959).

N. A. VOZNESENSKY, *The Economy of the U.S.S.R. during World War II* (Washington D.C., 1948).

JOHN W. WHEELER-BENNETT, *The Nemesis of Power: The German Army in Politics, 1918–1945* (London and New York, 1954).

CHAPTER XXV

RELIGION

World Religions

CHARLES S. BRADEN, *Modern Tendencies in World Religions* (New York, 1933).

KURT GALLING *et al,* (eds.), *Die Religion in Geschichte und Gegenwart,* Handwörterbuch für Theologie und Religionwissenschaft (Tübingen, 1957–)

KENNETH P. LANDON, *Southeast Asia, Crossroad of Religions* (Chicago, 1949).

SARVEPALLI RADHAKRISHNAN, *Eastern Religions and Western Thought* (2nd ed., London, 1951).

Christianity

DANIEL A. BINCHY, *Church and State in Fascist Italy* (London and New York, 1941).

JOHN S. CURTISS, *Church and State in Russia: The Last Years of the Empire, 1900–1917* (London and New York, 1940).

JOHN S. CURTISS, *The Russian Church and the Soviet State, 1917–1950* (Boston, 1953).

EDWARD DUFF, JR. *The Social Thought of the World Council of Churches* (London and New York, 1956).

CHARLES P. GROVES, *The Planting of Christianity in Africa* (London, 1948–1958), 4 vols.

WALDEMAR GURIAN, (ed.), *The Catholic Church in World Affairs* (Notre Dame, Ind., 1954).

G. L. H. HARVEY, (ed.), *The Church and the Twentieth Century* (London, 1936).

JULIUS F. HECKER, *Religion and a Changing Civilization* (London, 1935).

WILLIAM E. HOCKING, Commission of Appraisal of the Laymen's Foreign Missions Inquiry, *Re-thinking Missions: A Laymen's Inquiry after One Hundred Years* (New York, 1932).

KENNETH S. LATOURETTE, *A History of the Expansion of Christianity* (New York and London, 1937–45), 7 vols.

JOHN L. MECHAM, *Church and State in Latin America* (Chapel Hill, N.C., 1934).

ERICH MEISSNER, *Confusion of Faces: The Struggle Between Religion and Secularism in Europe* (London, 1946).

JOSEPH N. MOODY, (ed.), *Church and Society: Catholic Social and Political Thought and Movements, 1789–1950* (New York, 1953).

ARNOLD S. NASH, (ed.), *Protestant Thought in the Twentieth Century* (New York, 1951).

RUTH ROUSE and STEPHEN C. NEIL, *A History of the Ecumenical Movement* (Philadelphia, 1954).

HERBERT W. SCHNEIDER, *Religion in 20th Century America* (Cambridge, Mass., 1952).

GEORGE STEPHENS SPINKS et al., *Religion in Britain since 1900* (London, 1952).

FRANCIS HERBERT STEAD, *The Story of Social Christianity* (London, 1924), 2 vols.

ANSON P. STOKES, *Church and State in the United States: Historical Development and Contemporary Problems of Religious Freedom under the Constitution* (New York, 1950), 3 vols.

ROBERT TOBIAS, *Communist–Christian Encounter in East Europe* (Indianapolis, 1956).

Judaism (See also Chapter XXVIII)

JACOB B. AGUS, *Guideposts in Modern Judaism: An Analysis of Current Trends in Jewish Thought* (New York, 1954).

LOUIS FINKELSTEIN, (ed.), *The Jews: Their History, Culture and Religion* (2nd ed., New York, 1955), 2 vols.

ROBERT GORDIS, *Conservative Judaism* (New York, 1945).

DAVID PHILIPSON, *The Reform Movement in Judaism* (rev. ed., New York, 1931).

LEON ROTH, *Jewish Thought as a Factor in Civilization* (Paris, 1954).

Islam (See also Chapters XXVIII, XXIX)

CHARLES C. ADAMS, *Islam and Modernism in Egypt* (London, 1933).

HAMILTON A. R. GIBB, *Modern Trends in Islam* (Chicago, 1947).

ALPHONSE GOUILLY, *L'Islam devant le monde moderne* (Paris, 1945).

MUHAMMAD IQBAL, *The Reconstruction of Religious Thought in Islam* (London, 1934).

ROGER LE TOURNEAU, *L'Islam contemporian* (Paris, 1950).

WILFRED CANTWELL SMITH, *Islam in Modern History* (Princeton, N.J., 1957).

JOHN S. TRIMINGHAM, *Islam in West Africa* (Oxford, 1959).

GUSTAVE E. VON GRÜNEBAUM, (ed.), *Unity and Variety in Muslim Civilization* (Chicago, 1955).

Hinduism

JOHN N. FARQUHAR, *Modern Religious Movements in India* (New York, 1915).

KENNETH W. MORGAN, (ed.), *The Religion of the Hindus* (New York, 1953).

K. M. PANIKKAR, *Hindu Society at Cross Roads* (Bombay, 1955).

DITTAKAVI SUBRAHMANYA SARMA, *Studies in the Renaissance of Hinduism in the Nineteenth and Twentieth Centuries* (Benares, 1944).

Buddhism

CHAN WING-TSIT, *Religious Trends in Modern China* (New York, 1953).

EDWARD CONZE, *Buddhism: Its Essence and Development* (New York, 1951).

HIDEO KISHIMOTO, (ed.), *Japanese Religion in the Meiji Era* (trans. and adapted by John F. Howes, Tokyo, 1956).

KENNETH W. MORGAN, (ed.), *The Path of the Buddha* (New York, 1956).

T. R. V. MURTI, *The Central Philosophy of Buddhism* (London, 1955).

CHAPTER XXVI
EDUCATION

ROBERT FREEMAN BUTTS and LAURENCE A. CREMIN, *A History of Education in American Culture* (New York, 1953).

OLIVER CROMWELL CARMICHAEL, *Universities: Commonwealth and American, a Comparative Study* (New York, 1959).

MARGARET A. CLAPP, (ed.), *The Modern University* (Ithaca, N.Y., 1950).

STANLEY J. CURTIS and M.E.A. BOULTWOOD, *A Short History of Educational Ideas* (2nd ed., London, 1956).

STANLEY J. CURTIS, *Education in Britain since 1900* (London, 1952).

M. M. DEINEKO, *Forty Years of Education in the U.S.S.R.: Fact and Figures* (trans. by D. Myshne, Moscow, 1957).

HAROLD C. DENT, *Change in English Education: A Historical Survey* (London, 1952).

JOHN DEWEY, *School and Society* (rev. ed., Chicago, 1915).

ROBERT K. HALL, *Education for a New Japan* (New Haven, 1949).

NICHOLAS A. HANS, *Comparative Education: A Study of Educational Factors and Traditions* (London, 1949).

RICHARD HOFSTADTER and C. DEWITT HARDY, *The Development and Scope of Higher Education in the United States* (New York, 1952).

HUMAYUN KABIR, *Education in New India* (London, 1956).

HUGH L. KEENLEYSIDE and A. F. THOMAS, *History of Japanese Education and Present Educational System* (Tokyo, 1937).

EDMUND KING, *Other Schools and Ours* (London, 1960).

EDGAR W. KNIGHT, *Fifty Years of American Education: A Historical Review and Critical Appraisal* (New York, 1952).

ALEXANDER G. KOROL, *Soviet Education for Science and Technology* (New York, 1957).

INTERNATIONAL BUREAU OF EDUCATION and UNESCO, *International Yearbook of Education* (Geneva and Paris, 1933–).

RODERIC D. MATTHEWS and MATTA AKRAWI, *Education in the Arab Countries of the Near East* (Washington, D.C., 1949).

ADOLF E. MEYER, *The Development of Education in the 20th Century* (2nd ed., New York, 1949).

ARTHUR M. MOELMAN and JOSEPH S. ROUCEK, (eds.), *Comparative Education* (New York, 1952).

WALTER S. MONROE, (ed.), *Encyclopedia of Educational Research* (3rd ed., New York, 1960).

MARGARET H. READ, *Education and Social Change in Tropical Areas* (London and New York, 1955).

ROBERT ULICH, *History of Educational Thought* (New York, 1950).

UNESCO, *Basic Facts and Figures* (Paris, 1952–), biennial.

UNESCO, *Education in a Technological Society* (Paris, 1952).

UNESCO, *Humanism and Education in East and West* (Paris, 1953).

UNESCO, *National Programmes of Education for Social Development* (Paris, 1954).

UNESCO, *Progress of Literacy in Various Countries* (Paris, 1953).

UNESCO, *World Handbook of Educational Organization and Statistics* (1st ed., Paris, 1951).

WILLIAM D. WALL, *Education and Mental Health* (Paris, 1955).

HOWARD E. WILSON, *Universities and World Affairs* (New York, 1951).

JAMES Y. C. YEN, *The Mass Education Movement in China* (Shanghai, 1925).

CHAPTER XXVII

THE USE OF LEISURE

(See also Chapters XI and XXXI)

J. FREDERIC DEWHURST and ASSOCIATES, 'Recreation', in *America's Needs and Resources* (New York, 1955).

GEORGE A. LUNDBERG *et al.*, *Leisure: A Suburban Study* (New York, 1934).

HAROLD D. MEYER and CHARLES K. BRIGHTBILL, *Community Recreation: A Guide to Its Organization and Administration* (Boston, 1948).

MARTIN H. and ESTHER S. NEUMEYER, *Leisure and Recreation* (New York, 1949).

G. OTT ROMNEY, *Off-the-Job-Living* (New York, 1945).

BERNARD ROSENBERG and DAVID MANNING WHITE, (eds.), *Mass Culture: The Popular Arts in America* (Glencoe, Ill., 1957).

GILBERT SELDES, *The Public Arts* (New York, 1956).

THE ARTS COUNCIL OF GREAT BRITAIN, *The First Ten Years: Eleventh Annual Report* (London, 1956).

Reading

R. E. BARKER, *Books for All* (Paris, 1956).

MALCOLM COWLEY, *The Literary Situation* (New York, 1954).

JAMES D. HART, *The Popular Book: A History of America's Literary Taste* (New York, 1950).

FRANK LUTHER MOTT, *A History of American Magazines* (Cambridge, Mass., 1938–), 5 vols.

Motion Pictures

BOSLEY CROWTHER, *The Lion's Share: The Story of an Entertainment Empire* (New York, 1957).

FILM CENTRE, London, *The Film Industry in Six European Countries* (Paris, 1950).

GOVERNMENT OF INDIA, *Report of the Film Enquiry Committee* (New Delhi, 1951).

MOTION PICTURE ASSOCIATION OF JAPAN, *Japanese Motion Picture Industry* (Tokyo, 1955).

PARKER TYLER, *The Three Faces of the Film: The Art, the Dream, the Cult* (New York, 1960).

HORTENSE POWDERMAKER, *Hollywood, the Dream Factory* (Boston, 1950).

PAUL ROTHA, *The Film till Now: A Survey of World Cinema* (New York, 1949).

MARTHA WOLFENSTEIN and NATHAN LEITES, *Movies: A Psychological Study* (Glencoe, Ill., 1950).

Radio and Television

LEO BOGART, *The Age of Television* (rev. ed., New York, 1958).

BRITISH BROADCASTING CORPORATION, *The BBC Television Story* (London, 1956).

CHARLES A. SIEPMANN, *Radio, Television and Society* (New York, 1950).

Popular Music and Dance

RUDI BLESH, *Shining Trumpets: A History of Jazz* (rev. ed., New York and London, 1958).

MARGARET LLOYD, *The Borzoi Book of Modern Dance* (New York, 1949).

MARSHALL STEARNS, *The Story of Jazz* (New York, 1956).

BARRY ULANOV, *A History of Jazz in America* (New York, 1952).

Sports, Travel and Hobbies

FRANK G. MENKE, *The New Encyclopedia of Sports* (rev. ed., New York, 1953).

NATIONAL RECREATION ASSOCIATION OF THE USA, *Recreation and Park Yearbook, Mid-century Edition: A Review of Local and County Recreation and Park Developments, 1900–1950* (New York, 1951).

CHAPTER XXVIII

SELF IMAGE AND ASPIRATIONS OF NATIONS

(See also Chapters III, XXIII)

Liberal Democracy

JAMES B. BRYCE, *Modern Democracies* (London, 1921), 2 vols.

MICHAEL P. FOGARTY, *Christian Democracy in Western Europe, 1820–1953* (Notre Dame, Ind., 1957).

THEODORE M. GREENE, *Liberalism: Its Theory and Practice* (Austin, Texas, 1957).

THOMAS P. NEILL, *The Rise and Decline of Liberalism* (Milwaukee, 1953).

MICHAEL OAKESHOTT, *Social and Political Doctrines of Contemporary Europe* (Cambridge, 1939).

GUIDO DE RUGGIERO, *The History of European Liberalism* (trans. by R. G. Collingwood, London, 1927).

ARTHUR M. SCHLESINGER, Jr., *The Vital Center* (Boston, 1949).

JOHN A. SCOTT, *Republican Ideas and the Liberal Tradition in France, 1870-1914* (New York, 1951).

THOMAS VERNON SMITH and EDUARD C. LINDEMAN, *The Democratic Way of Life* (Chicago, 1926).

Marxist–Leninist Communism

RAYMOND A. BAUER, *The New Man in Soviet Psychology* (Cambridge, Mass., 1952).

COLUMBIA UNIVERSITY RUSSIAN INSTITUTE, (ed.), *The Anti-Stalin Campaign and International Communism: A Selection of Documents* (New York, 1956).

MICHAEL T. FLORINSKY, *Toward an Understanding of the U.S.S.R.* (rev. ed., New York, 1951).

MALCOLM D. KENNEDY, *A History of Communism in East Asia* (New York, 1957).

NIKITA S. KRUSHCHEV, *Speeches and Interviews on World Problems* (Moscow, 1958).

ANNA M. PANKRATOVA, *History of the U.S.S.R.* (comp. by K. V. Basilevich, Moscow, 1947–48), 3 vols.

G. V. PLEKHANOV, *History of Russian Social Thought* (trans. by B. Bakar *et al.*, New York, 1938).

MIKHAIL N. POKROVSKY, *Brief History of Russia* (trans. by D. S. Mirsky, New York, 1933).

ANDREW ROTHSTEIN, *A History of the U.S.S.R.* (Harmondsworth, Middx., 1950).

ERNEST J. SIMMONS, (ed.), *Continuity and Change in Russian and Soviet Thought* (Cambridge, Mass., 1955).

UNITED NATIONS, *Report of the Special Committee on the Problem of Hungary* (New York, 1957).

GEORG VON RAUCH, *A History of Soviet Russia* (trans. by P. and A. Jacobsohn, New York, 1957).

ALEXANDER S. VUCINICH, *The Soviet Academy of Sciences* (Stanford, Calif., 1956).

Anti-Liberal Authoritarianism

GERALD BRENAN, *The Spanish Labyrinth* (2nd ed., Cambridge, 1950).

CHARLES A. GULICK, *Austria from Habsburg to Hitler* (Berkeley, Calif., 1948), 2 vols.

NICHOLAS HORTHY, *Memoirs* (trans. by F. G. Renier and A. Cliff, New York, 1957).

EDWIN LIEUWEN, *Arms and Politics in Latin America* (New York, 1960).

BENITO MUSSOLINI, *The Doctrine of Fascism* (trans. by E. Cope, 2nd ed., Florence, 1937).

Racial Superiority

ALAN L. C. BULLOCK, *Hitler: A Study in Tyranny* (London and New York, 1952).

GEORGE H. CALPIN, (ed.), *The South African Way of Life: Values and Ideals of a Multi-Racial Society* (New York, 1953).

GWENDOLEN M. CARTER, *The Politics of Inequality: South Africa since 1948* (London and New York, 1958).

CORNELIUS W. DE KIEWIET, *The Anatomy of South African Misery* (London and New York, 1956).

HANS KOHN, (ed.), *German History: Some New German Views* (London, 1954).

DANIEL W. KRUGER, (ed.), *South African Parties and Policies, 1910–1960* (Cape Town and London, 1960).

LEOPOLD MARQUARD, *Peoples and Policies of South Africa* (2nd ed., New York, 1960).

FRIEDRICH MEINECKE *The German Catastrophe* (trans. by Sidney B. Fay, Cambridge, Mass., 1950).

KOPPEL S. PINSON, *Modern Germany, its History and Civilization* (New York, 1954).

HUGH R. TREVOR-ROPER, *The Last Days of Hitler* (3rd ed., London, 1956).

States of Religious Origin

DAVID BEN-GURION, *Rebirth and Destiny of Israel* (trans. by Mordekhai Nurock, New York, 1954).

MARTIN BUBER, *Israel and Palestine: The History of an Idea* (trans. by S. Godman, London, 1952).

ISRAEL COHEN, *The Zionist Movement* (rev. ed., New York, 1946).

J. B. DASGUPTA, *Indo–Pakistan Relations, 1947–55* (Amsterdam, 1958).

JACOB C. HUREWITZ, *The Struggle for Palestine* (New York, 1950).

S. M. IKRAM and PERCIVAL SPEAR, (eds.), *The Cultural Heritage of Pakistan* (Karachi and New York, 1955).

OSCAR I. JANOWSKY, *Foundations of Israel: Emergence of a Welfare State* (Princeton, 1959).

I. H. QURESHI, *The Pakistani Way of Life* (New York, 1956).

WILFRED CANTWELL SMITH, *Pakistan as an Islamic State* (Lahore, 1954).

RICHARD SYMONDS, *The Making of Pakistan* (London, 1950).

Independence in Face of European Expansion

HALIDÉ EDIB, *Turkey Faces West* (New Haven, 1930).

ELIOT G. MEARS et al., *Modern Turkey: A Politico–Economic Interpretation 1908–1923* (New York, 1924).

MARGERY F. PERHAM, *The Government of Ethiopia* (London, 1948).

IKBAL ALI SHAH, *Modern Afghanistan* (London, 1939).

DONALD EVERETT WEBSTER, *The Turkey of Atatürk: Social Process in the Turkish Reformation* (Philadelphia, 1939).

DONALD N. WILBER, *Iran, Past and Present* (4th ed., Princeton, 1958).

AHMED EMIN YALMAN, *Turkey in my Time* (Norman, Okla., 1956).

Awakening Nationalism—Africa

DAVID E. APTER, *The Gold Coast in Transition: A Case Study of Political Institutional Transfer* (Princeton, N.J., 1955).

WILLIAM R. BASCOM and MELVILLE J. HERSKOVITS (eds.), *Continuity and Change in African Cultures* (Chicago, 1958).

GWENDOLEN M. CARTER and WILLIAM O. BROWN, (eds.), *Transition in Africa: Studies in Political Adaptation* (Boston, 1958).

JAMES S. COLEMAN, *Nigeria: Background to Nationalism* (Berkeley, Calif., 1958).

BASIL DAVIDSON, *The African Awakening* (London, 1955).

ROBERT L. DELAVIGNETTE, *Freedom and Authority in French West Africa* (London, New York and Toronto, 1950).

JAMES DUFFY, *Portuguese Africa* (Cambridge, Mass., 1959).

THOMAS L. HODGKIN, *Nationalism in Colonial Africa* (London, 1956).

WILLIAM MALCOLM, LORD HAILEY, *An African Survey: A Study of Problems Arising in Africa South of the Sahara* (rev. ed., London and New York, 1957).

Z. A. MARSH and G. KINGSNORTH, *An Introduction to the History of East Africa* (Cambridge, 1957).

GEORGE PADMORE, *Pan-Africanism or Communism? The Coming Struggle for Africa* (London, 1956).

VIRGINIA M. THOMPSON and RICHARD ADLOFF, *The Emerging States of French Equatorial Africa* (Stanford, Calif., 1960).

CHAPTER XXIX
DRIVES FOR CULTURAL INTEGRITY AND RECOGNITION

India and Ceylon

FREDERICK G. BAILEY, *Tribe, Caste and Nation* (New York, 1960).

A. R. DESAI, *Social Background of Indian Nationalism* (Bombay and New York, 1948).

MOHANDAS K. GANDHI, *Gandhi's Autobiography: The Story of My Experiments with Truth* (trans. by Mahadev Desai, Washington, D.C., 1948).

JAWAHARLAL NEHRU, *Jawaharlal Nehru, An Autobiography: With Musings on Recent Events in India* (new ed., London, 1945).

JAWAHARLAL NEHRU, *The Discovery of India* (New York, 1946).

LEWIS S. S. O'MALLEY, (ed.), *Modern India and the West: A Study of the Interaction of their Civilizations* (London, New York, 1941).

K. M. PANIKKAR, *A Survey of Indian History* (3rd ed., Bombay and New York, 1956).

RICHARD L. PARK and IRENE TINKER, (eds.), *Leadership and Political Institutions in India* (Princeton, 1959).

SARVEPALLI RADHAKRISHNAN and J. H. MUIRHEAD, (eds.), *Contemporary Indian Philosophy* (rev. ed., London, 1952).

B. PATTABHI SITARAMAYYA, *The History of the Indian National Congress* (Bombay, 1946–47), 2 vols.

THOMAS G. P. SPEAR, *India, Pakistan, and the West* (2nd ed., London and New York, 1952).

WILLIAM HOWARD WRIGGINS, *Ceylon: Dilemmas of a New Nation* (Princeton, N.J., 1960).

China

O. BRIÈRE, *Fifty Years of Chinese Philosophy, 1898–1950* (trans. by L. G. Thompson, London, 1956).

CHIANG MONLIN, *Tides from the West, a Chinese Autobiography* (New Haven, 1947).

HERRLEE G. CREEL, *Chinese Thought, from Confucius to Mao Tse-tung* (Chicago, 1953).

CHARLES P. FITZGERALD, *Revolution in China* (London and New York, 1952).

HO KAN-CHIH, *A History of the Modern Chinese Revolution* (Peking, 1959).

ARTHUR N. HOLCOMBE, *The Chinese Revolution, a Phase in the Regeneration of a World Power* (Cambridge, Mass., 1930).

HU CHANG-TU et al., *China: Its People, its Society, its Culture* (ed. by Hsiao Hsia; New Haven, 1960).

KUO PIN-CHIA, *China: New Age and New Outlook* (London, 1956).

JOSEPH NEEDHAM, *Science and Civilisation in China* (Cambridge, 1954–).

SUN YAT-SEN, *San Min Chu I: The Three Principles of the People* (trans. by Frank W. Price, Shanghai, 1927; Taipei, 1953).

TENG SSÜ-YÜ and JOHN K. FAIRBANK, *China's Response to the West: A Documentary Survey, 1839–1923* (Cambridge, Mass., 1954).

Japan

RUTH BENEDICT, *The Chrysanthemum and the Sword: Patterns of Japanese Culture* (Boston, 1946).

HUGH BORTON et. al., *A Selected List of Books and Articles on Japan in English, French and German* (Cambridge, Mass., 1954).

HUGH BORTON, *Japan's Modern Century* (New York, 1955).

DELMER M. BROWN, *Nationalism in Japan* (Berkeley, Calif., 1955).

CENTENARY CULTURAL COUNCIL, *A Cultural History of the Meiji Era* (Tokyo, 1955–1958), 10 vols.

KAZUO KAWAI, *Japan's American Interlude* (Chicago, 1960).

E. HERBERT NORMAN, *Japan's Emergence as a Modern State* (New York, 1940).

EDWIN O. REISCHAUER, *Japan, Past and Present* (2nd ed., New York, 1953).

GEORGE B. SANSOM, *The Western World and Japan: A Study in the Interaction of European and Asiatic Cultures* (London, 1950).

South East Asia and Korea

WILLARD H. ELSBREE, *Japan's Role in Southeast Asian Nationalist Movements, 1940 to 1945* (Cambridge, Mass., 1953).

JOSEPH R. HAYDEN, *The Philippines: A Study in National Development* (New York, 1942).

GEORGE M. KAHIN, *Nationalism and Revolution in Indonesia* (Ithaca, N.Y., 1952).

GEORGE M. MCCUNE and ARTHUR L. GREY, *Korea Today* (Cambridge, Mass., 1950).

MAUNG MAUNG, *Burma in the Family of Nations* (2nd ed., Amsterdam and New York, 1957).

VIRGINIA M. THOMPSON, *Thailand: The New Siam* (New York, 1941).

AMRY VANDENBOSCH and RICHARD A. BUTWELL, *Southeast Asia among the World Powers* (Lexington, Kentucky, 1958).

RICHARD OLOF WINSTEDT, *The Malays: A Cultural History* (rev. ed., New York, 1950).

The Arabs

JAMAL MUHAMMAD AHMED, *The Intellectual Origins of Egyptian Nationalism* (London, 1960).

GEORGE ANTONIUS, *The Arab Awakening: The Story of the Arab National Movement* (London, 1938).

EDWARD S. ATIYAH, *The Arabs* (Harmondsworth, Middx., 1955).

x CARLETON S. COON, *Caravan: The Story of the Middle East* (rev. ed., New York, 1958).

NABIH A. FARIS, (ed.), *The Arab Heritage* (Princeton, N.J., 1944).

NABIH A. FARIS and MOHAMMED TAWFIK HUSAYN, *The Crescent in Crisis: An Interpretive Study of the Modern Arab World* (Lawrence, Kansas, 1955).

ALLAL AL FASSI, *The Independence Movements in North Africa* (trans. by H. Z. Nuseibeh, Washington, D.C., 1954).

x WALTER Z. LAQUEUR, (ed.), *The Middle East in Transition* (New York, 1958).

STEPHEN H. LONGRIGG, *Iraq 1900–1950: A Political, Social and Economic History* (London and New York, 1953).

GAMAL ABDUL NASSER, *Egypt's Liberation: The Philosophy of the Revolution* (Washington, D.C., 1955).

H. ST. JOHN B. PHILBY, *Sa'udi Arabia* (London and New York, 1955).

NICOLA A. ZIADEH, *Syria and Lebanon* (New York, 1957).

United States of America

x DANIEL J. BOORSTIN, (ed.), *The Chicago History of American Civilization* (Chicago, 1956–   ), 20 vols.

HENRY S. COMMAGER et al., *Years of the Modern: An American Appraisal* (New York, 1949).

HENRY S. COMMAGER, *The American Mind* (New Haven, 1950).

MERLE E. CURTI, *The Growth of American Thought* (2nd ed., New York, 1951).

RALPH H. GABRIEL, *The Course of American Democratic Thought: An Intellectual History since 1815* (2nd ed., New York, 1956).

RALPH H. GABRIEL, (ed.), *The Library of Congress Series in American Civilization* (Cambridge, Mass., 1951–54), 6 vols.

OSCAR HANDLIN *et al.*, *Harvard Guide to American History* (Cambridge, Mass., 1954).

LOUIS HARTZ, *The Liberal Tradition in America: An Interpretation of American Political Thought Since the Revolution* (New York, 1955).

RICHARD HOFSTADTER, *The Age of Reform* (New York, 1955).

HALVDAN KOHT, *The American Spirit in Europe* (Philadelphia, 1949).

ARTHUR M. SCHLESINGER, Jr., *The Age of Roosevelt* (Boston, 1957–60), 3 vols.

HARVEY WISH, *Society and Thought in America* (New York, 1950–52), 2 vols.

Canada, Australia, New Zealand

GEORGE W. BROWN, (ed.), *Canada* (Berkeley and Los Angeles, Calif., 1950).

JOHN B. CONDLIFFE, *New Zealand in the Making* (rev. ed., London, 1959).

GORDON GREENWOOD, (ed.), *Australia: A Social and Political History* (New York and Sydney, 1955).

ARTHUR R. M. LOWER, *Colony to Nation* (3rd ed., Toronto, 1949).

ALAN G. L. SHAW, *Story of Australia* (London, 1955).

Latin America

RICHARD N. ADAMS *et al.*, *Social Change in Latin America Today* (New York, 1960).

FERNANDO DE AZEVEDO, *Brazilian Culture* (trans. by W. R. Crawford, New York, 1950).

HARRY BERNSTEIN, *Modern and Contemporary Latin America* (Philadelphia, Pa., 1952).

WILLIAM R. CRAWFORD, *A Century of Latin American Thought* (Cambridge, Mass., 1944).

ROBERT A. HUMPHREYS, *Latin American History: A Guide to the Literature in English* (London and New York, 1958).

HENRY B. PARKES, *A History of Mexico* (rev. ed., Boston, 1950).

ANÍBAL SANCHEZ REULET, *Contemporary Latin-American Philosophy* (trans. by W. R. Trask, Albuquerque, New Mexico, 1954).

WILLIAM L. SCHURZ, *This New World: The Civilization of Latin America* (New York, 1954).

T. LYNN SMITH, *Brazil: People and Institutions* (rev. ed., Baton Rouge, La., 1954).

FRANK TANNENBAUM, *Mexico, the Struggle for Peace and Bread* (New York, 1950).

DANIEL COSÍO VILLEGAS, *Extremos de América* (Mexico, D. F., 1949).

GEORGE WYTHE *et al.*, *Brazil, an Expanding Economy* (New York, 1949).

Cultural Minorities

ALBERT H. HOURANI, *Minorities in the Arab World* (London and New York, 1947).

CLAUDE L. INIS, *National Minorities: An International Problem* (Cambridge, Mass., 1955).

CARLILE A. MACARTNEY, *National States and National Minorities* (London, 1934).

JOSÉ CARLOS MARIÁTEGUI, *Siete Ensayos de Interpretación de la Realidad Peruana* (2nd ed., Lima, 1934; Santiago de Chile, 1955).

VIRGINIA M. THOMPSON and RICHARD ADLOFF, *Minority Problems in Southeast Asia* (Stanford, Calif., 1955).

CHAPTER XXX
DRIVE FOR INDIVIDUAL FREEDOM AND RECOGNITION

Labour

MARGARET BONDFIELD, *A Life's Work* (London, 1948).

G. D. H. COLE, *A Short History of the British Working-class Movement, 1789–1947* (London, 1948).

JOHN R. COMMONS *et al.*, *History of Labour in the United States* (New York, 1918–35), 4 vols.

WILFRID H. CROOK, *The General Strike: A Study of Labor's Tragic Weapon in Theory and Practice* (Chapel Hill, North Carolina, 1931).

ISAAC DEUTSCHER, *Soviet Trade Unions: Their Place in Soviet Labour Policy* (London, 1950).

SAAD ED DIN FAWZI, *The Labour Movement in the Sudan* (London, 1957).

WALTER GALENSON, (ed.), *Comparative Labor Movements* (New York, 1952).

LEWIS L. LORWIN, *The International Labor Movement: History, Policies, Outlook* (New York, 1953).

VAL R. LORWIN, *The French Labor Movement* (Cambridge, Mass., 1954).

HILARY A. MARQUAND, (ed.), *Organized Labour in Four Continents* (London and New York, 1939).

H. A. MILLIS and R. E. MONTGOMERY, *Organized Labor* (New York, 1945).

ADOLF F. STURMTHAL, *Unity and Diversity in European Labor: An Introduction to Contemporary Labor Movements* (Glencoe, Ill., 1953).

Peasants

HENRY H. AYROUT, *The Fellaheen* (trans. by H. Wyament, Cairo, 1945).

RONALD P. DORE, *Land Reform in Japan* (London, New York and Toronto, 1959).

ERICH H. JACOBY, *Agrarian Unrest in Southeast Asia* (New York, 1949).

DAVID MITRANY, *Marx against the Peasant: A Study in Social Dogmatism* (Chapel Hill, North Carolina, 1951).

N. G. RANGA, *Revolutionary Peasants* (New Delhi, 1949).

ROYAL INSTITUTE OF INTERNATIONAL AFFAIRS, *Agrarian Problems from the Baltic to the Aegean: Discussion of a Peasant Programme* (London, 1944).

JOZO TOMAŠEVIĆ, *Peasants, Politics and Economic Change in Yugoslavia* (Stanford, Calif, 1955).

RUTH TROUTON, *Peasant Renaissance in Yugoslavia, 1900–1950* (London, 1952).

Women

SOPHONISBA P. BRECKINRIDGE, *Women in the Twentieth Century* (New York, 1933).

VERA BRITTAIN, *Lady into Woman: A History of Women from Victoria to Elizabeth II* (London, 1953).

MAURICE DUVERGER, *The Political Role of Women* (Paris, 1955).

SIDONIE M. GRUENBERG, *The Many Lives of Modern Woman* (Garden City, N.Y., 1952).

FANNINA W. HALLE, *Women in Soviet Russia* (trans. by M. M. Green, New York, 1933).

ASIZA HUSSEIN, *Women in the Moslem World* (Washington, D.C., 1954).

INTERNATIONAL INSTITUTE OF DIFFERING CULTURES, *Women's Role in the Development of Tropical and Sub-Tropical Countries* (Brussels, 1959).

RADEN ADJENG KARTINI, *Letters of a Javanese Princess* (trans. by A. L. Symmers, New York, 1920).

MARGARET MEAD, *Male and Female: A Study of the Sexes in a Changing World* (New York, 1955).

HANSA M. MEHTA, *The Woman Under the Hindu Law of Marriage and Succession* (Bombay, 1943).

ALVA MYRDAL and VIOLA KLEIN, *Woman's Two Roles: Home and Work* (New York, 1956).

ARTHUR H. NETHERCOT, *The First Five Lives of Annie Besant* (Chicago, 1960).

RACHEL C. STRACHEY, (ed.), *Our Freedom and Its Results* (London, 1936).

RACHEL C. STRACHEY, '*The Cause': A Short History of the Women's Movement in Great Britain* (London, 1928).

UNESCO and INTERNATIONAL BUREAU OF EDUCATION, *Access of Women to Education* (Paris, 1952).

UNITED NATIONS, *Legal Status of Married Women* (New York, 1950).

RUTH F. WOODSMALL, *Women and the New East* (Washington, D.C., 1960).

Race and Caste Groups

B. R. AMBEDKAR, *What Congress and Gandhi Have Done to the Untouchables* (2nd ed., Bombay, 1945).

MARGARET JUST BUTCHER, *The Negro in American Culture* (New York, 1956).

JOHN HOPE FRANKLIN, *From Slavery to Freedom* (2nd ed., New York, 1956).

E. FRANKLIN FRAZIER, *The Negro in the United States* (rev. ed., New York, 1949).

GOVIND S. GHURYE, *Caste and Class in India* (3rd ed., Bombay and New York, 1957).

OSCAR HANDLIN, *Race and Nationality in American Life* (Boston, 1957).

RAYFORD W. LOGAN, (ed.), *What the Negro Wants* (Chapel Hill, North Carolina, 1944).

GUNNAR MYRDAL, *An American Dilemma: The Negro Problem and Modern Democracy* (New York, 1944), 2 vols.

KAREL L. ROSKAM, *Interracial Relationships in the Union of South Africa and the International Community* (Leiden, 1960).

CHARLES H. WESLEY, (ed.), *The Negro in the Americas* (Washington, D.C., 1940).

CHAPTER XXXI
LITERATURE AND THE ARTS IN THE WESTERN CULTURE AREA

Visual Arts

ALFRED H. BARR, Jr., *H. Matisse, His Art and His Public* (New York, 1951.)

ALFRED H. BARR, Jr., *Masters of Modern Art* (New York, 1954).

ALFRED H. BARR, Jr., *Picasso: Fifty Years of His Art* (New York, 1946).

Encyclopedia of World Art (New York, 1961–   ), 15 vols.

GEOFFREY HOLME, (ed.), *Art in the U.S.S.R.: Architecture, Sculpture, Painting, Graphic Arts, Theatre, Film, Crafts* (London and New York, 1935).

PAUL KLEE, *The Thinking Eye: The Notebooks of Paul Klee* (trans. by Ralph Manheim, London and New York, 1961).

JOHN A. KOUWENHOVEN, *Made in America: The Arts in Modern Civilization* (Garden City, N.Y., 1948).

OLIVER W. LARKIN, *Art and Life in America* (rev. ed., New York, 1960).

MUSEUM OF MODERN ART, *Photography 1838–1937* (New York, 1937).

GEORGII V. PLEKHANOV, *Art and Society* (trans. by A. Goldstein *et al.*, New York, 1937).

MAURICE RAYNAL, (ed.), *Modern Painting* (trans. by Gilbert Stuart, Geneva, 1953).

HERBERT READ, *Concise History of Modern Painting* (New York, 1959).

ANDREW C. RITCHIE, *Abstract Painting and Sculpture in America* (New York, 1951).

ANDREW C. RITCHIE, (ed.), *German Art of the 20th Century* (New York, 1957).

ANDREW C. RITCHIE, *Sculpture of the Twentieth Century* (New York, 1952).

G. DI SAN LAZZARO, *Klee: A Study of His Life and Work* (trans. by Stuart Hood, New York, 1957).

EDWARD STEICHEN, (ed.), *The Family of Man* (New York, 1955).

Architecture

HERBERT BAYER, WALTER GROPIUS and ISE GROPIUS, (eds.), *Bauhaus 1919–1928* (New York, 1938).

LE CORBUSIER (C. E. JEANNERET-GRIS), *My Work* (trans. by J. Palmer, London, 1960).

LE CORBUSIER (C. E. JEANNERET-GRIS), *Towards a New Architecture* (trans. by F. Etchells, New York, 1927).

SIGFRIED GIEDION, *Space, Time and Architecture* (3rd ed., rev., Cambridge, Mass., 1956).

HENRY RUSSELL HITCHCOCK, *Architecture: Nineteenth and Twentieth Centuries* (Harmondsworth, Middx, 1958).

HENRY RUSSELL HITCHCOCK, *Latin American Architecture* (New York, 1955).

PHILIP JOHNSON, *Mies van der Rohe* (New York, 1947).

STAMO PAPADAKI, (ed.), *Le Corbusier, Architect, Painter, Writer* (New York, 1948).

MORRIS WEITZ, (ed.), *Problems in Aesthetics: An Introductory Book of Readings* (New York, 1959).

FRANK LLOYD WRIGHT, *A Testament* (New York, 1957).

Music

MERLE ARMITAGE, (ed.), *Schoenberg* (New York, 1937).

BORIS V. ASAFIEV, *Russian Music from the Beginning of the Nineteenth Century* (trans. by A. J. Swan, Ann Arbor, Mich., 1953).

GILBERT CHASE, *America's Music, from the Pilgrims to the Present* (New York, 1955).

HOWARD HARTOG, (ed.), *European Music in the Twentieth Century* (London, 1957).

PAUL HENRY LANG, *Music in Western Civilization* (New York, 1941).

ADOLFO SALAZAR, *Music in Our Time* (trans. by Isobel Pope, New York, 1946).

HALSEY STEVENS, *Life and Music of Bela Bartok* (New York, 1953).

HEINRICH STROBEL, *Stravinsky: Classic Humanist* (trans. by Hans Rosenwald, New York, 1955).

Literature

ANTUN BARAC, *A History of Yugoslav Literature* (trans. by P. Mijušković, Belgrade, 1955).

E. R. BENTLEY, *The Modern Theatre: A Study of Dramatists and the Drama* (London, 1948).

PIERRE BRODIN, *Présences Contemporaines* (Paris, 1954–57), 3 vols.

E. GORDON CRAIG, *On the Art of the Theatre* (London, 1911; New York, 1956).

RICHARD ELLMANN, *James Joyce* (New York, 1959).

ANGEL FLORES, (ed.), *The Kafka Problem* (New York, 1946).

JOHN GASSNER, *The Theatre in Our Times: A Survey of the Men, Materials and Movements in the Modern Theatre* (New York, 1954).

NIKOLAI M. GORCHAKOV, *Stanislavsky Directs* (trans. by M. Goldina, New York, 1954).

SIMON HALKIN, *Modern Hebrew Literature: Trends and Values* (New York, 1950).

PEDRO HENRÍQUEZ-UREÑA, *Literary Currents in Hispanic America* (Cambridge, Mass., 1945).

MANFRED KRIDL, *A Survey of Polish Literature and Culture* (trans. by O. Scherer-Virski, New York, 1956).

VICTOR LANGE, *Modern German Literature, 1870–1940* (Ithaca, N.Y., 1945).

C. K. OGDEN and I. A. RICHARDS, *The Meaning of Meaning* (2nd ed., London, 1927).

GEORGE D. PAINTER, *Marcel Proust, a Biography,* (London, 1959), 2 vols.

J. B. PRIESTLEY, *Literature and Western Man* (London and New York, 1960).

I. A. RICHARDS, *Principles of Literary Criticism* (2nd ed., London, 1926).

HAROLD V. ROUTH, *English Literature and Ideas in the 20th Century* (3rd ed., London, 1950).

RICHARD SAMUAL and R. HINTON THOMAS, *Expressionism in German Life, Literature and the Theatre* (Cambridge, 1939).

ERNEST J. SIMMONS, *Russian Fiction and Soviet Ideology: Introduction to Fedin, Leonov, and Sholokhov* (New York, 1958).

MARK L. SLONIM, *Modern Russian Literature* (London and New York, 1953).

HORATIO SMITH, (ed.), *Columbia Dictionary of Modern European Literature* (New York, 1947).

ROBERT E. SPILLER *et al.,* (eds.) *Literary History of the United States* (rev. ed., New York, 1953), 3 vols.

GLEB STRUVE, *Soviet Russian Literature, 1917–1950* (Norman, Okla., 1951).

WILLARD THORP, *American Writing in the Twentieth Century* (Cambridge, Mass., 1960).

ARTURO TORRES-RIOSECO, *The Epic of Latin American Literature* (rev. ed., New York, 1946).

RENÉ WELLEK, *A History of Modern Criticism, 1750–1950* (New Haven, 1955–).

EDMUND WILSON, *Axel's Castle* (New York, 1931).

Mass Media and the Arts

MAURICE BARDÈCHE and ROBERT BRASILLACH, *The History of Motion Pictures* (trans. and ed. by Iris Barry, London and New York, 1938).

SERGE M. EISENSTEIN, *The Film Sense* (trans. by Jay Leyda; new ed., London, 1948).

RICHARD GRIFFITH, *The World of Robert Flaherty* (London and New York, 1953).

JAY LEYDA, *Kino: A History of the Russian and Soviet Film* (London and New York, 1960).

HERBERT L. MATTHEWS, *The Education of a Correspondent* (New York, 1946).

PAUL ROTHA, (ed.), *Documentary Film* (3rd ed., London, 1952).

GILBERT SELDES, *The Seven Lively Arts* (New York and London, 1924; 1957).

CHAPTER XXXII

LITERATURE AND ARTS IN EASTERN CULTURE AREA

Literature

ARTHUR J. ARBERRY, (ed. and trans.), *Modern Arabic Poetry: An Anthology with English Verse Translations* (London, 1950).

PIERRE CACHIA, *Taha Hussein: His Place in the Egyptian Literary Renaissance* (London, 1956).

CHOU SHU-JÊN, *Selected Works of Lu Hsün* (pseud.) (trans. by Yang Hsien-yi and Gladys Yang, Peking, 1956–1959), 3 vols.

HU SHIH, *The Chinese Renaissance* (Chicago, 1934).

HUANG SUNG-K'ANG, *Lu Hsün and the New Culture Movement of Modern China* (Amsterdam, 1957).

TAHA HUSSEIN, *The Future of Culture in Egypt* (trans. by Sidney Glazer, Washington, D.C., 1954).

MUHAMMAD IQBAL, *Poems from Iqbal* (trans. by V. G. Kiernan, London and New York, 1955).

DONALD KEENE, *Japanese Literature: An Introduction for Western Readers* (London, 1953).

DONALD KEENE, (ed.), *Modern Japanese Literature, an Anthology* (New York, 1956).

KOKUSAI BUNKA SHINKOKAI, (ed.), *Introduction to Contemporary Japanese Literature* (trans. by Kenji Hamada, Tokyo, 1939).

BHARATAN KUMARAPPA, (ed.), *The Indian Literatures of Today* (Bombay, 1947).

YOSHIO OKAZAKI, (comp.), *Japanese Literature in the Meiji Era* (trans. and adapted by V. H. Viglelmo, Tokyo, 1955).

K. M. PANIKKAR, (comp.), *Modern Chinese Stories* (trans. by Huang K'un, Delhi, 1953).

PEGGY RUTHERFORD, (ed.), *Darkness and Light: An Anthology of African Writing* (London, 1958).

SAHITYA AKADEMI, *Contemporary Indian Literature* (New Delhi, 1957).

RABINDRANATH TAGORE, *Collected Poems and Plays* (New York, 1937).

EDWARD J. THOMPSON, *Rabindranath Tagore: Poet and Dramatist* (2nd ed., London, 1948).

WANG CHI-CHEN, (trans.), *Contemporary Chinese Stories* (New York, 1944).

RICHARD OLOF WINSTEDT, 'A History of Malay Literature', *Journal of the Royal Asiatic Society, Malayan Branch*, XVII, 3 (London, 1939).

Arts

FAUBION BOWERS, *Theatre in the East: A Survey of Asian Dance and Drama* (New York and Toronto, 1956).

FAUBION BOWERS, *The Dance in India* (New York, 1953).

MARG (Bombay, 1946–   ), quarterly.

P. R. RAMACHANDRA RAO, *Modern Indian Painting* (Madras, 1953).

MICHAEL SULLIVAN, *Chinese Art in the 20th Century* (Berkeley, Calif., 1959).

ARTHUR WALEY, *The Nō Plays of Japan* (London, 1921).

YUKIO YASHIRO, *2,000 Years of Japanese Art* (New York, 1958).

BERYL DE ZOETE and WALTER SPIES, *Dance and Drama in Bali* (London, 1938).

INDEX

APPENDIX A

FOREWORD*

by the

Director-General of UNESCO

At a time when man is preparing to launch out from this planet into space, it is well that History should hold him in contemplation of his trajectory through the ages.

Never before, indeed, has he shown so searching a curiosity about his past or such jealous care to preserve its vestiges. It is as though in some mysterious way a balance were now maintained in his thought between the exploration of space and that of time, the extroversion of the one being offset by the inwardness of the other.

Be that as it may, never more than now, when man finds himself hurtling at vertiginous speed towards a wondrous future, has there been a great need for the function of memory to ensure for mankind the appropriation of its creative actuality. If consciousness were not thus rooted in such reflection on its own process of becoming, many of the inventions we hail as conquests and advances would be no more than the uncontrollable workings of an alienated destiny.

To evoke this retrospective awareness is the first thing that this work which we now have the honour of introducing to the public sets out to do; it is an attempt to sum up the heritage of civilization to which we owe our present élan.

The ambition to write a universal history is a very old one indeed. Many have tried their hand at it before, particularly in the classical epochs—not without merit, nor without success. The present work belongs to that noble line of great syntheses which seek to present to man the sum total of his memories as a coherent whole.

It has the same twofold ambition, to embrace the past in its entirety and to sum up all that we know about the past. And it adopts the same intellectual approach—that of the interpretative as opposed to the descriptive historian—reducing events to their significance in a universal frame of reference, explicit or implicit.

However, this *History of Mankind* parts company with its predecessors on several essential points. In the first place, it deliberately confines itself to shedding light on one of mankind's many aspects, its *cultural and scientific development*.

In so doing it departs from the traditional approaches to the study of history, which, as we know, attach decisive importance to political, economic and even military factors. It offers itself as a corrective to the ordinary view of man's past. And those who initiated the enterprise may well have thought at first that this was, in itself, sufficiently useful and original for them to dispense with any further aim.

Admittedly, it rests with the science of history to decide objectively, *a posteriori* and according to the case, on the relative importance of the different elements and factors in particular situations. To that extent the approach deliberately adopted in this history may well be said to be an *a priori* postulate. This is the very postulate on which UNESCO itself is based, namely, the conviction that international relations, in their ultimate reality, are determined not merely by political and economic factors and considerations but spring as well, and perhaps even more surely, from the capabilities and demands of the mind.

Nevertheless, even from the strictly scientific point of view, this History, deliberately partial though it be, may well claim that, in restoring to the achievements of culture and science their full reality and significance, it has made an essential contribution to that sum of factual knowledge and right understanding which a complete history aspires to offer.

But the originality of the enterprise does not stop there. In point of fact, that is where it begins. For the facts of which this History treats are no ordinary ones. To put them back in their proper place is not merely to fill a long-standing gap and thus complete the sum, restoring its balance to the whole. It is to discover a new dimension of the historical object, perceptible only when approached from a particular intellectual angle.

Cultural or scientific facts, whatever their subject-matter, means, cause, pretext or circumstances, are essentially thoughts of man about man.

This is obvious in the cultural sphere, every value being a human ideal. But it is no less

* Published in Volume I of *The History of Mankind: Cultural and Scientific Development*.

true of science; for apart from the fact that truth, too, is a value, the essence of science is not knowledge, but the method by which knowledge is gained, the rule the mind prescribes itself in order to attain it; and every rule is a form of reflection and self-discipline; that is, doubled consciousness.

Thus, the history of what has no doubt been too simply described here as 'the cultural and scientific development of mankind' is, strictly speaking, the story of how, through the ages, men—individually and collectively—have conceived of humanity. Or, to be more correct, have conceived of *their* humanity, that is, the universal aspect of their experience. In short, the subject of this work is the gradual development, in its most expressive manifestations, of the consciousness of the universal in man.

As will be seen, great care is taken to describe the exchanges and influences which link the different foci of civilization across space or time. We are shown how this web of reciprocal influences is becoming more closely woven as spatial communications grow more numerous and rapid and relations in time more intensive.* Indeed by no means the least interesting feature of this work is the stress it lays upon this still too little known aspect of historical reality in which the 'intellectual and moral solidarity of mankind' referred to in the Preamble to UNESCO's Constitution can really be seen at work.

Yet even this is not the decisive discovery. That lies not so much in the evidence of inter-relation between the many and varied civilizations as in the fact, manifest in all forms of culture and science, that every civilization implies, produces or invokes an image of man in terms of the universal.

This immanence of the universal in every cultural and scientific experience is what gives its essential character to the spiritual solidarity of mankind. And it is in this form that the solidarity can serve as the foundation for the true peace described in UNESCO's Constitution, whereas the effect of intercultural relations upon the interplay of the forces conducive, in a given situation, to peace is, as well we know, extremely complex and indirect, and therefore contingent. In fact it is because the object of this History, as already pointed out, is the development of the consciousness of this solidarity that UNESCO regards such an understanding as both vital and necessary.

But straightway we are faced with another fact, no less rich in implications. In the actual experience of science and culture, sense and style, which constitute the universal element, remain indissolubly bound up with the singular act of invention or creation from which they derive. It may truly be said both of science and of culture, regarded as experiences, that 'the more one concentrates on the particular, the more universal one becomes'. And it is only by repeating the various operations of the act of creation, reduced to their objective characteristics—which make up what we call method—or by subjective communion with the mental atmosphere of that act—which is what we call intuition—that another person can understand and assimilate this sense and style.

It follows that for a history which aims to keep in constant touch with experience and restore it in its contingent truth, scientific and cultural facts have significance only for certain individuals, namely those who are capable of applying these methods and of exercising this intuition which give access to the secrets of creativeness in its unique aspects. However, to possess this ability, there is no doubt that one must belong to the particular context of civilization in which such unique phenomena occur. Accordingly a concrete history of science and culture can only be written from a plurality of viewpoints corresponding to the variety of civilizations.

To acknowledge the fact that there is more than one civilization is not to deny in any way the continuity or solidarity of human development. On the contrary, the study of the inter-relations, across time and space, of ideas, values and techniques restores this sense of continuity and solidarity, which have never before been so definitely and convincingly established as in this History. Similarly, to be aware of the originality of the works and symbols which make up each civilization is not to gainsay the universality of the human mind. As we have seen, true universality is no more than a dimension of this consciousness of a sense or style, which opens out to the potential totality of mankind only by rooting itself in the particularity of its initial emergence.

* Even in time, relations are reversible—not, of course, through any real causation, but owing to the perpetual reappraisal of the significance of events that take place in the course of man's constantly renewed, and renewing, retrospection.

The classical rationalism of the West conceived the history of the human mind as a process of development in which all scientific and cultural facts are arranged in order with reference to a single, constant subject that is universal by nature. There is no need to plunge into a philosophical discussion on ontological humanism in order to expose this myth. It would be only too easy, now of all times, to show how into this allegedly universal subject has been projected, out of pride or sheer naïveté, the subjectivity, in more or less sublimated form, of certain personalities eminently representative of their epoch, civilization or race.

The work you are about to read represents the first attempts to compose a universal history of the human mind from the varying standpoints of memory and thought that characterize the different contemporary cultures.

But in doing so, its main purpose was not to banish all subjectivity of interpretation. Indeed, such a pretension could not be entertained in a history which seeks to assess the significance of events and which takes as its starting points the positions adopted by the various cultures. For there is a kind of subjectivity, co-substantial, as it were, with culture, which causes the perspective opened by each culture on the universal in man to be a projection of that culture's humanity in its own particular circumstances. The originality of this attempt at a universal history lies in its having taken for its frame of reference the multiplicity of contemporary cultural perspectives and projections. For the first time an attempt has been made to present, with respect to the history of consciousness, the sum total of the knowledge which the various contemporary societies and cultures possess and a synthesis of the conceptions which they entertain. For the first time an attempt has been made to offer a history of human thought which is the product of the thought of mankind in every aspect of its present complexion. A universal history indeed, and doubly so—in both its object and it subject.

This aspiration, which is the essence of the whole undertaking, has determined the choice of method.

The History is the work, not of a team with a homogeneous cultural background, but of an International Commission which, by its very composition and even more by the spirit pervading it, embraces all the varied cultural traditions and modern ideologies which form the spiritual framework of our present-day world. What is more, the International Commission made it a rule that the contributions of the many scholars whose services it enlisted be submitted to the scrutiny of the National Commissions which, in the Member States of UNESCO, group together persons particularly qualified to represent the fields of education, science and culture. Subject always to the overriding considerations of scientific truth, the observations received in the course of these extensive consultations were scrupulously taken into account in drawing up the final text. Never before has what I may call the decentralization of viewpoints and interpretations been carried so far in the science of history.

Accordingly the work is also an act; for this historical study is itself a cultural achievement calculated to influence, by its spirit and its methods, the present trend of culture. And that, no doubt, is its ultimate end. For just as the awareness of mankind's intellectual and moral solidarity to which it stems leads less from the discovery of the interrelations of the past than from the effort of its scientific and cultural heritage, so the essential feature of this effort is not so much the complete restitution of the object which it is designed to achieve as the fact that the whole of the subject as it exists today is taking part in it and thus affirms its own unity in the process of achieving it.

In this humanism, whose universality springs not from a unique abstract nature but is being gradually evolved, on the basis of a freely acknowledged diversity, through actual contact and a continuous effort at understanding and co-operation, UNESCO recognizes both its own *raison d'être* and its guiding principle. The unity of mankind, we believe, has to be patiently built up, through mutual respect for the cultures which diversify it without dividing it, and by the establishment of more and more centres of science which spread man's technological power throughout the world, fostering equality of opportunity for progress and for the genuine preservation of his dignity.

Such, then, are the principal ideas and essential features of this work; they are, at the same time, the very reasons which led UNESCO, as the educational, scientific and cultural organization of the United Nations, to conceive the project and assist in its execution.

The author of this History is not UNESCO; it is the International Commission which, since 1950, has directed this venture in complete intellectual independence. It is to the Commission, therefore, and to it alone, that the full credit for this work is due. And at the same time—allow me to state—it also bears the sole responsibility for its scientific worth.

UNESCO is, however, proud to have organized this work and to have made possible its accomplishment by providing the necessary funds, administrative machinery and international background. In that sense this great venture, without precedent in many respects, is also in some measure its work, too.

It is, therefore, my pleasant duty to express the Organization's gratitude to all those who have, to whatever degree, participated in this undertaking and contributed to its success. Above all, its thanks are due to the distinguished members of the International Commission and to its eminent Chairman, Professor Paulo E. de Berrêdo Carneiro, who for thirteen years have given unsparingly of the wealth of their knowledge and talents, with a devotion and selflessness equalled only by the nobility of their thought. In this concept of scientific and cultural development in which consciousness is an act and all reflection a creation, it may be said without fear of exaggeration that, in presenting this vast panorama of the past history of the human mind, such as never was before, they have made a powerful contribution towards the advent of a consciousness of civilization on a scale encompassing the whole of mankind. With all my admiration, I wish to express to them UNESCO's gratitude.

RENÉ MAHEU

Paris, 1962.

APPENDIX B

PREFACE*

by the

*President of the International Commission
for a History of the Scientific and Cultural Development
of Mankind*

Among the great tasks assigned to UNESCO by its Constitution is the duty to promote and encourage mutual knowledge and understanding throughout the world. While many of the divergences which divide people date from a distant past, an analysis of their historical antecedents discloses links which draw them nearer to one another, brings to light their contributions to a common patrimony of humanity, reveals the ebb and flow of cultural exchanges and emphasizes their increasing tendency to become integrated into an international community.

Beyond differences of race, climate, economic structure and systems of ideas, history shows the fundamental identity of the various human groups, making it possible to discern, in many cases, profound analogies among the transformations they have undergone from the Palaeolithic era down to the present time. If we consider the human species as a whole, we perceive that the course of its evolution has been accomplished from one region and one people to another by way of a series of oscillations, greater or lesser in extent, longer or shorter in duration. The different civilizations which have arisen in the course of the ages correspond to distinct phases and patterns of this general movement. Almost every one of them is to be found somewhere in the world of today. Contemporary society appears as a mosaic in which the most widely-differing cultures adjoin and confront each other.

It was, I think, in order to know them better and to strengthen their solidarity that UNESCO took the initiative of entrusting to historians, men of science and of letters, recruited from all parts of the world, the task of preparing and of publishing this work. This, at least, is how I have understood the mandate of the International Commission over which I have the honour to preside. Our task was not to draw up a philosophy of history in the light of the economic, intellectual and moral laws which may govern social development but to describe, from a universal standpoint, the contribution of each age, each region, each people to the scientific and cultural ascent of humanity.

In the official reports which I have presented since 1951 to the General Conference of UNESCO will be found a detailed account of the steps taken in implementing this project which originated in a resolution submitted to the second session of the General Conference held in Mexico City in 1947. The idea had been put forward in 1946 by Dr Julian Huxley, then Executive Secretary of the Preparatory Commission for UNESCO:

'The chief task before the Humanities today would seem to be to help in constructing a history of the development of the human mind, notably in its highest cultural achievements. For this task, the help of art critics and artists will be needed as well as of art historians; of anthropologists and students of comparative religion as well as of divines and theologians; of archaeologists as well as of classical scholars; of poets and creative men of letters as well as of professors of literature; as well as the whole-hearted support of the historians. Throughout, of course, the development of culture in the various regions of the Orient must receive equal attention to that paid to its Western growth. Once more, UNESCO can help by being true to its many-sidedness, and by bringing men together from all these various fields to help in one or other facet of this huge work.' (UNESCO: *Its Purpose and Its Philosophy* [London, 1946].)

Several preparatory meetings were held and preliminary studies made in 1947 and 1948 with the participation of Professors Carl J. Burckhardt, Lucien Febvre, Joseph Needham, Georges Salles, Taha Hussein, and UNESCO officials, among whom were Dr Julian Huxley, then Director-General, Mr Jean Thomas and Professor Pierre Auger. In 1949, Professors Lucien Febvre and Migual Ozorio de Almeida were asked to prepare general reports on the basis of which the General Conference, at its fourth session, recommended that the work should proceed immediately.

* Published in Volume I of *The History of Mankind: Cultural and Scientific Development*.

In the same year a committee of experts was called to draft the plan to be submitted to the General Conference for the elaboration of a scientific and cultural history of mankind. It included the following scholars: R. Ciasca, L. Febvre, M. Florkin, J. Needham, L. Piaget, P. Rivet and R. Shryock. In opening the proceedings, Dr Jaime Torres-Bodet, at that time Director-General, evoked the spirit in which he considered the work should be accomplished:

'Through UNESCO, humanity must come to realize its common past and understand the significance of the sum total of endeavour, invention and enlightenment which have gone to make up the heritage we seek to serve today. If we can regard this moment in the world's history as UNESCO's hour, it is thanks to the slow and often unnoticed growth of an outlook of Mankind. . . .'

'We seek only to draw up the table of the major cultural events which have shaped Man's existence and slowly brought civilization into being. . . .'

'The important thing is to embark on it with the will to succeed and in a spirit of serene and dispassionate objectivity. . . .'

'Nevertheless, by publishing today a synthesis of our present knowledge of *humanity's scientific and cultural history*, UNESCO, far from lulling the critical spirit to sleep, will spur it to new and eager research. It is my profound conviction that there is nothing in the nature or the present state of historical science precluding the making of such a synthesis; indeed all circumstances invite us to it.'

In accordance with a resolution of the General Conference of 1950, consultations were held with the International Council of Scientific Unions (ICSU) and the International Council for Philosophy and Humanistic Studies (CIPSH) as to the appointment of an international commission to undertake, on behalf of UNESCO, full responsibility for the preparation and execution of the work. The following experts nominated by these two councils were invited by the Director-General to become active members of the Commission: Professors Homi Bhabha (University of Bombay), Carl J. Burckhardt (Switzerland), Paulo E. de Berrêdo Carneiro (University of Brazil), Julian Huxley, FRS (United Kingdom), Charles Morazé (University of Paris), Mario Praz (University of Rome), Ralph E. Turner (Yale University), Silvio Zavala (University of Mexico), and Constantine K. Zurayk (University of Damascus).

The International Commission met for the first time in December 1950 and again in March 1951 in Paris. It decided during these two meetings to invite a number of distinguished persons to become Corresponding Members, and to set up an Editorial Committee, under the chairmanship of Professor Ralph E. Turner, with Professors Constantine K. Zurayk and Charles Morazé as members. The Commission did me the honour of electing me as its President, with Dr Julian Huxley and Professor Carl J. Burckhardt as Vice-Presidents. A Bureau was created comprising the President, the Vice-Presidents and the Chairman of the Editorial Committee, Dr Armando Cortesao, a member of the Department of Cultural Activities of UNESCO, initially responsible for the secretariat of the Commission, was unanimously elected Secretary-General. In 1952 he was succeeded by Dr Guy S. Métraux.

Between 1952 and 1954 new members were added to the International Commission to enlarge its geographical, cultural and philosophical representation. The following scholars were appointed in agreement with the Director-General of UNESCO: Professors E. J. Dijksterhuis (Netherlands), Jacques Freymond (Switzerland), Mahmud Husain (Pakistan), Hu-Shih (China), Erik Lönnroth (Sweden), R. C. Majumdar (India), Percy E. Schramm (Federal Republic of Germany), Ali A. Siassi (Iran), and J. Pérez Villanueva (Spain).

As early as 1952 the International Commission approached scholars of countries which, at the time, were not members of UNESCO but which represented important cultural areas. Invitations were sent to national academies of sciences and arts, but met with no response. It was only in 1955 that the International Commission was able to welcome as new members historians and scientists from the Union of Soviet Socialist Republics and the People's Republics of Czechoslovakia, Hungary and Poland.

Since 1954 the Bureau, acting as delegate of the International Commission with additional responsibilities placed on it by the General Assembly, has been enlarged to comprise the President and six Vice-Presidents as follows: Sir Julian Huxley (United Kingdom), Professor R. C. Majumdar (India), Professor Ralph E. Turner (United States of America), Professor Gaston Wiet (France), Professor Silvio Zavala (Mexico), and Professor A. A. Zvorikine

(Union of Soviet Socialist Republics). Professor Louis Gottschalk (United States of America) was unanimously elected as a further Vice-President in 1961.

The first publication which the International Commission initiated, on the proposal of Professor Charles Marazé, was a quarterly review, the *Journal of World History*. Professor Lucien Febvre was the Editor until his death in 1956, when it came under the supervision of the Bureau, with Dr François Crouzet and Dr Guy S. Métraux as its editorial staff.

The main function of the *Journal of World History* has been to provide the International Commission with material for the final compilation of the History—documentary or biblio-graphical details about problems which have so far remained obscure; translations of docu-ments which may have appeared desirable; contributions to the History itself. This review has also enabled scholars in all countries to take part in an exchange of views on questions of interpretation and the actual presentation of the History.

The *Journal of World History* represents a considerable contribution on the part of the International Commission to historical knowledge and towards a better understanding of historical processes. Comprising articles of the highest scientific quality which bear the signature of scholars from every country and which express the most diverse ideological trends, it foreshadows to some extent the great work for which it has furnished basic materials.

The preparation of the History was examined in detail during the first and second meetings of the International Commission. Several courses of action presented themselves: the Commission could draft the final text, or it could be entrusted to a single editor, or to inde-pendent authors. It was decided that, while the Commission would retain the full authority conferred upon it by the General Conference of UNESCO, the wisest course would be to select individual author-editors for each of the six volumes. The author-editors would be fully responsible for the text, but they would work under the supervision of, and in collabora-tion with, the Editorial Committee and the Commission; they would benefit by the assistance of scholars, designated by them, to deal with certain chapters; and, if necessary, sections could be referred to specialists.

On the recommendation of the Editorial Committee, author-editors for five of the six volumes were at this time appointed. For Volume I, Jacquetta Hawkes and Henri Frankfort, both of the United Kingdom. On the death of Professor Frankfort in 1954, the late Sir Leonard Woolley (United Kingdom) was appointed to write the second part of this volume. For Volume III, René Grousset (France), with two co-authors, Vadime Elisséeff and Philippe Wolff (France). Professor Gaston Wiet (France) took over the author-editorship of this third volume in 1953 on the death of Professor Grousset. For Volume IV, Louis Gott-schalk (United States of America); for Volume V, Jorge Basadre (Peru), who afterwards resigned and was replaced later by Professor Charles Morazé (France); and for Volume VI, K. Zachariah (India), who was succeeded in 1956 by Dr Caroline F. Ware (United States of America), H.E. Dr K. M. Panikkar (India), and the late Dr. J. M. Romein (Netherlands).

In 1963 the late Professor Luigi Pareti (Italy) was appointed author-editor of Volume II, with Professors Paolo Brezzi and Luciano Petech of Italy as assistants.

By the spring of 1952 a first draft plan of the History was in circulation. Through the active interest of the author-editors, the members of the International Commission, and scholars consulted throughout the world on the initiative of the International Commission, this plan was slowly revised to constitute a general guide for the elaboration of the six volumes.

At a meeting of the International Commission in February 1954 it was decided, on my proposal, to include in its membership the author-editors of the six volumes and the editor of the *Journal of World History*. This measure was designed to enable those primarily responsible for the text of the volumes to take part in discussions and so to make a more effective contribution to the direction of the activities of the International Commission. In addition it was decided that one single body—the Bureau of the Commission—should be made entirely responsible for the co-ordination of the Commission's work. To ensure the unity of style and presentation essential to a work of such high intellectual standing and covering so wide a field, Professor Ralph E. Turner was entrusted with the task of editing the English texts.

In the course of the execution of its programme the International Commission benefited by the co-operation of UNESCO and of the General Conference which, at several of its sessions, had the opportunity to examine the work plans prepared for the History, and on two occasions took decisions which markedly influenced our work. The Ninth General Conference held in New Delhi in 1956 recommended that the texts of all volumes be submitted to the National Commissions set up in the Member States. The objective was to assist the International Commission in obtaining for each volume additional critical materials to enable the author-editors to revise and to perfect their texts. While not all National Commissions responded, the comments which were received proved most useful. All the author-editors have conscientiously noted the criticisms received and have taken them into account, wherever possible, when revising their texts. Furthermore, the International Commission has sought the advice of experts on several points.

Again at the invitation of the General Conference, following its tenth meeting held in Paris in 1958, the International Commission decided to appoint a number of historians to advise the Bureau and the author-editors on possible modifications of the text of each volume of the History, in the light of comments and criticisms received, and to suggest editorial notes on controversial issues. This step had become necessary as Professor Turner's illness had prevented him from accomplishing the editorial work. In pursuance of this policy, and in agreement with the members of the Bureau and with the author-editors, I selected a number of eminent historians, of different nationalities, particularly qualified to act as special consultants. Thus, at the end of each chapter of all volumes the reader will find grouped together editorial notes and bibliographical references that will provide him with summaries of historical opinions on those questions which can be variously interpreted.

The International Commission plans to issue a supplement to Volume VI, *The Twentieth Century*. While the first part treats of the history of our age in the same way as the history of previous periods was considered in all the volumes, this second tome will be devoted to an open debate on the main trends in scientific and cultural development at mid-century.

The six volumes include line drawings prepared by Mrs Stella Robinson at the request of the author-editors, photographic plates assembled by the Secretariat of the International Commission in co-operation with the author-editors and their assistants, and maps drawn specially by the Swiss firm, Hallwag, A.G.

At the time of publication I must recall with gratitude and regret the memory of those scholars whom the International Commission had the misfortune to lose in the course of its work and who contributed so much to the achievement of its task: Professors René Grousset, Henri Frankfort and K. Zachariah, Sir Leonard Woolley, Professors Luigi Pareti, Lucien Febvre, J. M. Romein, and H.E. Dr K. M. Panikkar.

I must hereby express, on behalf of the International Commission, my gratitude to the General Conference of UNESCO which made this project possible, to the Directors-General, Messrs Julian Huxley, Jaime Torres-Bodet, Luther Evans, Vittorino Veronese and René Maheu, and to the Secretariat of UNESCO which, through ten years, has extended assistance and guidance on every possible occasion.

The International Commission is greatly indebted to the author-editors who, often under difficult circumstances, fulfilled their task with the highest competence and devotion; to its Vice-Presidents, who constitute the Bureau, for assuming with me full responsibility for every phase of the execution of this project; and in particular to Professor Ralph E. Turner, Chairman of the Editorial Committee, for the elaboration of the general plan of the History and for his whole-hearted dedication to the success of the work to which he brought his own personal outlook of an integrated world history. I am particularly happy to acknowledge herewith the co-operation of the Corresponding Members, the consultants and the translators, whose work proved invaluable for the completion of this project.

The International Commission benefited throughout its work by the advice of the official Observers of the International Council of Scientific Unions, Professor R. J. Forbes; of the International Council for Philosophy and Humanistic Studies, Sir Ronald Syme; and of the International Social Science Council, Professor F. H. Lawson.

Lastly, I would like on behalf of the International Commission to thank the Secretary-General, Dr Guy S. Métraux, and his staff for their active and faithful collaboration which has contributed so much to the success of this scientific and cultural history of mankind.

PAULO E. DE BERRÊDO CARNEIRO